PHYSICS

FUNDAMENTAL PRINCIPLES FOR STUDENTS OF SCIENCE AND ENGINEERING

BY

GEORGE SHORTLEY, B.E.E., Ph.D.
Professor of Physics
The Ohio State University

AND

DUDLEY WILLIAMS, A.B., Ph.D.
Associate Professor of Physics
The Ohio State University

IN TWO VOLUMES

Volume II

NEW YORK
PRENTICE-HALL, INC.
1950

Copyright, 1950, by
PRENTICE-HALL, INC.
70 Fifth Avenue, New York

ALL RIGHTS RESERVED. NO PART OF THIS BOOK MAY BE REPRODUCED IN ANY FORM, BY MIMEOGRAPH OR ANY OTHER MEANS, WITHOUT PERMISSION IN WRITING FROM THE PUBLISHERS.

PRINTED IN THE UNITED STATES OF AMERICA

VOLUME II

PREFACE

This is the second volume of a book intended for use as a text in an introductory course in physics such as that normally taken by sophomore students in science and engineering in the Ohio State University. Although a somewhat detailed discussion of the general plan of the book is given in the Preface to the first volume, it seems desirable to include a few additional comments concerning the material in the second volume.

The chapter on Wave Motion lays the foundation for the later treatment of the properties of sound and light. In this chapter the problem of transverse waves in a string is treated rigorously; more complicated types of waves are then treated by analogy. In the chapters on Sound, many experimental aspects of acoustics are described; some of the sections on these subjects may be omitted.

In the part of the book dealing with Light, the new photometric standards are used throughout the sections on photometry. The chapters on Reflection and Refraction and on Optical Instruments give a fairly rigorous introductory treatment of geometrical optics; complete coverage of these chapters will probably be found desirable by all users of the book. The later chapters dealing with physical optics are somewhat long for complete coverage in the usual one-year physics course, and considerable discretion in making assignments must be exercised by the instructor; a somewhat cursory perusal of these chapters may serve as a satisfactory introduction to the subjects covered.

In the part of the text dealing with Electricity and Magnetism, a rigorous introductory treatment of electrical and magnetic phenomena is given in terms of the MKS electromagnetic system of units recommended by the International Electrotechnical Commission. Rationalized units are used for the magnetic quantities; the electrical quantities are handled in such a way that a foundation is laid for any of the several systems of units encountered in advanced treatments. A thorough discussion of the MKS units and of electrical standards is given in Chapter 41, and a comparison of various systems of electrical units is given in the Appendix. As in the other parts of the book, there are many sections and even complete chapters that can be omitted in a brief course without loss of continuity; the sections on Gauss's theorem and on the magnetic-pole concept and some of the chapters on magnetic phenomena are examples.

Although illustrative examples in all parts of the book have been drawn from 'modern physics' wherever possible, several important topics of wide interest not treated elsewhere have been included in the final part of the book under the heading Modern Physics. These final chapters give introductory, qualitative treatments of electronic circuits, radio-communication systems, and atomic energy. The book closes with a discussion of some of the as-yet-unanswered questions involving elementary particles.

GEORGE SHORTLEY
DUDLEY WILLIAMS

Washington, D. C.
Columbus, Ohio

VOLUME II

CONTENTS

PART III

Chapter 20. WAVE MOTION   475

1. Mechanical waves.................................... 476
2. Speed of a transverse wave in a string................. 481
3. Sinusoidal wave motion.............................. 482
4. Derivation of the speed of a transverse wave on a string..... 490
5. Speeds of waves of various types...................... 492
6. Energy associated with a transverse wave in a string........ 494
7. Interference phenomena; the superposition principle......... 496
8. Reflection of waves; production of standing waves.......... 503
9. Refraction... 506

Chapter 21. PRODUCTION OF SOUND   509

1. Sources of sound: vibrating solids..................... 510
2. Frequency measurements.............................. 518
3. Speed of sound: experimental measurements 521
4. Sources of sound: vibrating air columns................. 526
5. Sound characteristics: musical sounds and noise............ 529
6. Response of the ear to various types of sound............. 532
7. Electronic amplifiers for audio frequencies................ 535
8. Recording and reproduction of sound..................... 537

Chapter 22. PROPERTIES OF SOUND WAVES   539

1. Speed of sound waves in various media.................. 539
2. Sound intensities.................................... 545
3. Reflection of sound waves............................. 551
4. Refraction of sound waves............................. 553
5. Absorption of sound waves............................. 557
6. Interference and diffraction of sound waves................ 561
7. Doppler effect....................................... 564
8. Ultrasonic waves; sonar............................... 568

PART IV

LIGHT

Chapter 23. THE NATURE OF LIGHT AND ITS PROPAGATION   573

1. Nature of light...................................... 573
2. Emission of light.................................... 575

3. Rectilinear propagation	575
4. Vision	579
5. Speed of light	581

Chapter 24. ILLUMINATION AND PHOTOMETRY — 590

1. Light sources	590
2. Photometric quantities: source intensity, light flux, and illumination	592
3. Real light sources	598
4. Photometry	599
5. Efficiency of light sources	604

Chapter 25. REFLECTION AND REFRACTION OF LIGHT — 606

1. Reflection at plane surfaces	606
2. Reflection by concave spherical mirrors	611
3. Reflection by convex spherical mirrors	621
4. Refraction of light	624
5. Lenses	636

Chapter 26. OPTICAL INSTRUMENTS — 651

1. Definition of magnifying power	651
2. The magnifying glass	652
3. The photographic camera	656
4. The projection lantern	658
5. The compound microscope	660
6. The astronomical telescope	663
7. Terrestrial telescopes	667
8. The eye	669

Chapter 27. INTERFERENCE AND DIFFRACTION OF LIGHT — 676

1. Conditions for interference	676
2. Fresnel's experiments	677
3. Interference phenomena in thin films	679
4. The Michelson interferometer	687
5. Diffraction phenomena and Huygens' principle	690
6. Fresnel diffraction	693
7. Fraunhofer diffraction at a single opening	701
8. Resolving power of optical instruments	705
9. Diffraction gratings	708
10. Wave treatment of thin lenses	711

Chapter 28. DISPERSION, SPECTRA, AND COLOR — 713

1. Dispersion of white light	713
2. Prism spectrographs	715
3. Achromatic lenses	721
4. Grating spectrographs	724
5. Emission spectra	726
6. Absorption spectra	728
7. Spectrochemical analysis	730
8. Color sensation: mixtures of colors	731
9. Colors of nonluminous objects: mixtures of pigments	734
10. Scattering of light	738

Chapter 29. POLARIZATION OF LIGHT 740

1. Polarization by selective absorption.......................... 741
2. Polarization by reflection................................... 745
3. Polarization by scattering.................................. 748
4. Electromagnetic waves...................................... 750
5. Double refraction.. 751
6. Uses of polarized light..................................... 760
7. Magneto-optical and electro-optical effects.................. 763

Chapter 30. EMISSION AND ABSORPTION OF RADIATION 767

1. The black body... 767
2. Total radiation from a body; the Stefan-Boltzmann law....... 772
3. The spectrum of a black body; Planck's quantum theory...... 774
4. Line spectra... 779

PART V
ELECTRICITY AND MAGNETISM

Chapter 31. ELECTROSTATICS 785

1. Electric charges... 785
2. Electrical structure of matter; Coulomb's law............... 788
3. Electric field.. 796
4. Difference of potential..................................... 806
5. Charges on conductors; shielding............................ 812
6. Charging by induction; the electroscope..................... 820
7. Gauss's theorem.. 826

Chapter 32. CONDENSERS 833

1. Capacitance of a cylindrical condenser...................... 833
2. The spherical condenser.................................... 837
3. The parallel-plate condenser................................ 841
4. Dielectric constant... 843
5. Energy of a condenser...................................... 847
6. Condensers in parallel and series........................... 849
7. Dielectric strength... 852

Chapter 33. DIRECT ELECTRIC CURRENTS 855

1. Current arising from a condenser discharge.................. 855
2. Constant currents.. 857
3. Resistance; Ohm's law...................................... 859
4. Resistivity... 862
5. Temperature coefficient of resistance........................ 867
6. Resistance of insulators, semiconductors, and liquids........ 870
7. Terminal voltage of generators, motors, and batteries....... 873
8. Simple circuits; resistors in parallel and in series........... 876
9. Electrical networks; Kirchhoff's laws........................ 881

Chapter 34. ELECTROCHEMISTRY 890

1. The electron-volt (ev) as a unit of energy................... 891
2. Atomic weight; Avogadro's number; the mole; the faraday; the kilocalorie/mole.. 893

3. Charge transport in electrolysis................................ 896
4. Voltage necessary for electrolysis.............................. 901
5. The electrochemical series..................................... 905
6. The reversible-heat effect..................................... 907
7. Cells in current use... 909

Chapter 35. THERMOELECTRICITY 918

1. Thermoelectric effects... 918
2. The thermocouple.. 919

Chapter 36. MAGNETIC EFFECTS OF ELECTRIC CURRENTS 922

1. Introduction.. 923
2. Definition of the direction of the magnetic vectors; magnetic lines.. 925
3. Strength of a magnetic field; force on a current element...... 929
4. Discussion of the magnetic moment of a coil and of the forces on a current element.. 936
5. Magnetic fields set up by electric currents................... 938
6. Magnetic flux... 947
7. The pole concept; forces on thin solenoids and thin magnets.. 949
8. External fields of solenoids and magnets...................... 953
9. Ampere's line-integral law, with applications................. 956
10. Field of a solenoid... 961
11. Magnetic force on a moving charged particle; path of a particle in a magnetic field..................................... 964

Chapter 37. FERROMAGNETISM; PERMANENT MAGNETS; THE EARTH'S FIELD 969

1. Ferromagnetism.. 970
2. Permanent magnets... 973
3. The earth's field... 976

Chapter 38. IDEAL MAGNETIC MATERIALS; THE MAGNETIC CIRCUIT; REAL MAGNETIC MATERIALS 982

1. Definitions of magnetizing force $\mathcal{3C}$, ideal magnetic materials, permeability... 982
2. Magnetization of a toroid with distributed winding............ 984
3. A magnetic circuit of uniform cross section and permeability.. 988
4. Line-integral law for $\mathcal{3C}$....................................... 990
5. Series magnetic circuits...................................... 990
6. Real magnetic materials....................................... 994

Chapter 39. ELECTROMAGNETIC INDUCTION 999

1. Magnitude and direction of the induced EMF.................... 999
2. The relation between EMF and the rate of change of flux...... 1003
3. Homopolar DC dynamos.. 1006
4. AC and DC generators.. 1011
5. DC motors... 1017
6. Eddy currents; AC motors...................................... 1018
7. Mutual inductance... 1022

8. Self inductance.................................... 1024
9. Energy of self inductance........................... 1027
10. Growth and decay of current in inductive circuits........... 1028

Chapter 40. ALTERNATING-CURRENT CIRCUITS — 1033

1. The vector diagram................................ 1033
2. Circuit elements containing capacitance and resistance...... 1037
3. Circuit elements containing inductance and resistance....... 1041
4. Series circuits containing resistance, inductance, and capacitance; series resonance............................. 1044
5. Power in series circuits; effective values of voltage and current 1050
6. Parallel AC circuits; parallel resonance; oscillating circuits.... 1055
7. The transformer................................... 1058

Chapter 41. THE FUNDAMENTAL ELECTRICAL UNITS — 1064

1. Definition of the ampere............................ 1065
2. Definition of the volt.............................. 1066
3. Definition of the ohm.............................. 1067
4. Definition of the coulomb; the proportionality constant in Coulomb's law.................................... 1068
5. Maintenance of the units at the National Bureau of Standards 1070
6. Résumé.. 1071
7. Defining equations and dimensions of the electrical and magnetic units...................................... 1072

Chapter 42. ELECTRICAL MEASURING INSTRUMENTS — 1074

1. The d'Arsonval galvanometer........................ 1074
2. The DC voltmeter.................................. 1076
3. The DC ammeter................................... 1078
4. The electroynamometer 1080
5. The wattmeter, DC or AC........................... 1082
6. The watt-hour meter............................... 1085
7. Voltmeters and ammeters for use on AC.............. 1086
8. Measurement of resistance, inductance, capacitance......... 1088
9. Accurate comparison of voltages; the potentiometer......... 1089
10. The fluxmeter; the ballistic galvanometer................ 1091

PART VI
MODERN PHYSICS

Chapter 43. ELECTRONICS — 1097

1. Thermionic emission............................... 1098
2. Diode applications................................. 1104
3. The control grid: triode applications................. 1109
4. The electron-ray oscillograph........................ 1118
5. The electron microscope............................ 1124
6. The photoelectric effect............................. 1130
7. X rays... 1132
8. Conduction of electricity through gases................. 1134

Chapter 44. ELECTROMAGNETIC WAVES — 1138

1. Electromagnetic radiation: the work of Hertz 1140
2. Radiation from a dipole antenna 1142
3. Radio communication systems 1147
4. The electromagnetic spectrum 1152
5. Photons; waves associated with material particles 1157

Chapter 45. ELEMENTARY PARTICLES — 1164

1. Chemical elements; atoms 1164
2. The nuclear model of the atom 1166
3. Nuclear structure 1173
4. Particle accelerators 1181
5. The theory of relativity 1189
6. Mass-energy transformations; nuclear masses 1196
7. Atomic energy 1202
8. Nuclear forces; the meson 1212
9. Elementary-particle physics 1213

APPENDIX — 1215

1. Systems of electrical and magnetic units 1215
2. Fundamental physical constants 1220
3. Periodic table of the elements 1221
4. Physical properties of the elements 1222
5. Masses and abundances of naturally occurring isotopes 1224
6. Tables of conversion factors 1228
7. Natural trigonometric functions 1238
8. Table of logarithms to base 10 1242
9. Table of exponentials 1244

INDEX — 1247

Part III
SOUND

CHAPTER 20

WAVE MOTION

In everyday experience we meet with many usages of the term *wave*. We frequently read in the newspapers of 'cold waves,' 'heat waves,' 'crime waves,' 'waves of bombers,' and so on. The underlying conception in all these uses of the term *wave* is that a wave involves some quantity or disturbance that (a) changes in magnitude more or less regularly with time at a given location and (b) at a fixed time changes in magnitude from place to place in a more or less regular manner. For example, in the case of a 'cold wave moving eastward across the country,' (a) the temperature at Chicago may be high on one day, fall to a low value the next day when the 'crest' of the cold wave reaches the city, and rise to a high value the following day when the crest has passed; (b) on the day the crest of the cold wave is in Chicago, the temperature may be high at Denver, lower in Iowa, very low in Chicago, slightly higher in Cleveland, and high in New York. In this case, the quantity that is changing is temperature and the pattern of its variation *with time* at the Chicago location shows striking similarity to its variation *with geographical position* at any one time. The crest of the wave moves eastward across the country and may appear at Denver, Des Moines, Chicago, Cleveland, and New York on successive days.

The types of waves in which we are interested at present are the waves involved in the transfer of energy from one body to another. When two bodies are joined by some rigid mechanical connecting member such as a shaft, energy can be transferred from the first body to the second by motion of the shaft. However, when there is no rigid connecting member between the two bodies, there are in general only two ways in which energy can be transferred from one body to the other.* The first of these involves the motion of material from one body to the other; for example, energy may be transferred from a gun to a target by the passage of a projectile. The second of these ways involves the passage of a wave motion of some type through a medium separating the two bodies. For example, energy is transferred from a chapel bell to

* NOTE: There are certain borderline cases; for example, the transmission of electrical power over wires connecting two bodies. Whether the wires are to be considered a 'connecting member' or an 'intervening medium' depends to some extent on the frequencies used in transmitting the electrical power.

the ears of a distant listener by a *mechanical wave motion* in the air between; there is no transfer of material from the bell to the listener but only a transfer of energy by waves passing through the intervening medium. In the two chapters immediately following this one we shall concern ourselves with a discussion of these *sound waves*. In later chapters dealing with *light* and *radio transmission*, we shall discuss *electromagnetic waves;* although these electromagnetic waves are not mechanical waves like sound waves, the general principles we shall introduce in the present chapter are applicable to all types of wave motion and can therefore be used to advantage in discussing these electromagnetic waves.

In the present chapter, we shall first consider in detail the transmission of mechanical waves along a stretched string or wire. After we have derived the equations describing this simple type of wave motion, we shall treat more complicated types by analogy but shall not attempt detailed analyses.

1. MECHANICAL WAVES

In order for mechanical wave motion to occur, it is necessary to have a *source* that produces a displacement or *disturbance* of some kind and an *elastic medium* through which the disturbance can be transmitted. An elastic medium behaves as if it were a succession of adjoining particles with each particle occupying an equilibrium position; if one of the particles is displaced from its equilibrium position, this particle is immediately subjected to a restoring force as a result of attraction or repulsion by neighboring particles, which, in turn, are subjected to reaction forces exerted by the original particle. If one of the particles in a medium is given a sudden displacement by the *source*, this particle exerts forces on its immediate neighbors, which experience displacements; these immediately neighboring particles exert forces on *their* neighbors, which also undergo displacements, and so on. In this way, the initial disturbance at the source causes displacement of the particles in the surrounding medium. As a result of the inertia of the particles, the displacements of all the particles do not take place instantaneously; the displacements of the particles far removed from the source occur later than the displacements of particles close to the source. The energy imparted to the first particle by the source is transferred successively from one group of surrounding particles to the next and travels outward from the source; if there is no *absorption* arising from the dissipative effects of frictional forces, the initial mechanical energy continues to travel outward from the source. Thus, *energy is transferred from the source to distant parts of the surrounding medium without transfer of matter;* a motion of the type we have just described is called *wave motion*. A mechanical wave is an elastic deformation that travels through a medium.

We might construct a mechanical model of the medium we have just described; this model would resemble the model shown in Fig. 1 of Chap. 14, which we used in discussing conduction of heat. It should be noted, however, that although the *mechanism* involved in energy transfer is the same for heat conduction and wave transmission, the *motion* of the particles in the two cases is quite different; in the case of heat the motion is *random*, whereas in the case of wave transmission the motion is *ordered*. If the model were infinite in extent, the wave motion would continue to move outward from the source and *order* would be maintained. The

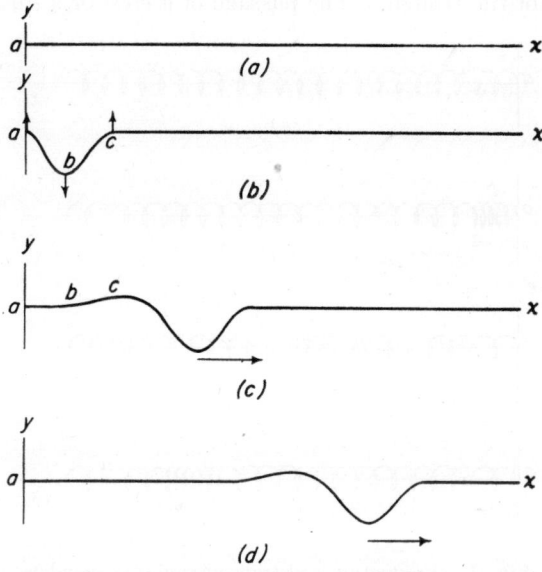

Fig. 1. Production and transmission of a transverse displacement (trough) in a stretched string. The end a of the string is either held in the observer's hand, or fastened, in such a way that tension is applied to the string.

motion involved in heat flow is *microscopic*—random motion of individual molecules—; the motion involved in wave transmission is macroscopic—ordered motion of many millions of molecules.

In beginning our discussion of wave motion, it will be desirable to consider the special case of wave motion in a single direction through a 'medium' such as a stretched string. For example, let us consider the case shown schematically in Fig. 1. In this figure a long string is shown in part (a); one end of the long string is held in the observer's hand; the other end is attached to a distant support not shown. In part (b), a portion of the string is distorted in the indicated manner by pulling downward at point b while points a and c are held at their initial positions; this distorted portion of the string is called a *trough*. If the string is suddenly released at points b and c, the displaced portion is pulled back to its equilibrium position as a result of the elastic properties of the string; but as a result of this action on the part of the string near b, the parts of the string immediately to the right are pulled downward and the trough moves to the right as shown in parts (c) and (d) of the figure. The speed with which the trough moves is determined solely by the tension in the string and the mass per unit length of the string; the speed of a trough in a tightly stretched string is greater than the speed of a trough in the same string when the tension is less. It might be mentioned that a *crest*, or upward displacement, would travel along the string in Fig. 1 at the same speed as that of the trough. The passage of a *crest* or a *trough* along the

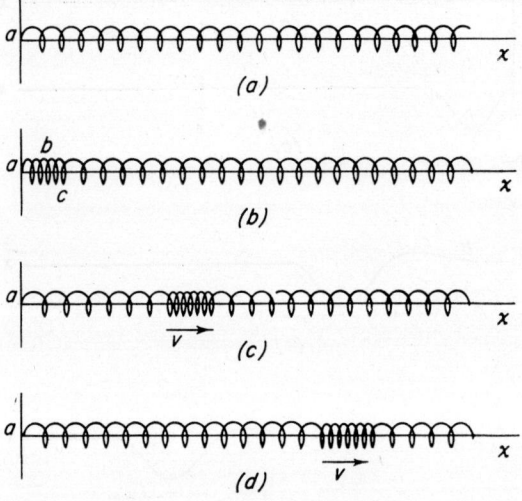

Fig. 2. Production and transmission of a 'condensation' along a helical spring.

stretched string shown in the figure is an example of a *transverse* wave motion.

In a transverse wave the displacements of the particles of the medium are perpendicular to the direction of propagation of the wave.

For example, if the crest or trough constituting the *transverse* wave is traveling in the $+x$-direction in Fig. 1, the displacements of the individual particles have only y-components. In general, the particles may have displacements with both y- and z-components if a transverse wave is traveling in the x-direction; but they do not have displacements with x-components.

Another type of wave, which can occur in a stretched spring, is illustrated in Fig. 2. Part (a) of the figure shows one end of a long coil spring with one end supported at point a; the support at the other end is not shown. If the spring is distorted in the manner indicated in Fig. 2(b) so that the coils of the spring are more closely spaced around point b than in other parts of the spring, the region in the vicinity of b is called a *condensation*. If the external forces producing the distortion are removed, the elastic restoring forces accelerate particles near b toward their equilibrium positions. When this acceleration occurs, the coils toward the right of the original condensation position are pushed closer together, and, as a result, the condensation moves toward the right as shown in Fig. 2(c) and (d).

Similarly, a *rarefaction*, in which the coils are initially pulled farther apart as in Fig. 3, will move to the right along the spring in the manner

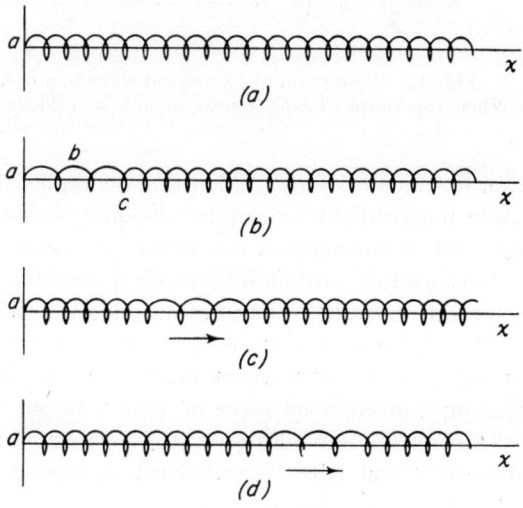

Fig. 3. Production and transmission of a 'rarefaction' along a helical spring.

shown. The speeds of motion of condensations and rarefactions are the same for a given coil spring and are determined by the force constant and the mass per unit length of the spring. The type of wave motion illustrated in Figs. 2 and 3 is known as *longitudinal* wave motion.

In a longitudinal wave the displacements of the particles of the medium are parallel to the direction of propagation of the wave.

For example, if the waves shown in Figs. 2 and 3 are moving in the positive x-direction, the particles in the spring undergo displacements with *only* x-components.

One other type of wave will be mentioned briefly. This is a *torsional* wave, in which each particle of the medium moves along a curve in a plane perpendicular to the direction of propagation of the wave. For example, consider a metal rod that is clamped firmly at one end and then twisted at the other end by a couple of torque $L=Fd$ as shown in Fig. 4. If the couple is suddenly removed, a torsional wave pulse will be propagated along the rod. In this type of wave, the particles in the rod move in circular arcs about the axis of the rod. A torsional wave is a particular type of transverse wave that is important in connection with 'torsional oscillation' of shafts transmitting power. We shall not consider this type of wave further, but the student of mechanical engineering will run into it again in later work.

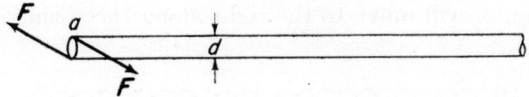

Fig. 4. Production of a torsional wave in a rod. When the couple $L=Fd$ ceases to act, a torsional wave disturbance will be transmitted along the rod.

Wave motion in solids is usually much more complex than the purely transverse, purely longitudinal, or purely torsional waves we have mentioned thus far. Most mechanical waves are a combination of these simple types. For example, although the wave in Fig. 1 is predominantly transverse, it actually has some longitudinal characteristics, since it is impossible to distort the string in the manner indicated in Fig. 1(b) without producing a slight rarefaction near point b. The limitations involved in treating a mechanical wave in a solid as purely longitudinal or purely transverse are similar to those accepted when the various elastic moduli were defined; if one effect is sufficiently greater than the others, we may get a fairly good physical analysis by ignoring the others. Thus, the motion of the string in Fig. 1 is a fair approximation of a purely transverse wave.

In the case of *surface* waves on a liquid, the motion is complex. The observant fisherman who watches a cork floating on the surface of a deep pond or lake notes that, when a wave passes, the cork does not merely move up and down in a direction perpendicular to the direction of wave propagation but also moves back and forth in a horizontal direction parallel to the direction of wave propagation. The cork moves horizontally in the direction of propagation when a crest passes and in the opposite direction when a trough passes. The motion of a water 'particle' on the surface of deep water is actually motion in a circular path. Surface waves of this type can therefore be considered as a combination of longitudinal and transverse wave motion. Waves or ripples on the surface of a *shallow* pool of water approximate longitudinal waves. Surface-tension effects predominate in the passage of ripples across a water surface, whereas gravitational effects predominate in the passage of large waves along the surface of deep bodies of water.

2. SPEED OF A TRANSVERSE WAVE IN A STRING

The speed of propagation of a transverse wave of small amplitude is given by the expression

$$v = \sqrt{T/\mu}, \tag{1}$$

where T is the tension in the string and μ is the mass per unit length of the string. The tension is equal to the magnitude of the stretching forces F applied to the ends of the string as shown in Fig. 5:

$$T = F. \tag{2}$$

The quantity μ is the ratio of mass to length:

$$\mu = m/l, \tag{3}$$

where m is the total mass of the string of length l. A derivation of (1) will be given in Sec. 4; problems involving this relation are given here for the benefit of those who may wish to omit the derivation.

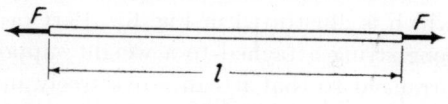

Fig. 5.

In equation (1), if T is in nt and μ in kg/m, v will be in m/sec; if T is in lbf and μ in slug/ft, v will be in ft/sec.

The expression (1) for the speed of a wave of small amplitude applies when the angle between the string and the x-axis is everywhere small compared to one radian. This equation would apply only approximately to a pulse of the exaggerated amplitude shown in Fig. 1, but would apply very well if the values of y were reduced by a factor of 5 in Fig. 1.

PROBLEMS

1. A string exactly 1 m long and with a mass of 5.0 g is under a tension of 10 nt. What is the speed of a transverse wave in this string? Ans: 44.7 m/sec.

2. What would be the speed of a transverse wave in the string mentioned in Prob. 1 if it were under a tension of 10 kgf?

3. A rope is 12 m in length. Experiment shows that a transverse wave passes from one end of the rope to the other in 1.5 sec when the rope is under a tension of 20 nt. What is the total mass of the rope? Ans: 3.75 kg.

4. What should be the tension in the rope mentioned in Prob. 3 in order for transverse waves to move along the rope at a speed of 24 m/sec?

5. A cord 36 ft long weighs 0.5 lbf. If tensile forces of magnitude 25 lbf are applied to the ends of this string, with what speed will transverse waves move along the string? Ans: 241 ft/sec.

6. What is the magnitude of the stretching forces that must be applied to the ends of the cord in Prob. 5 in order for transverse waves to move along the cord at a speed of 300 ft/sec? at 100 ft/sec?

7. Verify that the expression on the right of (1) actually represents the same unit as the speed on the left in the two unit systems mentioned in the next to the last paragraph of text above.

3. SINUSOIDAL WAVE MOTION

In the type of wave we have discussed thus far, a single nonrepeated disturbance, called a *pulse*, is initiated at the source and then travels away from the source through the medium. For example, in Fig. 1 the pulse is initiated when points b and c are released, and then travels to the right along the string. Another example of a pulse is the wave produced in a steel rail when it is given a single blow at one end by a hammer.

Another important type of wave motion is the *regular wave train* or *continuous wave*. In this type of wave, a regular succession of pulses is initiated at the source and transmitted through the medium. Thus, if a floating block of wood is pushed up and down regularly on a water surface, a regular train of waves will be propagated outward from the block along the surface.

The simplest type of regular wave train is a sinusoidal wave motion, which is illustrated in Fig. 6. Part (a) of this figure shows one end of a long string attached to a weight supported by a spring. The weight is arranged so that it can move freely in the vertical 'ways' of the frame shown. If the weight is pulled downward a distance A and then released, the weight will move in the vertical direction with simple harmonic motion of a certain frequency f. Since the end of the string is attached to the weight, the oscillating weight acts as a source of transverse waves which travel along the string in the manner indicated in Fig. 6(b), in which the velocities of the particles at various points on the string are shown by the small arrows. *The distance between adjacent crests or adjacent troughs in such a wave is called the wavelength;* in the figure the wavelength is denoted by λ. Each time the particle O attached to the weight makes a complete oscillation, the wave moves a distance λ in the x-direction. Since particle O makes f complete oscillations per second, the wave moves a distance $f\lambda$ in one second. Since the distance moved by the wave in a given direction in one second is just the speed v of the wave, the speed can be expressed in terms of the frequency of the source and the wavelength by

$$v = f\lambda. \tag{4}$$

Equation (4) is a general relation that holds for periodic wave motion of any type, not necessarily sinusoidal.

It should be noted that the wave of Fig. 6, as it moves to the right, carries *energy* away from the vibrating body at the left. If the wave is to have *constant amplitude*, as indicated in the figure, the body must be *driven* by a periodic force that supplies this energy loss. In the following discussion we assume that this is done and that the wave has constant amplitude A.

In a transverse wave like that shown in Fig. 6, the particles of the medium move about their equilibrium positions in a direction perpendicular to the direction in which the wave is moving; in the figure the particles move parallel to the y-axis and the wave moves in the $+x$-direction. All the particles execute simple harmonic motions of frequency f parallel to the y-axis, but the phases of their simple harmonic motions are not the same. For example, the motion of point P lags behind by that of particle O by $\tfrac{1}{2}\pi$ radians; the motion of point P' lags behind that of particle O

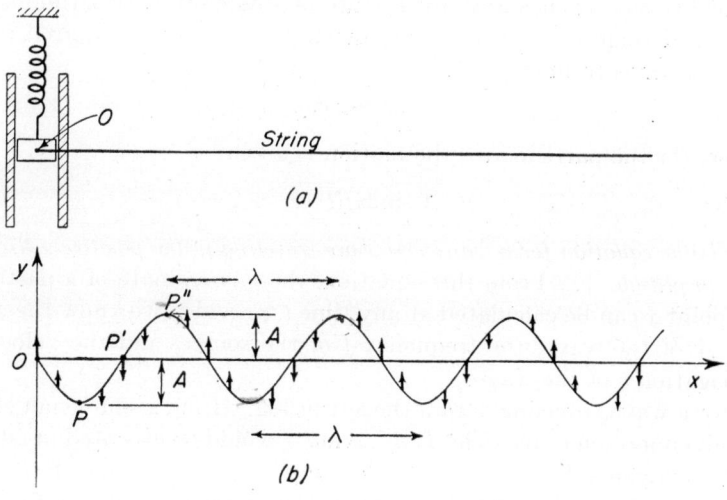

Fig. 6. Production and propagation of a sinusoidal transverse wave train in a long string The small arrows represent the velocities of particles at various points. The wave itself is moving toward the right in the figure.

by π radians; that of P'' by $\tfrac{3}{2}\pi$ radians; and so on. Thus, if the motion of particle O is given by

$$y = A \sin 2\pi ft,$$

one can see that the motion of the other particles is given by

$$y = A \sin(2\pi ft - \tfrac{1}{2}\pi) \quad \text{for particle } P,$$
$$y = A \sin(2\pi ft - \pi) \quad \text{for particle } P',$$
$$y = A \sin(2\pi ft - \tfrac{3}{2}\pi) \quad \text{for particle } P'',$$

where $-\tfrac{1}{2}\pi$, $-\pi$, and $-\tfrac{3}{2}\pi$ are called the initial phases of the motions of the particles. The greater the x-coordinate of the particle, the greater is the negative value of the initial phase angle.

From the above examples we see that the initial phase angle for a particle at coordinate x can be written as $-2\pi x/\lambda$, and hence that the motion of any point is represented by the equation

$$y = A \sin(2\pi ft - 2\pi x/\lambda) = A \sin 2\pi f(t - x/v),$$

since $f/v = 1/\lambda$ by (4). Another way of deriving this equation is to consider that the motion of the particle at x will be given by

$$y = A \sin[2\pi f(t-t_0)],$$

where t_0 denotes the time required for the wave to travel from O to the particle in question; the particle at x executes motion *similar* to that of particle O but reaches any given state of this motion at a time t_0 after this given stage was reached by particle O. The time required for the wave to travel from O to x is

$$t_0 = x/v.$$

Hence, for the particle at x the motion is given by

$$y = A \sin 2\pi f(t - x/v). \tag{5}$$

This is the equation for a transverse wave traveling in the positive x-direction with amplitude A. From this equation, the y-coordinate of a particle at any point x can be calculated at any time t, provided we know the amplitude A of the wave, the frequency f of the source, and the velocity of propagation v of the wave.

For a wave traveling *toward* the left in Fig. 6 from a source not shown, any given motion of particles P, P', and P'' would be executed in advance of the corresponding motion for particle O at the origin; that is, the motion of these particles has *positive* initial phase angles. Thus, the equation for the motion of O, P, P', and P'' could be written

$$y = A \sin 2\pi ft \qquad \text{for particle } O,$$
$$y = A \sin(2\pi ft + \tfrac{1}{2}\pi) \qquad \text{for particle } P,$$
$$y = A \sin(2\pi ft + \pi) \qquad \text{for particle } P',$$
$$y = A \sin(2\pi ft + \tfrac{3}{2}\pi) \qquad \text{for particle } P''.$$

Hence, by reasoning similar to that used above, we may write the equation

$$y = A \sin 2\pi f(t + x/v) \tag{5'}$$

for a transverse wave traveling in the negative x-direction.

Sinusoidal longitudinal waves in a long coil spring can be produced by the arrangement shown in Fig. 7. One end of the spring is attached to the steel ball supported at the end of a hacksaw blade; the other end of the hacksaw blade is held in the clamp as shown. If the ball is given a small displacement A to one side and then released, it will execute simple harmonic motion of frequency f and as a result of this motion will set up a sinusoidal longitudinal wave train in the spring. The appearance of the spring at a certain time after the wave train had been started is given in Fig. 7(b); *the wavelength λ is the distance between adjacent condensations or adjacent rarefactions*, as indicated in the figure. The wave speed v is given by the relation $v = f\lambda$.

Again we must assume that a driving force supplies the energy carried away by the wave, if the wave is to have constant amplitude.

In order to write the equation for the longitudinal wave traveling in the x-direction, we note that all the particles in the spring execute simple harmonic motions about their equilibrium positions and that these motions are parallel to the x-axis. Since the amplitude of the oscillation of the steel ball is A, this is also the amplitude of oscillation of point O at the end of the spring and, if there is no friction, of all other points in the

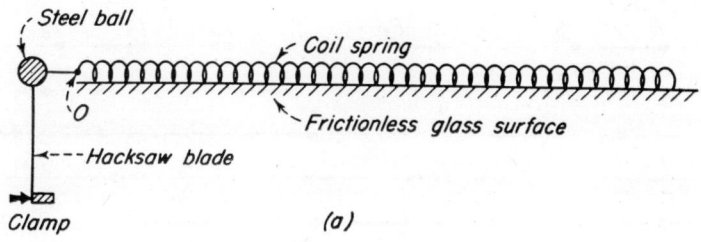

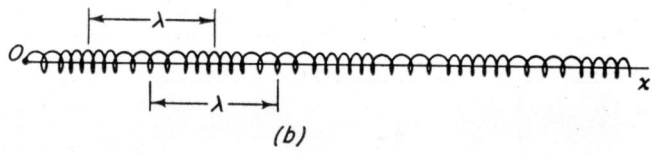

Fig. 7. Production and transmission of a sinusoidal longitudinal wave train in a long coil spring. The wave is moving to the right in the figure.

spring. In visualizing this motion, Fig. 8 may be of assistance. Part (a) of this figure shows the equilibrium positions of certain selected particles in the spring before wave motion starts. Parts (b)–(j) give the displacements X of these particles at various times during a complete cycle; a complete plot of the displacement of a particle during a complete cycle is given by the dotted curve. If we denote the displacement of a particle from its equilibrium position by X and express the displacement of particle P_1 at the origin by

$$X = A \sin 2\pi ft,$$

we can give the displacement of any other particle by the equation

$$X = A \sin 2\pi f(t - x/v), \qquad (6)$$

where x is the coordinate of the equilibrium position of the particle. This equation for a longitudinal wave traveling in the $+x$-direction can be derived by an argument similar to that used in deriving (5). For a longitudinal wave traveling in the $-x$-direction the equation is

$$X = A \sin 2\pi f(t + x/v). \tag{6'}$$

In representing the positions of the particles in a longitudinal wave at a given instant, the plots shown in Fig. 8 are rather inconvenient. A more convenient representation is given in Fig. 9, in which the ordinates

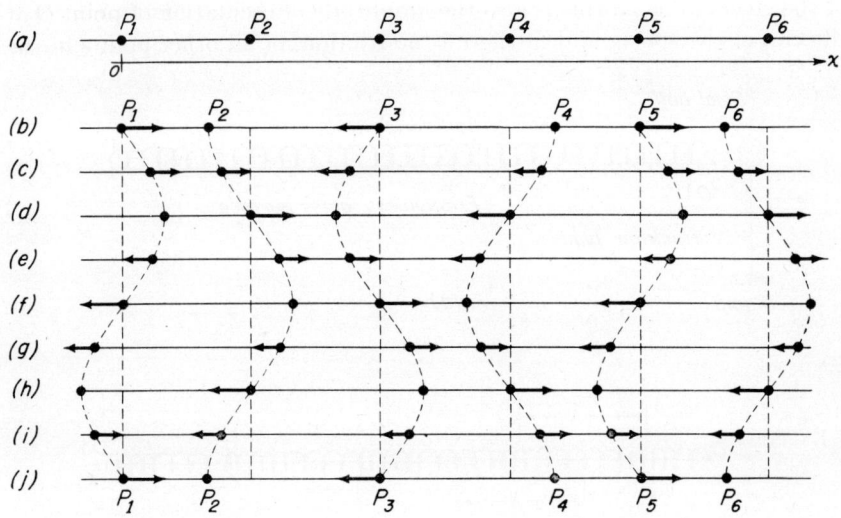

Fig. 8. The motion of six particles in a coil spring through which a longitudinal wave is moving toward the right, in the $+x$-direction. The particles are one-quarter wavelength apart. Part (a) shows the equilibrium positions of the particles. Parts (b)–(j) show the positions and velocities of the same particles at various instants during one complete cycle. For example, in (b) point P_1 is at its equilibrium position and has a maximum velocity toward the right. By following the dotted curve downward, we may find the positions and velocities of particle P_1 after successive intervals of $\frac{1}{8}$ of the period. Particle P_5 has the same motion as P_1 since it is exactly one wavelength away from P_1.

of the curves show the displacement X plotted against x as abscissa. The curves of Fig. 9 correspond to the plots given in Fig. 8. If we wish to find the actual position x' of a given particle at any time, we note that

$$x' = x + X,$$

where x is the coordinate of the equilibrium position of this particle; thus, we may write

$$x' = x + A \sin 2\pi f(t - x/v).$$

For reasons of convenience, we shall use plots like those shown in Fig. 9 in representing longitudinal waves.

There are other convenient ways in which the equations for sinusoidal

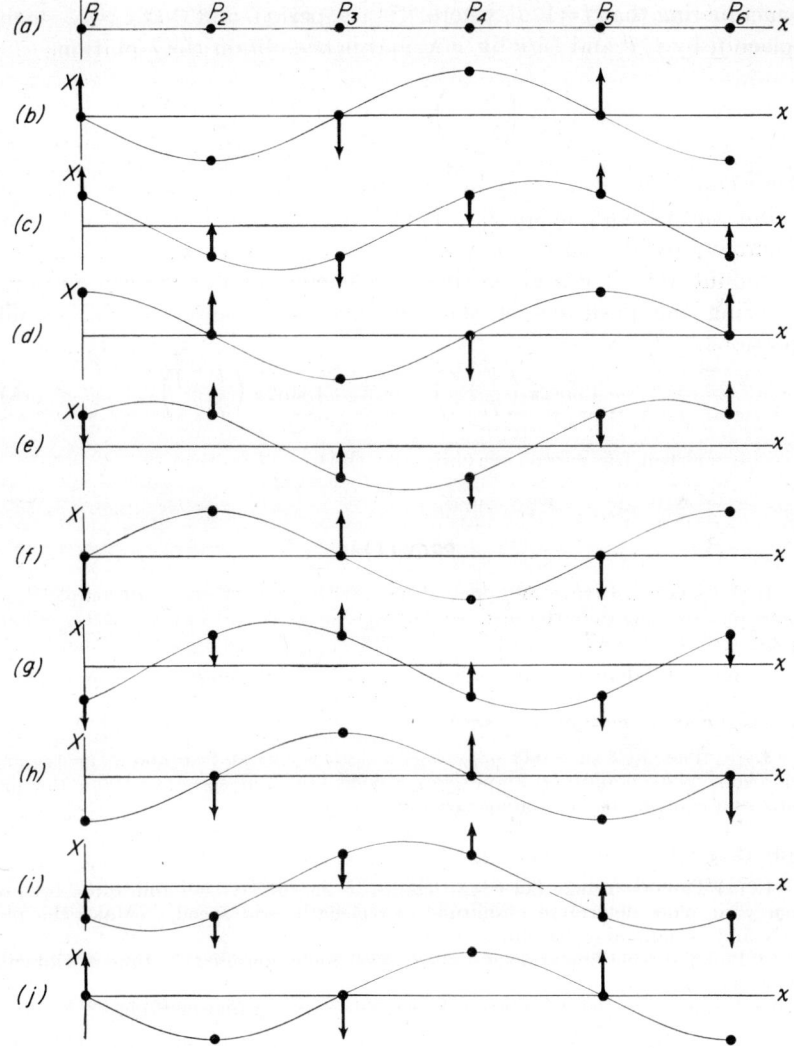

Fig. 9. Longitudinal *displacement* X for representative points in a coil spring at various times. The coordinate x of equilibrium positions of the points is plotted as abscissa; the horizontal displacement X as ordinate. The curves correspond to the plots of Fig. 8. The rate of change of X (the particle velocity) is denoted by the arrows.

waves can be written. One of these, for waves traveling in the $+x$-direction, is obtained as follows:

Transverse wave	*Longitudinal wave*
$y = A \sin 2\pi f(t - x/v)$	$X = A \sin 2\pi f(t - x/v)$
$y = A \sin 2\pi (ft - fx/v)$	$X = A \sin 2\pi (ft - fx/v).$

Remembering that $f = 1/T$, where T is the period, and that $v = f\lambda$, we may replace ft by t/T and fx/v by x/λ, and hence obtain the equations

$$y = A \sin 2\pi \left(\frac{t}{T} - \frac{x}{\lambda}\right), \qquad X = A \sin 2\pi \left(\frac{t}{T} - \frac{x}{\lambda}\right). \tag{7}$$

These equations are useful in showing that a wave motion is periodic in time and periodic in space. Thus, for a particle at a given position x, a complete oscillation of the particle takes place whenever t changes by an amount $\Delta t = T$; at a given time t, we encounter all phases of motion by observing the positions of the particles in a region $\Delta x = \lambda$. Similar equations:

$$y = A \sin 2\pi \left(\frac{t}{T} + \frac{x}{\lambda}\right), \qquad X = A \sin 2\pi \left(\frac{t}{T} + \frac{x}{\lambda}\right) \tag{8}$$

may be written for waves traveling in the $-x$-direction.

PROBLEMS

1. A fisherman sitting on a dock observes that his float makes 10 complete oscillations in 4 sec and that the distance between crests of the waves is 2 ft. What is the speed of the waves? *Ans: 5 ft/sec.*

2. A fisherman in an anchored boat observes that the crest of a wave passes him every 2 sec, and that it takes 4 sec for the crest to move the 40-ft length of the boat. What is the wavelength of the waves?

3. (a) Plot $y = 3 \sin 2\pi(60t - \tfrac{1}{2}x)$ against x (in cm) at $t = 0$ and at $t = \tfrac{1}{480}$ sec. From your plots determine amplitude, wavelength, and speed. (Make the plots neatly and explain your reasoning carefully.)

(b) Plot the same function against t at $x = 0$, and determine the time of vibration. Verify that in this case $\lambda = vT$.

4. (a) Plot $y = 3 \sin 2\pi(60t + \tfrac{1}{2}x)$ against x (in cm) at $t = 0$ and at $t = \tfrac{1}{480}$ sec. From your plots determine amplitude, wavelength, and speed. (Make the plots neatly and explain your reasoning carefully.)

(b) Plot the same function against t at $x = 0$, and determine the time of vibration. Verify that in this case $\lambda = vT$.

What is the essential difference between this case and that of Prob. 1?

5. The speed of transverse waves in a certain string is 50 ft/sec. This string is excited at one end by a device like that shown in Fig. 6. If the oscillation frequency of the body attached to the end of the string is 5 cycles/sec, what is the wavelength of the waves in the string? *Ans: 10 ft.*

6. If the tension in the string in Prob. 5 were doubled, what would be the speed of transverse waves in the string? What would be the wavelength of the waves produced when one end of the string is subjected to transverse displacements at a frequency of 5 cycles/sec? of 12 cycles/sec?

7. Sinusoidal transverse waves of frequency 8.0 cycles/sec are passing along a string. The distance between a crest and the adjacent troughs is 4.5 ft. What is the wavelength? What is the speed of the wave motion? *Ans: 9.0 ft; 72 ft/sec.*

8. If the tension in the string in Prob. 7 were doubled, what would be the speed of transverse waves? What would be the wavelength? What would be the distance from a crest to the following trough?

9. A sinusoidal wave train is moving along a certain string. The equation giving the displacement y m of a point at coordinate x m on the string as a function of time t sec has the following form:

$$y = 0.12 \sin[2\pi \cdot 8(t - x/50)].$$

Find the following quantities: (a) the amplitude of the wave motion, (b) the frequency of the wave motion, (c) the speed of the wave motion, and (d) the wavelength. (e) In which direction is the wave moving?
  Ans: (a) 12 cm; (b) 8 cycles/sec; (c) 50 m/sec; (d) 6.25 m; (e) $+x$-direction.

10. The equation describing a certain wave motion is

$$y = 0.08 \sin 20\pi (t - x/45) \text{ m}$$

at position x m and time t sec. Find (a) the amplitude of the waves, (b) the frequency of the motion, (c) the speed of propagation of the waves, (d) the wavelength, and (e) the period of oscillation of the source.

11. Sinusoidal longitudinal waves are sent out in a coil spring, from a vibrating source at one end of the spring as in Fig. 7. The frequency of vibration of the source is 20 cycles/sec. The distance between successive condensations in the spring is 30 cm. Find the speed of a condensation as it moves along the spring. The maximum longitudinal displacement of a particle in the spring is 4 cm. Write an equation for this wave motion for waves moving in the $+x$-direction if the source is at $x = 0$ and the displacement at the source is zero when $t = 0$.
  Ans: 6.00 m/sec; $X = 0.04 \sin 40\pi (t - x/6)$ m.

12. A source vibrating at a frequency of 12 cycles/sec produces longitudinal waves of amplitude 0.04 m in a coil spring. The speed of propagation of longitudinal waves in the spring is 20 m/sec. Write an equation describing this motion.

13. The equation for a transverse wave in a certain string is given by

$$y = 0.08 \sin 2\pi \left(\frac{t}{0.2} + \frac{x}{2} \right),$$

where x, y, and t represent numbers of meters and seconds. Find: (a) the amplitude of the waves, (b) the period of the motion of a particle in the string, (c) the wavelength, (d) the frequency, (e) the speed of propagation of the waves, and (f) the displacement of a particle at $x = 0.5$ when $t = 0$. In which direction is the wave moving? Plot a curve showing the displacement of a particle at the origin as a function of time.
  Ans: (a) 0.08 m; (b) 0.2 sec; (c) 2 m; (d) 5 cycles/sec; (e) 10 m/sec; (f) $+0.08$ m; the $+x$-direction.

14. Answer all questions asked in Prob. 13 for a transverse wave whose equation is

$$y = 0.05 \sin 2\pi \left(\frac{t}{0.10} - \frac{x}{1.5} \right).$$

Plot a curve showing the displacements at points along the string at time $t = 0$.

15. If $y = 0.12 \cos(5t - 4x)$ is the equation of a transverse wave on a string (x and y in cm, t in sec), (a) which way is the wave going? (b) what is the wavelength? (c) what is the frequency? (d) what is the period? (e) what is the speed of propagation?
  Ans: (a) $+x$-direction; (b) 1.57 cm; (c) 0.796 sec^{-1}; (d) 1.26 sec; (e) 1.25 cm/sec.

16. A transverse wave traveling along a rope is given by

$$y = 5 \sin(60t + 3x),$$

where y is the vertical distance in feet, x is measured in feet along the rope, and t is the time in seconds. (a) In what direction is the wave traveling if the positive direction of the x-axis is East? (b) What is the wavelength? (c) What is the frequency? (d) What is the amplitude? (e) What is the wave speed? (f) What is the time of one vibration of a small piece of the rope?

4. DERIVATION OF THE SPEED OF A TRANSVERSE WAVE ON A STRING*

We shall now write the differential equation satisfied by a simple sinusoidal wave of the type we have been discussing and use this equation in deriving an expression for the speed of a transverse wave on a string.

To obtain the desired differential equation, let us first write an expression for the second derivative of y with respect to t when x is constant† in (5):

$$y = A \sin 2\pi f(t - x/v)$$
$$\partial y/\partial t = 2\pi f A \cos 2\pi f(t - x/v)$$
$$\partial^2 y/\partial t^2 = -4\pi^2 f^2 A \sin 2\pi f(t - x/v)$$

or
$$\partial^2 y/\partial t^2 = -4\pi^2 f^2 y. \tag{9}$$

Similarly, we may take derivatives of y with respect to x when t is constant; thus,

$$\partial y/\partial x = -(2\pi f/v) A \cos 2\pi f(t - x/v)$$
$$\partial^2 y/\partial x^2 = -(4\pi^2 f^2/v^2) A \sin 2\pi f(t - x/v)$$

or
$$\partial^2 y/\partial x^2 = -(4\pi^2 f^2/v^2) y. \tag{10}$$

By combining (9) and (10) we obtain the differential equation

$$\frac{\partial^2 y}{\partial x^2} = \frac{1}{v^2} \frac{\partial^2 y}{\partial t^2}, \tag{11}$$

which applies to a transverse wave traveling in either the $+x$- or $-x$-direction; proof that (11) applies to waves traveling in the $-x$-direction is left as a problem. The corresponding differential equation for a longitudinal wave is

$$\frac{\partial^2 X}{\partial x^2} = \frac{1}{v^2} \frac{\partial^2 X}{\partial t^2}. \tag{12}$$

Although we derived equation (11) for a sinusoidal wave, it will be noted that neither frequency f nor wavelength λ appears in the equation. The equation actually applies to *any type* of transverse wave traveling in a direction parallel to the x-axis; similarly, equation (12) holds for any type of longitudinal wave.‡

Let us now derive an expression for the speed of a transverse wave in a string *when the amplitude of the motion is small*. Consider the element

---

* This section may be omitted without loss of continuity.

† The symbols $\partial/\partial t$ and $\partial^2/\partial t^2$ denote differentiation with respect to t when x is held constant; similarly $\partial/\partial x$ and $\partial^2/\partial x^2$ denote differentiation with respect to x at a constant value of t.

‡ See the discussion of Fourier's theorem in Sec. 7 for a verification of this assertion.

of length Δs in Fig. 10, which gives the configuration of the string at a certain instant. The tension T acts on the ends of the element as shown in the enlarged drawing of part (b). The y-component of the resultant force on this element of length has the value

$$\Sigma F_y = T \sin\theta_1 - T \sin\theta_2 = T(\sin\theta_1 - \sin\theta_2).$$

If the amplitude of motion is small, the angles θ_1 and θ_2 will be small in comparison with one radian, and we can set

$$\sin\theta_1 = \tan\theta_1 \quad \text{and} \quad \sin\theta_2 = \tan\theta_2.$$

However, the magnitude of $\tan\theta_1$ is simply the slope of the curve at point

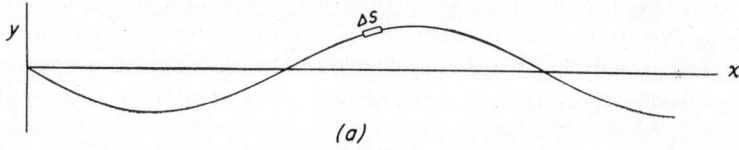

(a)

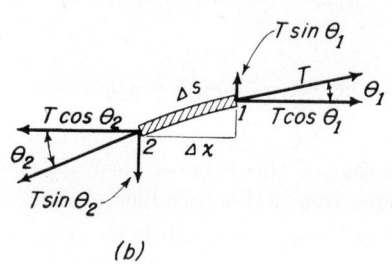

(b)

Fig. 10.

1 and $\tan\theta_2$ is the slope at point 2. Thus, denoting the slopes at points 1 and 2 by $[\partial y/\partial x]_1$ and $[\partial y/\partial x]_2$, respectively, we may write

$$\Sigma F_y = T([\partial y/\partial x]_1 - [\partial y/\partial x]_2).$$

Since Δs is small, we may approximate $[\partial y/\partial x]_1$ by

$$[\partial y/\partial x]_1 = [\partial y/\partial x]_2 + [\partial^2 y/\partial x^2]_2 \, \Delta x,$$

where Δx is the projection of Δs on the x-axis. This equation gives the approximate value

$$\Sigma F_y = T[\partial^2 y/\partial x^2]_2 \, \Delta x$$

for the y component of the resultant force.

This force will give a y-component of acceleration $\partial^2 y/\partial t^2$ of the center of mass of the element that can be obtained from Newton's second law:

$$\Sigma F_y = \mu \, \Delta s \, \partial^2 y/\partial t^2,$$

where $\mu \, \Delta s$ is the mass of the element. We now let point 1 approach point 2 so that Δs becomes infinitesimal. Then Δx approaches $\Delta s \cos\theta_2$. But since θ_2 is assumed small, $\cos\theta_2 = 1 - \tfrac{1}{2}\theta_2^2 + \cdots \approx 1$, and we can set $\Delta x = \Delta s$. Then

$$\Sigma F_y = T(\partial^2 y/\partial x^2)\, \Delta s = \mu\, \Delta s\, \partial^2 y/\partial t^2,$$

or
$$\frac{\partial^2 y}{\partial x^2} = \frac{\mu}{T} \frac{\partial^2 y}{\partial t^2}. \tag{13}$$

Equation (13) becomes identical with (11) if we identify the term T/μ with v^2; that is, to make (11) consistent with Newton's laws we must set

$$v = \sqrt{T/\mu}. \tag{14}$$

Equation (14) for the speed of a transverse wave in a string, derived by applying Newton's laws to the motion of an infinitesimal element of the string, has already been stated and used in Sec. 2. The above derivation of this speed is rigorous for the case of sinusoidal waves of small amplitude.

PROBLEM

1. Start with equation (5') for a wave traveling in the $-x$-direction and derive equation (11).

5. SPEEDS OF WAVES OF VARIOUS TYPES

The expression $v = \sqrt{T/\mu}$ for the speed of a transverse wave in a string is an example of the type of formula that applies to any wave motion. The force required to produce a given transverse displacement of a point in a stretched string is directly porportional to the tension T; hence we may consider the tension as a measure of the 'stiffness factor' or 'elasticity factor' of the string for transverse displacements. The mass per unit length μ can be considered as the 'inertia factor' for transverse motion. We may generalize the expression for wave speed in the form

$$\text{wave speed} = \sqrt{\frac{\text{stiffness factor}}{\text{inertia factor}}}. \tag{15}$$

This type of equation is applicable to mechanical wave motion in any type of medium, provided we select the appropriate quantities to measure the stiffness factor and the inertia factor. In this text we cannot attempt to derive expressions for the speeds of all the types of waves commonly encountered, but we can write down the expressions for the speed of several types of waves and show that they follow the form of (15).

First, let us write the expression for the speed of a *longitudinal wave* in a rod. In this type of wave, the adjacent molecules are alternately pushed closer together or pulled farther apart than their normal equilibrium separation. From our discussion in Chap. 9, we recall that the longitudinal stiffness of a rod is governed by Young's modulus E_Y. The inertia factor is the mass per unit volume of the rod, that is, the density ρ of the material of which the rod is composed. The expression for the speed v_L of a longitudinal wave in a rod is

$$v_L = \sqrt{E_Y/\rho}. \tag{16}$$

It should be noted that, although we may produce large variations in the speed of a transverse wave in a string by adjusting the tension T, we can do little to change the speed of a longitudinal wave in a rod, since the speed of a longitudinal wave is determined by properties of the *material* of which the rod is composed and not by the condition of stretch.

Formula (16), like all the other formulas we give for the speeds of waves, applies rigorously only to the case of waves of small amplitude, which means that the amplitude must be small compared to the wavelength in the case of sinusoidal waves.

The speed of a longitudinal wave in a coil spring is given by

$$v_L = \sqrt{k/\mu}, \tag{17}$$

where k is the force constant of the spring and μ again represents the mass per unit length.

Now let us write the expression for the speed of a *longitudinal wave* traversing an *extended solid*, rather than a thin rod or wire as in (16). The expression for this speed is

$$v_L = \sqrt{(E_B + \tfrac{4}{3}E_S)/\rho}, \tag{18}$$

where E_B is the bulk modulus, E_S the shear modulus, and ρ the density of the solid. In this case, the bulk modulus and shear modulus are both involved in the stiffness term and ρ is the inertia factor. In the case of a *transverse wave* in an extended solid body, the inertia factor is again given by the density but the shear modulus alone constitutes the stiffness factor; the speed v_T of a transverse wave is given by

$$v_T = \sqrt{E_S/\rho}. \tag{19}$$

Comparison of (18) with (19) indicates that the speed of a longitudinal wave in a solid is always greater than the speed of a transverse wave in the same solid.

An ideal fluid medium has no rigidity, so no transverse wave can be transmitted. The expression for the speed v_L of a longitudinal wave in a fluid is given by

$$v_L = \sqrt{E_B/\rho}, \tag{20}$$

where the bulk modulus E_B is the stiffness factor and the density ρ is the inertia factor. In the case of a gas the equation is the same, but one must use the adiabatic bulk modulus. We shall discuss this question further in connection with the transmission of sound waves through gases.

The above formulas are directly applicable to the transmission of sound through various media, and will be employed in the discussions of Chap. 22.

6. ENERGY ASSOCIATED WITH A TRANSVERSE WAVE IN A STRING

As we mentioned in the introduction to this chapter, one of the chief reasons for our interest in wave motion is that energy can be transmitted from one point to another by waves. In Chap. 22 we shall consider in some detail the transmission of energy by sound waves, but it may be well at this point to discuss the energy relationships involved in the passage of a transverse wave along a stretched string or flexible wire.

In such a wave, each point in the string is executing simple harmonic motion in a direction perpendicular to the direction of propagation of the wave motion. Thus, the mechanical energy of a particle in the string is given by

mechanical energy = kinetic energy + potential energy.

Also, as shown in Chap. 11, the mechanical energy of a particle executing simple harmonic motion is just equal to the maximum value of the particle's kinetic energy, or

mechanical energy = maximum value of kinetic energy.

The restoring force in this simple harmonic motion arises from the tension in the adjoining portions of the string, as discussed in Sec. 5.

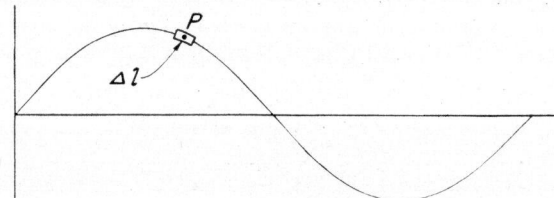

Fig. 11. The point P is at the center of mass of the element of length Δl.

Now let us treat an element of length Δl of the string as a 'particle' of mass $\mu \Delta l$ and calculate the mechanical energy associated with this particle. In treating a length element of string as a particle, we consider the motion of its center of mass indicated by point P in Fig. 11. The y-displacement of point P in this figure is given by the equation

$$y = A \sin 2\pi f(t - x/v),$$

where x is the x-coordinate of the point and A is the amplitude of vibration. Therefore, the velocity v_y of the particle is given by

$$v_y = \partial y/\partial t = 2\pi f A \cos 2\pi f(t-x/v).$$

Since the velocity is a maximum when $\cos 2\pi f(t-x/v) = 1$, we may write

$$v_{y\ \max} = 2\pi f A. \tag{21}$$

Therefore, the maximum value of the kinetic energy of a length Δl of the string is given by

$$\text{K.E.}_{\max} = \tfrac{1}{2}\mu \Delta l\, v_{y\ \max}^2 = \tfrac{1}{2}\mu \Delta l\, 4\pi^2 f^2 A^2 = 2\pi^2 \mu \Delta l\, f^2 A^2.$$

Since this is equal to the mechanical energy associated with a length element Δl of string, the mechanical energy W, *per unit length*, is given by

$$W = 2\pi^2 \mu f^2 A^2. \tag{22}$$

Thus, the *energy per unit length* in a string or flexible wire, along which a transverse wave travels, *is proportional to the square of the amplitude of vibration*. A similar expression can be derived for a longitudinal wave.

Since (22) gives the energy of each unit length of string, we may find the total energy transferred each second past a given point such as P by noting that the speed of the wave motion is v and asserting that all the mechanical energy in a length $v\,\Delta t$ of string passes point P in time Δt.*
From (22) this amount of energy is seen to be

$$Wv\,\Delta t = [2\pi^2 \mu f^2 A^2]\, v\, \Delta t,$$

and hence the energy passing point p per unit time is given by

$$2\pi^2 \mu f^2 A^2\, v,$$

where it should be noted that v *is used here to denote the speed of the wave.*

The expression above is just the *power P* transmitted by the wave:

$$P = 2\pi^2 \mu f^2 A^2\, v. \tag{23}$$

Thus, the power transmitted by a wave passing along a given stretched string is proportional to the square of the amplitude of the waves and to the square of the frequency of the source.

An expression similar to (23) can be developed for longitudinal waves in a wire. For waves in an extended isotropic medium, an expression analogous to (23) can be derived for the power transmitted through unit area by the wave. This will be done in Chap. 22, Properties of Sound Waves.

* We have not justified this assertion. It is reasonable, but a computation of the work done *by* each section of the string *on* the succeeding section is required to justify it. This justification is not difficult (see Prob. 8 at the end of this section).

PROBLEMS

1. Transverse waves of frequency 4 cycles/sec and wavelength 2.5 m are transmitted along a flexible rope. The amplitude of the wave motion is 20 cm. What is the speed of propagation of the wave? What is the magnitude of the maximum velocity of a particle in the rope? *Ans: 10 m/sec; 5.03 m/sec.*

2. Transverse waves of frequency 5 cycles/sec and wavelength 8.0 ft are transmitted along a flexible rope. The amplitude of the wave is 3 in. What is the speed of propagation of the wave? What is the magnitude of the maximum velocity of a particle in the rope?

3. If the rope in Prob. 1 is 20 m long and its mass is 1 kg, how much mechanical energy is associated with each meter of the rope as a result of the wave motion? How much energy is transmitted past a point in the rope each second?
Ans: 0.632 joule; 6.32 w.

4. If the rope in Prob. 2 is 75 ft long and weighs 3.0 lbf, how much energy is associated with each foot of the rope as a result of the wave motion? At what rate is energy transmitted past a point in the rope by the wave?

5. Transverse waves of 6-inch amplitude and 4-ft wavelength travel along a rope at a speed of 40 ft/sec. The rope is 100 ft long and has a mass of 0.16 slug. How much power is transmitted along the rope? *Ans: 31.6 ft·lbf/sec.*

6. A rope with a 'linear density' of 200 g/m transmits transverse waves of amplitude 15 cm and frequency 15 cycles/sec. If the speed of propagation of the wave in the rope is 9 m/sec, what power is transmitted through the rope by the wave?

7. A rope transmits a transverse wave described by the equation $y = A \sin 2\pi f(t - x/v)$. Find the magnitude of the maximum acceleration of a particle in the rope. *Ans: $4\pi^2 f^2 A$.*

8. Consider the transverse wave

$$y = A \sin 2\pi f(t - x/v),$$

traveling *to the right* along a string. Consider a typical point of the string, located at $x = x_0$. Let the tension be T, and assume that the angle of the string with the x-axis is always small.

(a) Show that the y-component of force exerted *by* the string to the left of x_0 *on* the string to the right of x_0 is

$$F_y = -T(\partial y/\partial x)_{x=x_0} = 2\pi f \mu A \cos 2\pi f(t - x_0/v).$$

(b) Show that the work done by the force component in (a) during one second is

$$\int_0^1 F_y \, (\partial y/\partial t)_{x=x_0} \, dt = 2\pi^2 \mu f^2 A^2 v.$$

Since this represents work done *by* the string to the left of x_0 *on* the string to the right, it represents power transmitted *to the right* and furnishes the derivation of (23).

9. Show that the right side of (23) has the unit *watt* when the quantities are in MKS units and the unit *ft·lbf/sec* when the quantities are in ft-slug-sec units.

7. INTERFERENCE PHENOMENA; THE SUPERPOSITION PRINCIPLE

Thus far, we have considered the passage of a *single* wave disturbance—a pulse or a continuous wave train—through a medium. However, it is possible for two or more waves to pass through a medium simultaneously. Let us now consider the effects when *two* transverse wave trains pass simultaneously along a stretched string. In this case, the resultant lateral displacement y of a point in the string is simply the sum of the displacements it would have if each wave train traveled along the string by itself. In other words, if the first wave train alone would produce displacement y_1, and if the second wave train alone would produce displacement y_2, the resultant displacement is given by

$$y = y_1 + y_2. \qquad (24)$$

In other words, *the effects of the two waves superpose*, and equation (24) gives a statement of this *superposition principle*.*

When two waves traveling in the same direction are superposed, the shape of the string at any instant can be determined by the method illustrated in Fig. 12. The displacements y_1 arising from the first wave are given by the light solid curve and the displacements y_2 arising from the

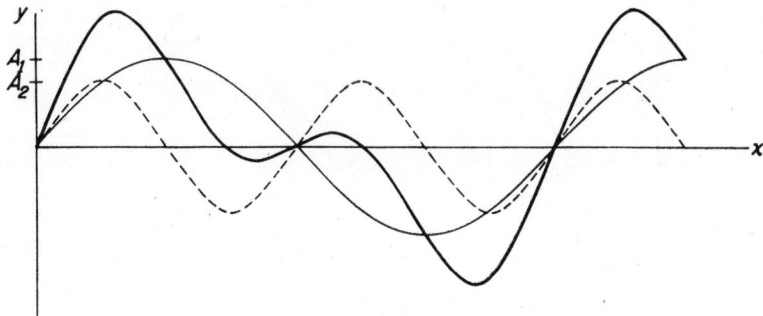

Fig. 12. Superposition of two waves moving in the $+x$-direction:

for the light curve $\quad y_1 = A_1 \sin 2\pi f_1(t - x/v)$,
for the broken curve $\quad y_2 = A_2 \sin 2\pi f_2(t - x/v)$,
$\quad$ where $\quad A_2 = \frac{3}{4} A_1 \quad$ and $\quad f_2 = 2f_1$,
for the heavy curve $\quad y = y_1 + y_2$.

second wave are given by the broken curve. The resultant displacements are given by the heavy curve, which was obtained by adding the displacements y_1 and y_2 for every point along the string. Since the speeds of the two wave trains in the string are the same, waves with the shape given by the heavy curve will travel along the string with the same speed as that of the component waves in the string.† A person watching the string would observe the passage of wave trains with the complicated shape given by the heavy curve in Fig. 12 and would not realize immediately that two *sinusoidal* wave trains were traveling along the wire.

* The superposition principle holds because the differential equation (11) is *linear*; that is, if $y_1(x,t)$ and $y_2(x,t)$ are solutions, so is $y = y_1 + y_2$.

† NOTE: In certain types of wave motion, the speeds of sinusoidal waves of different wavelengths in a given medium are not the same. In these cases, the apparent speed of a composite wave will be different from the speeds of the component waves. Two types of speed are defined, called the *group velocity* and the *phase velocity;* the medium is called a *dispersive medium*. Examples are found in the case of water waves, and in the passage of light waves through glass or water, which are dispersive media for light waves. Elastic media are not usually dispersive for mechanical waves of small amplitude, so we shall not discuss this subject in detail here.

One important case involves the passage of two wave trains of the same frequency, both traveling in the $+x$-direction. Let the equations of the two wave trains be given by

$$y_1 = A_1 \sin 2\pi f(t-x/v), \quad y_2 = A_2 \sin[2\pi f(t-x/v)+\phi], \quad (25)$$

where ϕ represents the phase difference between the waves.

In the case $\phi = 0$, the resulting wave train has the form

$$y = (A_1+A_2)\sin 2\pi f(t-x/v).$$

In this case in which the two wave trains are exactly in phase, the resulting wave train is similar to the component waves and has an amplitude

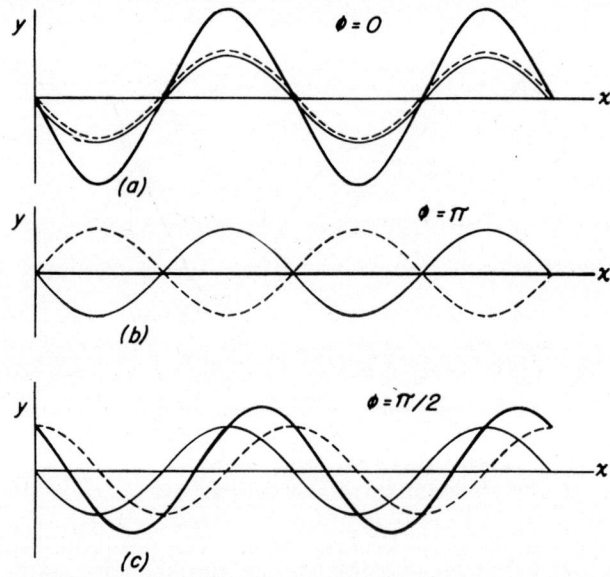

Fig. 13. Interference of two sinusoidal waves of the same amplitude and the same frequency, *traveling in the same direction*, for three values of phase difference. The two waves are represented by the light solid and broken curves, the resultant by the heavy curve. In (a) the interference is *constructive*, in (b) *destructive*, in (c) intermediate.

equal to the sum of the amplitudes of the component waves; the resulting configuration at a given time is given by Fig. 13(a). The two waves are said to 'interfere constructively.'

In the case $\phi = \pi$ in (25), the two component waves produce displacements in opposite directions since

$$\sin[2\pi f(t-x/v)+\pi] = -\sin 2\pi f(t-x/v).$$

Hence, by (24), the resultant displacement is

$$y = (A_1-A_2)\sin 2\pi f(t-x/v).$$

The two waves are said to 'interfere destructively.' A complete cancellation of the two component waves is obtained if $A_1 = A_2$; this case is illustrated in Fig. 13(b). An observer would see no wave at all.

A case intermediate between the two we have discussed is illustrated in Fig. 13(c). In this case, $\phi = \frac{1}{2}\pi$ and $A_1 = A_2$.

Now let us consider the important case of two sinusoidal transverse wave trains of *equal* amplitude and the same frequency traveling in *opposite directions* along a string. This is a case frequently met in practice, as we shall see in the next section. Let the first wave, traveling toward the right in Fig. 14(a), be described by the equation

$$y_1 = A \sin 2\pi f(t - x/v),$$

and the second wave, traveling toward the *left* in Fig. 14(b), be described by

$$y_2 = A \sin 2\pi f(t + x/v).$$

Then, from (24), the combination of these two waves is given by

$$y = A \sin 2\pi f(t - x/v) + A \sin 2\pi f(t + x/v). \tag{26}$$

Recalling the relations for sums and differences of angles:

$$\sin(a+b) = \sin a \cos b + \cos a \sin b, \quad \sin(a-b) = \sin a \cos b - \cos a \sin b,$$

we may write equation (26) in the form

$$y = [2A \cos 2\pi fx/v] \sin 2\pi ft$$

or
$$y = [2A \cos 2\pi x/\lambda] \sin 2\pi ft. \tag{27}$$

The wave pattern given by (27) is called a *standing wave*; the motion associated with this type of wave is illustrated in Fig. 14(c), (d), (e), and (f), for four positions of the component traveling waves. The particles in the standing wave (27) execute simple harmonic motion of frequency f about their equilibrium positions. However, the amplitude of their motion (given by $2A \cos 2\pi x/\lambda$) is not the same for all points along the string as in the case of a traveling wave, but varies from a maximum value of $2A$ at the points $x = 0$, $\frac{1}{2}\lambda$, λ, $\frac{3}{2}\lambda$, $\cdots$ at which $\cos 2\pi x/\lambda = \pm 1$ to zero at the points $x = \frac{1}{4}\lambda$, $\frac{3}{4}\lambda$, $\frac{5}{4}\lambda$, $\frac{7}{4}\lambda$, $\cdots$ at which $\cos 2\pi x/\lambda = 0$.

For the standing wave pattern shown in Fig. 14, the motions of all particles in the region between $x = 0$ and $x = \frac{1}{4}\lambda$ are exactly in time phase with one another and with the motion of particles in the region between $x = \frac{3}{4}\lambda$ and $x = \frac{5}{4}\lambda$, but are π radians out of phase with the motion of particles in the region between $x = \frac{1}{4}\lambda$ and $x = \frac{3}{4}\lambda$ and in the region between $x = \frac{5}{4}\lambda$ and $x = \frac{7}{4}\lambda$. This phase relationship is illustrated schematically in Fig. 15, which indicates that when particles in a length of the string equal to one-half wavelength are going *up*, the particles in the immediately neighboring parts of the string are going *down*.

It will be noted from Fig. 14 that at certain points in the string the particles never leave their equilibrium positions. These points, denoted by N in Fig. 16, are called *nodes*. The points midway between the nodes are points at which the amplitude of vibration is a maximum. These

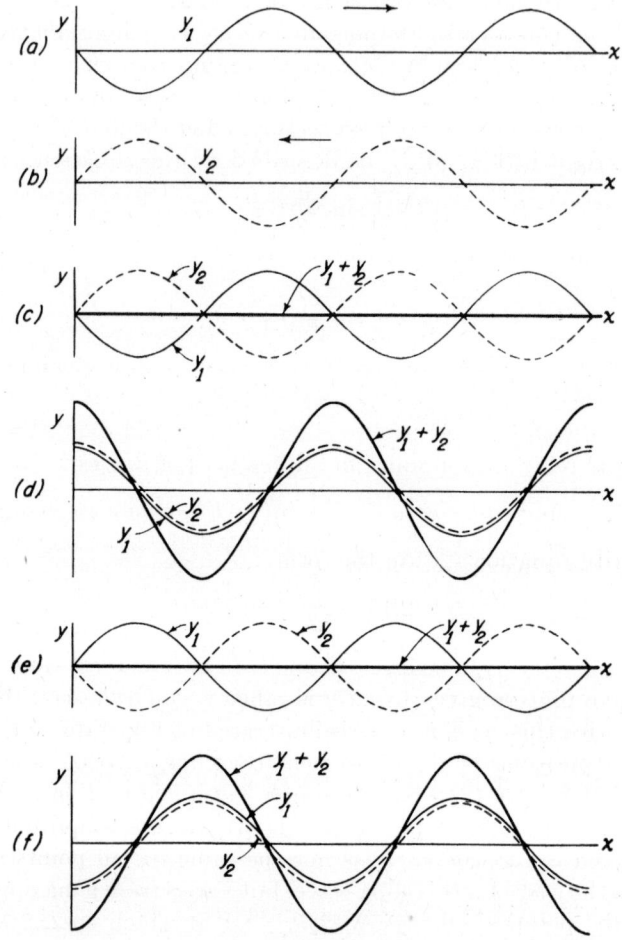

Fig. 14. A standing wave is produced when two waves of the same frequency travel *in opposite directions*. The traveling waves y_1 and y_2 are shown in (a) and (b). The resultant wave $y_1 + y_2$ is shown, at four times during a complete cycle, in (c), (d), (e), and (f).

points are called *antinodes* or *loops* and are denoted by L in Fig. 16. It should be noted that the wavelength λ of the component *traveling* waves which produce the standing wave is equal to the distance between *alternate* nodes or between *alternate* antinodes in the standing wave; that is, *twice* the distance between *adjacent* nodes or *adjacent* antinodes.

Sec. 7] INTERFERENCE PHENOMENA; THE SUPERPOSITION PRINCIPLE

A standing wave may be regarded as a *stationary interference pattern* produced when two traveling wave trains of the same wavelength traveling in opposite directions *interfere*. The interference is *destructive* at the nodes where there is no motion and *constructive* at the antinodes where the amplitude is equal to the sum of the amplitudes of the component waves. If two traveling waves of different wavelength are traversing a medium, no *stationary* interference pattern can be formed.

As somewhat of a digression, a further remark might be made concerning one aspect of the superposition principle. We have used the superposition principle for two waves, but the principle also holds for any

Fig. 15. Velocities of particles in a standing wave. When particles in a length of string equal to half a wavelength are going *up*, particles in the neighboring portions of the string are going *down*.

number of component waves. Thus, equation (24) could be generalized in the form

$$y = y_1 + y_2 + y_3 + y_4 + \cdots$$

for any number of components. As we have seen, two sinusoidal waves of different wavelength combine to form a resultant wave which is nonsinusoidal and which may appear quite complicated. This fact might lead us to wonder whether it might not be possible to approximate *any* periodic waveform whatever by the sum of a series of sinusoidal waves.

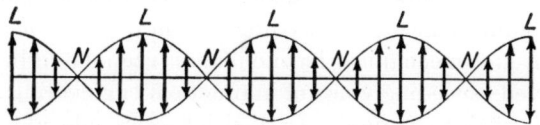

Fig. 16. A standing wave pattern. The curves show extremes of displacements for various points. At nodes N there is no displacement; at antinodes or loops L maximum displacements occur.

That this is indeed possible was discovered in 1807 by the French mathematician Fourier, who formulated the general theorem:

FOURIER'S THEOREM: *Any periodic function can be expressed as the sum of sine and cosine functions.*

This theorem is applicable not only to waves, which are periodic in both time and space, but to any periodic function of either time or space; for example, the periodic motion of a pendulum swinging with large amplitude can be described by a sum of sine and cosine functions of time. Fourier's theorem is important in the study of wave motion; by applying this theorem, we are able to solve problems in terms of sines and cosines, which are simple and familiar mathematical functions, instead of in terms of complicated functions expressible perhaps only numerically.

Methods have been developed for computing the component sine and cosine functions whose sum represents any given periodic function; the resulting sum of sinusoidal components is called the *Fourier series* of the function. If the equation of the arbitrary periodic function is *not* known

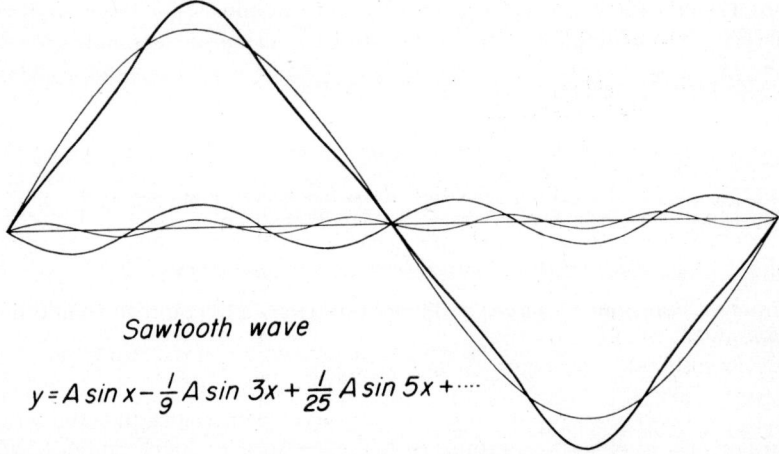

Fig. 17. The sawtooth wave can be approximated by a series of sine terms.

but a graph of the function is available, the component sinusoidal functions can be found by means of instruments known as *harmonic analyzers;* both electrical and mechanical harmonic analyzers have been developed and have proved exceedingly useful in practical engineering and in purely scientific work. As an example of a Fourier series, consider the sawtooth waveform. The Fourier series for such a wave is

$$y = A \sin x - \tfrac{1}{9} A \sin 3x + \tfrac{1}{25} A \sin 5x + \cdots.$$

The first three terms of this series are shown by the light lines of Fig. 17 and their sum is given by the heavy curve. The first three terms give a good rough approximation of the sawtooth wave-shape, and the addition of a few more terms would give a much closer approximation.

PROBLEMS

1. Plot the following curves from $x = 0$ to 4π:

$$y_1 = 4 \sin x \quad \text{and} \quad y_2 = \sin 2x.$$

By adding ordinates, find the resultant curve $y = y_1 + y_2$ formed by superposition of these two curves. The resultant curve might represent the configuration of a string at a given instant when two transverse waves are present.

2. Plot the following curves from $x=0$ to 4π:

$$y_1 = 4\sin x \quad \text{and} \quad y_2 = 3\sin 3x.$$

By adding ordinates find the curve $y = y_1 + y_2$ for superposition of these two curves.

3. Two transverse waves of equal amplitude and wavelength are traveling in opposite directions along a string. If the equations of the two waves are

$$y_1 = 2\sin 2\pi(t - \tfrac{1}{4}x) \quad \text{and} \quad y_2 = 2\sin 2\pi(t + \tfrac{1}{4}x),$$

compute and plot the shape of the string in the region between $x=0$ and $x=4$ at the times $t=0$, $t=\tfrac{1}{4}$, $t=\tfrac{1}{2}$, $t=\tfrac{3}{4}$, and $t=1$.

4. The distance between a node and the adjacent antinodes in a standing wave is 50 cm. What is the wavelength of the component waves?

5. The distance between adjacent nodes in a standing wave is 2 ft. What is the wavelength of the component waves? *Ans: 4 ft.*

6. Write the equation of a standing wave of wavelength 1.5 m and frequency 15/sec.

8. REFLECTION OF WAVES; PRODUCTION OF STANDING WAVES

Let us now consider what happens when a transverse pulse advancing along a stretched string arrives at the end of the string.

If the end of the string is attached to a *rigid* support, the end of the string must remain at rest. The arriving pulse exerts a force on the support, and the reaction force exerted on the string by the support sets up a reflected pulse with its displacement in the direction opposite to that of the original pulse. The result is shown schematically in Fig. 18 for a pulse in a string attached to a rigid wall. It will be noted that in reflection the *shape* of the pulse remains unchanged; that is, the leading portion of the incident pulse and the leading portion of the reflected pulse are both steep. However, in the incident pulse the particles of the string are displaced *upward* whereas in the reflected pulse the particles suffer *downward* displacements; in other words, an incident *crest* is reflected as a *trough*. Similarly, an incident *trough* would be reflected as a *crest*. These phenomena occur when the support is *rigid*. It might also be noted that no energy is transmitted to the rigid support, since the support does not move and, therefore, the string does no work on it. The energy associated with the reflected pulse is evidently the same as that associated with the incident pulse if the support is perfectly rigid.

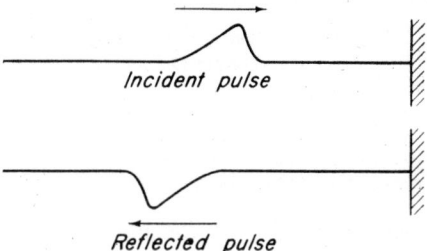

Fig. 18. Reflection of a transverse-wave pulse at a rigid wall. A *crest* is reflected as a *trough;* similarly, a *trough* would be reflected as a crest.

At the opposite extreme from a string with a rigidly fixed end would be a string with a perfectly *free* end. This case has little meaning in the case of a wave along a *stretched* string, since it is difficult to keep a string under finite and uniform tension if one end is *free*. However, reflection of a transverse wave from the free lower end of a rope hanging from a support can be observed, with the results shown in Fig. 19. By giving the rope a sudden sidewise thrust at a point near the support, an observer may produce a transverse pulse which travels down the rope as shown in part (a). After reaching the free end of the rope, the pulse is reflected as shown in part (b) and travels up the rope. It should be noted that the particles in both the incident and the reflected pulse are displaced toward the left. It might be mentioned that at the time when the incident pulse is reaching the free end and the reflected pulse is leaving the free end, the combined effects of both pulses result in a displacement of particles near the free end that is twice as large as the displacement arising from either pulse alone. To the observer standing near the upper end of the rope, the particles near the free end appear to 'overshoot' and in so doing set up the reflected wave. In the ideal case, the energy associated with the reflected pulse is just equal to the energy associated with the incident pulse.

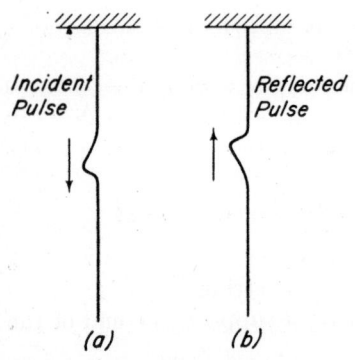

Fig. 19. Reflection of a transverse pulse from the free lower end of a rope hanging vertically. A *crest* is reflected as a *crest* and a *trough* is reflected as a *trough*. (At what part of the rope is the wave speed greatest?)

Whereas the rigidly fixed end of the string experiences *no* displacement when reflection occurs, the free end of a string experiences a *large* displacement. In reflection of a pulse at the fixed end of a string wave velocity and displacement are both reversed in direction; in reflection at a free end, wave velocity is reversed but displacement is unchanged.

Although reflection of transverse pulses at the free end of a string is not important to our present discussion of waves on *strings*, there are many analogous cases of importance. One of the cases encountered frequently is that of reflection of longitudinal vibrations in a solid. At a 'free' surface, in contact with air, a condensation is reflected in the solid as a condensation; similarly, a rarefaction is reflected as a rarefaction. At a fixed rigid boundary, the reverse is true; a condensation is reflected as a rarefaction, and vice versa. We shall discuss analogous types of phenomena in connection with reflection of sound waves in air columns and with reflection of light waves at boundaries between various media.

Just as transverse pulses are reflected at the ends of a string, so also will continuous transverse wave trains be reflected. When a continuous train of sinusoidal waves arrives at a fixed end of a stretched wire or string, a continuous train of reflected sinusoidal waves appears at the end and travels in the opposite direction. Thus, we have *two wave trains of the same wavelength traveling in opposite directions;* as we showed in the preceding section, this is the condition necessary for the production of a standing wave. It should be noted, however, that in the case of a stretched string there are *two* fixed ends; neither end of such a string can

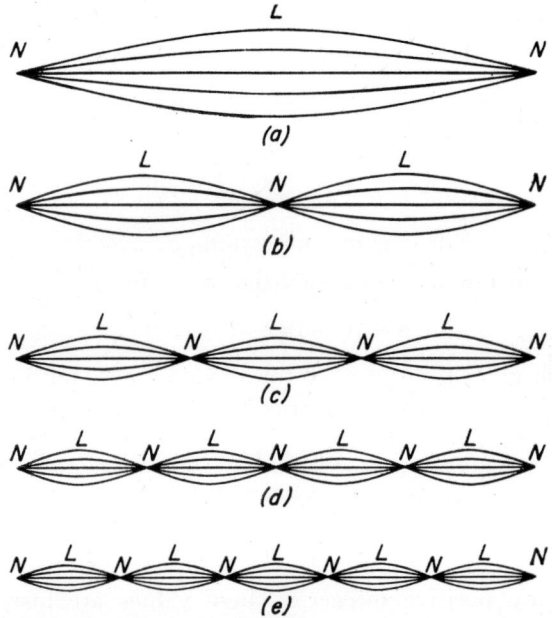

Fig. 20. Standing wave patterns in a stretched string. There is always a node at each end, where the string is attached to the rigid support. As we shall point out in Chap. 21, the simplest pattern shown in (a) gives the *fundamental mode of oscillation* of the string; the other patterns represent *higher modes of oscillation* of the string.

move, and therefore *the fixed ends of the string must appear as nodes in any standing wave pattern that may be formed.* This statement means that only for certain definite wavelengths will a standing wave pattern be formed in a given string; some of the possible wave patterns are shown in Fig. 20. The wavelength λ is equal to twice the distance between adjacent nodes. For the standing wave patterns shown in the diagrams of Fig. 20, the wavelengths are

(a): $\lambda = 2l = 2l/1$,

(b): $\lambda = l = 2l/2$,

(c): $\lambda = \tfrac{2}{3}l = 2l/3$,

(d): $\lambda = \tfrac{1}{2}l = 2l/4$,

(e): $\lambda = \tfrac{2}{5}l = 2l/5$.

Thus, the allowed values for the wavelengths that permit a standing wave pattern to be produced in a wire of length l are given by the general equation

$$\lambda = 2l/n, \qquad (n = 1, 2, 3, \cdots) \qquad (28)$$

when n can be any positive integer.

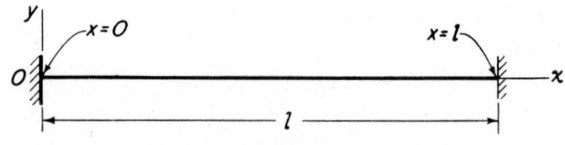

Fig. 21.

The analytic expression for the standing wave in a string with both ends fixed, as in Fig. 21, can be written in the form

$$y = [A \sin 2\pi x/\lambda] \cos 2\pi ft. \qquad (29)$$

This equation gives $y = 0$ at $x = 0$ for all values of λ, but in order for y to be zero also for $x = l$, we must restrict λ to the values that make

$$\sin 2\pi l/\lambda = 0.$$

These values for λ are given by $2\pi l/\lambda = n\pi$, or

$$\lambda = 2l/n,$$

where n is any positive integer. These values are just the ones we obtained in (28).

Thus, we see that reflections of transverse waves at the fixed ends of a stretched string can produce a standing wave pattern in the string only for waves of certain wavelengths λ. We shall have more to say on this subject in connection with the production of sound waves.

PROBLEMS

1. What is the longest wavelength of traveling waves that can produce a standing wave in a string 10 ft long? Ans: 20 ft.

2. Find the five longest wavelengths of traveling waves that can produce standing waves in a string 10 ft long.

3. Two waves, each of wavelength 5 ft, travel in opposite directions in a stretched string 20 ft long. How many loops are formed? Excluding the nodes at the *fixed* ends of the string, how many nodes appear in the string? Ans: 8 loops; 7 nodes.

4. A standing wave is set up in a string 10 ft long. There are 7 loops in the standing wave. What is the wavelength of the waves producing the pattern?

9. REFRACTION

We have considered the reflection of transverse waves at the fixed end of a string connected to a rigid support and at the *free* end of a string and in both cases have asserted that reflection was *complete*. These are limiting cases: (a) in the case of a *rigid* support the elastic force constant involved in the restoring forces *opposing the motions* of the particles of the support is so large (infinite) that the waves traveling down the wire can produce no displacement of the support and hence no energy can be imparted to the support; (b) at a *free* end there are *no* elastic restoring forces and hence no wave could be transmitted to the region of space beyond the free end. In these limiting cases, the wave motion is confined to the string and the energy remains confined to the string. However, these cases are never completely realized in practice; usually, some of the energy of the waves is transmitted into the 'medium' to which the ends of the string are attached. Thus, some of the energy of the wave

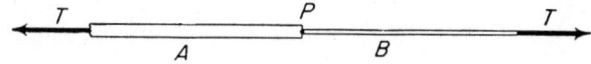

Fig. 22. A composite string.

reaching the ends of the string may be transmitted by waves produced in the not completely 'rigid' support at the fixed end or by longitudinal waves in the air at the 'free' end; in fact, if the string is in *air*, energy will be transferred from the string to the air along the whole length of the string.

Although we shall not give a quantitative discussion of the phenomena involved in the transmission of energy by waves passing from one medium to another, it may be desirable to give a few of the essential facts. Let us consider the string shown in Fig. 22; this string actually consists of two strings, of the same material but of different diameters, that have been joined together at point P. Since the *tension is the same in all parts of this composite string*, the speeds of transverse waves in the two parts of the string are different and their ratio is given by the expression

$$v_A/v_B = \sqrt{\mu_B/\mu_A},$$

since $v_A = \sqrt{T/\mu_A}$ and $v_B = \sqrt{T/\mu_B}$.

Therefore, if a wave travels toward the right in string A with speed v_A, waves are produced in string B as a result of the motion of point P, and these waves travel along string B with speed v_B; thus, a part of the energy associated with the incident wave in string A will be transmitted past point P into string B. However, some of the energy of the incident wave will be retained in string A as a result of partial reflection of the incident wave at point P. A part of the energy is transmitted and a part is reflected at the boundary at P between the two 'media'; this is always the case when any type of wave strikes a boundary between two media. The ratio of reflected energy to incident energy during any time interval is very large when the ratio of speeds in the two media is greatly different from unity; thus, in the case of two strings, a large fraction of the incident energy will be reflected if $v_A/v_B \gg 1$ or $v_A/v_B \ll 1$, and very little reflection will occur if $v_A \approx v_B$. These qualitative statements find application in many fields of physics: elasticity, acoustics, optics, and electromagnetic radiation.

As a result of velocity changes experienced by a wave in passing through a boundary between two extended media, the direction of a wave disturbance may be altered. This phenomenon is illustrated in Fig. 23, which shows a portion of a train of plane waves passing from medium A into medium B. The arrows give the direction of propagation. If $v_A < v_B$, the direction of propagation will change in the manner indicated. This effect is known as *refraction*. We shall discuss refraction fully in connection with light waves in Chap. 25; refraction is also important in certain acoustical phenomena.

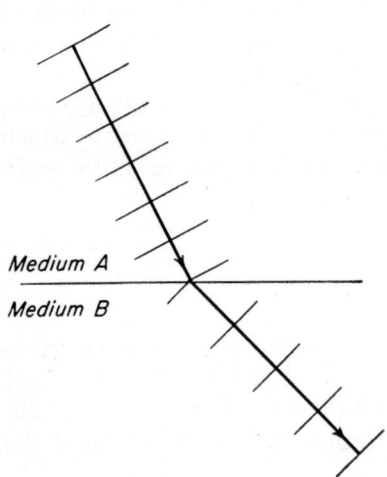

Fig. 23. Refraction at a boundary between two extended media. The direction of propagation is bent away from the normal to the boundary, as in the case shown, when $v_B > v_A$. By reversing the arrows showing the direction of propagation we would have illustrated the reverse effect encountered in the propagation of waves from B to A.

Thus far, we have ignored completely all frictional and dissipative phenomena encountered when mechanical waves are transmitted through a medium. Since mechanical waves involve the vibratory motion of macroscopic parts of bodies, we should expect dissipative effects to be present. They *are* always present and result in the conversion of the macroscopic mechanical motion of the medium in which the waves are traveling into random motion of the molecules; mechanical energy is transformed into heat. This effect is called *absorption* and its effects can be observed in a number of ways; for example, if there were no frictional effects, the amplitude of a sinusoidal traveling wave in a stretched string would be the same at points close to the source as at points remote from the source. This is not the case; in any type of string the amplitude of the wave motion decreases as the waves travel away from the source; the waves are said to be *attenuated*. The amount of attenuation is different for different types of string; for example, the amplitude decreases slowly as a transverse wave travels away from the source along a fine steel wire but decreases rapidly as a similar wave travels along a stretched piece of knitting yarn. The knitting yarn shows greater *absorption* than the steel wire.

CHAPTER 21

PRODUCTION OF SOUND

The term *sound* has two distinct uses. The physiologist or psychologist uses the word *sound* in connection with the sense of hearing and with the auditory sensations produced by certain types of disturbances in the air. The physicist uses the word *sound* to denote the disturbances themselves rather than the sensations produced; in other words, to denote the *waves* in the air or other media that are capable of producing the sensation of hearing. The frequencies of audible waves lie between about 20 cycles/sec and 20,000 cycles/sec, but the term *sound* is sometimes used by physicists to include disturbances having frequencies outside the range to which the normal human ear responds. Waves of frequency below the audible range are termed *infrasonic;* those of frequency above audible frequencies are called *ultrasonic*. Most of the characteristics of *infrasonic* (low-frequency) waves and *ultrasonic* (high-frequency) waves are essentially similar to those of ordinary sonic waves which can produce auditory stimulation; infrasonic, sonic, and ultrasonic waves are all mechanical waves traversing elastic material media. However, the physicist in his description of audible sound waves does attempt to correlate their psychological effects with the physical properties of the waves themselves; thus, as we shall show, the chief psychological characteristics of sound—*pitch, loudness,* and *quality*—can be correlated with certain physical properties—*frequency, intensity,* and *waveform*—of the sound waves themselves.

In order for sound waves to be produced, there must be a *source* which initiates a mechanical disturbance and an *elastic medium* through which the disturbance can be transmitted. The source may be a vibrating solid, such as the stretched strings of a piano or violin, the stretched membrane of a drum, or the walls of a bell, and the medium involved most frequently is air. A simple experiment will show the necessity of an elastic material medium to transmit the sound from the source to the ear. If an ordinary electric doorbell is suspended by fine wires inside a bell jar in such a way that it does not make contact with the walls of the jar, the sound of the ringing bell can be heard when air is inside the bell jar. However, if the air is removed from the bell jar by a vacuum pump, the sound can no longer be heard. This result indicates that a material medium such as air is necessary for the transmission of the sound from the bell. That sound waves can be transmitted by solids as well as by air can be shown by tilting the evacuated bell jar so that the bell touches the wall of the jar; as soon as contact is made between the bell and the wall, the sound can be heard again. That sound waves can also be transmitted by liquids can easily be shown by ringing a bell beneath the surface of oil or water in a large beaker.

Since shearing stresses are required for the transmission of transverse waves through a continuous medium, but not for the transmission of longitudinal waves, and since fluids cannot transmit shears, we conclude that *sound waves in gases and liquids are longitudinal.*

In the present chapter, we shall discuss in some detail the production of sound and some of the characteristic effects produced by sound waves. We shall postpone until the next chapter a detailed treatment of the mechanism of transmission.

1. SOURCES OF SOUND: VIBRATING SOLIDS

As we have mentioned above, vibrating solid bodies can act as sources of sound. Therefore we shall discuss the various ways in which solid bodies can vibrate; these ways in which bodies can vibrate are called the 'normal modes of oscillation' of the body. We shall show that the possible modes depend upon the shape of the body, the density of the body, the elastic properties of the body, and on the 'boundary conditions.' By *boundary conditions* we mean here the conditions imposed at the boundary of the body by restraints produced or imposed by other bodies or other media in contact with the body in question; for example, one boundary of the body may be considered 'fixed' in space as a result of restraints imposed by a rigid support, whereas another boundary may be regarded as 'free' if it is not connected to a support.

We have already discussed the vibration of a stretched string that has both ends fixed by connection to rigid supports. With these boundary conditions, there are certain normal modes of oscillations which for transverse motion correspond to the standing wave patterns shown in Fig. 20, p. 505. We shall refer to the mode of oscillation shown in part (a) of this figure as the *fundamental mode;* the more complicated modes are called *higher modes*. The wavelengths corresponding to these patterns are given by (28), p. 506 as

$$\lambda = 2l/n. \qquad (n = 1, 2, 3, \cdots) \qquad (1)$$

If we impart energy to the stretched string by plucking it or by stroking it properly with a violin bow, the string vibrates in one or more of the modes shown in this figure. As the string vibrates, some of the energy is transferred to the surrounding air in the form of sound waves; as the energy is transferred to the air, the vibrations in the string itself gradually die out.

The frequencies of the sound waves produced in the air are the same as those of the string, since the string is the source of the sound waves. We may write down an expression for the vibrational frequencies of the string by using the general expression $v = f\lambda$ for the wave motion in the string. Since the speed of transverse waves in a stretched string is $v = \sqrt{T/\mu}$, where T is the tension and μ is the mass per unit length, the characteristic vibrational frequencies of the string will be given by

$$f = \frac{v}{\lambda} = \frac{\sqrt{T/\mu}}{\lambda}.$$

By substituting the allowed values for λ as given in (1), we obtain

$$f = \frac{n\sqrt{T/\mu}}{2l} \qquad (n = 1, 2, 3, \cdots) \qquad (2)$$

for the allowed frequencies. The lowest possible frequency corresponds to $n = 1$; this is the frequency of the fundamental mode of the string and is called the *fundamental frequency*. The frequencies of higher modes of vibration are called *overtones*. We shall use the notation

$$f_1 = \frac{\sqrt{T/\mu}}{2l} \qquad (3)$$

for the fundamental frequency of the string.

Of the quantities occurring in (3), μ and l are determined by the geometrical dimensions of the string and by the mass of the string. These quantities are constants for a given string, and we have no way of changing them. However, it is possible for us to change the tension T over wide ranges and by this method to vary the fundamental frequency f_1 of a given string. Other things being equal, the frequency is proportional to the square root of the tension.

A comparison of equations (2) and (3) shows that for a string we may write the frequencies of all modes of oscillation in terms of the fundamental frequency f_1 by the simple relation

$$f = nf_1. \qquad (n = 1, 2, 3, \cdots) \qquad (4)$$

Thus, for $n = 1$, we have the frequency of the fundamental itself; for $n = 2$, we have a vibration of twice the frequency of the fundamental; and so on. Consequently, the frequencies of the higher modes of oscillation of the string are all integral multiples of the fundamental frequency; a set of frequencies bearing this type of relationship are called *harmonics*. The fundamental frequency, for which $n = 1$, is called the *first harmonic;* the frequency for which $n = 2$ is called the *second harmonic;* and so on. In general, the frequencies of the higher modes of oscillation of a body are called *overtones*. For a string, the fundamental and the overtones are harmonics; this is not the case for most vibrating bodies, as we shall see later.

For *any* vibrating body, *the lowest frequency is called the fundamental frequency;* the first frequency higher than the fundamental is called the *first overtone;* the second higher frequency is called the *second overtone;* and so on. *The overtones are not always simple integral multiples of the fundamental;* in the case of a drum, considered later, they are not simple integral multiples of the fundamental and they are said to be *inharmonic overtones.*

When the overtones *are* integral multiples of the fundamental, they are said to form a harmonic sequence, the successive terms f_n of which are given by the relation

$$f_n = nf_1,$$

where n is an integer. For a vibrating string, all harmonics are present. Thus, for the string, we may write

$$\text{Fundamental} = \text{first harmonic:} \quad f_1 = f_1,$$
$$\text{First overtone} = \text{second harmonic:} \quad f_2 = 2f_1,$$
$$\text{Second overtone} = \text{third harmonic:} \quad f_3 = 3f_1,$$
$$\cdots \qquad \cdots \qquad \cdots$$
$$(n-1)\text{th overtone} = n\text{th harmonic:} \quad f_n = nf_1.$$

Thus, the first harmonic for the string is the fundamental frequency itself and the overtones give all the multiples of the first harmonic. Although in the case of a string *all* harmonics are possible, this is not necessarily the case for vibrating bodies even though the overtones be harmonics. For some types of organ pipes and clamped bars the odd harmonics are present and all even harmonics are absent.

Let us now see how the various vibrational modes of a string may be excited. If a string is plucked at any point selected at random, several modes of oscillation may be produced simultaneously. However, by employing the proper procedure, we may excite *particular* modes of oscillation. Thus, if the string is plucked gently at its mid-point C in Fig. 1, the fundamental mode as shown in part (a) will be excited. However, if one plucks the string at point D one-quarter of its length from A while gently touching the mid-point C, the first harmonic will be excited as shown in part (b). Similarly, by plucking the string at point E one-sixth of its length from A and gently touching the string at point F one-third of the way between A and B, one can excite the second harmonic as shown in part (c). When a string vibrates, a number of modes of oscillation are usually excited simultaneously, but by applying a procedure like the one suggested we can reduce the amplitudes of all modes except the desired one to negligibly small values.

We have been considering only the modes of oscillation of a string or flexible wire in which *transverse* motions occur. However, there are also corresponding longitudinal modes of vibration. The frequencies of these modes are usually much higher than those of the transverse modes we have considered. The permitted wavelengths of longitudinal waves are also given by (1). Hence the frequencies for the various longitudinal vibrations can be written in terms of the speed v_L of longitudinal waves in the string in the form

$$f = \frac{nv_L}{2l} = \frac{n\sqrt{E_Y/\rho}}{2l}, \tag{5}$$

where we have inserted the value of v_L in terms of Young's modulus E_Y and the density ρ given by (16), p. 493.

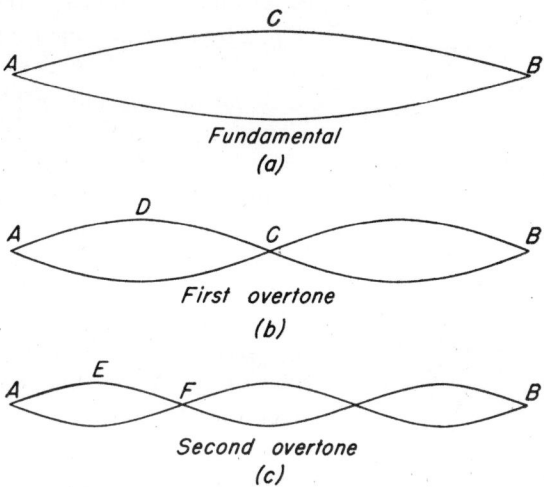

Fig. 1. A vibrating string.

In musical instruments such as the violin or piano, only the transverse oscillations are desired. In playing the violin, a novice usually manages to excite longitudinal vibrations by moving the bow lengthwise along the string; the resulting sound is an objectionable but unfortunately familiar shrill squeak.

As an example of a vibrating body whose overtones are *not* harmonics of the fundamental, let us now consider qualitatively the circular membrane used on a drum. The boundary condition is simple; the periphery of the membrane is fixed by clamps so that it cannot vibrate. If some part of the drumhead is given a blow, a wave pulse travels outward from the point receiving the blow and is reflected at the fixed periphery of the membrane; in this way a standing wave pattern is set up.

Some of the possible standing wave patterns or normal modes of vibration are shown in Fig. 2, which shows the nodal lines as dotted lines across the membrane. At these lines and at the periphery there is no motion; at points approximately midway between the nodal lines, displacements of maximum amplitude occur. Thus, in part (a) the center of the membrane is an antinode and the periphery is a nodal line; this mode of oscillation is the simplest mode and has the lowest frequency, the fundamental f_0. The mode giving the first overtone is shown in part (b); in this mode the motion of the part of the membrane to the right of the nodal line is 180° out of phase with the motion of the part of the membrane to the left of the nodal line; that is, when the part of the membrane to the right is moving toward the reader, the part to the left is moving away from the reader. It is easy to visualize the motion shown in the other parts of Fig. 2 by remembering that the motions of parts of the membrane on opposite sides of a nodal line are out of phase by 180°.

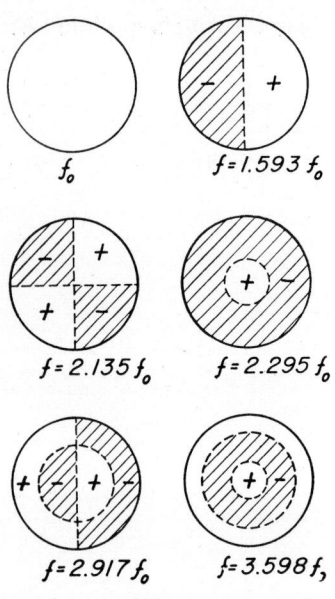

Fig. 2. Modes of oscillation of a circular membrane.

The frequencies of the various normal modes of oscillation are given in the figure in terms of the fundamental frequency f_0. The frequencies of the overtones are *not* integral multiples of the fundamental f_0; that is, the overtones are *not* harmonics.

The restoring forces in a flexible drumhead result from the tension of the stretched membrane, which is assumed to be the same in the various parts of Fig. 2. Calculation of the vibrational frequencies in terms of the tension and mass per unit area is beyond the scope of our present treatment. However, the characteristic frequencies and the mode of oscillation may be determined experimentally by subjecting the membrane to vibrations of known frequencies by placing a loudspeaker directly above the horizontal membrane and exciting the loudspeaker by means of an audio-frequency oscillator* whose frequency can be varied slowly. The drumhead will be set into vibration of large amplitude when the frequency of the sound waves from the loudspeaker coincides with the frequency of some mode of oscillation of the membrane; and if the drumhead is covered with a thin layer of fine powder such as chalk dust, the powder will move about over the drumhead and accumulate along the nodal lines. By noting the pattern of nodal lines and by noting the frequency at which the pattern occurs, one can determine the resonant frequencies for each of the modes of oscillation shown in Fig. 2.

* Oscillators using electronic tubes are described in Chap. 43.

A metal plate has modes of vibration similar to those of a stretched membrane. In this case the restoring forces appear as a result of bending stresses in the plate. Studies of vibrations of membranes and plates are of great importance to the engineer concerned with the design of diaphragms for loudspeakers, telephones, and microphones.

Now let us consider the modes of longitudinal oscillation of a metal bar subjected to various boundary conditions. For our first boundary condition, let us consider a flat bar with one end clamped firmly in the jaws of a vise and the other end 'free.' With this type of support, there will always be a *node* at the clamped end and an antinode at the free end.

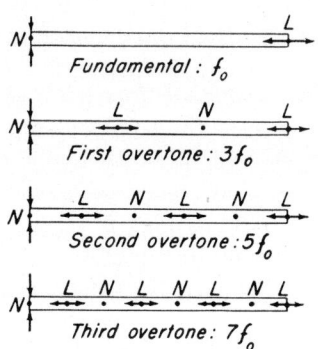

Fig. 3. Modes of *longitudinal* oscillation of a bar or rod clamped at the left end. These modes may be excited by stroking the bar at a loop with a rosined cloth and almost simultaneously touching an adjacent nodal point so as to damp out unwanted modes.

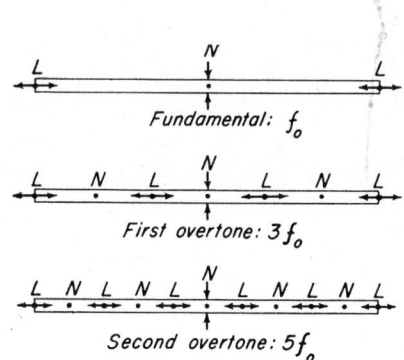

Fig. 4. Modes of longitudinal oscillation of a bar or rod clamped at the center. There is always a node at the center and loops at the ends. The fundamental frequency f_0 of a rod supported at the center is twice the fundamental frequency of the same rod supported at one end as in Fig. 3.

The first few of the characteristic modes of oscillation are shown in Fig. 3. By considering the wavelengths of the longitudinal waves in the rod which produce these vibration patterns, we can find the frequencies of the various overtones in terms of the fundamental f_0. These are indicated in the figure. It should be noted that the frequencies are all *odd*-integral multiples of the fundamental and the overtones are therefore harmonics. However, not *all* the harmonics are present among the overtones.

A bar supported rigidly only at the center has a node at the center and antinodes at the two free ends. The first few of its modes of oscillation are shown in Fig. 4. By considering the longitudinal waves required to produce the standing wave patterns, we may write the frequencies of the various overtones in terms of the fundamental f_0; the results are given in

Fig. 4. Again we see that the overtones are odd-integral multiples of the fundamental frequency. However, it should be pointed out that f_0 for the rod supported in the manner shown in Fig. 4 is *not* the same as f_0 for the same rod supported in the way shown in Fig. 3; the boundary conditions are important in determining the fundamental frequency.

A tuning fork [see Fig. 5(a)] is a U-shaped metal rod supported at the center that is widely employed as a standard of frequency or 'pitch' by piano tuners. Such a body vibrates transversely in such a manner that only the fundamental mode of oscillation is appreciably excited. The ends of the prongs of the fork experience displacements of maximum amplitude, and there is a nodal region near the lower part of the U. In the fundamental mode of oscillation, *the ends of the prongs alternately approach and recede from each other*, while the region near the point of support remains at rest. In order to make the existence of a nodal *region* seem reasonable, let us consider Fig. 5(b), which shows how a tuning fork might be made by bending a metal bar. In I the straight rod is supported at N and N, which are the nodal points. If the rod is gradually bent as in II, III, and IV, the nodes gradually approach each other and in the final fork IV may almost coincide at the point of support. A good tuning fork has no prominent overtones and is insensitive to temperature changes.

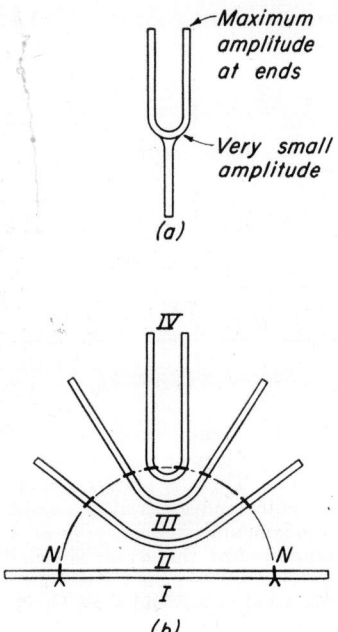

Fig. 5. A tuning fork.

We could discuss other types of solid bodies, such as bells, cymbals, and transversely vibrating bars, which are common sources of sound. In most such solid bodies there are many possible modes of oscillation and the sound waves produced have components of many different frequencies, so that the resulting wave forms are quite complex. We have omitted a treatment of the transverse modes of oscillation of a simple rod or bar. This problem is more difficult than that of longitudinal oscillation, since in transverse modes antinodes do not occur at the 'free' ends of the rod; rather, more complex boundary conditions must be satisfied at these ends.

Of the various vibrating solids we have mentioned thus far, the drumhead and the bell are most effective in the direct production of sound waves of *large amplitude*. Their large surface areas account for their great effectiveness. If a given amount of energy is imparted to a drumhead, this energy is quickly imparted to the surrounding air by the large, flat surfaces of the vibrating membrane. However, if an equal amount of energy is imparted to a stretched string, this energy is imparted very slowly to the surrounding air because the surface area of the string is small; hence, vibration of the string persists for a long time. In order to make a vibrating string or tuning fork more effective in setting up sound waves in the air, the string can be 'coupled' mechanically to a body of large area or volume which is effective in imparting vibrational energy to the surrounding air. The body to which the string is coupled is said to *amplify* the sound, since, by coupling the string to a suitable large body, we can produce sound waves of larger amplitude than could be obtained by using the string alone.

In selecting bodies for use as acoustic amplifiers, there are two cases to be considered. The first case involves the amplification of a single frequency. Let us suppose that we wish to amplify the sound from a tuning fork. In this case, we select a 'sound box' that has a normal mode of vibration of the same frequency as that of the fork. For example, the arrangement shown in Fig. 6 might be used; the tuning fork could be mounted on one face of a light wooden box that is open at one end. The top of the box is set into forced vibration as a result of its coupling to the stem of the fork.

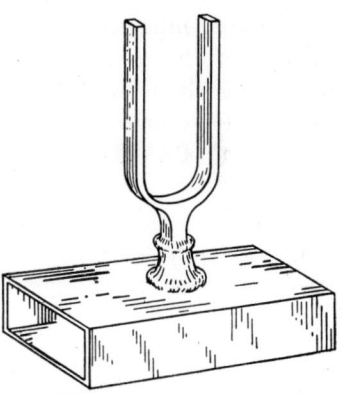

Fig. 6. Tuning fork mounted on a wooden box, which acts as an 'acoustic amplifier.'

The air inside the box is also set into oscillation by contact with the wall of the box. If the dimensions of the box are properly chosen, the fundamental frequency of the air column (see Sec. 3) can be made the same as the frequency of the tuning fork; therefore, oscillations of large amplitude are set up in the air column and transmitted to the surrounding air. If the fork is set into vibration by striking it with a rubber hammer, a much louder sound is heard when the fork is in contact with the box than when it is held in the air. It should also be noted that the vibrations of the fork die out more rapidly when it is in contact with the box, since its energy is imparted more rapidly to the surrounding air. A box such as the one just described is called a *tuned resonator*.

The second case to be considered is the design of an acoustic amplifier to be used to amplify a number of different frequencies; this is the case involved in the construction of the body of a violin, the sounding board of a piano, and the diaphragm of a loudspeaker. When an acoustic amplifier is to be used for several frequencies, it should have no characteristic modes of vibration with frequencies in the range of frequencies to be amplified; for example, if we wish to amplify frequencies of vibrating strings in the frequency range between 50 cycles/sec and 3000 cycles/sec, the 'sound box' or 'sound board' we use should have no natural frequencies within or near this range. The 'coupling' between the vibrating strings and the sound board or box should be made as 'tight' as possible; in other words, as much of the energy of the vibrating string should be transmitted to the box or board as possible. The string sets the sounding board or box into forced oscillation and the vibrating board or box sets up sound waves in the air.

The characteristics of the system used to amplify the sound have considerable influence upon the sound waves actually produced. For example, if the acoustic amplifier is more effective in amplifying high frequencies than low frequencies, the effects of overtones will be exaggerated; if the amplifier is more effective in amplifying low frequencies, 'distortion' of a different type occurs.*

PROBLEMS

1. What is the frequency of the fundamental transverse mode of oscillation of a steel wire of mass 25 g and length 2.0 m when the tension in the wire is 5 nt? What are the frequencies of the first three overtones? Ans: 5, 10, 15, 20 cycles/sec.

2. If the tension in the wire in Prob. 1 were 9 nt, what would be the frequencies of its fundamental and its first three overtones?

3. A wire 5 ft long under 25 lbf tension has a fundamental frequency of 512 cycles/sec when transverse oscillations are excited. What is the mass of the wire in lb? Ans: 15.3×10^{-5} lb.

4. What would be the fundamental frequency of the wire in Prob. 3 if the tension were decreased to 16 lbf?

5. A copper wire 0.1 cm in diameter is 4.0 m in length. Find the speeds of transverse and longitudinal waves in this wire when a tensile force of 12 nt is applied to each end. Find the frequency of the fundamental transverse and longitudinal modes of oscillation of this wire. ($E_Y = 11 \times 10^{10}$ nt/m² and $\rho = 8900$ kg/m³ for Cu.) Ans: 41.4 m/sec, 3520 m/sec; 5.18 cycles/sec, 440 cycles/sec.

6. Solve Prob. 5 for a steel wire with the same dimensions as the copper wire. ($E_Y = 20 \times 10^{10}$ nt/m² and $\rho = 7800$ kg/m³ for steel.)

7. String B has twice the length, twice the diameter, twice the tension, and twice the density (g/cm³) of string A. What overtone of B agrees in frequency with the fundamental of A? Ans: third.

2. FREQUENCY MEASUREMENTS

At the present time the most accurate method of measuring the frequency of a simple sound wave is to convert the sound wave by means of

---

* Everyone is familiar with similar distortion introduced by selective electronic vacuum-tube amplifiers. For example, the audio-frequency amplifiers used in the ubiquitous 'juke box' are most effective at low frequencies; the result is a pronounced exaggeration of the bass.

a microphone into an electrical voltage variation of the same frequency. The frequency of the electrical 'wave' can then be determined by means of an electron-ray oscillograph. On the oscillograph screen the unknown frequency of the wave can be determined by comparison with waves of known frequency from electronic oscillators. If high precision is desired, the frequency can be determined to 1 part in 1,000,000 by comparison with oscillators calibrated in terms of standard radio signals broadcast from the Naval Observatory (Station WWV) in Washington, D. C. However, precision of this order is not usually needed. The electrical methods are also the most convenient methods of determining frequencies in a well-equipped laboratory even when high precision is not desired, and accurate results can be obtained with simple apparatus.

However, it may be instructive to discuss some of the older methods of determining frequencies. One of these methods involves the direct comparison of the unknown frequency with the frequency of the sound from a siren. The sound from a siren is produced not by the vibration of a solid body but by the periodic interruption of an air jet; the interruption frequency can be accurately measured by means of a stop watch and a revolution counter.

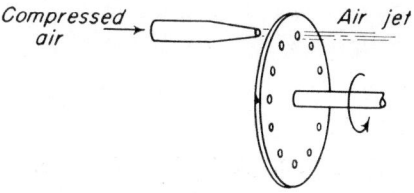

Fig. 7. A disk siren.

A schematic diagram of a simple disk siren is shown in Fig. 7. A circular disk mounted on the shaft of a motor whose speed can be varied rotates in front of a small nozzle through which a jet of compressed air flows. In the disk there is a set of small holes arranged in a circle concentric with the axis of the shaft. As the disk rotates, these holes move past the nozzle; the air stream passes through the disk when a hole passes the nozzle and is interrupted when a solid portion of the disk passes the nozzle. Each time a hole comes in front of the nozzle, a puff of air escapes and produces a compression. Then when the nozzle is closed, the inertia of the moving air produces a rarefaction. These periodic pressure variations are propagated through the air as sound waves. The frequency of the sound can be determined by a knowledge of the number n of holes in the disk and the rotational frequency f_m of the motor shaft. The rotational frequency in rev/sec can be determined by a revolution counter and a stop watch. The air jet is interrupted nf_m times per second, and this interruption frequency is just the frequency f of the sound produced:

$$f = nf_m.$$

In using the siren to measure the frequency of a given sound, the observer varies the rotational speed of the motor until the siren sound and the sound of unknown frequency are judged to have the same pitch. In this way, the frequency of the siren can be matched with the unknown frequency to within 1 cycle/sec even by an observer with limited experience. In matching the two frequencies, the observer makes use of the *beats* between the two frequencies; *beats* are periodic fluctuations in the loudness of the sound produced when two sources have nearly equal frequency, an effect to be discussed in some detail in Chap. 22.

Another method of measuring frequency involves observing, by means of a stroboscope, a vibrating body serving as the source of sound waves. A simple stroboscope can be constructed from a light source and a perforated disk like one used in the siren we have just described. If a person tries to observe the vibrations of a tuning fork illuminated by daylight, he will see only a blur between the extreme positions of each prong, since the motion is too rapid for the eye to follow in detail. However, by placing the vibrating fork in a darkened room and illuminating it by short properly spaced flashes of light, he can observe the vibration of the fork in 'slow motion.' In fact, if the repetition frequency of the light flashes coincides with the vibrational frequency of the fork, the fork will appear to stand still.

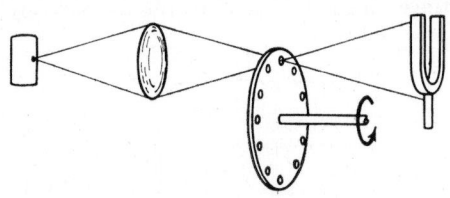

Fig. 8. A simple stroboscope.

We may produce light flashes by the simple arrangement shown in Fig. 8. Light from a concentrated-filament lamp is focused by means of a lens on one of the holes in a disk; the light passes through the hole to the tuning fork. The light passing through the hole is the only light reaching the fork; hence, an observer can see the fork only when a hole is in the light path. If the disk is at rest with a hole in the light beam, the vibrating fork is illuminated continuously and its appearance is the same as that of a fork illuminated by sunlight; the observer will see only a blur between the end positions of each prong. As the disk is set into rapid rotation, the motion of the fork appears to be slower. Finally, when the disk attains such a rotational speed that a light flash reaches the fork only once during each vibration, the vibrating fork appears to be at rest. This condition occurs when the product of the rotational frequency f_m of the disk and the number of holes n in the disk is equal to the frequency f of the tuning fork; that is, when

$$f = nf_m.$$

Since f_m can be determined by a rotation counter and a stop watch, this relation serves to determine f.

The stroboscopic method of determining frequency is carried out most conveniently by means of a Strobotac, an instrument containing a neon light that emits short flashes. The repetition frequency of the flashes is accurately controlled and measured by an electronic vacuum-tube circuit. The frequency-control dial of this instrument can be rotated until the fork illuminated *only* by the neon light appears motionless; frequencies are read directly from the dial.

3. SPEED OF SOUND: EXPERIMENTAL MEASUREMENTS

Owing to its relatively low value (approximately 1080 ft/sec in air), the speed of propagation of sound can be determined by direct measurement of the time required for sound to traverse a given distance. The problem is simplified considerably as a result of the fact that the speed of light (186,000 mi/sec) and the speed of transmission of electrical signals on wires (almost the speed of light) are so much greater than the speed of sound that the times required for light or electrical signals to traverse a given path length is negligible compared with the time for sound to traverse the same path; this makes it possible to use light or electrical signals to mark the beginning and end of a given time interval. In recent years, the development of electronic timing devices has simplified the problem still further.

Perhaps the simplest direct method of measuring the speed of sound is one in which a cannon is fired and a distant observer measures the time that elapses between the instant at which he sees the flash and the instant at which he hears the sound.* Fairly accurate results can be obtained by an observer who starts a stop watch when he sees the flash and stops it when he hears the sound. One of the chief sources of inaccuracy in measuring the time interval involves the reaction time of the observer in starting and stopping the watch. By employing electrical methods of recording these times, this source of error can be eliminated.

There are two other factors that introduce uncertainties in the determination of sound speeds by the method we have just described: First, if violent explosions are employed, a blast wave with a speed greater than that of sound is produced at the source, and not until the wave-front has moved a considerable distance from the source does the wave-front move with the speed characteristic of sound waves. Second, if large distances are used to give large, easily measurable time intervals, uncertainties arise from wind, temperature variations, and humidity variations. However, the development of electronic vacuum-tube circuits for the measurement of short time intervals and for amplification of sound signals has eliminated many of the inaccuracies of the time-interval method, since shorter path lengths and sounds of smaller intensity can be employed. A schematic diagram of two free-air experiments is shown in Fig. 9.

* The first experiment of this kind was performed by the French Academy in the middle of the eighteenth century.

In order to avoid the effects of the wind, measurements of the speed of sound in long tubes have been made by methods similar to those used in the free-air experiments. One famous experiment of this type was made by Regnault, who measured the speed of sound in empty underground water mains in Paris. The speed obtained in tube measurements is slightly different from the speed obtained in free-air experiments but can be converted to the free-air speed by making small corrections which vary

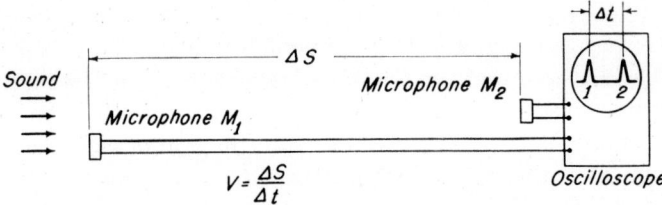

Time interval Δt measured by means of oscilloscope signals from microphones M_1 and M_2 located distance ΔS apart.

(a)

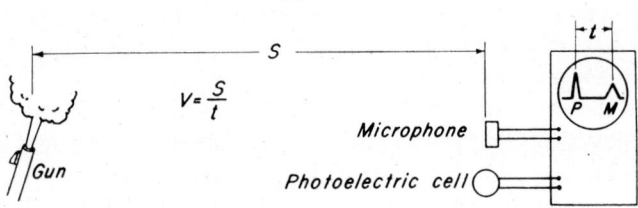

Photocell registers gun flash. Microphone registers sound signal. Time for sound to travel distance S measured by oscilloscope.

(b)

Fig. 9. Speed measurements.

inversely as the tube diameter and inversely as the square root of the frequency.

The speed of sound in lake water or sea water can be determined by methods essentially similar to those described for the free-air experiment. In one of the classical experiments on Lake Geneva, Switzerland, the source of the sound was a large bell. When the bell was struck with a hammer, a light flash was simultaneously produced above water. The receiving instrument was a *hydrophone*, which consisted of an ear trumpet with the large end closed by a membrane and inserted in the water. The observer recorded the time interval between the reception of the light signal and the reception of the sound signal from the bell.

If the *frequency* f of a sound wave is known, the speed of sound in air can be determined by measuring the *wavelength* λ and calculating the speed from the relation

$$v = f\lambda.$$

The wavelength can be measured most easily by producing a standing wave pattern in an air column by an arrangement such as that shown in Fig. 10. A vibrating tuning fork is held close to the open end of a cylindrical glass tube closed by a water seal at the other end. Sound waves are propagated down the tube through the air and are reflected at the water surface. A standing wave pattern will be set up if the air column has the proper length. The length of the air column can be varied by raising or lowering the reservoir connected to the glass tube by a

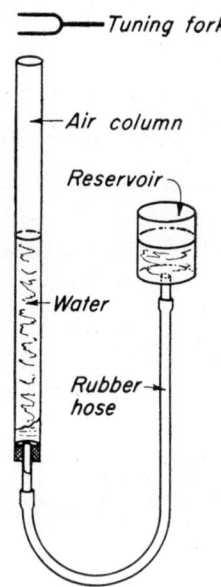

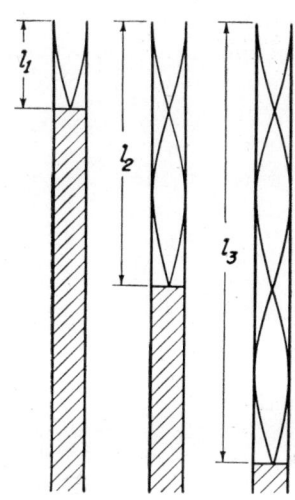

Fig. 10.

Fig. 11. Standing waves in an air column. The curves show the amplitudes of particle displacements at various points in the tube.

flexible rubber hose. It is easy to determine the lengths for which a standing wave pattern is set up in the air column, since resonance occurs at these lengths and at resonance the air column amplifies the sound waves in the surrounding air. The observer hears a much louder sound when the tube is resonant, that is, when a standing wave is set up in the tube.

After the lengths of the air column for which resonance occurs have been determined, the wavelength can be calculated from a consideration of the boundary conditions. Since the air at the closed lower end of the tube cannot experience downward displacements, this end of the column will appear as a *node* in any standing wave that may be produced; thus, the closed end of the air column is analogous to the *fixed* end of a wire or metal bar. The open end of the air column is analogous to the free end of a metal bar, and therefore an *antinode* will be produced near the open end of the air column when resonance occurs.

With these boundary conditions in mind, we can easily picture the standing wave patterns occurring in the tube; they are illustrated in Fig. 11. It should be noted that although this figure shows the amplitudes of the vibrations at various positions along the tube by the curves with lateral displacement, the wave motion is actually longitudinal and the particles actually vibrate in a direction parallel to the axis of the tube; that is, particle displacements are vertical for the arrangement shown in Fig. 11. Now we may write down expressions for λ in terms of the measured distances l_1, l_2, and l_3 shown in Fig. 11. From our earlier discussion of standing waves, we see that for a case in which the antinode near the end of the open tube occurs exactly at the end of the tube the wavelength λ can be obtained from any of the relations

$$\lambda = 4l_1, \quad \lambda = \tfrac{4}{3}l_2, \quad \text{or} \quad \lambda = \tfrac{4}{5}l_3. \tag{6}$$

In actual practice, the antinode near the open end always occurs slightly above the end of the tube; hence, we must add a small end correction k to each of the lengths l in equations (6). However, the value of k is the same in all these equations and hence can be eliminated between any pair of equations; this may be done in the following way:

Let $\quad \tfrac{1}{4}\lambda = l_1 + k \quad$ and $\quad \tfrac{3}{4}\lambda = l_2 + k$.

Subtraction and solution for λ leads to the value

$$\left. \begin{aligned} \lambda &= 2(l_2 - l_1). \\ \text{Similarly,} \quad \lambda &= 2(l_3 - l_2). \end{aligned} \right\} \tag{7}$$

Thus, the wavelength λ is equal to twice the difference in the tube lengths for which successive resonances are observed. If the tube diameter is small compared to the wavelength, the end correction k is small and equations (6) give fairly accurate values for λ, but equations (7) are preferable.

Once the wavelength λ has been determined, the speed of the sound waves in the tube can be determined by the relation $v = f\lambda$. As mentioned earlier, the speed in the tube is approximately, but not exactly, the same as the speed in free air. The measured speed for tubes can be corrected by known methods to the free-air speed if high accuracy is desired. Since the correction amounts to only a fraction of one per cent in ordinary cases, we shall consider the speed in a tube to be the same as in free air in the solution of problems.

The results of various types of measurements indicate that the speed of sound in air varies rapidly with temperature, only slightly with humidity, and is independent of pressure. Experimental measurements give

the value
$$v = 331 \sqrt{T/273°} \text{ m/sec},$$

where T is the absolute temperature on the Kelvin scale. This relation will be discussed further in Chap. 22 in connection with the theory of sound propagation in various types of media. In working the problems at the end of this section, the values 331 m/sec or 1090 ft/sec for the speed of sound in air at 0° C are to be used unless other values are specified. Direct measurements of the type we have described earlier in this section give the speed of sound in lake water at 15° C as 1440 m/sec and the speed of sound in sea water at 15° C as 1503 m/sec.

PROBLEMS

1. An observer sees the flash of a gun and hears the report 4.5 sec later. What is the distance between the observer and the gun if the temperature is 20° C?
Ans: 5080 ft.

2. A man sees the 'steam' from a locomotive whistle 2 sec before he hears the sound. What is the distance from the man to the locomotive if the temperature is 20° C?

3. An observer sees the flash of an explosion on the opposite shore of a lake. If the lake is exactly 1 mi wide, how long will it be before he hears the sound reaching him through the air? If the observer uses a hydrophone to receive the sound transmitted through the water, how long after the explosion does he receive the sound? Air and water are at 15° C. Ans: 4.73 sec; 1.12 sec.

4. If a charge of dynamite is set off on a railroad track, how long does it take the sound to travel through the steel rails to an observer exactly 5 mi away? How long after receiving the sound signal transmitted by the rails will the observer receive the sound signal transmitted through the air? Use (16) p. 493, with $E_Y = 29 \times 10^6$ lbf/in², $\rho = 487$ lb/ft³, to compute the speed in the rails. Take air temperature as 20° C.

5. When a tuning fork with a frequency of 256 cycles/sec is held above a tube like that shown in Fig. 11, resonance occurs when the length $l_1 = 33.5$ cm. Neglecting end corrections, calculate the speed of sound in air from these data. Assuming that the value obtained for the speed is correct, find the values to be expected for l_2, l_3, and l_4. Ans: 343 m/sec; 100.5, 167.5, 234.5 cm.

6. On a day when the speed of sound in air is 1100 ft/sec, what would be the tube lengths l_1, l_2, l_3, and l_4 at which resonances would be observed when a tuning fork of frequency 512 cycles/sec is held above the open end of a tube like that shown in Fig. 11, end corrections being neglected.

7. A sound of 612 vibrations/sec takes 0.744 sec to travel vertically from a point 200 m under water to a point 200 m in the air above the surface of the water. The speed in air is 330 m/sec. From these data alone calculate (a) the wavelength of this sound in air, (b) the wavelength of this sound in water.
Ans: (a) 0.539 m; (b) 2.37 m.

8. An observer drops a stone down a well, and notes with a stopwatch that 16 sec elapse from the time he lets the stone fall until he *hears the sound* of its striking at the bottom. How deep is the well if the temperature of the air in it is 10°C?

9. An electrically driven tuning fork is mounted 2.0 cm above the open end of a cylindrical tube 4.0 cm in diameter. The lower end of the tube is closed by a movable piston. Resonance (decided increase in volume of sound) occurs first at

a tube length of 24.5 cm, again at a length of 74.5 cm, and again at 124.5 cm. If the speed of sound in air is 330 m/sec, what is the frequency of the tuning fork?

Ans: 330 sec^{-1}.

10. What are the wavelengths in air at 20° C of sounds of frequency 20,000, 2000, 200, and 20 vibrations/sec?

4. SOURCES OF SOUND: VIBRATING AIR COLUMNS

Vibrating air columns like the ones shown in Figs. 10 and 11 are of special interest as sources of sound since they play an important role in many musical instruments. A tube like the one we have discussed operates in a manner similar to a *closed* organ pipe, which actually has one

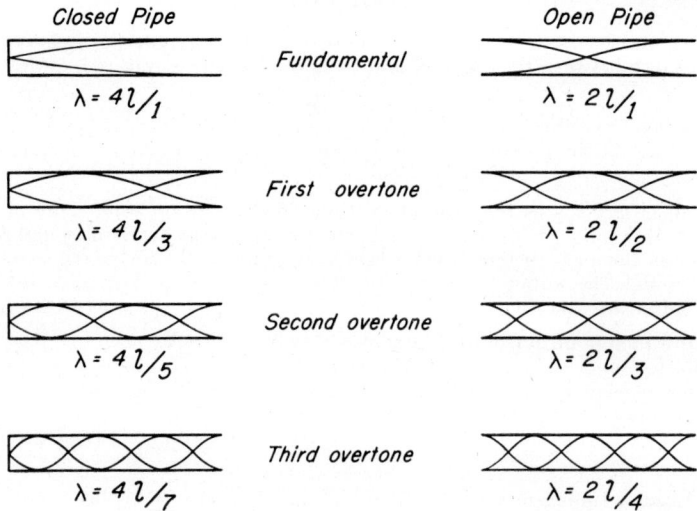

Fig. 12. Normal modes of oscillation of organ pipes.

end closed and the other open. Another type of organ pipe is the *open* pipe, which behaves as if it were open at both ends. The boundary conditions for an open organ pipe are such that an antinode is to be expected at each end.

A diagram showing several characteristic modes of vibration of an open organ pipe is given in Fig. 12, in which the corresponding modes for a closed pipe are repeated for comparison. The wavelengths of the sound waves to which the tubes are resonant are given in terms of the length l of the tube; one can easily verify the correctness of the values given by recalling that the wave length in the standing wave pattern is equal to the distance between *alternate* nodes or *alternate* antinodes.

Remembering that the speed of the waves in the tube is just the speed v of sound in the air, we can write down the frequencies for the various modes of oscillation from the relation $f = v/\lambda$. From Fig. 12 we see that for an open pipe $\lambda = 2l/n$, where n is an integer. Thus, the resonant frequencies of an *open* organ pipe can be written as

$$f = nv/2l. \qquad (n = 1, 2, 3, \cdots) \qquad (8)$$

If we denote the fundamental frequency of the open pipe by f_o, we may rewrite (8) in the form

$$f = nf_o, \quad \text{where} \quad f_o = v/2l.$$

We note (a) that the normal frequencies of an open organ pipe are harmonics and (b) that *all harmonics are present*, since n takes on all integral values.

The case of a *closed* organ pipe is somewhat different. From Fig. 12 we see that $\lambda = 4l/n'$, where n' can assume only *odd-integral* values. Hence the resonant frequencies are given by the expression

$$f = n'v/4l. \qquad (n' = 1, 3, 5, \cdots) \qquad (9)$$

If we denote the fundamental frequency of the closed pipe by f_c we may write (9) in the form

$$f = n'f_c, \quad \text{where} \quad f_c = v/4l.$$

We note (a) that the normal frequencies of a closed pipe are harmonics but (b) that *only odd harmonics are produced*.

Comparison of the expression for the fundamental frequency f_c of a closed pipe with the expression for the fundamental frequency f_o of an open pipe of the same length reveals that

$$f_o = 2f_c.$$

Thus, with a pipe of a given length one gets the lower frequency when it is closed.

There are many methods of producing vibrations in air columns. One method involves producing resonance by means of vibrating a solid body such as the tuning fork shown in Fig. 10. However, the method most frequently used involves an air jet. Everyone is familiar with the sound produced by blowing across the mouth of an empty bottle and with the various varieties of wooden whistles. In an organ pipe, vibration of the air column results from oscillations produced in an air jet that is blown upward through a narrow slot against a knife-edge or 'lip' forming a part of the pipe wall as shown in Fig. 13. The jet of air from the slot is deflected alternately into and out of the pipe at the knife-edge. This alternation occurs at the resonant frequency of the pipe, being controlled by air alternately entering and leaving the pipe as the air in the pipe near this end moves alternately up and down at resonant frequency. The air pressure and the distance from the slot to the knife-edge should be properly adjusted in order to produce the fundamental; usually the fundamental and many of the overtones are excited simultaneously. If the pressure of the air supplied to the lower part of the tube is too great, the fundamental may not be appreciably excited although many overtones will be produced. It should be noted that the lower end of an organ pipe is a region of maximum vibration, and therefore this end of the pipe should be regarded as *open*.

The knife-edge or lip of a flue organ pipe, like that shown in Fig. 13, is a rigid solid which does not vibrate at the frequency of the air column. In certain other wind instruments the vibrating air jet is replaced by a thin metal or wooden plate called a *reed*. The reed itself is caused to vibrate by the air stream. The reed may be mounted so that it vibrates freely or in such a way that it alternately opens and closes an air passage. The reed produces vibrations in the air column.

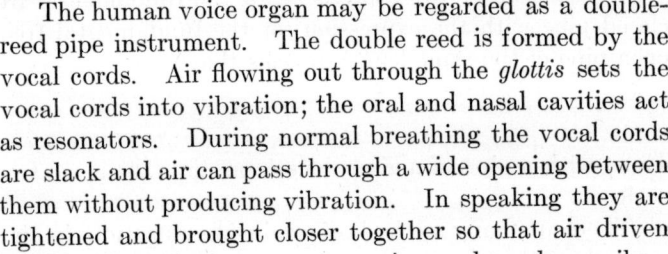

Fig. 13. Lower end of an organ pipe.

Metal reeds are used in reed organ pipes and mouth organs; wooden reeds are employed in clarinets, oboes, and bassoons. The reed principle is also used in brass wind instruments; in this case the lips of the player act as double reeds. Sounds produced by reeds are modified by the pipe or horn resonator used; in the clarinet and similar instruments the effective length of the pipe is varied by opening and closing small openings in the side.

The human voice organ may be regarded as a double-reed pipe instrument. The double reed is formed by the vocal cords. Air flowing out through the *glottis* sets the vocal cords into vibration; the oral and nasal cavities act as resonators. During normal breathing the vocal cords are slack and air can pass through a wide opening between them without producing vibration. In speaking they are tightened and brought closer together so that air driven out of the lungs flows through the narrow opening and produces vibration. The frequency of the resulting vibration can be controlled within certain limits by adjustment of the tension in the vocal cords. For vowel sounds of high frequency, the tension is large; for vowel sounds of low frequency, the tension is smaller.

PROBLEMS

NOTE: In working these problems, ignore end corrections.

1. On a day when the speed of sound in air is 1080 ft/sec, what are the frequencies of the fundamental and first three overtones of an organ pipe 16 ft long when the tube is operated as a *closed* pipe?   Ans: 16.9, 50.6, 84.4, 118/sec.

2. Solve Prob. 1 for the case where the pipe is used as an *open* pipe.

3. What should be the length of a closed organ pipe if the fundamental frequency is to be 256 cycles/sec? What should be the length of an open organ pipe to give this fundamental frequency? Assume $v = 1080$ ft/sec.   Ans: 1.05 ft; 2.11 ft.

4. What should be the length of a closed organ pipe if the fundamental frequency is to be 380 cycles/sec? What should be the length of an open pipe having this fundamental frequency? Assume $v = 1080$ ft/sec.

5. At a time when the speed of sound is 1080 ft/sec, the fundamental frequency of a closed organ pipe is 256 cycles/sec. What is the fundamental frequency of this pipe on a day when the speed of sound is 1112 ft/sec?   Ans: 264/sec.

6. When the speed of sound is 1130 ft/sec, the fundamental frequency of an open pipe is 380 cycles/sec. What is the fundamental frequency of this pipe on a day when the speed of sound is 1080 ft/sec?

5. SOUND CHARACTERISTICS: MUSICAL SOUNDS AND NOISE

Now let us turn to the question of the relationship between the psychological effects of sound waves and the physical properties of the sound waves. In terms of effects on the listener, we usually characterize sound by properties called *loudness, pitch,* and *quality.*

The meaning of the term *loudness* is well known from common usage. For example, we all know that the sound of a locomotive whistle is louder when the observer is close to the locomotive than when he is a mile away and that the music from the loudspeaker of a radio becomes louder when the volume control is 'turned up.' The loudness of a sound is intimately connected with the *intensity* of the sound wave, defined in the following way:

> The intensity of a sound wave is the energy transferred per unit time through unit area normal to the direction of propagation. It is commonly measured in watts/m².

Thus, the intensity of the sound waves reaching the man is greater when the man is close to the locomotive, since the wave disturbance has not spread out over as large an area as when the man is a mile away. Similarly, in turning up the volume control of the radio receiver, the listener causes more power to be delivered to the speaker and thereby increases the intensity of the sound reaching his ear.

The relationship between the loudness of a sound and its intensity is not a simple one. Loudness cannot be measured in physical terms, since it depends on the ear and judgment of the individual observer. It is relatively easy for two or more observers to agree that two sounds are equally loud, but different observers will not agree that one sound is 'twice as loud' as another. The difficulties of comparing the loudness of two sounds are even greater if the two sounds differ greatly in pitch and quality.

The intensities of sounds that can be heard by the ear vary over an enormous range. A sound that is so loud that it is almost painful may have an intensity as much as 10^{12} times that of a sound that is barely audible. In view of this wide range of intensities, it is convenient to use a logarithmic scale in defining an *intensity level* for use in comparison of sound intensities:

The *difference in intensity level* of two sounds, of intensities I and I_0, is specified in *decibels* (db),* and is defined as

$$10 \log_{10}(I/I_0) \text{ db.}$$

This logarithmic type of intensity-level scale corresponds roughly with the behavior of the ear. For example, the level of a sound of any intensity must be raised by about 3 db (a *factor* of 2 in intensity) before the ear perceives a very noticeable change in loudness.

If we take the intensity of the minimum detectable sound as I_0, the intensity I of a sound at the point of painfulness will be approximately $10^{12}I_0$, as mentioned above. Thus, the intensity level of this almost painful sound would be

$$10 \log_{10}(10^{12}I_0/I_0) \text{ db} = 120 \text{ db}$$

above the threshold of audibility.

In certain types of acoustical engineering work, it is desirable to select some standard reference intensity I_0 as the threshold of audibility and to specify the intensity level of any other sound of intensity I in terms of this reference level. By international agreement an intensity of 10^{-12} watt/m² has been selected as a *standard threshold of audibility* and is used as the value of I_0. Table I, included in order to give an idea of the intensity of various common sounds, is based on this convention.

TABLE I

INTENSITY LEVELS OF VARIOUS SOUNDS, IN DB ABOVE THRESHOLD OF AUDIBILITY*

Sound	Intensity level
Pain threshold	120 db
Riveting	95
Elevated train	90
Busy street traffic	70
Conversation in home	65
'Quiet' radio in home	40
Whisper	20
Rustle of leaves	10
Hearing threshold	0

* Typical values based on a survey made by the New York City Noise Abatement Commission.

In the following chapter we shall discuss the relationship between sound intensity and the amplitude of particle displacement in air.

Now let us consider the characteristic of sound known as *pitch*. This characteristic can best be demonstrated by striking various keys on a piano; all keys to the right of middle C produce sounds of higher pitch than that produced by middle C, and all keys to the left produce sounds of pitch lower than that produced by middle C. Pitch is designated by musicians by letters corresponding to the keys on the piano. Except for extremely loud sounds, there is a one-to-one correspondence between pitch and frequency, the higher the pitch, the higher the frequency. In going *up* the scale one octave, we double the frequency; thus, the A notes on the piano have the following frequencies: 27.5, 55, 110, 220, 440, 880, 1760, and 3520 cycles/sec. Audible sounds range in frequency from

* The bel, the unit used to specify $\log_{10}(I/I_0)$, was named in honor of Alexander Graham Bell (1847–1922), the inventor of the telephone. The smaller unit, the decibel, is more convenient for most work.

about 20 cycles/sec for sounds of the very lowest pitch to about 20,000 cycles/sec for sounds of highest pitch; the exact limits of the audible range vary from individual to individual. The most important frequency range for speech lies between 100 and 1000 cycles/sec; a telephone transmission system can operate satisfactorily even if it transmits only the frequencies in this range.

The only exceptions to the above statements concerning the one-to-one correspondence between pitch and frequency involve extremely loud sounds; for loud sounds the *pitch* tends to decrease slightly as the intensity of the sound increases, even though the frequency remains constant. This effect is most pronounced for frequencies lower than 1000 cycles/sec; for example, if we have a sound with a *fixed* frequency of 200 cycles/sec and increase the intensity of the sound from 10^{-8} watt/m² to 10^{-2} watt/m², the pitch of the sound decreases to the pitch associated with a frequency of approximately 188 cycles/sec for a sound of intensity 10^{-8} watt/m². These exceptions are not usually important, since such loud sounds are encountered infrequently; for example, the sound with intensity of 10^{-2} watt/m² just mentioned is comparable with the sound produced by a large automobile horn in a small living room. For most sounds normally encountered, we may rely on our earlier statement concerning the dependence of pitch on frequency alone.

Now let us consider the third sound characteristic: *quality*. The meaning of the term *quality* or *timbre* can be illustrated by sounding middle C successively on a trumpet, on a pipe organ, and on a violin. If these instruments are properly tuned, the fundamental frequencies of the three notes is the same, but we should have little difficulty in distinguishing between the sounds produced by the three instruments. The property of the three sounds which makes it possible for us to tell them apart is called *quality*. *The quality of a musical sound is determined by the relative intensities of the overtones present.* Thus, although the fundamental frequency of the note sounded by the three instruments mentioned above is the same, the note from each instrument has a different and distinctive pattern of overtone intensities which gives the note its distinctive *quality*. Hence, we may define sound quality as the psychological effect produced by the relative intensities of the overtones present in a sound.

In a good tuning fork only one mode of oscillation is excited, and hence the fork vibrates at only one frequency. The sound waves that are set up are therefore simple harmonic waves, that is, sinusoidal waves of a single frequency. A simple tone like that from a tuning fork is not particularly interesting. An interesting musical tone usually contains many overtones and these overtones are largely harmonics of the fundamental; that is, the overtone frequencies are simple multiples such as 2, 3, 4, or 5 times the frequency of the fundamental.

Recalling our discussion of the superposition principle in Chap. 20, we see that quality is related to the *wave-shape* of the sound waves produced by a given source. If the source consists of a tuning fork, the waves will be sinusoidal waves of a single frequency; but if the source is vibrating simultaneously in several different modes of different frequency, the wave produced will consist of the superposition of several sinusoidal waves with different frequencies and different amplitudes, and the resultant waveform will be quite complex. Thus, we see that our earlier statement that the quality of a sound depends on the number, frequencies, and relative intensities of the overtones is equivalent to the statement that *sound quality is determined by waveform*. However, two sound waves can differ in waveform and still have the same quality if the overtones in each have the same intensities but different phases relative to the fundamental.

A *noise*, in contrast to a musical sound, has no single fundamental frequency with harmonic overtones but consists of complex waves with many nonharmonic frequency components of varying amplitude. In other words, the sound 'wave' produced by a source of noise consists of a series of random displacements with little semblance of regularity of any kind.

6. RESPONSE OF THE EAR TO VARIOUS TYPES OF SOUND

An adequate treatment of the morphology and physiology of the human ear is beyond the scope of this textbook. Therefore, we shall content ourselves with a very brief description of the gross features of the ear and proceed to a discussion of the response of the ear to various types of stimuli.*

The ear consists of three major portions called the outer ear, the middle ear, and the inner ear (Fig. 14). Sound waves enter the outer ear, travel down the ear canal, and strike a thin membrane called the eardrum, which forms the boundary between the outer ear and the middle ear. In the middle ear, a mechanism consisting of three small bones called the hammer, the anvil, and the stirrup transmit vibrations from the eardrum to the oval window. The oval window is a membrane that transmits vibrations to the inner ear, which is filled with a liquid. In the cochlear spiral, which is a tube about 3.5 cm long and 1–2 mm in diameter, are the terminals of the auditory nerve. There are approximately 30,000 nerve terminals in the cochlea, and different frequencies have their greatest effects on nerve terminals located at different positions along the spiral. Sound signals are 'received' by these terminals, and are transmitted electrochemically to the brain in some type of pulse code.

* Much of the material in this section is taken from an excellent review article by Harvey Fletcher of the Bell Telephone Laboratories, which appeared in the REVIEWS OF MODERN PHYSICS for January, 1940. An interesting discussion of the physics of the human ear is given in an article by Francis M. Wiener in PHYSICS TODAY for December, 1949.

The vestibular apparatus shown in Fig. 14 is not associated with hearing. It consist of three fluid-filled semicircular canals in three orthogonal planes, and controls the sense of balance or equilibrium.

In earlier sections we have given approximate values for the limits of the intensities and frequencies of sound waves that can be heard by the 'normal' human ear. Actually, the ear is not a detector equally sensitive for all frequencies in the audio range. Extensive studies on the subject

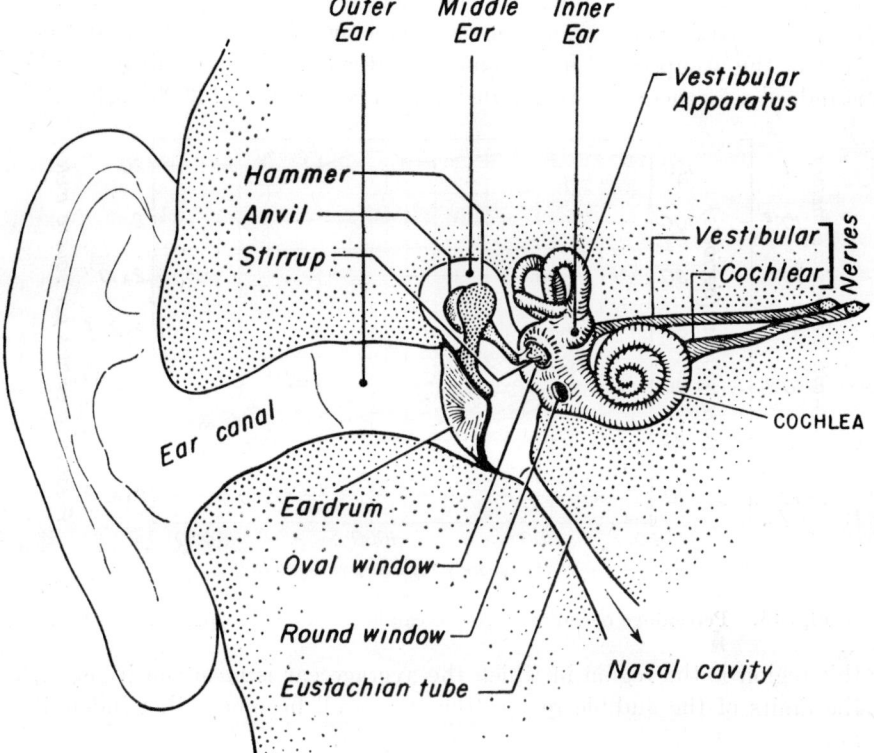

Fig. 14. The human ear.

of the range of audibility have been made by the United States Public Health Service and the Bell Telephone Laboratories. Some of the results of these studies are summarized in the graph shown in Fig. 15. The curves show plots of sound intensity as a function of frequency. Three different ordinate scales are shown: the first gives absolute intensities in watts/m², the second gives the intensity level in db above the standard reference level of 10^{-12} watts/m², and the third, which will be discussed in Chap. 22, gives the maximum variation in pressure produced by the sound wave. The uppermost curve shows at various frequencies the intensity of the sound that is loud enough to be almost painful;

sounds of this intensity can be felt as cutaneous sensations as well as heard. The height of this curve is almost constant at a level of 120 db above the standard reference level; this curve does not show extremely wide variations for various individuals. The lower curves represent the thresholds of hearing for various fractions of the group studied. Thus, 99 per cent of the individuals studied could hear sounds with lower intensities than those shown by the curve labeled 99 per cent, 95 per cent could hear sounds with intensities less than those given by the next lower curve labeled 95 per cent, and so on. The lowest curve shows that 1 per cent of the group could hear sounds of intensity nearly 10 db below the standard reference level in the region between 2000 and 3000 cycles/sec;

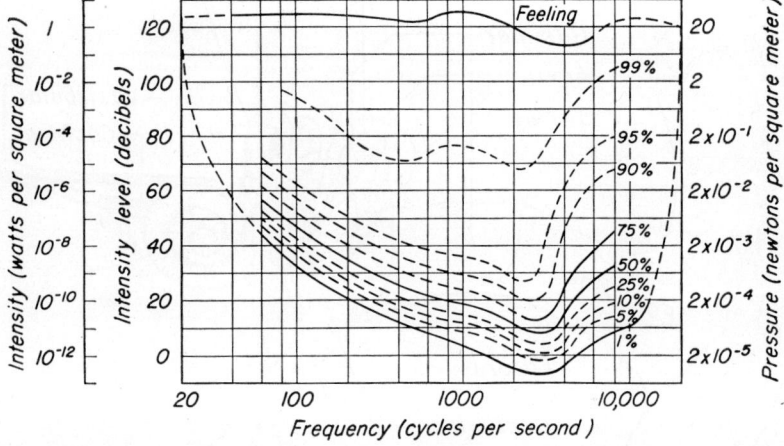

Fig. 15. Percentage of individuals who can hear sounds of various intensities.

this region is the region in which the average ear is most sensitive. At the limits of the audible region, the curves all become rather indefinite but approach the threshold of feeling or pain.

It should be emphasized once more that the curves shown in Fig. 15 give the results of a study of a large *group* of individuals. For a single individual the curve showing the hearing threshold may not resemble any of the curves in the figure. It is possible for an individual to have acute hearing for some frequencies in the range of normal audibility and to be quite deaf to other frequencies. Certain animals have ears that are sensitive to sounds outside the frequency range of the human ear. For example, dogs and cats can hear sounds of higher frequency than can humans, and an ultrasonic whistle can be used by the city dweller to summon a dog without disturbing the neighbors. There is one disadvantage in using such a whistle: if the dog fails to come, the owner never knows whether to suspect the dog of disobedience or to suspect the whistle of failure to produce sounds of sufficient intensity.

The ear is remarkable in its ability not only to respond to sound waves of widely different frequencies but also to respond to many different frequencies at one time. This latter property is especially important in interpreting speech, since speech involves a rapid succession of changes in intensity, quality, and frequency. The fundamental frequency is controlled primarily by the vocal cords, and most of the energy transmitted by the sound wave is associated with this fundamental frequency. The intelligibility of a spoken sound depends largely upon differences in higher frequencies. Two vowel sounds may have the same fundamental frequency but can be recognized as different by the differences in the overtones produced; these overtones are controlled by the resonating cavities of the mouth, throat, and nose. It is remarkable that a given vowel sound can be identified when spoken by different people speaking in quite different pitches; there may be large differences in both fundamental and overtone frequencies when a vowel sound is made by different people, but the frequency 'patterns' or waveforms are sufficiently similar for the two sounds to be identified as the same vowel.

Another noteworthy property of the ear is its ability to 'analyze' a complex wave into recognizable component waves. For example, the sound wave coming to a listener during an orchestral program is extremely complex, but the listener is able to identify the sound of individual instruments such as the violin, the flute, and the oboe from this complex wave; this phenomenon is all the more remarkable when we recall that the waves from each individual instrument are themselves complex. Another example of this analytical property of the ear is the feat of the experienced radio operator in the control room of an airport who can receive spoken communications from a pilot even when the power level of the verbal communication is below the average background noise; this feat is called receiving a signal 'down in the noise.' Apparently the trained ear of the operator can use to advantage the fact that there is some recognizable regularity in the communication signal but that the noise is a largely random disturbance.

7. ELECTRONIC AMPLIFIERS FOR AUDIO FREQUENCIES*

Although we shall postpone a detailed discussion of electronic amplifiers until Chap. 43, it might be desirable to say a few words at this point concerning some of the general principles involved in the design and use of such amplifiers for acoustics work. Electronic amplifiers operate in a fashion quite different from the so-called 'acoustic amplifiers' such as the tuned resonator used with the tuning fork in Fig. 6, the untuned sounding board of a piano, or the body of a violin. All the energy sent out in the sound waves from these acoustic amplifiers was supplied directly from the source; the acoustic amplifiers were used for the sole purpose of transferring energy to the air more rapidly and thereby producing sound waves of greater intensity. In an electronic amplifier, a small voltage is

* This section may be omitted without loss of continuity.

applied to the input terminals and a much larger voltage is produced at the output terminals; the output energy may be made many times greater than the input energy. This increase in energy is derived from the batteries or power line used to operate the amplifier. Thus, a sound source is used to operate a device such as a microphone that produces a signal voltage which has the same variation with time as the sound wave produced by the source. This signal voltage can be applied to the input of an electronic amplifier; and the output voltage from the amplifier can be used to operate a loudspeaker which emits sounds of much greater intensity than those produced by the source even when an acoustical amplifier is used with the source. It should be emphasized that the increase in signal power (energy per unit time transmitted by the sound

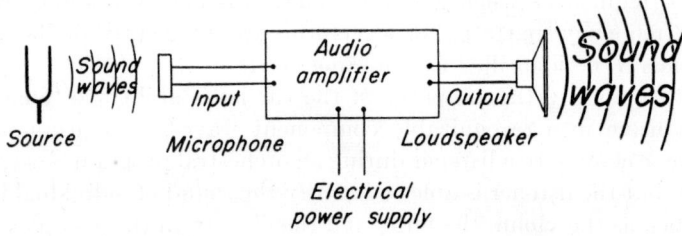

Fig. 16. Block diagram of electronic amplifier for audio frequencies.

waves) is made possible by energy derived from the electrical power supply of the amplifier.

The block diagram shown in Fig. 16 shows the basic principles. Sound waves of low intensity are sent out from the source represented by the tuning fork. These sound waves reach the microphone and produce slight mechanical displacements of a diaphragm or metal ribbon; the mechanical displacements of the moving parts in the microphone have the same frequency as the vibrations of the air waves. The mechanical motions in the microphone produce electrical voltage fluctuations,* which serve as the input signal voltage for the amplifier. At present we may regard the amplifier merely as a 'black box' that produces a large output voltage whenever a small voltage is applied at the input; in later chapters we shall discuss the processes taking place in the amplifier. The large electrical output power is used to operate the loudspeaker. At the speaker a large diaphragm undergoes mechanical oscillations of the same frequency as the frequency of the output voltage. Vibrations of the speaker diaphragm can produce sound waves of great intensity.

The key to the design of a perfect amplifier system is that all elements reproduce accurately the initial sound signal. If the system is to be used

---

* The voltages may be produced by electromagnetic induction or by variations in electrical resistance or capacitance or magnetic reluctance. Basic principles will be discussed in later chapters.

for the voice or for music, this statement means that the microphone, the amplifier, and the loudspeaker must respond in the same manner to *all* sound frequencies present in the initial sound signal. If this condition is to be fulfilled, none of the components—electrical or mechanical—should have any resonant frequencies in the audible-frequency range, since, as will be remembered from our discussion of forced vibrations in Chap. 11, the amplitude of the response of a body excited at its natural frequency is much greater than at other frequencies. The condition that all components give uniform nonresonant response to all audio frequencies cannot be realized in practice, and hence no amplifier is perfect. The most serious difficulties are encountered in loudspeaker design; in public-address systems two separate speakers are actually used in a single mount: a large speaker for low frequencies and a smaller one called a *tweeter* for high frequencies. Although no perfect amplifier system has been devised, there are, of course, many that are excellent over the audio-frequency range.

8. RECORDING AND REPRODUCTION OF SOUND*

As we have pointed out, a sound wave is a longitudinal wave in the air. The displacement of a given particle† of air is a function of time. Hence, if we had some method of plotting the displacement of a particle as a function of time, we should have a record of the sound wave producing the displacement. Since condensations are regions of local high pressure and rarefactions are low-pressure regions, a plot of instantaneous local pressure variations as a function of time would also give us a record of the sound. If such a record actually consisted of an ink trace on a chart, it would not be very useful unless we could devise an auxiliary device which could take the trace and from it produce a sound similar to the sound for which the record was made. Thus, there are really two problems involved in sound recording. The first is the problem of producing an accurate record; the second is the problem of obtaining an accurate reproduction of sound from the record. Both of these problems have been successfully solved in several ways.

The most familiar type of recording is that used in making the ordinary disk phonograph record. If we magnify the groove on a conventional record, it is found to be a wavy line. It gives a graph of the displacements or local pressure variations caused by the original sound as a function of time. If we place one corner of a card in the groove while the phonograph turntable is rotating, the card vibrates and sound waves are produced. If the phonograph turntable is rotating at the proper speed, the sound produced by the card will be a reproduction of the original sound; if the turntable is turning too rapidly, the sound produced by the card will have a higher frequency and therefore a higher pitch than the

---

* This section may be omitted without loss of continuity.
† The exact meaning of the term *particle* will be discussed in Chap. 22.

original sound; and if rotation is too slow, the sound produced will have a pitch lower than that of the original sound.

In the early phonographs the reproduction system was entirely mechanical and was essentially similar to the one involved in using the card mentioned above; the vibrations of the phonograph needle passing along the groove were first amplified mechanically and then imparted to a diaphragm. In a modern phonograph, the needle that follows the groove acts upon a magnetic device or upon a piezoelectric crystal, which produces an electrical signal that is amplified by an electronic amplifier and then used to operate a conventional loudspeaker.

There are two ways in which the grooves in a record can be cut. In addition to the lateral-displacement record just described, there is the scheme of recording the sound waves by variations in the *depth* of the groove, giving the so-called 'vertical-cut' record. This method makes it possible to put more grooves on a disk of a given diameter without danger of the needle's jumping from one groove to the next.

Another method of recording sound is that used in motion pictures. The record in this case, called the *sound track*, consists of a blackened strip of variable width or variable photographic density located at one edge of the film beside the pictures. Variations in the width or density of the track are proportional to the displacements of particles in the sound waves. In order to reproduce the sound recorded in this way, a beam of light is directed first through a fixed narrow slit, then through the sound track, and finally to a photoelectric cell. As the sound track on the film moves past the slit, the amount of light reaching the photoelectric cell varies with the width or density of the sound track. The variations in the light reaching the photoelectric cell produce variations in the electric current through the cell. The effects of the current variation can be amplified by an electronic amplifier, the output of which can be used to operate a loudspeaker.

One other widely used method of recording sound is magnetic wire recording. Here the sound waves are recorded as variations of the magnetization of a long steel wire that is drawn through the recording device. The intensity of magnetization varies in proportion to the displacements of particles in the sound wave. The wire bearing the magnetic record is wound on a spool for storage. In reproduction, the steel wire is unwound from the storage spool, pulled through the magnetic 'pickup,' and wound on a second spool in much the same way a movie film passes from one reel to another during projection. As the magnetized portions of the wire pass through the pickup, they produce electrical voltages which can be amplified and applied to a loudspeaker. Wire recording is popular for use in dictation work in business offices; after the wire recording has been read and transcribed by a stenographer, the whole wire may be completely demagnetized and used again. Magnetic tapes and magnetic drums are similarly used.

CHAPTER 22

PROPERTIES OF SOUND WAVES

In the preceding chapter we dealt in some detail with various sources of sound waves and with the psychological effects of sound waves but, except for a description of speed measurements, said very little about the transmission process. In the present chapter we shall devote our attention to the transmission process; we shall show how the speed of sound can be calculated from the mechanical properties of various media and how sound intensities are related to the motion of oscillation of the 'particles' of the medium. The phenomena of reflection, refraction, and absorption will be discussed and their bearing on problems involved in architectural acoustics, sound ranging, and other fields will be pointed out. Wave properties such as interference and diffraction will be discussed. We shall also point out the effects produced when the source, the observer, or the medium are in motion. A brief description of the properties of ultrasonic waves will be included at the end of the chapter.

1. SPEED OF SOUND WAVES IN VARIOUS MEDIA

In Chap. 20 we derived an expression for the speed of propagation of transverse waves along a stretched string. This expression involved a 'stiffness' or 'elasticity' factor and an 'inertia' factor. We asserted that the speed of waves with small amplitude through any medium is given by an analogous expression of the form

$$\text{speed} = \sqrt{\frac{\text{stiffness factor}}{\text{inertia factor}}}, \tag{1}$$

and gave formulas for various types of waves in Sec. 5 of Chap. 20.

The speed of a longitudinal wave traveling along a rod whose transverse dimensions are small compared to the wavelength of the wave (a *slender* rod) was given as

$$v_{\text{rod}} = \sqrt{E_Y/\rho}, \tag{2}$$

where E_Y is Young's modulus and ρ is the density of the rod material.

That equation (2) gives the correct value can easily be verified in the laboratory by a piece of apparatus known as *Kundt's tube*, which is shown diagrammatically in Fig. 1. A glass tube one meter or more in length is mounted in a horizontal position. Near the left end is an adjustable loose-fitting plug P. The other end is closed by a light metal disk D mounted at one end of a metal rod that is tightly clamped at its midpoint; the light disk D does not touch the walls of the tube and therefore has the same motion as the free end of the metal rod. By stroking the metal rod with a rosined cloth, we can excite longitudinal vibrations in the metal rod; with the rod clamped at its mid-point and with its ends free, there will be a node at the mid-point and antinodes at the ends. Provided the disk D is sufficiently light that it does not 'load' the rod heavily, the frequency of the fundamental mode of oscillation is given by

$$f = v_{\text{rod}}/\lambda_{\text{rod}}, \tag{3}$$

where λ_{rod} is the wavelength in the metal rod. The wavelength λ_{rod} is the distance between *alternate* antinodes in the rod and is therefore equal to

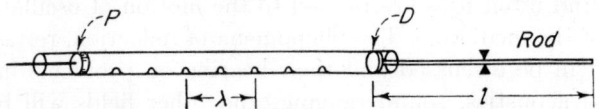

Fig. 1. Kundt's tube (schematic).

twice the length l of the rod, that is $\lambda_{\text{rod}} = 2l$. The expression for the frequency is therefore

$$f = v_{\text{rod}}/\lambda_{\text{rod}} = v_{\text{rod}}/2l. \tag{4}$$

In carrying out the Kundt's-tube experiment, a fine powder such as lycopodium powder, ground cork, or chalk dust is initially sprinkled uniformly along the bottom of the horizontal tube. When the distance between the disk D and the plug P has the proper value for resonance, standing waves will be produced in the air column in the tube when the metal rod is stroked. The light powder, set into motion by the vibrations in the air, is swept away from the loops and collects into ridges at the nodes as shown in Fig. 1. The wavelength λ_{air} of the sound in air is equal to twice the distance between nodes as shown in the figure and is therefore given by $\lambda_{\text{air}} = 2d$, where d is the distance between adjacent ridges of powder. We may express the frequency of the sound wave as

$$f = v_{\text{air}}/\lambda_{\text{air}} = v_{\text{air}}/2d, \tag{4'}$$

where v_{air} is the speed of sound in air. Equating the values given for the frequency in (4) and (4'), we obtain

$$v_{\text{rod}}/2l = v_{\text{air}}/2d.$$

Therefore, if v_{air} is known, we obtain

$$v_{\text{rod}} = v_{\text{air}}\, l/d. \tag{5}$$

The speeds measured in this way are found to be in excellent agreement with the values computed from (2).

The measured values of the speed of sound in slender rods of various materials are given in Table I.

TABLE I
Measured Speeds of Sound in Solid Rods
(From *Smithsonian Physical Tables*)

Material	Speed of Sound	
	(m/sec)	(ft/sec)
Aluminum	5104	16,750
Copper	3560	11,680
Iron	5130	16,830
Lead	1322	4,340
Nickel	4973	16,320
Glass (typical)	5500	18,050
Vulcanized rubber	54	177

TABLE II
Measured Speeds of Sound in Liquids
(From *Smithsonian Physical Tables*)

Material	Speed of Sound	
	(m/sec)	(ft/sec)
Alcohol, Methyl	1143	3750
Carbon bisulfide	1060	3477
Ether	1032	3386
Mercury	1407	4614
Turpentine	1326	4351
Water	1461	4794
Sea water	1500	4922

In extended solid media, both longitudinal and transverse sound waves can be transmitted. The speeds of these waves are given by formulas (18) and (19) of p. 493. It is seen that the longitudinal wave always travels much faster than the transverse. The difference in arrival times of these two types of wave is used in seismology to estimate the distance of an earthquake from the observing station. Measurement of the speed of sound waves is used in geophysical prospecting to determine the underlying structure of the earth.

The speed of sound waves in a liquid is given by the expression

$$\text{speed} = \sqrt{\frac{\text{bulk modulus}}{\text{density}}} = \sqrt{\frac{E_B}{\rho}}. \tag{6}$$

Experimental results obtained by the direct measurements of the speed of sound in lake water and sea water described in Chap. 21 are in agreement with equation (6). Speeds of sound in other liquid media are measured by special adaptations of the resonance-tube experiments mentioned in the preceding chapter and are also in agreement with values obtained from equation (6). The speeds of sound in various liquids are given in Table II.

Unlike the case in gases, the speeds of sound in solids and liquids vary only slowly with change in temperature, since the elastic constants and density both vary slowly.

Now we turn to the problem of calculating the speed of sound in gases.

Since, like liquids, a gas has no shear modulus, the speed of sound in a gas is given by the expression (6). However, formula (6) does not give a unique value for the speed of sound, since the experimental value obtained for the bulk modulus depends on the manner in which the measurements are made. Thus, we obtain one value of the bulk modulus for isothermal processes, another for adiabatic processes, and other values for other types of processes. Sir Isaac Newton obtained an expression for the speed of sound in a gas in which he used the isothermal bulk modulus; it was found later when accurate data were obtained that the Newtonian expression gave too low a value. Over a century later, in 1816, Laplace obtained the correct expression when he showed that gas compressions taking place at audio frequencies must be regarded as adiabatic. The correct expression for the speed of sound in a gas is

$$\text{speed} = \sqrt{\frac{\text{adiabatic bulk modulus}}{\text{density}}}.$$

It is convenient to express the bulk modulus in terms of the pressure. In order to see how this is done, let us recall that the bulk modulus is defined as the ratio of stress to strain, where the stress is the pressure variation dp and the accompanying strain is the change in volume per unit volume $-dV/V$. Hence

$$E_B = dp/(-dV/V) = -V\, dp/dV. \tag{7}$$

In order to find the desired expression for the adiabatic bulk modulus, we recall from p. 429 that the equation governing an adiabatic process in an ideal gas is

$$pV^\gamma = \text{const},$$

where γ is the ratio of the specific heat at constant pressure to the specific heat at constant volume. By differentiation, we obtain

$$\gamma p V^{\gamma-1}\, dV + V^\gamma\, dp = 0,$$

which leads to the expression

$$\gamma p = -V\, dp/dV. \tag{8}$$

Comparison of (8) with (7) shows that for an adiabatic process,

$$E_B = \gamma p. \tag{9}$$

Hence, the Laplace expression for the speed of sound in a gas is

$$v = \sqrt{\gamma p/\rho}. \tag{10}$$

Experiment shows that the expression given in (10) is correct. Table III gives the experimental values for the speed of sound in several gases.

Careful consideration of (10) reveals the interesting fact that at a

TABLE III
Measured Values of Speed of Sound in Various Gases
(From *Smithsonian Physical Tables*)

Gas	Temperature (C)	Speed (m/sec)	Speed (ft/sec)
Air	0°	331.36	1087.1
	20°	344	1129
	100°	366	1201
	500°	553	1814
	1000°	700	2297
Ammonia	0°	415	1361
Carbon dioxide	0°	258	846
Chlorine	0°	205.3	674
Helium	0°	971	3185
Hydrogen	0°	1269.5	4165
Methane	0°	432	1417
Oxygen	0°	317.2	1041
Ether vapor	0°	179.2	588
Water vapor	0°	401	1315
	100°	404.8	1328

given temperature, *the speed of sound in a gas is independent of the pressure.* From the general gas law, we recall that the density ρ is directly proportional to the pressure p. Thus, if we place air in a tank at an absolute pressure of 8 atm, the density of the gas is 8 times its density at atmospheric pressure; hence p/ρ and therefore the speed of sound in the air inside the tank is the same as in air at atmospheric pressure, provided the temperature is the same. This independence of pressure is experimentally verified at all pressures at which a gas obeys the ideal gas laws.

Now let us consider the effect of temperature variations on the speed of sound. From our discussion of the general gas law, we recall that

$$p/\rho = RT/M.$$

Substitution of this value in (10) gives

$$v = \sqrt{\gamma RT/M}. \tag{11}$$

Hence *the speed of sound in a given kind of gas depends* only *on the temperature.* The speed is directly proportional to the square root of the absolute temperature and may be calculated for any gas from formula (11), which is in complete agreement with experiment within the accuracy with which gases behave ideally.

It will be recalled that in Chap. 20 we obtained an expression for the speed of a transverse wave in a string on the assumption that the amplitude of the wave was *small*. For waves of large amplitude the equation we obtained does not apply. The same is true of all the expressions we have written in the present chapter for the speed of sound. The fact that the 'sound' from a violent explosion travels initially at a speed greater than that of ordinary sounds is readily explained by a reconsideration of our original assumption of small amplitude. An analytical treatment of blast waves can be found in more advanced texts on fluid dynamics. As noted in the preceding chapter, the speed of a blast wave from a cannon is appreciably greater than that of sound until the amplitude of the wave has fallen to the point where the pressure change involved is small compared to atmospheric pressure. Formula (11) applies only when pressure *changes* are small compared to the ambient pressure.

In setting up the equations for the speed of sound, we have not mentioned the fact that gases are composed of 'free' molecules and that the sound wave must actually be transmitted by collisions between these molecules. Thinking of the gas as a collection of 'free' molecules, we might expect the speed of sound to be of the same order of magnitude as the speed of the molecules. This is indeed the case; from the kinetic-theory analysis of Chap. 17 we found that the root-mean-square speed of the molecules was $\sqrt{3RT/M}$; the speed of sound given by (11) is $\sqrt{\gamma/3}$ times this value. For a diatomic gas, $\sqrt{\gamma/3} = 0.683$, so the speed of sound is 68 per cent of the root-mean-square molecular speed. Molecular speed, like the speed of sound, varies as $\sqrt{T}$ and is independent of p.

PROBLEMS

1. Calculate the speed of longitudinal waves in an aluminum rod, for which $E_Y = 7.0 \times 10^{10}$ nt/m² and $\rho = 2700$ kg/m³. Ans: 5090 m/sec.

2. Calculate the speed of longitudinal waves in a lead rod, for which $E_Y = 1.8 \times 10^{10}$ nt/m² and $\rho = 11,300$ kg/m³.

3. Calculate the speed of sound waves in an iron rod and compare your result with the value given in Table I. ($E_Y = 20 \times 10^{10}$ nt/m²; $\rho = 7900$ kg/m³.) Ans: 5030 m/sec.

4. Calculate the speed of sound waves in a copper rod and compare your result with that given in Table I. ($E_Y = 11 \times 10^{10}$ nt/m²; $\rho = 8900$ kg/m³.)

5. Calculate the speed of sound in water ($E_B = 2.1 \times 10^9$ nt/m²) and compare your result with that given in Table II. Ans: 1450 m/sec.

6. Compare the wavelength of sound waves of frequency 512 cycles/sec when the waves are traveling in water with the wavelength of the same sound in air.

7. If the speed of sound in air is 331 m/sec at 0° C, what is the speed at 25° C? at 1000° C? Ans: 346 m/sec; 697 m/sec.

8. From the speed of sound in hydrogen given in Table III, calculate the speed of sound in hydrogen at 100° C.

9. The observed value of γ for oxygen is 1.41. Using this value, find the speed of sound in oxygen at 0° C.
Ans: 316 m/sec.

10. The observed value of γ for helium is 1.66. Using this value, find the speed of sound in helium at 0° C.

11. What would be the frequency of the fundamental of an open organ pipe two feet long containing hydrogen at 0° C?
Ans: 1040 sec^{-1}.

12. Newton's formula for speed of sound was $v = \sqrt{p/\rho}$, derived on the erroneous assumption that the process of transmission of sound was isothermal. Show that this is the formula that would be obtained from (6) on the isothermal assumption.

13. The speed of sound, measured in hydrogen gas (H_2) at 140° K, is found to be 93,100 cm/sec. Find the values of γ and of the specific heats Mc_p and Mc_v for hydrogen at this temperature (see p. 387). Note that these specific heats are less than the NTP values (see p. 385).
Ans: $\gamma = 1.50$, $Mc_p = 2.99R$, $Mc_v = 1.99R$.

2. SOUND INTENSITIES*

In Chap. 21, the intensity of a sound wave was defined as the energy transferred by the wave through unit area per unit time. Let us now see how the intensity of a sound is related to characteristic properties of the wave motion such as the power of the source, the distance from the source, the speed of the vibrating 'particles' of the medium, the amplitude of the vibratory motions of the particles, and the pressure variations in the wave.

First of all, we note that all the energy in a sound wave comes from the source. Let us call the energy sent out by the source per unit time the power of the source and denote it by S; the source power is measured in watts. When a source sends out sound waves in an isotropic medium, the intensity I of the sound at any point is inversely proportional to the square of the distance r from the source. For example, let us consider the source S shown in Fig. 2. If energy is sent out uniformly in all directions, we can write down expressions for the intensity I at distances R_1 and R_2 by constructing the concentric spheres shown in the figure with the source at the center. The area through which S, the sound energy per second, passes is $4\pi R_1^2$ for the smaller sphere and $4\pi R_2^2$ for the larger sphere. Therefore, the intensities I_1 and I_2 at distances R_1 and R_2, respectively, are given by

$$I_1 = S/4\pi R_1^2 \quad \text{and} \quad I_2 = S/4\pi R_2^2.$$

From these expressions, we obtain $I_1 R_1^2 = I_2 R_2^2$, or

$$\frac{I_1}{I_2} = \frac{R_2^2}{R_1^2}, \tag{12}$$

which shows that *the intensity of the sound is inversely proportional to the square of the distance from the source.* Even if the energy is not sent out uniformly in all directions, equation (12) applies for the intensities at

---
* Much of this section may be omitted without loss of continuity. The significant points are summarized in equations (12) and (18).

points at distances R_1 and R_2 on a single radius; for example, at points at x_1 and x_2 on the x-axis in Fig. 2.

Now let us find the relation between the intensity I and the maximum speed u_{max} of the 'particles' of the medium. The 'particle speed' u is the speed that a small part of the medium has because of the wave motion. By 'small part' we mean a volume small compared to macroscopic objects such as pistons, cylinders, and tuning forks and small compared to the wavelength λ, but which contains so many molecules that we may attribute a definite meaning to the term *density* of the material in the volume and hence treat the material as being part of a *medium*. By 'particle velocity' we mean the *average* of the vector velocities of the molecules in

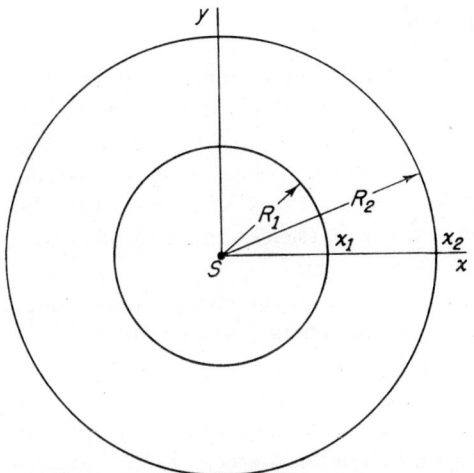

Fig. 2. Concentric spheres of radii R_1 and R_2 with sound source S at the center.

such a volume. This average corresponds to a macroscopic velocity of definite direction superposed on the microscopic motion of the molecules in random directions; it represents a velocity of *mass motion*. The term 'particle velocity' should not be confused with molecular velocity as used in the discussion of kinetic theory; the molecular velocities are much larger than the particle velocities we mention here.

If we make the radius R in Fig. 2 sufficiently large, the wave-front will appear to be plane if we consider only a small area. Let us consider such a plane sound wave. The energy of a small portion of the medium is the energy associated with the simple harmonic motion of the material in the medium. As we have seen, the energy of a particle executing simple harmonic motion continually alternates between kinetic and potential forms, but the magnitude of the energy is at all times equal to the maximum value of the kinetic energy. Thus, the total energy e associated with a unit volume of the medium in the wave is

$$e = \tfrac{1}{2}\rho u_{\max}^2,$$

where ρ is the density of the medium and $u_{\max}$ is the maximum particle velocity.*

Now let us consider the energy transferred through a small area ΔA of the wave-front shown in Fig. 3 by the wave each second. It can be

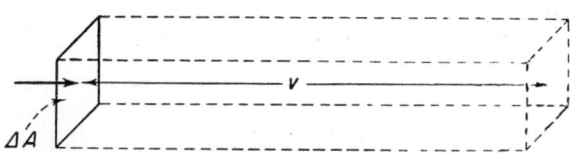

Fig. 3. A plane wave-front moves a distance v in one second. The energy associated with the material in the volume $v\,\Delta A$ crosses the area ΔA in one second.

shown that the energy transferred through this area each second is the energy associated with the material in a volume $v\,\Delta A$, where v is the wave speed. The energy per second through ΔA is $ev\,\Delta A$ and the intensity I is given by the power per unit area:

$$I = ev\,\Delta A / \Delta A = \tfrac{1}{2}\rho v u_{\max}^2. \tag{13}$$

Equation (13) gives the intensity as a function of maximum particle speed $u_{\max}$.

We recall that, for a particle executing simple harmonic motion of frequency f, the maximum particle speed $u_{\max}$ can be expressed in terms

---

* To be rigorous we should show that when a mass motion of velocity $\boldsymbol{u}$ is superposed on the random molecular velocity $\boldsymbol{V}$ of each molecule of a 'particle' the total kinetic energy is increased by $\tfrac{1}{2}mu^2$, where m is the total mass of the 'particle.' Superposition of the constant particle velocity $\boldsymbol{u}$ changes the velocity of a given molecule from $\boldsymbol{V}$ to

$$\boldsymbol{V'} = \boldsymbol{V} + \boldsymbol{u}.$$

By the trigonometric cosine law, the magnitude of $\boldsymbol{V'}$ is given by

$$V'^2 = V^2 + u^2 + 2Vu\cos\theta,$$

where θ is the angle between $\boldsymbol{V}$ and $\boldsymbol{u}$. If the molecule has mass μ its kinetic energy becomes

$$\tfrac{1}{2}\mu V'^2 = \tfrac{1}{2}\mu V^2 + \tfrac{1}{2}\mu u^2 + \mu Vu\cos\theta.$$

The total kinetic energy of the 'particle' is given by the product of N, the number of molecules in the 'particle,' by the average of this kinetic energy expression. *The average of the last term vanishes because the directions of $\boldsymbol{V}$ are distributed randomly in space so* $\overline{\cos\theta} = 0$. Hence the 'particle' has

$$\text{K.E.} = N\overline{\tfrac{1}{2}\mu V^2} + \tfrac{1}{2}N\bar{\mu}u^2,$$

of which the first term is the thermal kinetic energy in the absence of mass motion; this is increased by $\tfrac{1}{2}mu^2$ (since $m = N\bar{\mu}$) because of the mass motion, as we set out to prove.

of the amplitude a by the relation $u_{\max}=2\pi fa$ (see p. 495). By substituting this value for $u_{\max}$ in (13), we obtain

$$I = 2\pi^2 \rho v f^2 a^2, \tag{14}$$

which gives the intensity in terms of the amplitude a of vibration. This result shows that *for waves of equal frequency in a given medium, the intensity is proportional to the square of the amplitude; while for waves of equal amplitude in a given medium, the intensity is proportional to the square of the frequency.*

There is one other quantity in terms of which it is sometimes desirable to measure I; this quantity is $\delta p_{\max}$, the maximum difference between the local pressure at a point in the gaseous medium and the static pressure p_0 of the gas when no sound waves are present. The static pressure p_0 is atmospheric pressure in the case of sounds in free air.

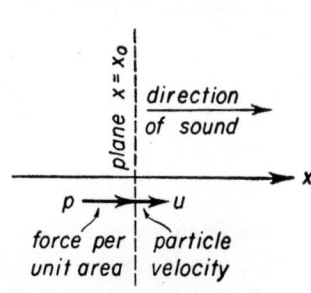

Fig. 4.

Consider a sound wave moving in the $+x$-direction, in which the x-components of velocity of the 'particles' are given by

$$u = u_{\max} \sin 2\pi f(t - x/v). \tag{15}$$

The adiabatic compressions and expansions associated with this velocity variation can be shown to give rise to pressure variations such that if we write

$$p = p_0 + \delta p, \tag{16}$$

then

$$\delta p = \delta p_{\max} \sin 2\pi f(t - x/v), \tag{16a}$$

where

$$\delta p_{\max} = \rho v u_{\max}, \tag{16b}$$

ρ being the undisturbed density and v the speed of sound.

From (15) and (16), we can compute the net work done by the gas to the left of the plane x_0 in Fig. 4 on the gas to the right of this plane. This net work, per unit time and unit area of wave front, represents power transmitted from left to right, and hence represents the intensity I of the sound wave. The work done in time dt by force p acting on a particle of velocity u is $pu\,dt$ and the power will be the integral of this for one second, or better f times the integral for one cycle from $t=0$ to $t=1/f$. Thus

$$I = f \int_0^{1/f} pu\,dt. \tag{17}$$

When (15) and (16), with $x = x_0$, are substituted in this integrand, we get no contribution from the first term of (16) but we do get a contribution from the second term. To see why the integral (17) has a net positive value, note that $p > p_0$ at times when u is positive, while $p < p_0$ at times when u is negative. Thus during the parts of the cycle when $u>0$ the positive work done has a larger magnitude than the negative work done while $u<0$.

The integral (17) is easily evaluated and gives

$$I = \tfrac{1}{2}\,\delta p_{\max}\,u_{\max},$$

which, in view of (16b), can be written as

$$I = \tfrac{1}{2}\rho v u_{\max}^2,$$

as in (13), or as

$$I = \tfrac{1}{2}\,\delta p_{\max}^2/\rho v,$$

which is the desired expression for sound intensity in terms of maximum pressure variation.

Thus we have obtained the following alternative expressions for the intensity of a sound wave, in terms of maximum particle speed $u_{\max}$, amplitude a of particle motion, and maximum pressure variation $\delta p_{\max}$, respectively:

$$I = \tfrac{1}{2}\rho v u_{\max}^2 = 2\pi^2 \rho v f^2 a^2 = \tfrac{1}{2}\,\delta p_{\max}^2/\rho v. \qquad (18)$$

The ordinate scales of Fig. 15 of Chap. 21 should now be re-examined. The scale on the right gives the values of $\delta p_{\max}$ corresponding to the values of intensity of sound in air shown on the scale at the left. In calculating particle speeds and amplitudes for sound waves of a given intensity, it is useful to note that the quantity ρv for sound waves in air at 0° C is 428 kg/m²·sec. The particle amplitude for sound waves of frequency 1000 cycles/sec and intensity 10^{-12} watt/m² has a value of approximately 5×10^{-12} m. Although this distance is only a fraction of the diameter of a single molecule, sound waves of this intensity can actually be heard by a person with acute hearing. Calculations of this kind give one great respect for the design of the human ear as a detector!

In *comparing* sound intensities, suitable microphones coupled with vacuum-tube amplifiers are usually employed. In order to be useful in measuring absolute intensities, these devices must be calibrated by means of some device that gives a reliable measurement of absolute intensity. Such a device is the Rayleigh disk. The operation of the Rayleigh disk is purely mechanical, and it is one of the few detectors that can be used to obtain absolute measurements of intensity.

The Rayleigh disk consists of a thin mica disk a few millimeters in diameter suspended by a fine quartz fiber attached to a point on the rim as shown schematically in Fig. 5(a). The action of this device depends on the fact that a flat object suspended in an air stream in such a way that it can rotate about an axis through its center tends to set itself at right angles to the air stream. The same type of action causes a falling leaf to assume a horizontal orientation when falling to the ground and a floating stick to tend to set itself at right angles to a stream.

If a Rayleigh disk is set at an angle of 45° to a stream of air, it experiences a torque proportional to the square of the speed of the stream. Comparison of the diagrams in Figs. 5(b) and (c) reveals that the torque has the same direction when the stream is moving to the left as when the stream is directed to the right. The disk experiences a static deflection when placed in an air stream that reverses its direction cyclically at a high frequency and therefore experiences a static deflection when placed in air through which sound waves are passing. Deflections are measured by observation of a light beam reflected from the disk. The deflection is directly proportional to the intensity of the sound waves.

The response of the disk is independent of frequency. The chief difficulty involved in using the Rayleigh disk is that deflections are

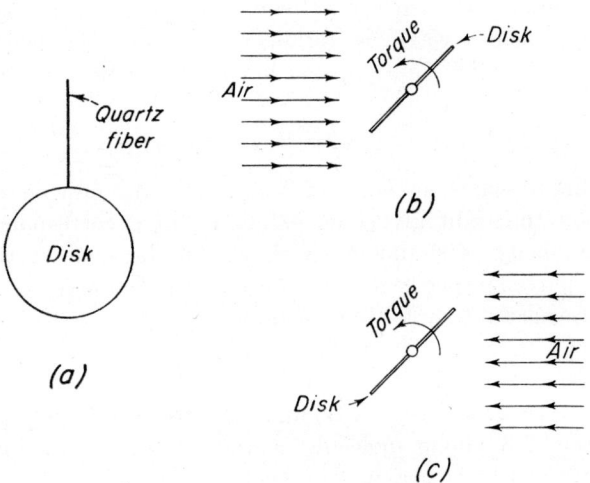

Fig. 5. The Rayleigh disk.

extremely small for sounds of moderate intensity. The disk is usually employed to measure the intensity of a loud sound (near the threshold of feeling), and other devices are used to measure the intensities of less intense sounds relative to the intensity of this loud sound whose absolute intensity was determined by means of the Rayleigh disk.

PROBLEMS

1. Plane sound waves of frequency 2000 cycles/sec are passing through air at NTP. If the sound intensity is 1.0 watt/m², find (a) the maximum particle speeds, (b) the amplitude of the motion of the particles, and (c) the magnitude of the maximum pressure variation associated with the wave motion. ($\rho = 1.293$ kg/m³.)

Ans: (a) 6.84×10^{-2} m/sec; (b) 5.44×10^{-6} m; (c) 29.3 nt/m².

2. Repeat Prob. 1 for hydrogen at 0° C.

3. Repeat Prob. 1 for a case in which the intensity of the sound wave corresponds to the 'zero reference level' of 10^{-12} watt/m².

Ans: (a) 6.84×10^{-8} m/sec; (b) 5.44×10^{-12} m; (c) 29.3×10^{-6} nt/m².

4. Repeat Prob. 3 for a sound wave of intensity 10^{-12} watt/m².

5. Find the sound level in decibels above the standard reference level for a sound wave in air at NTP with a frequency of 1000 cycles/sec and an amplitude of 10^{-6} cm.

Ans: 59.3 db.

6. From the relation between intensity and distance from the source, derive an equation for the amplitude when a sound wave is spreading spherically from a point source radiating isotropically at the rate S, in watts.

7. The expressions corresponding to (15) and (16a) for a wave traveling in the $-x$-direction are

$$u = u_{max} \sin 2\pi f(t+x/v)$$
$$\delta p = \delta p_{max} [-\sin 2\pi f(t+x/v)],$$

with δp_{max} given by (16b). Make a linear superposition of u and δp for the wave (15) traveling to the right and this wave, of equal intensity, traveling to the left, and show that the resulting *standing wave* has its velocity nodes at the antinodes of pressure variation, and vice versa, as assumed in the discussion of organ pipes in the preceding chapter. Ans: $u = 2u_{max} \sin\pi ft \cos 2\pi fx/v$; $\delta p = -2\,\delta p_{max}\cos 2\pi ft \sin 2\pi fx/v$.

8. Show that all terms of (18) have the same units, joule/m²·sec, in the MKS system.

3. REFLECTION OF SOUND WAVES

When sound waves in one medium strike a boundary between this medium and another medium, partial reflection occurs. The portion of the incident energy that is reflected is very large when the speed of sound

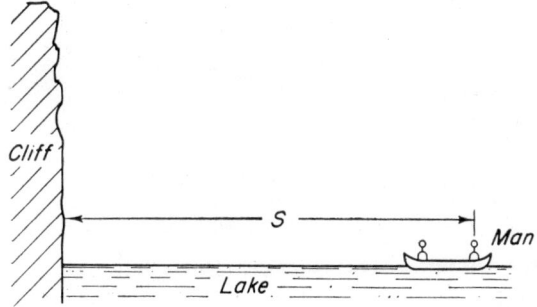

Fig. 6. Echo phenomenon.

in the second medium is greatly different from the speed of sound in the first medium.

Evidence that sound waves are reflected at the boundary between two media is found in the familiar phenomenon of echoes. For example, if a person in the canoe shown in Fig. 6 shouts some word, he hears his word 'repeated' as a result of reflection of sound waves at the face of the cliff; if the distance S between the canoe and the cliff is sufficiently great, the echo may repeat a whole sentence that has been shouted by the person. The echo phenomenon can be used effectively by the man in determining his distance from the cliff. If after shouting he finds that the time t

elapses before he hears the echo, he knows that his distance from the cliff is $S = \tfrac{1}{2}vt$, where v is the speed of sound in air.

If the canoe in Fig. 6 were on a small lake with parallel cliffs on both sides, multiple echoes would be produced when the man shouted. The sound waves might suffer repeated reflections before they finally died out.

In the above cases, the sound traveled in a direction normal to the cliff. Now let us consider the change in the *direction* of a sound wave that strikes a plane boundary between two media at some angle θ_i with the normal to the plane; θ_i is called the angle of incidence. In order to find the direction of the reflected sound wave, we might perform the simple experiment indicated schematically in Fig. 7. A ticking watch or small clock placed at one end of a long cardboard tube A serves as a source of sound for the experiment. The end of the tube near the watch is closed

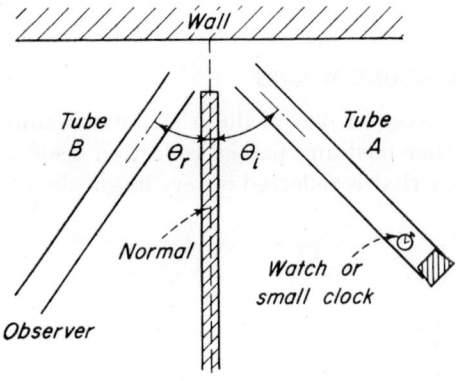

Fig. 7. In regular reflection $\theta_r = \theta_i$.

by a large cork stopper. The tube serves to collimate the sound waves sent out by the ticking watch. The sound waves emerge from the open end of the tube and strike the smooth plastered wall of a room. The observer takes a second cardboard tube B and puts one end to his ear and the other end close to the wall on which sound waves are incident. The observer gives tube B various orientations and notes the orientation at which he hears the watch most distinctly. He finds that this orientation is the one denoted by θ_r in the figure. θ_r, called the angle of reflection, is equal in magnitude to θ_i, and the axis of tube B lies in the same plane as the axis of tube A. The relation obtained by this experiment is called the law of regular reflection, which can be stated as follows:

The normal to the incident wave-front, the normal to the wall, and the normal to the reflected wave-front lie in the same plane, and the angle of reflection is equal to the angle of incidence. (LAW OF REGULAR REFLECTION)

It should be noted that the angle of incidence θ_i and angle of reflection θ_r are measured from a line perpendicular to the plane reflecting surface. The axes of the tubes are perpendicular to the wave-fronts of sound waves moving along the tubes. Figure 8(a) will help to make these points clear for the situation just described. Figure 8(b) shows the situation when a plane wave is reflected from a wall. The 'wave-front' mentioned here is a region in an advancing wave at which all particles have the same phase; for the sake of explicitness, we can consider the wave-fronts in Fig. 8 as being successive regions of maximum condensation.

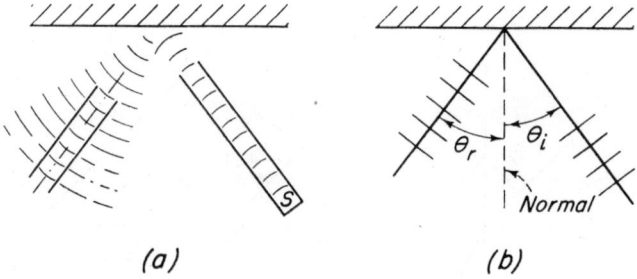

Fig. 8. Regular reflection.

Light waves obey the same law of regular reflection. Since the phenomenon of reflection is discussed in detail in the chapters on light, we shall not pursue the subject of sound reflection further at this point.

PROBLEMS

1. A man in a boat shouts and hears an echo after 3 sec. How far is the man from the object causing reflection of the sound waves if the temperature is 20° C?

Ans: 1690 ft.

2. A man is 500 ft away from a cliff. If he shouts, how long will it be before he hears an echo if the temperature is 20° C?

4. REFRACTION OF SOUND WAVES

In Chap. 20 we pointed out that the direction of propagation of a wave motion changes when the wave crosses a boundary between two media. In Fig. 23, p. 508, we see that the arrow giving propagation direction (denoted by the arrow drawn perpendicular to the plane wave-fronts) is bent *away from* the normal when the waves pass from one medium into another in which the propagation speed is greater. Let us now find a quantitative relationship describing this phenomenon. Let us call the angle between *the normal* and the propagation direction θ_A for medium A and θ_B for medium B as shown in Fig. 9(a). Now let us consider the position of a wave front at two instants as shown in Fig. 9(b). At the first instant a plane wave-front is just reaching the boundary at point O.

After an elapsed time interval t the other end of the wave-front initially at B has reached the boundary at point B' while the point on the wave front initially at O has advanced to O'. By constructing triangles OBB' and $OO'B'$, we see that

$$\sin\theta_A = BB'/OB' = v_A t/OB' \quad \text{and} \quad \sin\theta_B = OO'/OB' = v_B t/OB'.$$

Eliminating t/OB' from these equations, we have

$$\sin\theta_A/v_A = \sin\theta_B/v_B. \tag{19}$$

This relation holds for wave motions propagated in either direction across the boundary.

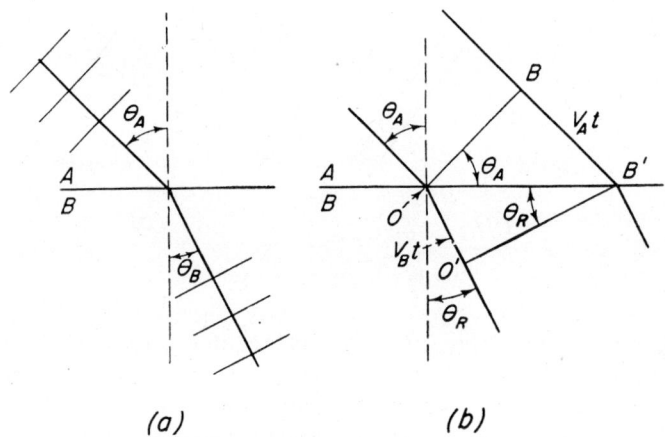

Fig. 9. Refraction of sound waves in the case $v_A > v_B$. The waves can travel in either direction.

To help visualize the situation depicted in Fig. 9, it is useful to think of a line of soldiers marching in a dry field A at speed v_A and entering obliquely a muddy field B where their speed is decreased to v_B. In order to keep in a 'dressed' line, the soldiers will have to march in a new direction after entering the muddy field.

It might be pointed out that if $v_A > v_B$, waves coming to the boundary from medium A will be propagated to some extent across the boundary for all values of θ_A, since

$$\sin\theta_B = (v_B/v_A)\sin\theta_A,$$

and therefore $\qquad\qquad \sin\theta_B < \sin\theta_A.$

However, there is a definite limit to the values θ_B can have when waves approach the boundary from medium B, since the equation

$$\sin\theta_A = (v_A/v_B)\sin\theta_B,$$

shows that $\sin\theta_A > \sin\theta_B$. But $\sin\theta_A$ cannot have a value greater than unity. Therefore θ_B cannot have a value greater than the maximum given by

$$\sin\theta_{B\ \text{max}} = v_B/v_A. \tag{20}$$

This statement does not mean that no waves can be incident at $\theta_B > \theta_{B\ \text{max}}$, but rather that if $\theta_B > \theta_{B\ \text{max}}$, no waves can cross the boundary into A. For $\theta_B > \theta_{B\ \text{max}}$, the waves are *totally reflected*. $\theta_{B\ \text{max}}$ is usually called the *critical angle*. The phenomenon of total reflection is very important in connection with light waves.

There are two applications of (20) that are worthy of note. One of these is illustrated by the case of sound waves in air that strike the surface of a body of water. Since the speed of sound in water at 15° C is 1440 m/sec and the speed of sound in air at this temperature is 341 m/sec, the air corresponds to medium B above, and

$$\sin\theta_{B\ \text{max}} = 341/1440 = 0.237, \quad \text{or} \quad \theta_{B\ \text{max}} = 13°\!.7.$$

Thus, all sound waves in air striking a water surface at an angle with the vertical greater than 13°.7 will be *completely* reflected. The corresponding critical angle for sound waves in air striking the surfaces of many solids is even smaller. Thus, we see that sound waves in air are to a considerable extent confined to the air.

Refraction plays an important role in the transmission of sound over great distances through the atmosphere. Near the earth's surface, the temperature of the air decreases as the altitude increases. Since the speed of sound in air is proportional to $\sqrt{T}$, the speed of sound in the air close to the earth's surface is greater than the speed of sound at higher altitudes. Hence, a sound wave traveling in an upward direction tends to be bent *toward* the vertical, as in Fig. 9 held upside down. Therefore, a plane sound wave initially moving almost horizontally

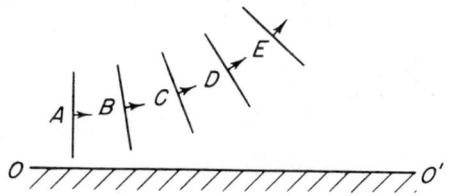

Fig. 10. Schematic diagram showing refraction of sound waves near the earth's surface.

would be deflected upward as shown schematically in Fig. 10, where A shows the initial position of the plane wave-front above the earth's surface OO' and B, C, D, and E show later positions of the wave-front. This drawing is highly schematic; the wave-front at B, C, and D is actually curved and the actual situation is considerably more complicated than that indicated in the figure. However, there is a pronounced tendency for sound waves to be deflected upward in still air near the earth's surface.

This tendency is reversed at higher altitudes in the vicinity of the temperature-inversion layers mentioned on p. 378. The effects of refraction and reflection at the inversion layers are observed in connection with the 'anomalous' transmission of sounds from large explosions, which may not be heard at all a few miles away but are heard distinctly over a hundred miles away. The reasons for this effect may be discussed in connection with Fig. 11, which shows a plot of the path of sound waves through the atmosphere. First the sound waves proceeding away from the source at low elevation angles are deflected upward in the manner described in connection with Fig. 10. These waves strike the inversion layer at large angles of incidence and are reflected toward the earth,

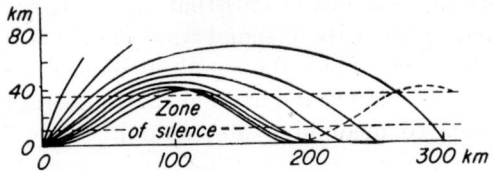

Fig. 11. Refracton of sound waves in the atmosphere.

reaching the earth's surface nearly 200 km from the explosion. Other sound waves proceeding away from the source at large elevation angles penetrate the inversion layer but are eventually returned to the earth as a result of refraction in the inversion layer; these sound waves return to the earth at points between 200 and 300 km from the initial explosion. The general effects observed at the ground are that sounds are heard close to the explosion and at points 200 km away, but between these two regions there is a 'zone of silence.' This zone of silence is indicated in Fig. 11 and is also shown in the typical 'map' of an explosion shown in Fig. 12.

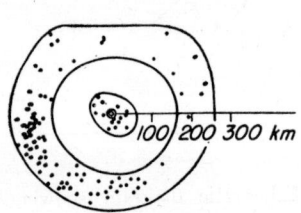

Fig. 12. Map showing region of audibility of an explosion.

The greatest explosion of which there is any record accompanied the volcanic eruption of Krakatao on August 26–27, 1883, which killed all the inhabitants of this small East Indian island and produced large tidal waves on neighboring islands, including Java and Sumatra. After several 'minor' explosions, the eruption culminated on the morning of August 27, when a large part of a mountain was blown into the air. The resulting wave in the air was observed in numerous parts of the world, and at a distance of 2000 mi from the island the sounds were like those accompanying heavy gunfire. The air wave proceeded entirely around the earth and culminated at a locality on the opposite side of the earth. From this 'focal point' the sound wave spread out again and did not entirely disappear for 127 hours after the explosion. The wave created by the Krakatao explosion was so violent that it can scarcely be classed as a sound wave at all; this unique wave actually involved the up-and-down motion of large portions of the earth's atmosphere and could be followed around the world several times as a wave of excess pressure on recording barometers.

PROBLEMS

1. In our discussion of sound through the atmosphere we assumed that there was no wind. Discuss the transmission of sound waves sent out from a source when a constant wind of velocity v_w is blowing. Find the wavelength of the sound waves sent out in various horizontal directions from the source.

2. Discuss qualitatively the refraction effects which would be produced by a steady west wind whose speed v_w increased with altitude h above the source according to the relation $v_w = v_{w0}(1+\alpha h)$, where v_{w0} is the wind velocity at the level of the source.

5. ABSORPTION OF SOUND WAVES*

In Chap. 21 we mentioned the fact that waves traveling in certain types of media are damped out or absorbed as a result of 'frictional' effects of various kinds. For sound waves† in air these frictional losses are very small, but absorption is very great in certain other media such as cork and certain types of fiberboard. The chief quantity of practical interest in connection with these absorbing materials is not the fraction of energy lost per unit path length within the material but the effectiveness of the material in *not* reflecting sound waves that are incident at the surface of the material.

To illustrate this point, let us consider a unidirectional sound wave like that emerging from the cardboard tube shown in Fig. 7. Let the intensity of the sound incident at the wall be denoted by I_0. Of the energy reaching the wall, part will be reflected, part will be transmitted through the wall, and part will be absorbed in the wall material. The acoustical engineer is usually concerned only with the energy *reflected* and regards all energy not reflected as being absorbed; he thus lumps energy transmitted through the wall and energy actually 'absorbed' in the wall material as 'absorbed,' since it is removed from the room in which he makes his measurements. If the intensity of the reflected unidirectional sound wave mentioned above is I, so that the sound 'absorbed' is $I_0 - I$, the *absorption factor* α for the wall material is defined by the relation

$$I_0 - I = \alpha I_0, \quad \text{or} \quad I = I_0(1-\alpha). \tag{21}$$

The factor α is a number ranging from zero for a hypothetical perfectly reflecting surface to unity for an open window, which from the point of view of the acoustical engineer is a perfect 'absorber.'

There are at least two reasons why the absorption factor or absorption

---

* This section may be omitted without loss of continuity.

† The absorption of waves at high ultrasonic frequencies will be discussed briefly in Sec. 8 of this chapter.

coefficient α cannot be determined by the experiment involving the cardboard tubes. In the first place, sound waves do not remain unidirectional after emerging from the tube; in the second place, the sound will be reflected not only at the wall shown in Fig. 7 but will suffer multiple reflections from other walls of the room in which the measurement is made. Reflection coefficients for various materials are usually determined in terms of the acoustical properties of a test room in which the materials in question serve as wall or floor covering. These methods were originally developed by W. C. Sabine, an American physicist, who was a pioneer in the development of scientific architectural acoustics.

By experiment Sabine discovered that when a source begins to send out sound waves at a constant rate into a large room the sound level I in the room begins to rise rapidly but then approaches a maximum intensity I_0 exponentially. The equation giving intensity I as a function of time is

$$I = I_0(1 - e^{-Bt}), \tag{22}$$

where B is a constant which depends on the volume of the room, the area of its walls, and the absorption coefficient of the wall materials. Similarly, if the source is turned off after the intensity has approached I_0 very closely, the intensity of the sound in the room decreases or 'decays' exponentially in a manner described by the relation

$$I = I_0 e^{-Bt}, \tag{23}$$

where B has the same value as in (22). If sufficient data are available, the value of B can be determined graphically from a semilog plot of the decay curve giving I as a function of time like that shown in Fig. 13.

In order to determine absorption coefficients for various materials from the measured values of the decay constant B, we may reason in somewhat the following way: The initial intensity I_0 of sound at the instant the source is cut off is decreased by a factor of $(1 - \alpha)$ for one reflection, to the value $(1 - \alpha)I_0$. After two reflections the intensity is $(1 - \alpha)^2 I_0$, and so on. If there are n reflections per unit time, the intensity I at the end of time t after the source is shut off is given by

$$I = (1 - \alpha)^{nt} I_0. \tag{24}$$

Equating the expressions for I given in (23) and (24), we obtain

$$(1 - \alpha)^{nt} I_0 = I_0 e^{-Bt} \quad \text{or} \quad (1 - \alpha)^{nt} = e^{-Bt}.$$

Taking the natural logarithm of both sides of this equation, we obtain

$$nt \log_e(1 - \alpha) = -Bt \quad \text{or} \quad n \log_e(1 - \alpha) = -B, \tag{25}$$

which would give us a value of α in terms of the measured value of B if we knew the value of n, the number of reflections per unit time. After considering rooms of different sizes and shapes, Sabine concluded that one could assume that the sound waves on the average travel a distance $4V/A$ between successive reflections, where V is the volume of the room and A the total wall area of the room. On this assumption, the number n of reflections per unit time is given by $n = vA/4V$, where v is the speed of sound in air. By making measurements of decay constant in rooms with

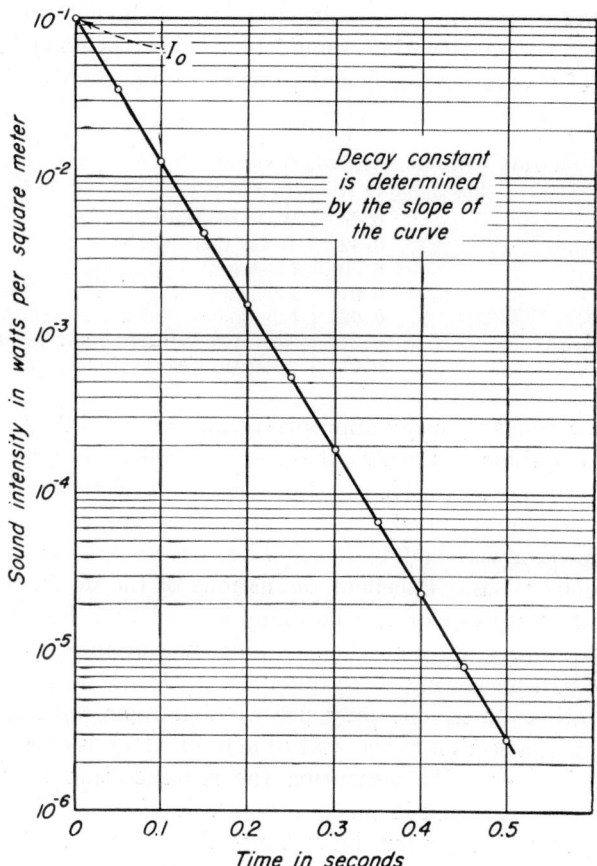

Fig. 13. Manner of decrease of sound intensity in a room after the sound source is turned off.

various types of walls, Sabine and later workers have determined the typical absorption coefficients listed in Table IV for various materials.

One of the major problems facing the acoustical engineer and architect is the design of rooms and auditoriums having proper acoustical properties. Sabine introduced a quantity, the time of reverberation T, in terms of which the acoustical properties of a room are judged. The time of reverberation T is arbitrarily defined as the time for a sound to decrease to one-millionth of its steady-state intensity I_0 after the source is stopped. As a result of numerous experimental studies, Sabine was able to select optimum values for the reverberation in rooms of different sizes. For speech, the optimum reverberation times vary from about 0.8 sec in a room with a volume of 1000 ft^3 to about 2.0 sec in a room with a volume of 1,000,000 ft^3. For music, optimum reverberation times are somewhat greater than for speech. A broadcasting studio should be quite 'dead'; that is, the reverberation time should be as short as possible. From a knowledge of absorption coefficients, one can do a great deal to control

TABLE IV
Absorption Coefficients for Various Building Materials
(For sound of frequency 512 cycles/sec)

Cork tile	0.08	Wood flooring	0.03
Hair felt	0.42	Wood paneling	0.06
Heavy draperies	0.50	Plaster	0.03
Brick wall	0.017	Fiberglas board 1 inch thick	0.65
Clay tile	0.028	Fiberglas board 2 inches thick	0.99
Concrete	0.015	Acoustex wall material 1 inch thick	0.81
Glass	0.027	Acoustic Celotex 1 inch thick	0.58

reverberation times by using appropriate wall materials. As a result of the studies of Sabine and others, it is now possible to design auditoriums scientifically, whereas previously the design was largely a hit-or-miss proposition to the architect. If the acoustical properties of the completed auditorium were bad, little could be done except to add wall hangings of various types. Excellent discussions of the design problems of architectural acoustics can now be found in books on this subject.

We might add a few details concerning measurements of absorption coefficients. In measuring these quantities in terms of decay constants or reverberation times, one may use a small room with hard, highly reflecting walls; a section of the wall or floor of which is covered with the material under test. By measuring the reverberation time with and without the test material in place, the additional absorption and hence the absorption coefficient for the test material itself can be determined. Another method involves making measurements on standing waves in a tube like the Kundt's tube shown in Fig. 1, with the test material used as a plug to close one end. Since reflection is not perfect, the amplitude of vibration at the nodes will not drop to zero. By means of a small microphone, the sound intensity at nodal and antinodal points can be measured, and the absorption coefficient of the plug material can be determined in terms of the ratio of intensity at the antinodes to the intensity at the nodes.

Absorption coefficients vary somewhat with sound frequency. The methods sketched in the preceding paragraph are capable of measuring absorption coefficients as a function of frequency.

PROBLEMS

1. By expanding the logarithm in (25) as a power series, show that for an absorption coefficient $\alpha \ll 1$, $B = n\alpha = vA\alpha/4V$ on Sabine's assumption. Also show that the reverberation time $T = 55.3V/\alpha vA$, for small α.

2. Using the formulas of Prob. 1, compute the reverberation time of a room $20 \times 20 \times 10$ ft with plaster walls and ceiling and wooden floor.

6. INTERFERENCE AND DIFFRACTION OF SOUND WAVES

We shall first discuss interference effects that occur when two sound waves of the same frequency arrive at the same point. The two waves can either come from the same source along different paths, or can come from different sources.

The first case involves the propagation of waves from a *single* source along *different paths* to a common point, where interference can be produced. This can be demonstrated by the arrangement shown in Fig. 14. A source of sound such as the diaphragm of a speaker is inserted at position S at the end of a tube. The diaphragm is set into oscillation by means of an audio-oscillator unit so that sound waves of a constant frequency are sent out in the air inside the tube. These waves travel to the opening O along two paths A and B. Path A has a constant length but the length of path B can be varied by means of the 'trombone' arrangement shown in the figure.

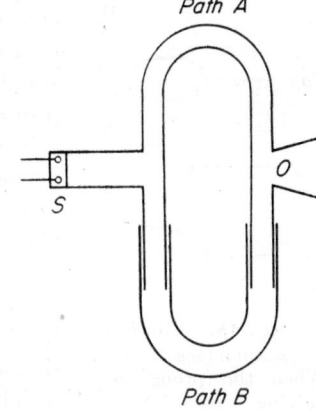

Fig. 14. Schematic diagram of apparatus for demonstrating interference between sound waves.

If the two paths are of *equal* length, the waves arrive exactly in phase at the opening O and sound will be heard by the auditor. If the length of path B is now varied slowly, the intensity of the sound wave decreases to a minimum when the difference between paths B and A is one-half wavelength. As the length of path B is increased still further, the intensity of the sound increases to a maximum when the difference between path A and B is equal to a whole wavelength. Further elongation of path B leads to successive minima and maxima of intensity of the sound heard. These observations can be summarized in terms of l_B and l_A, the lengths of paths A and B, respectively, in the following way:

Intensity maxima occur when $l_B - l_A = n\lambda$. $\quad (n = 0, 1, 2, \cdots)$

Intensity minima occur when $l_B - l_A = (n + \tfrac{1}{2})\lambda$. $\quad (n = 0, 1, 2, \cdots)$

The observed effects are readily explained on the basis of the superposition principle. When the path difference is an integral number of wavelengths, the waves arriving at O are effectively *in phase* and reinforcement occurs. When the path difference differs by an odd number of half wavelengths—that is, by $(n+\frac{1}{2})\lambda$—the waves arriving at O are 180° out of phase and destructive interference occurs.

The second case to be considered involves interference between waves from different sources having the same frequency. In this case there can be a stationary interference pattern only if there is a constant phase relationship between the vibrations of the sources. This condition is realized by a tuning fork, which actually acts as if it were a multiple source. That this is so can be understood by considering the vibration of one prong of the fork; as it moves in a given direction through the air, a compression is produced on the 'leading' side and a rarefaction on the 'trailing' side, and this situation is reversed when the prong moves in the opposite direction. Thus, the single prong acts as if it were *two sources* 180° out of phase. The other prong behaves in the same way. Hence, if the prongs are far apart, a single fork would behave like four simple sources; if the prongs are close together, it is possible to regard the two simple sources between the prongs as a single source and treat the fork as three simple sources. This situation can be understood by considering Fig. 15, which gives a diagram of the situation for several positions of the fork prongs during a complete cycle; here condensations are denoted by C and rarefactions by R.

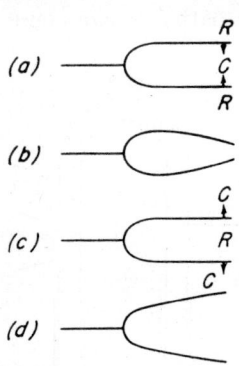

Fig. 15. Vibration of a tuning fork. When the prongs are moving toward each other, condensations are formed between the prongs and rarefactions beyond the outer surfaces of the prongs. When the prongs are moving away from each other, this situation is reversed.

As a result of the 'multiple-source' property of a tuning fork, a stationary interference pattern like that in Fig. 16 is produced. The crosshatched rectangles represent the ends of the tuning-fork prongs. The solid straight lines are drawn through points of maximum intensity and the dotted curves are drawn through points at which the intensity is a minimum. It is easy to verify the existence of such an interference pattern by walking around a table on which a vibrating tuning fork is standing or by rotating a vibrating tuning fork near one's ear.

If two wave trains of slightly *different frequency* traverse a medium, a stationary interference pattern will not be formed. However, if their frequencies are nearly equal, two sets of waves can interfere in such a way as to produce a sound with pulsating intensity at a given point; these pulsations in intensity are known as *beats*. From the superposition principle it is easy to see the reason for the production of beats. Let the magnitude of the displacement produced at a given point by one wave be given by

$$S_1 = A\ \sin 2\pi ft \qquad (26)$$

and the magnitude of the displacement produced by the second wave be

$$S_2 = A'\ \sin 2\pi f't. \qquad (27)$$

Then, by the superposition principle, the resultant displacement produced by the two waves is

$$S = S_1 + S_2 = A\ \sin 2\pi ft + A'\ \sin 2\pi f't.$$

For the sake of simplicity, let us consider a case in which $A = A'$; then

$$S = A(\sin 2\pi ft + \sin 2\pi f't).$$

By using the trigonometric relation for the sum of two sines, we can write

$$S = \left[2A\ \cos 2\pi \left(\frac{f-f'}{2}\right) t \right] \sin 2\pi \left(\frac{f+f'}{2}\right) t. \qquad (28)$$

Since we assume that f is close to f', this can be regarded as a wave of frequency $\tfrac{1}{2}(f+f')$ modulated by a slowly varying amplitude given

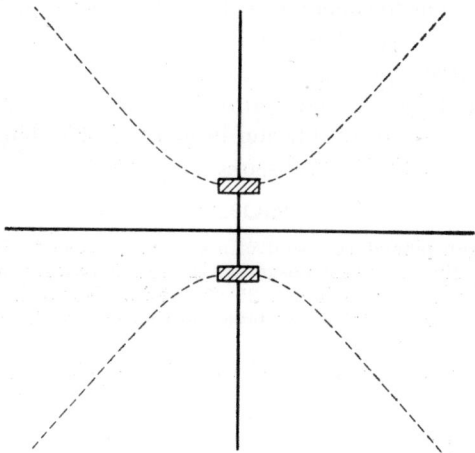

Fig. 16. Interference pattern near a tuning-fork. The heavy lines show regions of maximum intensity and the dotted curves regions of minimum intensity.

by the term in square brackets. A little consideration will reveal that the *magnitude* of this amplitude attains a maximum value $f-f'$ times per second. Thus, an observer will hear $f-f'$ *beats* per second. For example, if a tuning fork with a frequency of 256 cycles/sec and one with a frequency of 260 cycles/sec are sounded simultaneously, an observer will hear four beats each second of sound of frequency 258 cycles/sec. By counting beats it is possible to determine accurately the frequency difference between two sounds of nearly equal frequency.

When the difference between the frequencies of two sounds is more than 10 or 15 cycles/sec, the beats become difficult to distinguish. However, when the difference is great enough to correspond to an audible frequency, one may hear a *difference tone*. For example, if two intense sound waves having frequencies of 10,000 cycles/sec and 8500 cycles/sec reach the observer, he may hear a difference tone of 1500 cycles/sec. It is also sometimes possible to hear *summation tones;* for example, if waves of proper amplitude and with frequencies of 400 cycles/sec and 800 cycles/sec reach the ear, it is possible to hear a tone with a frequency of 1200 cycles/sec. Difference and summation tones are called *combination tones*.

There is another property of sound waves that should be mentioned at this point. This property is their ability to 'bend around corners,' called *diffraction*. This property becomes familiar to us early in life; a child can hear the voice of his mother in a neighboring room chiefly because sound waves are diffracted. Waves of a given frequency passing through an opening in a wall appear to spread out on the other side of the wall. If the width of the opening is of the same order of magnitude as the length of the sound wave, the spreading of the waves beyond the wall is by no means uniform; variations in intensity are noted as one moves from point to point, and we say that a *diffraction pattern* is formed. Since we shall treat the subject of diffraction in considerable detail in connection with light waves, we shall not discuss it further here.

PROBLEM

1. An open organ pipe at the front of a church is tuned to 264 cycles at 20° C, and an open organ pipe in the echo organ at the rear is tuned to 528 cycles at 20° C. On Sunday the rear of the church is at 25° C, the front at 20° C. How many beats occur between the fundamental of one pipe and the first overtone of the other when they are sounded together? Ans: 4.8.

2. Make a rough plot of (26), (27), and (28) for the case $A = A'$, $f = 10$/sec, $f' = 8$/sec.

7. DOPPLER EFFECT

When a source of sound is moving with respect to an observer or an observer is moving with respect to the source, the pitch of the sound heard by the observer is different from the pitch heard when the source and observer are both at rest. Casual observation by a man on a station platform shows that the pitch of a locomotive whistle is *higher* when the locomotive is approaching the station than when the locomotive is standing still; the pitch is *lower* when the locomotive is moving away from the observer than when the locomotive is standing still. The effect is very noticeable when an express train is moving at high speed past the station platform of a local stop. Careful measurement shows that the pitch does not depend simply upon the relative velocity of source and observer but also depends to some extent on whether the source or the observer is moving with respect to the air or other medium in which the sound travels. The change in frequency caused by the motion of the source or the observer is called the *Doppler effect*. We shall first consider the case of a moving source and a stationary observer, then the case of a stationary source and a moving observer, then the case in which both are moving.

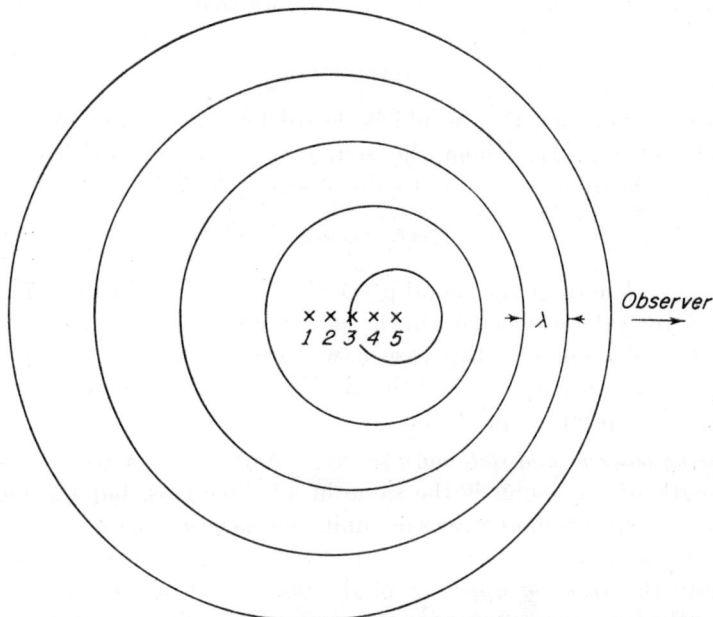

Fig. 17. Doppler effect: positions of successive condensations from a source moving toward the right with speed v_s. The wavelength λ is less than the normal wavelength λ_s by the distance the source moves is one period T_s, that is, $\lambda = \lambda_s - v_s T_s = \lambda_s - v_s \lambda_s / v$, since $T_s = \lambda_s / v$, where v is the speed of sound. Thus $\lambda / \lambda_s = (v - v_s)/v$, as in (29).

Moving source and stationary observer. When the source is moving, the motion causes a change in *wavelength* of the sound in air. In order to see how this change comes about, let v be the speed of sound in air, λ_s the wavelength in air when the source is at rest, and f_s the actual frequency of the source. If the source is traveling toward the right, the successive condensations produced by the source will have positions like those shown in Fig. 17. Each successive condensation is closer to the preceding condensation moving toward the right than it would be for a stationary source. The wavelength λ of the sound propagated to the right is given

by
$$\lambda/\lambda_s = (v-v_s)/v, \tag{29}$$

where v_s is the speed of the source. Since the speed of transmission of sound through the stationary air is unaltered by the motion of the source, the waves moving to the right will have a frequency f given by

$$f = v/\lambda \quad \text{rather than by} \quad f_s = v/\lambda_s. \tag{30}$$

This frequency of the sound waves in the air is higher than the frequency of the source. In order to find the frequency f of the sound waves in terms of the frequency of the source, we note that $f/f_s = \lambda_s/\lambda$ and hence that

$$f = f_s v/(v-v_s). \tag{31}$$

This is the frequency that would be heard by a stationary observer at the right of Fig. 17, whom the source is *approaching* with speed v_s. In this case the frequency heard by the observer would be

$$f_o = f_s v/(v-v_s). \tag{32}$$

The wavelength of the sound proceeding to the left in Fig. 17 would be longer than the wavelength in the case of a stationary source. Equation (32) still applies to this case if we consider that v_s, the speed of approach, has a negative value; that is, if we regard a speed of recession as a negative speed of approach.

Moving observer and stationary source. With a stationary source, the wavelength of the sound is the same in all directions, but the moving observer encounters more waves per unit time as he *approaches* the source. The effect observed is therefore a direct change in frequency. Using v_o to denote the *speed of approach* of the observer in moving toward the source, f the frequency of sound in the air, we may write

$$f_o/f = (v+v_o)/v,$$

since the number of waves received per second is proportional to the speed of the waves relative to the observer. Hence, for an observer moving with respect to the source the observed frequency f_o is given by

$$f_o = f(v+v_o)/v, \tag{33}$$

where v_o is the speed of approach of the observer. If the source is stationary, $f = f_s$, the frequency of the source, and

$$f_o = f_s(v+v_o)/v. \tag{34}$$

If the observer is moving away from the source, v_o assumes a negative value, and the frequency f_o is less than it would be if source and observer were both stationary.

Moving source and moving observer. With the source and observer both in motion, we can combine the results obtained in equations (31) and (33). In (33) we must substitute for f, not the frequency of the source, but the frequency in the air given by (31). This substitution gives the following expression for the frequency of the sound heard by the observer:

$$f_o = f_s(v+v_o)/(v-v_s), \qquad (35)$$

In this equation, v_o and v_s are positive when they represent speeds of approach, negative when they represent speeds of recession.

We have derived (35) for the case in which source and observer are moving along the line connecting them. In the more general case it can be shown that (35) is valid when v_s is the *component* of source velocity directed *toward* the observer, and v_o is the *component* of observer velocity directed *toward* the source.

PROBLEMS

1. The fundamental frequency of a certain locomotive whistle is 400 cycles/sec and the speed of the locomotive is 100 ft/sec. On a day when the speed of sound in air is 1100 ft/sec, what will be the fundamental frequencies of the sounds heard by an observer on a station platform as the locomotive passes the station with its whistle blowing?   Ans: approach: 440 cycles/sec; locomotive at station: 400 cycles/sec; recession: 367 cycles/sec.

2. What frequencies would be heard by the observer in Prob. 1 if the speed of the locomotive were 120 mi/hr?

3. If the fundamental frequency of a bell at a railroad crossing is 400 cycles/sec, what frequencies will the engineer of a locomotive hear as the locomotive passes the crossing at 100 ft/sec on a day when the speed of sound is 1100 ft/sec?
Ans: approach: 436 cycles/sec; at crossing: 400 cycles/sec; recession: 363 cycles/sec.

4. What sound frequencies would the engineer in Prob. 3 hear if the speed of his locomotive were 120 mi/hr.

5. The speed of a fighter plane is 280 m/sec. If a whistle on the plane has a frequency of 300 cycles/sec, what will be the frequency of the sound heard by an observer at an airport when the plane is receding if the speed of sound is 332 m/sec?
Ans: 163 cycles/sec.

6. What will be the frequency of the sound heard by the observer in Prob. 5 when the plane is moving directly toward him?

7. Locomotive A is moving southward at a speed of 100 ft/sec while locomotive B is moving northward at a speed of 100 ft/sec. If the whistle on locomotive A has a fundamental frequency of 256 cycles/sec, what will be the frequencies of the sounds heard by the engineer on locomotive B as the two locomotives pass each other? Take the speed of sound as 1100 ft/sec.
Ans: approach: 307 cycles/sec; adjacent: 256 cycles/sec; recession: 213 cycles/sec.

8. Solve Prob. 7 for a case in which the speed of locomotive A is 120 mi/hr and the speed of locomotive B is 80 mi/hr.

9. Discuss the effects of wind velocity on the Doppler effect.

10. What is the apparent pitch of a whistle of 700 vibrations/sec (a) if source and observer are approaching each other, each moving with $\frac{1}{8}$ the speed of sound? (b) if they are mutually receding, each at this same speed?

11. A man walks at 3 m/sec on a still day along the line between two fire stations The fire whistles on the two stations sound simultaneously at a frequency of 500 vibrations/sec. Find the apparent frequency of each whistle and the number of beats per second. Take $v = 330$ m/sec.   Ans: 495, 505, 9.06 sec^{-1}.

12. A man sounds a whistle of frequency f_s. This sound is reflected from an object that is approaching the man with speed v_r. Show that the frequency of the echo heard by the man is

$$f_s \frac{v + v_r}{v - v_r}.$$

Explain your reasoning carefully.

13. A man approaching a stationary wall at speed v_m blows a whistle of frequency f_s. Find the frequency of the echo heard by the man.

8. ULTRASONIC WAVES; SONAR*

As we have pointed out earlier, the upper limit of the audible frequency range is in the vicinity of 15 or 20 kilocycles per second (kc/sec). However, mechanical waves of much higher frequencies can be generated by suitable methods. These are known as *ultrasonic*† waves.

There are several types of sources used for producing ultrasonic waves. One of the oldest is the Galton whistle, which emits sounds as a result of oscillations produced in a small air column. The Galton whistle is not effective in producing waves of high intensity and its upper frequency limit is about 100 kc/sec. Ultrasonic waves are more readily initiated by vibrating solids, such as quartz crystals or short nickel rods. Vibrations of quartz crystals are excited by applying electric fields of high frequency to the crystal. With vibrating crystals, it is possible to produce ultrasonic waves with frequencies as high as 500 megacycles/sec (1 megacycle = 10^6 cycles); the wavelength corresponding to this frequency is about 6×10^{-7} m in air and about 2.4×10^{-6} m in water. Longitudinal vibrations can be initiated in rods of nickel by applying magnetic fields of high frequency. The upper frequency limit of these 'magnetostriction oscillators' is about 300 kc/sec, but waves of great intensity are more easily obtainable with these than with crystal oscillators.

Many interesting effects are produced by ultrasonic waves of high intensity. They can be used to produce stable emulsions from colloidal suspensions in liquids or from mixtures of normally immiscible liquids. On the other hand, ultrasonic waves 'coagulate' certain *aerosols* such as smoke or fine-powder suspensions in air. The biological effects produced by intense ultrasonic waves include destruction of certain micro-organisms and small animals in water, destruction of red blood corpuscles, and sterilization of milk. These effects are due in part to intense local heating and in part to the large accelerations imparted to the vibrating particles. Ultrasonic waves have proved useful in detecting flaws in the interior of

---

* This section may be omitted without loss of continuity.
† The term formerly used was *supersonic*, but this term is now generally reserved for phenomena occurring at *speeds* greater than the *speed of sound*.

solid bodies; flaws such as cracks produce reflections or cause absorptions that are easily detected. The graphite blocks used in the construction of the early atomic piles were tested in this manner.

One other interesting property of ultrasonic waves is that, for certain frequencies, they are absorbed very rapidly in air and other media. Experiments have shown that absorption by air shows marked variations with temperature and humidity. In this respect, ultrasonic waves differ considerably from audible sound waves, which are absorbed only slightly by air.

Underwater ultrasonic waves have proved useful in navigation problems and in submarine detection. Underwater waves of frequency in the neighborhood of 40 kc/sec travel many miles before absorption effects become troublesome. Waves in this general frequency range have been employed for underwater signaling. By varying the amplitude of these ultrasonic waves at an audio-frequency rate, it is possible to 'talk' from ship to ship. The way in which an 'amplitude-modulated' ultrasonic wave is used to carry voice messages is similar in many respects to the ordinary 'AM' radio-communication systems, which are discussed in Chap. 44, Electromagnetic Waves.

Another important application of ultrasonic waves is in the *sonar* systems used in the detection of underwater and surface vessels by employing the echo principle. By construction of 'arrays' of ultrasonic sources of the same frequency, it is possible to send out a narrow 'beam' of sound waves in any desired direction through water. In a sonar system on a submarine or destroyer, the ultrasonic sources producing such a beam are 'pulsed'; thus, an ultrasonic disturbance of short duration is sent out in a given direction. If this disturbance strikes a submarine or the submerged portion of a surface vessel, part of the energy will be reflected and returned to the ship from which the original pulse was transmitted, where it can be detected by suitable devices and registered as an 'echo.' The time interval between transmission of the original pulse and the reception of the echo is accurately measured by electronic timing devices; from a knowledge of this time interval and the speed of underwater sound, the distance from the source to the object producing the echo can be calculated. By noting the direction in which the beam was directed, one can also determine the direction of the object producing the echo. Thus, both the *direction* and the *range* of a reflecting object can be determined by the *sonar* system. By directing the ultrasonic beam downward from the bottom of a surface craft, one can make accurate depth measurements by means of echoes from the sea floor. This is the principle of the *fathometer* (1 fathom = 6 ft) in current use.

Part IV

LIGHT

Part IV

Light

CHAPTER 23

THE NATURE OF LIGHT AND ITS PROPAGATION

As we have noted in our study of heat, all objects are continually emitting and absorbing radiant energy. An object in thermal equilibrium with its surroundings emits as much radiation as it absorbs, so that there is no net transfer of energy between the object and its surroundings. If an object is at a higher temperature than its surroundings, it will emit more radiation than it absorbs, and a net transfer of energy from the object to its surroundings will take place. The thermal radiation from an object only slightly hotter than the human body is invisible but can be detected by the cutaneous senses. However, if the temperature of an object is gradually increased, a temperature will eventually be attained at which some of the emitted radiation becomes visible. Radiant energy that is capable of affecting the retina of the human eye is commonly called *light*.

In this and the following chapters, we shall discuss in detail some of the properties of light. Therefore, it is desirable at this point to give a brief survey of some of the more important optical phenomena and to outline the modern theories concerning the nature of light.

1. NATURE OF LIGHT

Light is emitted by matter when it is at high temperature, when it is electrically excited, and when it is undergoing certain chemical or physical processes. Objects that emit light are called *luminous* or *self-luminous* and are visible as a result of the emitted light. Nonluminous objects become visible only when they are *illuminated;* that is, when light from a luminous object strikes them. Whenever light strikes the surface of an object, some of the incident light is *reflected*, some is *absorbed*, and some is *transmitted*. The relative importance of these three effects determines the appearance of the object. In fact, we are accustomed to giving a qualitative estimate of these effects in describing an object. Thus, we say that a nonluminous object has a *bright* surface if a large fraction of the incident light is reflected. (For example, a freshly painted ceiling and a polished aluminum cooking utensil are said to have bright surfaces, while a soot-covered ceiling and a rusty iron pot are said to have dark surfaces.) Objects that transmit no light are said to be *opaque*. Materials like clear glass or water, which transmit light so well that a luminous object may be clearly seen through them, are called *transparent;* other materials such as frosted glass or paraffin, which transmit light but are not clear, are called *translucent.*

Many of our most frequent experiences with light involve *reflection* and *refraction.* We see our images in mirrors and other polished surfaces by means of light that has undergone *regular reflection;* in general, non-luminous objects are seen by means of light that has been *diffusely reflected* from their surfaces. We are also familiar with the change in direction of propagation of light as it passes from one medium to another. This change in direction, called *refraction,* causes an object submerged in water to appear closer to the surface than it actually is and causes a partially submerged stick to appear bent. Refraction of white light is usually accompanied by a splitting of the white light into its component spectral colors, as in the case of the rainbow; this phenomenon is called *dispersion.*

Three other phenomena not so frequently encountered are *interference, diffraction,* and *polarization.* The colors observed in thin layers of oil on a wet pavement are due to the *interference* of light waves that are reflected from the upper and lower surfaces of the oil film. Diffraction effects result when light passes through extremely narrow openings; a person looking through a narrow slit at the sky or at some distant light source sees a series of light and dark lines parallel to the sides of the slit. These light and dark lines are caused by *diffraction.* Light that has passed through certain crystals like tourmaline or through Polaroid films has become *polarized.* The effects of *polarization* are such that the light transmitted by one Polaroid film is abosrbed completely when intercepted by a second Polaroid film oriented at right angles to the first. These and other properties of light will be considered in detail in the chapters that follow.

Sir Isaac Newton and others attempted to explain optical phenomena in terms of a theory that pictured light as streams of minute *particles* emitted by luminous objects. This theory proved inadequate to account satisfactorily for phenomena involving interference, diffraction, and polarization, and predicted an incorrect value for the speed of light in media such as glass and water. Therefore, Newton's particle theory had to be abandoned in favor of a theory that treats light as a *wave motion.* The wave theory, in which the waves are *electromagnetic* in nature, is adequate to account for all phenomena involved in light transmission, and there is no reason to doubt its 'correctness.'

Careful observation of interference and diffraction phenomena enables us to measure wavelengths accurately. For visible light, the *wavelengths* vary from about 390 mμ* for violet to about 760 mμ for deep-red. To visualize these values, note that 1000 m$\mu = \frac{1}{1000}$ mm and that visible

* 1 micron (μ) = 10^{-6} meter; 1 millimicron (mμ) = 10^{-9} meter.

light has a wavelength of about half this value, or about $\frac{1}{2000}$ mm. Study of polarization phenomena indicates that the waves are *transverse*. Observations of the effects of electric and magnetic fields on light sources and on the transmission of light through media lead to the further conclusion that light waves are electromagnetic waves similar to radio waves except for differences in wavelength and frequency.

A luminous source may emit radiation of wavelengths both longer and shorter than those of visible radiation. These types of radiation are known as *infrared* and *ultraviolet*, respectively. Infrared, visible, and ultraviolet radiations are all portions of the *electromagnetic spectrum*, which includes radiation of all wavelengths from extremely long radio waves to extremely short X rays and the gamma rays from radioactive materials. The basic nature of all electromagnetic radiation is the same. In the present study we shall devote our attention chiefly to the visible radiation commonly called light, but it will be well to remember that electromagnetic radiations of other wavelength have many properties similar to those of light. In fact, the physical properties of infrared and ultraviolet radiations are so similar to those of light that these radiations are often referred to as 'infrared light' and 'ultraviolet light.'

2. EMISSION OF LIGHT

When the temperature of an opaque solid body such as a tungsten filament becomes sufficiently high, the body begins to emit light. In a darkened room, a tungsten filament begins to exhibit a reddish glow at about 500° C and becomes 'white-hot' at about 1300° C. While many liquids are vaporized before they reach a temperature high enough to cause them to emit light, this is not true of molten metals and some molten salts. The brilliance of molten steel is long remembered by visitors to a steel mill. Gases at high temperatures emit light and in fact are responsible for the radiation reaching us from the sun. Gases at low pressures can be caused to emit light by an electrical discharge through them; the blue-green mercury arc and the red neon tube provide familiar examples of light sources involving electrical discharges. Chemical transformations can cause the emission of light without production of high temperatures.

3. RECTILINEAR PROPAGATION

That light travels in straight lines in a uniform medium is a fact that is familiar to all of us. In fact, if this were not so, distinct vision would be impossible, and we would see only brightness and darkness. Straight-line propagation may be demonstrated by means of the arrangement shown in Fig. 1. The light from the source can be seen only if the small holes in the screens are in a straight line. Since light consists of waves, we might expect light to pass as readily around obstacles as sound does.

Actually, the wavelength of light is so short compared to that of sound that bending of light can be neglected except when extremely small openings or extremely small obstacles are involved. For most practical purposes such as surveying and navigation, the assumption of rectilinear propagation is a sufficiently close approximation to permit highly accurate measurements of position.

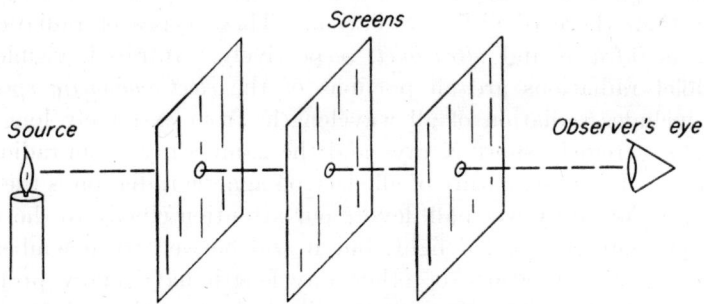

Fig. 1. Rectilinear propagation.

The direction or path of propagation of light may be represented by a straight line called a *ray*. Since light actually consists of waves emitted by the source of light and advancing outward through the surrounding medium, as indicated in Fig. 2, a ray is actually only a normal to the advancing wave-front. The rays perpendicular to such a wave-front constitute a *beam of light*. When all the rays defining the beam are parallel, a *parallel beam* results. When the rays approach one another, the beam is *convergent;* when the rays are separating, the beam is *divergent*.

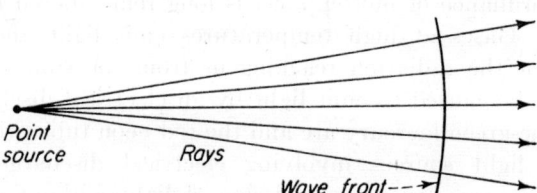

Fig. 2. Light rays and a typical wave-front. The wave-front is spherical if the medium is isotropic.

The limitation on the size of the beam, if propagation is to be essentially rectilinear, is that it must be many wavelengths wide. Since the wavelength is extremely small, this limitation actually permits use of very narrow beams indeed. It is sometimes convenient to think of a ray as such a narrow beam.

One of the simplest consequences of the straight-line propagation of light is the production of shadows; in fact, the production of sharp shadows is a proof of rectilinear propagation. Thus, the point source of light S in Fig. 4 will illuminate all parts of the screen above A and below B, but all points between A and B will be in darkness, since light from the source is stopped by the opaque body O. When a point source is involved, the boundary of the shadow is sharply defined and has the shape of the opaque body as seen from the source.

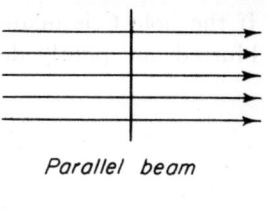
Parallel beam

Most actual sources are too large to be approximated by points, so that the boundaries of shadows are not sharply defined. In Fig. 5 the parts of the screen between A and B are in complete shadow; the regions between C and A and between B and D are in partial shadow; the portions of the screen beyond C and D are fully illuminated. In a shadow of this type, the regions of complete and partial shadow are called the *umbra* and *penumbra*, respectively.

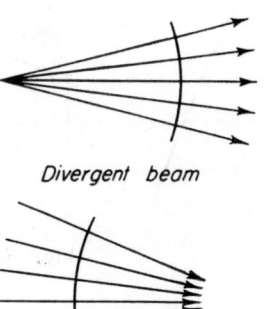
Divergent beam

Rectilinear propagation is used directly in the so-called pinhole camera. This arrangement is illustrated in Fig. 6. An opaque screen with a small hole in it is placed between a luminous or strongly illuminated object and a second screen. From every point such as A on the object a ray of light passes through the small hole C in the first screen and falls on point A' of the second screen; rays from all points on the *object*

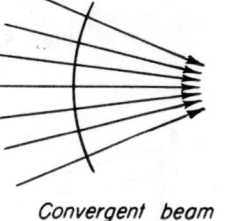
Convergent beam

Fig. 3. Light beams.

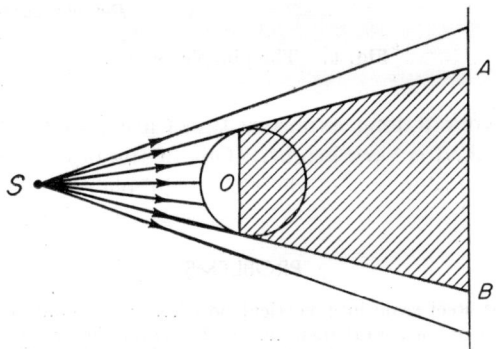

Fig. 4. Shadow cast by an opaque object illuminated by a point source of light.

reach the second screen after passing through the hole in the first screen and form an inverted *image* on the second screen in the manner indicated in the figure. If the opening C is extremely small compared with the distance to the screen, the image is sharp and well-defined but is rather dim. If the hole C is made larger, the image becomes brighter but becomes blurred and poorly defined. A pinhole camera can actually be used in

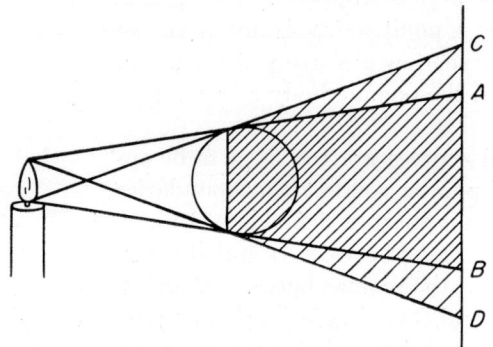

Fig. 5. Shadow cast by an opaque object illuminated by an extended source.

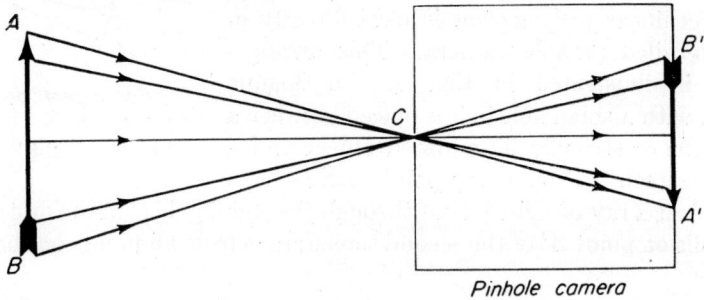

Fig. 6. The pinhole camera.

photographic work if long exposure times are possible or if the object being photographed is very bright. One of the best pictures of the first atomic-bomb explosion was made with a pinhole camera of the type just described.

PROBLEMS

1. A one-foot steel scale in a vertical position is illuminated by a point source of light located at a horizontal distance of 2 ft from the scale. A shadow of the scale is formed on a vertical wall 8 ft away from the scale. What is the length of the shadow? Draw a ray diagram. What effect does the vertical position of the point source have on the length of the shadow?   Ans: 5 ft; none.

2. A point source of light is located at a horizontal distance of 4 ft from a suspended pendulum bob. The pendulum bob is 2 in long and casts a shadow 6 in long on the wall of the room. What is the horizontal distance from the pendulum bob to the wall on which the shadow is formed? Draw a ray diagram.

RECTILINEAR PROPAGATION

3. An incandescent lamp with small filament and clear bulb is suspended 3 ft above the center of a table top. If the area of the table top is 4 ft^2 and if the distance from the table top to the floor is 3 ft, what is the area of the shadow formed on the floor?
Ans: 16 ft^2.

4. A small flashlight bulb is located at a distance of 2 ft from an opaque screen in which a circular hole of 3 in^2 cross-sectional area has been cut. A circular light spot is formed on a wall at a distance of 4 ft from the screen by light passing through the circular opening. What is the area of the light spot on the wall?

5. A vertical incandescent filament 1 in long is located at a horizontal distance of 6 in from an opaque object of 3-in vertical height. The opaque object casts a shadow on a vertical screen 6 in away from the object. What is the total vertical height of the resulting shadow? What is the vertical height of the umbra?
Ans: 7 in; 5 in.

6. A candle flame 3 cm long is placed 6 cm from the center of an opaque sphere 3 cm in diameter as in Fig. 5. If a shadow is formed on a screen 6 cm from the center of the sphere, what is the total vertical height of the shadow? What is the height of the umbra?

7. A circular opening 4 cm in diameter is cut in an opaque card which is placed close to the surface of a large frosted light bulb. The circular opening serves as a source of illumination for a circular piece of sheet metal 2 cm in diameter located 6 cm away from the opening. If a circular shadow of the metal is formed on a screen, find the limiting screen position beyond which no umbra could be observed. This limiting distance is sometimes called *the length of the conical umbra*.
Ans: 6 cm from metal to screen.

8. If the sun's diameter is 400 times that of the moon and if the distance from the sun to the moon is 93,000,000 mi, what is the length of the conical umbra of the moon's shadow? (See Prob. 7.)

9. A pinhole camera is used to form an image of an object 2 ft tall located 10 ft in front of the pinhole. If the distance from the pinhole to the camera screen is 5 in, what is the height of the image?
Ans: 1 in.

10. The diameter of the sun is 864,000 mi and that of the moon is 2160 mi. A 'pinhole camera,' consisting of a small hole in a window shade and a white card held 10 ft from the hole, is used to obtain an image of the sun at a time when the sun is at a distance of 92,900,000 mi from the earth and to obtain an image of the full moon at a time when the moon is 236,000 mi from the earth. Find the diameters of the images produced.

11. It is pointed out in the text that if the size of the pinhole used in a pinhole camera is increased, the image becomes brighter but also becomes blurred. The reason is that the light from a point on the object is actually spread out over a finite area on the screen. If the distance from a *point* source to the pinhole is 1 m and if the diameter of the pinhole is 2 mm, what will be the diameter of the image if the plate of the camera is 30 cm away from the pinhole? What would be the diameter of the image produced by this pinhole camera if the pinhole were reduced to 0.5 mm?
Ans: 2.6 mm; 0.65 mm.

12. A pinhole camera is used to take a picture of a flat object 2 ft^2 in area located 9 ft in front of the pinhole. The distance from the pinhole to the film is 4 in. What is the area of the image? If the diameter of the pinhole is 0.01 in, what is the diameter of the image of a single point of the object?

4. VISION

It may be well at this point to consider briefly some of the physical processes involved in vision. If light proceeding from a luminous point enters the eye, the luminous point is the apex of a divergent beam, or cone of rays, the base of the cone being the pupil of the eye as shown in Fig. 7. Whenever such a cone of rays enters the eye, the eye 'sees' the luminous point.* Each point of a luminous source acts as such a point source, and the eye sees the source as a collection of luminous points so closely spaced as to give the impression of continuity. Bodies that are not self-

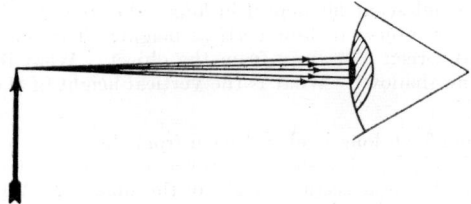

Fig. 7. Light rays entering the eye from a point on a luminous object.

luminous are not visible unless light falls upon them and is diffusely reflected in all directions. Each point on the illuminated body then behaves like a luminous point source.

The knowledge of our surroundings that is obtained from visual sensations depends on perception of relative brightness, of the apparent size and shape of objects, of their relative positions, and of their color. A combination of our perception of these aspects, combined with other knowledge derived from the sense of touch in handling visible objects,

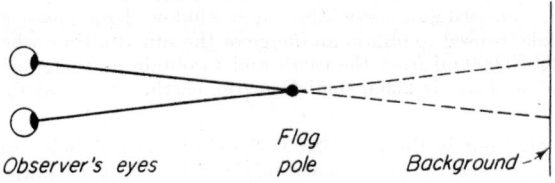

Fig. 8. Binocular vision.

gives us a mental picture of things seen at a distance. Relative brightness and, to some extent, color are useful guides in judging distance. Observed outline and shading are guides to shape.

Probably the most valuable means of judging relative distance results from the fact that our two eyes give us slightly different pictures of each scene. Thus, as indicated in Fig. 8, a near-by flagpole would be seen against a slightly different background of trees and buildings when viewed by each of our eyes. These two pictures are transmitted to the brain, which interprets them in the light of earlier experiences as meaning

* The actual optical mechanism of the eye will be discussed in Chap. 26.

that the flagpole is closer than the buildings or trees. This is, in essentials, a process similar to the triangulation technique used in surveying; the 'base line' in the present case is the distance between the two eyes.

PROBLEMS

NOTE: The unit solid angle is called the *steradian* and is the solid angle subtended at the center of a sphere by unit area of a sphere of unit radius. The solid angle subtended at the center of a sphere of radius R by area A is given by $\omega = A/R^2$; the total solid angle about a point at the center of a reference sphere is therefore equal to the total area of the sphere divided by the square of the radius, that is by $\omega = 4\pi R^2/R^2 = 4\pi$ steradians.

1. A point on a luminous object is 40 cm from the eye of an observer. If the pupil of the observer's eye is 2 mm in diameter, what is the size of the solid angle ω defining the cone of rays entering the observer's eye? (In this problem the angle subtended by the pupil at the point is sufficiently small for us to consider the area of the pupil to be an area on a reference sphere.)   Ans: 1.96×10^{-5} steradian.

2. A point source on a luminous object is located 50 cm in front of an observer's eye. If the pupil of the observer's eye is 1.5 mm in diameter, what is the solid angle ω defining the cone of rays entering the observer's eye?

3. A vertical pin is located 40 cm in front of an observer. If the pupils of the observer's eyes are 6.0 cm apart, what angle is subtended at the pin by the observer's optical 'base line,' that is, by the distance between his eyes?   Ans: $8°.6$.

4. A vertical wire is located 50 cm in front of an observer. If the pupils of this observer's eyes are 5.5 cm apart, what angle is subtended at the wire by the distance between his pupils?

5. SPEED OF LIGHT

We have stated that light consists of electromagnetic radiation of certain short wavelengths, emitted by sources and transmitted through the surrounding medium. The fact that we are able to see light from a hot filament inside an evacuated bulb indicates that *no material medium is needed for the transmission of light waves;* our reception of light from the sun and distant stars is a further indication that no material medium is necessary. The mechanism of the transmission of electromagnetic waves will be discussed in Chap. 44 in connection with radio transmission.

The *speed of light* is so great that early attempts at its measurement proved unsuccessful. Galileo conducted an experiment in which two observers stationed in towers some distance apart flashed signals at each other with lanterns. The second observer was supposed to flash a signal as soon as he received a light signal from the first observer. Galileo hoped that after the transmission of repeated signals, he could determine the speed of light by dividing the total distance the light traveled by the time required for transmission. The experiment was unsuccessful, and he concluded that the speed of light was too great for measurement by this method and that light transmission might indeed be instantaneous. In view of our present knowledge, it is easy to recognize that the reaction times of the observers were much greater than the time of transit of light between the towers.

The first successful measurement of the speed of light was reported by the Danish astronomer Olaus Roemer in 1675, when he announced a calculation of the speed of light from observations of irregularities in the times between successive eclipses of the innermost moon of Jupiter by that planet. The general argument used by Roemer can be understood by a consideration of Fig. 9, which shows certain relative positions of Jupiter and the earth. For simplicity, we shall consider Jupiter at rest in its orbit, since its motion is slow compared with that of the earth and

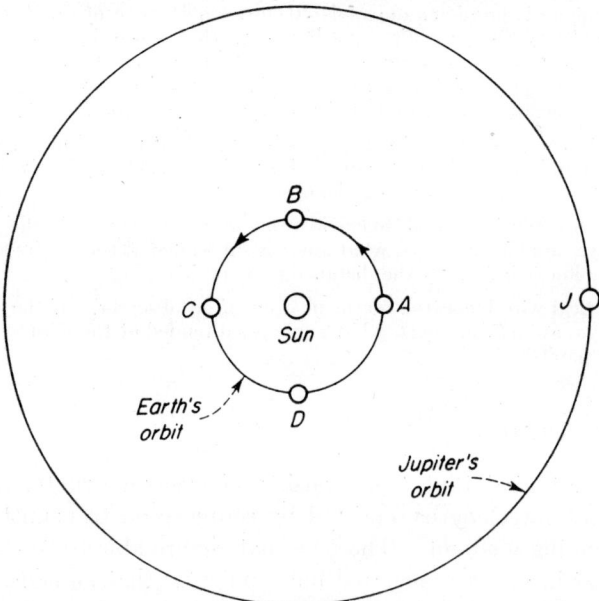

Fig. 9. Roemer's determination of the speed of light.

can easily be taken into account in actual calculations. Roemer noted that the observed interval between successive eclipses of Jupiter's moon as it passes behind the planet is the same (about 42.5 hr) when the earth is at positions A and C but that the interval between successive eclipses is greater when the earth is at B, and less when the earth is at D. These variations, Roemer correctly asserted, are not due to irregularities in the motion of Jupiter's moon, but are caused by variations in the times required for light to travel from Jupiter to the earth. Because the distance between Jupiter and the earth is increasing when the earth is at B, the time required for light to travel from Jupiter to the earth is increasing, and the measured interval between successive eclipses increases accordingly. A similar line of reasoning accounts for the shorter eclipse intervals noted when the earth is at D. This change in frequency of the eclipses is analogous to the apparent change in frequency of sound in the Doppler effect.

From observations made when the earth was at A, Roemer predicted the exact time at which a certain eclipse would take place when the earth was at C if one neglected the time required for light to traverse the distance AC, the diameter of the earth's orbit. He found, however, that the eclipse occurred about 16 min later than the predicted time. He concluded that 16 min represented the approximate time required for light to traverse a distance equal to the diameter of the earth's orbit. More recent measurements show that this time is approximately 1000 sec, or about $16\tfrac{2}{3}$ min. Since the diameter of the earth's orbit is 186,000,000 mi, this determination gives 186,000 mi/sec as the speed of light.

Roemer's conclusions, not credited at the time, were confirmed in 1727 by James Bradley, who employed quite a different astronomical method of determining the speed of light. Bradley observed that the apparent positions of the distant stars varied with the direction of orbital motion of the earth relative to the stars, the *maximum* angular change in apparent direction being approximately the same for all stars. Bradley interpreted this result in terms of the velocity of light and the varying direction of the velocity of the earth relative to the distant stars.

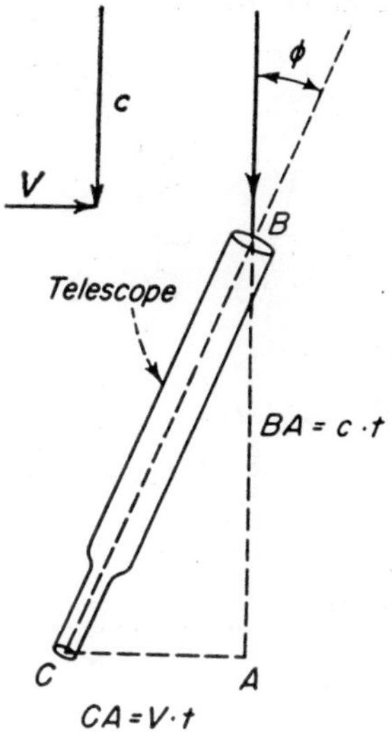

Fig. 10. Aberration of light. The light is traveling vertically downward in this figure.

In observing the position of the fixed stars at different times of the year, Bradley found a small displacement in apparent position, always in the direction the earth was traveling at the time the observation was made. This effect is due to the motion of the earth relative to the light coming from the star. If the earth and telescope were at rest, the telescope would have to be pointed in direction AB in Fig. 10. Since the earth is moving with velocity V, the telescope must be tilted so as to point in direction CB. This phenomenon is known as the *aberration of light*. Passage of light through the telescope is analogous to the passage of raindrops through a hollow tube. If the raindrops fall vertically, they can pass through a stationary tube without striking the walls, provided the tube is upright. However, if the tube is being carried by a man who is walking, the tube must be tilted forward in order for the raindrops to pass through without striking the walls.

The angle CBA in Fig. 10 can be determined by considering the conditions that permit light to pass down the telescope. From the figure, it can be seen that while the light moves the distance BA, the telescope must move the distance CA. If c is the speed of light and V the orbital speed of the earth, we may set

$$CA = Vt \quad \text{and} \quad BA = ct,$$

where t is the time required for the light to travel from B to A. Hence, we see that $\tan\phi = CA/BA = V/c$. The angle ϕ can be accurately determined by observing the annual apparent motions of stars near the pole star about their mean positions. The angle ϕ is $20''.492$; from this and

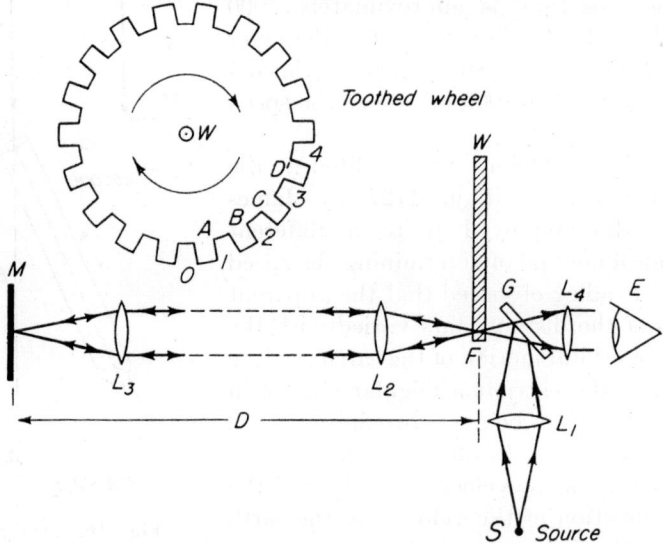

Fig. 11. Schematic diagram of Fizeau's apparatus for the determination of the speed of light.

the known value of approximately 18.5 mi/sec for the orbital speed of the earth, the speed of light is found to be 186,300 mi/sec. Bradley's method is more accurate than Roemer's, but both have been surpassed in accuracy by direct terrestrial observations of the speed of light.

The first successful terrestrial measurement was made by A. H. L. Fizeau in 1849. The principle of his method was the obvious one of sending out a brief flash of light and measuring the time for this light flash to travel to a distant mirror and return to the observer. The equipment used in the measurement is shown in Fig. 11. Light from an arc at S, passing through lens L_1 and reflected by the half-silvered mirror G, is brought to a focus at F. (A half-silvered mirror is a piece of glass with a very thin layer of silver—so thin that only half the light is reflected; the other half is transmitted.) The toothed wheel WF rotates at high speed so that it interrupts the light beam passing through the rim at F and produces a series of short flashes. A flash is sent out each time the wheel is in such a position that light can pass through the slot between adjacent teeth. The light beam passing through the slot is rendered parallel by the lens L_2 and, after traversing a large, accurately measured distance, is focused by the lens L_3 on a plane mirror M. The distance D used in Fizeau's experiment was 5.36 mi. After reflection from M, the light retraces its path to L_2 and is again focused on the rim of the wheel by the lens L_2. If during the time required for the light to travel from F to M and back to F the wheel has turned through such an angle that a tooth is interposed at F, this light flash will be intercepted by this tooth.

With the wheel at rest in such a position that light passes through the opening 0, the observer at E will see the image of the source formed by light returning from M. If the wheel is now rotated with increasing speed, a rotational speed will be reached in which the light passing through slot 0 on its outward trip will be stopped by tooth A on its return trip; at the same rotational speed the light transmitted through slot 1 will be stopped by tooth B on its return trip, and so on. The image will be completely 'eclipsed'. A further increase in speed will cause the image to reappear when these flashes pass through openings 1, 2, $\cdots$; a second eclipse will occur at the speed at which the flashes in question are stopped by teeth B, C, $\cdots$. Fizeau's wheel had 720 teeth, and the total light path was 2×5.36 mi $= 10.72$ mi. The wheel had to turn through $\frac{1}{1440}$ rev in the time required for the round trip in order for the first eclipse to occur. The time required for the round trip was 10.72 mi/c, if c is the speed of light in mi/sec. The time required for the wheel to travel $\frac{1}{1440}$ rev was $\frac{1}{1440}/f$ if f is the angular speed in rev/sec. Therefore

$$\frac{10.72 \text{ mi}}{c} = \frac{\frac{1}{1440}}{f} \quad \text{or} \quad c = 10.72 \cdot 1440 \, f \text{ mi,}$$

if f is the angular speed in rev/sec for first eclipse. Fizeau observed the first eclipse at $f = 12.6$ rev/sec, which gave $c = 195{,}000$ mi/sec.

In 1850, J. B. L. Foucault devised a second terrestrial method for determining c by observation of the displacement of an image formed by light returning to a rotating mirror after it had traversed a known distance. The distances in Foucault's experiments were relatively short—4 meters in one experiment and 20 meters in another. His work was of importance chiefly in that he measured the speed of light in water as well as in air and found that the speed in water is less than the speed in air, a result which had been predicted on the wave theory of light, but which was in contradiction to Newton's particle theory.

The most accurate measurements of the speed of light are those of A. A. Michelson and his colleagues in the years following 1926, made with apparatus similar to that of Foucault. A diagram of the apparatus is shown in Fig. 12. Light from an arc light S passes through a slit and is reflected from one face a of the octagonal rotating mirror R. From this face the light passes to the small fixed plane mirrors b and c which reflect it to the large concave mirror M_1. Mirror M_1 renders the beam parallel and sends it to a similar concave mirror M_2. Mirror M_2 reflects the light to a small mirror f that reverses the direction of the beam, which now retraverses its path to mirror M_1. After reflection at M_1, the light passes to plane mirrors c', b', a', and p and finally reaches the observer's eye E. It should be noted that mirror M_1 is tilted in such a manner that the light reflected toward M_2 does not strike the rotating mirror R. Since the distance from R to M_1 is actually about 30 ft, the necessary

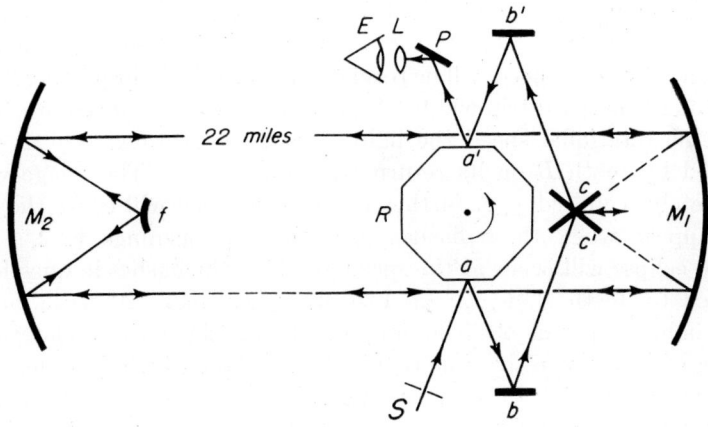

Fig. 12. Schematic diagram of Michelson's apparatus for the determination of the speed of light. As noted in the text, the figure is highly distorted. The rotor size is of the order of an inch, while the distance from c, c' to M_1 is about 30 feet. The rotor is actually slightly to one side of the direct path from M_1 to M_2.

angle of tilt is small. Also c and c' are so placed that they do not interfere with each other; one can consider them as located one above the other in the diagram of Fig. 12.

Mirror M_1 was located on Mount Wilson in California, and mirror M_2 was located on Mount San Antonio, about 22 mi away. The intervening distance D was measured by the United States Coast and Geodetic Survey as $35,385.53 \pm 0.32$ m; this is probably the most accurate survey ever made.

In Michelson's experiment, when the rotating mirror R is at rest, the path traversed by the light is that shown in Fig. 12, and an image of the source slit is observed at cross hairs in the eyepiece L. As the mirror R begins to rotate, the final image at the cross hairs is displaced laterally. As the rotational speed f is increased, the displacement becomes so large that no image is observed. Finally, a sufficient rotational speed is attained so that the mirror turns through one-eighth of a revolution during the transit time of the light to mirror M_2 and return, so that the next mirror face is at position a'. At this speed, an image is again observed at the cross hairs. If this speed f_1 is known, the speed of light can be determined from the relation

$$c = \frac{\text{distance traveled by the light}}{\text{time required for mirror to turn } \frac{1}{8} \text{ rev}}.$$

As the rotational speed is further increased, the image again disappears and later reappears at the cross hairs at a speed twice as great as pre-

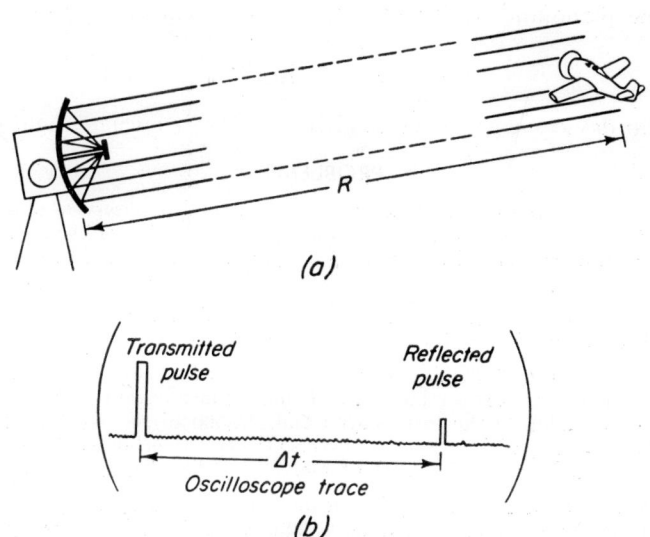

Fig. 13. Pulsed microwave radar system.

viously, so that the mirror turns $\frac{1}{4}$ rev in the time taken by the light to traverse its path.

The results obtained in this experiment and later experiments in an evacuated tube one mile long give

$$c = 299{,}776 \pm 4 \text{ km/sec},$$

as the present best value of the speed of light in a vacuum. The speed in air is less by a factor of $1/1.0003$.

One important application in which use is made of the knowledge of the speed of light occurs in *radar* (*ra*dio *d*irection *a*nd *r*anging) systems. Short radio waves called *microwaves*, which travel with the speed of light, are sent out from radiators backed by parabolic reflectors of the type shown schematically in Fig. 13(a). If this radiation strikes an object such as an airplane or a ship, some of the radiation is reflected to the parabolic reflector and detected by a receiver. The radiation is not sent out continuously but in pulses of extremely short duration. Electronic devices are used to indicate the interval between the time at which a pulse is sent out and the time at which reflections are received. Reflected signals are displayed on an oscilloscope. A typical oscilloscope display is shown in Fig. 13(b). The time between transmission of a pulse of radiation and reception of an 'echo' can be accurately determined. Let us call this time Δt. Since c, the speed of light, is well known, the total distance traversed by the radiation is given by $d = c\,\Delta t$. This distance is actually twice the range R, since the waves must travel from the radar set to the plane and back to the radar set. Therefore, the range R is given by

$$R = \tfrac{1}{2} c\,\Delta t.$$

Such radar devices can be used to give an accurate measurement of range.

PROBLEMS

1. Let us suppose that in Galileo's experiment the two observers were stationed in towers 6 mi apart. Using present knowledge of the value of the speed of light, calculate the time of transmission of a light signal from one tower to the other.
Ans: 32.2 μsec.

2. An observer sees lightning strike a tree on a hill 10 mi away. How long after the lightning has struck does the observer see the flash?

3. Roemer first gave 22 min for the time required for light to traverse a distance equal to the diameter of the earth's orbit. Using the more recent values of 92,900,000 mi as the mean radius of the earth's orbit and 186,300 mi/sec as the speed of light, calculate the time required for light to traverse the earth's orbit and find the per cent error in Roemer's determination of this time. Ans: 997 sec or 16.6 min; 32%.

4. The best value Roemer had for the diameter of the earth's orbit was 172,000,000 mi. Using Roemer's original value of 22 min for the time required for light to travel this distance, calculate the speed of light.

5. Using 92,900,000 mi as the radius of the earth's orbit, 1 year as the time for one revolution of the earth about the sun, and 20″.49 of arc as the aberration angle denoted by ϕ in Fig. 10, calculate the speed of light. Ans: 186,000 mi/sec.

6. Aberration of light will occur as a result of the rotation of the earth on its axis. Taking 7900 mi as the diameter of the earth, calculate this aberration angle and compare with the value of 20″.49 arising from orbital motion.

7. Consider a Fizeau experiment in which the wheel has 600 teeth and the distance between stations is 15 km. What must be the number of revolutions per second of the toothed wheel in order that light passing through a slot on the outward journey may be stopped by the adjacent tooth on the return journey?
Ans: 8.33 rev/sec.

8. Fizeau's measurements of the speed of light were continued by later investigators. M. A. Cornu (1841–1902) used Fizeau's apparatus with a path length $2D$ of 45.8 km. One of the wheels used had 180 teeth. Find the angular velocity at which this wheel should rotate in order that light transmitted through one slot will return through the next slot.

9. In an experiment in which an eight-sided rotating mirror was used, Michelson measured the speed of light by means of the arrangement shown in Fig. 12. Taking

35,386 m as the distance between the stations on Mount Wilson and Mount San Antonio, find the lowest rotational speed at which the image will again be observed at the cross hairs after the rotation of the mirror has begun. Ans: 529 rev/sec.

10. During the years 1930–1933, Michelson's group made a direct measurement of the speed of light in vacuum by using an evacuated tube approximately 1 mi long. The rotating mirror had 32 faces and the light traveled back and forth between mirrors at the ends of the tube a total distance of 8 mi during the time of replacement of one of the 32 mirror faces by the next one. What is the approximate value of the minimum rotational speed required for the image to be observed in the following mirror face?

11. A short pulse of radiation is sent out by a radar set such as that in Fig. 13, and a reflection is received 45 μsec later. How far away is the object that produced the reflection? Ans: 4.19 mi.

12. A reflection of radiation from an airplane is noted by a radar operator 628 μsec after a pulse of radiation has been sent outward. What is the distance of the plane from the radar station?

13. On a day when the speed of sound is 1080 ft/sec, a gun is fired 54 ft away from an observer. By the time the sound of the shot reaches the observer, how far has the light from the muzzle flash traveled? Ans: 9320 mi.

14. On a day when the speed of sound is 1100 ft/sec, a speaker is using a microphone in a broadcasting studio. How far beyond the microphone should an observer stand if he wishes to hear the speaker's voice at the same time the voice reaches a radio loudspeaker 500 mi away via radio? (The time of transmission through radio transmitter and receiver may be considered as negligible.)

CHAPTER 24

ILLUMINATION AND PHOTOMETRY

In this chapter we shall describe various types of light sources. We shall show how the present system of photometric units is set up and shall define units for the quantities *source intensity*, *light flux*, and *illumination*. The measurement of these quantities involves comparison of sources with a standard source, which will be described in some detail. Several types of photometers and 'light meters' will also be discussed.

1. LIGHT SOURCES

Our great natural source of light is the sun. Radiant energy from the luminous portion of the sun must traverse the relatively cold gases of the outer portion of the sun, the relatively empty space between the sun and earth, and the earth's atmosphere before reaching us at the surface of the earth. Energy is received just above the earth's atmosphere at the rate of 19.4 kcal/min per m^2 of area (see p. 364); about one-third of this incident radiation is absorbed in the atmosphere. Much of the radiation reaching the earth from the sun consists of infrared and ultraviolet radiation, which is invisible to the eye but can be easily detected by photographic or electrical methods. The amount of visible radiation reaching us at the earth's surface varies considerably with the path in the atmosphere traversed by the incident radiation as well as with local atmospheric conditions.

Man has developed many 'artificial' sources of light. These include, in order of development, the torch, the oil lamp, the candle, the gas lamp with mantle, the carbon arc lamp, the incandescent-filament electric lamp, the luminous gas tube, and the fluorescent lamp.

The carbon arc, once employed for street lighting, is now used chiefly in searchlights and in slide and film projectors. It consists of a pair of carbon rods connected with a series resistance to electric power lines, usually direct-current. The arc is initiated by bringing the ends of the carbon rods together and then separating them. While the arc is in operation, the ends of the carbons gradually burn away, so that frequent adjustment of the separation of the ends of the rods is necessary. This adjustment was accomplished by an automatic mechanism in the old street lights but is usually made manually in slide projectors. Most of the arc light comes from a crater that is formed in the tip of the positive carbon; the crater temperature is in the neighborhood of 3500° C and furnishes an extremely brilliant concentrated light source. Carbon arcs can be used with alternating current, but both carbons become equally bright and the results are not so satisfactory for projection purposes.

The incandescent-filament lamp consists of a filament of some material of high melting point which can be raised to high temperatures by an electric current. One early form of incandescent lamp was the Nernst glower, which consisted of a small rod composed of a mixture of refractory oxides that are semiconductors of electricity. This glower can be operated in air, but it is rather fragile and must be heated by a flame before the electric current can be established. These inconvenient features have led to the abandonment of ceramic glowers of this type in favor of the glass-enclosed incandescent lamp.

The original incandescent lamp of this type, developed by Edison in 1879, consisted of a carbon filament mounted in a glass bulb evacuated to prevent oxidation. The carbon filaments, made from carbonized horsehair or bamboo fibers, were extremely fragile and inefficient. About 1910, techniques were developed for drawing tungsten into small wires, and evacuated bulbs using tungsten filaments were introduced. This early tungsten lamp was more efficient than the carbon lamps because it could be operated satisfactorily at higher temperatures. However, after continued use there was a gradual blackening of the bulb because of deposition of tungsten evaporated from the hot filament. The more recent practice of filling the glass bulb enclosing the metal filament with an inert gas such as nitrogen reduces the rate at which the filament material is evaporated. The introduction of closely coiled or doubly coiled filaments has also resulted in improved operation. Tungsten filaments operate at temperatures of 2100–2700° C

Another form of light source now used for special purposes is the gas-discharge tube. The mercury-vapor lamp, employed for industrial lighting and photographic purposes, utilizes an arc discharge in an evacuated glass bulb between two mercury pools or between a mercury pool and an iron electrode. The lamp can be started by tilting the tube so as to connect the electrodes by a thin stream of mercury. When the tube is allowed to resume its normal position, the steam of mercury is broken and an arc discharge is maintained in the mercury vapor. The light from the mercury arc is bluish green in color.

Long glow-discharge tubes containing gas at low pressure are widely used for display purposes, neon being commonly used for orange-red light, helium for reddish-white light, and argon for blue light. These discharge tubes are operated at high potentials of the order of 10,000 to 15,000 volts, produced by step-up transformers from the usual 110–120-

volt alternating-current lines. The currents are of the order of 30 milliamperes.

The most recently developed light source is the fluorescent lamp, which utilizes a discharge in mercury vapor at low pressure. The discharge occurs in a glass tube coated on the inside with a material that fluoresces when exposed to the ultraviolet radiation emitted by the mercury vapor. The light emitted through the glass walls of the tube gives the impression of white light when proper mixtures of fluorescent powders are used. Actually, the light is quite different in spectral distribution from the light of an incandescent filament. The color can be adjusted by suitable choices of fluorescent powders; these include cadmium borate for pink, zinc silicate for green, calcium tungstate for blue, and mixtures for white.

2. PHOTOMETRIC QUANTITIES: SOURCE INTENSITY, LIGHT FLUX, AND ILLUMINATION

We have defined light as radiant energy that is capable of affecting the retina of the eye. This definition suggests immediately that the intensity of a given source of light might be measured in terms of the number of joules of visible light radiated per second, and specified as radiated power in watts. This procedure would be desirable from many points of view, but unfortunately there are numerous difficulties involved in measuring the intensities of light sources directly in absolute units of power. We must remember that we are interested only in that part of the radiant energy that affects the eye. One of the difficulties is that any detecting device that is equally sensitive to all colors of light is usually also sensitive to infrared and ultraviolet radiation. The problem is further complicated by the fact that the eye is *not* equally sensitive to equal amounts of energy of different colors, and in connection with light we are not really interested in amount of energy but in effect on the eye. These difficulties force us to use the eye itself as the basic detecting device. The usual method employed in determining the intensity of a light source consists of the visual comparison of the source with some other arbitrarily chosen standard source by means of a photometer, which will be described in Sec. 4. The luminous intensity of the source is then expressed in terms of the standard source.

In order to understand the concepts involved in the measurement of light sources and to see how a consistent system of photometric quantities can be set up, let us first consider an idealized situation in which we have a certain point source that radiates *isotropically*, that is, uniformly in all directions. We shall arbitrarily define the *intensity of this source* as 1 candle.

Now imagine a sphere circumscribed about the point source in the manner indicated in Fig. 1. Light travels outward from the source and strikes the inside surface of the sphere. We need a unit in terms of which to measure the rate of flow or *flux* of visible radiation. The unit is called the *lumen* and we may define it by saying that *the total flux emitted by a source whose intensity is 1 candle is 4π lumens*. Since there are 4π steradians in the total solid angle surrounding a point source, this statement is equivalent to saying that *an isotropic point source of unit intensity radiates 1 lumen per steradian.*

A third light quantity we shall use frequently is *illumination*, which is defined as *light flux per unit area* and can properly be measured in $lumens/ft^2$ or $lumens/m^2$. Thus, if the radius of the hollow sphere with a point source of 1 candle at its center is 1 ft, the illumination of the inner surface of the sphere is 4π lumens/4π ft^2 = 1 lumen/ft^2. One *lumen per square foot* is sometimes called a *foot-candle*, but this term is gradually becoming obsolete.

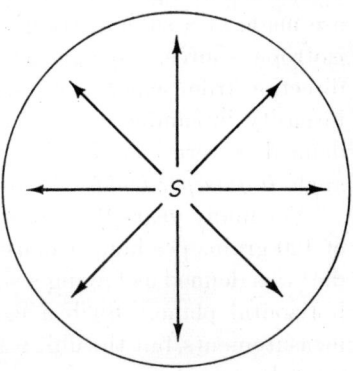

Fig. 1. Isotropic point source at the center of a hollow sphere.

The light quantities we have introduced are denoted by the symbols indicated below:

Quantity	Symbol	Unit
Source intensity	I	candle (candlepower)
Light flux	F	lumen
Illumination	E	lumen/ft^2 (foot-candle) or lumen/m^2 (meter-candle)

From the discussion above, it can be seen that the total light flux F from a point source of intensity I, in candles, is given by the relation

$$F = 4\pi I, \quad \text{in lumens.} \tag{1}$$

Similarly, the illumination E of the inner surface of a sphere of radius R by an isotropic point source of intensity I at the center of the sphere is given by the relation

$$E = \frac{F}{A} = \frac{4\pi I}{4\pi R^2} = \frac{I}{R^2}, \tag{2}$$

in lumens/ft^2 or lumens/m^2 according to whether R is in ft or m.

The above discussion serves to introduce the quantities *source intensity*, *light flux*, and *illumination* and to indicate the principles by which a system of photometric units could be set up. Actually, as a *practical* scheme for defining light units, the method indicated is meaningless, since in practice *it is impossible to produce an isotropic point source*. A real source, such as a candle flame or an incandescent filament, can be considered as a point source, provided that measurements of illumination are made at a sufficiently great distance, but it cannot be treated as an isotropic source. We get around this difficulty by defining a particular direction from which a standard source is to be observed, and define its intensity in candles *when viewed from this direction*. The lumen is then defined in terms of the light flux per unit solid angle for a *small* solid angle *in this particular direction*.

For many years the flame of a spermaceti candle burning at the rate of 120 grains per hour was used as a standard. This 'international candle' was defined as having a source intensity of 1 candle when viewed in a horizontal plane. Such a candle was inconvenient to use in practical measurements, but the unit was long retained. Later, carefully calibrated incandescent lamps, viewed in a particular direction, were used as practical secondary standards in most national standards laboratories. A serious objection to the use of a candle or incandescent lamp as a standard source is that a source of this type is not accurately reproducible.

A new accurately reproducible standard source, developed by the United States National Bureau of Standards, has been adopted by the International Committee on Weights and Measures, and became effective on January 1, 1948.

The new standard source consists of a glowing cavity with temperature equal to that of solidifying platinum. A schematic diagram of the cross section of the source is shown in Fig. 2. The platinum, contained in a fused thoria (thorium-oxide) crucible* and surrounded by powdered thorium oxide acting as an insulating material, is placed in an alternating magnetic field and heated by currents induced in the platinum itself. A sighting tube, also composed of fused thorium oxide and containing some powdered thorium oxide, extends into the molten platinum and serves as a 'black-body' cavity radiator.† Thorium oxide is chosen because it is a material that is very white and that is still solid at the melting point of platinum. When the radiation from this tube is viewed in the indicated direction, the source intensity is defined as 60 candles per square centimeter of opening when the platinum in cooling reaches its solidifying temperature.

> The new standard candle is defined as one-sixtieth of the luminous intensity per square centimeter of opening in the above cavity at the temperature of solidifying platinum.

* Fused thoria is a refractory ceramic material. After thorium oxide has once been melted or fused and then resolidified, its refractory properties are improved. By *fused* thoria we do not mean molten material but rather material that has been melted and resolidified.

† See Chap. 30 for definition of a 'black body.'

The new candle is slightly smaller than the older international standard candle. Secondary standard lamps calibrated in terms of the new standard were delivered to European countries in 1947. The new standard source has the advantage of being accurately reproducible. A photograph of the source parts is shown in Fig. 3. It should be noted that the circular opening at the end of the sighting tube is only 1.5 mm

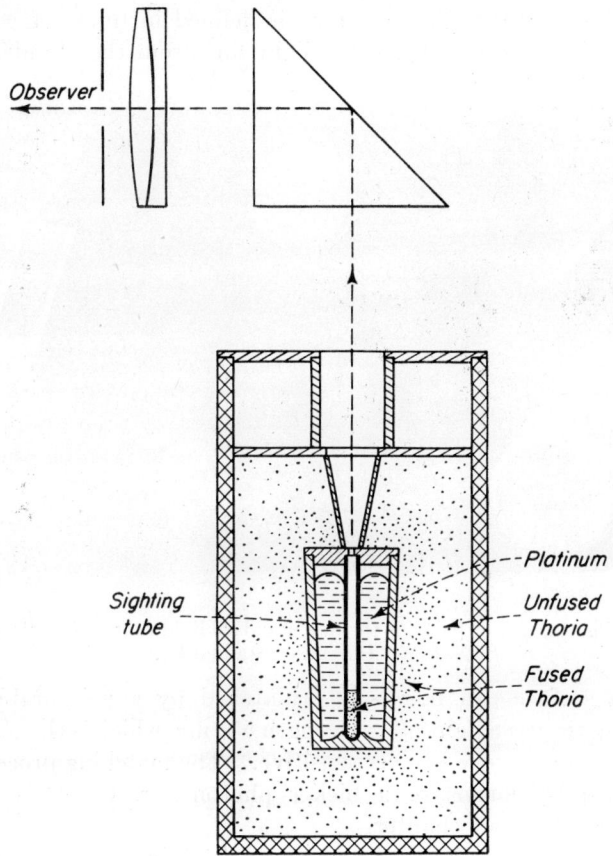

Fig. 2. Cross section of the new standard light source.

in diameter; thus, the opening is a fair approximation of a point source when viewed in the prescribed direction. If the area of opening were exactly $\frac{1}{60}$ cm², the source intensity would be 1 candle and give out 1 lumen/steradian in directions very near the vertical.

> The lumen is defined by the statement that the flux, per $\frac{1}{60}$ cm² of opening of the new standard source, proceeding in a small solid angle $\delta\omega$ in the vertical direction, is $\delta\omega$ lumens.

Having defined the lumen, we can immediately define the *illumination* of a surface as follows:

> The illumination of a surface is defined as the light flux per unit area of surface. The units of illumination are lumens/ft² or lumens/m².

Since the lumen is essentially a unit of power, it is desirable to relate it to the watt. Although the lumen is defined in terms of white light from the new standard source, the light flux from the standard source

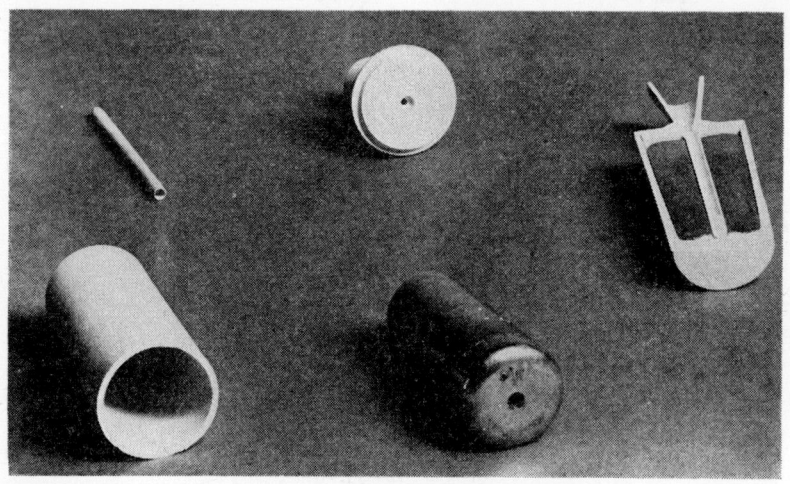

Fig. 3. Photograph of parts of the new standard light source (Courtesy of the National Bureau of Standards).

reaching a surface can be visually matched by a measurable flux of monochromatic green light of wavelength 555 mµ, which is the wavelength to which the human eye is most sensitive. The matching process can be accomplished by means of a flicker photometer, which is discussed briefly in Sec. 4 of this chapter.

After extensive studies of the response of the human eye to radiation, the National Bureau of Standards has found that one watt of radiation of wavelength 555 mµ is equivalent to 621 lumens. Thus, so far as the response of the eye is concerned:

> *One lumen is equivalent to 0.00161 watt of monochromatic light of wavelength 555 mµ.*

In order to give some idea of illuminations frequently encountered, we might point out that on a clear day the illumination from direct sunlight is about 8000 lumens/ft² and the illumination from direct sunlight plus skylight is as great as 10,000 lumens/ft². On a 'dark' day illumination outdoors drops to 100 lumens/ft² or less. The full moon gives an illumination of 0.03 lumen/ft². Indoors one rarely encounters illumination of more than 20 lumens/ft². The following are *recommended values of illumination* for spaces of various types:

Classrooms	12 lumens/ft²	Laboratories	12 lumens/ft²
Club lounges	5	Library reading rooms	12
Drafting rooms	25	Offices	10
Hallways	3	Railway cars	8
Hotel lobbies	8	Sidewalks	0.5

PROBLEMS

1. An isotropic point source of light has a source intensity of 5 candles. (a) What is the total light flux from this source? (b) Calculate the illumination at a point on a surface 10 ft away from the source if the light strikes this surface perpendicularly. Ans: 20π lumens; 0.05 lumen/ft².

2. An isotropic point source of light emits a flux of 320 lumens. (a) What is the source intensity? (b) Calculate the illumination of the inner surface of a sphere of 2-m radius if the point source is located at its center.

3. A certain light source emits only light of wavelength 555 mμ and radiates at the rate of 0.05 watt. What is the luminous flux? Ans: 31.1 lumens.

4. A certain light source emits only green light of wavelength 555 mμ and has a total flux of 300 lumens. At what rate in watts is energy radiated in the form of visible radiation? By comparison it is found that a source of blue light also has a flux of 300 lumens. Does this second source emit energy more or less rapidly than the first source?

5. The new standard candle is defined as one-sixtieth of the luminous intensity per square centimeter of opening in the cavity of the standard source. The diameter of the opening is actually only 1.5 mm. By treating this small opening as a point source, compute the total source intensity of this opening when viewed along the axis of the sighting tube in Fig. 2 without the lens in position. Ans: 1.06 candles.

6. What is the total light flux from an isotropic point source that has an intensity equal to that of the opening in the new standard when viewed from the prescribed direction? Use the data given in Prob. 5. Does the new standard have this total flux?

7. A certain suspended light source has an effective source intensity of 300 candles when viewed from below. At what distance above a drafting table should this source be suspended in order to give the recommended illumination of 25 lumens/ft²? At this distance, what would be the illumination in lumens/m² of the table surface immediately below this lamp? Ans: 3.46 ft; 269 lumens/m².

8. In order to provide the recommended illumination of 12 lumens/ft² on a library table, a certain lamp must be suspended at a height of 10 ft above the table. What is the effective source intensity of this lamp?

9. A certain 100-watt tungsten filament has a flux of 1630 lumens. (a) What would be the intensity of an isotropic point source that has this total flux? (b) At what distance from this equivalent point source would the illumination be equal to the illumination of direct sunlight, 8000 lumens/ft²? Ans: (a) 130 candles; (b) 0.127 ft.

10. A 1000-watt projection light has an initial luminous flux of 21,500 lumens. (a) What would be the candlepower of an isotropic point source that has a flux of this magnitude? (b) At what distance from this equivalent point source would the

illumination be equal to 10,000 lumens/ft², the full daylight illumination from direct sunlight plus skylight?

11. A 150-candle light hangs at the geometrical center of a cubical room 20 ft on an edge. Assuming the source to be isotropic and considering only the direct illumination, find:
  (a) the total number of lumens striking the floor;
  (b) the average illumination of the floor;
  (c) the maximum and minimum values of the illumination of the floor [see (6), p. 600].   Ans: 100π lumens; 0.785 lumen/ft²; 1.50, 0.287 lumen/ft².

12. If a 16-candle lamp placed 2 ft above the surface of a table is switched on for 2 min, how many lumens fall on a square inch of table top directly below the lamp during the time the light is on?

13. The light of the full moon, 240,000 mi from the earth, gives an illumination of 0.03 lumen/ft².
  (a) Neglecting absorption in the earth's atmosphere, determine the candlepower of the moon.
  (b) How far away from a 40-watt, 35-candle tungsten lamp must a screen be placed to have the same illumination as in full moonlight?
      Ans: 4.8×10^{16} candles; 34 ft.

14. The light of the sun, 93,000,000 mi from the earth, gives a direct illumination of 8000 lumens/ft².
  (a) Neglecting absorption in the earth's atmosphere, determine the candlepower of the sun.
  (b) How far away from a 40-watt, 35-candle tungsten lamp must a screen be placed to have the same illumination as in sunlight?

3. REAL LIGHT SOURCES

A real light source can be considered as a point source when it is viewed from a distance large compared to the dimensions of the source. So considered, a real source rarely radiates equally in all directions. Hence, the apparent intensity of the source will be a function of the angle from which it is viewed. Suppose, in Fig. 4, that the source were an isotropic

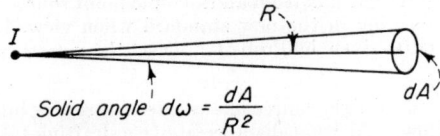

Fig. 4. Radiation in a given direction from a light source.

point source of intensity I candles. In solid angle $d\omega$, it would then emit $dF = I\, d\omega$ lumens, since it emits one lumen per unit solid angle per candle. If now the source in Fig. 4 is a real source, the distance R large compared to the dimensions of the source, and light flux dF passes through area dA subtending solid angle $d\omega$ at the 'center' of the source, the candlepower of the source, *as viewed in this particular direction*, is defined as

$$I = dF/d\omega. \tag{3}$$

The *mean candlepower* of the source is defined as the average of this, averaged over all directions in the sphere. This average is the integral of I over the sphere, divided by 4π, the total solid angle in a sphere. That is,

$$I_{\text{mean}} = \frac{1}{4\pi} \int I \, d\omega = \frac{1}{4\pi} \int \frac{dF}{d\omega} d\omega = \frac{1}{4\pi} \int dF = \frac{F_{\text{total}}}{4\pi}, \quad (4)$$

where F_{total} is the total light flux emitted in all directions.

Now consider the *illumination* of the surface dA in Fig. 4 by the real source of candlepower I in this particular direction. The illumination E is defined as the number of lumens striking the surface per unit area of surface. In this case,

$$E = dF/dA = dF/(R^2 \, d\omega),$$

or, substituting from (3), we find that

$$E = I/R^2. \quad (5)$$

Hence, the illumination from a real source is given by the same formula as derived for an isotropic source in (2), except that I will vary with direction for a real source.

PROBLEMS

1. A certain tungsten lamp is suspended from the ceiling of a room and gives an illumination of 8 lumens/ft² on the floor 7 ft below the lamp. What is the flux per unit solid angle in this direction? What is the candlepower of the lamp as viewed from below? *Ans*: 392 lumens/steradian; 392 candles.

2. A certain lamp produces an illumination of 12 lumens/ft² at a point on a surface a distance of 4 ft in a certain direction from the lamp. What is the flux per unit solid angle in this direction? What is the candlepower of the lamp as viewed from this direction? (The light beam is normal to the surface.)

3. An incandescent lamp has a flux of 10 lumens/steradian in a certain direction. What is the illumination at a point on a surface 9 ft away when the light beam from the source is normal to the surface at this point? What is the candlepower of the source when viewed from this direction? *Ans*: 0.123 lumen/ft²; 10 candles.

4. A small fluorescent lamp has a flux of 300 lumens/steradian in a particular direction. What is the maximum illumination on a surface 8 ft away in this direction?

4. PHOTOMETRY

We have seen in (5) that the illumination on a surface a distance R from a source of intensity I is given by $E = I/R^2$, provided the light rays are perpendicular to the surface. Thus, the illumination of a surface is inversely proportional to the square of the distance of the surface from the source, providing the light rays are perpendicular to the surface.

Let us now consider the illumination of a surface to which the light rays are not perpendicular. In Fig. 5, dA represents an element of area whose normal makes an angle θ with the rays of light reaching this element from source S. This element subtends the solid angle $d\omega = ds/R^2$ at source S. Since $ds = \cos\theta \, dA$,

$$d\omega = \cos\theta \, dA/R^2.$$

Therefore, in view of equation (3), the flux dF through this element of area is given by

$$dF = I\, d\omega = I\, \cos\theta\, dA/R^2.$$

The illumination E of this area is by definition the flux per unit area, that is,

$$E = dF/dA = I\, \cos\theta/R^2. \qquad (6)$$

When the surface is tilted by the angle θ shown in Fig. 5, the illumination is reduced to $\cos\theta$ times the illumination for normal incidence.

From the above considerations, a simple method for comparing the luminous intensities becomes immediately evident. If two sources of

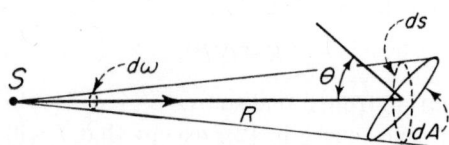

Fig. 5. Light incident at an angle θ to the normal to a surface.

intensities I_1 and I_2 at distances R_1 and R_2, respectively, from a screen on which the light is incident at the same angle θ produce equal illumination on the screen, then

$$E_1 = E_2,$$

so, from (6),

$$\frac{I_1}{R_1^2} = \frac{I_2}{R_2^2}. \qquad (7)$$

This relation is fundamental to the theory of the photometer, which compares the intensities of two sources by matching the illumination of a surface by the two sources. The eye itself is incapable of directly comparing two luminous sources with accuracy, but it can determine with remarkable precision whether or not the illumination of similar adjacent surfaces is equal. An illumination difference of one part in 150 can be detected. Thus, if R_1 and R_2 for sources I_1 and I_2 are varied until $E_1 = E_2$, relation (7) applies, and the ratio of the source intensities I_1 and I_2 can be determined. The measurement of relative source intensity is called *photometry*, and the instruments used in this measurement are called *photometers*.

One of the simplest instruments used for comparing the intensities of sources by matching illuminations from the sources is the Bunsen grease-spot photometer shown schematically in Fig. 6. The essential part of this photometer is a flat screen of opaque white paper having a translucent grease spot at the center. The grease spot reflects less light and transmits more light than the balance of the paper. The screen is illuminated on its two sides by the light from the two sources S and X that are to be compared. If the illumination is more intense on one side of the screen, the grease spot will appear dark from this side but bright if viewed from the side with weak illumination. The spot will very nearly disappear when the illumination is equal on the two sides; this condition can be realized by moving the screen to the proper position between the two sources. The mirrors M allow both sides of the screen to be seen at the same time; this feature is of considerable importance in matching the illuminations. If I_S and I_X are the intensities of the sources S and X, respectively, and the distances are R_S and R_X when the illuminations are equal, then

$$\frac{I_S}{R_S^2} = \frac{I_X}{R_X^2}. \qquad (8)$$

The sharper the boundary between two areas, the more accurately the adjustment to equal illumination can be made. One of the best devices

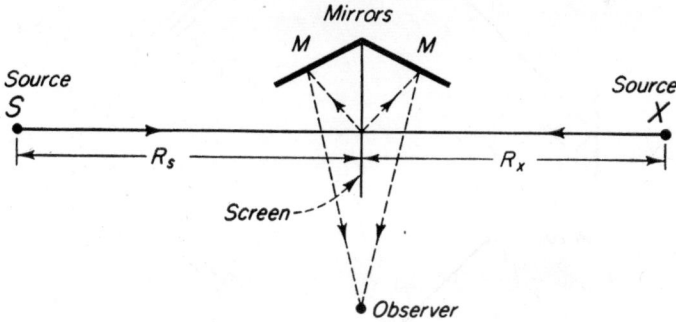

Fig. 6. Diagram of Bunsen's grease-spot photometer.

for obtaining a sharp boundary is the 'comparison cube' used in the Lummer-Brodhun photometer. This cube, shown at the bottom of Fig. 7, consists of two right-angled glass prisms; the hypotenuse of one prism is ground or etched away except for a circular area in the center which is cemented to the hypotenuse of the other prism. By means of two auxiliary mirrors light from one side of a chalky white screen is sent through the center of the cube, while light from the other side of the screen is totally reflected (see Chap. 25) from the surrounding ring. Since the boundary of the central ring is very sharp, an accurate adjustment to equal illumination can be made. Adjustment is accomplished by varying the distances between the sources being compared and the screen.

In discussing the Bunsen and Lummer-Brodhun photometers we have assumed that the light from the sources being compared is of the same color. If this is not the case, no photometric balance can be attained with these photometers. Comparison of sources of different color is considerably more difficult. One method of comparing light sources of different color makes use of the *flicker photometer*, in which the screen seen by the observer is illuminated alternately by light from the two sources. If the frequency of the alternation has the proper value, the color difference disappears, because of persistence of vision, before brightness differences become unobservable. After the frequency of alternation has been adjusted to the proper value, the source intensities are compared by noting source distances R_S and R_X at which the brightness flicker disappears.

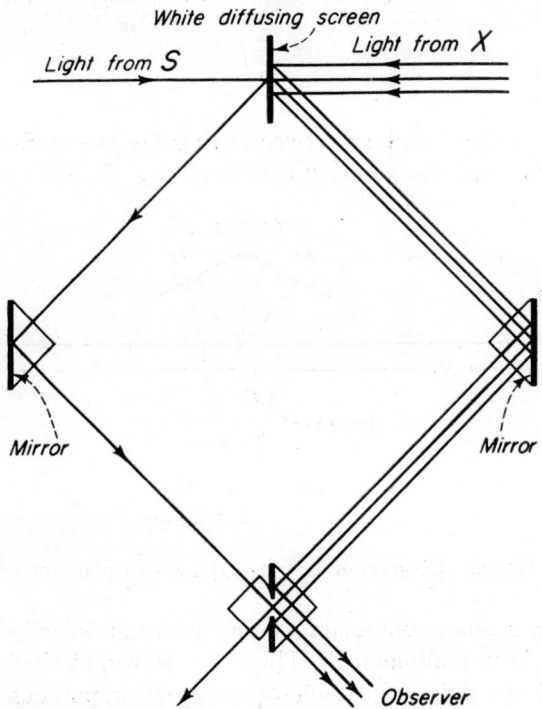

Fig. 7. Lummer-Brodhun photometer 'head' showing comparison cube.

Another method of comparing sources of different color involves the use of photoelectric cells provided with optical filters; combinations of photoelectric cells and filters can be chosen so as to have a color response that reproduces that of the eye. This method is not yet in wide use.

In practical problems such as planning lighting installations or arranging for proper photographic exposure times it is often necessary to have a fairly accurate measurement of illumination. Instruments using photoelectric cells are sufficiently accurate for this purpose. These instruments are known as 'foot-candle meters' or 'light meters.' In these meters, the light reaching the sensitive surface of a photoelectric cell produces an electric current which within definite limits is proportional to the light flux striking the sensitive surface. Although the sensitivity of the photoelectric cell for various colors is not quite the same as the sensitivity of the eye, the cell can be used to obtain approximate values for illumination.

PROBLEMS

1. An incandescent lamp with a frosted bulb, suspended 8 ft above a floor, produces an illumination of 12 lumens/ft^2 at a point on the floor immediately below the lamp. Assuming that the lamp radiates isotropically, calculate the illumination at a point on the floor 6 ft away from the point immediately below the lamp.
Ans: 6.14 lumens/ft^2.

2. A workbench 8 ft long is illuminated by a single lamp suspended 4 ft above the center of the bench. If this lamp produces an illumination of 20 lumens/ft^2 on the bench immediately below the lamp and can be assumed to radiate isotropically, what is the illumination at the end of the bench?

3. On March 22 the noon sun at Quito, Ecuador, produces an illumination of 8000 lumens/ft^2 on level ground when the sun is directly overhead. What is the illumination at this position due to direct sunlight at 2 P.M.? At 4 P.M.? (Neglect atmospheric absorption.) Ans: 6930 lumens/ft^2; 4000 lumens/ft^2.

4. On a certain day direct sunlight produces an illumination of 8000 lumens/ft^2 on a surface tilted so that the sun's rays are perpendicular to the surface. What is the corresponding illumination on level ground if the sun is 60° above the horizon?

5. In using a Bunsen grease-spot photometer, a standard 40-candle lamp is mounted at the zero mark on a 1-m optical bench and a lamp of unknown intensity is mounted at the 100-cm mark. It is found that the two sides of the screen are equally illuminated when the screen is at the 70-cm mark. What is the intensity of the lamp being tested? Ans: 7.35 candles.

6. In a Bunsen grease-spot photometer, a lamp of unknown intensity is placed above the zero mark of a 2-m optical bench and a standard 150-candle lamp is placed above the 200-cm mark. In order to have the two sides of the screen equally illuminated, the screen must be placed at the 120-cm mark. What is the source intensity of the lamp being tested?

7. A 50-candle standard lamp is placed 30 cm away from the diffusing screen of a Lummer-Brodhun photometer. At what distance from the screen should a 100-candle lamp be placed if both sides of the screen are to have equal illumination? Calculate the screen illumination in lumens/m^2. Ans: 42.4 cm; 556 lumens/m^2.

8. A standard 100-candle lamp is placed 40 cm away from the diffusing screen of a Lummer-Brodhun photometer. A lamp of unknown source intensity must be placed 70 cm from the screen if both sides of the screen are to be illuminated equally. What is the source intensity of the test lamp? What screen illumination would the test lamp produce if it were located 50 cm away from the screen?

9. A workbench 16 ft long is illuminated by three 300-candle lamps suspended at a height of 6 ft above the bench. One of the lamps is located above the center of the bench and the other two are located above its ends. What is the illumination immediately below the center lamp? (Assume isotropic radiation from the lamps.)
Ans: 11.9 lumens/ft^2.

10. For the workbench described in Prob. 9, calculate the illumination immediately below one of the end lamps.

11. A certain street intersection is illuminated by a 1000-watt lamp suspended at a height of 15 ft above the street. The lamp has a total flux of 21,000 lumens, and can be considered as an isotropic radiator.

(a) Calculate the source intensity of the equivalent point source.

(b) Calculate the illumination of the pavement at a distance of 50 ft from the point immediately below the lamp.   Ans: (a) 1670 candles; (b) 0.176 lumen/ft².

12. Find the illumination of the pavement at distances of 0, 25, and 75 ft from the point immediately beneath the lamp described in Prob. 11.

5. EFFICIENCY OF LIGHT SOURCES

In the case of mechanical devices, it is customary to define efficiency as the ratio of useful work done by the device to the total energy input; if no energy is stored, the ratio of useful power output to total power input can also be used as a measure of efficiency. Therefore, by using the power ratio we might define the efficiency of an electrically operated lamp as the ratio of the light output in watts to the total input power. This ratio is called the *true efficiency* of the lamp. However, since light flux is usually measured in lumens instead of watts, we shall adopt the following definition for the over-all efficiency of electrical lamps:

> The over-all efficiency of a light source is the ratio of total light flux emitted by the source to the total power supplied to the source. This efficiency is measured in lumens per watt.

Tables I and II give values of over-all efficiency for present-day tungsten and fluorescent lamps.* These values apply to the lamps when new.

TABLE I
Efficiency of Tungsten Lamps

Input power (watts)	Flux (lumens)	Efficiency (lumens/watt)
6*	40	6.6
10*	78	7.8
25*	260	10.4
40†	465	11.7
60†	835	13.9
100†	1,630	16.3
200	3,650	18.3
500	9,950	19.9
1000	21,500	21.5

TABLE II
Efficiency of Fluorescent Lamps

Input power (watts)	Length (inches)	Flux (lumens)	Efficiency (lumens/watt)
4	6	73	18.2
6	9	210	35.0
8	12	330	41.2
14	15	490	35.0
20	24	960	48.0
30	36	1500	50.0
40	48	2320	58.0
100	60	4400	44.0

* Vacuum; lamps above 25 watts are gas-filled.   † Coiled-coil filament.

A comparison of the tables shows that a 40-watt fluorescent lamp gives five times as much light as a 40-watt incandescent lamp. Most of

---

* The data given in the tables are taken from articles by C. E. Weitz and Harris Reinhardt in the Ohio State University Engineering Experiment Station News for February, 1947.

the energy input to a tungsten lamp appears as heat rather than visible light; the larger-size lamps have a higher filament temperature than the smaller sizes and hence are more efficient as light producers. Much less 'heat' is generated in a comparable fluorescent lamp.

For sources like candles, gas jets, or kerosene lamps, it is customary to use a different definition of efficiency, called the *luminous efficiency:*

> The *luminous efficiency* of a source is the ratio of the light flux from the source to the total radiation flux. The unit is lumens/watt.

If this definition is applied to electrically operated sources, the luminous efficiency is always greater than the over-all efficiency, since some of the electrical input power is always lost by convection and conduction of heat, rather than by radiation.

PROBLEMS

1. After continued use a certain 75-watt tungsten lamp has a total flux of 850 lumens. What is the over-all efficiency of this lamp if the total input power is still 75 watts?   *Ans:* 11.3 lumens/watt.

2. A tungsten lamp for which the input power is 60 watts gives a total light flux of 795 lumens. What is the over-all efficiency of this lamp?

3. (a) Using the data on typical lamps given in Table I, find how many 100-watt tungsten lamps would be required to produce total light flux approximately equal to that of a single 1000-watt tungsten lamp. (b) Explain the advantages, if any, in using the 100-watt lamps, rather than the single 1000-watt lamp, for the direct illumination of a large room.   *Ans:* (a) 13.

4. How many 10-watt tungsten lamps would be required to produce total luminous flux approximately equal to the flux from a 1000-watt tungsten lamp? Remembering that a consumer is charged for electrical energy in kilowatt-hours, calculate the costs of producing a flux of 21,500 lumens for 8 hr by a single 1000-watt lamp and by the set of 10-watt tungsten lamps if electrical energy costs 6 cents per kilowatt-hour.

5. A certain room is illuminated by five 40-watt fluorescent lamps. How many 200-watt tungsten lamps would be required to produce an approximately equivalent light flux in the room? Compare the costs of illuminating the room by these two methods for a 10-hr day if electrical energy costs 6 cents per kilowatt-hour.
    Ans: 3; 12 cents, 36 cents.

6. Considering all lamps listed in the tables, select the most expensive and the least expensive method of maintaining a light flux of 9280 lumens. Calculate the costs of maintaining this light flux for 12 hr by the two methods, with electrical energy at 6 cents per kilowatt-hour.

7. What is the theoretical maximum over-all efficiency that an electrically operated light source can have?   *Ans:* 621 lumens/watt.

8. Using the response curve of the eye (Fig. 18 on p. 675), estimate the over-all efficiency of an ideal source of white light that radiates a uniform amount of energy in each mμ range between 400 and 700 mμ, and radiates no energy outside this range. This might be considered the goal in fluorescent-lamp design.

CHAPTER 25

REFLECTION AND REFRACTION OF LIGHT

In this chapter we shall consider in detail some of the optical phenomena involving reflection and refraction. After a statement of the laws of regular reflection, we shall use these laws to explain diffuse reflection and the process of image formation by mirrors of various types. We shall then proceed to state Snell's law of refraction in its original form and to interpret this law in terms of the speeds of propagation of light waves in various media. We shall use Snell's law as a guide to the study of refraction and internal reflection at plane surfaces. The process of image formation by thin lenses will then be discussed. We shall use light rays extensively in our treatment of reflection and refraction, keeping in mind that a light ray is physically just the normal to a wave front and gives the direction of propagation of that wave front.

Those parts of optics in which light can be treated by means of rays rectilinearly propagated in a homogeneous medium, as in this chapter and Chap. 26, are known as *geometrical optics;* those aspects of the subject in which the wave nature of light plays a fundamental role (treated in Chaps. 27–30) are called *physical optics.*

1. REFLECTION AT PLANE SURFACES

When light travels through a single medium, it moves progressively outward from the source in straight lines in the manner we have described in Chap. 23. But whenever the light strikes a smooth boundary between two media, such as an air-water interface, an air-metal interface, or a glass-metal boundary similar to that of the familiar silver-backed glass mirror, some of the light will be turned back or *reflected*. At the surface of polished metals in air nearly all incident light is reflected. Reflection of light occurs in accordance with two definite laws:

FIRST LAW OF REFLECTION: *The reflected ray lies in the plane containing the incident ray and the normal to the reflecting surface at the point of incidence.*

SECOND LAW OF REFLECTION: *The angle of incidence is equal to the angle of reflection.* (The angle of incidence is the angle between the incident ray and the normal; the angle of reflection is the angle between the reflected ray and the normal.)

These two laws summarize the results of experience and have been known since the third century B.C.

The laws of reflection can be understood from a consideration of Fig. 1. The line ABC represents a plane reflecting surface which is perpendicular to the plane of the paper. The normal BN is in the plane of the paper.

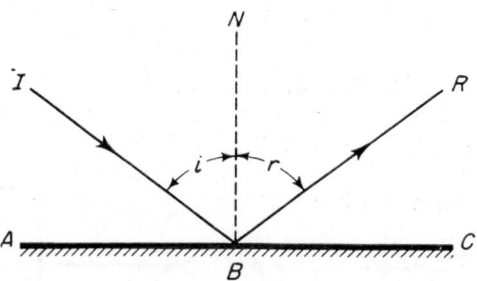

Fig. 1. Reflection at a smooth surface. The angle of incidence i is equal to the angle of reflection r.

If an incident ray IB is in this plane, the first law states that the reflected ray BR is also in the plane of the paper. The second law states that the angle of incidence $i = \angle IBN$ is equal to the angle of reflection $r = \angle RBN$.

Reflection of light from a smooth surface of the type just discussed is called *regular reflection* or *specular reflection*. Reflection from a rough or 'mat' surface like that of cement, newsprint, or the bark of a tree occurs in many directions when a parallel beam of light is incident on the surface, as indicated in Fig. 2. Although the laws of regular reflection are obeyed by any single ray, the irregular surface causes the reflected rays to travel in many different directions. The incident beam of light is said to be *diffused* at the rough surface and reflection at a rough surface is called *diffuse reflection*.* It is by diffuse reflection that we are able to see nonluminous bodies when light strikes them. The reflected rays from any small portion of a rough surface travel in so

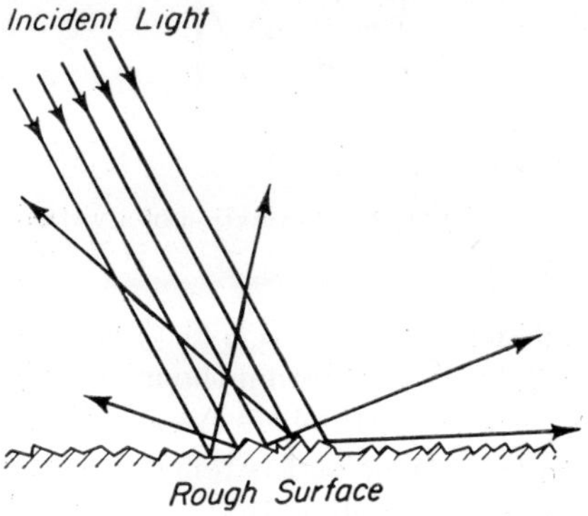

Fig. 2. Diffuse reflection at a rough surface.

---

* The above discussion is not completely satisfactory, because of course all surfaces are rough on an atomic scale. But the scale of atomic size is small in comparison with the wavelength of light. The dividing line between regular and diffuse reflection is not sharp, but if the width of the hills in Fig. 2 is large compared with

many different directions that the small area is visible to us in essentially the same manner as a similar small area on the surface of a luminous body. However, if the incident light is shut off we can no longer see the nonluminous body. On the other hand, we cannot really 'see' a perfect mirror. Diffuse rather than regular reflection is required to make the surface of a body visible.

Let us next consider the reflection of light by a plane mirror when the light is emitted by a point source near the mirror. Light is emitted in all directions from a point source, but for the sake of simplicity we shall devote our attention to only a few rays. Figure 3(a) shows three rays coming from the point source O (called the *object*) and making angles of

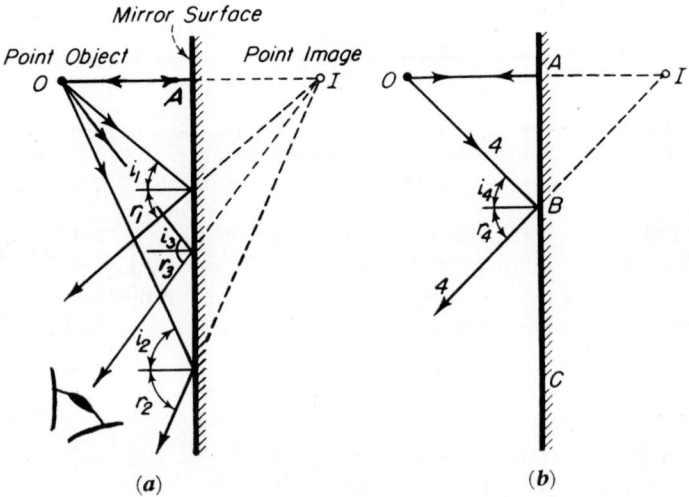

Fig. 3. Formation of a virtual image of a luminous point source by a plane mirror.

incidence i_1, i_2, and i_3 at the reflecting surface of the mirror. These rays will be reflected from the mirror with angles of reflection $r_1 = i_1$, $r_2 = i_2$, and $r_3 = i_3$, respectively. An additional ray is shown which proceeds normally to the mirror and is reflected back along itself. It is a simple matter of geometry to show that all such reflected rays, when extended back of the mirror as shown by broken lines, pass through a common point I known as the *image*. As a demonstration, we can use Fig. 3(b), where OAI is the normal to the mirror and OB is any other ray whatsoever. From the fact that $i_4 = r_4$, we see that $OA = AI$ in length, and hence infer that *all*

---

the wavelength of the light, the reflection is diffuse as in the figure. On the other hand, if the width of the hills in Fig. 2 were small compared with the wavelength of the light, the reflection would be regular, as in Fig. 1. Consequently, in order to make a good mirror, a glass or metal surface must be polished so that its irregularities are small in size compared with the wavelength of light.

reflected rays will seem to come from a common image point at a distance behind the mirror equal to the distance of the object in front.

When an observer places his eye in the position indicated, all the reflected rays that enter his eye appear to come from the point I, and he apparently sees a luminous point source at I. Since I is behind the mirror, and the rays that seem to come from I do not really pass through the point I at all, I is said to be the *virtual* image of the object O.

A plane mirror forms a virtual image of a point object, the image being behind the mirror at a distance equal to that of the object in front, along the normal from the object to the mirror.

If we call the distance from the object to the mirror the *object distance* and the distance from the image to the mirror the *image distance*, we conclude that for a plane mirror

$$\text{image distance} = \text{object distance}.$$

If the object is not a point object, it is possible to treat the object as if it were equivalent to a collection of point sources as indicated in Fig. 4, in which rays are drawn from two 'point objects' O and O'. By reasoning similar to that used above for a single point object, we see that point images I and I' are formed at positions given by

$$IA = OA \quad \text{and} \quad I'B = O'B.$$

Consideration of Fig. 4 also shows that $II' = OO'$; that is, the image size is equal to the size of the object. Since the arrow points of both object and image in the figure are pointing upward, we may also conclude that the image is *upright*. Thus, we may summarize our discussion of the plane mirror by saying that it forms a virtual, upright image whose size is equal to that of the object, with image distance equal to object distance. These considerations apply whether the object is self-luminous or whether it is nonluminous with a diffusely reflecting surface which, when illuminated, reflects light rays in all directions.

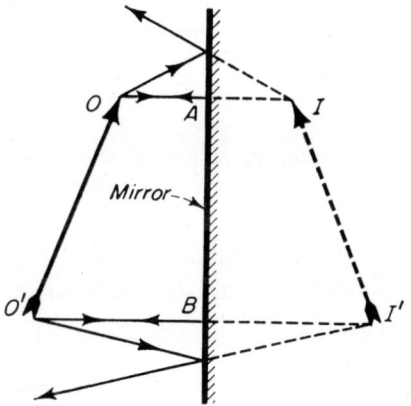

Fig. 4. Formation of a virtual image of an extended object by a plane mirror.

The rotation of a plane mirror upon which a ray of light is incident causes the reflected ray to be changed in direction by an angle that is twice the angle through which the mirror has been rotated. In order to demonstrate that the rotation of the reflected ray is twice the rotation of the mirror, consider the arrangement shown in Fig. 5. A ray of light SO strikes the mirror normally when the mirror is in its initial position M and is reflected back along itself in the direction OS. Then the mirror is rotated through angle θ into the position M'. The angle of incidence i is now equal to θ, since the normal has been moved through angle θ. The angle of reflection r is also equal to θ. Hence, the reflected ray has experienced a rotation equal to 2θ. The use of a light beam reflected from a mirror is common in connection with the reading of galvanometers

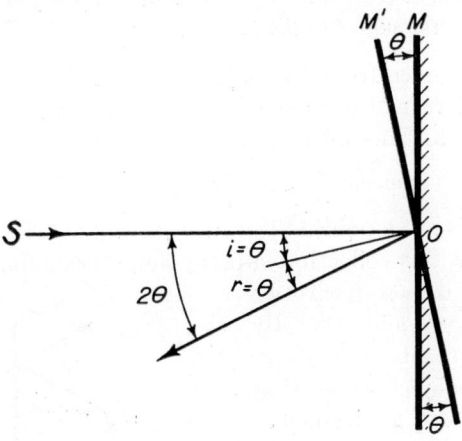

Fig. 5. When a plane mirror rotates through angle θ, a reflected light ray is rotated through angle 2θ.

and other instruments in which a small rotation must be indicated or recorded. Essentially, this arrangement uses the light beam as an 'inertialess pointer' or 'optical lever.'

PROBLEMS

1. At a time when the sun is at an angle of 40° above the southern horizon, the sun's rays strike a horizontal plane mirror. (a) What is the angle of incidence of the light rays at the mirror surface? (b) What is the angle of reflection? (c) In what direction does the reflected light travel?
                Ans: (a) 50°; (b) 50°; (c) northward, 40° above the plane of the mirror.

2. At a time when the sun is observed at an angle of 40° above the southern horizon, the sun's rays strike a vertical plane mirror whose reflecting surface faces south. (a) What is the angle of incidence of the light rays at the mirror surface? (b) What is the angle of reflection? (c) In what direction does the reflected light travel?

3. Rays of sunlight after reflection at a smooth water surface reach an observer standing on the bank of a pool. If the reflected rays reaching the observer on the bank come from a direction of 30° below the horizontal, at what elevation angle above the horizon would the sun be observed? What is the angle of incidence of the sun's rays at the water surface? What is the angle of reflection?   Ans: 30°; 60°; 60°.

4. Light from a street lamp suspended at a height of 14 ft strikes a puddle of water on the pavement at a horizontal distance of 21 ft from the point immediately below the lamp. Find the angles of incidence and reflection of the light beam at the puddle.

5. A man strikes a match in a dark room and sees the virtual image of the match by light reflected by a plane mirror. If the image *appears* to be 16 ft from the lighted match, what is the distance from the match to the mirror? Ans: 8 ft.

6. A man 6 ft tall stands 4 ft in front of a large vertical plane mirror. Where will a virtual image of the man be formed? How tall will the image be?

7. A young woman 5 ft 2 in tall wishes to purchase a mirror just long enough to enable her to see a full-length image of herself. How long should the mirror be? Ans: 31 in.

8. Two plane mirrors are placed in contact in such a way that the reflecting surfaces form a right angle as shown in Fig. 6. By application of the laws of reflection, show that rays in the plane of the figure incident upon either mirror will be reversed in direction after reflection. NOTE: It can also be shown that when three plane mirrors are arranged at right angles so that they form a 'corner' like the corner of a room, all rays incident upon any of the three mirrors will be reversed in direction after single or multiple reflections. Such 'retrodirective reflectors' find wide application as highway markers for night driving.

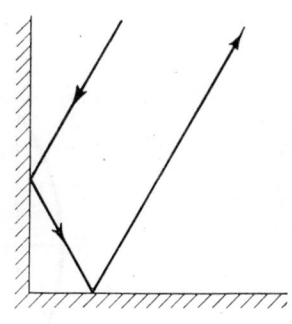

Fig. 6.

9. A narrow light beam is reflected as in Fig. 5 from the suspended mirror of a galvanometer to a straight scale 2 m away from the mirror. If the scale is parallel to the mirror in position M, and the mirror then turns through an angle of $7°.5$, what will be the displacement of the light spot on the scale? Ans: 53.6 cm.

10. If a deflection of the galvanometer mirror in Prob. 9 causes the spot of light to move 61.1 cm along the scale, what is the angle through which the mirror has rotated?

11. Show that if two adjacent walls of a rectangular room are mirror surfaces, an observer sees exactly three images of himself and of all other objects in the room. Locate the images for arbitrary position of the object, and trace the rays associated with each image. The rays should be traced from a point of the object to the observer's eye.

12. Show that if the mirror walls of Prob. 11 include an angle of 60°, there are five images. Locate the images and trace rays as in Prob. 11.

13. What does an observer see if two adjacent walls and the ceiling of a rectangular room are mirror surfaces? Explain clearly. Ans: Seven images.

14. What does an observer see if two opposite walls of a rectangular room are mirror surfaces? if three walls are mirror surfaces?

15. A woman's eyes are 5 ft from the floor while she is wearing shoes. The top of her hat is 6 ft from the floor. At what height from the floor should the lower edge of a 3-ft vertical mirror be placed so that she can see herself, with hat, at full length? Show that the answer is independent of the distance the woman stands from the mirror, and draw a ray diagram to illustrate this point clearly. Ans: 2.5 ft.

2. REFLECTION BY CONCAVE SPHERICAL MIRRORS

A spherical mirror is a mirror whose surface can be obtained by cutting off a portion of a reflecting sphere. We shall consider mirrors that might be cut from a sphere by a plane in the manner indicated in Fig. 7. The line *PN* represents the cutting plane, and arc *PSN* is the portion of the sphere to be used as the mirror. For reasons that we shall discuss later, the mirror must be only a small portion of the total spherical surface if it is to be of any value in optical instruments. In other words, the *angular aperture* defined by the angle α in the figure must be small. If the *inner* surface of the spherical segment *PSN* is the reflecting surface, the spherical mirror is said to be *concave;* if the *outer* surface is used as the reflecting surface, the mirror is said to be *convex*.

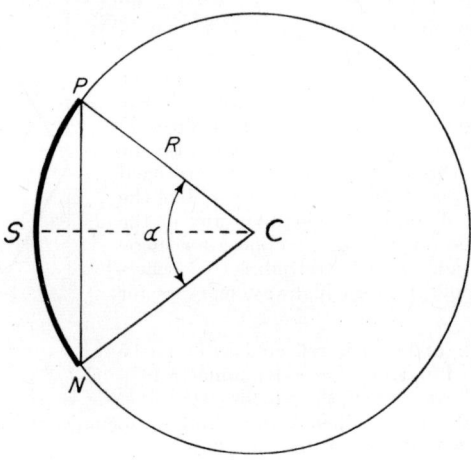

Fig. 7. Construction of a spherical mirror of radius of curvature R. The mirror diameter PN is called the *linear aperture*, the angle α the *angular aperture*.

The *axis* of a spherical mirror is a line CS drawn from the center of the original sphere to the center of the mirror. A spherical mirror can be used to produce images of luminous or illuminated objects placed near its axis. In order to see how images are produced by a concave mirror, let us consider rays from a point object on the mirror axis as shown in Fig. 8(a). Let OA be a ray which strikes the mirror at point A; after reflection, this ray traverses the path AI, where I is on the mirror axis. The normal to the mirror surface at point A can be constructed by drawing the radius R from the center of curvature C to the mirror surface. We may set the angle of reflection r equal to the angle of incidence i. Remembering that the exterior angle of a triangle is equal to the sum of the opposite interior angles, we may write for triangle OAC:

$$\beta = \alpha + i \quad \text{or} \quad i = \beta - \alpha,$$

and for triangle CAI: $\quad \gamma = \beta + r \quad \text{or} \quad r = \gamma - \beta.$

Since $r = i$, we arrive at the result

$$\gamma - \beta = \beta - \alpha,$$

or

$$\alpha + \gamma = 2\beta.$$

Now the angle β equals the arc AS divided by the radius $R = CS$. We must now introduce the condition that the angles α and γ be small (mean-

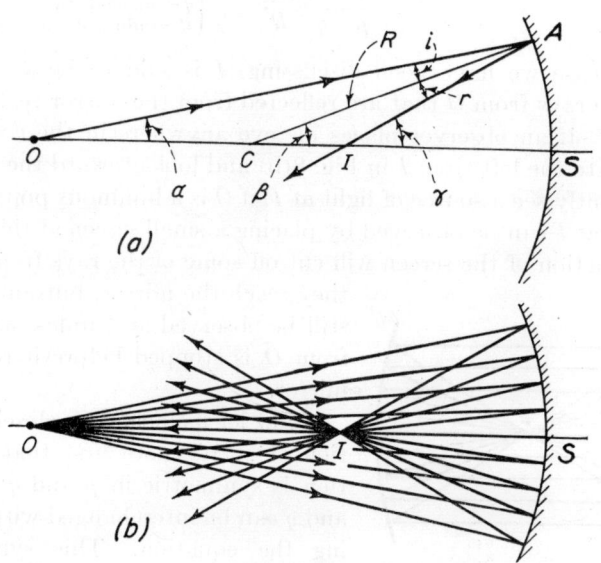

Fig. 8. Formation of a real image of a point object by a concave mirror.

ing a small fraction of a radian). If these angles are small, they can be measured to a good approximation by the ratios

$$\alpha = AS/OS; \quad \gamma = AS/IS.$$

In this case the equation $\alpha + \gamma = 2\beta$ becomes

$$\frac{AS}{OS} + \frac{AS}{IS} = 2\frac{AS}{R}, \quad \text{or} \quad \frac{1}{OS} + \frac{1}{IS} = \frac{2}{R}.$$

This is the equation that determines the distance IS in terms of the distance OS and the radius R. The distance IS is seen to be independent of the angle α, provided the angles α and γ are both small. If α and γ are both small, their sum 2β will be small; and since 2β is the angular aperture of the mirror as defined above, this angular aperture must be small. When the angular aperture is small, the distance IS will be independent of the angle α, and all rays starting from O will pass through the same point I, as indicated in Fig. 8(b). This point will then be an *image* of the object O.

It is customary to call OS the *object distance* and to designate it by the symbol p; and to call IS the *image distance* and to designate it by the symbol q. In terms of these symbols, the above equation becomes

$$\frac{1}{p}+\frac{1}{q}=\frac{2}{R}. \qquad \begin{cases} p=\text{object distance} \\ q=\text{image distance} \\ R=\text{radius of curvature} \end{cases} \qquad (1)$$

In the case we have been discussing, I is said to be a *real image*, because the rays from O that are reflected from the mirror really do pass through I. If an observer places his eye anywhere in the cone of rays proceeding to the left from I in Fig. 8(b) and looks toward the mirror, he will apparently see a source of light at I, if O is a luminous point. Or the real image at I can be observed by placing a small screen at this position; the introduction of the screen will cut off some of the rays from O before they reach the mirror, but an image can still be observed at I unless *all* the light from O is stopped before it reaches the mirror.

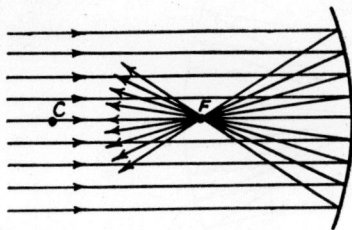

Fig. 9. Parallel light rays converge at the principal focus F.

Now let us look more closely at equation (1). We note first that the equation is symmetric in p and q; that is, p and q can be interchanged without altering the equation. This symmetry is associated with the physical fact that object and image positions can be interchanged in Fig. 8. If the object were placed at point I in Fig. 8 and rays were then drawn from this point *to* the mirror, they would be reflected back to a focus at point O. In fact, they would be just the rays shown in Fig. 8 *traced backwards*.

Equation (1) tells us that when $p=R$, q also equals R. This statement is correct because a set of rays proceeding outward from the center of curvature would all strike the mirror normally and be reflected right back through the center of curvature. Now let us see what happens as the object distance increases. As p increases in (1), q decreases. The largest value p can have is ∞; in this case $1/p=0$ and $q=\tfrac{1}{2}R$ (see Fig. 9). 'Object at infinity' means, physically, that the rays coming from the object are parallel. The image position in this case—the position at which *parallel light* is focused—is called the *principal focus* of the mirror, and the distance $\tfrac{1}{2}R$ of the principal focus from the mirror is called the *focal length* of the mirror. Thus, the focal length of a concave mirror, denoted by f, is

$$f=\tfrac{1}{2}R. \qquad (2)$$

If equation (1) be rewritten in terms of the focal length, it takes the form

$$\frac{1}{p}+\frac{1}{q}=\frac{1}{f}. \qquad (3)$$

Study of this equation shows that as the object distance p decreases from ∞ to f, the image distance q increases from f to ∞. But what happens when the object distance is less than f—that is, when the object is 'inside' the principal focus of the mirror? Formal application of (3) would give a *negative* value for q, which would suggest that the image was *behind* the mirror, and hence *virtual*. Accurate analysis of this case, similar to the above analysis of Fig. 8(a), shows that these suppositions are correct. We omit this analysis, which shows that we arrive at the situation of Fig. 10, where the object O is inside the principal focus, marked F, and the image is virtual. *Equations* (1) *and* (3) *still apply when the object distance p is less than $f = \tfrac{1}{2}R$; the fact that the image distance q comes out negative in this case indicates that the image is virtual and behind the mirror.*

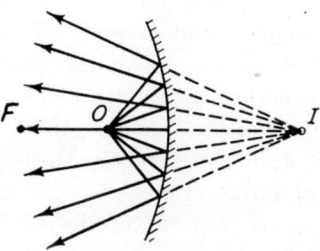

Fig. 10. Formation of a virtual image of a point object by a concave mirror.

So far, we have considered only the image of a point. Now we shall consider the image of an extended object AO lying in a plane normal to

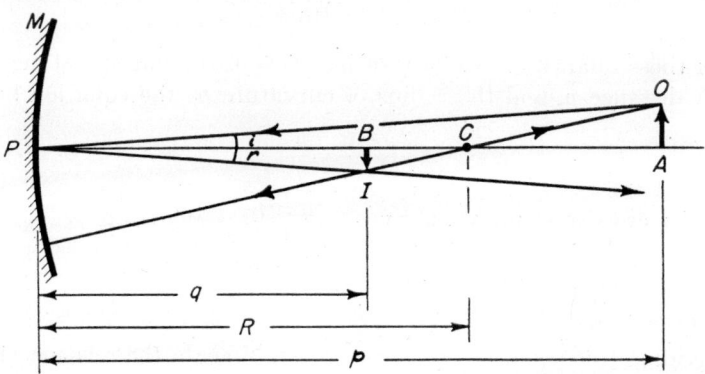

Fig. 11. Formation of a real image BI of an extended object AO by a concave mirror.

the mirror axis in Fig. 11. We know that an image of A is formed at a position B given by equation (1). By the previous analysis we know also that an image of O will be formed at some point I along the radius OC of the sphere, provided none of the rays from O to the mirror make too large an angle of incidence. Since we know that under these conditions all rays from O are focused at a common point, we can determine the position of this point from any two rays. Using the two rays of Fig. 11, we shall show that the point I lies immediately beneath B, and hence that *a plane object has a plane image.* Of the two rays chosen, one passes through the center of curvature C and is reflected back along itself; the other strikes the mirror at point P on the axis and is reflected with angles i and r equal. To prove the above statements we shall show that the distance q of the point of intersection of these two rays satisfies exactly the relation (1).

For the moment, then, forget that B in Fig. 11 is the image of A and consider it merely as the foot of the perpendicular dropped from the point of intersection I to the axis. The ray from O that passes through C forms portions of the similar triangles OAC and IBC, and from these triangles we may write the following proportionality:

$$\frac{OA}{IB} = \frac{CA}{BC}.$$

The ray from O to P to I forms portions of the similar triangles OPA and IPB; from these triangles we may write the proportionality

$$\frac{OA}{IB} = \frac{PA}{PB}.$$

Combining these relations, we obtain

$$\frac{CA}{BC} = \frac{PA}{PB}.$$

When these quantities are written in terms of the image distance q, the object distance p, and the radius of curvature R, the equation becomes

$$\frac{p-R}{R-q} = \frac{p}{q},$$

which by cross multiplication gives

$$pq - Rq = Rp - pq$$

or
$$Rq + Rp = 2pq.$$

On dividing this equation by pqR, we obtain again the relation (1):

$$\frac{1}{p} + \frac{1}{q} = \frac{2}{R},$$

which is called the *mirror equation.* This completes the demonstration that the image I of O lies at the same distance from the mirror as the image B of A.

An exactly similar argument can be applied to the case in which the image is virtual. This is left to the student as an exercise.

The best understanding of the characteristics of image formation by concave mirrors is obtained by plotting principal-ray diagrams. Such diagrams are plotted for a concave mirror in Fig. 12 for the cases in which the object is (a) beyond the center of curvature, (b) between the principal focus and the center of curvature, and (c) inside the principal focus.

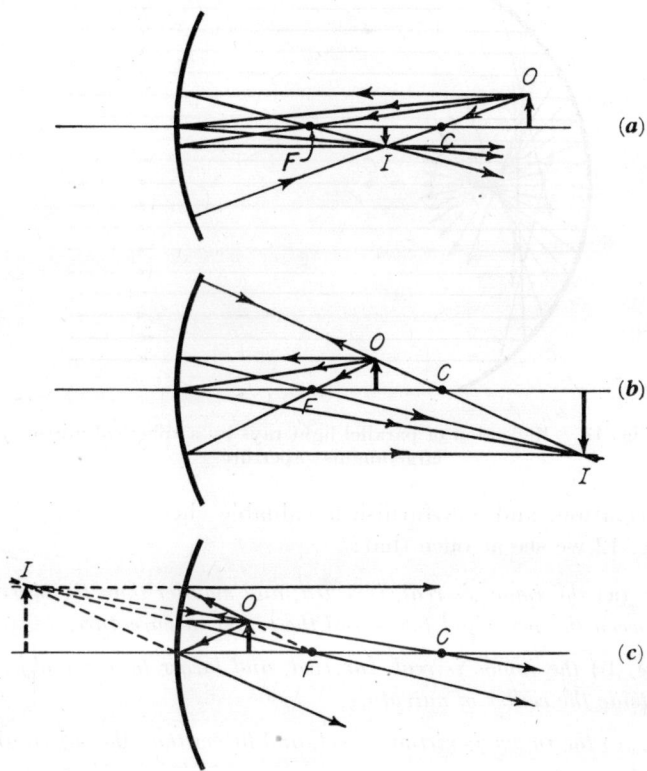

Fig. 12. Image formation by a concave mirror: principal-ray diagrams.

The so-called *principal rays* are four in number and are very easy to plot in these diagrams. The principal rays are

(1) the ray that leaves O parallel to the axis and is reflected back through the principal focus (a ray of Fig. 9),
(2) the ray that leaves O along the line through the principal focus and is reflected parallel to the axis (a reversed ray of Fig. 9),
(3) the ray that leaves O along the line through the center of curvature and is reflected back along itself, and
(4) the ray that strikes the mirror at the axis and is reflected back at an equal angle on the opposite side of the axis.

These four rays intersect at the point I, and serve to locate the position, size, and orientation of the image graphically.

The student will find that the sketching of rough principal-ray diagrams like those of Fig. 12 will assist him in the understanding of

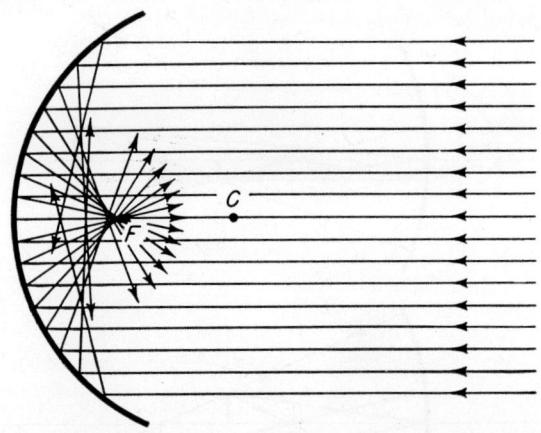

Fig. 13. Reflection of parallel light rays by a spherical mirror of large angular aperture.

image formation, and will furnish a valuable check on analytical work. From Fig. 12 we see at once that:

In case (a) *the image is real, inverted, and smaller than the object, and lies between the principal focus and the center of curvature.*

In case (b) *the image is real, inverted, and larger than the object, and lies outside the center of curvature.*

In case (c) *the image is virtual, erect, and larger than the object, and lies behind the mirror.*

From Fig. 12 we can derive immediately the analytical rule that gives image size. We see that in each case principal ray (4) in the above list, together with the object, the image, and the axis, form two similar triangles. From these triangles we see directly that

$$\frac{\text{image size}}{\text{object size}} = \frac{\text{image distance}}{\text{object distance}}. \tag{4}$$

In applying this rule, the sign attached to the image distance q is to be ignored.

It is good practice to sketch a principal-ray diagram in connection with *every* problem on optical image formation.

In our discussion of the formation of images by concave mirrors, we have assumed that the mirrors were of small angular aperture. The mirror equation can be used only for such mirrors. If the mirror has a large angular aperture, image formation is imperfect because the reflected rays do not all pass through a single point. This effect is known as *spherical aberration*. Figure 13 shows a concave spherical mirror of large

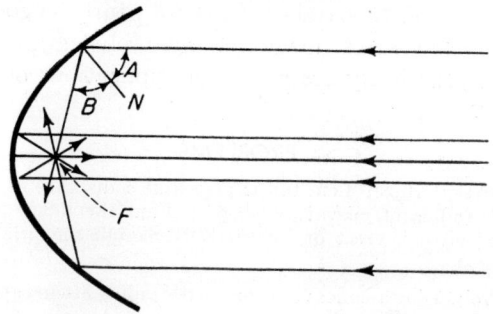

Fig. 14. Reflection of parallel rays by a parabolic mirror.

aperture, on which parallel rays are incident. It will be noted that reflected rays cross the mirror axis farther and farther from the principal focus as the paths of the incident rays are drawn farther and farther from the axis. The envelope of these rays forms a 'caustic curve' which has a cusp at the principal focus F.

It is possible to eliminate spherical aberration for distant objects by using a mirror that is not spherical but is in the shape of the paraboloid of revolution obtained by rotating a parabola about its own axis. Such a mirror is usually called a *parabolic mirror* (rather than a paraboloidal mirror). The parabolic section of such a mirror is shown in Fig. 14. It is a well-known property of the parabola that the normal to the curve at any point bisects the angle between a line drawn to that point parallel to the axis of the parabola and a line drawn from the focus of the parabola to the point in question. Therefore, the angles A and B in Fig. 14 are equal for all lines drawn parallel to the axis. Since this equality of angles is also the condition for regular reflection, it follows that all rays parallel to the axis pass through the focus F after reflection and also that all rays emanating from a point source at the principal focus are reflected from the mirror as rays parallel to the axis.

The parabolic mirror may therefore be used either to concentrate parallel rays from a distant point source at a sharply defined focus or to send out a parallel beam of light from a point source at F. The first use is illustrated in the large reflecting mirrors in astronomical telescopes. The second use is illustrated in the parabolic reflectors used in automobile and locomotive headlights and in searchlights of all kinds. Generally, a slightly divergent beam is needed from a searchlight; this may be obtained by placing the electric-arc source slightly inside or outside F. With the source between F and the mirror, the beam diverges immediately; with the source beyond F, the beam first converges and then diverges.

Although a parabolic mirror has the unique advantages indicated above with regard to formation of an image of a point object at a great distance *on the axis* of the parabola, it is not nearly so good as a spherical mirror in the formation of images of point objects at other locations; hence its use is practically restricted to applications of the types cited above.

PROBLEMS

1. An illuminated object 4 cm tall is placed at a distance of 50 cm from a concave mirror with radius of curvature 40 cm. Find the image distance, size, and character (real or virtual, erect or inverted?). Sketch the principal-ray diagram.
 Ans: 33.3 cm; 2.67 cm.

2. Repeat Prob. 1 for a concave mirror with radius of curvature 10 cm.

3. An illuminated object 4 cm tall is placed 30 cm from a concave mirror with radius of curvature 40 cm. Find the image distance, size, and character. Sketch the principal-ray diagram. Ans: 60 cm; 8 cm.

4. An illuminated object 2 cm tall is placed 6 cm from a concave mirror of 10 cm radius of curvature. Determine image distance, size, and character. Sketch the principal-ray diagram.

5. An object 4 cm tall is placed 10 cm away from a concave mirror with radius of curvature 40 cm. Find the image distance and the image size. Sketch the principal-ray diagram. Ans: −20 cm; 8 cm.

6. An object 0.5 cm tall is placed 1.5 cm away from a concave mirror of radius of curvature 10 cm. Determine image distance, size, and character. Sketch the principal-ray diagram.

7. An object 4 cm tall is placed 40 cm away from a concave mirror of 40 cm radius of curvature. Determine the image distance, size, and character. Sketch the principal-ray diagram. Ans: 40 cm; 4 cm.

8. An object 8 cm tall is placed 20 cm away from a concave mirror of 40 cm radius of curvature. Determine the image distance. Place the head of the object 4 cm above the axis, the tail 4 cm below the axis, and draw a ray diagram showing clearly the course of a number of rays from each end of the object and from the mid-point of the object, after reflection from the mirror. Be prepared to discuss thoroughly this important case of an object at the principal focus. Discuss the image character as a limiting case of what happens if the object moves toward the focus (a) from positions slightly inside, (b) from positions slightly outside.

9. By an argument exactly like that used in the text in connection with Fig. 11, derive the mirror equation for the case in which the object is inside the principal focus and the image is virtual. Draw a new diagram similar to Fig. 11 for this case, and denote the distance of the image behind the mirror by $-q$.

10. A certain concave mirror has a radius of curvature of 30 cm. Where should a luminous point object be placed in order to have a parallel beam of light reflected from the mirror?

11. Let R be the radius of curvature and f be the focal length of a concave mirror. Five possible object positions are (1) $p > R$, (2) $p = R$, (3) $f < p < R$, (4) $p = f$, (5) $0 < p < f$. Which ones of these five positions give
  (a) an inverted diminished image?
  (b) an inverted enlarged image?

(c) an inverted image equal in size to the object?
(d) no finite image?
(e) an erect image equal in size to the object?
(f) an erect enlarged image?
(g) a real image?

12. When a luminous object is placed 10 cm in front of a concave mirror, a virtual image is formed 20 cm away from the mirror surface. Find the focal length and radius of curvature of the mirror. Sketch the principal-ray diagram.

13. When an illuminated object is placed 40 cm away from a concave mirror, a real image is produced 20 cm from the mirror. Find the focal length and radius of curvature of the mirror. Sketch the principal-ray diagram. Ans: 13.33 cm; 26.67 cm.

14. A real object is placed x cm in front of a concave mirror of radius of curvature 10 cm. What are the least and greatest values of x for which
(a) the image is real?
(b) the image is erect?
(c) the image is larger than the object?

15. A concave mirror has a linear aperture (diameter) of 10 cm and a focal length of 10 cm. Find the angular aperture. Ans: 28°.

16. Concave mirror A has a linear aperture of 10 cm and radius of curvature 10 cm, and concave mirror B has an aperture of 15 cm and focal length 12 cm. For which of these mirrors will the effects of spherical aberration be the more troublesome? Why?

17. It is shown in the text that if a point source is placed at the focus of a parabolic mirror, all reflected rays will be parallel. Recalling the geometrical properties of an ellipse, determine what will happen if a point source is placed at either focus of an ellipsoidal mirror, cut from one end of an ellipsoid of revolution obtained by rotation of an ellipse around its major axis.

3. REFLECTION BY CONVEX SPHERICAL MIRRORS

When a luminous or illuminated point object is placed on the axis of a *convex* mirror, the rays from the object clearly *diverge* after reflection from the mirror. This statement is true for any position of the object. However, if the angle of incidence of all the rays is small, which implies that the angular aperture of the mirror is small, the rays diverge from a common point as indicated schematically in Fig. 15. This point constitutes a virtual image of the object. A person looking into the convex mirror of Fig. 15 sees a mirrored image of O at I, much as in the case of a plane mirror.

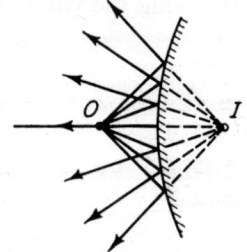

Fig. 15. Formation of a virtual image of a point object by a convex mirror.

A proof that such an image is formed can be given by methods similar to those we used in connection with Fig. 8. Also, we can show that a plane object such as OA in Fig. 16 has a plane image IB. We shall omit these proofs; but granted that an image of point O in Fig. 16 is formed at some point I, we shall determine the location of I by finding the intersection of the two rays shown in Fig.

16. One of these rays heads from O toward the center of curvature and is reflected back along itself; the other strikes the mirror at the axis and is reflected symmetrically. As is customary in the case of convex mirrors, *the radius of curvature R is considered to be a negative number;* hence, the distance from the mirror to the center of curvature is represented by $-R$. As is customary in the case of virtual images, *the image distance q is con-*

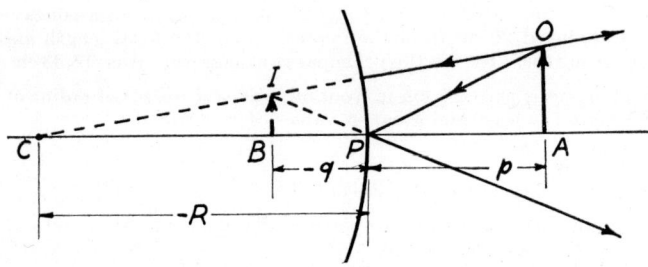

Fig. 16. Image formation by a convex mirror.

sidered to be a negative number; hence, the distance from the image to the mirror is represented by $-q$.

From the similar triangles IBP and OAP, we see that

$$OA/IB = PA/BP.$$

From the similar triangles IBC and OAC, we see that

$$OA/IB = CA/CB.$$

Hence
$$\frac{PA}{BP} = \frac{CA}{CB}.$$

Inserting the values of these lengths in terms of p, q, and R gives

$$\frac{p}{-q} = \frac{(-R)+p}{(-R)-(-q)} = \frac{p-R}{q-R}.$$

Clearing of fractions gives

$$-pq + qR = pq - pR$$

or
$$qR + pR = 2pq.$$

When this equation is divided through by pqR, we obtain the *mirror equation* again:

$$\frac{1}{p} + \frac{1}{q} = \frac{2}{R}. \tag{5}$$

For a convex mirror we must remember that R is a negative number; this convention makes q come out negative for any positive value of p, indicating that *the image is always virtual and behind the mirror.*

A study of equation (5) shows that as the object distance p varies from

0 to ∞, the image position varies from $q=0$ to $q=\tfrac{1}{2}R$. Object at infinity corresponds to parallel light incident on the mirror as in Fig. 17. The virtual-image point in this case is called the *principal focus* of the convex mirror. The distance $q=\tfrac{1}{2}R$ of the principal focus is called the *focal length* and is denoted by f. Just as R is taken as a negative number,

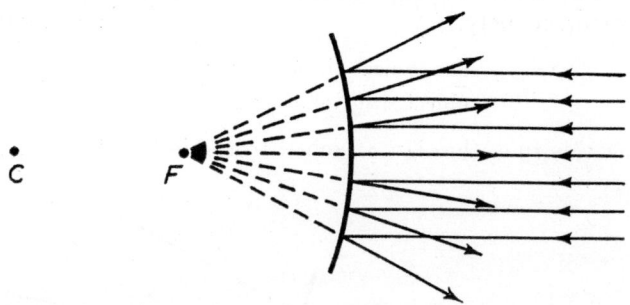

Fig. 17. Parallel light rays diverge from the principal focus F of a convex mirror. The principal focus is behind the mirror, halfway between the mirror and the center of curvature C. (The rays coming from the right in this figure are drawn parallel; an optical illusion makes them seem to curve.)

the focal length $f=\tfrac{1}{2}R$ *is a negative number in the case of a convex mirror*. In terms of focal length the mirror equation takes the form

$$\frac{1}{p}+\frac{1}{q}=\frac{1}{f}=\frac{2}{R}.$$

It is convenient that *equation (6) applies to all types of spherical mirrors with the sign conventions we have adopted:*

> p is positive for any real object (later we shall define a virtual object for which p is negative).
> f and R are positive for a concave (converging) mirror.
> f and R are negative for a convex (diverging) mirror.
> If q is positive, the image is real (in front of the mirror).
> If q is negative, the image is virtual (behind the mirror).

In the case of a convex mirror, one can again make good use of a principal-ray diagram such as that in Fig. 18. The four principal rays shown in Fig. 18 are

(1) the ray that leaves O parallel to the axis and is reflected back along a line through the principal focus (as in Fig. 17),
(2) the ray that leaves O along the line through the principal focus and is reflected back parallel to the axis (the reverse of one of the rays of Fig. 17),
(3) the ray that leaves O along the line through the center of curvature and is reflected back along itself, and

(4) the ray that strikes the mirror at the axis and is reflected at an equal angle on the opposite side of the axis.

From Fig. 18, we conclude that the image is always erect, virtual, and smaller than the object. From triangles IBP and OAP of Fig. 16 we obtain the same analytical expression (4) for image size as in the case of a concave mirror, namely,

$$\frac{\text{image size}}{\text{object size}} = \frac{\text{image distance}}{\text{object distance}}$$

In applying this rule, the sign attached to the image distance q is again to be ignored.

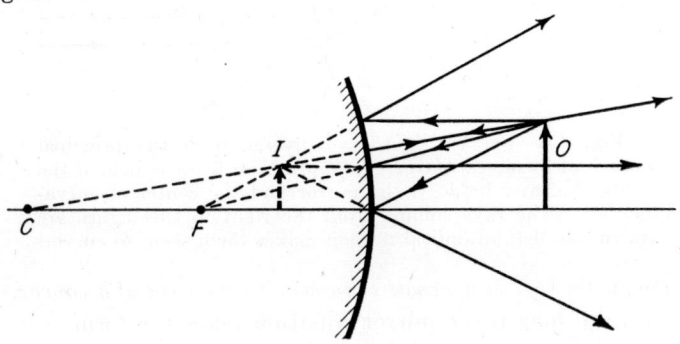

Fig. 18. Principal-ray diagram for a convex mirror.

PROBLEMS

1. An illuminated object 4 cm tall is placed on the axis at a distance of 50 cm from a convex mirror with radius of curvature 40 cm. Find the image distance, size, and character. Sketch the principal-ray diagram. Ans: -14.3 cm; 1.14 cm.

2. An illuminated object 4 cm tall is placed on the axis at a distance of 10 cm from a convex mirror of radius of curvature 40 cm. Find the image position, size, and character. Sketch the principal-ray diagram.

3. How far from a convex mirror with radius of curvature 40 cm should an illuminated object be placed in order to produce an image one-half as tall as the object? Ans: 30 cm.

4. When an illuminated object is placed 30 cm away from a convex mirror, a virtual image one-third as tall as the object is produced. Find the focal length and radius of curvature of the mirror.

4. REFRACTION OF LIGHT

We have stated that light travels in straight lines in a homogeneous medium and that reflection occurs at the surface separating two media. However, the reflection is not generally complete; some of the light striking a boundary between two media usually passes from the first medium into the second. When light strikes a highly polished metal surface, the fraction of incident light that penetrates the metal is small; however, when light strikes the surface of a *transparent* substance like glass, a considerable fraction of the incident light penetrates the glass.

A ray of light passing from one medium to another ordinarily experiences an abrupt change in direction. This bending of the light ray at a surface is called *refraction*. Some of the results of refraction are familiar to all of us. An oar dipped obliquely through the surface of water appears to be bent sharply at the surface. A coin placed on the bottom of a cup in such a manner as to be hidden by the walls of the cup when the cup is empty may become visible when the cup is filled with water. Objects appear enlarged and distorted when viewed through a drinking glass filled with water.

The behavior of light in passing from one medium such as air into another medium such as water or glass will now be considered quantita-

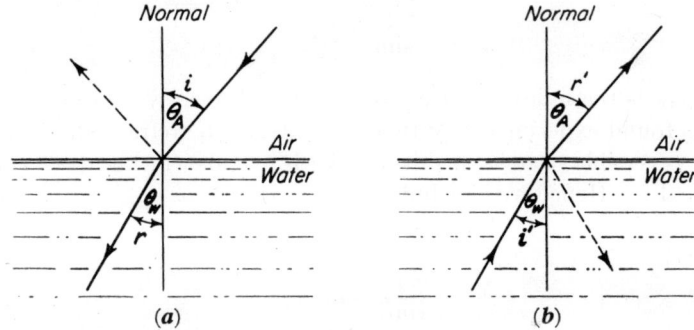

Fig. 19. Refraction at a plane surface. Broken lines indicate reflected rays.

tively. Rays passing from air to water or glass are bent *toward* the normal at the interface; rays passing from water or glass into air are bent *away* from the normal. These phenomena are illustrated in Fig. 19. Water and glass are said to be *optically denser* than air. It will be noted from the figure that a portion of the light is reflected at the interface and a portion is transmitted. The ratio of the light transmitted to that reflected depends upon the nature of the media and upon the angle of incidence. At present we are concerned with the change in direction (the *refraction*) experienced by rays passing from one medium into another.

Refraction takes place in a manner described by the following laws:

FIRST LAW OF REFRACTION: *The refracted ray lies in the plane containing the incident ray and the normal to the interface at the point of incidence.*

SECOND LAW OF REFRACTION: *The ratio of the sine of the angle of incidence to the sine of the angle of refraction when light passes from one* given medium into a second is a constant that is independent of the angle of incidence, but that may depend on the wavelength of the light. (*Angles of incidence and of refraction are measured from the normal.*)

In Fig. 19 the incident ray, the refracted ray, and the normal to the interface are all in the plane of the paper; the plane surface of the water is oriented at right angles to the plane of the paper. The second law of refraction can be written for the case shown in Fig. 19(a) in the form

$$\frac{\sin i}{\sin r} = \mu_{WA}, \qquad (7a)$$

where μ_{WA} is called the *index of refraction* of water with respect to air. The second law of refraction for the case shown in Fig. 19(b) can be written in the form

$$\frac{\sin i'}{\sin r'} = \mu_{AW}$$

where μ_{AW} is the index of refraction of air with respect to water.

It is found experimentally that the path of the refracted ray is completely reversible; that is, if i' in Fig. 19(b) equals r in Fig. 19(a), then r' will equal i. Hence we conclude that

$$\mu_{AW} = 1/\mu_{WA},$$

so that
$$\frac{\sin r'}{\sin i'} = \mu_{WA}. \qquad (7b)$$

Comparison of equations (7a) and (7b) points to the desirability of writing the law of refraction in a form that is independent of which way the light is travelling and applies equally well to Fig. 19(a) and to Fig. 19(b). If we let θ_A be the angle between the normal and the ray in air, and θ_W be the angle between the normal and the ray in water, as indicated in Fig. 19, equations (7a) and (7b) both take the form

$$\frac{\sin \theta_A}{\sin \theta_W} = \mu_{WA}. \qquad (8)$$

The first law of refraction has been known since the third century B.C.; the second law of refraction is known as *Snell's law* and was discovered early in the seventeenth century.*

Refraction can be readily understood in terms of a difference of the speed of light in the two media. Consider the situation shown in Fig. 20. OA and PB represent two rays normal to a plane wave-front, a portion of which is represented by a line such as AB. Seven successive

* The Dutch astronomer Willebrord Snell (1591–1626) was the first to discover the second law of refraction, but the results of his investigations were not published until after his death. The law was discovered independently and first reported by René Descartes (1596–1650).

positions of this wave-front are shown in Fig. 20. After refraction of the light, the wave-front reaches position CD. Now $\angle BAD = i$, since the sides of the angles BAD and i in Fig. 20 are mutually perpendicular; $\angle ADC = r$ for the same reason. Thus, Snell's law (7a) can be written as

$$\mu_{WA} = \frac{\sin i}{\sin r} = \frac{\sin BAD}{\sin ADC} = \frac{BD/AD}{AC/AD} = \frac{BD}{AC}. \tag{9}$$

Since A and B are points on an incident plane wave and C and D are points on the same wave-front after refraction has occurred, it follows that the time required for the wave-front to move from B to D in air must

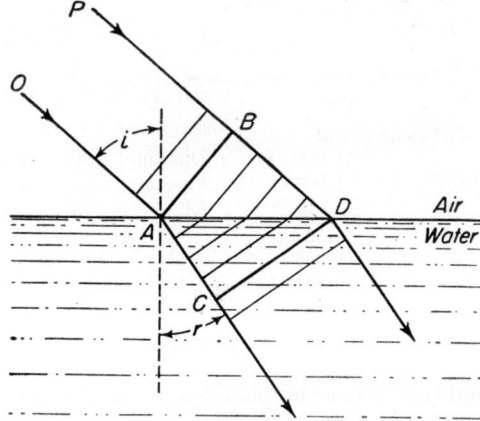

Fig. 20. Refraction at a plane surface. The wave-front turns because the speed of light in water is less than in air. It is useful to visualize a line of soldiers marching from a dry field (air) into a muddy field (water) where the marching speed is less. The line would have to turn as indicated.

be equal to the time for the refracted wave-front to move from A to C in water. If c_A represents the speed of light in air and c_W the speed of light in water, equating these two times gives

$$\frac{BD}{c_A} = \frac{AC}{c_W}.$$

Therefore, in equation (9), $\mu_{WA} = \dfrac{BD}{AC} = \dfrac{c_A}{c_W}.$ (10)

Equation (10) states that the index of refraction of water with respect to air is equal to the ratio of the speed of light in air to the speed of light in water. Direct experimental measurements of the speeds of light in air and water are in agreement with this equation and furnished early support for the wave theory of light.

In view of the result given by equation (10) and in view of the fact that the speed of light is greater in vacuum than in any other transparent medium, it is desirable to refer the indices of all optical media to vacuum. The *absolute index of refraction* of any medium is defined as the index of refraction of the medium relative to vacuum; that is,

$$\mu_M = c/c_M,$$

where μ_M is the absolute refractive index of medium M, c the speed of light in vacuum, and c_M the speed of light in medium M.

Table I gives absolute indices of refraction for various gases, liquids, and solids, for light of a particular wavelength. Since the absolute index of refraction of air is so nearly equal to 1, it is possible to treat it as unity in many problems.

TABLE I
Absolute Indices of Refraction of Various Media for Yellow Light of Wavelength 590 mμ

Gases at NTP		Solids at 20° C	
Dry air	1.00029	Diamond	2.419
Carbon dioxide	1.00045	Fluorite	1.434
Liquids at 20° C		Glass (typical values)	
Benzene	1.501	Crown	1.517
Carbon disulfide	1.642	Commercial plate	1.523
Carbon tetrachloride	1.461	Light flint	1.574
Ethyl alcohol	1.354	Dense flint	1.656
Water	1.334	Quartz (fused)	1.458

The relative index of refraction μ_{WA} occurring in equation (8) can now be rewritten in terms of the absolute indices for air and water as follows:

$$\mu_{WA} = \frac{c_A}{c_W} = \frac{c/c_W}{c/c_A} = \frac{\mu_W}{\mu_A}.$$

When this expression is substituted in (8), we get the most convenient form of Snell's law:

$$\frac{\sin\theta_A}{\sin\theta_W} = \frac{\mu_W}{\mu_A},$$

or
$$\mu_A \sin\theta_A = \mu_W \sin\theta_W.$$

This relation can be immediately generalized to apply to the passage of a light ray through the interface between any two media I and II:

$$\boxed{\mu_I \sin\theta_I = \mu_{II} \sin\theta_{II},} \qquad (11)$$

where μ_I and μ_{II} are the absolute refractive indices of media I and II and θ_I and θ_{II} are the angles between rays and normals in media I and II, respectively. Equation (11) applies equally well for rays incident on either side of the interface. This is probably the easiest form in which to remember and to use Snell's law.

We are now in a position to discuss the phenomenon of *total reflection*. Figure 21 shows the interface between two media I and II, of which medium II is assumed to have the higher index of refraction—one says that II is *optically denser* than I. According to (11), if $\mu_{II} > \mu_I$, then $\theta_{II} < \theta_I$. A ray passing from I into II is bent toward the normal, and no peculiarities arise. But consider the three rays (a), (b), (c) *within the denser medium* in Fig. 21, heading toward the interface. Ray (a) has a small angle of incidence and is refracted away from the normal. As the angle of incidence increases, we reach the situation shown in (b) where the angle of refraction is 90°. The angle of incidence for which the angle of

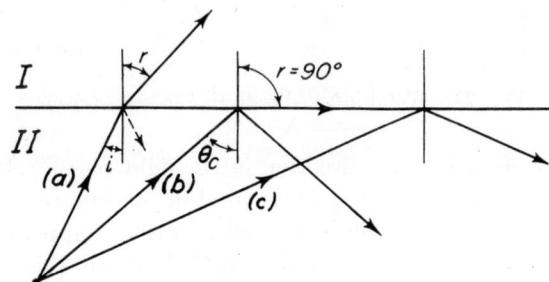

Fig. 21. Total reflection. If $\mu_{II} > \mu_I$, all light from the source is totally reflected when the angle of incidence is greater than the critical angle θ_C.

refraction is 90° is called the *critical angle* θ_C. Substituting $\theta_I = 90°$ ($\sin\theta_I = 1$) in (11) gives the formula

$$\sin\theta_C = \mu_I/\mu_{II}. \qquad (\mu_I < \mu_{II}) \quad (12)$$

Substitution of a value of θ_{II} larger than the critical angle in (11) gives a value for $\sin\theta_I$ that is greater than unity and does not correspond to any real angle. No refracted ray is possible. For angles of incidence greater than θ_C, as in the case of ray (c) in Fig. 21, the ray is *totally reflected* at the interface, and no light passes into the other medium. Notice that *total reflection takes place only for light within a medium of higher optical density at a surface of contact with a medium of lower optical density.*

The relation (12) furnishes the basis for a number of types of convenient refractometers designed to determine an unknown index of refraction by measurement of a critical angle. For example, the index of refraction of a small drop of liquid can be measured by placing the drop on the surface of glass of known index and measuring the critical angle for total reflection of light traveling within the glass and reflected at the surface of liquid contact, provided that the liquid has lower optical density than the glass.

Because total reflection is really *total*, it furnishes the basis for a perfect mirror which is utilized in various ways in optical instruments. A beam of light may be turned through 90° or 180° by a glass prism with 45° and 90° angles. These applications of total reflection are shown in Fig. 22, (a) and (b). Another utilization of total reflection is illustrated in Fig. 22(c), which shows a glass prism that can be used to invert an

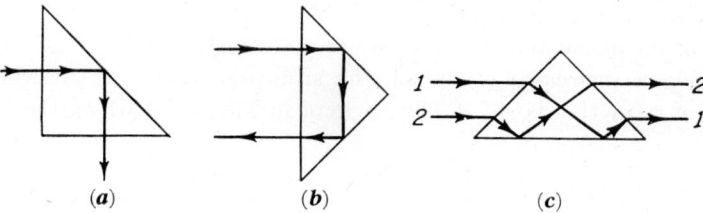

Fig. 22. Total internal reflection in glass prisms.

image without changing the direction of the light beam. Prisms giving total internal reflection are frequently used in binoculars.

Refraction causes an object immersed in water to appear closer to the surface than it actually is. In order to understand this phenomenon, let us consider Fig. 23. In this sketch, O represents a point on a submerged object. A ray of light from O strikes the surface at point P, the ray making an angle i with the normal. The angle of refraction is r and to an observer in the air, the ray would appear to come from point D. Now $\angle AOP = i$ and $\angle ADP = r$. Therefore,

$$\frac{\tan i}{\tan r} = \frac{AP/AO}{AP/AD} = \frac{AD}{AO}$$

$$= \frac{\text{apparent depth}}{\text{actual depth}}.$$

Now if i is small, the tangents of i and r are almost equal to the sines of i and r, and we may write

$$\frac{\sin i}{\sin r} = \frac{AD}{AO} = \frac{\text{apparent depth}}{\text{actual depth}}.$$

But

$$\frac{\sin i}{\sin r} = \frac{1}{\mu_W},$$

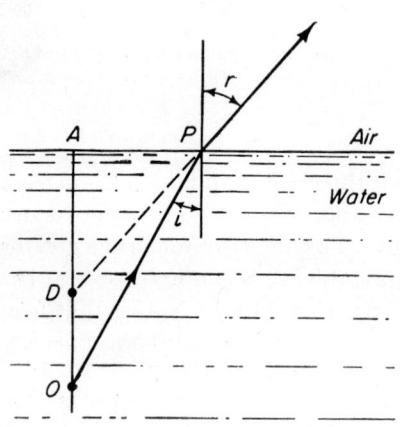

Fig. 23. Apparent depth of a submerged object.

where μ_W is the refractive index of water and the refractive index of air is taken as 1. Therefore, we may write the following equation for the apparent depth of a submerged body *when viewed almost vertically:*

$$\text{apparent depth} = (\text{actual depth})/\mu_W. \tag{13}$$

In deriving equation (13), we have used only a single ray. Actually, many rays will reach the eyes of an observer looking vertically downward at the object in the water, but these rays will all have angles of incidence and refraction small enough to permit the tangents to be approximated by sines. Equation (13) will apply to all such rays, so we see that point D will be the image of O. Submerged objects viewed from directions other than the vertical appear closer to the surface than is indicated by equation (13).

Let us now consider the deviation of a light beam by a prism. In a triangular prism, the amount of deviation depends on the refracting angle of the prism, the material of the prism, and the angle of incidence. Deviation of a ray of light by a prism is illustrated in Fig. 24. The angle

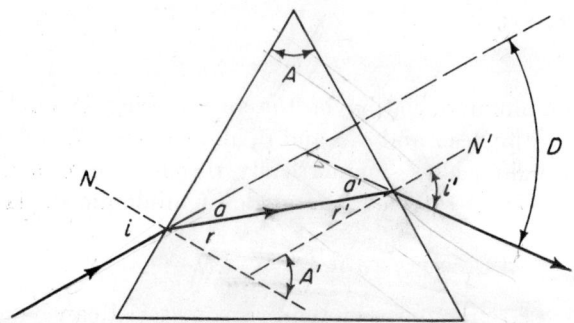

Fig. 24. Deviation of a light ray by a triangular prism of refracting angle A.

D in this figure is called the *angle of deviation* and A the *refracting angle*.

We shall now prove that the angular deviation is a minimum when the light ray passes symmetrically through the prism, and derive the relation giving the angle of minimum deviation in terms of the index of refraction of the prism material and the refracting angle of the prism. We shall need this relation later.

Consider a ray of light striking one face of the prism at an angle i with the normal N and being refracted at an angle r with the normal. The ray will then go through the prism and emerge from the second face making angles r' and i' with the normal N'. The refracting angle A of the prism is equal to the angle A' because the sides of these angles are mutually perpendicular. We may set $A' = r + r'$, since A' is the exterior angle of the triangle of which r and r' are the opposite interior angles; it follows that $A = r + r'$. For the same reason, the angle of deviation D is equal to $a + a'$. But $a = i - r$ and $a' = i' - r'$. Therefore, we may write

$$D = a + a' = i - r + i' - r' = i + i' - A.$$

Taking μ as the index of refraction of the prism material relative to air, we may write

$$\sin i = \mu \sin r,$$

and
$$\sin i' = \mu \sin r' = \mu \sin(A - r).$$

Thus
$$D = \arcsin(\mu \sin r) + \arcsin[\mu \sin(A - r)] - A$$

is a general expression for the deviation.

In order to find the value of r that will make the deviation a minimum, we must differentiate the above expression for D with respect to r and then equate the derivative to zero:

$$\frac{dD}{dr} = \frac{\mu \cos r}{\sqrt{1 - \mu^2 \sin^2 r}} - \frac{\mu \cos(A - r)}{\sqrt{1 - \mu^2 \sin^2(A - r)}} = 0.$$

This equation is satisfied if $\quad r = A - r$

and hence if $\quad r = r'$.

Therefore, minimum deviation of the ray passing through the prism occurs when the angles r and r', i and i', and therefore a and a' are equal, that is, when light passes symmetrically through the prism. With the symmetry conditions satisfied, the angle of minimum deviation can be written as

$$D_{\min} = a + a' = 2a = 2(i - r).$$

The index of refraction μ of the prism material can be expressed in terms of the angle of minimum deviation $D_{\min}$ and the prism angle A by noting that, for minimum deviation, $2r = A$ and

$$i = \tfrac{1}{2}D_{\min} + r = \tfrac{1}{2}(D_{\min} + 2r) = \tfrac{1}{2}(D_{\min} + A).$$

From Snell's law, we obtain

$$\mu = \frac{\sin i}{\sin r} = \frac{\sin \tfrac{1}{2}(D_{\min} + A)}{\sin \tfrac{1}{2}A}. \tag{14}$$

This equation, which implicitly gives $D_{\min}$ in terms of μ and A, and explicitly gives μ in terms of $D_{\min}$ and A, will be of considerable use in our later discussion of spectrographs (Chap. 28).

We have thus far considered chiefly the refractive properties of solids and liquids. Although gases have rather small indices of refraction, their refractive properties can sometimes be important. The refractive properties of the atmosphere can produce interesting effects, some of which we shall now consider.

Air changes considerably in density with changes in pressure and temperature, and variations in density are accompanied by changes in index of refraction. Approximately, the difference between the index of refraction and unity is proportional to the density. The decrease of air density with altitude is accompanied by a decrease in index of refraction. Therefore, light from a star or from the sun experiences gradual refraction toward the vertical in passing through the atmosphere. The effects of this refraction are much exaggerated in Fig. 25, in which the light from

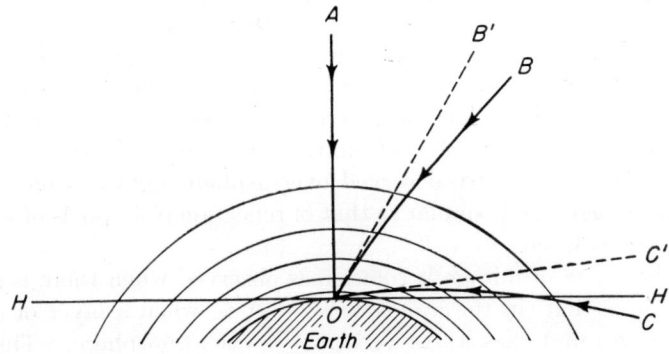

Fig. 25. Refraction of light by the atmosphere.

star B is refracted in passing through the atmosphere in such a way as to appear to come from B'. The observed altitude angle HOB' is always greater than the true altitude angle except for a body at the zenith. It should be noted that as a result of atmospheric refraction, it is possible

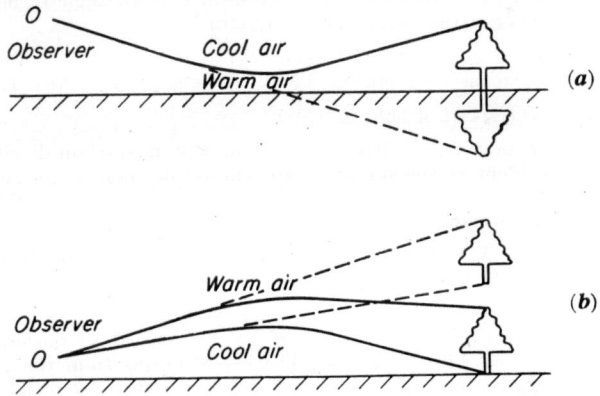

Fig. 26. Optical phenomena arising from atmospheric refraction: (a) mirage, (b) looming.

for an observer at O to see bodies such as C that are slightly below the geometrical horizon HOH. The deviations are actually small. For example, the deviation for a ray coming from star 10° above the horizon is only 5' of arc. For a body on the horizon, the deviation is 35' of arc, which is greater than the apparent diameter of the sun or moon, so that these bodies are seen entirely above the horizon when they are actually entirely below.

Another atmospheric effect frequently observed is the *mirage*. On still, sunny days there is sometimes a layer of warm air of low density close to the ground. This warm air has a smaller index of refraction than the colder, denser air above it, and light entering obliquely from a distant object is refracted in such a way as to appear to come from an inverted object below ground. This observed effect, illustrated in Fig. 26(a), is similar to the effect of reflection from the surface of a lake. Mirages on a small scale are frequently observed over asphalt highways on still, hot days; the appearance is similar to that of reflection from pools of water on the highway surface.

Another type of mirage is sometimes observed when there is a 'temperature inversion' in the atmosphere; that is, when a layer of cool air near the earth underlies warm air higher in the atmosphere. This effect is illustrated in Fig. 26(b). It occurs frequently along the seacoast when cool sea breezes blow, and is sometimes known as *looming*.

PROBLEMS

NOTE: In working most of these problems, the refractive index of air can be taken as unity. Take other indices of refraction from Table I.

1. A ray of light in air strikes a water surface at an angle of incidence of 30°. What is the angle of refraction? Show diagram. Ans: 22°.0.

2. A ray of light in air strikes a water surface at an angle of incidence of 60°. What is the angle of refraction? Show diagram.

3. The index of refraction of a certain type of glass is 1.52. Taking $c = 3 \times 10^8$ m/sec, calculate the speed of light in this type of glass. Ans: 1.97×10^8 m/sec.

4. What is the speed of light in water?

5. A shallow tank with a flat glass bottom contains carbon disulfide. A ray of light in air is incident at the surface of the carbon disulfide at an angle of 45°. If the refractive index of the glass is 1.517, find the angle of refraction of the light inside the glass. Show diagram. Ans: 27°.8.

6. If the tank described in Prob. 5 were filled with water instead of carbon disulfide, what would be the angle of refraction of the light ray inside the glass? Show diagram.

7. A ray of light in air has an angle of incidence of 30° at the surface of a plate of glass 4.0 cm thick, with $\mu = 1.523$. The ray emerging from the glass is parallel to the incident ray but is displaced laterally with respect to the incident ray. What is the magnitude of the lateral displacement? Show diagram. Ans: 0.796 cm.

8. A ray of light in air has angle of incidence of 60° at the surface of a plate of glass 4.0 cm thick, with $\mu = 1.523$. What is the magnitude of the lateral displacement of the emerging ray with respect to the incident ray? Show diagram.

9. An observer looks from directly above at a small stone at the bottom of a pool of water. The stone appears to be 3 ft beneath the surface of the water. What is the actual depth of the pool? Ans: 4.00 ft.

10. A tank containing carbon disulfide is viewed from directly above. What is the apparent depth of the tank if its actual depth is 4 in?

11. A ray of light in water strikes the horizontal surface of the water at angle of incidence of 30°. What is the angle of refraction in air? What is the angle of incidence in water when the angle of refraction in air is 90°? Show diagrams. What is the critical angle for water? Ans: 41°.8; 48°.6; 48°.6.

12. What is the critical angle for carbon disulfide? What is the critical angle for diamond? A ray of light in dense flint glass strikes the surface at an angle of 45°; will any of the light emerge into the air beyond the surface?

13. What is the angle of minimum deviation for light passing through a 60° dense flint-glass prism? Ans: 51°.8.

14. What is the angle of minimum deviation for light passing through a 60° fluorite prism?

15. What is the angle of incidence (i in Fig. 24) that gives minimum deviation in the case of a 60° dense flint-glass prism? Ans: 55°.9.

16. What is the angle of incidence (i in Fig. 24) that gives minimum deviation in the case of a 60° fluorite prism?

17. What is the angle of deviation when light is incident at an angle of 50° on a 60° dense flint-glass prism? Ans: 52°.7.

18. What is the angle of deviation when light is incident at an angle of 70° on a 60° dense flint-glass prism?

19. Neglecting the curvature of the earth, compute the deviation of starlight incident at an angle of 80° (the star is 10° above the horizon) on the top of the earth's atmosphere if the index of refraction of the air at the earth's surface is 1.00030.
Ans: 0°.097 = 5′.8.

20. The index of refraction of air depends only on temperature, pressure, and humidity. An astronomer reads temperature, pressure, and humidity at the earth's surface, and measures the apparent angle of a star from the zenith. He then looks up in a table the correction to be applied to give the true angle. To the approximation in which the curvature of the earth can be neglected and in which the atmosphere can be assumed to have characteristics that vary with altitude but do not vary in any given horizontal plane, show that these tables can be rigorously compiled because the angle of deviation depends only on the index of refraction at the earth's surface and is independent of the manner in which this index varies as one ascends to the top of the atmosphere.

21. Why do stars twinkle?

22. Why does the air over a hot radiator seem to shimmer?

23. What is the minimum index of refraction glass can have and still give total reflection in the case of the 90° prisms shown in (a) and (b) of Fig. 22? Ans: 1.414.

24. What is the minimum index of refraction glass can have and still give total reflection for the light paths shown through the 90° prism of Fig. 22(c)?

25. What is the critical angle for diamond? Ans: 24°.4.

26. Explain how the high index of refraction of diamond accounts for its extraordinary 'sparkle' when cut as a gem.

27. A large slab of glass of index 1.650 has a small air bubble a short distance below the surface. A dime (diameter 1.75 cm) placed on the surface of the glass is just large enough to completely prevent the bubble from being seen through the surface. How far down is the air bubble? Ans: 1.15 cm.

28. Why is a camera lens with a 180° field of view called a 'fish-eye lens'? What is the angle of the cone in which a fish would see the whole of the world above the level surface of a fresh-water lake?

5. LENSES

Having discussed the refractive properties of various materials, we are now in a position to consider the ways in which the refractive properties of transparent substances can be used in the design of the lenses used to produce images in optical instruments. Lenses are made of transparent materials with polished surfaces, at least one of which is curved. The commonest form of simple lens has two surfaces, which can be considered as parts of spheres; the line joining the centers of the two spheres is called the *principal axis*, or merely the *axis* of the lens, as shown in Fig. 27. We shall consider chiefly lenses made of dense optical materials such as glass, and designed for use in air. Lenses are usually classified as *converging* or *diverging*, depending upon their effects upon incident

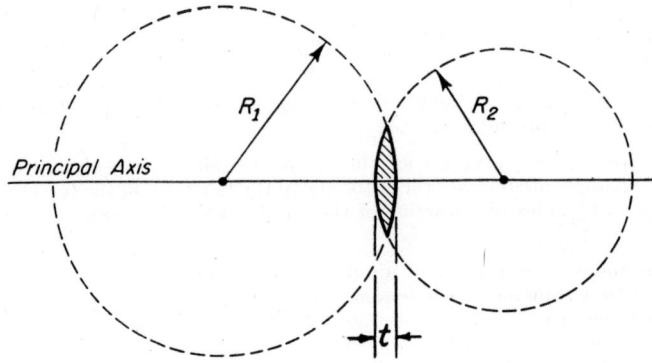

Fig. 27. Geometry of lens surfaces. In the figure R_1 and R_2 are the radii of curvature of the lens surfaces on the right and left, respectively.

parallel rays. A glass lens is regarded as 'thin' if the lens thickness t is small compared to the radii of curvature of the lens surfaces denoted by R_1 and R_2 in Fig. 27.

We have already studied the way in which glass prisms produce deviation of light rays. We might consider the cross section of a lens as roughly equivalent to the cross section of prisms as indicated in Fig. 28. A glass lens thicker in the middle, like a pair of glass prisms joined base to base, tends to *converge* parallel rays. A lens thicker at the edges than in the center, like a pair of prisms joined at the refracting angles, tends to *diverge* incident parallel rays. The cross sections of common types of simple thin lenses are shown in Fig. 29.

Lenses produce images of luminous or illuminated objects. In order to show how images are produced, let us consider Fig. 30. Part (a) of this figure shows a ray leaving a point object O on the lens axis at a distance p from the lens; after passing through the lens, this ray again reaches the lens axis at point I at a distance q from the lens. Part (b) shows the refraction of the ray at the first surface only. By Snell's law, we may write

$$\sin\theta_1 = \mu \sin\phi_1,$$

where the index of refraction of air is taken as unity and that of the glass as μ, and where θ_1 and ϕ_1 are the angles between the normal and the rays

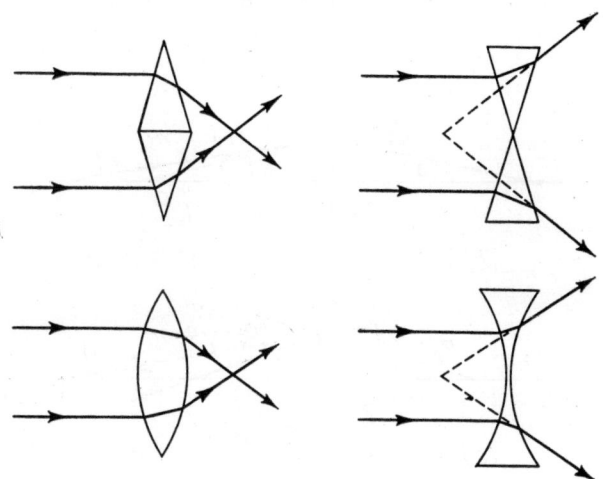

Fig. 28. Deviation of light rays by lenses and by analogous prism pairs.

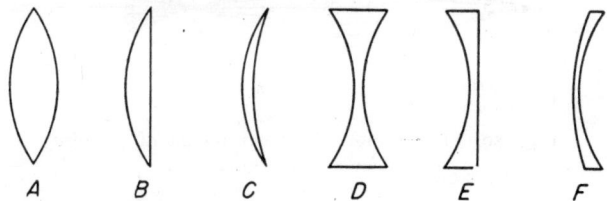

Fig. 29. Common lens types: A, double-convex; B, plano-convex; C, concavo-convex; D, double-concave; E, plano-concave; F, convexo-concave. The first three are converging; the last three diverging.

in air and glass, respectively. If θ_1 and ϕ_1 are sufficiently small, the sines of these angles may be replaced by the angles themselves, and Snell's law gives

$$\theta_1 = \mu \phi_1.$$

By consideration of the exterior angles of the triangles in part (b) of Fig. 30, it can be seen that

$$\theta_1 = A + B \quad \text{and} \quad \phi_1 = B - C;$$

therefore,
$$A + B = \mu(B - C). \tag{15}$$

Similarly, Fig. 30(c) shows the refraction at the second lens surface. The ray coming from the left in this figure is the same ray, in the glass, as that which proceeds to the right in (b). By writing Snell's law for the

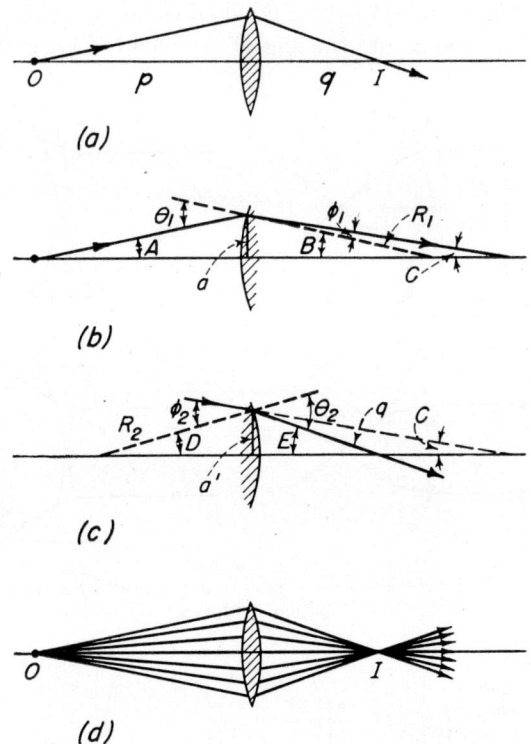

Fig. 30. Formation of a real image of a point object by a converging lens.

second lens surface and considering the triangles shown in part (c) of Fig. 30, we may write, for small angles,

$$\theta_2 = \mu\phi_2;$$

or
$$D + E = \mu(D + C). \qquad (16)$$

By adding relations (15) and (16), we obtain

$$A + B + D + E = \mu(B + D)$$

or
$$A + E = (\mu - 1)(B + D). \qquad (17)$$

If we assume that the thickness of the lens is negligible compared with p, q, R_1, and R_2, then it does not matter from exactly what point of the lens p and q are measured, and the height a in Fig. 30(b) can be set equal to the height a' in (c). Then by considering that all angles are small enough to be replaced by their sines or tangents, we can write the following approximate values for the angles:

$$A = a/p, \quad E = a/q, \quad B = a/R_1, \quad D = a/R_2.$$

Substituting these values for the angles in (17) and dividing by a gives the *lens equation:*

$$\frac{1}{p} + \frac{1}{q} = (\mu - 1)\left(\frac{1}{R_1} + \frac{1}{R_2}\right), \tag{18}$$

where p is the object distance, q is the image distance, and R_1 and R_2 are the radii of curvature of the lens surfaces.

Since there is nothing unique about the particular ray shown in Fig. 30, this relation holds for all rays passing from the object to the lens, provided that only small angles are involved, and we may therefore conclude that all such rays passing from the point object O to the lens also pass through point I, as indicated in part (d) of Fig. 30. Hence, a real image appears at point I. Although we have derived the above relation only for a point source on the axis, the same relation holds for point objects slightly off the axis, provided the angles of incidence at the first lens surface are small. Since objects of finite size may be

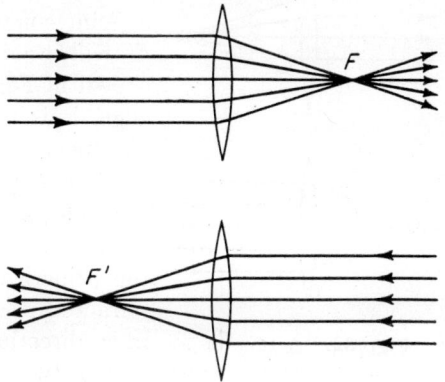

Fig. 31. Action of a converging lens on parallel light rays. Parallel rays intersect at the principal focal points of the lens.

treated as collections of point sources, the lens can be used to produce an image of an object of finite size lying in a plane perpendicular to the axis, provided all angles of incidence are small. For objects of finite size, p in the above equation is the distance from the lens to the plane in which the object lies and q is the distance from the lens to the plane in which the image lies.

In discussing the formation of images by thin lenses, let us first consider the effects of a thin lens on incident parallel light rays. If we have a lens like that shown in Fig. 31, we find that parallel rays coming from the left are brought to a focus at point F. This point is called a *principal focal point* of the lens, and its distance from the lens is known as the *focal length f* of the lens. We can determine the focal length by setting $p = \infty$ in (18), corresponding to incident parallel rays, in which case q becomes equal to f and we find that

$$\frac{1}{f} = (\mu - 1)\left(\frac{1}{R_1} + \frac{1}{R_2}\right). \tag{19}$$

Unlike a mirror, a lens is two-sided, and light can pass through it in either direction. Furthermore, because (18) is symmetric with respect to R_1 and R_2, we see that even though the radii of curvature may be different, the image-forming properties are identical for light traveling in the two directions. Consequently, in Fig. 31, parallel rays coming from the right will be brought to a focus at point F', which is at the same distance f from the lens as point F. The points F and F' are called the two *principal foci* of the lens. They are equidistant from the lens, at the distance given by (19), even though the two radii of curvature of the lens surfaces be different.

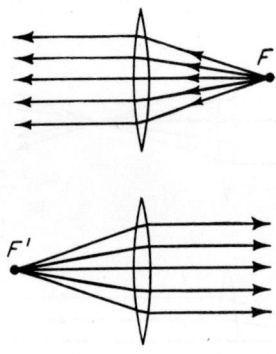

Fig. 32. Action of a converging lens on light rays from point objects at the principal foci.

As a result of the reversibility of light rays, a point source of light placed either at F or at F' will produce a parallel beam of light, as shown in Fig. 32. On the basis of this knowledge, it is possible to find image positions by graphical methods, since (a) any ray coming to the lens parallel to the principal axis passes through the principal focus beyond the lens after refraction, and (b) any ray passing through the principal focus in front of the lens will be refracted in such a manner as to leave the lens in a direction parallel to the principal axis. These two rules are correct so long as the diameter of the lens is small compared with the focal length, so that all angles occurring in Figs. 31 and 32 are small.

In order to illustrate the graphical method of locating images formed by a converging lens, let us consider Fig. 33, in which an object is located at position O. Principal ray 1 leaves a reference point on the object in a direction parallel to the principal axis and after refraction passes through the principal focus F. Principal ray 2 leaves the reference point on the object, passes through the principal focus F', and after refraction leaves the lens in a direction parallel to the principal axis. The principal rays 1 and 2 intersect at a point. The point of intersection is the reference point on a real image formed at position I. It is now possible for us to define a third principal ray shown by 3 in the figure. This ray is defined by a straight line joining the reference points on object and image and intersects the principal axis at point X, which is called the *optical center* of the lens. All rays passing through point X traverse the lens without deviation, since there is no 'prism effect' for rays passing through the center of the lens.

It is instructive to derive the relation between p, q, and f from the principal-ray diagram. Consider Fig. 34, in which principal rays 1 and 3 are used to locate the real image I formed by a converging lens. In this

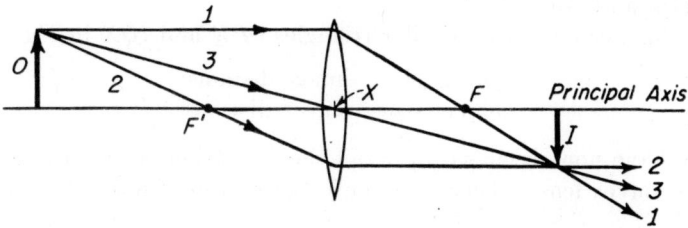

Fig. 33. Principal-ray diagram showing image formation by a converging lens.

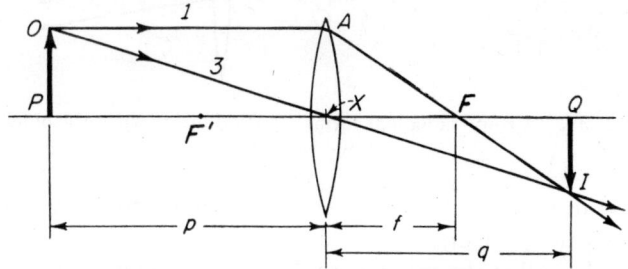

Fig. 34. Principal-ray diagram for a converging lens showing object distance p, image distance q, and focal length f.

figure, the right triangles OPX and IQX are similar. Therefore, we may write

$$OP/IQ = PX/QX.$$

Triangles AXF and IQF are also similar, and we may write

$$AX/IQ = XF/QF.$$

But since $AX = OP$, this relation can be rewritten as

$$OP/IQ = XF/QF.$$

By equating the two expressions for OP/IQ, we obtain

$$\frac{PX}{QX} = \frac{XF}{QF}.$$

Rewriting this relation in terms of the object distance p, the image distance q, and the focal length f, we obtain

$$\frac{p}{q} = \frac{f}{q-f},$$

which can be rewritten in the form

$$\frac{1}{p}+\frac{1}{q}=\frac{1}{f}, \tag{20}$$

as in (18) and (19).

We further note from similar triangles OPX and IQX in Fig. 34 that

$$\frac{\text{image size}}{\text{object size}}=\frac{\text{image distance}}{\text{object distance}}. \tag{21}$$

We have now discussed in detail the formation of a real image by a double-convex lens. There are many other cases of image formation by

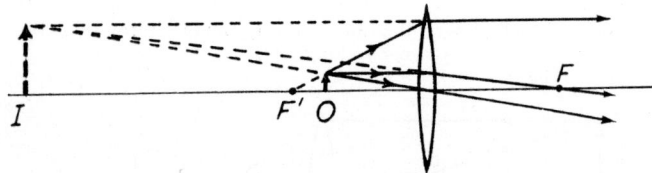

Fig. 35. A converging lens forms a virtual image when the object is inside the focus.

lenses to be discussed. These we shall treat less rigorously, making full use of principal-ray diagrams to achieve an understanding of the phenomena involved. All of the subsequent discussion can be rigorously justified by methods similar to those used above.

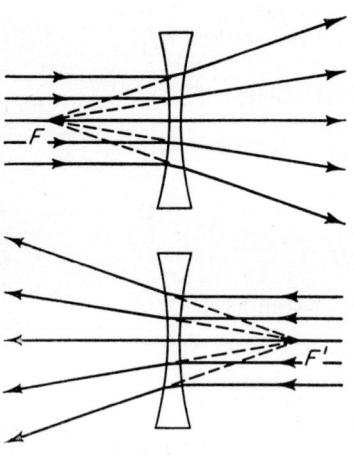

Fig. 36. Action of a diverging lens on parallel light rays.

First we note that the image formed by a converging lens is not necessarily real. If we insert a value of p less than f in (20), q comes out negative. As shown by the principal-ray diagram for this case in Fig. 35, this negative value of q implies a virtual image in front of the lens rather than a real image in back of the lens. (The *front side* of a lens is the side from which the light comes, and the *back side* is the side from which the light emerges; 'back of the lens' means to the right of the lens in Figs. 34 and 35.) From similar triangles in Fig. 35, we again see that (21) gives the image size.

A glass lens thinner at the center than at the edge acts, as we have noted, as a *diverging* lens. Fig. 36 illustrates its action on parallel rays. It will be noted that parallel rays incident from the left upon a diverging lens are refracted in such a manner as to make them *appear* to come from a point called the principal focus F on the left side of the lens. Similarly, parallel rays reaching the lens from the right are refracted in such a way as to make them *appear* to come from a point called the principal focus F' on the right side of the lens.

A diverging lens cannot be used to produce a parallel beam from a diverging beam as is done in Fig. 32. However, if a converging beam of

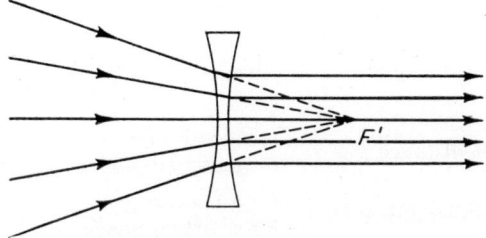

Fig. 37. Rays directed toward the principal focus behind a diverging lens become parallel after passing through the lens. This figure is the same as the lower part of Fig. 36 with the directions of the rays reversed.

light is incident upon a diverging lens, it is possible for the lens to render the beam parallel. Such a situation is indicated in Fig. 37. If a beam of light converging toward the point F' approaches the lens from the left, the diverging lens will render the beam parallel. A converging beam like that incident on the lens in Fig. 37 can be considered to represent a

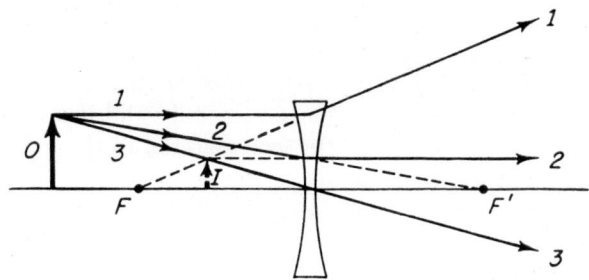

Fig. 38. Principal-ray diagram for a diverging lens.

virtual object at F'. The converging beam would have come to a point focus at F' if the beam had not been intercepted by the diverging lens.

Graphical construction of the images formed by diverging lenses can be carried out by the use of principal rays as in Fig. 38. Principal ray 1 approaches the lens in a direction parallel to the principal axis and is refracted in such a way that it *appears* to come from principal focus F. Principal ray 2 approaches the lens in such a direction that it would pass through principal focus F' if the lens were absent; after refraction, it leaves the lens parallel to the principal axis. Principal ray 3 passes without deviation through the center of the lens. After passage through the lens, these three rays appear to come from a point which defines the end of the virtual image I. Again we see from similar triangles that the relation (21) will give the image size.

The equation
$$\frac{1}{p}+\frac{1}{q}=\frac{1}{f} \qquad (22)$$

applies to all types of lenses (and mirrors) with the following sign conventions:

Object distance p is $\begin{cases} + \text{ for a real object} \\ - \text{ for a virtual object} \end{cases}$

Image distance q is $\begin{cases} + \text{ for a real image} \\ - \text{ for a virtual image} \end{cases}$

Focal length f is $\begin{cases} + \text{ for a converging lens or mirror} \\ - \text{ for a diverging lens or mirror} \end{cases}$

Equation (21), with signs of p and q ignored, will always give the image size. Whether the image is erect or inverted is best determined by sketching a principal-ray diagram.

The focal length of a thin lens is determined correctly as to magnitude and sign in every case by the *lensmaker's equation:*

$$\frac{1}{f}=(\mu-1)\left(\frac{1}{R_1}+\frac{1}{R_2}\right). \qquad (23)$$

In using this equation we must take the radii R_1 and R_2 as *positive for convex surfaces, negative for concave surfaces.* Equation (23) assumes that the lens is immersed in material, such as air, having index of refraction unity. If this is not true, equation (23) is still valid if μ represents the ratio of the index of refraction of the lens material to the index of refraction of the material in which the lens is immersed.

We should mention the unit used by opticians in describing lenses. Opticians measure the *power* of a lens in *diopters*. A lens having a focal length of 1 meter has a power of 1 diopter. The power of a lens in diopters may be expressed as

$$P=1/f, \qquad (24)$$

where f is the focal length of the lens in meters. Opticians call diverging lenses *negative lenses;* converging lenses are termed *positive lenses.*

If light from an object passes through two lenses one after the other, the combined action of the two can be deduced by considering that the image which would be formed by the first lens is the object for the second lens. If the first lens produces an image in front of the second lens, this first image may be treated as a real object for the second lens. If the lenses are in contact or close together, the image from the first lens may not be formed before the light beam is intercepted by the second lens; in this case the image which would have been formed by the first lens must be treated as a *virtual object* for the second lens. These two cases are illustrated in Fig. 39.

In the lens arrangement shown in Fig. 39(a), lens L_1 forms a real image I_1 of object O_1. Image I_1 can be treated as a real object O_2 for lens L_2. Lens L_2 forms a real image I_2 at the position indicated. It should be noted that only one of the three principal rays drawn through

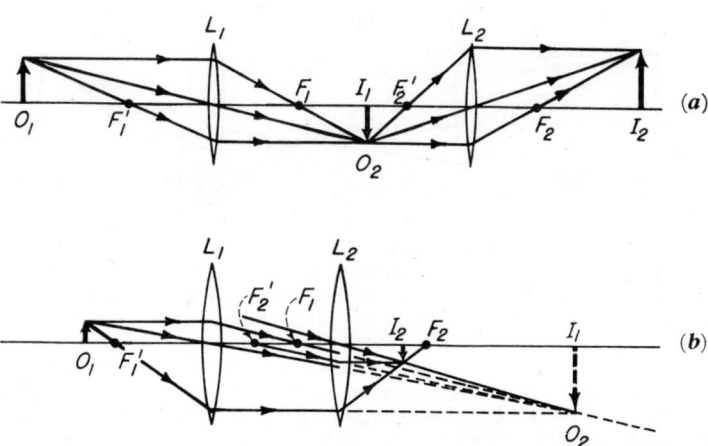

Fig. 39. Formation of images by lens combinations. In (a) the image formed by the first lens acts as a real object for the second lens, in (b) this image acts as a *virtual object*. Note that all the principal rays used in locating the image formed by the second lens need not actually be present. In (a) two of the principal rays drawn from O_2 through the second lens would not be present, but use of these rays for graphical purposes is permissible (see Fig. 40).

the second lens L_2 would actually reach the second lens if the aperture of lens L_2 is as small as indicated in the figure. Nevertheless, the use of all three rays gives a correct location for the final image, which is actually produced at position I_2 by nonprincipal rays as shown in Fig. 40.

In the lens arrangement shown in Fig. 39(b), lens L_1 would have formed a real image I_1 if the light beam had not been intercepted by the second lens L_2. In finding the position of the final image I_2 formed by the second lens, we must treat I_1 as the virtual object O_2 for the second lens. It will be remembered that the object distance of a virtual object is regarded as negative when used in the lens equation.

As an example of a lens combination, let us consider the case of two thin lenses in contact as shown in Fig. 41. The focal length of the first lens is f_1, that of the second lens is f_2. Consider parallel rays reaching the

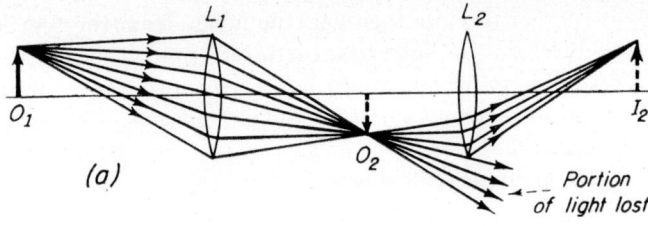

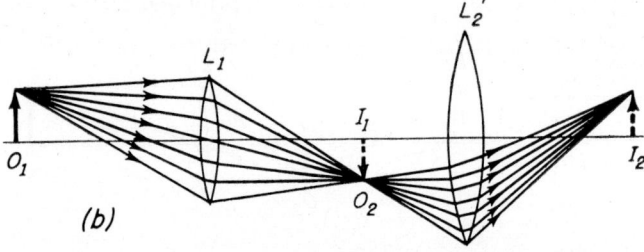

Fig. 40. Diagram showing the cone of rays, from one point on the object, that passes through the first lens. Part (a) shows the situation for the lenses shown in Fig. 38(a). This arrangement is not good from the standpoint of optical design, since a portion of the light transmitted by the first lens misses the second lens. The arrangement shown in (b) utilizes a lens L_2' of the same focal length as L_2 but of larger aperture so that all rays passing through L_1 pass through L_2'; this arrangement is more desirable in many applications.

first lens from an infinitely distant point object. Then the lens equation for the first lens is

$$\frac{1}{\infty}+\frac{1}{q_1}=\frac{1}{f_1},$$

which gives the expected result $q_1 = f_1$. Now let the image formed by the first lens serve as a *virtual object* for the second lens. Neglecting the thicknesses of these thin lenses, we can write the following equation for the second lens:

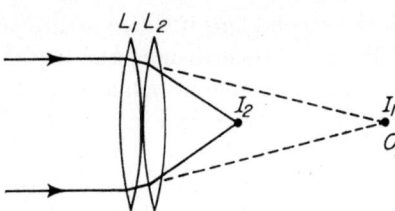

Fig. 41. Image formed by two thin lenses in contact.

$$\frac{1}{-f_1}+\frac{1}{q_2}=\frac{1}{f_2}, \quad \text{or} \quad \frac{1}{q_2}=\frac{1}{f_1}+\frac{1}{f_2}.$$

It is possible to treat the two thin lenses in contact as a compound lens. Remembering that the focal length of a lens is the image distance when the object distance is infinite, we note that q_2 in the above equation is equal to the focal length of the lens combination, and we may write

$$\frac{1}{f_{\text{comp}}} = \frac{1}{f_1} + \frac{1}{f_2}, \tag{25}$$

where f_{comp} is the focal length of the compound lens. This relationship will be found useful in Chap. 28 when we consider the problems involved in the design of *achromatic lenses*.

We have thus far treated thin lenses as if they were infinitely thin and produced perfect images. Real lenses, of course, are not infinitely thin and do not produce perfect images. We shall now indicate some of the problems involved in the treatment of real lenses.

First we shall consider the problem of simple or compound lenses whose thickness is not negligible compared with the focal length. Actually, when we deal with thick lenses, the term 'focal length' has no definite meaning, since we do not ordinarily know what reference point at

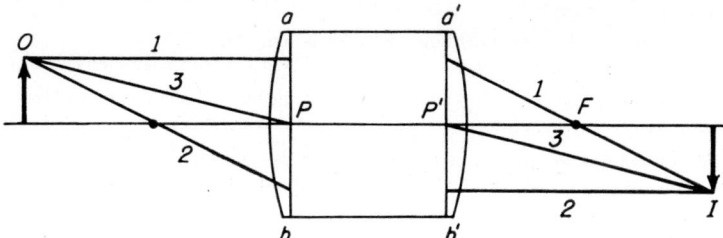

Fig. 42. Principal-ray diagram for a thick lens.

the lens is to be used in measuring the focal length. However, it is still possible to calculate image positions by a method devised by Gauss. This method amounts to eliminating the central portion of the lens from consideration as illustrated in Fig. 42. The planes ab and $a'b'$ are called the *principal planes* and bound the part of the lens that is eliminated from consideration. All distances should be measured from the principal planes. In Fig. 42, p should be measured from ab, and f and q should be measured from $a'b'$. The points P and P' are called *principal points*. It will be noted from the figure that image positions may be located graphically in much the same manner as that used for thin lenses. Principal ray 3 is drawn through the principal points instead of through the optical center as in the case of a thin lens. A detailed treatment of thick lenses is beyond the scope of this book.

Next, we shall list some of the ways in which lenses fail to produce perfect images. First, rays parallel to the axis striking the lens at points far from the axis do not pass through the principal focus defined for rays close to the axis. This defect, called *spherical aberration*, can be minimized by using a diaphragm to limit the useful portion of the lens to an area close to the axis. A second defect results from the fact that the index of refraction of a lens material is not the same for all colors; hence, if white light is incident upon a lens, the rays of the component colors are not brought to a focus at the same point. This defect, called *chromatic aberration*, can be corrected by the use of compound lenses composed of simple lenses made of different glasses; a compound lens of this type is called an *achromatic lens*. In addition to spherical and chromatic aberration, there are several other defects of a spherical lens. One of the more important of these defects, called *astigmatism*, arises from the fact that rays of light that pass through the lens obliquely from an object removed from the principal axis do not converge at a common image point. A full discussion of lens defects can be found in many intermediate optics texts but is beyond the scope of the present book.

PROBLEMS

1. A double-convex lens of crown glass has surfaces with radii of curvature of 40 cm and 50 cm, respectively. What is the focal length of this lens?   Ans: 43.0 cm.

2. A double-concave lens of dense flint glass has surfaces with radii of curvature of 30 cm and 40 cm, respectively. What is the focal length of this lens?

3. What should be the radius of curvature of the curved surface of a plano-convex crown-glass lens if the lens is to have a focal length of 20 cm?   Ans: 10.3 cm.

4. What should be the radius of curvature of the curved surface of a plano-convex fused-quartz lens if the lens is to have a focal length of 30 cm?

5. A luminous object 4 cm tall is placed near the axis of a thin converging lens at a distance of 33.3 cm from the lens. If the focal length of the lens is 20 cm, where will the image be formed and what will be the size of the image? Sketch the principal-ray diagram.   Ans: 50 cm behind; 6 cm.

6. A luminous object 2 cm tall is placed 10 cm away from a diverging lens of 10 cm focal length. Where will the image be formed? What will be the size of the image? Sketch the principal-ray diagram.

7. A converging lens has a focal length of 10 cm. Determine the distances of the images produced when a small illuminated object is placed at the following distances from the lens: 25 cm, 20 cm, 15 cm, 10 cm, and 5 cm.
   Ans: $+16.7$ cm; $+20$ cm; $+30$ cm; ∞; -10 cm.

8. A converging lens has a focal length of 12 cm. Locate the images produced when a small illuminated object is placed at the following distances from the lens: 30 cm, 24 cm, 18 cm, 12 cm, and 6 cm.

9. A small luminous object is placed 10 cm away from a converging lens of focal length 20 cm. Locate the image produced and compute the ratio of image size to object size. Sketch the principal-ray diagram.   Ans: 20 cm in front; 2.

10. A diverging lens has a focal length of 10 cm. Locate the images produced when a small luminous object is placed at the following distances from the lens: 25 cm, 20 cm, 15 cm, 10 cm, and 5 cm.

11. When a small illuminated object is placed 20 cm from a certain converging lens, a real image is formed on a screen at a distance of 50 cm from the lens. Find the power of this lens in diopters.   Ans: 7 diopters.

12. A plano-concave lens is made of crown glass. If the radius of curvature of the concave surface of the lens is 50 cm, what is the power of the lens in diopters?

13. Two converging lenses are placed 10 cm apart. The focal length of the first lens is 20 cm and that of the second is 30 cm. If a small illuminated object is placed

Sec. 5]   LENSES   649

40 cm in front of the first lens, where will the final image be formed? Sketch the principal-ray diagram.   Ans: 15 cm behind second lens.

14. A converging lens of focal length 10 cm is placed 20 cm in front of a diverging lens of focal length 10 cm. If a small luminous object is placed 40 cm in front of the converging lens, where will the final image be formed? Sketch the principal-ray diagram.

15. Two converging lenses of focal lengths 40 and 50 cm are placed in contact. What is the focal length of this lens combination? What is the power of the combination in diopters?   Ans: 22.2 cm; 4.5 diopters.

16. A 4-diopter converging lens and a 2-diopter diverging lens are placed in contact. What is the focal length of the resulting compound lens?

17. A converging lens of focal length 20 cm is placed in front of a converging lens of focal length 4 cm. What is the distance between the lenses if parallel rays entering the first lens leave the second lens as parallel rays?   Ans: 24 cm.

18. A converging lens of focal length 50 cm is placed in front of a diverging lens of focal length 5 cm. What is the distance between the lenses if parallel rays entering the first lens leave the second lens as parallel rays?

19. An object is placed 8 cm in front of a diverging lens of focal length 8 cm. A converging lens of focal length 15 cm is placed behind the diverging lens and forms a final image at infinity. What is the distance between the lenses? Sketch the principal-ray diagram.   Ans: 11 cm.

20. An object is placed 16 cm in front of a converging lens of focal length 8 cm. A diverging lens of focal length 12 cm is placed behind the converging lens and forms a final image at infinity. What is the distance between the lenses? Sketch the principal-ray diagram.

21. An object is placed 8 cm in front of a converging lens of focal length 8 cm. A diverging lens of focal length 12 cm is placed 4 cm behind the converging lens. Find the position, size, and character of the final image. Sketch the principal-ray diagram.

Ans: Erect, virtual image at same location as object; 1.5 times object size.

22. An object is placed 8 cm in front of a converging lens of focal length 8 cm. A converging lens of focal length 12 cm is placed 4 cm behind the first lens. Find the position, size, and character of the final image. Sketch the principal-ray diagram.

23. A converging lens of focal length 20 cm is placed 20 cm from a diverging mirror of focal length 10 cm. A candle is midway between the lens and the mirror. Where should a screen be placed to catch a real image of the candle flame? What is the image size? Is the image erect or inverted? Sketch the principal-ray diagram.
   Ans: 100 cm from the lens; twice the size of the flame; inverted.

24. A converging lens of focal length 20 inches is placed 20 inches from a converging mirror of focal length 4 inches. A candle is placed midway between the lens and the mirror. Describe the two images of the candle flame (position, size, character) seen when one looks through the lens. Sketch the principal-ray diagram.

25. An image of the sun is formed by a converging lens of 2-m focal length. The sun's apparent diameter is 32' of arc. What is the diameter of the image? Sketch the principal-ray diagram.   Ans: 1.10 cm.

26. Two distant stars are imaged on a photographic plate by a converging telescope mirror of 8-m focal length. The distance between the images is 1 mm. What is the angular separation of the stars in the sky?

27. A concavo-convex spectacle lens has a power of +2 diopters. If the glass has a refractive index of 1.6 and the concave surface a radius of 1 m, what is the radius of the convex surface?   Ans: 23.1 cm.

28. A convexo-concave spectacle lens has a power of -2 diopters. If the glass has a refractive index of 1.6 and the convex surface a radius of 1 m, what is the radius of the concave surface?

29. A converging lens is made of glass of refractive index 1.523 and has a focal length of 10 cm. What is its focal length when immersed in water?   Ans: 13.3 cm.

30. If the lens of Prob. 29 is immersed in carbon disulfide, what is its focal length?

31. By an argument similar to that used in the text in connection with Fig. 30, derive the lensmaker's equation for the focal length of a lens immersed in material of refractive index different from unity.

32. Why does a piece of glass of irregular shape become invisible when it is immersed in a liquid of the same index of refraction?

33. By arguments similar to those used in the text in connection with Fig. 34, derive the lens equation for the following specific cases:
  (a) a converging lens with the object inside the focus, forming a virtual image;
  (b) a diverging lens with a real object;
  (c) a converging lens with a virtual object;
  (d) a diverging lens with a virtual object.

34. Two converging lenses A and B have focal lengths of 4 cm and 7 cm, respectively. At what distance apart should these lenses be placed so that a parallel beam of light falling on A will leave B as a parallel beam of light, and a parallel beam of light falling on B will leave A as a parallel beam of light?

35. A converging lens A has a focal length of 10 cm, and a diverging lens B has a focal length of 5 cm. How far apart should these lenses be placed so that a parallel beam of light falling on A will leave B as a parallel beam of light, and a parallel beam of light falling on B will leave A as a parallel beam of light?   Ans: 5 cm.

CHAPTER 26

OPTICAL INSTRUMENTS

In the preceding chapter, the laws of reflection and refraction were stated and the properties of mirrors and lenses were described. The present chapter deals with optical instruments of which lenses and mirrors are the component parts. Although the lenses actually used in good optical instruments are compound lenses and in accurate computations must be treated as thick lenses, here they will be treated as thin simple lenses. The basic theory of these optical instruments is not altered by this simplification. The instruments to be discussed are the simple magnifying glass, the camera, the projector, the telescope, and the microscope. The chapter will be concluded with a brief discussion of some of the optical properties of the human eye.

1. DEFINITION OF MAGNIFYING POWER

Magnifying glasses, microscopes, and telescopes enable us to see objects more clearly than is possible with the unaided eye. The greater clarity is obtained because, with the aid of the optical instrument, a larger image is formed on the retina of the eye than would be formed if the object were viewed directly. The ratio of the sizes of these images on the retina is known as the *magnifying power* of the optical instrument. Although the words *magnification* and *enlargement* have other meanings, such as ratio of image size to object size in the case of a projection lantern or other optical system, the term *magnifying power* is restricted to the dimensionless ratio defined as:

$$\left\{\begin{matrix}\text{magnifying power of}\\ \text{an optical instrument}\end{matrix}\right\} = \frac{\left\{\begin{matrix}\text{length of image on retina when}\\ \text{object is viewed through the}\\ \text{optical instrument}\end{matrix}\right\}}{\left\{\begin{matrix}\text{length of image on retina when}\\ \text{object is viewed by the unaided}\\ \text{eye in the most favorable manner}\end{matrix}\right\}} \quad (1)$$

In Fig. 1, rays are traced from the ends of the object (or from any two definite points of the object) through the center of the lens of the eye. The distance from the lens of the eye to the retina does not change when the focal length of the eye lens is changed to view objects at different distances. Hence we see in Fig. 1 that the ratio of image lengths in (1) equals the ratio of angles subtended at the eye by rays from the ends of the object, provided these angles are small. The assumption of small angles is always valid, because the eye sees distinctly only the small central portion of the field of view, which subtends a small angle α. In connection with Fig. 1, we must consider that the rays are drawn from two points of the object sufficiently close that the angle α_1 will be small enough to justify the proportionality $i_1/i_2 = \alpha_1/\alpha_2$. These considerations lead to the following useful expression for magnifying power:

$$\left\{\begin{array}{l}\text{magnifying power of}\\ \text{an optical instrument}\end{array}\right\} = \frac{\left\{\begin{array}{l}\text{angle } \alpha_1 \text{ subtended at lens of eye}\\ \text{when object is viewed through}\\ \text{the optical instrument}\end{array}\right\}}{\left\{\begin{array}{l}\text{angle } \alpha_2 \text{ subtended at lens of eye}\\ \text{when object is viewed directly}\\ \text{in the most favorable manner}\end{array}\right\}}. \quad (2)$$

The denominators of the above expressions contain the phrase 'in the most favorable manner,' which we must now discuss. As we shall see in Sec. 8, the normal adult eye has a lens of variable focal length so that the normal eye can focus on the retina an image of an object at any distance between 25 cm and ∞. But for a given object size, the size of the image on the retina varies inversely as the object distance. When this page is held at 25 cm, the words on this page form images on the retina that are twice as large as when the page is held at 50 cm. Hence the normal eye can distinguish letters at

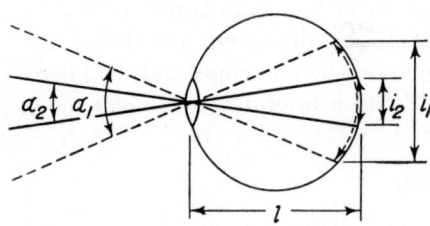

Fig. 1. Magnifying power $= i_1/i_2 = \alpha_1/\alpha_2$, where i_1 and α_1 refer to observation through an optical instrument, i_2 and α_2 refer to direct observation. The angle of the field of view is much exaggerated in this sketch.

25 cm (10 in) that are just half the size of those that can be distinguished at 50 cm (20 in). The normal adult eye cannot focus comfortably at less than 25 cm (in childhood and youth the eye can normally focus comfortably at closer distances). *Twenty-five centimeters is called the distance of most distinct vision.* In defining the magnifying power of a magnifying glass or a microscope, we assume that observation with the unaided eye, in the denominator of (1) or (2), is made with the object held at 25 cm, the distance of most distinct vision.

On the other hand, a telescope or opera glass is specifically intended for viewing *distant* objects. Hence, in defining their magnifying powers we must assume that, in the denominator of (1) or (2), the object is viewed at the distance of its actual location.

2. THE MAGNIFYING GLASS

A single converging lens can be used as a magnifying glass to form enlarged virtual images of small objects. A magnifying glass can be employed in two ways. According to its method of employment, we shall call it either a *simple microscope* or a *reading glass*.

When a magnifying glass is used as a *simple microscope*, the eye of the observer is placed close to the lens. The familiar jeweler's lens used by instrument makers is one example of a simple microscope; the linen microscope used in textile work is another. Although any converging lens can be used as a simple microscope, the lens must have a short focal length if it is to have a high magnifying power.

In using a converging lens as a simple microscope, the object is placed between the focus and the lens as in Fig. 2(a), and an enlarged erect virtual image is formed at some distance $-q$ given by

$$\frac{1}{p}+\frac{1}{q}=\frac{1}{f}. \qquad (3)$$

The eye is placed close to the lens as in Fig. 2(b) and sees the virtual image at a distance D. Since D is 25 cm or greater, and the lens is held very close to the eye, we make little error by setting $D=-q$.

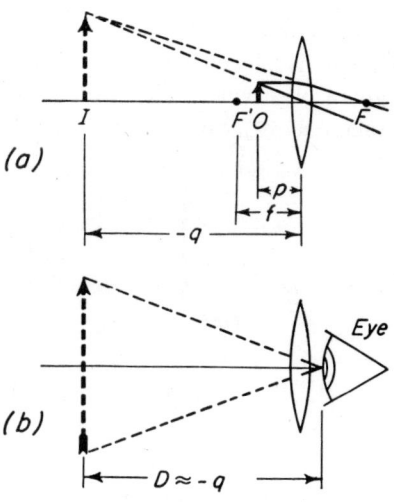

Fig. 2. Simple microscope.

If we let O be the length of the object and I the length of the image, then, for small angles,

$$\left\{\begin{array}{l}\text{angle subtended at lens of eye}\\\text{when object is viewed through}\\\text{simple microscope}\end{array}\right\}=\frac{I}{D},$$

$$\left\{\begin{array}{l}\text{angle subtended at lens of eye}\\\text{when object is viewed directly}\\\text{at 25 cm}\end{array}\right\}=\frac{O}{25\text{ cm}}.$$

Hence, according to (2),

$$\text{magnifying power}=M=\frac{I/D}{O/25\text{ cm}}=\frac{I}{O}\times\frac{25\text{ cm}}{D}.$$

But $\quad\dfrac{I}{O}=\dfrac{-q}{p}=\dfrac{D}{p};\quad$ hence, $\quad M=\dfrac{D}{p}\times\dfrac{25\text{ cm}}{D}=25\text{ cm}\times\dfrac{1}{p}.$

From (3), we see that $\quad\dfrac{1}{p}=\dfrac{1}{f}-\dfrac{1}{q}=\dfrac{1}{f}+\dfrac{1}{D}.$

Substituting this in the above expression for M gives the expression

$$M=\frac{25\text{ cm}}{f}+\frac{25\text{ cm}}{D} \qquad (4)$$

for the magnifying power of a simple microscope.

In order that the eye may focus the image I, the image distance D must be somewhere between 25 cm and ∞. If f is small compared to 25 cm, the magnification does not vary much with D. As D varies from 25 cm to ∞, M varies from

$$M = \frac{25 \text{ cm}}{f} + 1 \quad \text{to} \quad M = \frac{25 \text{ cm}}{f}.$$

For example, if $f = 5$ cm, M varies from 6 to 5. At what distance D the image is placed will depend on the most restful focus for the eye of a given observer. This value is usually assumed to be the focus with the image at ∞, which is the resting position of the normal eye and leads to

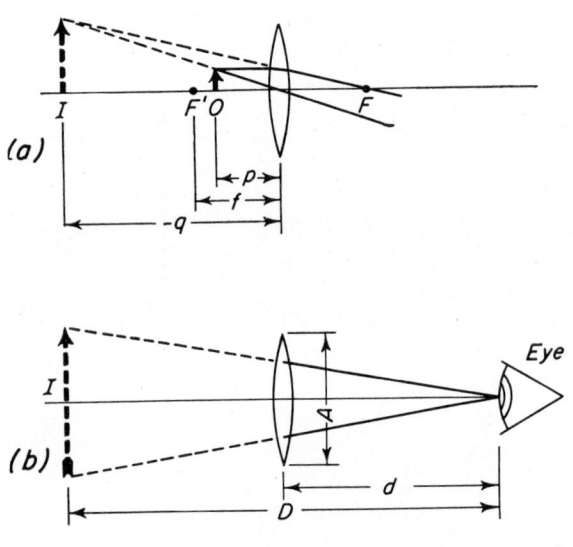

Fig. 3. Reading glass.

least eyestrain. The position of the image I has little effect on the size of the retinal image because as D increases, the image size grows larger in almost direct proportion.

It is seen from (4) that the shorter the focal length f, the greater the magnifying power of the lens when used as a simple microscope.

When a magnifying glass is used as a *reading glass*, it is not held close to the eye but is held fairly close to the object being observed. The object is between the focal point and the lens as in Fig. 3(a), and an enlarged virtual image is formed at a considerable distance from the lens. The lens is held at some distance d from the eye as in Fig. 3(b), and the image is formed at a large distance D from the eye. By comparison of Fig. 3(b) and Fig. 2(b), it is seen that the lens must have a much larger aperture A when used as a reading glass than when used as a simple microscope, and hence that it cannot be made of so short a focal length if the radii of curvature are to be large compared to the aperture in order to avoid spherical aberration.

If the image I is at ∞ in Fig. 3, it is seen that the angle subtended at the eye is the same as if the object were viewed directly at distance f; hence the magnifying power in this case is $25 \text{ cm}/f$. If the image is closer, the magnifying power is less. An argument like that used above for the simple microscope shows that the general formula for the magnifying power of the reading glass is

$$M = \frac{25 \text{ cm}}{f}\left(1 - \frac{d}{D}\right) + \frac{25 \text{ cm}}{D}. \tag{5}$$

Derivation of this formula is left as a problem. It reduces to formula (4) if we set $d = 0$.

A typical reading glass will have a focal length $f = 10$ cm and be held at $d = 15$ cm from the eye. In this case, (5) gives $M = 2.5 - (12.5 \text{ cm}/D)$. For distinct vision, D must lie between 25 cm and ∞. We have $M = 2.5$ if $D = \infty$, corresponding to $-q = \infty$, $p = 10$ cm. At the other extreme, $M = 2$ if $D = 25$ cm, corresponding to $-q = 10$ cm, $p = 5$ cm. So this reading glass, when at 15 cm from the eye, may be held between 5 and 10 cm from the book, giving magnifying powers varying from 2 to 2.5.

PROBLEMS

NOTE: When British units are used, it is customary to replace 25 cm by exactly 10 inches in formulas (4) and (5).

1. A converging lens has a focal length of 1 cm. If this lens is to be used as a simple microscope, at what distance from the lens should the object be placed in order that an enlarged virtual image may be formed at a distance of 25 cm from the lens? What is the magnifying power in this case?   Ans: 0.962 cm; 26.

2. If the lens in Prob. 1 were used in such a way as to produce a virtual image 50 cm from the lens, where would the object be placed? What is the magnifying power in this case? What are the advantages and disadvantages of using this arrangement rather than the arrangement described in Prob. 1?

3. Calculate the magnifying power of a simple microscope focused to form a virtual image 10 in from the eye if the focal length of the lens is 1.5 in. Sketch the principal-ray diagram.   Ans: 7.7.

4. What should be the focal length of the lens of a simple microscope if a magnifying power of 12 is to be obtained when the virtual image is formed 10 in from the lens?

5. What is the magnifying power of a reading glass whose focal length is 5 in if it is held 4 in from a book and if the observer's eyes are 12 in from the lens? Sketch the principal-ray diagram.   Ans: 1.56.

6. How far from the lens in Prob. 5 should the book be located in order for the maximum magnifying power of 2 to be produced?

7. What should be the focal length of a linen microscope for it to have a magnifying power of 20 when the image is formed at the distance of most distinct vision? What should the object distance be?   Ans: 1.32 cm; 1.25 cm.

8. An observer wishes to design a simple microscope that will form images 50 cm from the lens and have a magnifying power of 15. What should the focal length of the lens be?

9. Derive formula (5).

3. THE PHOTOGRAPHIC CAMERA

One of the simplest optical instruments is the photographic camera, in which a lens is used to produce a real image of an illuminated or luminous object. The essential features of a camera are shown in Fig. 4. The lens L is mounted at the end of a light-tight bellows which excludes all light except that entering through the lens. The lens is equipped with a shutter S which can be opened in order to admit light when desired. The lens position can be adjusted by the rack and pinion R until a clearly defined image is formed at the plate position P. In adjusting the lens position, a ground-glass translucent screen is placed at position P. After the lens position has been adjusted in such a way as to produce a sharply defined image on the screen, the shutter is closed and a photographic plate or film is inserted at position P. The shutter is then opened briefly and a real image is formed on the light-sensitive plate. The portions of the plate illuminated during the exposure experience chemical changes which are later made visible during the process of developing. This process is followed by treatment of the plate in a fixing bath in order to remove further sensitivity to light.

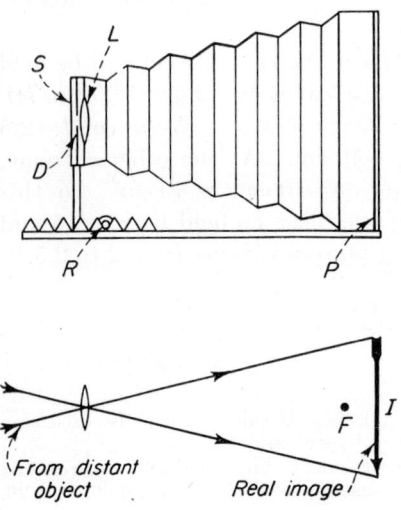

Fig. 4. Photographic camera.

Usually, the object being photographed is at a considerable distance from the camera, and a diminished real inverted image is formed on the plate. If the object is at a distance large compared to the focal length, the image is formed in the plane of the principal focus of the lens; the plate position P is permanently fixed in this plane in so-called 'box cameras,' which can be used satisfactorily in photographing distant objects. In photographing near-by objects, the distance between lens and plate must be increased and a camera equipped with a movable lens must be used. If the object distance is equal to $2f$, the image distance is also $2f$ and the image and object are of equal size; special copying cameras arranged in this way are used for reproducing drawings or manuscripts without change in size. Enlarging cameras and cameras employed in microphotography are used with the object distance less than $2f$, and produce an enlarged image at the plate position.

A photographic lens is frequently given a rating that measures its photographic 'speed' or 'relative exposure time.' This rating is given as the ratio of the focal length to the effective diameter of the lens opening as defined by the stop or diaphragm denoted by D in Fig. 4. The use of this ratio, usually called the f-number, as a speed rating can be justified by a consideration of the plate illumination. Since all light reaching the plate must pass through the lens, the lens can be regarded as a source illuminating the plate. The illumination of a surface by a uniform extended source is directly proportional to the area of the uniform source and is inversely proportional to the square of the distance to the source. In the case of the camera, this proportionality can be expressed as $E \propto A/q^2$, where E is the illumination of the plate, A the effective area of the lens, and q the distance between lens and plate. However, A varies as the square of the diameter d of the diaphragm, and for distant objects q may be set equal to the focal length f of the camera lens. Therefore, we may write, approximately,

$$E \propto d^2/f^2.$$

The ratio f/d is known as the 'f-number' of the stop. The higher the f-number, the lower the illumination and the greater the exposure time for a given object being photographed. The illumination varies inversely, and hence *the exposure time varies directly as the square of the f-number*. The lower the minimum f-number of a given camera lens (diaphragm wide open), the 'faster' the lens. The series of stops marked on most diaphragms—a series such as f:1.6, 2.3, 3.2, 4.5, 6.3, 9, 13, 18—are a set such that the square of each f-number is approximately double the square of the preceding one. Hence, a shift to the next slower stop requires double the exposure time for given lighting or double the illumination for given exposure time.

As an example, a lens of focal length 12 inches with a useful aperture ¾ inch in diameter would have a rating of f:16. Used in a camera, this lens would require exactly the same exposure time as a lens of 6-in focal length stopped down to a ⅜-inch aperture. Of course the first lens admits four times as much light, but this is distributed over a plate area four times as great to cover the same field of view.

PROBLEMS

1. A camera lens has a focal length of 10 cm. What should be the distance between lens and plate when the object being photographed is 2 m from the lens? Sketch the principal-ray diagram. Ans: 10.5 cm.

2. What should be the distance between lens and plate in the camera of Prob. 1 if an object 50 cm from the lens is to be photographed? Sketch the principal-ray diagram.

3. A certain camera lens has a focal length of 4 in and is to be used in photographing an object 2 ft tall. How far from the object should the lens be placed if the photographic image is to be 2 in tall? What should be the distance from the lens to the photographic plate when the photograph is taken?   Ans: 52.0 in; 4.33 in.

4. A lens is to be used in a box camera in which the plate distance has a fixed value of 4 in. What should be the focal length of the lens? By consideration of ray diagrams, show why a 'slow' lens of small aperture is used in cameras of this type.

5. The housing of a camera lens is marked f:3.2, 9 cm. What is the diameter of the lens? If the correct exposure time for a certain scene is $\frac{1}{20}$ sec at f:6.3, what is the correct exposure time at f:3.2?   Ans: 2.8 cm; $\frac{1}{80}$ sec.

6. A camera lens has a focal length of 8 cm and a diameter of 2.5 cm. What is the f-number of this lens? What is the proper exposure time for photographing a scene with this lens if an exposure meter indicates that the correct exposure is $\frac{1}{200}$ sec at f:2.8?

7. A camera lens has a focal length of 8 in and a diameter of 2.5 in. With the lens 'wide open,' the correct exposure for a certain photographic plate and a certain illumination is $\frac{1}{80}$ sec. What exposure would be correct with a stop rating of f:18?   Ans: 0.4 sec.

NOTE: When a scene is photographed, it is desirable to have objects at various distances in reasonably good focus. If light from an object at distance p is perfectly focused on the plate, light from a point on an object at different distance p' will not fall at a single point on the plate, but will fall within a small circle, known as the *circle of confusion*.

8. Show that for a given lens, and given values of p and p' in the note above, the diameter of the circle of confusion is directly proportional to the diameter d of the aperture, and hence inversely proportional to the f-number of the stop used. Hence show that the 'depth of focus' increases as the f-number of the stop increases.

9. Show that for given values of p and p' in the note above, and for a given f-number, the absolute diameter δ of the circle of confusion is approximately proportional to the square of the focal length f of the lens; hence that δ/f, which is a measure of the ratio of diameter of circle of confusion to plate size, is approximately proportional to f. Hence in order to keep down the size of the circle of confusion relative to the plate size, and still be able to use low f-numbers for high speed, it is desirable to use a lens of short focal length and a small plate size, as in the *Leica* camera. These results seem reasonable if we consider that when $p \gg f$ and $p' \gg f$, both p and p' will focus at image distances very near to f, and the circle of confusion will be very small. Now, the smaller the value of f, the larger will be the ratios p/f and p'/f for given values of p and p', and the more closely will objects at p and p' behave as if they were both at infinity.

4. THE PROJECTION LANTERN

Optically, the slide or film projector is somewhat similar to a camera, since a lens is used to form a real image of an illuminated object. Thus, the lens L in Fig. 5 produces an image I of the slide O upon the screen. The slide O is located at a distance from the lens only slightly greater than the focal length, and the image is enlarged, real, and inverted. Great enlargement is possible provided the slide is sufficiently well illuminated. The primary source of illumination may be a carbon arc or an incandescent lamp with its filament concentrated in a small flat zone. A converging mirror and a converging lens (condensing lens) are usually used to cause as much as possible of the light of the source to pass through the slide or film and head in the direction of the projection lens. While these optical parts are necessary in order to get adequate illumination on the screen, they have no role in forming the image on the screen and need not be of high quality. The projection lens L must be of high optical quality and is usually compound.

The slide projector differs from the camera in that the projector is used to produce a greatly enlarged image of a near-by object, whereas the usual operation of a camera involves the formation of a diminished image

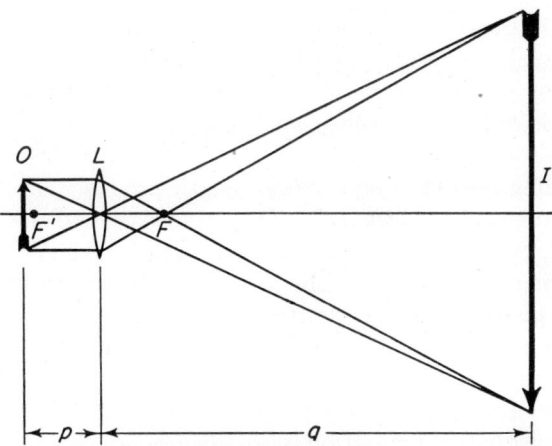

Fig. 5. Image formation by the lens of a projection lantern.

of a distant object. The enlargement produced by the projector is given by the ratio of image size to object size, which is equal to the ratio of image distance to object distance; that is,

$$\text{enlargement} = I/O = q/p. \tag{6}$$

PROBLEMS

1. The total distance between a slide in a projection lantern and the screen is 4 m. If the projection lens has a focal length of 36 cm, what should be the distance between the slide and the lens?   *Ans: 40 cm.*

2. The total distance between a slide and a screen is 30 ft. If the projection lens has a focal length of 18 in, what should be the distance between the slide and the lens?

3. A lantern slide has dimensions 3 in ×5 in. This slide is to be projected in such a way as to produce an image 3 ft ×5 ft on a screen 20 ft from the projection lens. What should be the focal length of the projection lens? What should be the distance from the slide to the lens?   *Ans: 18.5 in; 20 in.*

4. A lantern slide in a projector has dimensions 3 in ×4 in, and an image 6 ft ×8 ft is to be formed on a screen 15 ft from the projection lens. What should be the focal length of the projection lens? Where should the slide be placed?

5. It is desired to produce an image of a 3-in ×4-in lantern slide on a screen 30 ft from the projection lens. The image on the screen is to be 6 ft by 8 ft. (a) What should be the focal length of the projection lens? (b) Where should the slide be placed? (c) If the illumination at the slide is 1000 lumens/ft², what is the maximum possible illumination at the screen?

Ans: (a) 1.20 ft; (b) 15 in from lens; (c) 1.74 lumens/ft².

6. An image of a 3-in ×4-in slide is formed on a screen 40 ft from a projection lens. If the distance from the slide to the lens is 12 in and if the illumination at the slide is 10,000 lumens/ft², what is the focal length of the projection lens and what is the maximum possible illumination at the screen?

5. THE COMPOUND MICROSCOPE

When it is desired to view a small object with very great magnifying power, it is usually necessary to utilize two lenses or two combinations of lenses, each of which contributes to the magnifying power. Such an arrangement is called a *compound microscope* and is shown schematically in Fig. 6(a).

A converging lens O of short focal length produces an enlarged real image CD of the small object AB. This lens O is called the *objective*. A second lens E, called the *eyepiece*, is then used to form an enlarged virtual image FG which is viewed by the observer. The role played by the objective can be seen more clearly from Fig. 6(b), which gives a principal-ray diagram for this lens. It can be seen that the objective acts like a projector in forming an enlarged real image CD of the small object AB. As in the case of the slide in the projector, the object AB must be well illuminated; adequate illumination is usually accomplished by means of an auxiliary incandescent lamp and concave mirror located so as to illuminate the object either from in front or from behind. The role played by the eyepiece is indicated in Fig. 6(c); the eyepiece is used as a simple microscope to view the real image formed by the objective. The principal-ray diagram shows how an enlarged virtual image is formed by the eyepiece.

The total magnifying power produced by a compound microscope is equal to the product of the enlargement M_O produced by the objective and the magnifying power M_E of the eyepiece, because the simple microscope which constitutes the eyepiece can form on the retina an image of CD which is M_O times as large as the image it could form of the object AB. This magnifying power can be expressed in terms of the distances given on the simplified diagram of the microscope shown in Fig. 7. In this figure the object AB and images CD and FG are shown as before; p and q denote object and image distances from the objective; and the final virtual image FG is formed at the distance D (between 25 cm and ∞) from the eyepiece. Under these conditions, the enlargement M_O produced by the objective is given by the relation $M_O = q/p$, as in equation (6) for the projector. The magnifying power M_E of the eyepiece is given by equation (4) for the simple microscope. Therefore, the total magnify-

Sec. 5]   THE COMPOUND MICROSCOPE

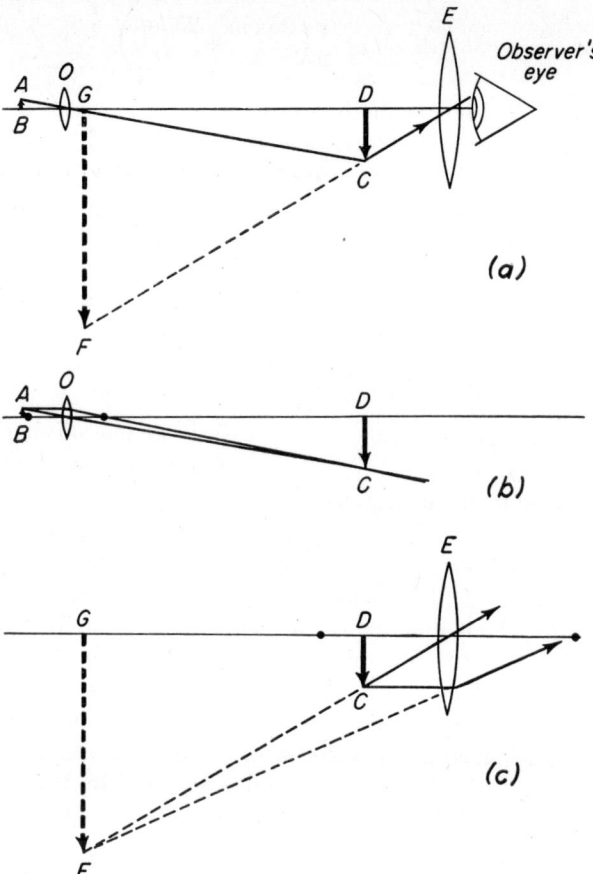

Fig. 6. Image formation by the components of a compound microscope.

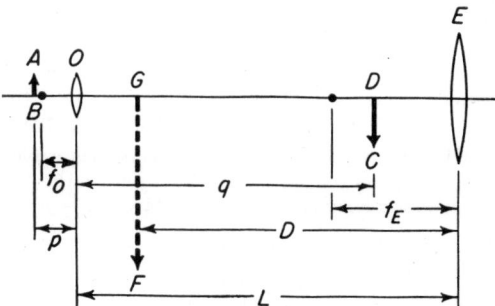

Fig. 7. Positions of object and images in a compound microscope.

ing power is
$$M = M_O M_E = \frac{q}{p}\left(\frac{25 \text{ cm}}{f_E} + \frac{25 \text{ cm}}{D}\right), \qquad (7)$$

where f_E is the focal length of the eyepiece.

A useful approximation to this formula is obtained by noting that in actual cases (a) f_E is small compared to D, so that the term $25 \text{ cm}/D$ can be neglected in comparison with $25 \text{ cm}/f_E$; (b) p is only negligibly larger than f_O, so that we can write f_O for p; (c) f_E is small compared to the 'tube length' L, so that we introduce little error by replacing q by L. With these approximations, the formula for the magnifying power becomes

$$M = \frac{L}{f_O} \times \frac{25 \text{ cm}}{f_E} = \frac{L (25 \text{ cm})}{f_O f_E}.$$

From this expression, it can be seen that for large magnifying power, the focal lengths of eyepiece and objective should be very small and the tube length should be made as large as convenience permits.

There are several practical limitations to the magnification obtainable with a compound microscope. One of these is the illumination that can be used on the object; for biological specimens, the maximum illumination tolerable without damage to the specimen is sometimes rather low. A second limitation to magnification is involved in the increasingly serious problem of lens aberrations; the compound lenses used in good microscopes must be carefully designed to minimize chromatic and spherical aberration and other types of distortion. A third and more fundamental limitation to magnification is imposed by the wave properties of light itself; this limitation will be discussed in Chap. 27.

PROBLEMS

NOTE: Use the accurate formula (7) in working the following problems.

1. In a certain compound microscope, the focal length of the objective lens is 1.0 cm and that of the eyepiece is 5 cm, and the distance between the lenses is 20 cm. If the observer places the final image at a distance of 25 cm from his eye, what is the distance from the object to the objective lens? What is the magnifying power?
Ans: 1.07 cm; 89.

2. In a certain compound microscope the focal length of the objective is 0.5 cm and that of the eyepiece is 4 cm. If the distance between the lenses is 30 cm, what should be the distance from the object to the objective lens if the observer is to see an image at a distance of 25 cm from his eye? What is the magnifying power?

3. The objective lens of a compound microscope has a focal length of 0.5 cm and the eyepiece has a focal length of 2 cm. What is the maximum obtainable magnifying power when the lenses are 10 cm apart? Ans: 206.

4. In the microscope described in Prob. 2, what is the enlargement produced by the objective lens? the magnifying power of the eyepiece?

5. A compound microscope has an objective of 3.0 mm focal length and a draw-tube length of 250 mm. Employing the approximations mentioned in the text, calculate the magnifying power when an eyepiece with a magnifying power of 12 is employed. Ans: 1000.

6. If the objective of a compound microscope has a focal length of 5 mm, where should the object be placed in order that the objective produce a magnification of 100 diameters? What would be the focal length of the eyepiece needed to give an over-all magnifying power of 2000 for the microscope when the final image is 25 cm from the eyepiece? Are there any objections to this type of design for a microscope?

7. A compound microscope has an objective lens of focal length 5 mm and an eyepiece of 8-mm focal length. How far apart should the lenses be in order to obtain a magnifying power of 500 when the final image is formed at infinity? Ans: 9.3 cm.

8. If the illumination at the object being studied by means of the microscope in Prob. 6 is 50,000 lumens/ft², what is the maximum possible apparent illumination at the final image?

9. In a biological laboratory a certain specimen is to be examined at as high a magnification as possible. However, an illumination greater than 10,000 lumens/ft² cannot be used without injury to the specimen. If the effective illumination at the final image at the distance of most distinct vision must be at least 1 lumen/ft² for satisfactory observation, what is the maximum possible magnifying power?
Ans: 100.

10. A compound microscope has an objective of focal length 4 mm, an eyepiece of focal length 6 mm, and a drawtube length of 20 cm. If the illumination at the object is 10,000 lumens/ft² (full sunlight plus skylight), what is the maximum possible effective illumination at the final image if the final image is formed 25 cm from the eyepiece?

6. THE ASTRONOMICAL TELESCOPE

Telescopes are instruments used for the purpose of improving the observer's vision of distant objects. Like the compound microscope, the

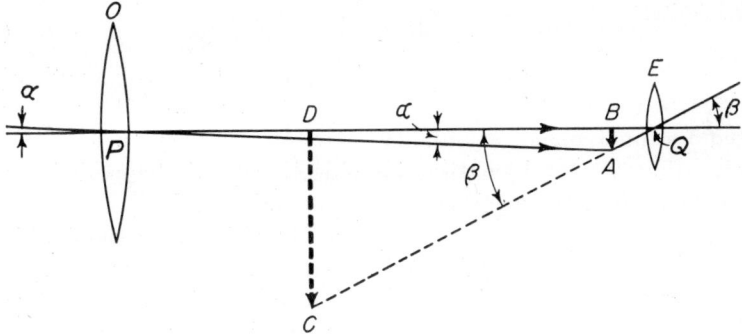

Fig. 8. Image formation in a refracting astronomical telescope.

telescope consists essentially of two components: the objective and the eyepiece. In the case of the telescope, the objective forms a real image of a distant object and hence serves the same purpose as a camera lens; the eyepiece is used to produce an enlarged virtual image of the real image produced by the objective and hence serves as a simple microscope.

Figure 8 shows a diagram of a refracting astronomical telescope. O represents the objective lens that forms a real image AB of a distant object, which might be a planet whose diameter subtends an angle α at the objective. This real image AB is then viewed through the eyepiece E which produces the enlarged virtual image CD. The virtual image CD subtends the angle β at the eyepiece.

Owing to the great distance of the object, the rays from any point of it can be considered parallel on reaching the instrument; hence, the real image AB is formed in the principal focal plane of the objective, and the image distance PB is simply the focal length of the objective. In observing distant objects, it is their apparent size that is important, and this is determined by the angle they subtend at the eye. Without the telescope, the angle subtended would be α; with the telescope, the angle subtended is β. Hence, the magnifying power of the telescope is given by

$$M = \beta/\alpha.$$

As in previous discussions, these angles α and β may be approximated by their tangents, and we may write

$$M = \frac{AB/QB}{AB/PB} = \frac{PB}{QB}.$$

In focusing the telescope, let us assume that the observer arranges the eyepiece position for parallel rays so that the image CD is at infinite distance, and the distance QB is the focal length of the eyepiece. Since PB is simply f_O, the focal length of the objective, the above expression for the magnifying power can be written as

$$M = f_O/f_E. \tag{8}$$

The magnifying power is equal to the ratio of the focal length of the objective to the focal length of the eyepiece, provided the telescope is focused for final image at infinity. Hence, in order to achieve high magnification, the focal length of the objective should be made large and the focal length of the eyepiece should be made small.

Slightly greater magnifying power can be obtained if the final image is brought in to a distance D (not less than 25 cm) from the eyepiece since this involves a decrease of QB with no change in PB. The formula for this case, whose derivation is left for a problem, is

$$M = \frac{f_O}{f_E}\left(1 + \frac{f_E}{D}\right). \tag{9}$$

Since f_E is ordinarily small compared to 25 cm, the last term in this formula gives only a small correction to formula (8), no matter where the final image is formed.

In astronomical work, although a certain amount of attention must be paid to magnifying power, the principal emphasis is on seeing fainter and fainter objects by increasing the *light-gathering power* of the telescope. Because of inherent limitations imposed by the wave nature of light, we cannot hope to see any star outside of our own solar system as other than a point; but in order to see fainter and more distant objects, it is desirable to gather as much light as possible from the object, all focused as accurately as possible at a point on a photographic plate. Hence emphasis is placed on increasing the size of the telescope objective. There are difficult problems involved in increasing the size of an objective lens, since both the production of large pieces of glass of high optical quality and the grinding and polishing of the large compound-lens components needed to correct aberrations involve great difficulties. The largest

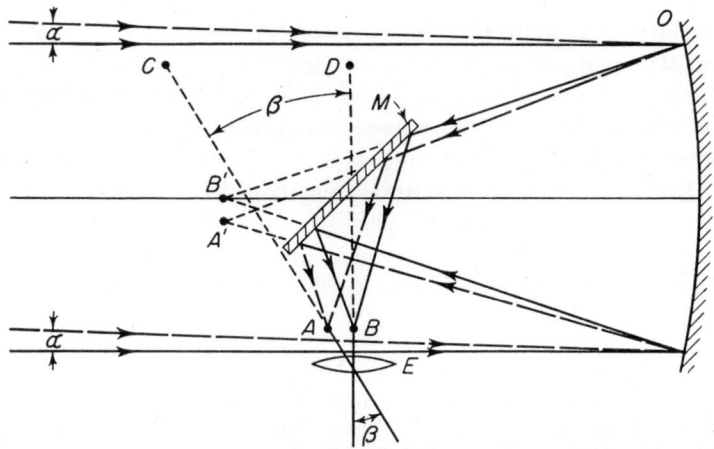

Fig. 9. Reflecting telescope. Incoming light from one point of the object, located on the axis, is shown in solid lines. Light from a point of the object located at an angle α away from the axis is shown by long dashes. The focal length of the objective is ordinarily much longer in comparison with its aperture than shown here, so the mirror M cuts off a smaller fraction of the incoming light.

objective lens that has been made is the one of 40-inch diameter at the Yerkes Observatory.

One method of overcoming some of these optical problems is to replace the objective lens by a large concave front-surface mirror. With an objective of this type, glass of high optical quality is not needed, since the light is reflected from the surface and does not traverse the glass; furthermore, in the case of a concave mirror, there is only one optical surface to be ground and polished.

There are various ways in which a *reflecting telescope* may be arranged; one is shown diagrammatically in Fig. 9. In the mounting of Fig. 9, the concave objective mirror O is placed at one end of the mounting tube. Light from a distant object or from two neighboring stars, subtending angle α at the mirror surface, is focused by the objective in such a manner as to form a real image at $A'B'$. A small plane mirror M is placed on the mirror axis in order to change the direction of the reflected light in such a way that the real image is actually formed at AB, where it may be viewed through the eyepiece E. At the eyepiece the image subtends angle β. The magnifying power is given by $M = \beta/\alpha$, and formulas (8) and (9) apply to this case if f_o is the focal length of the objective mirror. Since an astronomical telescope is used only for viewing distant objects very nearly on the telescope axis, the objective mirror is ground with a paraboloidal surface so as to avoid difficulties involving spherical aberration. The largest objective mirror is the one of 200-in diameter at Mount Palomar.

We have discussed only the simplest type of eyepiece for an astronomical telescope arranged for visual observation. There are a number of other important arrangements, particularly those designed for photographic observation. If the telescope is arranged to follow the stellar motion accurately, a photographic plate can integrate the light received over a period of many hours, and hence can detect objects very much fainter than can be visually observed. In photographic observation, either the plate can be put directly at the position of the image formed by the objective, or a camera can be used to photograph this image with further linear magnification.

PROBLEMS

1. An astronomical telescope has an objective of focal length 10 ft and an eyepiece of focal length 1 in. What is the magnifying power of the telescope when it is adjusted so that parallel rays reach the observer? *Ans:* 120.

2. When the telescope described in Prob. 1 is adjusted in the manner indicated, what is the distance between the lenses? If this telescope were adjusted in such a way as to form a real image of the sun 4 in behind the eyepiece, what would be the separation of the lenses? Show diagrams.

3. A small telescope has a distance of 28.4 cm between the objective and the eyepiece. If the magnifying power of this telescope when parallel light reaches the observer is 20, find the focal lengths of eyepiece and objective.
Ans: 27.0 cm; 1.35 cm.

4. If an astronomical telescope has a magnifying power of 100 when used with an eyepiece of 3-cm focal length and the final image at infinity, what is the focal length of the objective?

5. The telescope at the Yerkes Observatory has an objective of diameter 40 in and focal length 65 ft. What is its magnifying power when used with an eyepiece of focal length 1 in and the final image at infinity? *Ans:* 780.

6. The illumination from direct sunlight on a certain day is 8000 lumens/ft². If the Yerkes telescope were used to view the sun, what would be the illumination measured at the image of the sun's disk in the focal plane of the objective? (NOTE: The diameter of the sun subtends an angle of approximately 0°.5.)

7. A telescope objective has a diameter of 12 in and a focal length of 10 ft. When the sun is being observed, the lens is illuminated with 8000 lumens/ft² of direct sunlight. An eyepiece of focal length 3 in is used to focus a real image of the sun on a plane surface 8 ft from itself. Assuming that all the sunlight striking the objective appears in this real image, and that the sun's apparent diameter is 0°.5, find the intensity of illumination of the image. *Ans:* 1090 lumens/ft².

8. In taking a photograph of the moon, the eyepiece of a telescope is removed and a photographic plate is inserted in the focal plane of the objective lens. How large a photograph of the moon can be obtained if the telescope objective has a focal length of 80 cm? The diameter of the moon is 2163 mi and the distance to the moon is 240,000 mi.

9. Derive formula (9).

7. TERRESTRIAL TELESCOPES

When a telescope is used for astronomical purposes, the fact that the image is inverted is of no inconvenience; but when terrestrial objects are to be viewed, it is necessary to have an erect final image. The erection can be accomplished by introducing a third lens, called the *erecting lens*, between the objective and eyepiece. The arrangement is shown schematically in Fig. 10. In this figure two defining rays are shown passing

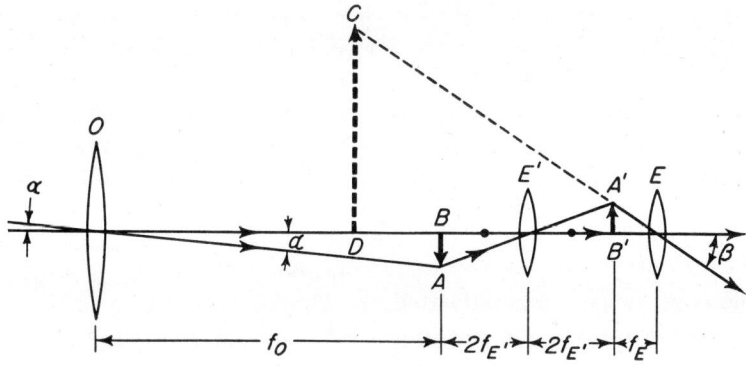

Fig. 10. Terrestrial telescope.

through the objective O, the erecting lens E', and the eyepiece E. If the erecting lens E' is placed twice its focal length from the real inverted image AB, it forms a reinverted image $A'B'$ of equal size, which is then viewed through the eyepiece E. Since there is no difference in the sizes of AB and $A'B'$, the magnifying power is still given by (8) or (9). However, it should be noted that a terrestrial telescope is longer by $4f_{E'}$ than an astronomical telescope giving equal magnification.

This increased length is sometimes inconvenient and can be avoided by using totally reflecting prisms (described in Chap. 25) instead of an erecting lens for producing the reinversion. Such an arrangement is shown in Fig. 11, in which a single ray is traced. Light from the object O reaches prism P_1, which produces a right-left inversion. From prism P_1 the light passes to prism P_2, which produces a vertical inversion. As a result of these two inversions the real image produced by the objective is erect and properly oriented and can be observed through the eyepiece E in the usual manner. Owing to the reflections occurring at P_1 and P_2, the optical length of the instrument is almost three times the actual distance between objective and eyepiece. Hence, an objective of longer focal length can be used and higher magnification can be obtained than for an instrument of the same length without prisms. Since these instruments are usually made in pairs, one for each eye, the combinations are generally termed *prism binoculars*. One other optical property of prism binoculars may be noted briefly. With this construction it is possible to have the distance between the two objectives greater than the distance between the observer's eyes. This feature increases the stereoscopic effect involved in binocular vision by providing a longer 'base line' for use in 'triangulation' and hence enhances the observer's perception of differences in distance.

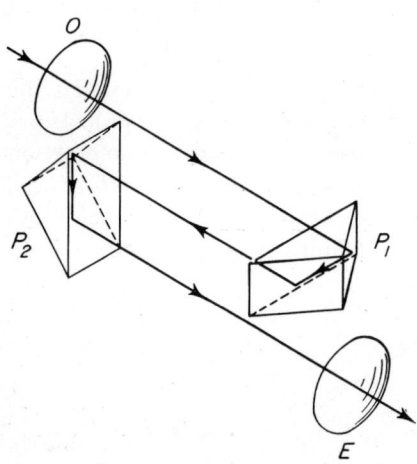

Fig. 11. Arrangement of lenses and prisms in the prism binocular.

One other type of telescope that can be used for terrestrial purposes is the very earliest form of telescope, which was invented by Galileo in 1609. This instrument yields rather low magnification and survives today almost exclusively in the opera glass. The magnification is usually about 3. The essentials of a Galilean telescope, indicated in Fig. 12, consist

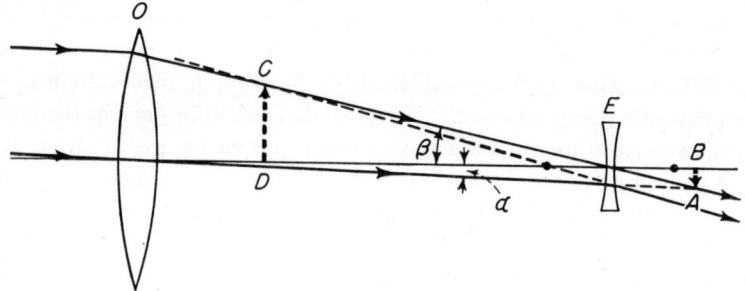

Fig. 12. Galilean telescope (opera glass).

of a converging lens as objective and a diverging lens as eyepiece. Two rays are shown reaching the objective from a point of a distant object at an angle α off the axis. The objective would produce a real inverted image at position AB if the eyepiece E were not present. However, since the eyepiece is present, the image AB forms a virtual object for the eyepiece. The observer sees the erect virtual image CD formed by lens E. The magnification produced by this telescope is given, as usual, by the ratio of angle β to angle α. When the final image CD is at infinite distance the image AB is at the principal focus of the eyepiece and the magnifying power is given by

$$M = f_O/f_E,$$

as in the case of the astronomical telescope. In this relation the negative sign usually attached to the focal length f_E of a diverging lens is to be ignored. It is noted that the tube length is shorter than for an astronomical telescope and much shorter than for a terrestrial telescope of the same magnifying power; hence the compact size of opera glasses.

PROBLEMS

1. The objective of a terrestrial telescope has a focal length of 80 cm and the telescope has a magnifying power of 20 when adjusted in such a way that parallel rays reach the observer. If the erecting lens has a focal length of 18 cm, what is the total length of the telescope? Show diagram. Ans: 156 cm.

2. The objective of a terrestrial telescope has a focal length of 3 ft. The erecting lens has a focal length of 4 in and the total length of the telescope is 4.5 ft. What is its magnifying power?

3. The total length of the optical path between objective and eyepiece in a pair of prism binoculars is 18 in, although the over-all length of each tube is only 7 in. If the magnifying power of this instrument is 8, what would be the length of an equivalent terrestrial telescope using a similar objective and eyepiece and having an erecting lens of focal length 3 in? Ans: 30 in.

4. A terrestrial telescope has a magnifying power of 10, uses an erecting lens of focal length of 2 in, and has a length of 28 in. If the same objective and eyepiece were used in a prism binocular, what would be the length of the optical path between objective and eyepiece? Would the actual geometrical length of the binocular be this large?

5. An opera glass (Galilean telescope) measures 3 in between objective and eyepiece. The focal length of the objective is 5 in. What is the magnification? Ans: 2.5.

6. An opera glass measures 6 in between objective and eyepiece. If the focal length of the objective is 8 in, what is the magnification?

7. Prove that the magnifying power of the Galilean telescope of Fig. 12 is f_O/f_E when the final image is formed at infinity.

8. THE EYE

Optically, the human eye is similar in many respects to the camera since it contains a lens system equipped with a shutter (the eyelid), a variable diaphragm (the iris), and a screen (the retina) on which are produced real inverted images of external objects. The eye is really a very complex piece of apparatus, but the complexity arises chiefly from the mechanisms required for making various adjustments and from the as-yet-little-understood processes of detection at the retina. The chief optical properties are discussed briefly in the following paragraphs.

The eye consists of a roughly spherical eyeball supported in a bony socket in the skull, a system of muscles for moving the eyeball, and tear ducts for moistening the anterior surface of the eyeball. The chief features of the eyeball itself are shown in cross section in Fig. 13. Light enters the eye through a transparent curved shell called the *cornea*, the space immediately behind which is filled with a liquid material called the *aqueous humor*. Next the light passes through the *pupil*, a circular aperture in a colored membrane called the *iris;* the diameter of the pupil

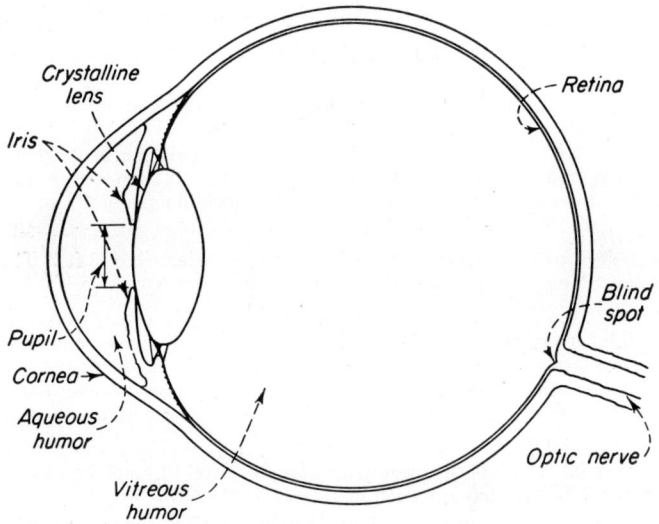

Fig. 13.   Parts of the human eye.

can be changed by the expansion or contraction of the iris. In bright light the pupil automatically contracts so as to prevent injury to the eye by the admission of too much light. Immediately behind the iris is the *crystalline lens*, a somewhat plastic lens, the curvature of whose surfaces are controlled by muscles around the edge. The focal length of the crystalline lens is varied by these muscles. The interior portion of the eyeball is filled with jellylike substance called *vitreous humor*, and the inner coating of the back wall is the light-sensitive surface called the *retina*.

Constituent	*Refractive index*
Cornea	1.351
Aqueous humor	1.337
Crystalline lens	1.437
Vitreous humor	1.337

Approximate values for the indices of refraction of the transparent portions of the eye are given in the accompanying table. Since these indices range only from 1.34 to 1.44, light experiences the greatest refraction as it first enters the eye at the cornea. The cornea, aqueous humor, crystalline lens, and vitreous humor must all be considered as components of the lens system of the eye. The effect of all the refractions is to form a real image on the retina in the manner we have already discussed for simple lenses. If the eye muscles are relaxed, sharply defined images of *distant objects* are produced on the retina of a normal eye. In order to produce sharp images of nearby objects, the muscles attached to the crystalline lens increase the curvature of the lens surfaces, decreasing the focal length sufficiently to bring the desired images into sharp focus. This adjustment of focus is called *accommodation*. It is possible for the normal adult eye to deform the crystalline lens sufficiently to produce sharp images of objects as close as 10 in, the distance of most distinct vision mentioned earlier in the present chapter. Children can see

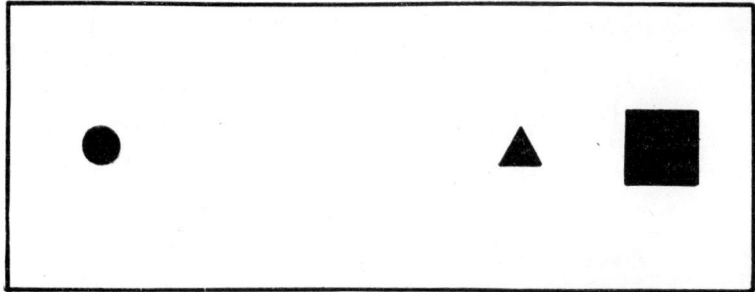

Fig. 14.

objects clearly at shorter distances, since the crystalline lens is more readily deformable in early life.

The retina includes many millions of light receivers called *rods* and *cones* because of their shapes. These are imbedded in the tissue with their lengths normal to the retinal surface. Each of these receivers is connected to a ramification of the optic nerve. These nerve fibers are gathered together and leave the eyeball as the optic nerve; just at the point of departure there is an insensitive retinal area known as the *blind spot*. The existence of the blind spot can be verified by closing the left eye and looking with the right eye at the circle in Fig. 14. As the page is brought toward the eye, the square will become invisible when the page is about 12 in from the eye; at a closer position the square will reappear and the triangle will disappear. Disappearance occurs when the image falls on the blind spot. To one side of the blind spot there is a region containing only numerous, closely spaced cones; here vision is much more acute than on the remainder of the retina. It is this portion of the retina, about 0.3 mm in diameter, which is always used when an observer looks directly at an object; the muscles of the eye rotate the eyeballs until the image in each eye falls on the *fovea centralis*, as the sensitive spot is called.

Another point involving image formation at the retina deserves mention. Since the lens system of the eye acts effectively as a simple lens, it follows that the real image on the retina is inverted, as indicated in Fig. 15. The brain, however, is conscious of the presence of the object in the erect position AB. This automatic reversal is not surprising, since it must be remembered that we have no direct experience whatever of the processes occurring inside our own eyes but have learned early in life that the stimulus produced by the inverted image $A'B'$ indicates the presence of an erect object AB.

There are several rather common defects of vision that deserve brief consideration. The normal eye, as we have already mentioned, produces sharp images of distant objects when the eye muscles are relaxed;

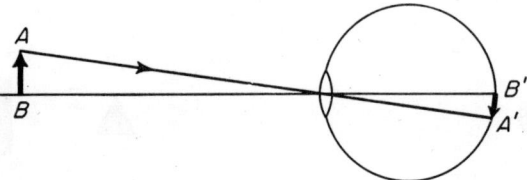

Fig. 15. The image formed on the retina is inverted.

the action of a normal eye is illustrated in Fig. 16(a). However, the size and shape of the eyeball and the focal length of the lens system are not always properly matched. If the lens is effectively too convergent, the images of distant objects will fall in front of the retina so that on the retina itself the image will be blurred. Only objects close to the eye can be focused sharply on the retina; eyes with this type of defect are said to be *myopic* or *nearsighted*. As indicated in Fig. 16(b), this defect can be remedied by using a suitable diverging spectacle lens. An insufficiently convergent lens leads to farsightedness, or *hypermetropia*, which, as indicated in Fig. 16(c), can be remedied by the use of converging spectacle lenses.

A third common type of defect in vision occurs when one or more of the refracting surfaces of the eye, such as the cornea or crystalline lens, are not perfectly spherical. In this case light from a point source will not be focused in a point image but in two short *line images* perpendicular to each other and at different distances from the eye lens. When such an eye is focused upon an object, one of these line images is focused upon the retina, but vision will be blurred and indistinct except for straight lines that lie in such a direction that their images are parallel to the line image of each point. An eye having this characteristic is said to be *astigmatic*.

The existence of astigmatism can be detected by examining with one eye at a time the sets of parallel lines shown in Fig. 17. If astigmatism is present, one set of lines will appear sharper than the others. This defect can be corrected by using a cylindrical spectacle lens so placed in front of the eye that its unsymmetric curvature corrects the asymmetric curvature of the crystalline lens or cornea.

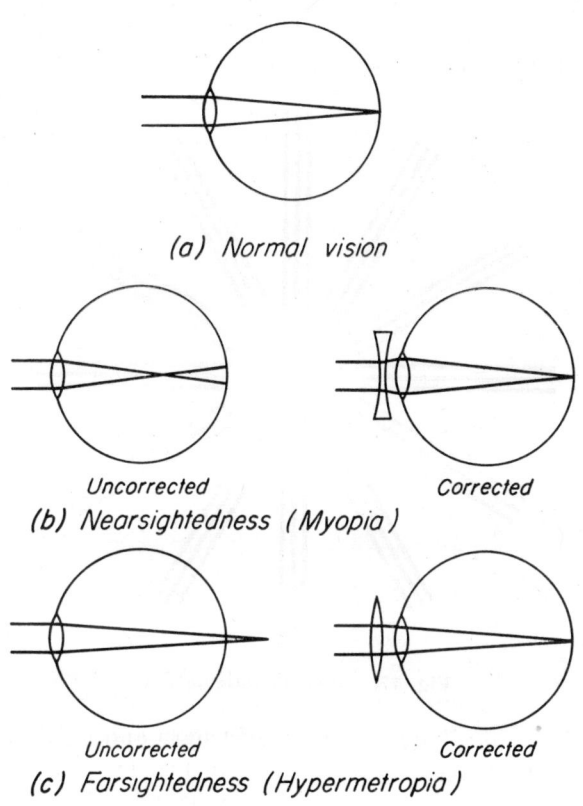

Fig. 16.

Although the exact process involved in the detection of light by the receivers at the retina is not understood, it is well known that the eye can detect extremely small amounts of light energy; it can detect an amount as small as that which would be received from a single candle at a distance of about 15 miles if there were no atmospheric absorption. The eye is more sensitive to light in a dark room than in a well-illuminated one. When a person first goes from a sunny street into a darkened movie theater, he cannot see surrounding objects, but after ten or twenty minutes his vision improves so that he has little difficulty in perceiving nearby objects. This improvement in vision comes in part from the dilation of the pupil but chiefly from the replenishment of a dye, the so-called *visual purple*, which increases the sensitivity of the eye. When illumination is intense, this dye is bleached by the light and the amount present is small. In a dimly lighted room, the dye accumulates and the sensitivity of the eye gradually increases. The eye is said to become 'dark-adapted.'

The sensitivity of the eye varies for different wavelengths. Under conditions of moderate or strong illumination the eye is most sensitive to yellow-green light of wavelength 555 millimicrons. The spectral sensi-

Fig. 17. Test for astigmatism.

tivity curve has a maximum at this wavelength and falls off rapidly for longer and shorter wavelengths as shown in Fig. 18. Most eyes do not respond appreciably to wavelengths below 400 mμ or above 700 mμ.

Although the eye receives different stimuli or sensations from different wavelengths, it has no power of *analyzing* the sensation produced by a mixture of light of different wavelengths. In this respect it is quite different from the ear, since a trained ear can analyze the tone complex of an entire orchestra into the tones of individual instruments. There are in general an infinite number of wavelength combinations that produce indistinguishable color sensations in the eye. Just how these color sensations are produced is not yet fully understood. One useful working hypothesis concerning the *behavior* of the eye is found in the Young-Helmholtz theory. This theory assumes the existence of three independent types of radiation detectors, each responsive to a wide range of wavelengths but with maximum sensitivity in the red, green, and violet respectively. Although it is known that only the cones are sensitive to color differences, there is no anatomical evidence for the existence of three types of receivers. Hence, though any color stimulus can be matched by combining lights of three wavelengths in the red, green, and violet, this fact cannot be regarded as direct evidence for the Young-Helmholtz hypothesis of three definite and different color detectors, since a match

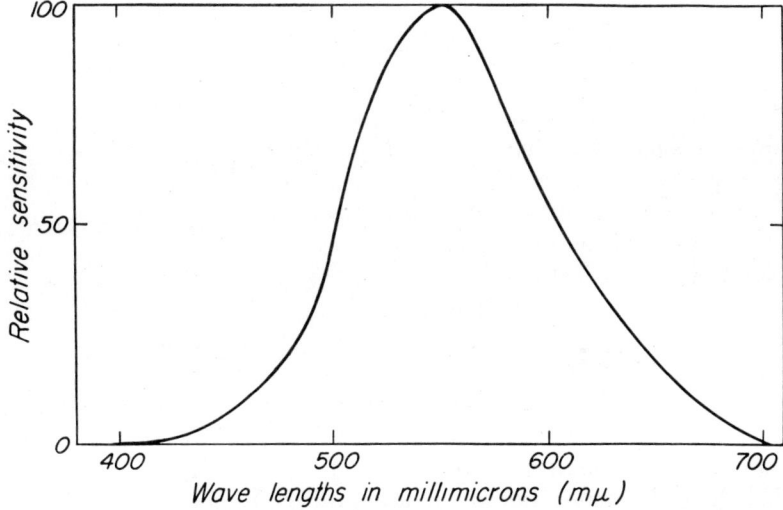

Fig. 18. Relative sensitivity of the human eye to light of various wavelengths.

can also be produced by many sets of three wavelengths in various parts of the spectrum if the proper proportion is chosen.

PROBLEMS

1. A nearsighted person cannot see objects clearly when they are farther than 10 in away. What is the focal length of the lens needed to enable this person to see distant objects clearly? Ans: −10 in.

2. A nearsighted person cannot see objects clearly at distances greater than 12 cm. What power of lens is needed to make reading at 25 cm possible? What power of lens does this person need in order to see distant objects clearly?

3. If a man needs spectacles having a power of +2 diopters in order to see an object distinctly when the object is 25 cm from his eyes, what is the shortest distance at which he can see an object without using spectacles? Ans: 50 cm.

4. What focal length of spectacle lenses is needed by a person who cannot see objects distinctly when they are closer than 250 cm?

CHAPTER 27

INTERFERENCE AND DIFFRACTION OF LIGHT

In the discussion of optical phenomena thus far, attention has been devoted to phenomena that can be adequately described in terms of rays. This treatment of optical problems by means of rays is called *geometrical optics*. Although a ray was originally defined in Chap. 23 as a normal to a wave-front, the actual wave properties of light are not intimately involved in geometrical optics.

There are many optical phenomena that cannot be described in terms of geometrical optics. These phenomena are encountered whenever light strikes objects whose physical dimensions are comparable to the wavelength of the light. The dimensions involved might, for example, be the width of a narrow slit, the diameter of a fine wire, or the thickness of a thin film of oil on a wet pavement. The optical phenomena involved are known as *diffraction* and *interference* and can be adequately described only in terms of the wave properties of light. Treatment of phenomena from the wave point of view is usually called *physical optics*. *All* optical problems must be treated by the methods of physical optics if a minutely detailed analysis is desired. Geometrical or ray optics can be regarded as an approximation which proves adequate for many practical optical problems not involving objects with small physical dimensions.

In the present chapter, certain simple problems involving interference and diffraction will be treated. A brief discussion of the ultimate limitations of optical instruments will be given from the point of view of physical optics.

1. CONDITIONS FOR INTERFERENCE

The general conditions for interference have been discussed in Chap. 20, Wave Motion. We recall that if, as in Fig. 1, we have two sources S_1 and S_2 of waves, a stationary interference pattern can be produced only (a) if the frequencies of the sources are equal and (b) if there is some definite and constant phase relationship between the vibrations of the two sources. Let us assume that the frequencies of the two sources are equal and that the vibrations of the two sources are exactly *in phase*. The sources send out waves in all directions. Hence, any point such as

P receives waves from both sources and therefore interference occurs at P. The effects of this interference are determined by the distances d_1 and d_2. If the path difference $d_2 - d_1$ is equal to an odd number of half wavelengths, destructive interference occurs; if $d_2 - d_1$ is equal to a whole number of wavelengths, constructive interference occurs.

It is possible to construct sources of equal frequency and to arrange for a definite phase relationship when mechanical waves and even radio waves are concerned. However, although it is relatively easy to produce optical sources of equal frequency, the problem of arranging for definite phase relationships between two independent light sources is probably insoluble. Interference between two independent light sources such as two electric arcs or two luminous flames has never been observed. However, we shall see that there are a number of ways in which interference of light waves does occur.

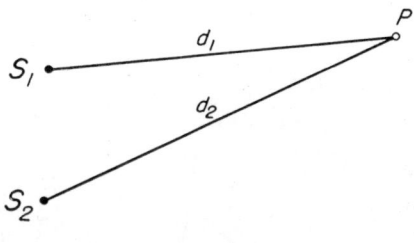

Fig. 1.

2. FRESNEL'S EXPERIMENTS

Although Thomas Young was actually the first (in 1802) to produce effects directly and unambiguously interpretable as interference between light waves, it is desirable to consider first another set of historically important experiments originally performed by Augustin Jean Fresnel (1788–1827). One of the arrangements used by Fresnel is shown in Fig. 2. Two plane mirrors M_1 and M_2 meet each other along a straight line K. The two mirrors are inclined toward each other so that there is a small angle, actually only a few minutes of arc, between their planes. At a distance of a few centimeters from the mirrors, a narrow slit S is set up in such a way that it is parallel to the line of intersection K. The slit is illuminated from behind by a sodium arc or some other bright source of monochromatic (single-frequency) light so that light passing through the slit reaches both mirrors and is reflected by them. The mirrors are made of black glass so that the light is reflected from the front surfaces of the mirrors. After reflection by the mirrors, the light reaches the screen. Defining rays are shown in Fig. 2.

The slit S is imaged in mirror M_1 at S_1, and light diverging from S_1 reaches the screen in the region between A and A'. The image formed by mirror M_2 is at S_2, and light diverging from S_2 reaches the screen in the region between B and B'. Thus, the portion of the screen between A and B' receives light from both images, S_1 and S_2. In this way we have created two 'sources' of illumination on the screen that have not only *identical frequencies* but also *a definite phase relationship*. Therefore, the conditions for interference are fulfilled. The interference gives rise to alternate bright and dark bands on the white screen. The bands, or *interference fringes*, as they are usually called, are parallel to the line K and to the slit S. In the center of the interference pattern there is an unusually bright band at position M on the perpendicular bisector of the line S_1S_2; for this bright band the light paths S_1M and S_2M are equal.

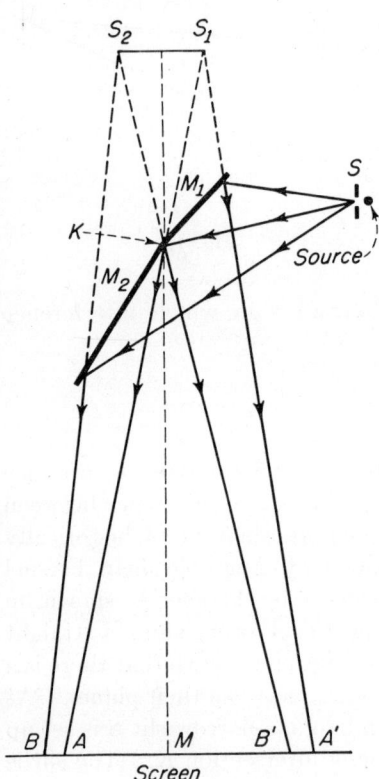

Fig. 2. Fresnel's double mirror.

If a sodium arc (a monochromatic source) illuminates the slit S, the interference pattern consists of alternate yellow and black fringes or bands. If, however, white light is used, all the bright bands except the central one exhibit spectral colors like a rainbow. This effect is due to the fact that the wavelengths corresponding to different colors are different and hence the positions of destructive and constructive interference are different for different wavelengths. If the interference fringes are close together, only the margins of the bright fringes are colored. If the fringes are sufficiently far apart, as they will be on a distant screen, each of the first few bright fringes has the form of a complete spectrum.

A second method of producing interference patterns involves the use of a slit and a biprism as shown in Fig. 3. This arrangement was also devised by Fresnel. Light from the slit S is refracted by the prism so that the light reaching the screen appears to come from two sources S_1 and S_2. In the portion of the screen where the beams apparently coming from S_1 and S_2 overlap, interference fringes are observed.

Determination of the location of the bright and dark fringes on the screens of Figs. 2 and 3 from the conditions for constructive and destructive interference is merely a problem in geometry. The centers of the bright fringes will be located at those points of the screen whose distances from S_1 and S_2 differ by a whole number of wavelengths; the centers of the dark fringes will be located at those points whose distances from S_1

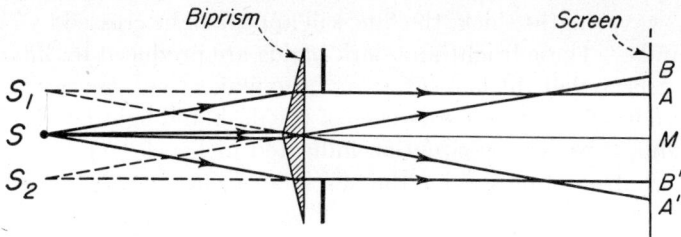

Fig. 3. Fresnel's biprism.

and S_2 differ by an odd number of half wavelengths. Examples of these computations will be furnished by the following problems.

PROBLEMS

1. A narrow slit is located near a Fresnel double mirror in the manner indicated in Fig. 2. If the separation of the virtual sources S_1 and S_2 is 0.1 mm and the perpendicular distance from the virtual sources to the screen is 50 cm, find the distance between the central bright fringe and the center of the first bright fringe on either side when the slit is illuminated with violet light of wavelength $\lambda = 400$ mμ.

Ans: 2.0 mm.

2. When the slit in the double-mirror experiment of Prob. 1 is illuminated by light of another wavelength, it is found that the distance between the central bright fringe and the center of the first bright fringe at one side is 3 mm. What is the wavelength of the light?

3. A narrow slit used in a Fresnel biprism experiment of the type illustrated in Fig. 3 is illuminated by red light of wavelength 700 mμ. If the separation of the virtual source-slits S_1 and S_2 is 0.2 mm and if the perpendicular distance from these virtual sources to the screen is 1 m, what is the distance from the central bright fringe to the nearest bright fringes on either side? Ans: 3.5 mm.

4. If light of another color is used in the experiment of Prob. 3, and the distance between the central bright fringe and the next fringe is found to be 2.4 mm, what is the wavelength of the light?

3. INTERFERENCE PHENOMENA IN THIN FILMS

Interference phenomena are also produced by reflection of light from thin films. The colors observed in thin films such as soap bubbles, thin layers of oil on water, and thin layers of oxide on metal surfaces (for example, blued steel and the blacksmith's temper colors) are familiar to everyone. Such films are usually observed by reflection when white light is incident, and the colors are due to the interference of light waves reflected at the front and back surfaces of the films.

The reflection involved in this phenomenon is regular reflection. If, as indicated in Fig. 4, the film is illuminated by a broad source S of monochromatic light such as a yellow Bunsen flame in which sodium chloride salt is present, the eye will receive light from all parts of the source by reflection at the film. Hence, it is possible to observe the virtual image S' of the source. However, if the eye is focused on the film, and the film is a few wavelengths thick, the film will appear to be crossed by light and dark bands. These bright and dark bands are produced by interference of light reflected at the two surfaces of the film.

In order to explain the existence of the dark and light bands observed in the film, consider the situation indicated in Fig. 5. AB represents a plane wave-front approaching the film in air from some distant source; at

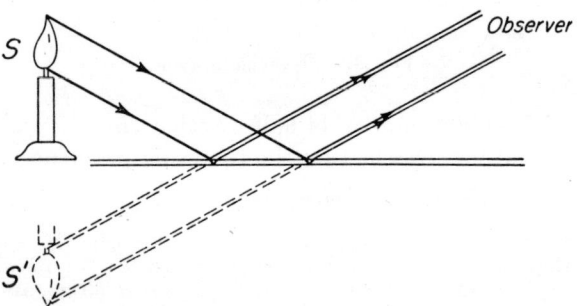

Fig. 4. Reflection from a thin film.

all points such as a and b on this wave-front the phase is the same. Let us then draw rays 1 and 2 perpendicular to the plane wave-front at these two points. On striking the film, ray 1 is partially reflected at the front surface CD; in the figure this reflected ray is shown as ray $1'$ with $A'B'$ as the corresponding wave-front. On reaching the film, ray 2 is partially

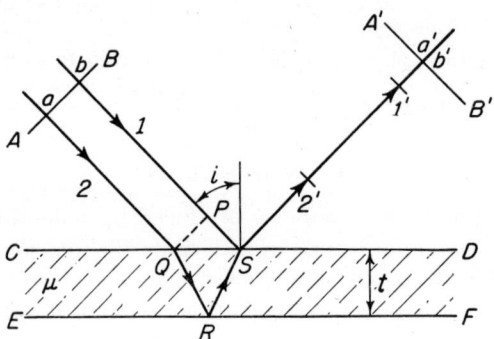

Fig. 5. Light paths in a transparent thin film.

refracted at the front surface CD, is reflected at the back surface of the film EF, and eventually re-emerges from the front surface as ray $2'$, which is now coincident with ray $1'$. Therefore, the plane $A'B'$ could also be considered as a wave front corresponding to ray $2'$. However, whether the light waves reaching $A'B'$ by the path traversed by ray 1 are in phase with the light wave reaching $A'B'$ by the path traversed by ray 2 is determined by the difference in time taken by the two rays in going from AB to $A'B'$.

Now, in Fig. 4, as the eye is focused on various portions of the film from which light is reflected, the angle i of Fig. 5 will at some locations be such as to give destructive interference between the rays reflected from the front and back surfaces. At other locations i will be such as to give constructive interference. The result will be a series of interference bands in the film running in a direction perpendicular to the paper in Fig. 4.

In order to obtain the conditions on i for constructive and destructive interference, note that the path difference between rays 1 and 2 in Fig. 5 arises from the fact that 1 follows the route QRS while 2 traverses the path PS. One cannot, however, merely subtract the length PS from the length QRS and determine the number of wavelengths in this path difference, because the wavelengths in the film and in air are different.

In order to handle problems like this, involving paths in material media, it is convenient to define a quantity called the *optical path length:*

> The optical path length of a ray in a material medium is the path length in vacuum that would contain the same number of wavelengths as does the actual path length in the material medium.

Two rays of the same frequency will take the same times to traverse the same optical path lengths since a distance equal to one wavelength is traversed in the fixed periodic time $T = 1/f$.

Since the speed of light in a material medium of index of refraction μ is c/μ, where c is the speed in vacuum, and since the frequency is the same in the material and in vacuum, the wavelength in the material will be λ/μ, where λ is the wavelength in vacuum. Since the wavelength is less by a factor μ, we see that the number of waves in the material path will be greater by a factor μ, and from the above definition that

$$(\text{optical path}) = \mu(\text{actual path}).$$

It is readily seen that the conditions for interference that we have previously stated can be applied to the difference between the total *optical* paths of two interfering rays when comparison is made with the vacuum wavelength.

In Fig. 5, then, if we take the index of refraction of air as unity, we see that

$$\text{difference in optical path} = \mu(QR+RS) - PS.$$

For normal incidence, PS is zero and $QR + RS$ is simply twice the film thickness t. Therefore, for normal incidence, the optical path difference is $2\mu t$, and we might expect that the light waves traversing paths 1 and 2 would come into phase and interfere constructively as the film thickness t approaches zero. That is, we might expect extremely thin films to appear bright when viewed by reflected light at almost normal incidence. A simple experiment with a soap film shows the reverse to be the case; in a region where the soap film is so thin that it is about to break, the film appears *black* when viewed by reflected monochromatic or white light. This effect can be observed by viewing a soap bubble; the thinnest part of the bubble becomes dark just before the bubble bursts. Note that the reflection processes for rays 1 and 2 are not identical. The reflection at the front surface takes place in a medium of low refractive index (air) at the boundary of a medium of high refractive index (film material); reflection at the back surface occurs in a medium of high refractive index (film material) at the boundary of a medium of low refractive index (air). The above and similar experiments show that, under these circumstances, there is always a phase difference of 180° between the two reflected waves in addition to phase differences caused by differences in optical path. This 180° phase difference is analogous to the difference in the character of the reflections in Figs. 18 and 19 on pp. 503–504. It can be allowed for by adding a distance of $\frac{1}{2}\lambda$ to the optical-path difference to obtain what is sometimes called the *total retardation*. Thus, for a thin soap film in air at normal incidence,

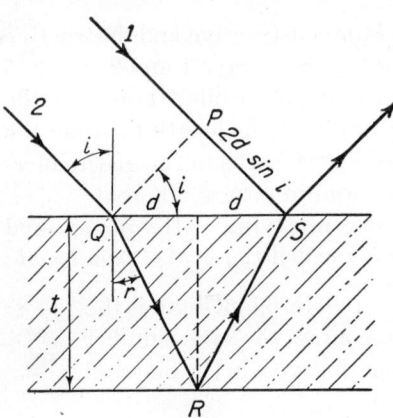

Fig. 6. Optical paths in a transparent film.

$$\text{total retardation} = 2\mu t + \tfrac{1}{2}\lambda. \tag{1}$$

Maximum constructive interference occurs if the total retardation is equal to a whole number of wavelengths; maximum destructive interference occurs if the total retardation is equal to an odd number of half wavelengths.

The total retardation in the case when the incident light does not strike the film normally can be determined from a consideration of Fig. 6, which is essentially an enlargement of a part of Fig. 5. It can be seen that the distance traversed in the film is $2t/\cos r$, so the optical path in the film is $\mu(2t/\cos r)$. The path PS in air is given by $2d \sin i$; but since distance d is equal to $t \tan r$, the optical path in air can also be written as

$$PS = 2t \tan r \sin i = \frac{2t \sin r \sin i}{\cos r} = \frac{2\mu t \sin^2 r}{\cos r}.$$

Remembering that the optical path in the film is $\mu(2t/\cos r)$, we can write the difference in optical path as

$$\text{difference in optical path} = 2\mu t \left(\frac{1-\sin^2 r}{\cos r}\right) = 2\mu t \cos r = 2t\sqrt{\mu^2 - \sin^2 i},$$

since $\mu \cos r = \sqrt{\mu^2 - \mu^2 \sin^2 r} = \sqrt{\mu^2 - \sin^2 i}$. Thus, the total retardation can be written as

$$\text{total retardation} = 2t\sqrt{\mu^2 - \sin^2 i} + \tfrac{1}{2}\lambda. \tag{2}$$

It should be noted that the values for total retardation given in equations (1) and (2) are applicable to the case of a thin film of a liquid or solid in air. If the thin film consists of a liquid film on the surface of a liquid of higher refractive index, the additional term $\tfrac{1}{2}\lambda$ does not appear.

One well-known phenomenon involving interference of light waves in thin films gives rise to *Newton's rings*, first observed scientifically by Sir Isaac Newton. The effect (Fig. 9) can easily be produced by placing a plano-convex lens with a long focal length (approximately 4 meters) on a flat piece of plate glass in the manner indicated in Fig. 7. If the arrangement is illuminated by white light and viewed by reflected light, the point of contact of the lens and plate is surrounded by a system of colored concentric circular rings. If the arrangement is illuminated with monochromatic light, a system of light and dark rings can easily be observed either by reflected or transmitted light; the rings that appear light when observed by reflection appear dark when observed by transmission, whereas the rings that appear dark when observed by reflection appear light when observed by transmission.

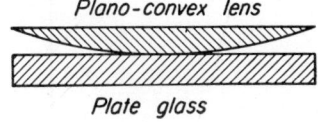

Fig. 7.

It might be remarked that these thin-film phenomena, which we today are inclined to interpret immediately in terms of interference of light waves, were explained in a quite different way by Newton, who believed light to consist of streams of minute *particles* emitted by luminous sources. According to Newton, streams of these particles striking a refracting surface are subjected to 'fits of easy transmission and of easy reflection' which occur at regular intervals along the surface. If the particles passing through one surface of the film at a fit of easy transmission strike the second surface at a fit of easy transmission, none of these particles will be reflected, and a dark region will be observed by reflection. The reason for the existence of fits of easy transmission and easy reflection is difficult to understand and must be attributed to special properties of the particles constituting light. To us today, Newton's explanation of the existence of the observed rings seems rather forced, since their existence can be so easily explained on the basis of interference of waves. However, until Young's conclusive experiments in 1802, Newton's particle theory of light was widely accepted. Young's experiments, on the diffraction of light by slits, will be discussed later, in Sec. 5.

The modern explanation of Newton's rings considers the air layer between the lens and plate glass as a film of varying thickness. In the arrangement shown in Fig. 8, a parallel beam of monochromatic light coming from the right strikes a piece of plate glass MM which acts as a mirror to reflect part of the light vertically to the lens-plate combination. Reflected light from surfaces HHH, HOH, FF, and GG returns to the plate glass MM, is partially transmitted by the plate, and can be seen by

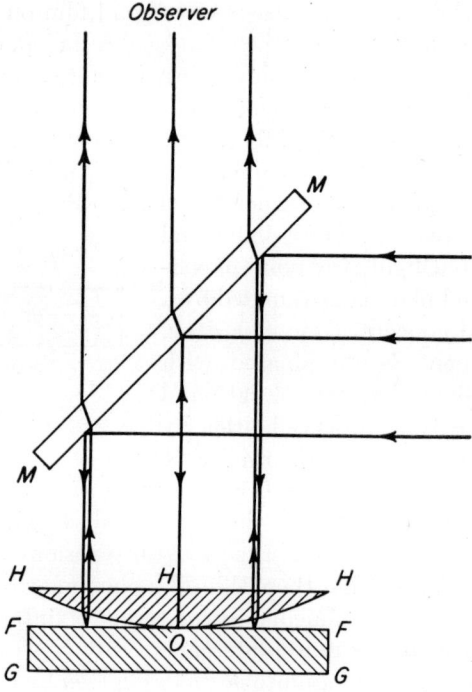

Fig. 8. Diagram of apparatus used in observing Newton's rings.

the observer. The distances involved are such that only reflections from surfaces HOH and FF produce interference. Since the lens curvature is small, the light can be considered as normally incident on the air film. Under this condition, constructive interference occurs when the total retardation is equal to a whole number of wavelengths, and destructive interference occurs when the total retardation is equal to an odd number of half wavelengths. Since the index of refraction of air is approximately 1, these conditions are:

$$\text{total retardation} = 2t + \tfrac{1}{2}\lambda = n\lambda \quad \text{for constructive interference,} \quad (3)$$

$$\text{total retardation} = 2t + \tfrac{1}{2}\lambda = (n - \tfrac{1}{2})\lambda \quad \text{for destructive interference,} \quad (4)$$

where t is the thickness of the air film and n is an integer. $n = 1, 2, 3, \cdots$ in (3) and (4) give, in order of increasing thickness, the thicknesses corresponding to constructive and destructive interference. $n = 1$ in (4) gives $t = 0$, as we have already noted. Since the film thickness t varies in a regular manner as the horizontal distance from the point of contact O increases in the plane defined by FF, a clearly defined symmetrical interference pattern results.

The pattern observed by reflection is shown in Fig. 9. The central region around the point of contact between lens and plate is dark, since in this region the film is extremely thin, as in the case of a soap film just before rupture. Beyond this region the conditions for constructive and destructive interference are realized alternately as the distance from the point of contact increases.

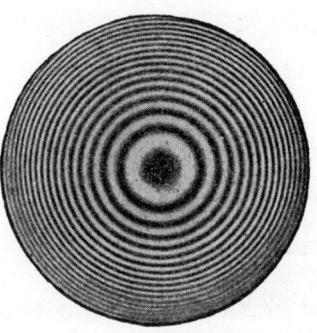

Fig. 9. Photograph of Newton's rings taken with monochromatic light. (*Courtesy of Jemima B. Dutcher.*)

Since the thickness of the air film can be determined from geometrical considerations, the wavelength of light can be determined from a meas-

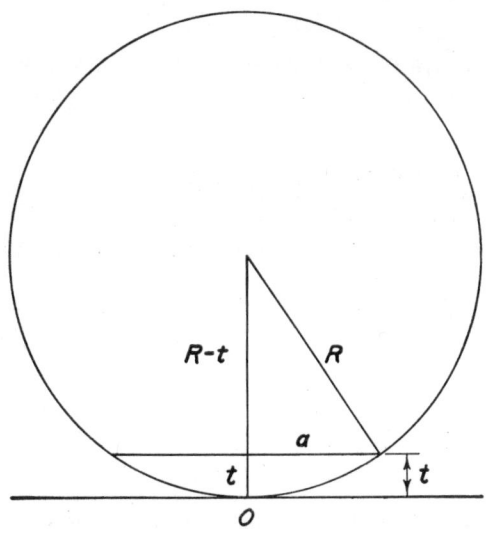

Fig. 10.

urement of the radii of the observed rings. In order to see how this measurement may be accomplished, consider Fig. 10, in which R is the radius of curvature of the lens surface, t is the thickness of the air film, and a is a distance measured from the point of contact O. By the Pythagorean theorem, we may write

$$R^2 = (R-t)^2 + a^2$$

or

$$R^2 = R^2 - 2Rt + t^2 + a^2.$$

In the case of the thin films involved in Newton's rings, the term t^2 is negligibly small in comparison with Rt. If we drop this term and solve for t, we obtain

$$t = a^2/2R. \tag{5}$$

Returning to equation (3), let us write the conditions for the $(n+1)$th and nth bright rings,

$$2t_{n+1} + \tfrac{1}{2}\lambda = (n+1)\lambda,$$

$$2t_n + \tfrac{1}{2}\lambda = n\lambda,$$

where t_{n+1} and t_n are the air-film thicknesses producing the constructive interference at the $(n+1)$th and nth ring, respectively. The difference in the thickness of the film for these two rings is given by

$$2(t_{n+1} - t_n) = \lambda. \tag{6}$$

The values for t_{n+1} and t_n can be determined from equation (5). Substitution of these values in (6) gives

$$\lambda = (a_{n+1}^2 - a_n^2)/R, \tag{7}$$

where a_{n+1} and a_n are the radii of the $(n+1)$th and nth bright rings and can be measured directly. The value of R can also be measured directly by means of a spherometer. Therefore, the wavelength λ can be determined from equation (7).

PROBLEMS

1. What is the minimum thickness of a soap film of refractive index 1.33 if the film gives strong reflection when viewed by yellow light of wavelength 600 mμ at normal incidence? Ans: 1.13×10^{-5} cm.

2. Find the thickness of a soap film that gives strong second-order reflection of red light of wavelength 700 mμ. Take $\mu = 1.33$ for the film and assume normal incidence. NOTE: Second-order reflection occurs when the total retardation is equal to two wavelengths.

3. A thin film of oil on a wet pavement reflects red light of wavelength 700 mμ when illuminated by white light. If first-order interference at normal incidence is involved, what is the thickness of the oil film? Refraction index for oil = 1.46.
Ans: 1.20×10^{-5} cm.

4. What thickness of oil film on a glass plate will give first-order reflection for red light of wavelength 700 mμ? Assume normal incidence and take 1.46 as the refractive index of the oil. What is the wavelength of red light in the oil?

5. A beam of sodium light ($\lambda = 589$ mμ) strikes a film of olive oil floating on water, and interference fringes are observed. The refractive index of the oil is 1.46. When the film is viewed at an angle of 30° from the normal, the eighth *dark* band of the system is seen. This band corresponds to a total retardation of $15\tfrac{1}{2}\lambda$. What is the thickness of the film? Ans: 1.50 μ.

6. A glass plate 0.50 micron thick is illuminated by white light. The refractive index of the glass is 1.50. What wavelength in the visible spectrum (400 mμ to 700 mμ) will be intensified in the reflected light observed at an angle of 45° from the normal?
Ans: 529 mμ.

7. A parallel beam of sodium light ($\lambda = 589$ mμ) falls normally on the plane surface of a plano-convex lens whose convex surface is in contact with a plane glass surface. The radius of curvature of the lens surface is 50 cm. Find the radius of the 51st dark ring observed by reflection, counting the central dark spot as the first ring.
Ans: 0.384 cm.

8. A parallel beam of red light of wavelength 650 mμ is incident normally on the plane surface of a plano-convex lens whose curved surface is in contact with a plane glass plate. If the radius of curvature of the curved surface of the lens is 300 cm, find the diameter of the third bright ring in the interference pattern observed by reflection.

9. The flatness of glass plates such as are used in interferometers (discussed in the next section) can be tested in the following way: Two such plates are placed in contact along one edge, separated by the thickness of a sheet of thin paper along the opposite edge, and observed by monochromatic light at normal incidence.

(a) Show that if the plates are perfect, a system of straight, parallel, uniformly spaced interference fringes will be observed. Determine the spacing of the fringes in terms of the thickness of the paper, the dimensions of the plates, and the wavelength of the light.

(b) A plate is perfect except for one low spot. This plate is tested against a perfect plate and the fringe pattern photographed. What will be the appearance of the fringe pattern? Show how, by measurements on the photograph, the depth of the low spot can be determined to within an accuracy of a fraction of the wavelength of light.

4. THE MICHELSON INTERFEROMETER

One of the most ingenious methods of producing interference is used in the Michelson interferometer, which is shown diagrammatically in Fig. 11. The method consists of dividing a beam of light by partial transmission and partial reflection and sending the two beams over different routes to two mirrors, where they are reflected in such a way as to cause them to recombine and produce interference. Incident monochromatic light shown as ray S is incident at an angle of 45° on a plane half-silvered mirror M. Part of the light is transmitted and is shown as ray 1; the rest of the light is reflected and is shown as ray 2. Ray 1 reaches mirror M_1 and ray 2 reaches mirror M_2. In both cases incidence is normal, and hence the direction of each ray is reversed as indicated in the figure; for the sake of clearness, the reflected rays shown in Fig. 11 have been displaced laterally. On their return journey the two rays reach half-silvered mirror M again and part of the light represented by each ray reaches the observer; the remaining light shown by the dotted ray returns to the source.

If the optical distances of the two mirrors M_1 and M_2 from the half-silvered mirror M are equal, the two rays 1 and 2 traverse identical paths; the glass plate N is introduced to make the path in glass approximately the same for both rays. Therefore, the light waves associated with rays 1 and 2 emerge in the observer's direction in phase and reinforce each other. Reinforcement also occurs when the optical paths traversed by rays 1 and 2 differ by a whole number of wavelengths. To the observer's eye, focused for parallel rays, the field of view appears alternately bright and dark when one of the mirrors M_1 or M_2 is moved toward M. The field changes from bright to dark when one of the mirrors is moved a distance equal to a quarter wavelength, since this movement changes the optical path by a half wavelength. It follows that the Michelson interferometer can be used for the absolute measurement of wavelength if the mirror M_2 is moved in the direction of ray 2 through a distance that can be measured

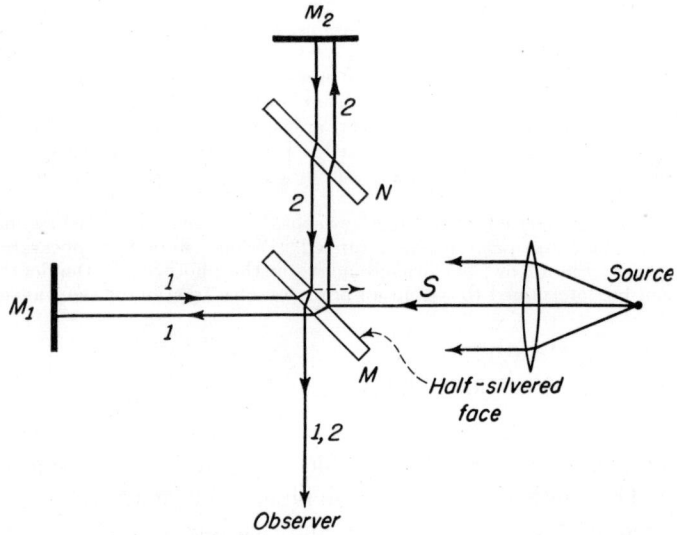

Fig. 11. Plan of Michelson's interferometer.

by a micrometer screw, and if the alternations of light and darkness in the field of view are observed while the mirror is being moved.

In order to see more clearly how this measurement is accomplished, consider the diagram shown in Fig. 12. Suppose that the mirror M_2 is moved through a distance S to position M_2' and that N successive bright fields, after the original one, have been observed. The total optical path traversed by ray 2 has changed by an amount $2S$; the fact that N bright fields have been seen indicates that this change is equivalent to a change of N wavelengths. Thus, we may write

$$N\lambda = 2S,$$

where the distance S can be measured by a micrometer.

The field of view does not actually appear uniformly bright or dark but, if the mirrors are accurately aligned, exhibits concentric circles if an extended source is used. However, this variation is of minor importance in making observations, since it is necessary only to observe some arbitrary point such as the center of the field of view. If mirror M_1 is very slightly tilted, the field is crossed by parallel fringes, which move in a direction normal to their length as mirror M_2 is moved. The value of N can be observed by 'counting the fringes' that move past the crosshairs of an eyepiece. The interferometer is usually used in this way.

One extremely important application of the Michelson interferometer is in the evaluation of the length of the standard meter in terms of wavelengths of light. Michelson and his colleagues originally performed this

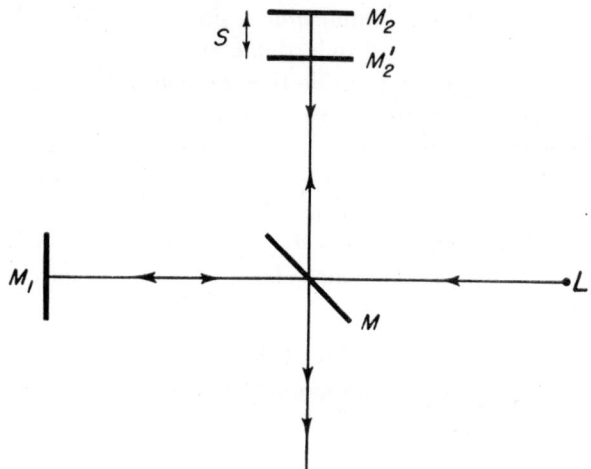

Fig. 12. Measurement of wavelengths by Michelson's interferometer.

measurement in terms of light from an electric-spark source with cadmium electrodes. The details of the apparatus are somewhat complicated, but the method is similar in essentials to that described above. The results of the experiments give

$$1 \text{ meter} = 1{,}553{,}161.1 \; \lambda_R$$
$$= 1{,}966{,}249.7 \; \lambda_G$$
$$= 2{,}083{,}372.1 \; \lambda_B,$$

where λ_R, λ_G, and λ_B are, respectively, the wavelengths of the red, green, and blue light emitted by cadmium; these are the wavelengths in dry air at a pressure of 760 mm of mercury and a temperature of 15° C. An even more accurate evaluation of the meter has recently been made in terms of green light emitted by the mercury isotope 198, which can now be produced in quantity from gold. This evaluation in terms of green light from mercury 198 can be made more precise than the evaluation in terms of light from cadmium for several reasons. Since cadmium has several isotopes, light of a given color (such as red light from a cadmium spark) can never be strictly monochromatic but involves several nearly but not exactly equal frequencies. The fact that mercury sources can be operated at lower temperatures is also advantageous, since at low temperatures the Doppler effect arising from motion of the emitting atoms does not interfere as seriously with the production of strictly monochromatic light. The result of the evaluation of the meter in terms of the green light of wavelength λ_{Hg} from mercury is

$$1 \text{ meter} = 1{,}831{,}249.21 \ \lambda_{Hg}.$$

This evaluation is of great importance, since it provides a method of duplication of the primary standard meter. If the primary standard were destroyed, it would be possible to construct a new one which would agree with the original standard meter within 1 part in 10,000,000.

It is very likely that in the near future the fundamental unit of length, the meter, will be redefined in terms of the wavelength of the above mercury green line, since this wavelength is more reproducible, and can be measured to higher accuracy, than the distance between two scratches on a platinum-iridium bar that may be suffering unknown mechanical distortions as time passes.

PROBLEMS

1. While moving one mirror of Michelson's interferometer a distance of 0.250 mm, an observer counted 909 fringes. Calculate the wavelength of the light used.
Ans: 550 mμ.

2. While moving one mirror of a Michelson interferometer a distance of 1.000 mm, an observer counted 4218 fringes. What was the wavelength of the light used?

3. In order to check the accuracy of a certain precision micrometer gauge, an observer uses the micrometer to measure the distance moved by an interferometer mirror. Using the red light from a cadmium source, an observer counts 4162 fringes while the mirror is being moved a distance of 1.330 mm *as measured by the gauge*. What is the actual distance moved? What is the per cent error in the distance as given by the gauge? Ans: 1.3398 mm; 0.7%.

4. In order to check the accuracy of a certain instrument-maker's gauge, an observer uses the gauge to measure the movement of an interferometer mirror. Using the red light from a cadmium spark, an observer counts 4198 fringes while the mirror is moved a distance of 1.350 mm *as measured by the gauge*. What is the actual distance moved? What is the per cent error in the gauge reading?

5. DIFFRACTION PHENOMENA AND HUYGENS' PRINCIPLE

When light waves pass through an aperture, they always spread to some extent into regions that would not be traversed by rays drawn from the original incoming wave-front. In other words, rectilinear propagation is not realized when light passes through a narrow opening or passes a small opaque object. This phenomenon is called *diffraction*.

In order to explain this bending of light, Christian Huygens (1629–

1695) introduced an hypothesis known today as *Huygens' principle*. According to this hypothesis, every point on an advancing wave-front can be considered as a source of *secondary waves* which in a homogeneous medium spread out as spherical wavelets at a speed equal to the speed of the original wave disturbance. A later position of the *primary wave-front* is given by the envelope of the spherical wavelets traveling in the forward direction.

The application of Huygens' principle to spherical waves in free space can be understood by consideration of Fig. 13. If W_1 is a wave-front spreading out from a source S with speed c, then according to the Huygens hypothesis every point of this wave-front is to be considered as the source of a secondary wavelet whose radius after t seconds would be ct. A later position of the primary wave-front such as W_2 is given by the envelope of the secondary wavelets, which combine to give the advancing primary wave-front. In order to be consistent, one should also consider the secondary wavelets combined to give a resultant wave-front moving *backward*—something that is not observed. The wavelets are effective only in producing a forward-moving wave. It should be noted that the secondary wavelets start from all points of a primary wave-front *in the same phase*. The laws of reflection and refraction are readily interpretable in terms of Huygens' principle, but the chief utility of this hypothesis is the interpretation of diffraction phenomena.

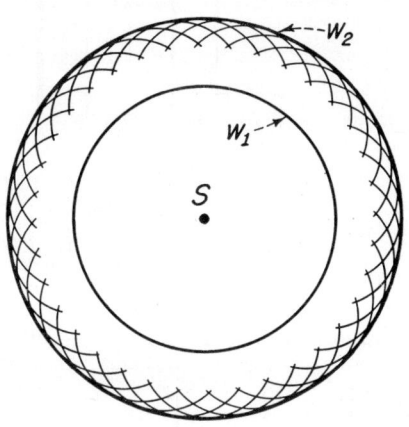

Fig. 13. Huygens' principle for a spherical wave-front.

In order to explain the spreading of light passing through a narrow opening, consider plane waves approaching a barrier, as shown in Fig. 14. Let AB represent the barrier and let S be an opening of width small compared with the wavelength of the advancing plane waves. At all points on the barrier except S the waves will be absorbed or reflected. The narrow opening S will transmit a disturbance to the region beyond the barrier. According to Huygens' principle, the disturbance in this region will be transmitted in the manner shown in the figure; a cross section of the advancing wave-front would consist of semicircles. Experimentally, it is found that the region of screen CD that is illuminated by a narrow slit at position S becomes broader as the slit width is made narrower. The central portion of the screen is always brighter than the more remote portions, and hence it must be assumed that the amplitudes of the secondary wavelets is greatest in the forward direction; more detailed theory indicates that the amplitude of the wavelet is proportional to $(1+\cos\theta)$, a quantity sometimes called the *obliquity factor*.

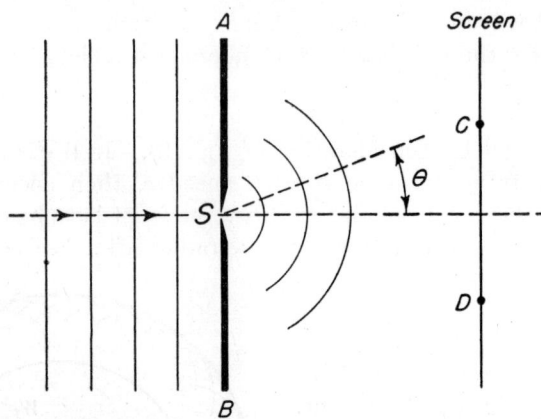

Fig. 14. Diffraction by a narrow slit.

The original experiment on interference performed by Thomas Young made use of the diffraction of light in passing through a narrow slit. Young's experimental arrangement is shown schematically in Fig. 15. Sunlight is first allowed to pass through slit S, and then at a considerable

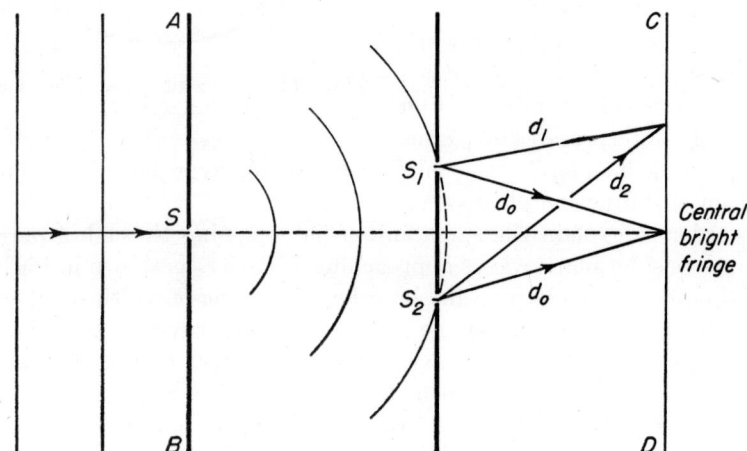

Fig. 15. Young's experiment.

distance away the diffracted light passes through the slits S_1 and S_2. If the slits S_1 and S_2 are at equal distances from S, the light waves from S reach these slits in the same phase. Light waves passing through slits

S_1 and S_2 therefore produce interference fringes on the screen CD in exactly the same manner as in the interference experiments of Fresnel that involved a double mirror or a biprism.

In our discussion of diffraction thus far, we have mentioned only the spreading of a plane light wave in passing through a slit that is extremely narrow. This phenomenon is satisfactorily explained in terms of the wave theory of light with the aid of Huygens' principle. We have not discussed quantitatively the way in which the light is *distributed* after passing through the aperture or past the edges of an obstacle in the light beam. The light reaching a screen behind the slit or obstacle forms a *diffraction pattern*, which we shall now discuss in terms of the wave theory.

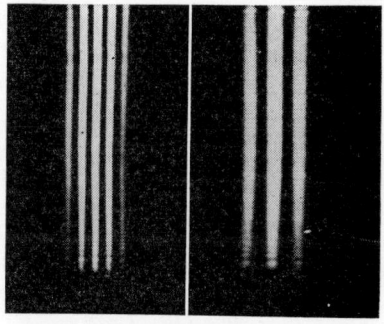

Fig. 16. Photographs of diffraction patterns formed in Young's experiment. The pattern on the left is formed by slits of twice the separation of those giving the pattern on the right.*

For the purpose of our discussion, it will be convenient to divide diffraction phenomena into two classes: (1) *Fresnel diffraction* and (2) *Fraunhofer diffraction*. Fresnel diffraction consists of diffraction phenomena in which either the source or the screen or both are at a finite distance from the aperture, whereas in Fraunhofer diffraction the diffraction phenomena involve parallel light beams. In the observation of Fresnel diffraction, no lenses are necessary. In observing Fraunhofer diffraction, light from a source such as an illuminated slit is rendered parallel by a lens; after the light has passed through the aperture at which diffraction occurs, a second lens is placed in such a manner that an image of the source is formed on a screen, where diffraction effects can be observed. In effect the use of these lenses makes source and image distances infinite.

6. FRESNEL DIFFRACTION

As an example of Fresnel's approach to diffraction problems, we shall first consider his method of finding the effect produced by a plane wave at a point ahead of the wave. Let us consider a plane wave advancing to the right in Fig. 17 and attempt to find the effect of this wave at point P by combining the results produced by secondary wavelets from all points of the primary plane wave-front. Let the wavelength of the incident light be λ and let the distance OP normal to the wave front be r. Now with P as a common center construct a series of spheres which intersect

---

* The photographs of Figs. 16, 19, 20, 22, 23, 25 and 29 are reproduced by permission from *Principles of Physics III* by F. W. Sears (Addison-Wesley Press, 1945).

the plane wave-front and which have radii $r+\frac{1}{2}\lambda$, $r+\lambda$, $r+\frac{3}{2}\lambda$, $r+2\lambda$, $\cdots$. The intersections of these spheres with the plane wave-front divide the wave-front into a series of zones; the first zone is a circle and the others are rings having O as a center. It is evident from the method of construction that the average distance from the point P to successive zones will increase by $\frac{1}{2}\lambda$ in passing from one zone to the next. All the secondary waves from any one zone can be considered to produce a certain resultant vibration at P, and the amplitudes of the resultants from

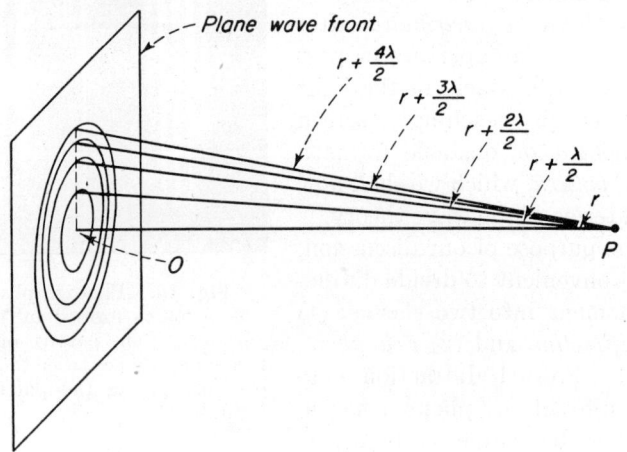

Fig. 17. Construction of a zone plate.

the successive zones can be represented by M_1, M_2, M_3, $\cdots$. The total amplitude of the disturbance at point P depends on the amplitudes and the phases of the disturbances reaching P from the different zones. Since the secondary waves start with the same phase from all points on the wave-front, their phase at point P will depend simply on the distance traveled to P. Since the distance traveled increases by $\frac{1}{2}\lambda$ from zone to zone, the disturbance from zone 2 will be a half wavelength behind that from zone 1, and so on for successive zone pairs. Consequently, the amplitudes of the resultant disturbances M_1, M_3, M_5, $\cdots$ will be in phase with one another but will be out of phase by 180° with resultants M_2, M_4, M_6, $\cdots$. Hence, in order to obtain the total amplitude A at point P, we should add the successive M's, using $+$ and $-$ signs alternately:

$$A = M_1 - M_2 + M_3 - M_4 + \cdots. \tag{8}$$

From the relation (5) derived from Fig. 10 we can see that all the zones have the same area provided their radii are small compared to OP in Fig. 17. However, it has been pointed out that the amplitude of secondary waves decreases as the angle between the direction of propagation and the normal to the wave-front increases. Therefore the M's slowly decrease:

$$M_1 > M_2 > M_3 > M_4 > \cdots.$$

The expression for A in equation (8) can be rewritten in the form

$$A = \tfrac{1}{2}M_1 + (\tfrac{1}{2}M_1 - \tfrac{1}{2}M_2) - (\tfrac{1}{2}M_2 - \tfrac{1}{2}M_3) + (\tfrac{1}{2}M_3 - \tfrac{1}{2}M_4) - \cdots.$$

Since the M's decrease slowly, the quantities in the parentheses are very

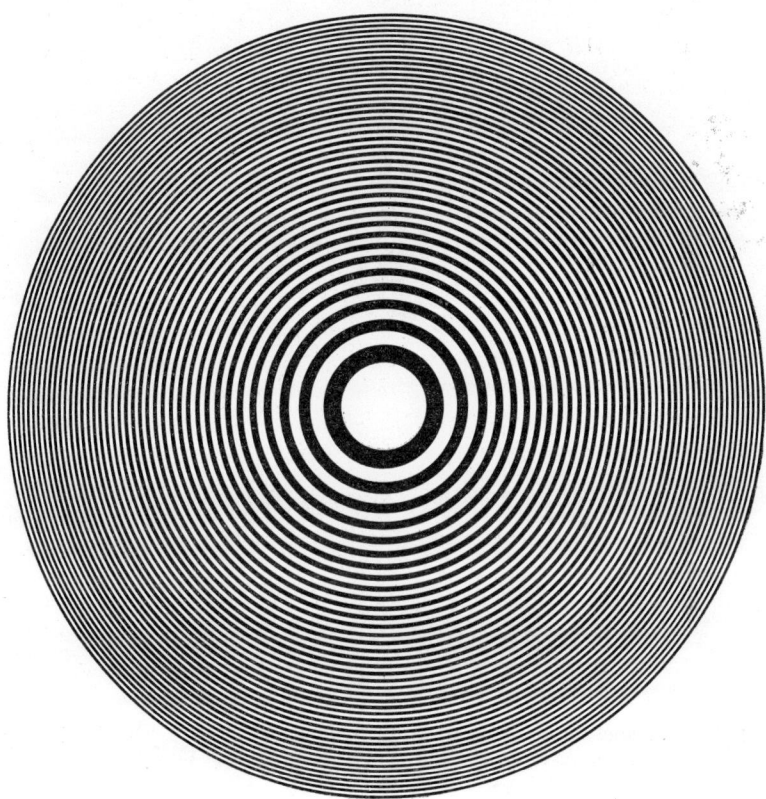

Fig. 18. Circular zone plate.

small and occur alternately with positive and negative signs. It can be shown that the sum of the series is actually

$$A = \tfrac{1}{2}M_1.$$

In other words, the effect of the plane wave at point P is equal to half of the resultant disturbance from the first zone; the effects from the remainder of the wave-front annul one another. This statement can be directly checked experimentally by blocking out all but the first zone;

the intensity at P quadruples when this is done, since the intensity is proportional to the square of the amplitude.

On the basis of this analysis, it would be expected that blocking out the alternate zones 1, 3, 5, · · · (or 2, 4, 6, · · ·) by opaque rings drawn

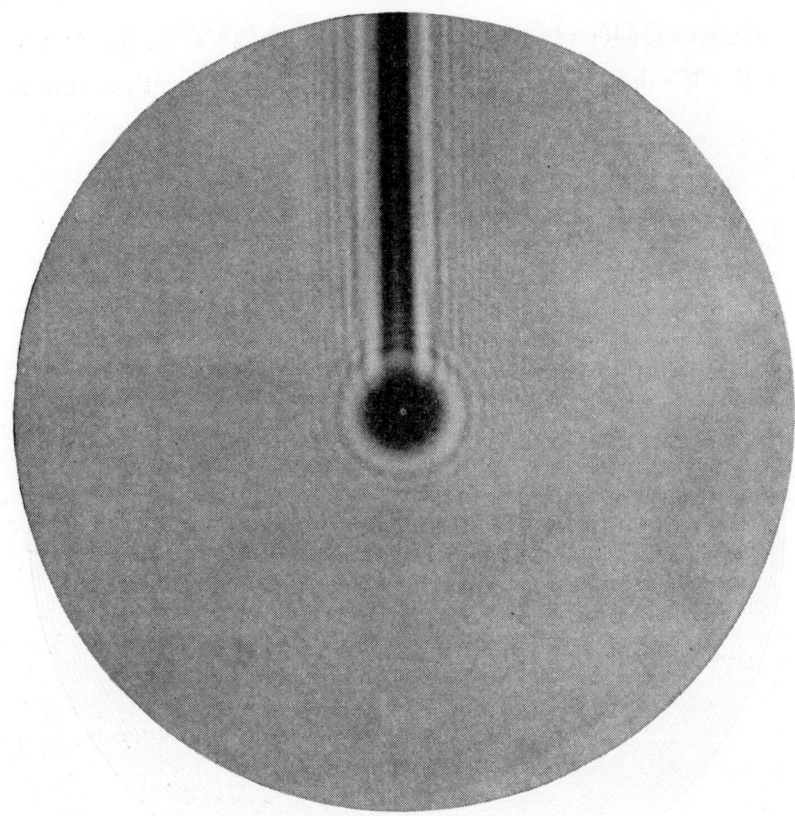

Fig. 19. Fresnel diffraction pattern of a small ball bearing supported by a needle. Note the bright spot at the center of the ball.

to the proper size on a transparent plate would considerably increase the amplitude of the disturbance at P, since the effects of all remaining zones would be in phase and the amplitude A could be written

$$A = M_2 + M_4 + M_6 + \cdots.$$

Plates so constructed are called *zone plates*. They do produce a strong increase in intensity at point P when placed in a parallel beam of light; in fact, they can be used to produce real images of distant objects in somewhat the same manner as does a converging lens. The fact that a zone plate does increase the intensity at point P is further evidence that the effect of a source at a point is not necessarily transmitted simply along the ray connecting the source and the point but does involve *diffraction* effects. A circular zone plate is shown in Fig. 18. This figure is accurate. If it is photographed, the photographic negative can be used as an effective zone plate.

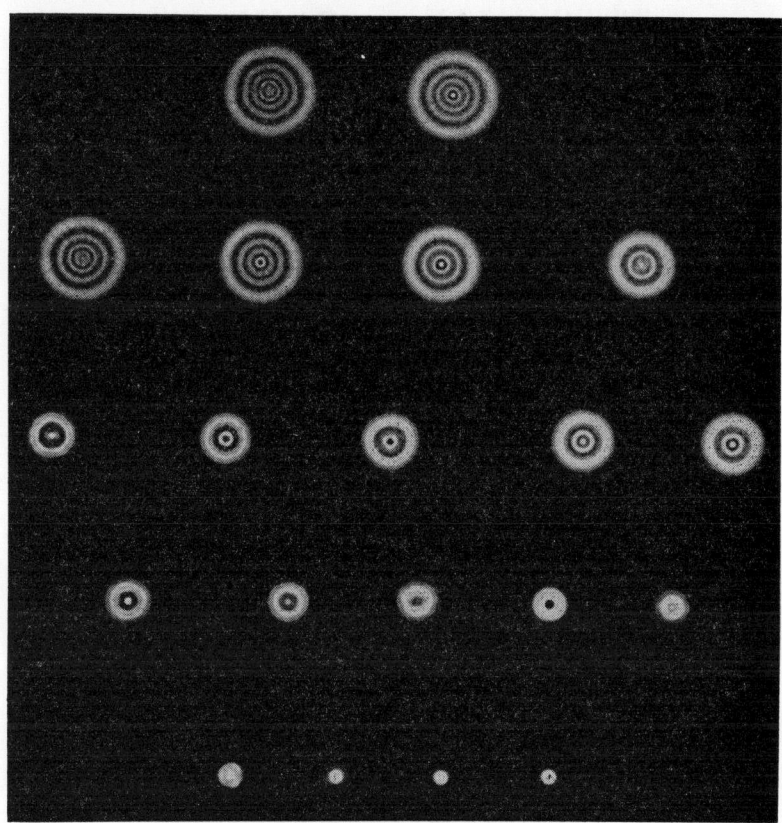

Fig. 20. Fresnel diffraction patterns of circular holes of various sizes. Largest holes are at the top, smallest at the bottom. The center is light or dark according to whether an odd or even number of zones is exposed by the hole.

Fresnel used arguments based on the discussion of the circular zone plate in explaining the diffraction effects observed when a parallel beam of light strikes a small circular opaque object. Some rather interesting diffraction patterns can be observed within and near the geometrical shadow. The same type of analysis can be used to explain the diffraction patterns produced by light passing through small circular apertures; in this case, all but a few of the central zones in the plane wave-front are removed. Photographs of diffraction patterns observed for circular obstacles and circular apertures are shown in Figs. 19 and 20. Our simple discussion of the zone plate enables us to predict intensities only at a point P at the center of the geometrical shadow of an obstacle or at the central point in a beam of light passing through a circular aperture. A more detailed analysis shows that point P is surrounded

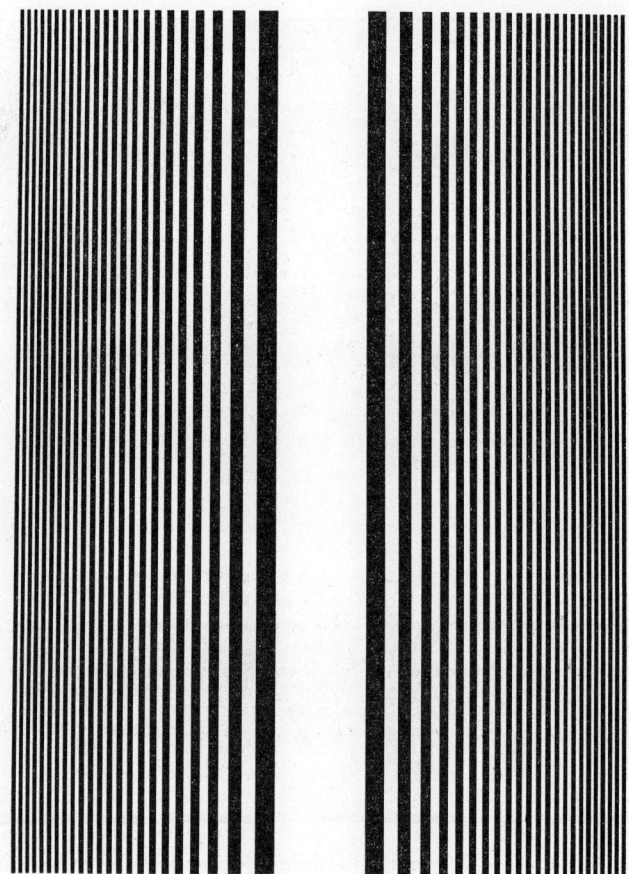

Fig. 21. Cylindrical zone plate.

by a system of concentric circular diffraction fringes of the type shown in the photographs.

In discussing the diffraction patterns produced when light passes a straightedge, passes through a narrow slit, or passes by a narrow opaque strip, Fresnel used a somewhat similar treatment involving zones. In cases of this kind, the diffraction pattern consists of parallel fringes, and the problem is essentially one of finding the intensity produced by a wavefront along a *line* rather than at a *point* in advance of the approaching wave-front; in other words, it is necessary to divide an approaching plane

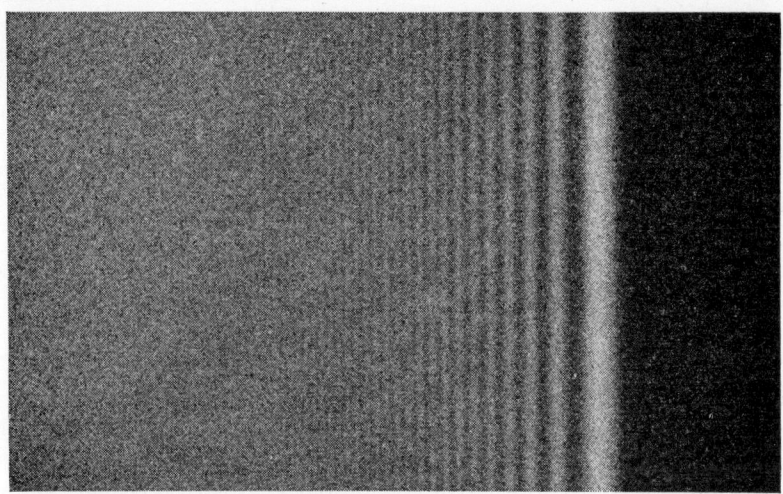

Fig. 22. Shadow of a straight edge, showing Fresnel diffraction pattern.

Fig. 23. Fresnel diffraction effects in the shadow of a razor blade.

wave-front into zones that are strips rather than into zones that are circular. The strip zones are formed by constructing cylinders of radii $r+\frac{1}{2}\lambda$, $r+\lambda$, $r+\frac{3}{2}\lambda$, $\cdots$ around the reference *line* as axis and finding the lines at which these cylinders intersect the plane wave-front. This method of construction is analogous to the method already described for the construction of circular zones. If a zone plate is constructed by blanking out successive zones, a cylindrical zone plate like that shown in Fig. 21 is obtained.

The effect of a narrow slit or a narrow obstacle on the intensity of the light received along the reference line can be determined by ascertaining the effect of the obstacle or slit in blocking out zones in the incident wave-front. Observed fringes are shown in the photographs of Figs. 19, 22, and 23. The observed patterns are adequately explained in terms of Fresnel zones, but the mathematical details involved in determining the intensity distributions are beyond the scope of the present work.

It is fairly easy to observe diffraction patterns with relatively simple apparatus. For example, by making a small pinhole in a piece of cardboard and viewing the daytime sky through the pinhole, one can observe well-defined diffraction patterns. In order to observe the diffraction pattern of a slit, one can hold his hand at arm's length toward a window and obtain a narrow band of light shining between two fingers. By viewing this first slit through a similar very narrow slit formed by the fingers of the other hand, one can observe a diffraction pattern when the two slits are parallel. The illuminated first slit appears wider than when viewed directly and on both sides of the first slit parallel rows of bright and dark diffraction fringes are observed.

PROBLEMS

1. Light of wavelength 600 mμ from a distant point source passes through a circular opening, and the resulting Fresnel diffraction pattern is observed on a screen 1 m beyond the opening. Find the radius of the opening if it is just large enough to include the central Fresnel zone. *Ans: 0.775 mm.*

2. Compute the radius of a circular zone plate having a 'focal length' of 1 m for light of wavelength 500 mμ if the plate has only 10 zones, with zones 1, 3, 5, 7, and 9 open and the even-numbered zones blacked out.

3. If the circular opening described in Prob. 1 is enlarged sufficiently to include the first four Fresnel zones, what will be the diameter of the opening? *Ans: 3.10 mm.*

4. Find the radius of the central zone of a Fresnel zone plate that has a focal length of 2.00 m for red light of wavelength 700 mμ.

5. Find the radius of a circular hole in an opaque screen if the hole is just equal in size to the central Fresnel zone for a parallel beam of green light from a mercury lamp (546.1 mμ) when the observer's eye is exactly 3 m from the hole. *Ans: 1.28 mm.*

6. Show that the hole described in Prob. 5 must have a radius approximately $\sqrt{2}$ times as large to uncover the first two Fresnel zones, $\sqrt{3}$ times as large to uncover the first three Fresnel zones, and so on.

7. Why is there always a bright spot at the center of the Fresnel diffraction pattern of a small circular obstacle, such as the ball of Fig. 19?

8. (a) From measurements made on Fig. 18, determine the 'focal length' (r in Fig. 17) of this circular zone plate for light of 500-mμ wavelength.

(b) Do the same for the cylindrical zone plate of Fig. 21.

7. FRAUNHOFER DIFFRACTION AT A SINGLE OPENING

As indicated in Sec. 5, the term *Fraunhofer diffraction* refers to diffraction phenomena occurring when parallel light beams are incident upon an aperture or an obstacle. The experimental production of Fraunhofer diffraction is more complicated than that of Fresnel diffraction, since a lens must be used to render the light from a source parallel and another lens must be used to focus the diffracted beam on a screen. However, the details of the Fraunhofer patterns are much easier to compute.

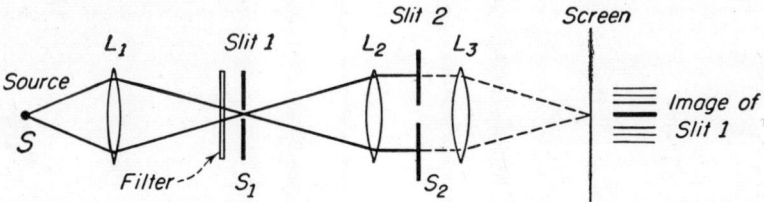

Fig. 24. Arrangement for observing the Fraunhofer diffraction pattern of a slit.

A typical arrangement for observing the Fraunhofer diffraction pattern of a slit is shown in Fig. 24. Light from a source S is focused by lens L_1 on slit 1 after the light has been made monochromatic by the filter inserted between lens L_1 and the slit S_1. The light passing through slit 1 is rendered parallel by the lens L_2. Before slit S_2 is introduced, the parallel light beam is focused by lens L_3 in such a manner as to produce a real image of slit S_1 on the screen. When slit S_2 is inserted parallel to slit S_1, a diffraction pattern is observed on the screen. The bright central portion of the diffraction pattern coincides with the original image of slit 1 but is considerably broader. If slit 2 is very narrow, several bright and dark fringes will appear on the screen on each side of the central image. The width of the central image and the spacing of the diffraction fringes are determined by the width of slit 2. The width of the central image on the screen is approximately twice that of the fainter bright fringes at the side, as shown in Fig. 25.

The explanation of the observed diffraction pattern is relatively simple, since only plane wave-fronts reaching the lens L_3 are focused on the screen. The simplified drawing in Fig. 26 will be useful in understanding the observed diffraction patterns; in this figure the magnitudes of the slit width and wavelength are enlarged for purposes of clarity. In the figure the lines I represent the path traversed in the forward direction by the secondary Huygens wavelets from the two edges of the slit. Since the light approaching the slit consists of a parallel beam, the original wave-front is plane and all sources of Huygens wavelets in the slit opening are in phase. Therefore, the secondary waves traversing the paths I and all similar paths drawn in the forward direction from the plane of the slit are in phase, and the lens produces a bright image in the forward direction; this bright image is the central maximum of the diffraction pattern. The intensity of images produced at other points on the screen depends on the differences in optical paths traversed by secondary waves from different parts of the slit. If we are interested in the intensity on the screen at a point making angle θ (measured at the slit) with the center of

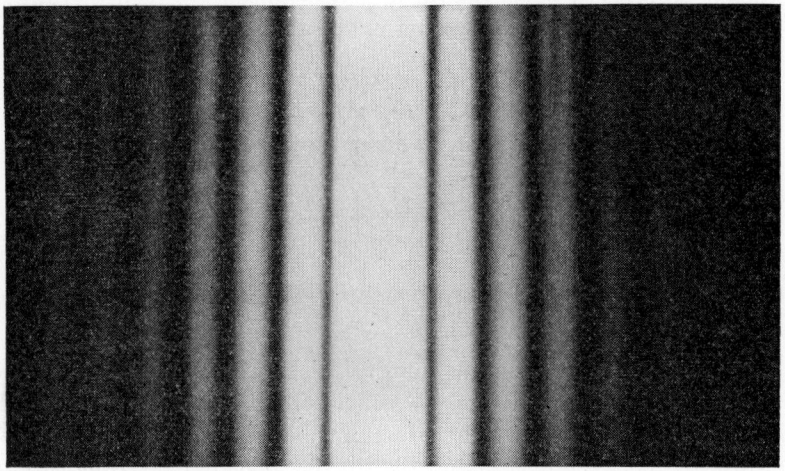

Fig. 25. Fraunhofer diffraction pattern of a single slit.

the pattern, we must consider the portions of the Huygens' wavelets that leave the slit at angle θ in Fig. 26. The lines II_a and II_b represent paths traversed by such secondary waves. It will be noted that path II_a traversed by waves from the upper limit of the slit is longer than path II_b by an amount Δp. If this path difference Δp is λ, the slit can be divided into two zones indicated in the figure by AB and BC, respectively; the *mean difference* in path length for the secondary waves coming from the two zones is then $\frac{1}{2}\lambda$ and the waves from the two zones cancel completely when the lens brings the waves together on the screen. Therefore, at an angle θ for which Δp is λ, complete cancellation occurs, and a dark fringe or region of zero intensity results. Similar reasoning shows that the intensity is zero when Δp is equal to 2λ, 3λ, 4λ, 5λ, $\cdots$.

The situation is different when Δp is equal to an odd number of half wavelengths. For example, consider the case for $\Delta p = \frac{3}{2}\lambda$. The slit can be divided into three zones, and the mean difference in path traversed by the secondary waves coming from successive zones is $\frac{1}{2}\lambda$. Therefore, the waves from two of the zones will lead to cancellation at the screen, but the secondary waves from the third zone are not canceled and a bright fringe or maximum will appear on the screen. Apart from the obliquity factor, which is close to unity if θ is small, the amplitude of this maximum will be $\frac{1}{3}$ the amplitude of the central maximum, so the intensity will be $\frac{1}{9}$. Similar arguments show that bright fringes occur when Δp is equal to $\frac{5}{2}\lambda$, $\frac{7}{2}\lambda$, $\cdots$. Since the first dark fringe occurs at

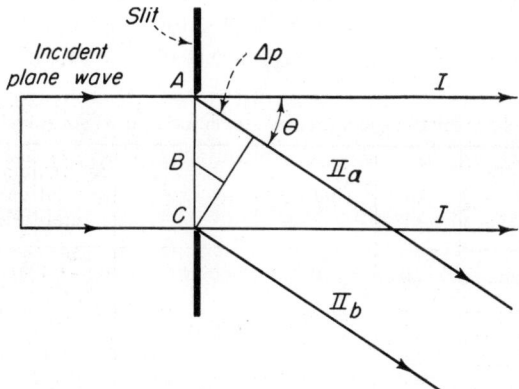

Fig. 26. Enlargement of slit 2 of Fig. 24.

$p = \lambda$, and $p = 0$ gives a maximum, the distance between the centermost dark fringes is twice as great as that between succeeding dark fringes; the result is that the observed central maximum is twice as wide as the other maxima.

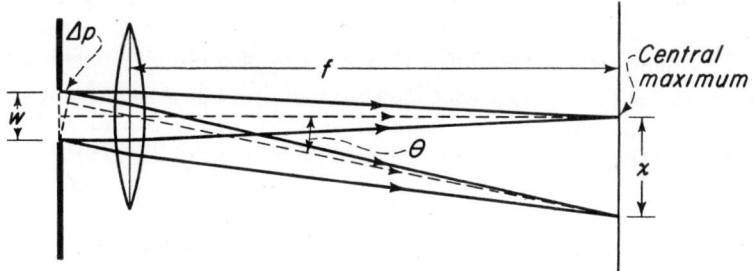

Fig. 27. Fraunhofer diffraction patterns on a screen.

As for the angles at which the maxima and minima occur, it will be noted that in Fig. 26 $\sin\theta = \Delta p/w$, where w is the slit width. Fig. 27 shows the way in which the light is focused on the screen. Since parallel light is focused at a point, the distance from the lens to the screen must equal the focal length f of the lens. Parallel light making angle θ with the axis of the lens will be focused at the point x for which $x/f = \tan\theta$, as shown by the broken ray drawn through the center of the lens. Since the angle θ is small for those parts of the diffraction pattern that have appreciable intensity, we may replace $\tan\theta$ by $\sin\theta$ and write

$$\sin\theta = \frac{\Delta p}{w} = \frac{x}{f}.$$

Table I gives the angles θ, screen positions x, and approximate values for relative amplitudes and intensities for the diffraction pattern. The approximate values for the amplitudes shown in the table are obtained from a consideration of the relative areas of the uncanceled zones con-

TABLE I
Fraunhofer Diffraction Pattern for a Single Slit

	Δp	$\sin\theta \approx \theta$	x	Approximate relative amplitude	Approximate relative intensity
Central maximum...	0	0	0	1	1
First minimum......	λ	λ/w	$(\lambda/w)f$	0	0
First maximum......	$3/2\lambda$	$3/2\lambda/w$	$3/2(\lambda/w)f$	$1/3$	$1/9$
Second minimum....	2λ	$2\lambda/w$	$2(\lambda/w)f$	0	0
Second maximum....	$5/2\lambda$	$5/2\lambda/w$	$5/2(\lambda/w)f$	$1/5$	$1/25$
Third minimum.....	3λ	$3\lambda/w$	$3(\lambda/w)f$	0	0
Third maximum.....	$7/2\lambda$	$7/2\lambda/w$	$7/2(\lambda/w)f$	$1/7$	$1/49$
Fourth minimum....	4λ	$4\lambda/w$	$4(\lambda/w)f$	0	0
Fourth maximum....	$9/2\lambda$	$9/2\lambda/w$	$9/2(\lambda/w)f$	$1/9$	$1/81$

structed at the slit in the manner described above; the intensities are proportional to the squares of the amplitudes. The values shown in the table are good approximations for cases in which the diffraction angles are small.

The calculation of the diffraction pattern of a circular opening for a point source is similar in essentials to the above calculation for a narrow slit. However, since the details of the calculation are considerably more complicated, we shall merely state the results for the angle at which the first minimum is observed. As we have seen, the first minimum in the diffraction pattern of a slit occurs at an angle $\theta = \lambda/w$. In the case of a circular opening, the first minimum occurs at angle $\theta = 1.22\,\lambda/a$, where a is the diameter of the circular opening (the linear aperture).

In the above discussion and in that of Fig. 11 we have employed implicitly the following important theorem:

When a lens forms a point image of a point object, the optical path lengths of all rays through the lens are equal; hence rays leaving the object in phase will arrive at the image in phase. When a parallel beam is focused at a point, the optical path length of all rays from a plane wave-front to the point are equal; a similar statement applies when light from a point is rendered parallel by the lens.

This property of a lens, which is necessary to permit interference between light passing through different parts of the lens, will be demonstrated in a particular case in Sec. 10.

PROBLEMS

1. A lens of focal length 40 cm is used to form a Fraunhofer diffraction pattern of a slit 0.3 mm wide. Calculate the distance on the screen from the center of the central maximum to the center of the first dark band and to the next bright band when the slit is illuminated by yellow light ($\lambda = 589$ mμ) from a sodium flame.

Ans: 0.79 mm; 1.18 mm.

2. Parallel light of wavelength 546.1 mμ is incident normally on a slit 1 mm wide. If a lens of 100-cm focal length is mounted just behind the slit and the light is focused on a screen, what will be the distance from the center of the diffraction pattern to (a) the first minimum, (b) the first maximum, and (c) the third maximum?

3. In the Fraunhofer diffraction pattern of a single slit, the distance between the first minimum on one side of the central maximum to the first minimum on the other side of the central maximum is 6.75 mm. If the wavelength of the light is 546.1 mμ and the lens used to form the diffraction pattern has a focal length of 60 cm, find the width of the slit.

Ans: 0.097 mm.

4. Parallel white light is incident normally on a slit; a lens of focal length 60 cm mounted behind the slit focuses the light on a screen. Find the wavelength of light for which the *third* maximum coincides in position with the *second* maximum for red light of wavelength 640 mμ.

5. Parallel light of wavelength 600 mμ is incident normally on a narrow slit and is focused on a screen 80 cm away by a lens just behind the slit. If the distance from the center of the central image to the first maximum is 2.0 mm, what is the width of the slit?

Ans: 0.36 mm.

6. Light of wavelength 500 mμ is incident normally on a slit 0.6 mm wide and is brought to a focus by a lens of focal length 200 cm. Find the distance between the first and second maxima in the resulting diffraction pattern.

8. RESOLVING POWER OF OPTICAL INSTRUMENTS

Let us now consider the case of diffraction effects in which there are two sources focused on a screen. Such a situation could be realized by placing a second source slit S_1' just above and parallel to the original source slit S_1 in Fig. 24, both slits being illuminated by use of an extended rather than a point source S. Light from slits S_1 and S_1' would be furnished by different parts of the source and would have no definite phase relationship. With such an arrangement there would be two central maxima I_m and I_m' formed on the screen. Each central image would be bordered by a set of bright and dark fringes, which would overlap if the source slits S_1 and S_1' were sufficiently close together. Indeed, if the two source slits were brought sufficiently close together, the two diffraction patterns would overlap to such an extent that the eye would be unable to distinguish two separate central images. It has been found that the two images can just be seen as separate or just *resolved*, if the central maximum I_m' coincides with the first minimum of the diffraction pattern to which I_m belongs. This situation is illustrated in Fig. 28, which shows a plot of intensity as a function of screen separation for the two patterns. According to Table I, the screen separation of the two central maxima in Fig. 28 is $(\lambda/w)f$. This value corresponds to an angular separation of λ/w, where w is the width of slit S_2. Hence, we can state that two images can be resolved only if their angular separation α is at least equal to λ/w, where w is the opening of the slit through which the light passes. The condition for resolution, $\alpha = \lambda/w$, is known as the *Rayleigh criterion*.

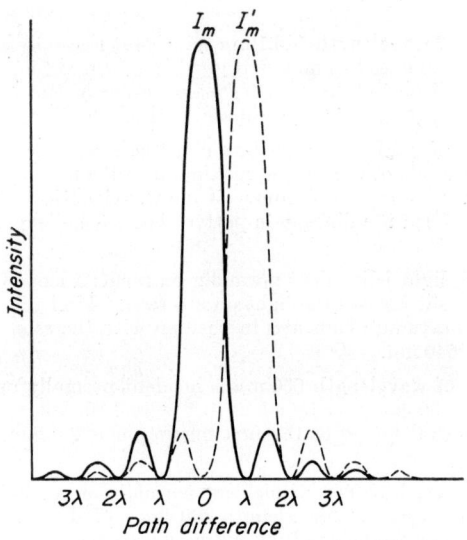

Fig. 28. Rayleigh criterion: The diffraction patterns from two closely-spaced sources at the limit of resolution where the central maximum of one pattern falls at the first minimum of the other.

Note that in the above discussion the 'sources' S_1 and S_1' are assumed to be very narrow slits, and that the limit of angular resolution of the images of these slits formed by the lenses L_2 and L_3 in Fig. 24 is determined by the width of slit S_2 that limits the lens aperture. *Widening* the slit S_2 *increases* the resolving power, that is, *widening* S_2 permits resolution of the images of *more closely spaced* slits S_1 and S_1'.

If the opening that gives the Fraunhofer diffraction pattern is circular, a *point source* forms a circular central image with circular diffraction rings around it. As stated earlier, the first dark ring is formed at an angle of $1.22\lambda/d$ with the direction of the original incident light beam. Therefore, the Rayleigh criterion for a circular opening of diameter d is that two point sources can be resolved only if their angular separation is greater than

$$\alpha = 1.22\lambda/d. \qquad (9)$$

This criterion is illustrated by the photographs of Fig. 29.

If the diaphragm containing the slit S_2 in Fig. 24 is removed, we still have a diffraction pattern on the screen, but this pattern is very narrow because the width of the slit has been replaced by the whole width of the lens L_3. But this type of diffraction pattern furnishes a limit to the resolving power of an optical instrument. For example, if the objective lens of an astronomical telescope is illuminated by the parallel light from two distant stars, the images of the two stars formed by the lens can-

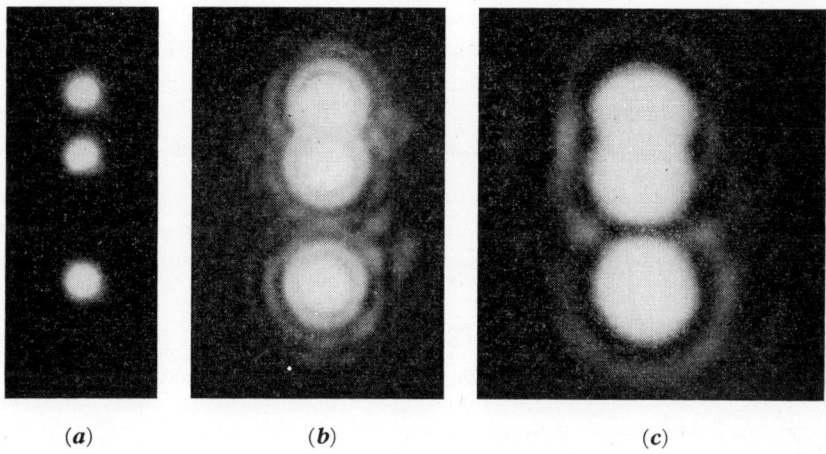

Fig. 29. Fraunhofer diffraction patterns of three 'point' sources obtained with a circular opening in front of the lens. Part (a) shows the results obtained with a large opening; in part (b) the circular opening has been closed until the patterns of the upper holes are just resolved, according to the Rayleigh criterion; in part (c) the circular opening is so small that these patterns are no longer resolved.

not be resolved if the angle between the stars is less than that given by (9) with d equal to the diameter of the objective.

Diffraction effects set the ultimate limitation on the usefulness of optical instruments such as telescopes and microscopes. In Chap. 26, Optical Instruments, we discussed the magnification obtainable with these instruments and indicated that limits of *useful* magnification were imposed by the wave nature of light itself. Now we see that it is useless, for example, to try to resolve two stars by increasing the magnifying power of a telescope merely by using an eyepiece of shorter focal length if the stars subtend an angle of less than $\alpha = 1.22\lambda/d$, where d is the diameter of the objective. If the angle subtended is less than α, the objective can produce only a fuzzy image consisting of overlapping diffraction patterns in which separate images of the two stars cannot be distinguished, regardless of the power of the eyepiece used. The wavelength normally used in Rayleigh's criterion for ultimate resolution is an average value of 500 m$\mu = 5 \times 10^{-5}$ cm when white light is involved.

The reasoning used in determining the ultimate resolution attainable with a microscope is somewhat similar. In order to be resolved by a microscope, two points must subtend an angle at the objective at least as large as $1.22\lambda/d$, where d is the diameter of the microscope objective. However, there is a way in which the resolving power of a microscope can be increased. If ultraviolet light is used to illuminate the object, the limiting angle α is smaller, since ultraviolet light is of shorter wavelength than visible light. It is necessary to use a photographic plate to receive the image in an ultraviolet microscope.

The *resolving power* of an optical instrument like the telescope or microscope is defined as the reciprocal of α. For an instrument using circular lenses or mirrors,

$$\text{resolving power} = (\text{diameter of objective})/1.22\lambda.$$

The simple expressions for α and resolving power that we have stated for the microscope are only approximate, since parallel light beams are not involved and since additional factors involving the illumination of the object should be considered.

PROBLEMS

1. What is the angular separation of two luminous point objects that can just be resolved by a small telescope having an objective lens of 8-cm diameter?   Ans: $1''.57$.

2. What is the resolving power of the telescope described in Prob. 1?

3. The focal length of the objective of a certain microscope is 3.2 mm and its diameter is 4.0 mm. What is the *approximate* value of the separation of two point objects that can just be resolved when they are illuminated by light of mean wavelength 500 mμ?
Ans: 488 mμ.   NOTE: Calculation on basis of more detailed theory gives 380 mμ.

4. What would be the *approximate* value for the smallest separation of two point objects that could just be resolved if ultraviolet light of wavelength 230 mμ were used with the microscope described in Prob. 3 and photographic methods of detection were used?

5. What is the theoretical angular limit of resolution of the Yerkes telescope, whose objective is 40 inches in diameter? What is its resolving power?
Ans: $0''.124$; 1.67×10^6.

6. Calculate the limit of angular resolution in seconds, and the resolving power of the 200-in reflecting telescope at Mount Palomar.

7. The pupil of the eye is approximately 2 mm in diameter under conditions of moderate illumination. Considering the eye as a telescope, compute the eye's limit of angular resolution for $\lambda = 550$ mμ. Is the resolving power of the eye greater at night or in bright daylight?   Ans: 3.4×10^{-4} rad, or approximately $1'$.

8. Using the value computed in Prob. 6 for the limit of angular resolution for the Mount Palomar telescope and taking 240,000 mi as the distance from the earth to the moon, find the linear separation of two objects on the moon's surface that can just be resolved by the 200-in telescope.

9. DIFFRACTION GRATINGS

When a large number of narrow slits are placed side by side, a device known as a *diffraction grating* is formed. Diffraction gratings are extensively used in the study of light emitted and absorbed by various materials.

In Fig. 30 a parallel beam of monochromatic light is shown approaching a transmission grating consisting of a large number of extremely narrow slits, only a few of which are shown. The distance between adjacent slits is d. Since the beam is parallel and normal to the grating, all Huygens sources in the plane of the grating are in the same phase. The secondary waves are in phase in the forward direction, since the paths traversed by all waves in this direction are of equal length. If the light waves traveling in the forward direction are focused on a screen, a bright

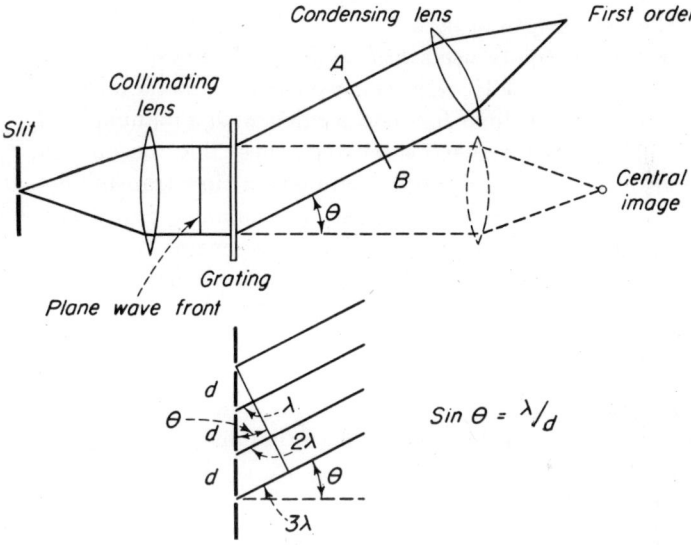

Fig. 30. Transmission grating.

central image of the original slit is formed. In certain other directions, the secondary waves will also form plane wave-fronts. One of these directions is denoted by θ in Fig. 30. At this angle the paths traversed by secondary waves from successive slits differ by an amount equal to the wavelength of the light. Hence, along the plane AB all points are essentially *in phase* and a lens placed in this beam will produce an image of the original slit on an appropriately placed screen; this image is called the *first-order* image. Consideration of Fig. 30 shows that the angle θ for the first order is defined by the relation

$$\sin\theta = \lambda/d,$$

where θ is the angle measured from the direction of the incident light, λ is the wavelength of the light, and d is the distance between adjacent slits.

Other directions in which secondary waves from the slits can produce a common plane wave-front are those directions in which the paths traversed by the secondary waves from successive slits differ by 2λ, 3λ, 4λ, $\cdots$. The directions in which diffraction maxima may be produced are accordingly given by the general relation

$$\sin\theta_n = n\lambda/d,$$

where $n = 1, 2, 3, 4, \cdots$, but n cannot exceed d/λ, the number of wavelengths in the grating spacing. These values of n give the *order number* of the diffraction maxima. Since θ_n can be accurately measured and d is known for a given grating, it is possible to use a grating to measure the wavelength of light.

The gratings actually used in most research investigations are reflection gratings. Essentially, reflection gratings are metal mirrors on which equally spaced narrow lines have been ruled with a diamond. When the grating is illuminated, the strips between these lines become the sources of Huygens wavelets, just as do the parallel slits in a transmission grating. Since the spacing of grating lines must be constant for all parts of a grating surface and since optical gratings have several thousand lines per centimeter, the fabrication of a grating is a difficult and expensive process. However, it is possible to produce *replicas* of an original grating by coating the grating surface with a collodion film. After the collodion film has dried, it can be removed from the grating surface. The collodion film has ridges corresponding to the ruled lines; hence, the smooth spaces between the rulings can be used in the same manner as slits in a transmission grating. In recent years, Prof. R. W. Wood has developed an excellent method for producing replicas that can be used as reflection gratings; this method involves evaporating aluminum on the collodion surface in a vacuum. Gratings prepared by this method have proved extremely satisfactory and are being used in many research laboratories.

PROBLEMS

1. A transmission grating has 4000 lines/cm. Calculate the angular deviation of the second order for sodium light of wavelength 589.3 mμ when a parallel beam of light strikes the grating at normal incidence. Show diagram. Ans: 28°.1.

2. When a parallel beam of light is normally incident, a certain transmission grating produces a diffraction pattern in which the third-order maximum for sodium light appears at an angle of 45° away from the central image. Find the distance between the lines on the grating.

3. When plane light waves are normally incident, a diffraction grating ruled with 6000 lines/cm forms the first-order diffraction maximum for light of a certain wavelength at an angle of 18°.0. What is the wavelength of the light? Show diagram. Ans: 515 mμ.

4. A diffraction grating is ruled with 6000 lines/cm. If a parallel beam of light consisting of light of wavelengths 500 mμ and 550 mμ strikes the grating normally, what is the angular separation between the diffraction maxima for 500-mμ and 550-mμ radiation, in the first order? in the second order?

5. Plane monochromatic waves of wavelength 600 mμ are incident normally on a plane transmission grating having 5000 lines/cm. Find the angles at which the first-, second-, and third-order diffraction maxima appear. Show diagram.

Ans: 17°.5; 36°.9; 64°.2.

6. A transmission grating ruled with 8000 lines/cm forms a second-order diffraction maximum at an angle of 42°.0 from the central maximum when a parallel beam of monochromatic light strikes the grating at normal incidence. What is the wavelength of the incident light?

10. WAVE TREATMENT OF THIN LENSES*

Having discussed some of the optical phenomena that can be interpreted only in terms of the wave theory of light, we shall return to one of the problems discussed earlier in terms of geometrical optics and show

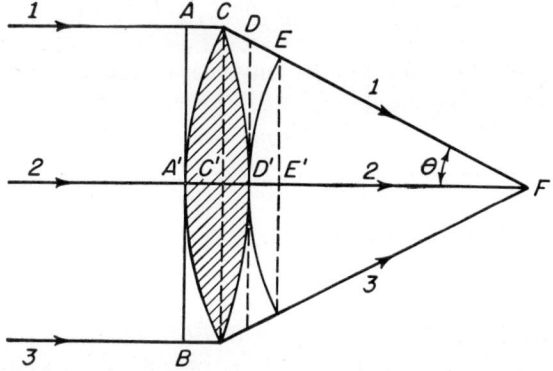

Fig 31. Wave treatment of a thin lens. (For the sake of clarity, the lens in the sketch is rather thick; it must be imagined that the angle θ is very much smaller than indicated.)

how this problem can be treated from the viewpoint of physical optics. We shall derive the *lensmaker's equation*

$$\frac{1}{f} = (\mu - 1)\left(\frac{1}{R_1} + \frac{1}{R_2}\right) \tag{10}$$

for the focal length of a thin double-convex lens having R_1 and R_2 as the radii of the surfaces. This equation can be easily derived by consideration of the optical paths traversed by various parts of a plane wave-front incident upon the lens.

In Fig. 31 a plane wave-front AB is shown approaching a thin double-convex lens. Since all Huygens sources on the wave-front are in phase, the light represented by the plane wave-front can be brought to a focus at F only if the optical paths traversed by secondary waves from different parts of the plane wave-front are equal. Let us consider the paths

---

* This section may be omitted without loss of continuity.

denoted by 1 and 2 in the figure. Path 1 passes through the periphery of the lens and traverses distance $AC+CE$ while waves on path 2 through the center of the lens traverse distance $A'D'$. Since the distance $AC+CE$ includes only an extremely short path length through the lens material, we can consider the path AE as being entirely in air; the distance $A'D'$ is entirely within the lens material. In order for the secondary waves along paths 1 and 2 to be in phase at point F, the optical path $AC+CE+EF$ must be equal to the optical path $\mu A'D'+D'F$. Since EF and $D'F$ are radii of the same circle and are therefore equal, it is necessary to consider only the optical-path elements $AC+CE$ and $\mu A'D'$. The sphere $D'E$ must represent one position of the wave-front that converges toward F. In order for the secondary waves to arrive at point F in phase, it is necessary that

$$AC+CE = \mu A'D'. \tag{11}$$

If θ is sufficiently small so that $\cos\theta$ may be set equal to unity, we see that $CE = C'E'$, and (11) becomes

$$A'E' = \mu A'D'.$$

For reasons that will be apparent later, it is desirable to restate this relation in the form

$$A'C'+C'D'+D'E' = \mu(A'C'+C'D')$$

or

$$D'E' = (\mu-1)(A'C'+C'D'). \tag{12}$$

In order to express the above distances in terms of the radii of the lens surfaces and the focal length, it is necessary to make use of the so-called *sagitta formula*, which was actually derived by considering the geometrical configuration shown in Fig. 10 and was stated in equation (5): the sagitta t of a chord of half length a of a circle of radius R is given by

$$t = a^2/2R,$$

provided R is large compared to a. In the case of Fig. 31, each of the path elements can be obtained from this formula if the appropriate radius is introduced; the term a for each of the path elements can be taken as AA' if the lens is sufficiently thin and θ sufficiently small. Thus

$$D'E' = \frac{(AA')^2}{2f}, \quad A'C' = \frac{(AA')^2}{2R_1}, \quad C'D' = \frac{(AA')^2}{2R_2}.$$

Substitution of these values in equation (12) above gives the lensmaker's equation (10) directly.

In a manner similar to the above, all relations that can be derived by the methods of geometrical optics can also be derived by the methods of physical optics. Furthermore, this type of derivation proves the important theorem, stated on p. 704, that *rays focused by a lens all arrive at the image point in phase.*

CHAPTER 28

DISPERSION, SPECTRA, AND COLOR

In Chap. 23 it was asserted that light consists of electromagnetic waves and that the range of wavelengths in the visible region extends from about 390 mμ for deep-violet light to 790 mμ for deep-red light; in Chap. 27, methods of determining wavelengths from measurements of interference and diffraction patterns were described. In the present chapter we shall discuss some of the ways in which light from a source can be divided or *dispersed* into its component wavelengths. The component wavelengths of a light source constitute the *spectrum* of the source; a spectrum can be displayed by focusing the dispersed radiation on a screen, on a photographic plate, or in the focal plane of an eyepiece. Emission and absorption spectra of various types of sources will be described and compared. The latter part of the present chapter is concerned with the color effects produced by optical filters and pigments. Some phenomena involving scattering of light will be discussed briefly.

1. DISPERSION OF WHITE LIGHT

During the discussion of refraction, it was pointed out that the bending of light rays passing from one medium to another is governed by Snell's law. The index of refraction that occurs in Snell's law is not the same for all wavelengths and for most transparent media is slightly greater for shorter wavelengths; that is, it is slightly greater for violet light than for red light. As a result of this difference in refractive index, rays of violet light are bent more sharply than rays of red light in passing from air into most transparent media. For example, when parallel rays of violet and red light are incident on a water surface as

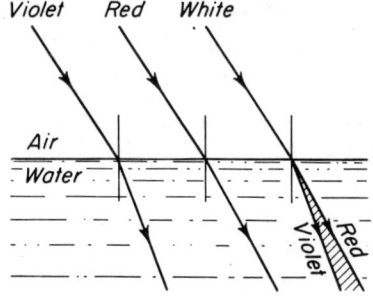

Fig. 1. Dispersion of white light by refraction at a water surface. (The amount of dispersion is exaggerated in this sketch.)

shown schematically in Fig. 1, they are no longer parallel after experiencing refraction.

If a ray of white light is incident on the water surface at the same angle as the violet and red rays, it splits after passing through the water surface into a group of colored rays with a violet ray at one boundary of the group and a red ray at the other boundary. This phenomenon is called *dispersion*. It can readily be observed when a narrow pencil of sunlight is incident on the surface of water in an aquarium. The explanation of the splitting of the white light ray into colored rays appears obvious now; we immediately conclude that the original white light is a complex wave motion that can be analyzed into components of different frequencies corresponding to the colored components, which are separated from one another by refraction at the water surface. In other words, white light is actually a compound wave produced by superposition of the waves corresponding to the different colors. Before Newton's time

Fig. 2. Newton's experiments on dispersion. (From Voltaire's *Elémens de la Philosophie de Newton*, Amsterdam, 1738, p. 116.)

it was thought that the colors were somehow *created* in the refracting medium. Using glass prisms to produce dispersion as in Fig. 2, Newton showed that the colored light produced by dispersion could be recombined to produce white light, but that a single color produced by dispersion was not changed into still other colors by a second refraction process. In Newton's own words:

> "And so the true Cause of the Length of that Image was detected to be no other, than that *Light* is not similar or Homogenial, but consists of Difform Rays, some of which are more Refrangible than others."

The observed spectrum or band of colors produced when white light is dispersed actually varies in hue continuously from the violet to the red end of the spectrum, but we are still accustomed to use the terminology of Newton in dividing these 'colors of the rainbow' into the seven bands: violet, indigo*, blue, green, yellow, orange, and red, in order of increasing

* The term *indigo* is obsolescent.

wavelength. Since Newton did not believe that light transmission involves a wave motion, he did not, of course, attribute a different frequency and wavelength to each spectral color as we do today. None the less, we are indebted to him for his clear demonstration that the spectral colors are merely components of white light.

When light contains colored components in the same proportion in which they are present in sunlight, the light appears *white*. If some components are relatively more abundant than in sunlight, the light appears slightly colored; for example, the light from an ordinary tungsten lamp contains a larger proportion of red light than does sunlight, and hence the light from a tungsten lamp appears slightly more orange than the *white* light from the sun.

2. PRISM SPECTROGRAPHS

The separation of light into its spectral colors can be accomplished by the use of a prism. Since a prism has two useful refracting surfaces, the resulting angular separation is greater than that at a single surface. The

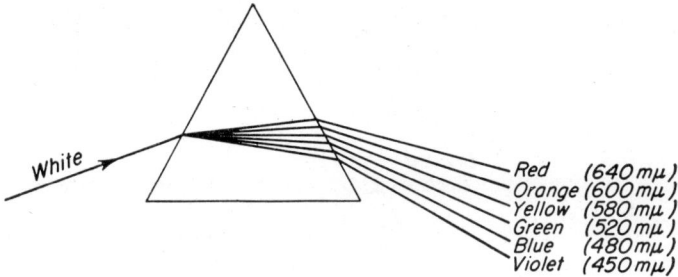

Fig. 3. Dispersion of white light by a prism. Typical values of wavelength associated with the different colors are indicated at the right.

path of a ray of white light through a prism is shown schematically in Fig. 3.

To show that the dispersed radiation can be recombined to produce white light, Newton introduced a second prism in the manner shown in Fig. 4. The reverse orientation of the second prism just reverses the angular separation of rays produced by the first prism. Beyond the second prism all the colored rays are parallel to the initially incident ray of white light. These laterally displaced parallel colored rays are converged by the lens so that a white image of the small opening defining the initial ray is formed at the principal focus of the lens.

A simple instrument for visual study of spectra is the prism *spectroscope*. The arrangement of such an instrument is shown in Fig. 5. Light from the source X passes through a lens L_1 and is imaged at slit S.

Slit S is located at the focal plane of a second lens L_2; therefore, the light leaves L_2 as a parallel beam. The slit S and lens L_2 are mounted at the ends of a tube, and the combination is called a *collimator*. Light from the collimator passes to the prism P, which produces angular separation of the light into its component wavelengths. The dispersed radiation

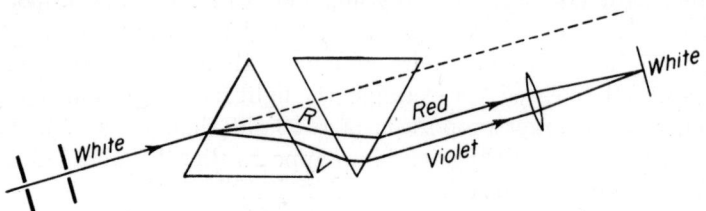

Fig. 4. Recombination of dispersed radiation into white light by a second prism and a lens.

then passes to the *telescope* objective L_3, which produces real images of the slit in the focal plane ab of the eyepiece E. If the light from source X is monochromatic, a single image of the slit will be observed. If the light from the source is polychromatic, an image of the slit will be observed for each spectral color emitted by the source; these colored images will be

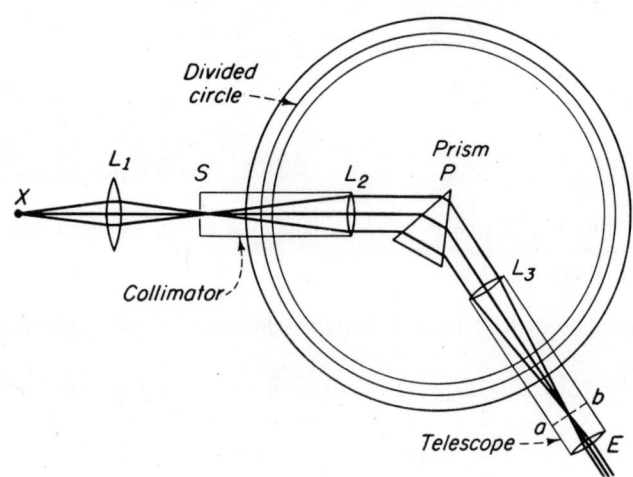

Fig. 5. Schematic diagram of a prism spectrometer.

separated from one another since, as a result of the angular separation produced by the prism, the beams of different colors are incident at the objective L_3 at slightly different angles. The images of the slit appear to the observer as narrow vertical lines, and hence it is customary to speak of them as *spectral lines*. In the simplest type of spectroscope, a small engraved glass scale is inserted at the focal plane ab of the eyepiece and the spectral lines are viewed adjacent to this reference scale; such an instrument can be used for qualitative work. If accurate measurements are desired, modifications must be made in this instrument. As shown in Fig. 5, the collimator can be kept fixed in position and the telescope can be rotated about a vertical axis located at the center of an accurately divided circle. Angular positions of the collimator and telescope can be determined by means of attached verniers. At the focal plane of the eyepiece is a set of fine crosshairs. Spectral lines can be brought into coincidence with the crosshairs by moving the telescope; by means of the vernier and the divided circle, accurate data on angular separation of the light of different wavelengths can be obtained. A spectroscope provided

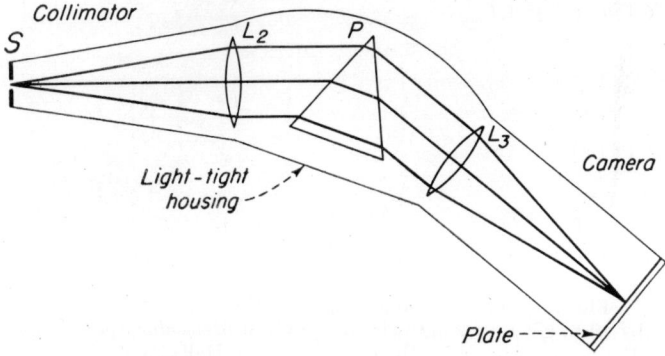

Fig. 6. Schematic diagram of a prism spectrograph.

in this manner with devices for measuring angular positions of spectral lines is called a *spectrometer*.

In much actual research and industrial work, it is desirable to make a photographic record of the spectra from various sources. This record may be made by replacing the telescope by a camera focused for parallel light. Such a device is called a *spectrograph*. A typical spectrograph arrangement is shown in Fig. 6, in which the slit S is illuminated by light from the source being studied. Parallel light from the collimator is dispersed by the prism, and the dispersed radiation passes to the camera lens. Colored images of the slit are formed at the photographic-plate position, and a photograph of the spectrum lines can be obtained. Such a picture is called a *spectrogram*. A reproduction of a spectrogram is shown in Fig. 7.

The angular separation of spectral colors obtainable with a prism spectrograph or spectroscope is determined by the angle A of the prism used and the optical properties of the prism material. In order to understand the effect of the optical properties of the prism material, let us

consider the relation
$$\mu = \frac{\sin\frac{1}{2}(D_{min}+A)}{\sin\frac{1}{2}A}$$

which was given in equation (14), p. 632. This equation gives the exact relationship between refractive index μ, prism angle A, and angle of minimum deviation D_{min}. However, the equation is also approximately correct for the deviation of light incident at angles close to the angle of incidence that gives minimum deviation. That is, because D_{min} is at an extremum of the curve giving the deviation as a function of angle of incidence, the angle of deviation θ will be approximately equal to D_{min} so long as the angle of incidence is in the neighborhood of the angle for minimum deviation. A further approximation can be made for small-angled

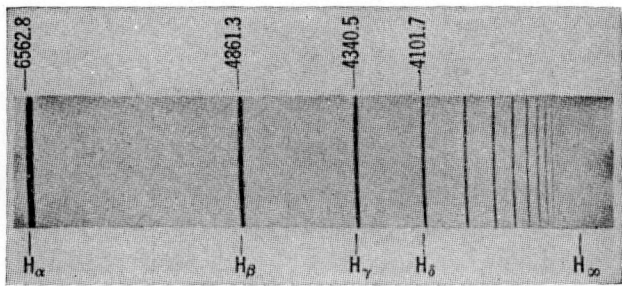

Fig. 7. Spectrogram of atomic hydrogen. Divide numbers by 10 to get wavelengths in mμ. [From *Molecular Spectra and Molecular Structure* by Herzberg (Prentice-Hall).]

prisms by setting the sines of angles equal to the angles; thus, if A is small and the angle of incidence is close to that giving minimum deviation, we may write

$$\mu \approx \frac{\frac{1}{2}(\theta+A)}{\frac{1}{2}A}, \quad \text{or} \quad \theta \approx A(\mu-1), \qquad (1)$$

where θ is the angle of deviation. Thus, if the refractive index of the prism has values μ_1 and μ_2 for light of wavelengths λ_1 and λ_2, respectively, the approximate angular separation of the light of these wavelengths is given by

$$\Delta\theta = \theta_1 - \theta_2 \approx A(\mu_1-1) - A(\mu_2-1),$$

or
$$\Delta\theta \approx A(\mu_1-\mu_2) \qquad (2)$$

when a prism of small angle A is used.

Since we are usually interested in obtaining wide separation of spectral lines, it is desirable to use prisms made of materials with refractive indices that change as rapidly as possible with change in wavelength, so that the ratio $\Delta\theta/\Delta\lambda$ will be large. When the approximation (2) is valid, we may express this quantity (the mean angular dispersion) as

$$\frac{\Delta\theta}{\Delta\lambda} \approx \frac{A(\mu_1-\mu_2)}{\lambda_1-\lambda_2} = A\frac{\Delta\mu}{\Delta\lambda}.$$

In the limit,
$$\frac{d\theta}{d\lambda} \approx A\frac{d\mu}{d\lambda}. \tag{3}$$

The quantity $d\mu/d\lambda$ is usually negative; $-d\mu/d\lambda$ is called the *dispersive power* of the prism material. The quantity $d\theta/d\lambda$ is called the *angular dispersion*; to get a large (negative) value of angular dispersion so that spectral lines will be well separated, it is desirable to use a prism material of high dispersive power.

In order to find the plate separation of two spectral lines produced in a prism spectrograph, we recall that the photographic plate is located in the principal focal plane of the camera lens. Therefore, if light of different

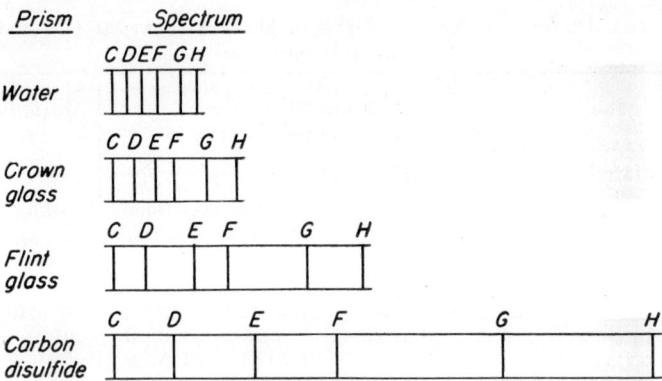

Fig. 8. Spectra obtained with the same spectrograph using different prisms of the same shape. See p. 729 for an explanation of the letters C, D, E, F, G, H.

wavelengths λ_1 and λ_2 is incident at the camera lens at angles differing by $\Delta\theta$, the plate separation ΔX of the slit images is given by

$$\Delta X = f\,\Delta\theta,$$

provided the plate separation ΔX is small compared to the focal length f of the camera lens. In the limit, we may write

$$dX = f\,d\theta. \tag{4}$$

The expression for *linear dispersion* $dX/d\lambda$ can therefore be written, in accordance with (4) and (3), as

$$\frac{dX}{d\lambda} = f\frac{d\theta}{d\lambda} \approx fA\frac{d\mu}{d\lambda}. \tag{5}$$

The wiggly equal signs in the above formulas imply two approximations: (1) that the prism angle A is small, (2) that the light is incident near the angle that gives minimum deviation. Condition (1) is seldom satisfied, condition (2) usually satisfied, in actual prism spectrographs. However, equations (3) and (5) are useful in giving a qualitative idea of the action of a prism in dispersing light even in the general case of large A, where the accurate formulas are very complex.

Figure 8 shows the positions of certain spectral lines as observed by using prisms of the same size and shape but made of different materials; in the case of the water and carbon-disulfide prisms, the liquid prism materials were poured into hollow glass prisms with thin windows. As we see from the figure, the linear dispersion is greatest for carbon disulfide; and since the prism angles are the same and the same camera arrangement was used in each case, we may conclude that $d\mu/d\lambda$ for carbon disulfide is greater than $d\mu/d\lambda$ for the other materials.

TABLE I

Refractive Indices of Several Optical Materials at 20° C for Light of Various Wavelengths

Materials	Refractive index for wavelength			Mean dispersive power
	λ_C (red) 656.3 mμ	λ_D (yellow) 589.3 mμ	λ_F (blue) 486.1 mμ	$\dfrac{\mu_F - \mu_C}{\lambda_C - \lambda_F}$
Water....................	1.3312	1.3330	1.3372	35×10^{-6}/mμ
Carbon disulfide............	1.6182	1.6276	1.6523	201
Crown glass (typical)........	1.5145	1.5172	1.5240	56
Flint glass (typical)..........	1.6221	1.6270	1.6391	100

In Table I are given the refractive indices of several optical materials for wavelengths λ_C, λ_D, λ_F, in the red, yellow, and blue, respectively. These designations C, D, and F were given by Fraunhofer and are still widely used. The C- and F-lines appear in the spectrum of hydrogen and the yellow D-line appears in the spectrum of sodium.

PROBLEMS

NOTE: Use refractive indices given in Table I.

1. A light ray consisting of wavelengths 656.3 mμ and 486.1 mμ is incident on the surface of carbon disulfide contained in a beaker. If the angle of incidence is exactly 30°, find the angles of refraction in carbon disulfide. Show diagram.

Ans: 18°.00; 17°.61.

2. A ray of light containing only wavelengths 656.3 mμ and 486.1 mμ strikes a water surface at angle of incidence of 45°. Find the angular separation of the two refracted rays beneath the water surface.

3. Find the angles of minimum deviation produced by a 60° flint-glass prism for light of C- and F-wavelengths. Ans: 48°.37; 50°.06.

4. A parallel beam of light is incident upon a hollow glass prism with a prism angle of 60°. If this prism is filled with carbon disulfide, what will be the angle of minimum deviation for red C-light? for blue F-light?

5. What is the function of the *collimator* in a prism spectroscope? A 4-diopter converging lens is to be used in a collimator; how far from this lens should the slit be placed?
Ans: 25 cm.

6. What is the function of the telescope used in a prism spectrometer? of the camera lens in a spectrograph? Why do we use the term *spectral lines* in discussing the spectrum emitted by a given source? In a certain spectrograph the focal length of the collimator lens is 40 cm and the focal length of the camera lens is 20 cm; if the length of the entrance slit of the spectrograph is 1.5 cm, what will be the length of the spectral lines on the photographic plate?

7. What is the resulting approximate angular separation between C- and F-light when sunlight passes through a 10° flint-glass prism oriented in such a way as to give minimum deviation for D-light?
Ans: 0°.17.

8. A 12° crown-glass prism is arranged in a spectrograph in such a way as to give minimum deviation for sodium D-light. What is the approximate value for the deviation angle as given by equation (1) of this chapter? What is the exact value for minimum deviation of sodium light produced by this prism?

9. What is the mean dispersive power of carbon disulfide in the spectral region between the wavelengths 656.3 mμ and 589.3 mμ? in the spectral region between the wavelengths 589.3 mμ and 486.1 mμ?
Ans: 140×10^{-6} mμ^{-1}; 239×10^{-6} mμ^{-1}.

10. Find the mean dispersive power of flint glass in the spectral region between the wavelengths 656.3 mμ and 589.3 mμ; in the region between the wavelengths 589.3 mμ and 486.1 mμ.

11. Find the approximate mean angular dispersion produced by a 10° carbon-disulfide prism in the spectral region between the C- and F- lines.
Ans: 2.00×10^{-3} degrees/m$\mu = 7''.21$/mμ.

12. Find the approximate mean angular dispersion produced by a 10° crown-glass prism in the spectral region between the C- and F-lines.

13. What is the total angular separation produced by the prism in Prob. 11 between C- and F-light? If this prism is used in a spectrograph that employs a camera lens of 2-m focal length, what will be the plate separation between the C- and F-lines? What is the mean linear dispersion produced by this spectrograph?
Ans: 0°.341; 11.9 mm; 6.99×10^{-2} mm/mμ.

14. A prism used in a prism spectrograph gives a mean angular dispersion of 0°.015/mμ in the visible region. If the camera lens used in this spectrograph has a focal length of 150 cm, what is the mean linear dispersion? Find the total plate separation between the C- and F-lines.

15. A ray of white light is incident at an angle of 60° with the normal to the face of a 60° flint-glass prism. Make a large drawing showing the passage of rays of C-, D-, and F-light through this prism, including accurate values of all angles involved. Compare the deviations with the angles of minimum deviation given in Prob. 3.
Ans: resultant deviations are 49°.01, 49°.45, 50°.56.

3. ACHROMATIC LENSES

It will be noted from Table I that the refractive indices for a given wavelength are different for different materials and also that the values of $\Delta\mu = \mu_F - \mu_C$ are different for different materials. These properties make it possible to correct in part the *chromatic aberration* always associated with simple thin lenses. We recall from Chap. 25 that chromatic aberration results from the fact that the index of refraction of a lens material is not the same for all wavelengths. The result of this variation in μ can be seen from the drawing of a simple lens in Fig. 9(a). Here white light is incident on the lens; but as a result of the variation of refractive index with wavelength, colored images are produced at different points by the lens. By making a compound lens from two simple lenses of different materials I and II, such as crown and flint glass, it is possible to make the red C- and blue F-images coincide, as in Fig. 9(b). When the lens is so constructed that red and blue images coincide, it is found that the images of colors of intermediate wavelengths also coincide fairly accurately. Such a compound lens is said to be *achromatic* (Gk: without color, colorless).

In the selection of simple lenses to use in a converging achromatic combination of the type shown in Fig. 9(b), we note that the converging

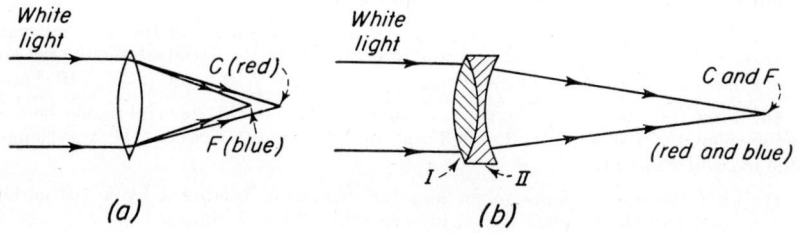

Fig. 9. Construction of an achromatic lens. Typically, component I would be crown glass, II flint glass.

lens of material I would by itself produce colored images in the manner indicated in Fig. 9(a). The separation of these images depends on the variation of refractive index with wavelength; this variation is conveniently measured by the *mean dispersive power* of material I as defined in Table I. By properly selecting a diverging lens of material II, we may bring the colored images into *coincidence* at a greater distance from the lens. The diverging lens must have a focal length of smaller magnitude than that of the converging lens if the combination is still to act as a converging lens, and the material II of the second lens must have a mean dispersive power higher than the mean dispersive power of material I if the colors are to be returned to coincidence. From the values given in Table I, it can be seen that crown and flint glass are suitable for use in making an achromatic combination, since the refractive indices of these materials are not greatly different but the mean dispersive power of flint glass is nearly twice that of crown glass. Therefore, we might choose a converging crown-glass lens I and a diverging flint-glass lens II for making an achromatic combination. These ideas are expressed quantitatively in the following discussion.

Equation (25) of Chap. 25 (p. 647) gives the relation between the focal length f_{comp} of a compound lens and the focal lengths f_I and f_{II} of the component simple lenses. Since we wish the focal length f_{comp} of the compound lens of Fig. 9(b) to be the same for C- and F-wavelengths, we may write the condition for achromatism in the form

$$(f_{\text{comp}})_C = (f_{\text{comp}})_F$$

or
$$\left(\frac{1}{f_\text{I}}+\frac{1}{f_\text{II}}\right)_C = \left(\frac{1}{f_\text{I}}+\frac{1}{f_\text{II}}\right)_F, \tag{6}$$

where the subscripts I and II refer to the materials I and II and the subscripts C and F refer to C- and F-wavelengths. Substitution of the expression given by the lensmaker's equation (23), p. 644, for the focal lengths leads to a relation between the radii of curvature of the four surfaces of the lenses:

$$(\mu_{\text{I}C}-1)\left(\frac{1}{R_{\text{I}1}}+\frac{1}{R_{\text{I}2}}\right)+(\mu_{\text{II}C}-1)\left(\frac{1}{R_{\text{II}1}}+\frac{1}{R_{\text{II}2}}\right)$$
$$=(\mu_{\text{I}F}-1)\left(\frac{1}{R_{\text{I}1}}+\frac{1}{R_{\text{I}2}}\right)+(\mu_{\text{II}F}-1)\left(\frac{1}{R_{\text{II}1}}+\frac{1}{R_{\text{II}2}}\right).$$

Here $R_{\text{I}1}$ and $R_{\text{I}2}$ denote the radii of curvature of the first and second surfaces of the lens composed of material I, $R_{\text{II}1}$ and $R_{\text{II}2}$ the radii for the lens of material II. Rearranging the above equation, we obtain

$$(\mu_{\text{I}C}-\mu_{\text{I}F})\left(\frac{1}{R_{\text{I}1}}+\frac{1}{R_{\text{I}2}}\right) = (\mu_{\text{II}F}-\mu_{\text{II}C})\left(\frac{1}{R_{\text{II}1}}+\frac{1}{R_{\text{II}2}}\right). \tag{7}$$

The second surface of the first lens is usually cemented to the first surface of the second lens in an achromatic combination; therefore the magnitude of their radii of curvature must be equal. We are free to choose any convenient radius of curvature R for these surfaces. Thus, setting $R_{\text{I}2}=R$ and $R_{\text{II}1}=-R$, since the one surface is convex and the other is concave, we may rewrite equation (7) in the form

$$(\mu_{\text{I}C}-\mu_{\text{I}F})\left(\frac{1}{R_{\text{I}1}}+\frac{1}{R}\right) = (\mu_{\text{II}F}-\mu_{\text{II}C})\left(-\frac{1}{R}+\frac{1}{R_{\text{II}2}}\right). \tag{8}$$

This equation gives the relation between $R_{\text{I}1}$ and $R_{\text{II}2}$ that is necessary to assure achromatism. In order to assign specific values to these radii, we must use the relation for the desired focal length f_{comp} of the compound lens. Since $(f_{\text{comp}})_F = (f_{\text{comp}})_C$, we can write

$$\frac{1}{f_{\text{comp}}} = \frac{1}{(f_{\text{comp}})_C} = \left(\frac{1}{f_\text{I}}+\frac{1}{f_\text{II}}\right)_C$$

or
$$\frac{1}{f_{\text{comp}}} = (\mu_{\text{I}C}-1)\left(\frac{1}{R_{\text{I}1}}+\frac{1}{R}\right)+(\mu_{\text{II}C}-1)\left(-\frac{1}{R}+\frac{1}{R_{\text{II}2}}\right). \tag{9}$$

Equations (8) and (9) can now be solved simultaneously for $R_{\text{I}1}$ and $R_{\text{II}2}$. Equation (8) is the condition for achromatism; (9) is the condition for the desired focal length of the compound lens.

With white light incident on the achromatic lens shown in Fig. 9(b), the red and blue light corresponding to the C- and F-lines is brought to a common focus. The lens exhibits no chromatic aberration so far as these two colors are concerned. However, in general, light of other colors is not focused at exactly the same point. Therefore, a compound lens with only two components is not *strictly* achromatic. By using more components, the achromatic properties of the lens can be further improved, but chromatic aberration cannot be *entirely* removed.

PROBLEMS

1. A flint-glass lens has a focal length of 50.00 cm for sodium D-light. What is the focal length of this lens for C- and F-light?   Ans: 50.39 cm; 49.05 cm.

2. A crown-glass lens has a focal length of 80.00 cm for D-light. What is the focal length of this lens for C- and F-light?

3. A parallel beam of white light from a distant point object is incident on a plano-convex flint-glass lens. If the radius of curvature of the curved surface of this lens is 40.00 cm, what is its focal length for C-light? for F-light?
Ans: $+64.30$ cm; $+62.59$ cm.

4. A plano-convex lens of crown glass has a curved surface whose radius of curvature is 25 cm. What is the focal length of this lens for C-light? for F-light?

5. By cementing a diverging lens of crown glass to the flint-glass lens described in Prob. 3, it is possible to make an achromatic lens. Suppose that a plano-concave crown-glass lens is chosen for this purpose and that the plane surfaces of the two lenses are cemented together. What should be the radius of curvature of the curved surface of the crown-glass lens?   Ans: -22.4 cm.

6. By cementing the plane surface of a plano-concave flint-glass lens to the plane surface of the lens described in Prob. 4, it is possible to construct an achromatic lens. What should be the radius of curvature of the curved surface of the flint-glass lens?

7. What is the focal length of the achromatic combination composed of the lenses described in Probs. 3 and 5?   Ans: -134 cm.

8. What is the focal length of the achromatic combination composed of the lenses described in Probs. 4 and 6?

9. It is desired to make a converging achromatic lens of focal length 40 cm from a flint-glass lens and a crown-glass lens. Each of the component lenses has one plane surface, and it is the plane surfaces that are in contact. What should be the radius of curvature of the curved surface (a) of the flint-glass lens and (b) of the crown-glass lens?   Ans: (a) -11.9 cm; (b) $+6.67$ cm.

10. It is desired to make a diverging achromatic lens of focal length 25 cm from flint- and crown-glass lenses. If the lens surfaces that are in contact are plane, what should be the radii of curvature of the outer curved surfaces?

4. GRATING SPECTROGRAPHS

Instruments in which prismatic dispersion is used to produce a spectrum do not furnish an *absolute* determination of the actual wavelengths corresponding to the observed spectral lines. The wavelengths must be determined by *comparison* with spectral lines of *known* wavelengths. The situation is quite different in the case of spectrometers that utilize diffraction gratings to disperse the light from a source. The grating equation derived in Chap. 27 (p. 710) gives the convenient relation

$$\sin\theta = nN\lambda, \tag{10}$$

where θ is the angle, measured from the direction in which the incident light is traveling, at which the nth diffraction maximum occurs; N is the number of grating lines per unit length, and λ is the wavelength. This relation can be conveniently used in determining absolute wavelengths from spectrograms obtained with grating spectrometers.

A simple grating spectrometer is shown diagrammatically in Fig. 10. The slit S of the collimator is illuminated with light from the source being studied. A parallel beam of light from the collimator strikes the grating G at normal incidence. With the telescope in position I the central image of the slit [$n = 0$ in (10)] is observed at the crosshairs of the eyepiece. The telescope is then rotated about a vertical axis located at the ruled sur-

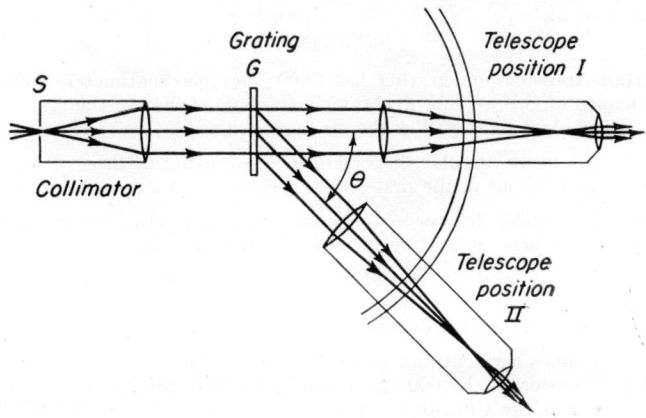

Fig. 10. Schematic diagram of a transmission-grating spectrometer.

face of the grating until at position II a slit image is again observed at the crosshairs. This image is produced from light in the first order ($n = 1$) of the diffraction pattern of the grating. The angular separation θ of the two telescope positions can be read by means of a vernier on a divided circle. The wavelength of the observed spectral line is then determined from the grating equation (10). The grating spectrometer just described could be converted into a grating spectrograph by replacing the telescope by a camera focused for parallel light. In actual practice the arrangement used is somewhat different but the principles involved are the same.

In order to find the angular dispersion $d\theta/d\lambda$ obtainable with a grating spectrograph, we may differentiate the grating equation (10) and obtain

$$\cos\theta \, d\theta = nN \, d\lambda,$$

which gives
$$\frac{d\theta}{d\lambda} = \frac{nN}{\cos\theta} \qquad (11)$$

for the angular dispersion. If the focal length of the camera lens is f, the linear dispersion $dX/d\lambda$ at the plate can be written

$$\frac{dX}{d\lambda}=f\frac{d\theta}{d\lambda}=\frac{nNf}{\cos\theta}. \qquad (12)$$

The dispersion obtainable with grating spectrographs is usually much higher than that obtainable with prism instruments. However, since the light from a diffraction grating is ordinarily distributed in many orders in addition to the undispersed radiation at the central image, the intensity of the light in any single order of the spectrum is much lower than the intensity of the light in the single spectrum produced by a prism instrument. Both types of instruments find important applications in research and industry.

PROBLEMS

1. A certain transmission grating has 5000 lines per centimeter. What is the angular dispersion of this grating in the vicinity of the D-line in the first-order spectrum when the incident light strikes the grating normally? Ans: $1!80/m\mu$.

2. What is the mean angular dispersion of the grating in Prob. 1 in the region between the C- and F-lines in the first-order spectrum? Assume normal incidence.

3. What is the angular dispersion of the above grating in the vicinity of the D-line in the second order when the grating is used at normal incidence? Ans: $4!25/m\mu$.

4. What is the angular dispersion of the above grating in the vicinity of the C-line in the third-order spectrum? How does the intensity of the third-order spectrum compare with that of the first-order spectrum?

5. How many lines per centimeter must a plane grating have in order to give the same angular dispersion in the 600-mμ region in the first order as that obtainable in the 600-mμ region in the third-order spectrum from a grating with 5000 lines/cm? Both gratings are used at normal incidence. Ans: 15,000 lines/cm.

6. What is the maximum angular dispersion near the C-line obtainable in any order of a grating with 8000 lines/cm?

7. A 5000-line/cm grating is used at normal incidence in a spectrograph in which the camera lens has a focal length of 150 cm. What is the linear dispersion at the plate in the vicinity of 600 mμ when the first-order spectrum is photographed?
Ans: 0.786 mm/mμ.

8. What is the linear dispersion obtainable in the vicinity of 450 mμ in the first-order spectrum formed by a grating with 6000 lines/cm used in a spectrograph in which the camera lens has a focal length of 2 m? Assume normal incidence.

5. EMISSION SPECTRA

The spectrum produced when the light from a luminous source is dispersed is called the *emission spectrum* of the source. Its appearance is determined by the composition and physical state of the source.

Incandescent solids and liquids, and incandescent gases under extremely high pressure produce *continuous spectra*, which include light of all colors. Thus, the spectrum of a hot tungsten filament consists of all colors from the violet end of the spectrum to the red end. The spectrum is not interrupted by any dark regions.

Luminous gases and vapors at low pressure have spectra quite different from the spectra of incandescent solids. The emission spectra of such materials consist of distinct lines and are called *line spectra*. It is found that every chemical element emits a characteristic *line spectrum* when the atoms of the element are excited in a flame, a furnace, or an electric discharge. Thus, if different materials containing sodium are introduced into a hot Bunsen flame or an electric arc, the yellow D-lines* appear in the spectrum at the same position as the D-lines in the spectrum of a sodium-vapor light such as is used for highway illumination. Therefore, we might conclude that the mechanism involved in the emission of the sodium D-lines is to be found in the sodium *atom* itself. This conclusion is correct and can be generalized by the statement that *line spectra originate in the atoms of the chemical elements*. Figure 7 shows the spectrum of the hydrogen atom in the visible and near-ultraviolet regions.

It should be pointed out that the number of lines in the spectrum emitted by a given element is determined to some extent by the type of excitation used to produce emission. For example, the spectrum of an element heated in a high-temperature electric *arc* may include more lines than the spectrum of the same element excited in a much cooler Bunsen flame. The excitation of the same element in a high-voltage *spark* discharge results in the appearance of still more lines in the emission spectrum.

Other types of emission spectra are sometimes produced by incandescent gases at low pressure. These spectra are called *band spectra* and

267.71 mμ   238.13 mμ

Fig. 11. Band spectrum. [From *Molecular Spectra and Molecular Structure* by Herzberg (Prentice-Hall).]

consist of large numbers of spectral lines closely spaced in groups called *bands*. In the bands, the lines are usually so closely spaced that they cannot be separated by low-dispersion instruments. *Band spectra have their origin in molecules*. The molecules of any compound will emit a characteristic band spectrum if excitation can be produced without causing the molecules to dissociate. Many types of molecules dissociate at relatively low temperatures; for example, when sodium chloride is placed in a Bunsen flame, the molecules are readily dissociated and only the bright D-lines of atomic sodium are observed in the spectrum of the hot vapor. In other gases such as air, molecular excitation results in the emission of band spectra characteristic of the O_2 and N_2 molecules.

---

* What we have called the D-line previously is actually a closely spaced pair of lines of wavelengths 589.0 and 589.6 mμ that are unresolved in a spectrograph of low dispersion. Because two lines are present, we shall in the future call these the D-lines.

To summarize, solids, liquids, and high-pressure gases give *continuous spectra*, atoms give *line spectra*, and molecules give *band spectra* when light is emitted because of thermal or electrical excitation.

6. ABSORPTION SPECTRA

When light from a source with a continuous spectrum is allowed to pass through a relatively cool gas or vapor before entering the spectrograph, the observed spectrum consists of the continuous spectrum of the source crossed by dark lines or bands. The dark lines or bands are present as a result of selective absorption by the cool gas or vapor. For example, if light from an incandescent tungsten-filament lamp is allowed to pass through a tube containing sodium vapor, the observed spectrum is continuous except for two closely spaced dark lines appearing in the yellow region. These lines correspond to wavelengths *absorbed* by the sodium vapor. These two dark lines appear at exactly the same positions as the pair of D-lines appear in the emission spectrum of sodium. This correspondence between position of lines in the emission and absorption spectra is quite general. The wavelengths absorbed by a given material are identical with wavelengths emitted when the emission spectrum of the material is excited. The dark regions in the spectrum, observed when white light is allowed to pass through an absorbing material, constitute the *absorption spectrum* of the material. Gases and vapors are characterized by absorption *line spectra* or *band spectra* in which individual absorption lines can be observed with suitable spectrographs. Liquids and solids have broad regions of absorption exhibiting no line structure. For example, the ruby glass commonly used in photographic darkrooms has an absorption region covering the entire visible spectrum except the red and deep orange; the absorption is very intense and shows no line structure. An aqueous solution of copper sulfate absorbs strongly in most regions of the visible spectrum except in the blue and green.

Dark lines are observed in the otherwise continuous visible spectrum of the sun. Although these lines were first observed by William Hyde Wollaston in 1802, they are known as the *Fraunhofer lines*, since Joseph von Fraunhofer made the first careful study of them in the years following 1814. Fraunhofer observed about 600 dark lines in the solar spectrum and assigned letters of the alphabet to the more prominent ones, beginning with A in the extreme red and ending with H in the violet. The correct explanation of these dark lines in the solar spectrum was given by Kirchhoff in 1859. The visible portion of the sun's surface, called the *photosphere*, consists of gases at high pressure that emit a continuous spectrum. The photosphere is much hotter than the outer gaseous solar envelopes known as the *reversing layer* and the *chromosphere* The photosphere emits a continuous spectrum. The light from the photosphere in passing through the reversing layer and chromosphere experiences selective absorption by the relatively cool gases in these layers. The radiant energy absorbed by these gases is actually re-emitted, but the re-emission takes place in all directions, and hence only a small fraction of the light of these wavelengths that started toward the observer actually reaches him. The net result is that the light selectively absorbed is much less intense, and dark lines appear in the sun's spectrum. The *reversing layer* is the inner layer in which most of the line absorption takes place. The name arises from the fact that it gives a *reversed* spectrum of *dark* lines on a *bright* background. The *chromosphere* is the layer further out that gives a colored bright-line spectrum at the time of a solar eclipse.

Tens of thousands of Fraunhofer lines have now been measured, and their chemical origin identified. The first large table of wavelengths was compiled by Rowland at Johns Hopkins University, in 1893, after he had made a diffraction grating of much higher dispersive power than any previous grating. Some of the Fraunhofer lines are *telluric* in origin, meaning that they result from absorption in the atmosphere of the earth rather than in that of the sun. Such telluric lines can be distinguished by the fact that they increase in intensity when the sun is low on the horizon and the light penetrates a thicker layer of the earth's atmosphere, and by the fact that they show no Doppler effect from the sun's rotation. Fraunhofer's A- and B-lines turned out to be of telluric origin.

Fraunhofer's letter designations, which are still widely used, refer to the following lines:

A	759.4 mμ (O_2 telluric band)		F	486.1 mμ (H, called Hβ)
B	686.7 mμ (O_2 telluric band)		G	430.8 mμ (blend of Fe lines and
C	656.3 mμ (H, called Hα)			molecular bands)
D	589.6 mμ (Na, called D_1)		H	396.8 mμ (Ca)
	589.0 mμ (Na, called D_2)		K	393.4 mμ (Ca)
E	527.0 mμ (Fe)			

The designation K for the strong near-ultraviolet Ca line represents an extension by Rowland of Fraunhofer's letter designations.

By comparison of the wavelengths of the Fraunhofer lines with those of lines observed in terrestrial sources, one can identify the chemical elements occurring in the solar atmosphere. Over 60 of the chemical elements have been identified in the sun's spectrum, and there are good reasons for expecting the spectra of the balance to be difficult to observe, so it seems highly probable that all the stable elements that occur terrestrially also occur in the sun.

The spectra of other stars are similar in many respects to that of the sun, although the faintness of these light sources precludes the observation of the spectra with the detail possible in the case of the sun.

7. SPECTROCHEMICAL ANALYSIS

The detailed study of emission and absorption spectra is called *spectroscopy*. This field of study is of importance not only in giving us detailed theories of the structure of atoms and molecules based on interpretation of the observed spectra but also in providing methods of chemical analysis. Spectroscopic investigations have been extended from the visible to the ultraviolet and infrared portions of the electromagnetic spectrum. Since glass has absorption bands in these regions, other optical materials must be used in the spectrographs. In the near-ultraviolet region, quartz lenses and quartz prisms are frequently used;

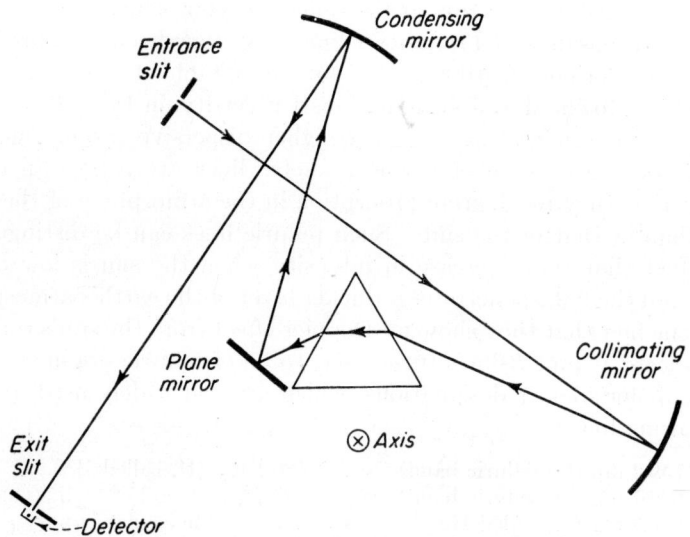

Fig. 12. Prism spectrograph for the infrared.

photographic plates or photoelectric cells are used as detectors for the radiation. In the near infrared, metallic mirrors are used in place of lenses in the optical systems of spectrographs, as indicated in Fig. 12. Prisms of fluorite, rock salt, or potassium bromide, or coarse reflection gratings are used to disperse the infrared radiation, and electrical methods of detection are generally employed.

In the analysis of a chemical for constituent elements, a sample of the unknown is usually placed on the carbon electrodes of an electric arc and the resulting emission spectrum is observed. Extremely small quantities of elements can be detected by their characteristic emission lines. The method can be used in quantitative chemical analysis by comparison of the emission spectrum of an unknown sample with the spectra of known mixtures of the components. The degree of photographic blackening can be used as a measure of line intensities, and from these the concentration of material in the sample can be inferred. The processes of analysis are rapid and accurate and have the advantage of requiring only very small samples. Special analyses for impurities in certain metallurgical processes are obtainable in a matter of seconds.

Another valuable application of spectroscopic methods of analysis is in the field of organic chemical analysis. Chemical methods of analyzing mixtures of organic compounds are sometimes laborious and time-consuming. The infrared absorption spectrum of an organic compound includes characteristic bands which can be used in identifying the compound. These bands can frequently be used in detecting the compound and in measuring its concentration when it is mixed with other compounds. Infrared methods of analysis find many industrial applications.

8 COLOR SENSATION; MIXTURES OF COLORS

In Chap. 26 we pointed out that *different* combinations of pure spectral colors are capable of producing *indistinguishable color sensations*. In other words, the eye is incapable of resolving a light stimulus into

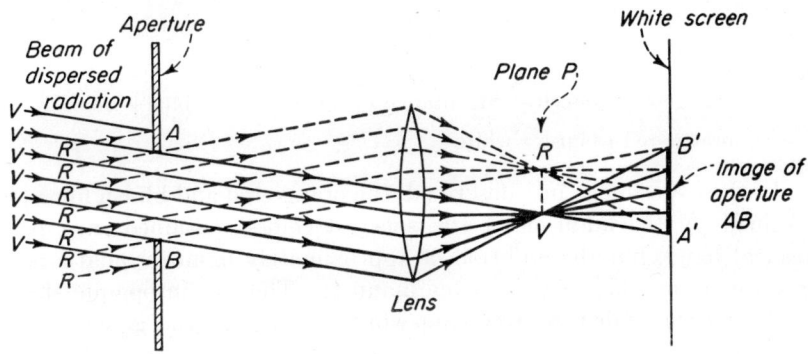

Fig. 13. Observation of the color sensations produced by different combinations of pure spectral colors.

spectral colors and gives only an integrated response called a *color sensation*. The Young-Helmholtz theory of color vision is a useful hypothesis in explaining how different spectral color combinations produce similar color sensations. In our present discussion, we shall merely indicate the *color sensation* resulting when quantities of light of various *spectral colors* are mixed without interpreting the results in terms of a theory of color vision.

Let us consider the experimental arrangement indicated in Fig. 13. A beam of dispersed radiation from a transmission grating on which white light is incident enters from the left and passes through a rectangular aperture AB. The converging lens produces a spectrum at plane P, where colored images of the entrance slit of the grating spectrograph are produced. However, instead of placing the white screen at plane P, we shall place it in the indicated position where the image $A'B'$ of the aperature AB is formed. The image $A'B'$ will be white since all colors pass through aperture AB and are all spread out over the entire image $A'B'$. Thus, used in this manner, the lens essentially recombines the colors separated by the transmission grating.

With the arrangement shown in Fig. 13, we can perform a number of experiments by inserting opaque shutters in plane P so as to remove different portions of the spectrum displayed in this plane and noting the effects upon the color of the image $A'B'$. Thus, if the opaque shutters remove all spectral colors except the violet, the image $A'B'$ appears unchanged in shape but is violet in color. If the shutter cuts off the green, blue, and violet by removing the lower half of the spectrum at P, the image $A'B'$ has an *orange-red* hue; if the shutter cuts off the red, orange, and yellow by removing the upper half of the spectrum at P, the image $A'B'$ has a *bluish* hue. The bluish hue and the orange-red hue are said to be *complementary colors*, since their sum produces white light.

$$\begin{aligned}
\text{orange-red} &= \text{red} + \text{orange} + \text{yellow} \\
\text{bluish} &= \text{green} + \text{blue} + \text{violet} \\
\text{orange-red} + \text{bluish} &= \text{red} + \text{orange} + \text{yellow} + \text{green} + \text{blue} + \text{violet} \\
\text{orange-red} + \text{bluish} &= \text{white}
\end{aligned}$$

In the experiment just described, the orange-red and bluish hues were obtained by the addition of the spectral colors contained in a broad spectral band, but the addition of approximately monochromatic colors produces other colors in the same manner. Thus, if an opaque shutter in plane P has fairly narrow slits which allow only the green and red spectral colors to pass, the image $A'B'$ will *appear* yellow, although no light of spectral yellow is actually present. Similarly, the addition of spectral green and violet produces an image $A'B'$ which *appears* greenish-blue; the addition of spectral red and violet produce an image $A'B'$ which appears purple, a nonspectral color. If the shutter in plane P has three slits which pass narrow bands of spectral red, green, and violet, the image $A'B'$ has a white color that to the eye is indistinguishable from the normal white composed of all spectral colors.

The results of the described experiments can be summarized by the following set of equations which state the *additive effects* produced by combining light of different colors:

$$\text{green} + \text{violet} = \text{green-blue}, \qquad \text{(I)}$$
$$\text{violet} + \text{red} = \text{purple}, \qquad \text{(II)}$$

$$\text{red} + \text{green} = \text{yellow}, \qquad \text{(III)}$$
$$\text{red} + \text{green} + \text{violet} = \text{white}. \qquad \text{(IV)}$$

In order to test the additive properties of color mixtures, let us treat these equations as if they were algebraic equations. Thus, by subtracting (I) from (IV), we obtain

$$\text{red} = \text{white} - \text{green-blue},$$
or
$$\text{red} + \text{green-blue} = \text{white}. \qquad \text{(V)}$$

Experiment verifies the correctness of equation (V), which states that red and green-blue light are complementary. Combining (II) with (IV) and (III) with (IV) in a similar manner gives the relations

$$\text{green} + \text{purple} = \text{white}, \qquad \text{(VI)}$$
$$\text{violet} + \text{yellow} = \text{white}. \qquad \text{(VII)}$$

Relations (VI) and (VII) can also be verified by experiment. Thus, we can conclude that the combination of colored lights is an additive process.

Another way of demonstrating this additivity of colors is shown in Fig. 14, in which S_1, S_2, and S_3 are three sources of white light. Red, green, and violet filters are placed in the positions indicated. The regions on the screen where the light beams from the three filters overlap appear white. It might be pointed out that the light transmitted by a filter may be a pure spectral color but usually consists of several spectral colors which in combination give the desired color sensation. For example, the light from the red filter may be spectral red; the light from the green filter may contain orange, yellow, green, and blue spectral colors; the light from the violet filter may be spectral violet. Thus, all spectral colors may actually be present in the white region of the screen. The white region of the screen may be illuminated with only spectral red, green, and violet, and the screen will still appear white. The eye is unable to distinguish the difference.

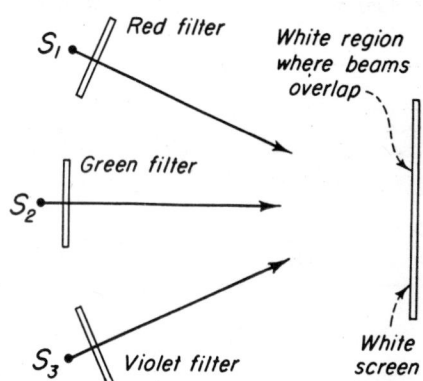

Fig. 14. Observation of the effects produced by mixing light transmitted through filters of different colors.

From the above discussion, it is evident that *color sensation* and *spectral color* are quite different concepts. Spectral color is determined by the wavelength or frequency of a light wave. Thus light of wavelength 560 mμ is *spectral yellow* and produces a *yellow color sensation*. However, a beam of light consisting only of light of the two wavelengths 720 mμ (*spectral red*) and 520 mμ (*spectral green*) can produce a *yellow color sensation* that is indistinguishable from the yellow color sensation produced by spectral yellow. The eye *synthesizes* but does not *analyze* light.

PROBLEMS

1. What color sensation would be produced by mixing green and purple light on a white screen? Explain. Ans: white.

2. What color sensation would be produced by mixing red light and yellow light? Explain.

9. COLORS OF NONLUMINOUS OBJECTS; MIXTURES OF PIGMENTS

Objects that are not self-luminous can be seen only by transmitted or reflected light. Their colors are determined by the wavelengths of the incident light that are transmitted or reflected. As indicated in Fig. 15, light incident on an object may be (a) reflected at the surface, (b) reflected by particles just below the surface, (c) absorbed within the body, or (d) transmitted by the body. All of these processes occur simultaneously, and the appearance and color of the object are determined by the relative magnitudes of the different effects.

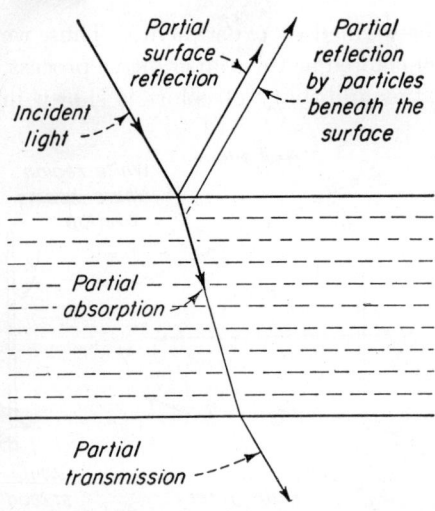

Fig. 15. Effects influencing the color and appearance of a material object. (NOTE: The reflection is usually diffuse.)

Some substances appear differently colored when viewed by reflected light and when viewed by transmitted light. Such materials owe their color chiefly to selective reflection at the surface. In this case certain wavelengths are highly reflected at the surface, and the rest of the incident light is transmitted or absorbed. Thus, if a very thin film of gold is illuminated by white light, it appears yellow when viewed by reflected light and appears green when viewed by transmitted light. Similarly, as a result of selective surface reflection, very thin films of silver appear blue when viewed by transmitted light. Certain aniline dyes such as fuchsin also produce strong selective surface reflection, and thin layers of oxide can produce the same effect by interference, as in the case of blued steel.

A white surface is one that reflects all spectral colors equally well and is highly reflecting for all colors. In general, the term *white* is applied only to surfaces sufficiently rough to produce *diffuse* reflection, so that no mirror images are formed; the surface appears white regardless of the direction of the incident light. Surfaces coated heavily and uniformly with magnesium-oxide powder are sometimes used as standards of whiteness. Black surfaces absorb all spectral colors strongly and equally well. Surfaces heavily coated with lampblack or surfaces covered with black velvet cloth are sometimes used as standards of surface blackness, although a small hole in the wall of a light-tight cavity is a closer approximation to a true black body. If lampblack and powdered magnesium oxide are intimately mixed, the resulting mixture is *gray;* a true gray surface *partially* reflects all wavelengths equally well. Thus, the difference between whiteness and blackness is determined merely by the percentage of incident light reflected; a perfectly white surface reflects all light incident upon it, a gray surface reflects a part of the incident light but shows no selectivity for any particular color, and a perfectly black surface absorbs all incident light.

If a white surface is illuminated by red light, it appears red; if illuminated with blue light, the surface appears blue. Since all wavelengths are equally well reflected by a white surface, the surface always has the color of the incident light. A black surface appears black regardless of the color of the light that illuminates the surface.

Perfectly transparent bodies are invisible when surrounded by material of the same refractive index. For example, a piece of flint glass disappears when immersed in carbon disulfide, which has approximately the same index of refraction. Partially transparent bodies such as colored glass transmit certain spectral colors and absorb others. Thus, a piece of ruby glass transmits red and some orange light and appears red when illuminated by white or red light; it appears red when viewed by transmission and also when viewed by reflected light, since some of the light that penetrates the first surface is reflected from particles inside the glass. It would appear black when illuminated by green or blue light, since it absorbs all green and blue.

The color of most opaque bodies, like that of partially transparent bodies, is due to selective absorption. In the case of opaque bodies, incident white light penetrates only a short distance below the surface and then returns to the surface by reflection from particles within the body. The re-emerging light has lost some spectral colors by absorption and hence appears colored. Extremely thin layers of the material from an opaque body transmit the same color reflected by the body. In the reflection of white light from an opaque body, some of the incident light is reflected from the surface itself without penetrating; if there is not selective surface reflection, the light reflected from the surface includes all the spectral colors present in the incident light and hence makes the color of the body lighter. Surface scratches enhance this effect. Pulverizing a material increases the surface effect; for example, blue copper sulfate crystals appear almost white when they are ground into small fragments.

Most paints consist of small particles of colored materials or pigments suspended in a clear varnish or drying oil called a *vehicle*. Most pigments absorb several spectral colors; reflected light of the colors not absorbed gives a single color sensation to the observer. The reflection of white light from a yellow painted surface is shown schematically in Fig. 16. If the pigment is cadmium yellow, the blue and violet spectral colors are absorbed and the remaining spectral colors are reflected from points near the surface. The spectral red, orange, and green combine with the spectral yellow to give a yellow color sensation to the observer.

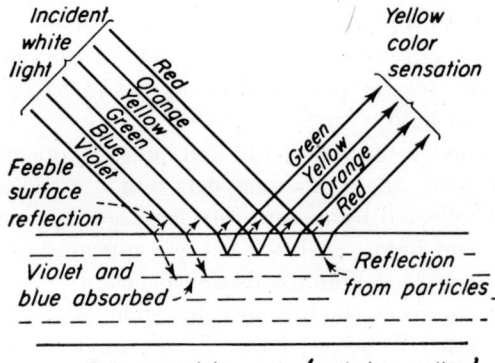

Fig. 16. The colors produced by pigments depend primarily on selective absorption. (The reflection from the particles is actually diffuse.)

It should be remembered that the reflection from the painted surface is actually diffuse and that there is also a slight reflection of all wavelengths at the surface itself. If the paint contains only cadmium yellow as a pigment, the painted surface will appear black when illuminated by violet light except for the effects of the feeble surface reflection. In most common varieties of paint, a white pigment is present in addition to the colored pigment, so the reflected colored light is 'diluted' with white.

Before considering the phenomena observed when pigments are mixed, it might be desirable to discuss the subtractive effects of filters on white light. A yellow filter absorbs blue and violet and transmits the other spectral colors as indicated in Fig. 17(a), whereas a blue filter absorbs red, orange, and yellow and transmits the other spectral colors as shown in Fig. 17(b). When these filters are combined in either of the ways shown in Fig. 17(c) and (d), the only light transmitted through the resulting combination is green. The effect of *adding filters* in a light beam is therefore a *subtractive* process and is quite different from the *additive* effect involved in mixing light of different colors.

Since the effects produced by pigments depend upon selective absorption, mixing pigments is essentially subtractive and is similar to combining the action of successive filters on a beam of white light. For example, the pigment 'cadmium yellow' absorbs blue and violet and the blue pigment 'French ultramarine' absorbs red, orange, and yellow; if these

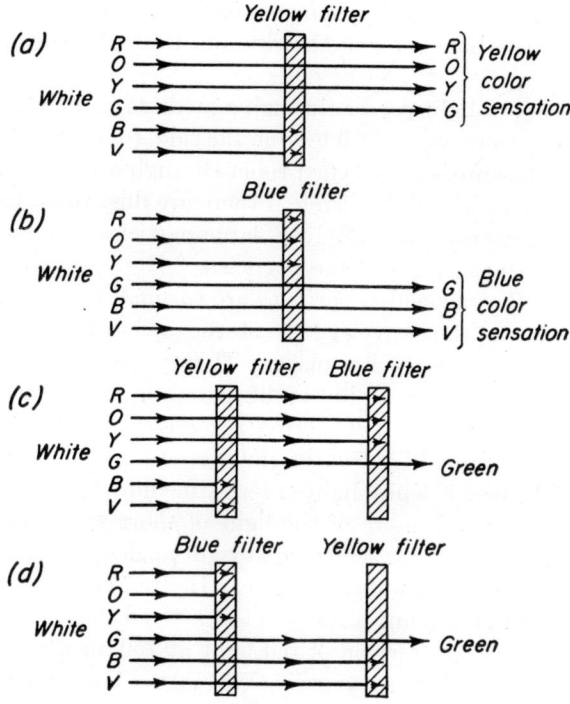

Fig. 17. Schematic diagram showing light transmitted by filters.

pigments are mixed, all light except the green is absorbed. Therefore, these two pigments can be combined to produce a bright-green pigment.

PROBLEMS

1. Red light only is incident on a blue rug on the floor of a certain room. What is the apparent color of the rug to an observer in the room? Explain. Ans: black.

2. A yellow pigment is mixed with a green pigment. What is the color sensation produced by the resulting mixture when white light is incident? Explain.

3. A white wall is illuminated by light passing through a red filter. How does the surface of the wall appear to the eyes of an observer? If the observer views the wall through a blue filter, what is the apparent color of the wall? Explain.
Ans: red; black.

4. When spectral red light and spectral violet light strike a white screen, the screen appears purple. What is the appearance of the resulting mixture when a red pigment and a violet pigment are mixed and white light is incident on the mixture? Explain.

10. SCATTERING OF LIGHT

Before concluding our discussion of color, it might be well to mention one other phenomenon which, like diffraction, refraction, and selective absorption, involves the partial separation of white light into its component spectral colors. This phenomenon is known as *scattering* and is responsible for the blue color of the sky and the red color of the sun at sunset.

When a beam of light passes through a medium in which particles are suspended, its path becomes visible from the side; for example, if a narrow pencil of sunlight enters a darkened room through a small hole in a window shade, its path is plainly visible if there are dust particles in the air. This type of 'scattering' by relatively large particles results from reflection of light by the surfaces of the particles.

However, if the suspended particles are so small that their diameters are comparable to the wavelengths of the incident light, a different type of scattering process takes place. This type of scattering involves not ordinary reflection but a kind of diffraction in which each particle in the light path behaves as if it were a secondary light source, and the intensity of the scattered light varies inversely as the fourth power of the wavelength. Hence, if white light enters a medium in which such small particles are suspended, more of the light of short wavelength near the violet end of the spectrum is scattered at right angles to the original beam than of the light of long wavelength near the red end of the spectrum. Of the violet light at 450 mμ, a fraction is scattered that is approximately 8 times as great as the fraction of red light at 750 mμ that is scattered. The ratio 8 in the previous sentence is $(750/450)^4$. Thus, a pencil of white light traversing a suspension of small particles appears bluish when viewed from the side because a preponderance of the scattered light is of short wavelength; it appears reddish when viewed along the beam in the direction of the source because little of the red and orange light has been scattered out of the beam. This effect can be noted when tobacco smoke is viewed in sunlight; the smoke appears blue-gray but the 'shadow' of the smoke has a red-gray tint.

The red color of the sun at sunrise and sunset is due to selective scattering by dust particles in the air near the earth's surface and by the molecules of the gases in the atmosphere. When the sun is at the horizon, the sunlight reaching an observer at the earth's surface has an effective atmospheric path that is approximately 50 times greater than the path traversed by light passing vertically through the atmosphere. This longer atmospheric path accentuates the effects of molecular scattering, and, since a larger portion of the actual path is through dust-filled air at low altitudes, the effects of scattering by dust particles are more pronounced than when the sun is high above the horizon. Therefore, since much of the violet, blue, and green in the original sunlight is scattered, the sun appears redder at sunrise and sunset than at midday.

The blue color of the sky can be explained in terms of scattering by molecules. The effects involved can be understood by consideration of

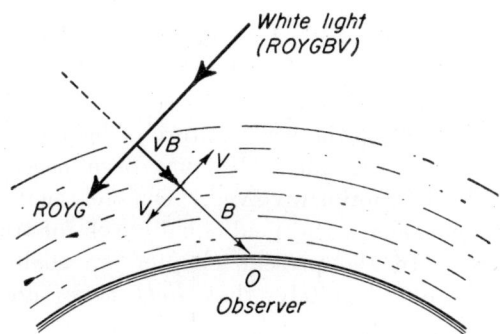

Fig. 18. Scattering of sunlight in the atmosphere.

Fig. 18. In this figure a beam of white light is shown coming from the sun. In the atmosphere the blue and violet components are scattered in the indicated manner toward the observer at point O at the earth's surface. Before the scattered light reaches the observer, the violet components experience secondary scattering in the layers of dense air near the earth's surface; hence, the light reaching the observer appears blue instead of blue-violet. When observed from balloons at great altitudes, the sky has a blue-violet appearance, since the secondary scattering of the violet occurs chiefly at low altitudes.

CHAPTER 29

POLARIZATION OF LIGHT*

In our discussion of the optical phenomena involved in interference and diffraction, we have shown that the observed effects can be readily explained on the basis of the wave properties of light. Although we have made extensive use of the wave nature of light in our explanation of optical phenomena, thus far it has not been necessary for us to specify the type of wave motion involved. Our treatment of interference and diffraction phenomena would hold equally well for transverse or for longitudinal waves. In the present chapter we shall discuss other phenomena that show definitely that *light waves are transverse in character*.

In longitudinal waves such as sound waves, there is always symmetry around an axis in the direction of propagation, since the vibrations are in this direction. In transverse waves the vibrations are at right angles to the direction of propagation, and hence symmetry around an axis in this direction may not exist. For example, a transverse wave traveling along a horizontal string may involve up-and-down vertical motion of the particles of the string, or it may involve left-and-right horizontal motion, or any combination of these. Similarly, a transverse elastic wave in a solid may involve particle motions in various different directions all perpendicular to the direction of propagation; we say that the wave may have different *polarizations*.

Whenever there is a lack of symmetry around an axis in the direction of propagation of a wave motion, we say that the wave motion is *polarized*. Polarization can occur only with transverse waves. Since a beam of light can be polarized, we conclude that light waves are transverse waves. The ways in which polarization of light can be produced include (a) selective absorption, (b) reflection, (c) refraction, and (d) scattering. In this chapter we shall discuss the methods of production of polarized light and the properties of polarized light.

It is noted that what we refer to as 'light vibrations' in the first three sections are actually the vibrations of the *electric vector* of the electromagnetic wave that constitutes light. The electromagnetic wave is discussed in Sec. 4 of this chapter and in Chap. 44.

* If desired, this chapter may be given a somewhat hasty reading in a first treatment of the subject, in order that the important *ideas*, but not necessarily the details, may be assimilated.

1. POLARIZATION BY SELECTIVE ABSORPTION

The production of polarized light by selective absorption is exhibited by crystals of certain minerals and organic compounds. The best known of these minerals is *tourmaline*. When a light beam passes through a single properly cut slab of clear tourmaline, it emerges somewhat diminished in intensity but not otherwise changed in appearance so far as the human eye can discern. However, if two slabs of tourmaline are introduced into a light beam, the intensity of the transmitted light depends on the relative orientation of the two slabs.

The observed effects are illustrated in Fig. 1, in which are shown two slabs cut in an identical manner from tourmaline crystals. In (a) the two slabs are oriented with crystalline axes parallel and light is transmitted. In (b) one of the slabs has been rotated through an angle θ with

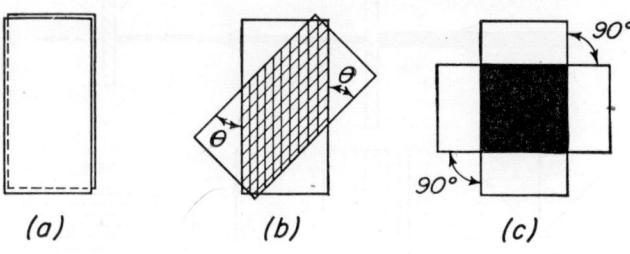

Fig. 1. Transmission of light through tourmaline crystals.

respect to the other slab; with the crystals in this position, less light is transmitted than when the crystalline axes are parallel. In (c) one of the slabs is oriented at 90° with respect to the other slab and *no light is transmitted through the pair*. These effects can be interpreted *only* if light waves are assumed to be transverse.

Let us assume that light consists of transverse waves and that in an ordinary light beam the transverse vibrations have no preferred direction with respect to the direction of propagation; in other words, that the different 'pieces' of the light wave which originated in different atoms of the radiating source have their vibrations randomly oriented in all possible planes transverse to the direction of propagation. Then a pencil of light approaching the reader would involve the transverse vibrations shown in Fig. 2(a); in this figure the arrows represent the transverse vibrations associated with the different 'pieces' of the wave and have all possible orientations in a plane perpendicular to the direction of propagation indicated by the arrow point ⊙. Now let us assume that a properly cut tourmaline slab transmits vibrations having a given orientation with respect to the slab and absorbs all light associated with vibrations at right angles. For example, assume that the tourmaline slab shown in Fig. 2(b) transmits only the light associated with vibration components in the vertical direction and absorbs all the light associated with vibration components in the horizontal direction. If the tourmaline slab is placed in the light beam approaching the reader, the transmitted light has only vibrations in the vertical direction as indicated in Fig. 2(c). If a second tourmaline slab oriented at right angles to the first is placed in the approaching light beam as shown in Fig. 2(d), it can transmit only light associated with horizontal vibrations. Since light associated with horizontal vibrations has already been removed by the first tourmaline slab, no light reaches the observer. This explanation is necessary to account for the observed phenomena depicted in Fig. 1 and many similar phenomena, and hence we must conclude that light waves are transverse.

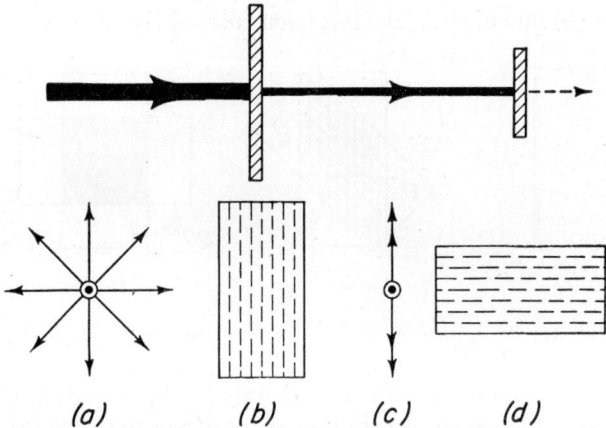

Fig. 2. Schematic diagram showing transmission of light waves through 'crossed' tourmaline crystals.

Owing to the fact that most tourmaline crystals are colored, they are not ordinarily used in optical instruments. There have been numerous unsuccessful attempts to grow large clear crystals having optical properties similar to those of tourmaline. Small needle-shaped crystals of the organic compound quinine iodosulphate having similar optical properties were grown as early as 1852. On account of their small size, they were not useful in optical work until 1935, when Edwin H. Land developed a method of orienting large numbers of crystals of this type. The material (called *Polaroid*) that was developed by Land consists of a film of cellulose acetate or nitrocellulose in which are suspended large numbers of minute crystals having optical properties similar to those of tourmaline. These minute crystals are given the same orientation by giving the film a stretch in one direction during the manufacturing process. Films of large area can be prepared and are finding many practical applications. As indicated in Fig. 3, two Polaroid films can be used to produce effects similar to those produced by tourmaline crystals. A Polaroid film is usually mounted between a pair of glass plates, the combination being called a Polaroid plate.

As we have seen, the first tourmaline crystal or Polaroid plate inserted in a light beam transmits only those light waves having vibrations in a

Fig. 3. Photograph showing transmission of light through Polaroid films. (*Courtesy of the Polaroid Corporation.*)

given direction. The transmitted light is said to be *plane-polarized*, since the vibrations are in a single plane. For example, the vibrations shown in Fig. 2(c) are in a vertical plane containing the propagation vector. (The *propagation vector* is a vector showing the direction of propagation; it is represented by ⊙ in Figs. 2 and 4.)

The device, such as the first tourmaline slab or first Polaroid plate, that produces the polarization is called the *polarizer*. Ordinarily, the eye cannot detect any difference between polarized and unpolarized light without the assistance of a second tourmaline slab, Polaroid plate, or similar device; the second device is usually called the *analyzer*.

In ordinary light, the vibrations of the different 'pieces' of the light originating in different atoms of the source take place in all directions at right angles to the propagation vector. However, each of these vibrations can be resolved vectorially into components along any two axes normal to the propagation vector. Since the energy of a light vibration is proportional to the square of the amplitude, this resolution is energetically correct, the sum of the squares of the two rectangular components of a vector being equal to the square of the length of the vector. Thus, if a beam of light is approaching the reader as shown in Fig. 4(a), the vibrations take place in all directions, including those shown. We may treat these vibrations as vectors, and resolve each of them into components along a pair of transverse x- and y-axes. The whole unpolarized light wave may be considered as composed of, or equivalent to, two resultant vibrations along the x- and y-axes as shown in Fig. 4(b).

One method we shall use for picturing the transverse waves associated with a light beam is shown in Fig. 5. The heavy arrows give the propagation vectors, the vertical arrows represent light vibrations in the plane of the paper, and the circles represent light vibrations perpendicular to the plane of the paper. Thus, the light shown in Fig. 5(a) is polarized in the plane of the paper, that shown in Fig. 5(b) is polarized in a plane at right

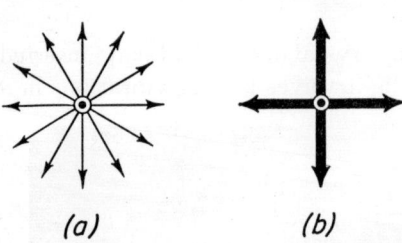

Fig. 4. Resolution of unpolarized light into two plane-polarized components.

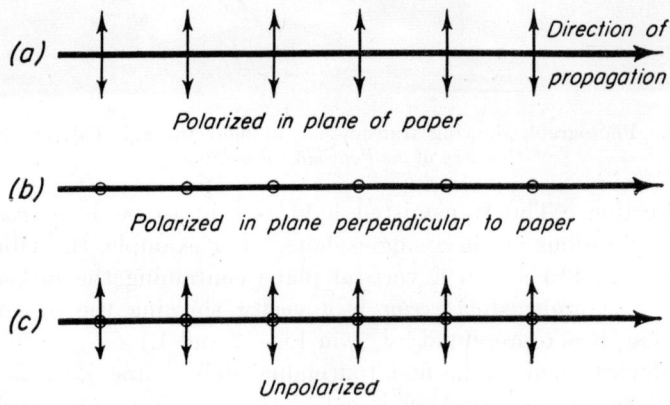

Fig. 5.

angles to the paper, and that in Fig. 5(c) is unpolarized. The *plane of polarization* is the plane in which the propagation vector and the light vibrations lie.

PROBLEMS

NOTE: By a *perfect* polarizing plate, we mean one that transmits *all* light polarized along a given transverse axis, called the *axis of the plate*, and absorbs *all* light polarized in a direction normal to this axis. In the following problems, assume that the polarizing plates are *perfect*.

1. Show that a polarizing plate absorbs 50 per cent of the intensity of an unpolarized beam.

2. Show that two polarizing plates such as those in the window of Fig. 26, p. 762, with axes making an angle θ with each other, transmit $\frac{1}{2}\cos^2\theta$ of the intensity of an incident unpolarized beam.

3. Three polarizing plates are stacked. The first and third are crossed; the one between has its axis at 45° to the axes of the other two. Find the fraction of the intensity of an incident unpolarized beam that is transmitted by the stack. Ans: ⅛.

4. Three polarizing plates are stacked. The first and third have their axes parallel; the one between has its axis at 30° to the axes of the other two. Find the fraction of the intensity of an incident unpolarized beam that is transmitted by the stack.

2. POLARIZATION BY REFLECTION

Perhaps the simplest method of polarizing light is the one discovered by Étienne Louis Malus in 1808. This method involves reflection of light at the surface of a polished nonmetallic medium such as glass. Malus discovered that light reflected from a glass surface is partially polarized and that when the light is incident at one particular angle the reflected light is completely plane-polarized.

Nowadays we can use a Polaroid analyzer in order to detect this polarization. Consider an unpolarized incident light ray SO striking a glass surface at an angle of incidence θ, as shown in Fig. 6. There is always a reflected ray OR and a refracted ray OT at such a surface. If the reflected light is examined with an analyzer placed at the indicated position, it is found that the reflected light is partially polarized in such a way that light associated with vibrations parallel to the surface and perpendicular to the plane of incidence is more highly reflected than light associated with vibrations in the plane of incidence. The plane of incidence is the plane of the paper in Fig. 6. When the angle of incidence at a glass surface is about 57°, the reflected light is completely polarized and all vibrations present in the reflected light are parallel to the glass surface and perpendicular to the plane of incidence. The angle 57° is called the *polarizing angle* (or *Brewster's angle*) for glass. At this angle approximately 8 per cent of the incident light is reflected.

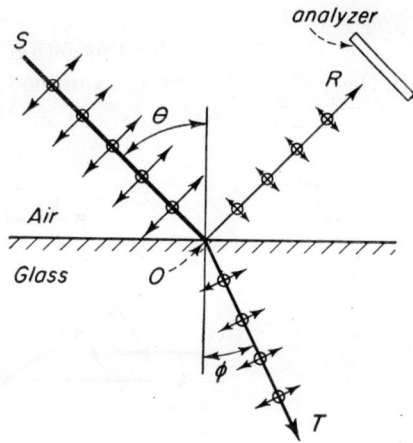

Fig. 6. Partial polarization by reflection.

It was Sir David Brewster (1781–1868) who first noted that when light is incident at the polarizing angle p, the reflected and refracted rays are exactly 90° apart. This situation is shown in Fig. 7. The reflected ray is plane-polarized as shown. Brewster's discovery that rays OR and OT are 90° apart enables us to write a relation between the polarizing angle and the index of refraction of a medium. Snell's law for the case under consideration is

$$\sin p = \mu \sin r,$$

where μ is the refractive index of the reflecting medium. Since the angle between the reflected and refracted rays is 90°, we may write (Fig. 7)

$$p + r + 90° = 180°, \quad \text{or} \quad p + r = 90°.$$

Hence, $\sin r = \cos p.$

Substituting this value for $\sin r$ in Snell's law, we get

$$\mu = \sin p / \cos p = \tan p. \tag{1}$$

This relation between refractive index and polarizing angle is known as *Brewster's law*.

Let us now consider the action of the surface on the refracted light. If the refracted light is examined with an analyzer, it is found to be

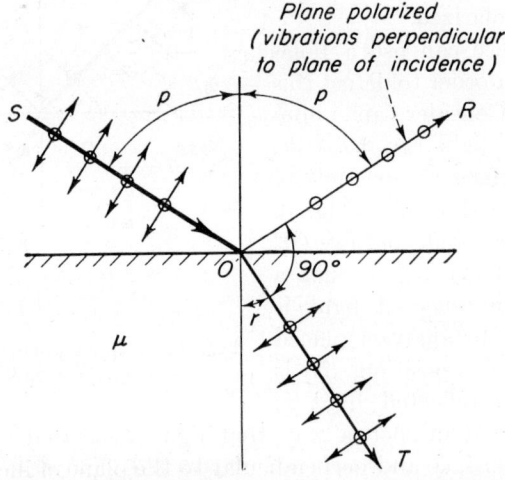

Fig. 7. Complete polarization by reflection: Brewster's law.

partially polarized for all angles of incidence, but for no angle of incidence is the refracted light *completely* plane-polarized. Since more light is *reflected* with polarization normal to the plane of incidence than with polarization in the plane of incidence, more light is *refracted* with polarization in the plane of incidence than with polarization normal to this plane. Since the refracted light always includes some light with vibrations in each reference plane, it is said to be *partially plane-polarized*. The ratio of light with vibrations in the plane of incidence to the light with vibrations perpendicular to the plane of incidence is greatest when the initial beam is incident at the polarizing angle.

Plane polarization of the refracted light can be approximated by the use of several glass plates as shown in Fig. 8. If a beam of unpolarized light is incident at the polarizing angle on a pile of glass plates, some light

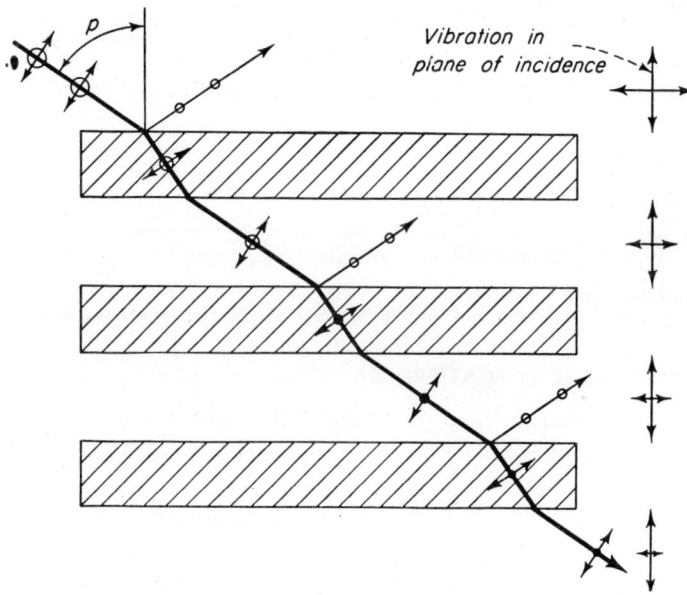

Fig. 8. Polarization by transmission through a series of glass plates.

with vibrations perpendicular to the plane of incidence is reflected at each surface and all light with vibrations in the plane of incidence is refracted. The net result is that the refracted beam becomes more nearly plane-

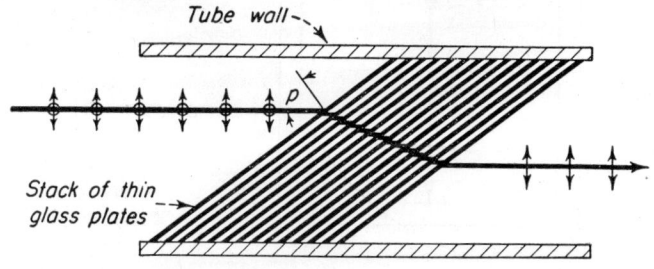

Fig. 9. Polarizer constructed from a stack of glass plates.

polarized with vibrations in the plane of incidence as the beam traverses successive glass plates. The approach to plane polarization is shown qualitatively in the figure. Although plane polarization is never completely attained by transmission, it can be approached by using a large number of plates. In fact, an effective polarizer can be constructed by mounting a stack of microscope cover glasses in a tube in such a manner that light entering the tube strikes the cover glasses at the polarizing angle as shown in Fig. 9. The reflected light is absorbed by the blackened inner wall of the tube and the refracted light passes through the tube as shown.

PROBLEMS

1. Calculate the polarizing angles of crown glass and flint glass for sodium D-light.
Ans: $56°6;\ 58°4$.

2. A beam of sunlight strikes a piece of glass at an angle of incidence of $58°$ and the reflected beam is completely polarized. What is the angle of refraction of the transmitted light?

3. At what angle with the normal can one view the smooth surface of a lake through Polaroid spectacles and eliminate glare completely? Ans: $53°$.

4. Find the angle of refraction of sodium D-light in carbon disulfide when light of this wavelength strikes a carbon-disulfide surface at the polarizing angle.

3. POLARIZATION BY SCATTERING

As we have seen in Chap. 28, some of the light in a beam traversing a medium containing small particles in suspension is scattered. Examina-

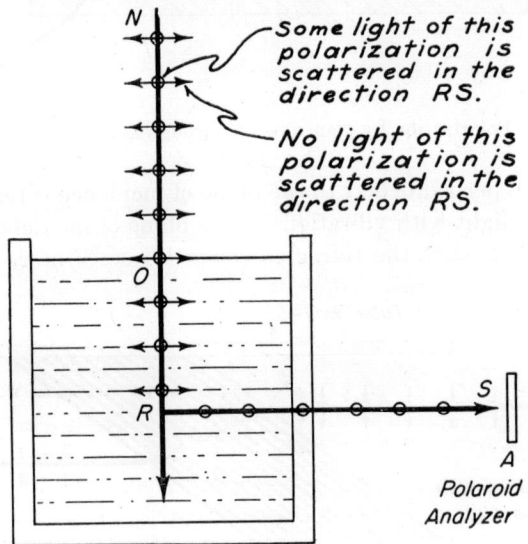

Fig. 10. Polarization by scattering.

tion by means of an analyzer reveals that the scattered light is plane-polarized.

In order to determine the plane of polarization of the scattered light, let us consider the arrangement shown in Fig. 10. A beam of unpolarized light indicated by the propagation vector NO enters a liquid at normal incidence. If the liquid holds fine particles in suspension, some of the light will be scattered. Let vector RS represent a typical path of scattered light and let A represent an analyzer. By rotating the analyzer it is found that the scattered light is completely polarized with its plane of vibration perpendicular to the plane of the paper, as indicated in Fig. 10.

Part of the light of the incident beam that has its vibration vector perpendicular to the plane of the paper in Fig. 10 is scattered at 90° by the small particles and still has its vibration vector in the *same direction*, perpendicular to the paper. None of the light of the incident beam NR with its vibration vector in the plane of the paper is scattered in the direction RS (although it will be scattered directly out of the paper into the reader's eyes and directly into the paper). This result is reasonable if one considers that such scattering would necessarily require a 90° change in direction of the vibration vector, since the scattered wave must be transverse.

Sunlight scattered by the earth's atmosphere (the blue of the sky) is similarly polarized. It is completely polarized when scattered through 90°, partially polarized when scattered through other angles. This effect can also be illustrated by Fig. 10. Let N be the sun more or less directly overhead; let the scattering medium be the earth's atmosphere, S the observer, and R a point in the blue sky near the horizon. Then the blue skylight from R will be polarized in a horizontal plane.

Although some of the blue skylight is due to scattering by small dust particles, most of it is due to scattering by random density fluctuations in the atmospheric gas itself. The polarization phenomenon is the same for these two types of scattering. On the other hand, scattering by particles large in size compared to the wavelength of light, such as water droplets in a cloud, does not result in polarization. One does not usually speak of *scattering* in such cases, but of *reflection*.

Since an ordinary photographic plate is about equally sensitive to the blue of the sky and the white of the clouds, clouds do not show up well in ordinary photography. The older way of bringing them out against a darker sky background was to use a yellow filter which failed to transmit the blue light of the sky but passed most of the white light of the clouds. A newer method which takes advantage of the polarization of the skylight and the availability of Polaroid filters is to place in front of the camera lens a Polaroid filter turned so that it transmits only vertically polarized light. The horizontally polarized blue skylight is then almost completely eliminated while half the unpolarized light reflected from clouds and other objects being photographed gets through. This is illustrated in Fig. 25 a few pages further on.

4. ELECTROMAGNETIC WAVES

We have seen that, in order to explain polarization effects, it is necessary to treat light as a transverse wave motion. Although we have spoken of 'displacements' and 'vibrations' associated with light waves, we have not yet attempted to specify the nature of the displacements. For reasons that will become apparent in the part of the text dealing with electricity, light is regarded as consisting of associated electric and magnetic 'fields.' Thus, a simple plane-polarized light wave traveling in the x-direction and polarized in the y-direction is pictured in the manner

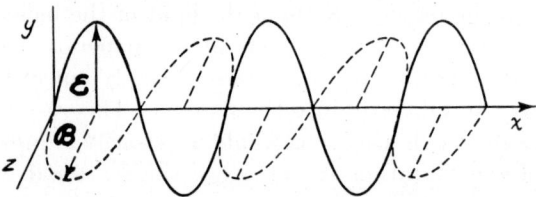

Fig. 11. Electromagnetic wave plane-polarized in the xy-plane.

indicated in Fig. 11. The electric field $\mathcal{E}$ is in the y-direction and of magnitude given by the equation

$$\mathcal{E}_y = \mathcal{E}_0 \sin 2\pi f(t - x/c), \qquad (2)$$

where $\mathcal{E}_0$ is the amplitude, f is the frequency, and c is the speed of light. In terms of wavelength λ, this equation becomes

$$\mathcal{E}_y = \mathcal{E}_0 \sin 2\pi (ct - x)/\lambda. \qquad (2')$$

The magnetic field $\mathcal{B}$ is in the z-direction, of magnitude given by

$$\mathcal{B}_z = \mathcal{B}_0 \sin 2\pi (ct - x)/\lambda, \qquad (3)$$

where $\mathcal{B}_0$ is the amplitude and the other symbols are the same as those in the equations for the electric field. Thus, a plane-polarized beam of light traveling in the x-direction consists of a transverse electric wave given by equation (2) and a transverse magnetic wave given by equation (3); the magnetic vibrations are in phase with the electric vibrations but are perpendicular to the electric vibrations.

Consideration of this twofold character of light waves leads us to the question of whether the electric component $\mathcal{E}_y$ or the magnetic component $\mathcal{B}_z$ is to be identified with the vibrations we have used in our discussions of light waves. In every interference and diffraction phenomenon, the electric waves influence one another in precisely the same way as the magnetic waves. However, in interactions with matter the electric component of the light wave is usually the more important. The forces exerted on electrical charges in matter are proportional to the electric field $\mathcal{E}$. It is the electric component of a light wave that affects photographic plates. There is good reason to suppose that the electric component is the one that affects the retina of the eye. Therefore, we may identify the *electric* vibrations with the light vibrations we have discussed earlier. The magnetic wave, which always accompanies the electric wave, is less important in interactions with matter. Therefore, in terms of our conventional picture of light waves, the simple wave shown in Fig. 11 would be represented in the manner indicated in Fig. 12.

The speed with which light is transmitted in a given medium is determined largely by the interactions between the electric components

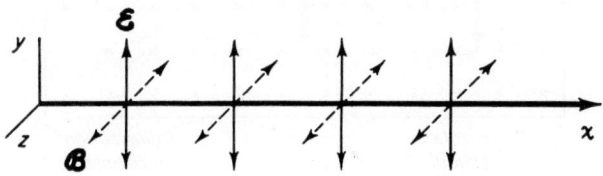

Plane polarized light - showing $\mathcal{E}$ and $\mathcal{B}$ vibrations

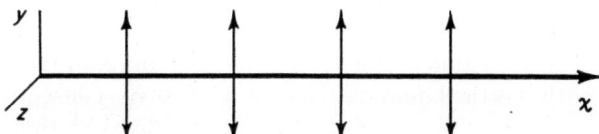

Plane polarized light - showing conventional 'vibrations'

Fig. 12.

of the wave and the electric charges associated with the atoms and molecules present in the medium. Since no charges are present in vacuum, the speed of light in a vacuum is independent of frequency. In other media the interaction between the light vibrations and the charges depends on the frequency; hence, light of different frequencies travels with different speed. In glass, red light travels with a greater speed than violet light; the index of refraction of glass is therefore greater for violet light than for red light.

The subject of electromagnetic waves will be treated more fully in Chap. 44 after electric and magnetic fields have been studied in detail.

5. DOUBLE REFRACTION

Our treatment of refraction so far applies only to refraction in isotropic media. By an *isotropic medium* we mean one whose physical properties are the same in all directions. The speed of light in such a medium does not depend on the orientation of the electric vibrations. For example, consider the idealized situation shown in Fig. 13. The small crosses represent the positions of molecules or atoms in an isotropic medium traversed by plane-polarized light beams with electric displacements in the vertical direction and horizontal direction, respectively. The arrangements of the atoms or molecules relative to vibrations in

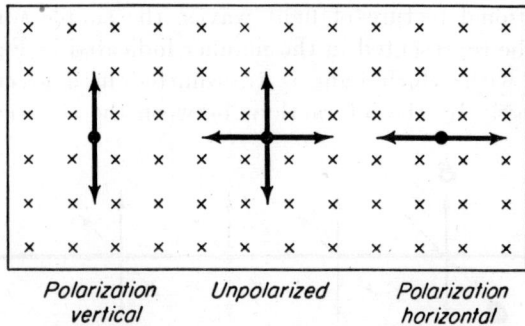

Fig. 13. Schematic diagram showing transmission of light through an isotropic material.

these two directions are identical. The vertical and horizontal vibrations interact in the same manner with the medium, and the light waves associated with vertical and horizontal vibrations consequently have the same speed. The speed of the unpolarized light in this case is the same as that of the polarized light, since vibrations associated with

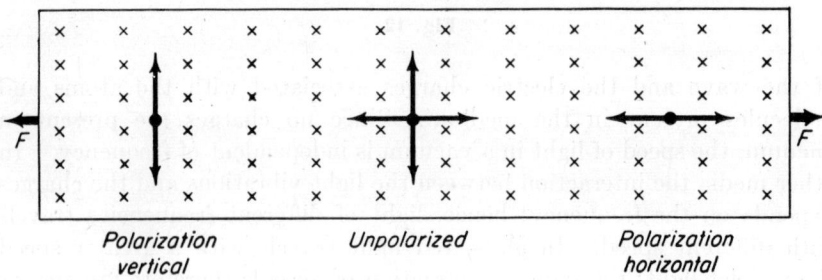

Fig. 14. Transmission of light by an anisotropic material.

the unpolarized light can be resolved into vertical and horizontal components in the manner shown. In Fig. 13 and the succeeding diagrams, all vectors are again the electric vectors which define the plane of polarization. The magnetic vector can be completely ignored.

Let us now consider the situation resulting when the isotropic medium is subjected to a tensional stress as shown in Fig. 14. As indicated, the resulting strain involves a change in the relative positions of the atoms and molecules of the medium, which is therefore no longer isotropic. The polarized light with vertical vibrations will not interact with the medium in the same manner as the light with horizontal vibrations and will therefore have a different speed in the strained medium. The unpolarized light will actually be divided by the medium into two disturbances traveling with different speeds. A medium with properties like those just described is called *doubly refracting* or *birefringent*. An isotropic medium like glass or Lucite becomes doubly refracting when strained; certain crystals like quartz and calcite are naturally nonisotropic and exhibit double refraction even when not subjected to external forces.

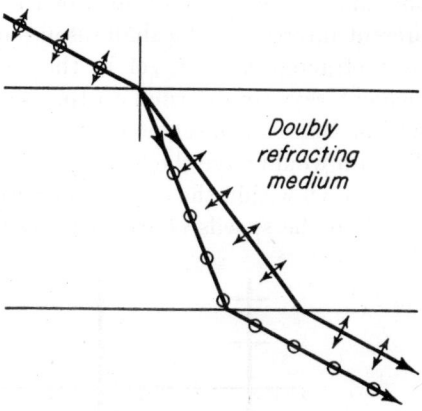

Fig. 15. Double refraction by an anisotropic medium such as a calcite crystal.

Since a doubly refracting medium has two different indices of refraction, a ray of unpolarized light incident at an angle with the normal to the surface is usually split into two refracted rays polarized at right angles, as

Fig. 16. Photograph of a printed word viewed through a doubly refracting crystal, and through ordinary glass. No polaroid is involved, but the photograph was furnished through the courtesy of the Polaroid Corporation.

shown in Fig. 15. This phenomenon can lead to some rather interesting effects such as the one depicted in Fig. 16, in which the incident light is separated into polarized components traveling in different directions in a manner somewhat analogous to that shown schematically in Fig. 15.

Figure 16 shows the appearance of a printed word when viewed through a piece of doubly refracting calcite crystal.

The subject of crystal optics is an interesting but very complicated one, and a general treatment of the subject is beyond the scope of our present interests. We shall discuss only the particular case in which the two refracted rays travel in the same direction, as they would if the incident ray were normal to the surface of a doubly refracting medium such as that shown schematically in Fig. 14. In this simple case, the ray diagram would have the form shown in Fig. 17, in which the lengths of the rays shown within the doubly refracting medium have been made proportional to the speeds of the polarized light in the medium. In the case

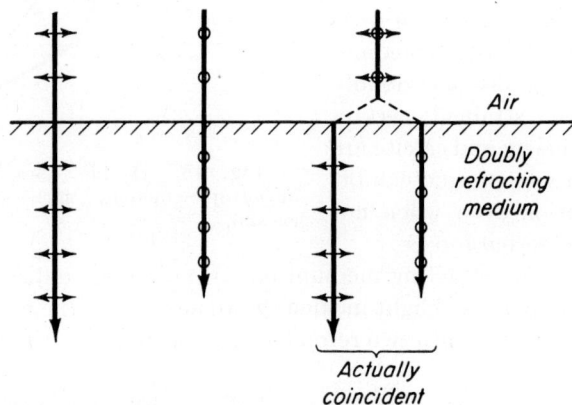

Fig. 17. This is essentially a front view of Fig. 14, showing the difference in speed of transmission of light polarized in the two planes of symmetry of the anisotropic medium, and the splitting of unpolarized light into two coincident beams of different wavelength.

when unpolarized light is incident, the two refracted rays are actually coincident but the light represented by the two rays travels with different speeds, so that the two rays get out of phase.

Let us now consider what happens when a beam of plane-polarized light strikes the surface of a doubly refracting medium in such a way that the plane of polarization is not parallel to a plane of symmetry of the medium. Such a situation is shown schematically in Fig. 18, in which the plane of polarization is oriented at an angle of 45° to the symmetry planes. Let us suppose that the plane-polarized light beam directed away from the reader enters the surface of the doubly refracting medium at normal incidence. The initial displacement of the light wave is represented by I_0. This initial displacement can be resolved into two component displacements V_0 and H_0 in the vertical and horizontal directions, respectively. The speeds of the component light waves having original displacements V_0 and H_0 are not equal. Therefore, the waves with horizontal and vertical displacements will have different wavelengths and will not remain in phase after they have traveled into the medium. Consequently, the resultant of the V and H displacements at a given position in the medium will not necessarily add in such a way as to give a resultant in the original plane of polarization. This statement will be true in particular after the wave has traversed the medium and again emerged into the air.

In order to understand the effects of the doubly refracting medium on plane-polarized light incident in the manner indicated in Fig. 18, let us consider the diagrams shown in Fig. 19. The light of Fig. 18 is incident normally on a sheet of doubly refracting material, and the diagrams in Fig. 19 show the light wave at the point of emergence for several phase

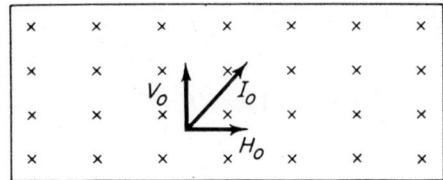

Fig. 18. Light beam plane-polarized in the plane of I_0, traveling directly away from the reader, and entering a slab of anisotropic material.

differences between the two plane-polarized waves. In each case the series of diagrams (1), (2), (3), (4), (1) follow the wave through a complete period of vibration $T = 1/f$, always just at the point of emergence. In part (a) of this figure, the phase difference is zero and the resultant displacements at times equal to various fractions of the period T are shown in (1), (2), (3), and (4). The drawing at the right shows the locus of the resultant displacement during a complete vibration. As might be expected, the resultant is polarized in the same plane as the plane of polarization of the incident light. Part (b) gives similar information for the case in which the phase difference between the horizontally and vertically polarized component waves is 90° at the point of emergence. It will be noted that the resultant displacement is never zero; as shown at the right, the locus of the resultant displacement during a complete vibration is actually a *circle*. Thus, if the light completes its passage through the doubly refracting medium when the phase difference between waves with vertical and horizontal polarization is 90°, the emerging light is said to be *circularly polarized*. If the light of part (b) is coming out of the paper toward the eye of the observer and the electric vector rotates counterclockwise as shown, the polarization is said to be *left circular;* if the rotation is clockwise, it is said to be *right circular.* Part (c) of Fig. 19

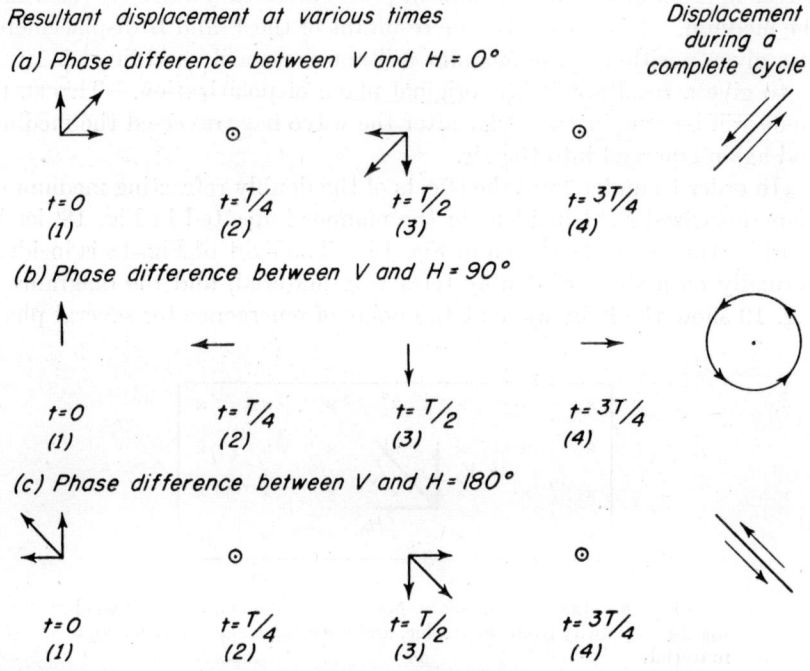

Fig. 19. When the light of Fig. 18 emerges from the slab, the character of its polarization depends on the phase difference between the H and V components. A slab that gives the 90° phase difference of (b) is called a *quarter-wave plate.*

shows the situation when the phase difference between the vertically and horizontally polarized waves is 180° at the point of emergence. Here the resultant vibrations are similar to those for which the phase difference was

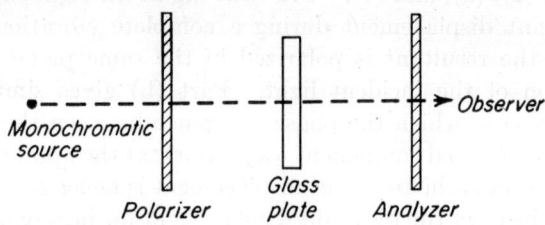

Fig. 20. Photoelastic polariscope (schematic).

zero except for the fact that they have been rotated through 90°. The locus of the displacements for a complete vibration is actually a straight line perpendicular to the straight line shown in (a). Therefore, if the light completes its passage through the doubly refracting medium when the phase difference is 180°, the emerging light is polarized in a plane perpendicular to the plane of polarization of the incident light. When the phase difference between the vertically and horizontally polarized

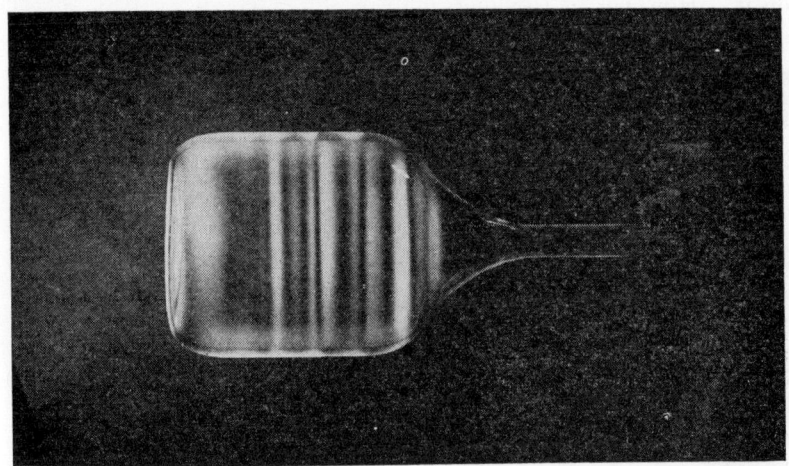

Fig. 21. Use of polarized light in detecting strains in glassware.

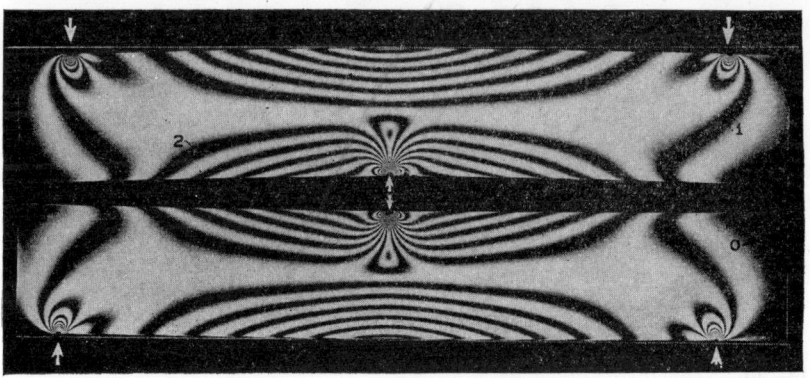

Fig. 22. Photoelastic pattern.

waves is given by angles other than 0°, 90°, 180°, and 270°, the locus of the resultant displacement during a complete vibration is an ellipse, and the light is said to be *elliptically polarized*.

Let us now consider an arrangement by which polarized light can be used to detect strains in transparent materials. Figure 20 shows a polarizer-analyzer combination oriented in such a way that the plane-polarized light from the polarizer is not transmitted by the analyzer; the polarizer and the analyzer are 'crossed' and no light is transmitted. Now a plate of glass or some other transparent, normally isotropic material is placed in the light beam between polarizer and analyzer. If there are no strains in the glass plate, the plate will have no effect on the light incident upon it. However, if the glass plate is subjected to a stress, the glass

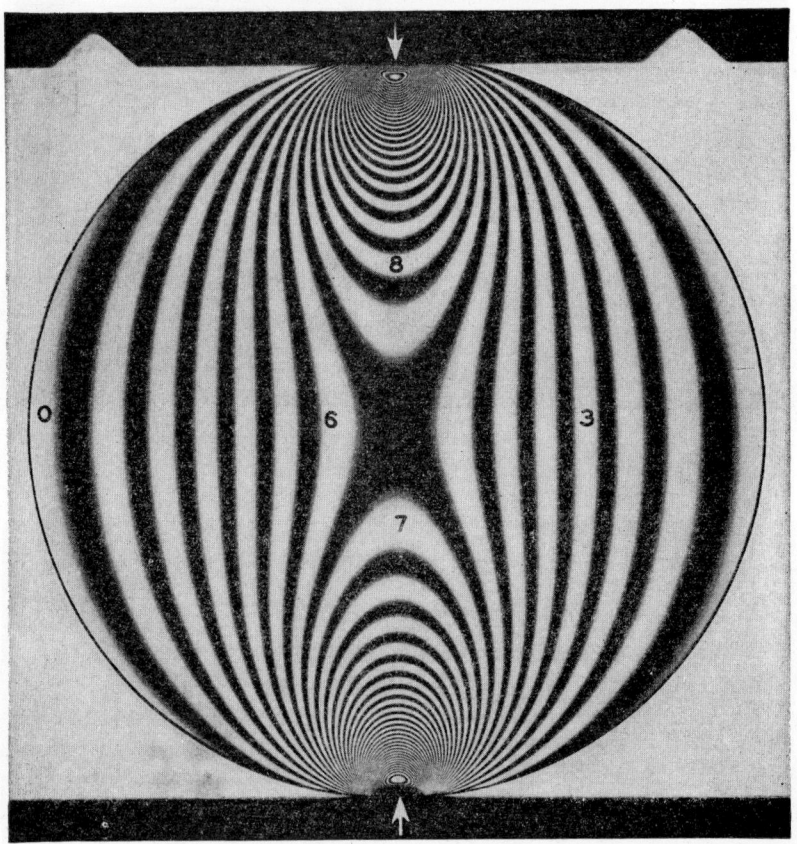

Fig. 23. [The photographs for Figs. 22 and 23 reproduced by permission from *Photoelasticity*, Vol. I, by Frocht (Wiley).]

becomes doubly refracting. As a result of the double refraction, the plane-polarized light entering the plate will not necessarily be polarized in the same plane when it emerges from the plate. Therefore, some of the light transmitted by the plate will also be transmitted by the analyzer and can be seen by the observer. He will be able to see the strained portions of the glass plate through the analyzer; the plate will appear to be crossed by alternate light and dark bands which are contours of constant phase difference between the component beams on emergence.* Glassblowers use such a system for locating the strains appearing in glassware. A photograph of a piece of strained glass observed in the above manner is shown in Fig. 21.

This method of using polarized light to reveal strains in transparent materials is finding extensive application in the field of mechanical stress analysis. The distribution of internal stresses in structural units or machine parts may be determined by passing polarized light through scale models made of celluloid or transparent bakelite, which are subjected to external forces simulating those in the actual structures or machines. The internal strains can be determined from the patterns observed through an analyzer. The method is illustrated by the photographs in Figs. 22 and 23. This important method of solving problems in the theory of elasticity is called *photoelasticity*.

PROBLEMS

1. Consider light incident upon a quartz crystal in the manner indicated in Fig. 17. The index of quartz for the 'extraordinary ray' is 1.553 and for the 'ordinary ray' is 1.544 when the wavelength of the incident light in vacuum is 589.0 mμ. What are the two wavelengths of the light in the crystal? Ans: 379.3 mμ; 381.5 mμ.

2. The 'ordinary' index of refraction of calcite is 1.6584 and its 'extraordinary' index of refraction is 1.4864 when light of wavelength 589.0 mμ is incident in the manner indicated in Fig. 17. What are the wavelengths of this light in calcite?

3. What minimum thickness of crystalline quartz is required for a quarter-wave plate for 589.0-mμ light? The phase difference of the waves emerging from a quarter-wave plate is 90°. (Compare with Prob. 1.)   Ans: 1.6×10^{-3} cm.

4. What minimum thickness of calcite is required for a quarter-wave plate for 589.0-mμ light? The phase difference of the waves emerging from a quarter-wave plate is 90°. (Compare with Prob. 2.)

5. A thin plate of calcite is cut from a crystal in the proper manner and light is incident normally, so that the situation depicted in Fig. 17 is realized. If the plate is placed between *crossed* Polaroids and oriented at 45° to the incident polarized light as in Fig. 18, what should be the minimum thickness of the plate in order that no light be transmitted by the second Polaroid? Use the indices of refraction in Prob. 2.   Ans: 3.43×10^{-4} cm.

6. If a piece of quartz is properly cut and placed between *crossed* Polaroids in the manner indicated in Prob. 5, what should be the minimum thickness in order that no light be transmitted by the second Polaroid? Use the indices of refraction given in Prob. 1.

7. Let Fig. 18 represent a quartz quarter-wave plate in which the index for the V component is the extraordinary index, 1.553, and the index for the H component is the ordinary index, 1.544, for light of wavelength 589.0 mμ. Will light of this wave-

---

* This description is oversimplified. The simple patterns described here and shown in Figs. 22 and 23 result only when circularly polarized light is used instead of plane-polarized light. A 'circular polarizer' consists of a Polaroid followed by a 'quarter-wave plate' which generates, say, left-circularly polarized light in the manner of Fig. 19(b). A 'circular analyzer' consists of another quarter-wave plate followed by a Polaroid. The circular analyzer is 'crossed' with the circular polarizer when it is so arranged that the analyzer transmits only right-circularly polarized light and absorbs all the left.

length, incident on the plate with plane polarization in the plane I_0, emerge with right- or left-circular polarization? Show that light incident with plane polarization in the plane perpendicular to I_c will give the opposite type of circular polarization. (Remember that in Fig. 18 you are looking in the direction of propagation but that before you can apply the definitions of the text to decide the type of polarization, you must reverse your point of view and imagine the light entering your eye.)

Ans: right-circular.

8. Show that if circularly polarized light is incident on a quarter-wave plate, it emerges as plane-polarized light. Show that if the sense of the circular polarization is reversed, the plane of polarization of the emergent light turns through 90°, and hence that a combination of a quarter-wave plate and a Polaroid can be arranged as a circular analyzer which will transmit light with one type of circular polarization and will completely absorb light circularly polarized in the opposite sense.

9. Show that circularly polarized light incident on a Polaroid plate is transmitted equally well for all orientations of the plate, and hence that a Polaroid plate used alone as an analyzer cannot distinguish circularly polarized light from unpolarized light.

6. USES OF POLARIZED LIGHT

In addition to the application of polarized light in stress analysis, it has numerous other practical uses. One of these applications is in the field of quantitative chemical analysis.

Certain materials have the property of rotating the plane of polarization of light by an amount directly proportional to the length of the light path in the sample; this property is called *optical activity*. These materials include the following liquids: turpentine, Rochelle salt solutions, sugar solutions, and solutions of quinine sulfate, nicotine, and camphor. Some of these liquids cause a rotation that is clockwise when viewed toward the source of light; these are called *dextrorotatory*. Other liquids cause a counterclockwise rotation and are called *levorotatory*.* The most important of these 'optically active' materials are the sugars, such as dextrose, which is dextrorotatory, and levulose, which is levorotatory. The analysis of the concentration of sugar solutions by measurement of optical rotation finds numerous practical applications. For example, the import duties on liquids containing sugar are based on the concentration, which is quickly and accurately determined by optical measurements.

In making the measurement, a device called a *polarimeter* or *saccharimeter* is used. A simple polarimeter is shown schematically in Fig. 24. Light from a monochromatic source, usually a sodium flame, passes through a collimating lens to the polarizer P. Before the tube containing the solution of unknown concentration is placed in the indicated position, the analyzer A is rotated until no light is transmitted. When the tube containing the solution is inserted, the analyzer A must be rotated

---

* It is useful to think of dextrorotatory molecules as having some of the characteristics of an ordinary right-handed corkscrew; levorotatory molecules as having some of the characteristics of the left-handed corkscrew which proverbially fools the drunk. This picture actually makes good sense from the standpoint of molecular structure.

through angle α before the polarized light is again completely removed by the analyzer. This angle α, the angle through which the plane of polarization has been rotated by the solution, is directly proportional to the path length l, to the 'concentration' d (mass per unit volume of the optically active material), and to the specific rotatory property of the

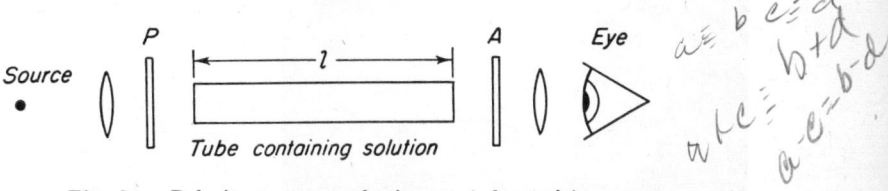

Fig. 24. Polarimeter or saccharimeter (schematic).

optically active material being studied. Therefore, the expression for α can be written as

$$\alpha = Sld.$$

In actual practice, the path length l is measured in decimeters (1 decimeter = 10 cm), d is measured in g/cm³, and α is measured in degrees. S is then called the 'specific rotation'; it is the angle of rotation in degrees

Fig. 25. Photographs of the same scene taken (left) without and (right) with a Polaroid filter. (*Courtesy of the Polaroid Corporation.*)

produced by passage through a 1-decimeter path length in a liquid containing 1 gram of active material per cubic centimeter of solution.

Various refinements can be made in the simple polarimeter shown schematically in Fig. 24. These refinements make it possible to measure α accurately. If a solution containing an unknown amount of an optically active material with known specific rotation S is introduced

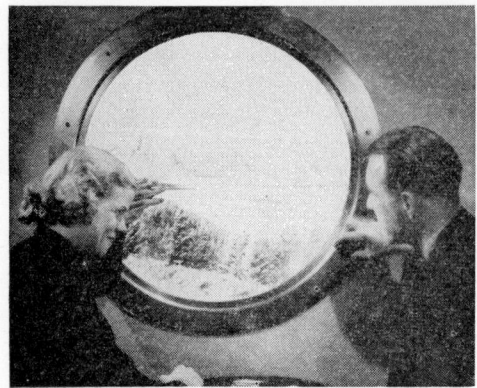

Fig. 26. Variable-density window. In the top picture the two sheets of Polaroid have their axes parallel; in the center picture the axes are in an intermediate orientation; in the bottom picture they are crossed. (*Courtesy of the Polaroid Corporation.*)

in the light path in a tube of length l, α can be measured and d can be determined. This type of optical analysis has been used for many years in the sugar industry.

Since the development of Polaroid, many new developments involving polarization effects have been possible. The use of Polaroid goggles for the elimination of glare arising from the reflection of sunlight from water surfaces or highway surfaces is well known. Much of the glare consists of light with vibrations in the horizontal plane; this type of light can be eliminated by the use of Polaroid sheets oriented in such a manner as to transmit only light waves having vibrations in the vertical direction. Therefore, Polaroid goggles in which the films are properly oriented can be quite useful to automobile drivers and to others engaged in activities in which glare is objectionable. The use of Polaroid for the elimination of glare is illustrated in Fig. 25, in which it will be noted that the building is much brighter in comparison with the water surface in the photograph made with a Polaroid filter. These photographs also illustrate the reduction in intensity of the polarized blue light of the sky in comparison with the unpolarized light from the clouds.

Another use for Polaroid is the curtainless window of variable density that is beginning to appear in railway club cars. This contains two Polaroid sheets that can be rotated relative to each other. The effect is illustrated in Fig. 26.

PROBLEMS

1. An aqueous solution of cane sugar in a tube 20 cm long produces a rotation of the plane of polarization of $13°30$ for a concentration of 0.1 g of sugar per cm^3. What is the 'specific rotation' for cane sugar?

Ans: $S = 66°5$ per g/cm^3 per decimeter path length.

2. What rotation of the plane of polarization would be produced by a 25-cm tube of a sugar solution containing 0.2 g of sugar per cm^3? The value of S is given in the answer to Prob. 1.

3. A column of a certain sugar solution 20 cm long and 125 cm^3 in volume is found to rotate the plane of polarization by $5°42$. How much sugar does the solution contain? Use the value of S found in Prob. 1. Ans: 5.09 g.

4. A tube 20 cm long is filled with a solution containing cane sugar and is placed in a beam of polarized light. The plane of polarization is rotated through $28°4$. Using the value of S given in the answer to Prob. 1, find the concentration of sugar in grams per liter.

7. MAGNETO-OPTICAL AND ELECTRO-OPTICAL EFFECTS

In Sec. 4 of this chapter we pointed out that light consists of electromagnetic waves with the electric and accompanying magnetic vectors at right angles. Hence we should expect the optical properties of materials

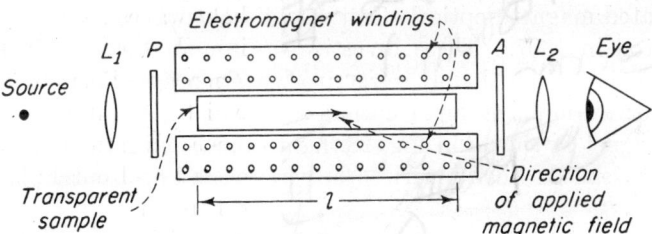

Fig. 27. Rotation of the plane of polarization by a magnetic field: Faraday effect.

to be influenced to some extent by externally applied magnetic and electric fields. This is indeed the case.

The first connection between magnetism and optics was discovered by Michael Faraday in 1845. Faraday found that the plane of polarization of light is rotated when polarized light is allowed to pass through an isotropic medium located in a strong magnetic field if the light travels in a direction parallel to the direction of the magnetic field. An arrangement for demonstrating this *Faraday effect* is shown schematically in Fig. 27. Monochromatic light from a source such as a sodium flame passes through a collimating lens L_1 and polarizer P and then through a transparent rod of glass or a tube of carbon disulfide to an analyzer A and lens L_2 to the observer's eye. The transparent sample is located inside a large coil of wire like the coils used in electromagnets. Before the direct electric current in the coil is turned on, the analyzer is rotated until no light is transmitted. When the electric current is started, a magnetic field is produced in a direction parallel to the direction in which the light is traveling. Light now comes through the analyzer to the observer, and the analyzer must be rotated through an angle θ before the light is again extinguished. This angle θ represents the angle through which the plane of polarization has been rotated. The magnitude of θ depends on the strength of the magnetic field $\mathfrak{B}$, the length of the light path l through the magnetic field, and the optical properties of the transparent material; the relation can be written as

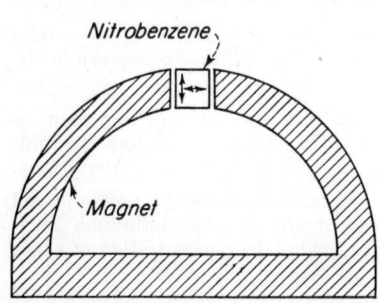

Fig. 28. Schematic diagram: Cotton-Mouton effect.

$$\theta = V l \mathfrak{B},$$

where V is called *Verdet's constant*. This constant depends on the material used and on the wavelength of the light.

A related magneto-optical effect was discovered by A. A. Cotton and H. Mouton in 1907. These investigators found that certain isotropic optical media become doubly refracting when placed in a strong magnetic field. For example, if nitrobenzene is placed between the poles of a strong magnet as shown in Fig. 28, light approaching the reader travels at different speeds when polarized in vertical and horizontal planes.

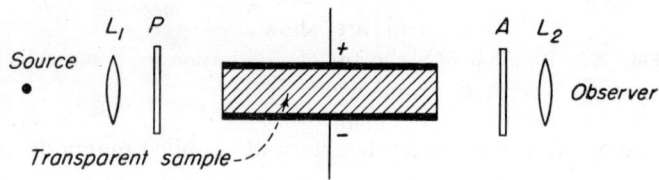

Fig. 29. The Kerr effect.

The electrical analogue of this *Cotton-Mouton effect* had been discovered by John Kerr in 1875. Kerr found that an *isotropic* optical medium between the plates of an electric condenser becomes doubly refracting when the condenser is charged. The *Kerr effect* can be demonstrated by the arrangement shown in Fig. 29. Collimated light from a monochromatic source is plane-polarized by the polarizer P. Examination of the light transmitted through the cell shows that the transmitted light becomes elliptically polarized when the condenser plates are charged.

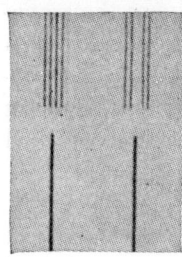

Fig. 30. Zeeman effect.

The processes of producing double refraction in a normally isotropic medium by the application of mechanical deforming forces, magnetic fields, and electric fields have a basic similarity; in each case, strains are produced inside the medium, which accordingly becomes anisotropic.

The effects thus far mentioned have involved changes produced by magnetic and electric fields in a material medium through which light passes. These effects therefore influence light waves during the *transmission* process. Magnetic and electric fields can also affect the processes involved in *emission* and *absorption* of light.

As we have already noted, each chemical element has a characteristic line spectrum. Therefore, we conclude that the processes involved in the emission and absorption of line spectra take place within the atoms of the elements. For example, the two D-lines are emitted as a result of processes taking place within the sodium atom. In 1896, Peter Zeeman discovered that when a sodium flame is placed between the poles of a strong magnet, these two yellow D-lines are split into a number of components; this discovery therefore indicates that the process of emission can be influenced by a magnetic field. Figure 30 shows the *Zeeman effect* observed in the emission spectrum of the D-lines. The two D-lines in the absence of a magnetic field are shown at the bottom of this figure. At the top is an exposure on the same plate of the lines when the emitting atoms are in a magnetic field. The Zeeman effect can also be observed in absorption, and therefore it can be concluded that absorption processes are also influenced by magnetic fields.

In 1913, Johannes Stark observed an analogous effect arising from an external electric field. He discovered that when the hydrogen spectrum is excited in a strong electric field, each line in the normal hydrogen spectrum is split into a number of components. The *Stark effect* on a line of helium is shown in Fig. 31. In the absence of an electric field this line has only one com-

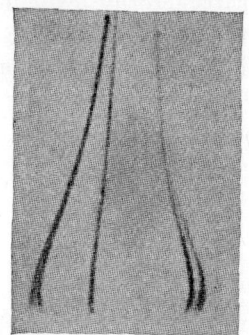

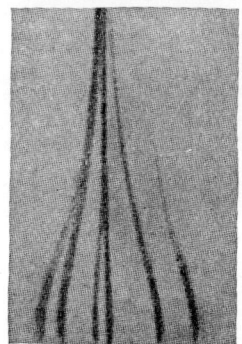

Fig. 31. Stark effect. [Figures 30 and 31 are reproduced from *Atomic Spectra and Atomic Structure* by G. Herzberg (Prentice-Hall).]

ponent. In the spectrograms the electric field is not constant, but increases as one goes from the top of the pattern to the bottom, where the splitting is greatest. The upper spectrum shows the wavelengths of the emitted light that is polarized parallel to the direction of the electric field; the lower spectrum is made with light polarized perpendicular to the field. The observed effects indicate that electric fields influence emission processes. Since the Stark effect can also be observed in absorption, we can conclude that absorption processes are also influenced by electric fields.

The fact that processes of emission, transmission through material media, and absorption of light can be affected by external magnetic and electric fields leaves little doubt that the electromagnetic theory of light is correct. All phenomena involved in the transmission of light can be satisfactorily explained in terms of electromagnetic waves. In the following chapter we shall consider in more detail the processes involved in emission and absorption.

CHAPTER 30

EMISSION AND ABSORPTION OF RADIATION

We have now considered various optical phenomena and have shown evidence that light consists of transverse electromagnetic waves which are similar except in wavelength to the much longer electromagnetic waves used in radio transmission. The electromagnetic theory of light was developed by an English theoretical physicist, James Clerk Maxwell, in 1864—long before radio waves were experimentally observed and measured. Maxwell's electromagnetic theory, presented in elegant mathematical form, gives a satisfactory description of most phenomena involved in the *transmission* of light and forms the basis of what is now called the *classical electromagnetic theory*. In the present chapter we shall discuss phenomena involved in the *emission* and *absorption* of radiation. It will not be possible for us to give a complete and rigorous treatment of the subject, but we shall attempt to indicate the general lines of development of the modern theories of emission and absorption.

According to classical electromagnetic theory, the ultimate sources of electromagnetic radiation are accelerated electric charges. A charge executing simple harmonic motion of frequency f about an equilibrium position would be expected to emit radiation of frequency f. For the radiation of relatively low frequency emitted by a radio-broadcast antenna, the predictions of classical theory are in complete agreement with experiment. *For the radiation of higher frequency corresponding to visible light, emission and absorption processes cannot be satisfactorily treated by classical theory.* In particular, (a) the observed wavelength distribution of intensity in the continuous spectrum of an incandescent solid is different from that predicted by the classical theory, and (b) the observed line spectra characteristic of atoms cannot be interpreted in terms of classical theory. The *quantum theory* was developed to account for the experimental results that were at variance with the predictions of classical theory. Since the quantum theory was first proposed by Max Planck in connection with observed intensities in continuous spectra, we shall first consider some of the phenomena observed in the emission of continuous spectra.

1. THE BLACK BODY

As we have noted before, all materials at temperatures above absolute zero are continually emitting and absorbing radiation. As the temperature of a solid is increased, the total radiation flux from the solid increases and there is a variation in the relative abundance of emitted radiation of various wavelengths. The resulting changes in the appearance of a solid body as its temperature is increased are well known; as the temperature of a solid is gradually increased, the solid appears successively red-hot, orange, and white. These changes in appearance can be readily observed in a darkened room by increasing the current through the tungsten filament of an incandescent lamp with a clear bulb. Not all solids radiate in precisely the same way at the same temperature. For this reason, it is helpful to define an 'ideal radiator' or 'perfect radiator,' which obeys simpler laws than do real radiators but which approximates the behavior of real radiators. This procedure is somewhat analogous to our use of the concept of a 'perfect gas,' which approximates the behavior of real gases but obeys simpler laws.

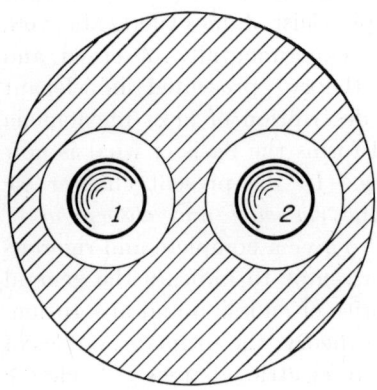

Fig. 1. Two spherical bodies of the same size but of different materials concentrically placed within spherical cavities of the same size.

It is impossible, from a consideration of *emission* only, to decide what an ideal radiator should be. By comparing, with a thermopile or some other nonselective radiation detector, the radiant flux emitted by different surfaces of the same area and at the same temperature, we could select the surface from which the emission was greatest and define this as the ideal radiator, but we should have no assurance that there might not be some other surface of equal area that would give greater emission at the same temperature. The fact that there is an upper limit to the rate at which energy is emitted as radiation from a given body at a given temperature can be deduced only by considering the inverse process, absorption.

Let us consider the solid object shown in Fig. 1, which is maintained at a uniform temperature T throughout. Within this solid there are two evacuated cavities containing opaque bodies 1 and 2 of the same size. The bodies 1 and 2 may be made of quite different materials; for example, 1 may be of metal with a mirror surface, and 2 may be made of wood. It is found by experiment that as a result of radiative interchanges of heat, the temperatures of bodies 1 and 2 eventually become equal to the temperature T of the enclosing walls and remain at that temperature.

In order to be able to study the processes taking place at the surface of each body after equilibrium is reached, let us further assume that the inner walls of the cavities are perfectly absorbing. (This condition can be closely approximated in practice by coating these inner walls with lampblack.) Then the only radiation reaching bodies 1 and 2 is directly radiated by the inner walls of the cavities; these cavity walls do not reflect any radiation and return it to the bodies. Under these circumstances, the radiant energy incident per second on unit area of each body will be the same; call it E, in watts/m². Of the incident radiation E, a certain fraction will be reflected and the remainder will be absorbed. Let ρ denote the fraction of the incident radiation that is reflected and α denote the fraction that is absorbed; ρ is called the *reflection factor* or *reflectivity* or *albedo*, and α the *absorption factor* or *absorptivity*. These quantities are dimensionless and their sum is unity for the surface of any opaque body: $\alpha+\rho=1$. The product $\rho_1 E$ gives the radiation reflected

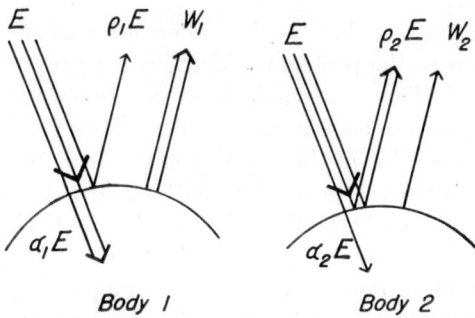

Fig. 2. Diagrammatic representation of the rates of absorption, reflection, and emission by unit areas of the surfaces of the two bodies in Fig. 1 when they are in thermal equilibrium with the surrounding solid object.

from unit area of body 1 and $\rho_2 E$ the radiation reflected from unit area of body 2, in watts. Similarly, $\alpha_1 E$ and $\alpha_2 E$ give the radiation absorbed per unit area of bodies 1 and 2, respectively, in watts. These quantities are represented diagrammatically in Fig. 2.

In the absence of other processes, the absorbed energy would produce an increase in the temperatures of the two bodies. However, experiment shows that the temperatures of the two bodies remain equal to the temperature of their surroundings. This result is understandable if we remember that bodies 1 and 2 are also emitting radiation. Let the rate of radiation be W_1, in watts/m², for body 1 and W_2, in watts/m², for body 2; we shall call W_1 and W_2 the *emissive powers* of the surfaces at temperature T. Now, if the temperatures of the bodies are to remain constant, as much energy must be lost per second by emission as is gained by absorption and we may write

$$\text{rate of absorption} = \text{rate of emission}$$

$$\alpha_1 E = W_1,$$
$$\alpha_2 E = W_2.$$

Dividing the first equation by the second, we find that

$$\frac{\alpha_1}{\alpha_2} = \frac{W_1}{W_2}, \tag{1}$$

or
$$\frac{W_1}{\alpha_1} = \frac{W_2}{\alpha_2}. \tag{2}$$

Equation (1) states that

> The ratio of the emissive powers (rates of radiation) of any two surfaces at the same temperature is equal to the ratio of the absorption factors of the two surfaces. (KIRCHHOFF'S LAW)

Qualitatively, we can say that 'good radiators are good absorbers.'

Now we return to the problem of defining a perfect radiator. As we have already noted, there is no *a priori* way in which we could immediately set an upper limit on the emissive power W. However, it is evident that there *is* a maximum value of the absorption factor α; since no surface can absorb *more* than *all* of the incident radiation, the maximum value α can have is unity. In view of equation (1), we may say that a surface having the maximum emissive power is one that has the maximum absorption factor and is therefore one that absorbs all radiation incident upon it; such a surface is *black* to radiation of all wavelengths. Therefore, we may define a perfect radiator as follows:

> A perfect radiator is a body that absorbs all incident radiation and is therefore called a **black body**. A perfect radiator is a perfect absorber.

Such a body would appear black unless its temperature were high enough for the body to be self-luminous.

We shall denote the emissive power of a black-body or perfect-radiator surface by W_0. If we substitute this value and the black-surface absorption factor $\alpha = 1$ for W_2 and α_2 in equation (2), and write W and α for W_1 and α_1, we find

$$\frac{W}{\alpha} = \frac{W_0}{1} = W_0,$$

or
$$W = \alpha W_0. \tag{3}$$

The quantities W and α denote the emissive power and absorption factor for any surface whatever at the same temperature as the perfect radiator. This equation therefore states that the amount of radiation from any surface is proportional to its absorption factor.

Thus, a dull black surface may absorb 95 per cent of the incident radiation; it would then radiate 95 per cent as much energy as a perfect black body. A polished metal surface may absorb only 5 per cent of the incident radiation; it would then radiate only 5 per cent as much energy as a perfect black body. Such a surface is used in a thermos bottle to inhibit radiation of thermal energy if the contents are hot or to inhibit absorption of thermal energy if the contents are cold.

No material surface absorbs *all* of the radiation incident upon it; even lampblack reflects about one per cent of the incident radiation. In practice, a perfect black surface can be most closely approximated by a small opening in the wall of a cavity such as the one shown schematically

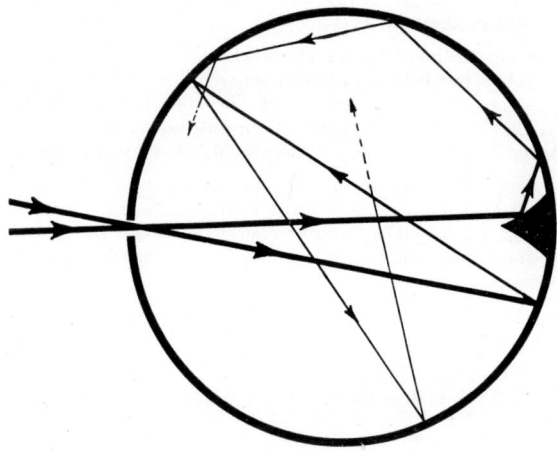

Fig. 3. A small hole in the wall of an enclosure is a good black body. If the cavity walls are rough or dull, reflection from the cavity walls is largely diffuse and the projection on the wall opposite the opening is not necessary and can be omitted. Complete absorption of two representative rays entering the hole is shown schematically.

in Fig. 3; radiation may enter or leave the cavity through the opening. Of the radiation entering through the opening, a part is absorbed by the interior walls of the cavity and a part reflected. Of the part reflected, only a small fraction escapes through the opening, and the remainder is again partially absorbed and partially reflected by the walls. After repeated reflections, all of the entering radiation is absorbed except for the small portion that escapes through the opening. The opening therefore approximates a *black surface* or *perfect absorber*.

The inside walls of the cavity are radiating as well as absorbing, and a part of this radiation escapes through the opening. It can be shown that if the walls are at a uniform temperature T, the radiation that escapes is identical with that which would be emitted by a perfect radiator at temperature T. The hole behaves in all respects like the surface of a black body, and the radiation from it is *black-body radiation*.

PROBLEMS

1. Radiant energy is incident on a certain opaque body at the rate of 30 watts/m². The surface absorbs 20 watts/m². (a) What is the reflectivity of the surface? (b) What is the absorptivity? (c) If the body is in thermal equilibrium with its surroundings and can exchange energy with its surroundings only by radiation, what is the emissive power of the body?   Ans: 0.333; 0.667; 20 watts/m².

2. Radiant energy is incident on a certain opaque body at the rate of 50 watts/m². The surface absorbs 20 watts/m². (a) What is the reflectivity of the surface? (b) What is the absorptivity? (c) If the body is in thermal equilibrium with its surroundings and can exchange energy with its surroundings only by radiation, what is the emissive power of the body?

3. Radiant energy is incident on the surface of a black body at the rate of 50 watts/m². (a) At what rate is radiant energy reflected from each unit area of the surface? (b) At what rate is radiant energy absorbed by each unit area of the surface? (c) If the black body is in radiative equilibrium with its surroundings, what is its emissive power?   Ans: (a) 0; (b) 50 watts/m²; (c) 50 watts/m².

4. Radiant energy is incident on the surface of a black body at the rate of 100 watts/m². (a) At what rate is radiant energy reflected from each unit area of the surface? (b) At what rate is radiant energy absorbed by each unit area of the surface? (c) If the black body is in radiative equilibrium with its surroundings, what is its emissive power?

5. What would be the emissive power of a black body at the same temperature as the opaque body described in Prob. 1?   Ans: 30 watts/m².

6. What would be the emissive power of a black body at the same temperature as the opaque body described in Prob. 2?

7. The emissive power of the surface of a certain opaque body is 45 watts/m². The emissive power of a black body at the same temperature is 50 watts/m². What is the absorption factor for the surface of the opaque body?   Ans: 0.9.

8. The emissive power of the surface of a certain opaque body is 8 watts/m². The emissive power of a black body at the same temperature is 100 watts/m². What is the absorption factor for the surface of the opaque body?

2. TOTAL RADIATION FROM A BODY; THE STEFAN-BOLTZMANN LAW

It is a familiar fact that the total radiation emitted from the surface of a body increases rapidly as the temperature of the surface is increased. A quantitative relationship between emissive power and surface temperature was first correctly determined by Josef Stefan in 1879. On the basis of experimental data, Stefan concluded that the emissive power of a surface is proportional to the fourth power of its absolute temperature. Later, Ludwig Boltzmann derived the same relation from theoretical consideration of an ideal radiator or black body. This relationship for a black body is called the *Stefan-Boltzmann law* and is written in the form

$$W_0 = \sigma T^4, \qquad (4)$$

where W_0 is the emissive power of a black body at absolute temperature

T. The proportionality constant σ is called the *Stefan-Boltzmann constant* and has the value 5.672×10^{-8} watt/m^2(K deg)^4.

The total radiation from many surfaces that are definitely not black is also very nearly proportional to the fourth power of the absolute temperature. This is true of surfaces composed of platinum, iron, tungsten (wolfram), carbon, and many other materials. In every case, however, the proportionality constant is less than that for an ideal-radiator surface. The relation for the emissive power W of such a surface is

$$W = e\sigma T^4, \tag{5}$$

where σ is the Stefan-Boltzmann constant and e is a fraction called the *emissivity* of the surface.

> The emissivity of a surface is the ratio of the emissive power of the surface to the emissive power of a black body at the same temperature.

The emissivity of a tungsten surface in a lamp filament is about 0.33.

A comparison of equations (3) and (5), which can be rewritten in the forms

$$W = \alpha W_0 \quad \text{and} \quad W = e W_0,$$

shows that the emissivity is just equal to the absorption power:

$$e = \alpha. \tag{6}$$

So far we have been talking about total radiation of all wavelengths, and in our discussion of absorption have assumed that there was a single absorption factor, independent of wavelength. A body whose absorption factor is independent of wavelength is called a *gray body*. There are many bodies whose absorption is highly variable with wavelength; all colored bodies are of this sort. An extension of the above type of argument shows that if such a body has absorption factor α_λ for radiation of wavelength λ, then its thermal radiation at this wavelength is exactly the fraction α_λ of what a perfect black body would radiate at this wavelength. The distribution in wavelength of black-body radiation is discussed in the following section.

PROBLEMS

1. What is the emissive power of a black body at a room temperature of 27° C? at 327° C? at 727° C? Ans: 459, 7350, 56,700 watts/m^2.

2. What is the emissive power of a black body at liquid-nitrogen temperature ($-196°$ C)?

3. A certain body has a surface with a reflectivity of 0.8 at 727° C. What is the emissive power of this body at this temperature? Ans: 1.134×10^4 watts/m^2.

4. A silver surface has a reflection factor of 0.97 at a certain temperature. What is the emissivity of a silver surface at this temperature?

5. From measurements of solar radiation received on the earth, it is concluded that the sun radiates at the rate of 6250 watts per square centimeter of its surface area. Assuming that the sun is a perfect black body (such a gaseous mass certainly has close to zero reflectivity for incident radiation), compute its surface temperature.

Ans: 5760° K.

6. A radiation pyrometer is used to measure the amount of radiation emerging from a hole of area 1 cm² in the wall of a furnace. If 115 watts emerge, what is the temperature of the interior of the furnace?

7. The surface temperature of the sun is now 6000° K if it is assumed to radiate like a black body. If the sun were to cool to 5000° K, what fraction of the energy now received by the earth would then be received? Ans: 48.2%.

8. Compare the total radiation of the sun at 6000° K and of Betelgeuse, the giant red star in Orion, whose diameter is 290 times that of the sun and whose surface temperature is 3000° K. Assume that both stars radiate like black bodies.

9. What diameter should a tungsten lamp filament of emissivity 0.33 have in order that it will come to a temperature of 3000° K when it is *radiating* 5 watts per cm length?

Ans: 0.105 mm.

3. THE SPECTRUM OF A BLACK BODY; PLANCK'S QUANTUM THEORY

As we have seen, the Stefan-Boltzmann law enables us to determine the emissive power W_0 of a perfect radiator at absolute temperature T. However, thus far we have said nothing concerning the spectrum of the radiation emitted by a perfect radiator and nothing concerning the relative abundance of radiation of different wavelengths. We can immedi-

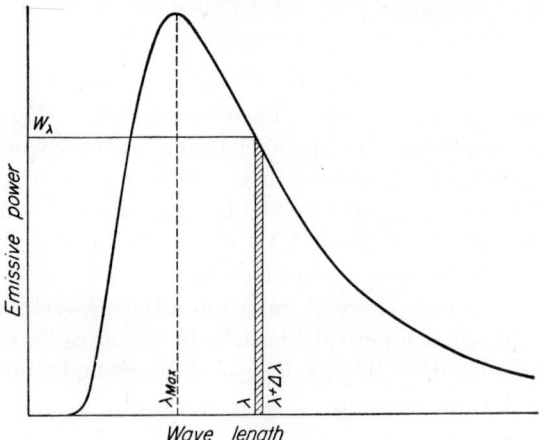

Fig. 4. Measurement of the spectral emissive power of a black body (curve is schematic only).

ately assert that the spectrum of a perfect radiator is continuous; that is, radiation of all wavelengths is emitted from a black body. In order to discuss the relative abundance of radiation of different wavelengths in the spectrum, it is necessary to introduce the quantity W_λ, called the *spectral emissive power*; this gives a measure of the emissive power of a body for radiation in a unit wavelength range at wavelength λ.

In order to see how this quantity can be determined for a black body, let us consider an experiment in which the radiation from a black body is dispersed by means of an instrument like the infrared spectrograph described in Chap. 28, which employs a nonselective electrical receiver such as a thermopile. By noting the receiver voltages produced by radiation of various wavelengths passing through the exit slit of the spectrograph, it is found that the voltage is a maximum for some particular wavelength and gradually decreases to unobservably small values for wavelengths on either side in the manner indicated in Fig. 4. From the observed thermopile voltages and the constants of the spectrograph, a value may be found for the spectral emissive power of the black body for any wavelength λ as indicated in the figure. What is actually observed is the amount of radiation in a short wavelength interval between λ and λ+Δλ, where Δλ gives the 'band' of wavelengths transmitted by the slit, which of course has a finite width. The rate of emission of radiant energy in this wavelength range is given by $W_\lambda \Delta\lambda$ as represented by the shaded area in Fig. 4. *The unit in which the spectral emissive power W_λ is measured is watts/m² per unit wavelength interval;* for example watts/m² per millimicron.

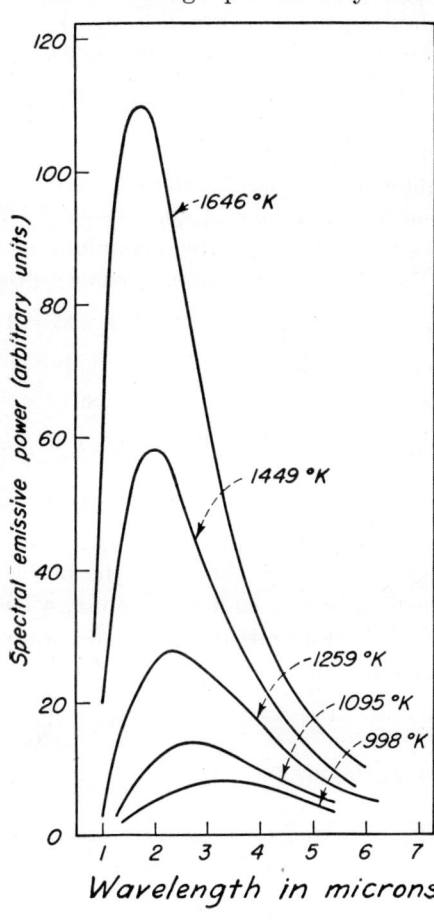

Fig. 5. Experimental radiation curves for a black body.

If the experiment just described is repeated for different black-body temperatures, curves of the type shown in Fig. 5 are obtained. The curves, called *black-body radiation curves*, all have certain basic similarities in form. The curves for higher temperatures are always above the curves for lower temperatures; the maxima of the curves are displaced toward shorter wavelengths as the temperature of the black body is increased. The progressive shift of maximum toward the violet end of the spectrum accounts for the change in color of a body from red through white to blue as its temperature is increased. Sunlight has the characteristics of black-body radiation corresponding to a temperature of about 6000° K and serves to define 'white.' Incandescent-lamp filaments are much cooler and give light that is more orange than daylight. Certain stars, such as Vega (12,000° K) are much hotter and appear blue.

It should be noted that the area under the radiation curve for any absolute temperature T is equal to the total emissive power W_0 and is therefore equal to the value given by the Stefan-Boltzmann law:

$$\int_0^\infty W_\lambda \, d\lambda = W_0 = \sigma T^4. \tag{7}$$

Hence, looking back at the curves of Fig. 5, we see that the total area under the curves, which represents the total radiated energy, varies as the fourth power of the absolute temperature. It turns out that the wavelength λ_m of the maximum of the curve varies inversely as the absolute temperature, according to the law

$$\lambda_m = A/T, \tag{8}$$

where A is a constant whose value is

$$A = 2.8972 \times 10^6 \text{ m}\mu \cdot \text{K deg}.$$

Equation (8) is called *Wien's displacement law*, after Wilhelm Wien (1864–1928).

Many attempts were made to derive an analytical expression for the detailed shape of the curves of Fig. 5 by application of classical electromagnetic theory to the problem of black-body radiation, but all such attempts ended in failure. The correct form of the equation for the spectral emissive power W_λ was first given by Max Planck in 1900 on semiempirical grounds. This expression is

$$W_\lambda = \frac{2\pi \times 10^{-9} hc^2}{\lambda^5 (e^{hc/\lambda kT} - 1)}, \tag{9}$$

in watts/m$^2 \cdot$mμ, where

λ is the wavelength in *meters*,
$c = 2.99776 \times 10^8$ m/sec is the speed of light,
$k = 1.3803 \times 10^{-23}$ joule/K deg is Boltzmann's constant,
$h = 6.623 \times 10^{-34}$ joule·sec is a new universal constant called *Planck's constant*.

The successful attempt of Planck to derive this expression on theoretical grounds represented the beginning of *quantum* theory, which has revolutionized our concepts of the nature of the processes taking place in the emission and absorption of radiation. The radical assumption that Planck made—an assumption completely contrary to the ideas of classical electromagnetic theory according to which emission and absorption are essentially continuous processes, but an assumption that has since been well confirmed by many lines of experimental evidence—is the following:

Radiation of frequency f cannot be emitted or absorbed in arbitrary amounts but is always emitted or absorbed in a discrete quantity, or quantum, of energy hf, where h is a universal constant. In the radiation field in an enclosure, *the radiation of frequency f cannot exist in arbitrary amounts but must consist of an integral number of such energy quanta.*

(QUANTUM HYPOTHESIS)

The complete formulation of the above statement is due partly to Planck and partly to Einstein, who drew his conclusions from an analysis of the photoelectric effect. In the photoelectric effect, which will be more fully discussed in Chap. 42, light falling on a metal surface in a vacuum tube ejects electrons whose energy can be measured. If the surface is illumi-

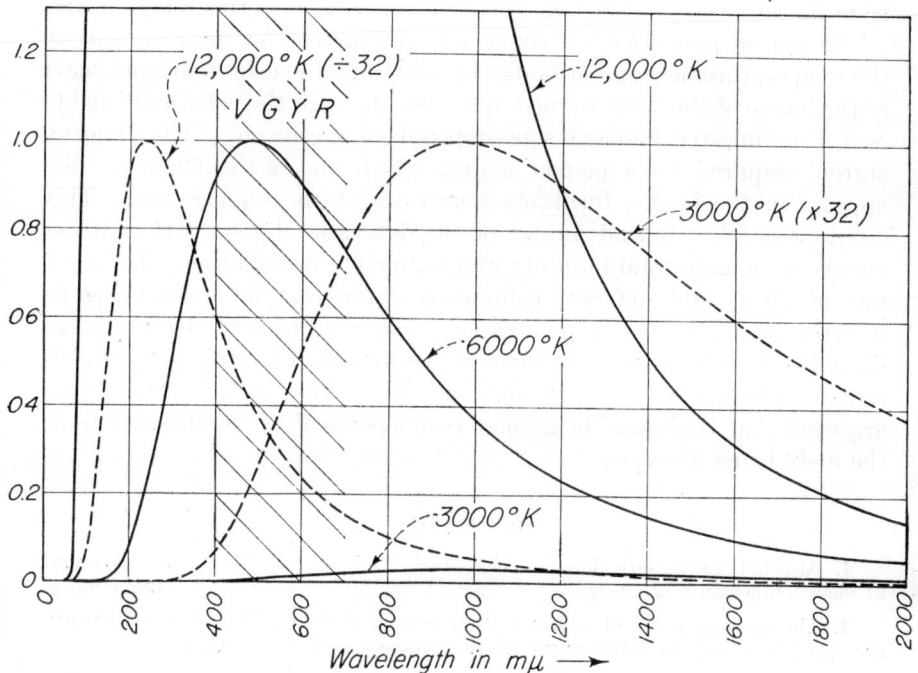

Fig. 6. Accurate plots of Planck black-body radiation curves for temperatures of 3000°, 6000°, and 12,000° K. The ordinates are relative values of spectral emissive power. Broken lines show the 3000° curve with ordinates multiplied by 32 and the 12,000° curve with ordinates divided by 32; this brings the maxima of these curves to the ordinate 1.0, which is the maximum of the 6000° curve. The ordinate 1.0 actually represents $W_\lambda = 1.000 \times 10^5$ watts/m² per mμ.

nated with monochromatic light, it is found that the energy given to the ejected electrons varies directly with the frequency $f = c/\lambda$ of the light and in fact equals hf. If the intensity of the light is decreased, the *number* of ejected electrons decreases, but the *energy* of each ejected electron remains the same, indicating definitely in this process the absorption of one quantum at a time.

There are now a large number of independent lines of evidence for the validity of the quantum hypothesis as stated above, and there is no contradictory evidence whatsoever. The statement in italics above is fundamental to the whole of the development of modern physics that has taken place in the twentieth century.

Figure 6 gives accurate plots of the spectral emissive powers (9) of black bodies at three temperatures. As seen from this plot, the curves for different temperatures are related in shape. One can go from the 6000° curve to the 12,000° curve in two steps: first squeeze the 6000° curve to the left, dividing all wavelengths by 2 (the temperature ratio) to get the broken curve; then multiply the ordinates of the broken curve by 32 (the fifth power of the temperature ratio). A similar procedure will lead from the curve for one temperature to the curve for any other temperature.

An *optical pyrometer* is a convenient instrument for measurement of the temperature of very hot bodies by matching the color and brightness of the image of the body formed in a telescope with the color and brightness of a tungsten filament superimposed on the image. The filament current required for a perfect match, which makes the filament 'disappear' in the image, furnishes a measure of the temperature. This instrument takes full advantage of the details of the spectral emission curves, both as to total intensity and as to color distribution. Different sets of filters and different calibration curves are used according to whether the instrument is pointed at a hole in a furnace, which radiates like a black body, or at a hot ingot or the surface of molten metal, which radiates like a gray body of emissivity 0.4. The optical system is so arranged that the image brightness is independent of the distance from the body being observed.

PROBLEMS

1. At what wavelength does the black-body emission curve have its maximum at room temperature (27° C)? Ans: 9.657 μ.

2. The melting point of wolfram (tungsten) is 3400° C. At what wavelength does the black-body radiation curve for this temperature have its maximum?

3. The maximum of the radiation curve for the sun occurs at 470 mμ. What would be the temperature of a black body for which the radiation curve would have a maximum at this wavelength? Ans: 6160° K.

4. What would be the temperature of a black body for which the intensity maximum occurred in the infrared at 1000 mμ? in the ultraviolet at 100 mμ?

5. From Planck's formula, compute the relative spectral emissive powers for gray-body radiation at 400 mμ (deep violet), 500 mμ (green), and 600 mμ (orange), setting the emissive power at 500 mμ equal to 1 in each case, for
  (a) a tungsten filament at 3000° K,
  (b) the sun at 6000° K,
  (c) Vega at 12,000° K.   Ans: (a) 0.28:1:1.99; (b) 0.91:1:0.90; (c) 1.60:1:0.63.

6. Compare Betelgeuse (3000° K) and Vega (12,000° K) with the sun (6000° K) with regard to
  (a) total emissive power,
  (b) spectral emissive power at 400 mμ,
  (c) spectral emissive power at 600 mμ.
Assume that all three stars radiate like black bodies.

7. By counting squares under the 6000° curve of Fig. 6, estimate the total emissive power and compare with the value 7.4×10^7 watts/m² given by the Stefan-Boltzmann formula.

4. LINE SPECTRA

The quantum theory was initially developed to account for the shape of the black-body radiation curves giving spectral emissive power as a function of wavelength. Now let us see how this theory can be applied to another emission process—the emission of *line spectra* by atoms. In this case, we have to account not only for source intensity but also for the discrete frequencies present in the observed spectra.

At first glance, there does not appear to be any order or regularity in the appearance or spacing of the spectral lines. Certainly, there are no frequency sequences analogous to the fundamental and overtones that might be expected if a radiating atom were comparable in any way with an electrical oscillator. Actually, much time was spent in looking for sequences of this type, but none were found. Finally, in 1885, Johann Jakob Balmer found a simple formula that gives the frequencies of the hydrogen lines appearing in the visible spectrum (see Fig. 7, p. 718). Balmer found that the frequencies of this series of spectral lines are given by the relation

$$f = cR \left(\frac{1}{4} - \frac{1}{n^2} \right), \tag{10}$$

where c is the speed of light, R is a quantity called the *Rydberg constant* whose value is 10,967,758 m⁻¹, and n is a number that takes the integral values 3, 4, 5, 6, $\cdots$ for the various lines of the series. The frequencies of the lines in this series converge to the limit $\frac{1}{4}cR$ as n becomes large. Further examination of the spectrum of atomic hydrogen in regions outside the visible region revealed the existence of still other similar spectral series which have been named for their discoverers:

Lyman series: $\quad f = cR \left(\dfrac{1}{1^2} - \dfrac{1}{n^2} \right), \quad$ where $\quad n = 2, 3, 4, \cdots \quad$ (ultraviolet)

Balmer series: $\quad f = cR \left(\dfrac{1}{2^2} - \dfrac{1}{n^2} \right), \quad$ where $\quad n = 3, 4, 5, \cdots \quad$ (visible)

Paschen series: $\quad f = cR \left(\dfrac{1}{3^2} - \dfrac{1}{n^2} \right), \quad$ where $\quad n = 4, 5, 6, \cdots \quad$ (infrared)

Brackett series: $\quad f = cR \left(\dfrac{1}{4^2} - \dfrac{1}{n^2} \right), \quad$ where $\quad n = 5, 6, 7, \cdots \quad$ (infrared)

Pfund series: $\quad f = cR \left(\dfrac{1}{5^2} - \dfrac{1}{n^2} \right), \quad$ where $\quad n = 6, 7, 8, \cdots \quad$ (far infrared)

The frequencies of *all* observed lines of atomic hydrogen are contained in the above series.

It will be noted that the frequency of any observed spectral line of hydrogen can be written as the difference of two frequencies, usually called *term frequencies* or *term values*. For example, the second line of the Balmer series can be written as

$$f = \tfrac{1}{4}cR - \tfrac{1}{16}cR. \tag{11}$$

The number of term values is considerably smaller than the number of lines; every possible difference between two term values gives the fre-

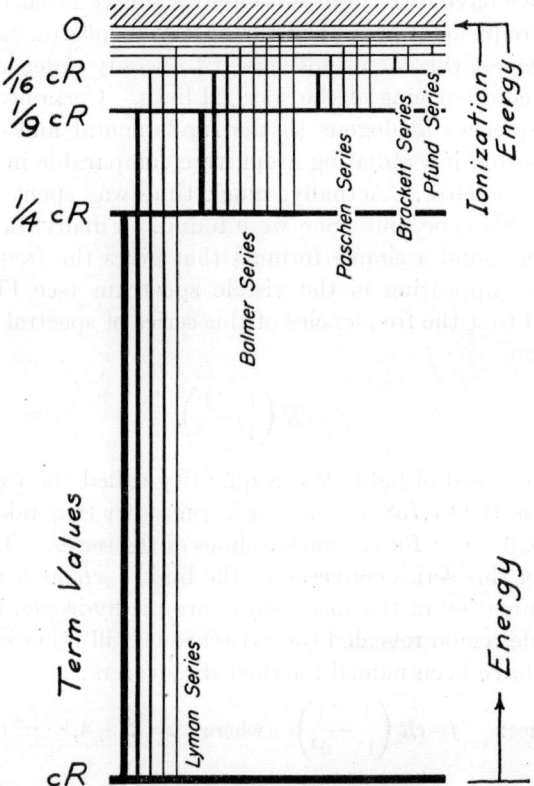

Fig. 7. The spectrum of atomic hydrogen. The horizontal lines represent allowed energy levels of the atom. When the atom makes a transition from one energy level to another it emits (or absorbs) radiation of frequency proportional to the energy difference, that is, proportional to the *length* of the vertical line connecting the two energy levels in this diagram.

quency of a spectral line. In the case of hydrogen, the terms are represented by the horizontal lines in Fig. 7; the lengths of the various vertical lines represent term differences and are proportional to the frequencies of the spectral lines in the various series as indicated. The term values are plotted down from a zero at the top for a reason that will be made clear in a moment.

Similar regularities were found in other spectra more complicated than that of hydrogen, and resulted in the formulation by Ritz in 1908 of the *combination principle*, according to which each atom may be characterized by a set of numbers called *term values*, dimensionally like frequencies, such that the actual frequencies of the spectral lines are given by the differences between these term values.

It remained for Niels Bohr in 1913 to suggest that each term value represents an energy level of the atom. This hypothesis was the beginning of the *quantum mechanics* of atomic structure, as distinguished from the quantum theory of radiation which we have been discussing. According to quantum mechanics, an atom (or a molecule) cannot have an arbitrary amount of internal energy; rather, it must at any time be in one of a discrete set of states, each having a particular value of energy. When it is not already in its state of lowest energy, it will spontaneously make a transition to one of the states of lower energy, the energy released appearing as a single quantum of radiation of frequency f such that the energy released equals hf. Correspondingly, if radiation falls on the atom it can absorb a single quantum, but of only such frequencies f that the quantum energy hf is exactly the energy needed to excite the atom to one of its possible states of higher energy.

These ideas can be clarified by returning to the term diagram for hydrogen, Fig. 7. The horizontal lines can now be interpreted as energy levels. At normal temperatures all the hydrogen atoms are in the state of lowest energy at the bottom of the diagram, called the *ground state*. In the ground state the electron is at an average distance of about 0.5×10^{-10} m from the proton. According to any classical theory of the negatively charged electron revolving around the positively charged proton in planetary fashion under the influence of the electrical force of attraction, the accelerated electron would radiate away its energy and fall right into the proton, but this does not happen. When in this ground state, the electron loses no energy by radiation.

The possible states of motion of the electron are said to be *quantized*. There are only certain allowed states; and when the electron is in any one of these states it does not radiate—it radiates or absorbs energy only when it shifts from one state to another. The states above the ground state are called *excited states*. These are states of higher energy; and since energy is required to pull the electron away from the proton, it is accurate to think of them as states in which the electron is farther and farther from the proton as the energy increases. The allowed states get closer and closer together in energy in accordance with our previous discussion of the terms and finally end at the ionization energy, which is the energy required to pull the electron completely away from the proton.

Hydrogen molecules can be dissociated into atoms and the atoms raised to excited states so as to excite the emission spectrum by either (a) raising the temperature of the gas sufficiently, (b) using an electrical discharge, or (c) illuminating the gas with the proper frequencies of ultraviolet light.

Emission of radiation corresponds to transitions downward in Fig. 7; absorption of radiation corresponds to transitions upward. In each case the frequency of radiation is exactly proportional to the energy change, the proportionality factor being Planck's constant h. Hence, the frequency of the radiation is proportional to the length of the vertical lines in Fig. 7, since this length represents the magnitude of the energy change.

There is a large body of experimental evidence of various types, all confirming the correctness of the above picture. We shall describe only one type of experiment, first performed by James Franck and Gustav Hertz in 1913, that gives very direct confirmation of the energy-level interpretation of spectral terms. A beam of hydrogen atoms (not molecules) in the ground state is sent down a vacuum tube; the beam is bombarded from the side by electrons of known and controlled energy, and a spectrograph is focused on the beam. When the electrons have energy below the quantum energy hf of the first line of the Lyman series (compare Fig. 7), no spectrum appears. When the electron energy exceeds the quantum energy of the first Lyman line but is less than that of the second, only the first Lyman line appears in the spectrum. When the energy exceeds the quantum energy of the second Lyman line but is less than that of the third, the first two Lyman lines *and* the first Balmer line appear in the spectrum. And so on. Similar experiments performed with a large number of different types of atoms completely confirm the correspondence of energy levels and term values.

Each element of the periodic table has an energy-level diagram similar to Fig. 7, in which the energy differences correspond to observed spectral lines. In no other case is this diagram so simple as that for hydrogen. The energy values, and hence the spectral-line frequencies, for any atom are given by the formulas of the *quantum mechanics* initiated by Schrödinger and Heisenberg in 1925.

Each chemical molecule also has a characteristic energy-level diagram. In the case of molecules, the energy levels occur in closely spaced groups, so the lines also occur in closely spaced groups called bands—hence the term *band spectrum*.

PROBLEMS

1. What is the wavelength of the first line of the Lyman series in the spectrum of hydrogen? In what spectral region is it found? Ans: 122 mμ.

2. What is the wavelength of the first line in the Balmer series of hydrogen? In what spectral region does it occur?

3. What energy, in joules, must an electron have in order to excite the first Lyman line of hydrogen in the Franck-Hertz experiment? What is the quantum energy of the radiation in the first Lyman line? Ans: 1.63×10^{-18} joule; same.

4. What energy, in joules, must an electron have in order to excite the first Balmer line in the Franck-Hertz experiment? What is the quantum energy of the radiation of the first Balmer line?

Part V
ELECTRICITY AND MAGNETISM

CHAPTER 31

ELECTROSTATICS

Electrostatics is that branch of science which deals with the laws of electricity at rest.*

Almost everyone has had the experiences, especially in dry interiors in winter, of getting a shock when touching a doorknob after walking across a rug, of having his comb crackle in his hair, and of having sheets of writing paper cling obstinately together. Of course he has seen lightning; he may have had the interesting experience of standing on a dock during the approach of a summer thunderstorm and seeing everyone's hair pulled tautly erect by the electrical forces that precede a lightning discharge. These are all manifestations of static electricity—electricity at rest, as distinguished from the currents of electricity in wires with which we are so familiar nowadays.

The laws of static electricity are not only fundamental to a study of those of current electricity, they are also directly applied in describing the performance of many familiar modern devices such as the condensers and vacuum tubes in every radio set. We therefore begin the systematic study of electricity by considering the basic laws governing static electricity, that is, by a study of *electrostatics*.

1. ELECTRIC CHARGES

We can electrify, or charge, a hard-rubber rod by rubbing it with cat's fur. We can charge a glass rod by rubbing it with silk. The electrified rods acquire the power of attracting bits of paper or small balls made of some light material such as pith or cork and suspended by silk threads. By playing with pith balls coated with metal foil or painted with metal paint, we can easily convince ourselves that there is a difference between the type of electric charge on the hard rubber and that on the glass. The pith ball is attracted by either charged rod until it is permitted to touch the rod; then it bounces away from the rod it has touched and is thereafter strongly repelled by it. The pith ball has become charged by contact with the charged rod. A charged pith ball

* Throughout the chapters on electricity and magnetism we shall employ the *American Standard Definitions of Electrical Terms* as published by the American Institute of Electrical Engineers in 1942. Where these definitions are quoted, they are identified by the AIEE reference number. The definition of electrostatics quoted here is AIEE definition 05.15.005.

that is repelled by the hard-rubber rod is attracted by the glass rod, and one that is repelled by the glass rod is attracted by the hard-rubber rod. Furthermore, a pith ball that has touched a charged glass rod and another that has touched a charged hard-rubber rod attract each other; but if two pith balls have touched the same charged rod, they repel each other. Hence, a pith ball that has touched a charged glass rod behaves differently from one that has touched a charged hard-rubber rod. Evidently the charged pith balls, and likewise the two charged rods, must have two different *kinds* of electric charge. Any two dissimilar materials when brought into contact or rubbed together become more or less charged, but two centuries of search have produced no more than the two kinds of electric charge that are produced in considerable quantity on hard rubber and glass when rubbed with cat's fur and silk, respectively. Thus we conclude that there are two and only two different kinds of electric charge.

The two kinds of electric charge are arbitrarily called *positive* and *negative*, or $+$ and $-$, according to the following conventions:

Positive electricity is the kind of electricity which predominates in a body composed of glass after it has undergone electrification by rubbing with silk.*

Negative electricity is the kind of electricity which predominates in a body composed of resin after it has undergone electrification by rubbing with wool.†

From the experiments with pith balls discussed above, we conclude that charged objects exert forces on each other in accordance with the following laws:

Two positively charged objects repel each other.

Two negatively charged objects repel each other.

A positively charged object and a negatively charged object attract each other.

These laws are summarized in the statement:

Like charges repel each other and unlike charges attract each other.

For example, the pith ball that touches the positively charged glass rod acquires a positive charge like the rod and is repelled by the rod, but it will be attracted to the negatively charged hard-rubber rod or to the negatively charged ball that has touched the hard-rubber rod.

* AIEE definition 05.10.030.
† AIEE definition 05.10.125. Sealing wax, hard rubber, amber, or Bakelite rubbed with either cat's fur or wool would serve equally well for purposes of definition of negative electricity. Hard rubber and cat's fur seems to be the favorite lecture-table combination. It is interesting that the words *electric*, *electron*, and so on, come from the Greek word for *amber*, whose electrical properties were noted by the Greeks before 600 B.C.

A little further experimenting with charged pith balls will show that the electrostatic force between a given pair of charges decreases rapidly as the distance between the charges increases. The law of dependence on distance was first determined experimentally by Coulomb* in 1785. Using a torsion balance to measure the forces, he showed that *the mutual force between two given charges varies inversely as the square of the distance between them:*

$$f \propto 1/d^2. \tag{1}\dagger$$

Thus, if the distance between two charges is doubled, the force between them is decreased to $\frac{1}{4}$ its original value; if the distance is halved, the force is increased to 4 times its original value; and so forth. Of course, by Newton's third law, the electrical force with which one charge acts on a second charge is equal in magnitude but opposite in direction to the force

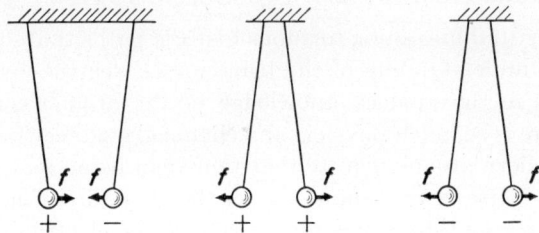

Fig. 1. Unlike charges attract; like charges repel.

with which the second charge acts on the first. The directions of the force vectors are along the line connecting the charges, in an attractive or repulsive sense according to the signs of the charges, as illustrated in Fig. 1.

PROBLEMS

1. Two small pith balls, each suspended by a 15-inch silk thread from a horizontal east-west wooden rod, hang a short distance apart. Each is negatively charged. The west ball is subjected to an electrical force of 0.02 newton because of the presence of the east ball.
(a) What is the direction of the electrical force on the west ball?
(b) What is the direction of the electrical force on the east ball?
(c) What is magnitude of electrical force on the east ball?
    Ans: (a) toward the west; (b) toward the east; (c) 0.02 nt.

2. Two small pith balls hang at the ends of 15-inch silk threads from a horizontal north-south wooden rod. The ball to the north is positively charged. It experiences

---

* Charles Augustin Coulomb (1736–1806), French physicist; discoverer of the inverse-square laws of electrostatics and magnetostatics.

† This law holds rigorously only for 'point' charges or, more practically, for charged bodies, such as pith balls or atomic ions, separated by distances large compared with the dimensions of the bodies. Charges that are physically very small compared with distances of interest will be referred to as *point charges,* the word *point* to be understood in this physical sense and not in the idealized mathematical sense.

an electrical force toward the south.
  (a) What is the sign of the charge on the south ball?
  (b) What is the direction of the force on the south ball?
  (c) How do the electrical forces on the two balls compare in magnitude?

3. If two point charges each experience an electrical force of repulsion of 0.06 nt when they are 10 cm apart, what will be the force when they are (a) 100 cm apart? (b) 50 cm apart? (c) 5 cm apart? (d) 2.5 cm apart? (e) 1 cm apart?
    Ans: (a) 0.0006 nt; (b) 0.0024 nt; (c) 0.24 nt; (d) 0.96 nt; (e) 6 nt.

4. If two point charges each experience an electrical force of attraction of 0.04 nt when they are 5 cm apart, what will be the force when they are (a) 100 cm apart? (b) 50 cm apart? (c) 10 cm apart? (d) 2.5 cm apart? (e) 1 cm apart?

5. (a) Make a plot on rectangular coordinate paper of force versus distance for the charges of Probs. 3 and 4. (b) Write the equations of these curves.

6. Replot the same data as in Prob. 5 on log-log paper (preferably 4-decade). Show how these curves fit the equations obtained in Prob. 5.

2. ELECTRICAL STRUCTURE OF MATTER; COULOMB'S LAW

Instead of stumbling along tortuous historic paths that eventually led to a complete understanding of the behavior of electric charges, we can profitably utilize the modern knowledge of the atomic constitution of matter. There is so much physical and chemical evidence for the correctness of the modern atomic picture that there can be no reasonable doubt of its validity. Use of this knowledge of the structure of matter greatly simplifies the presentation and understanding of electrical phenomena.

An atom contains a positively charged central core, or *nucleus*. Most of the mass of the atom is in the nucleus, which has a diameter of only about 10^{-15} m. Revolving around the nucleus, out to a distance of the order of 10^{-10} m, are a number of negatively charged particles called *electrons*. The electrons are all alike; each is of much smaller mass than the nucleus and carries a charge denoted by $-e$. Ordinarily, the atom as a whole appears to be electrically neutral or uncharged, so we say that *the total negative charge on all the electrons is equal in magnitude to the positive charge on the nucleus*. The number of electrons in an atom equals the atomic number and varies from 1 to 96 through the known periodic table.* Thus,

> H has a nucleus of charge $+e$ and 1 electron,
> He has a nucleus of charge $+2e$ and 2 electrons,
> Li has a nucleus of charge $+3e$ and 3 electrons,
>   and so forth, to curium:
> Cm has a nucleus of charge $+96e$ and 96 electrons.

If one or more electrons are removed from a normal atom, we have a positive ion, familiar from the study of chemistry; if one or more extra electrons are added to a normal atom, we have a negative ion.

* Note added to proof: The discovery of elements 97 and 98 has been reported in 1950. The names berkelium and californium have been proposed by the discoverers.

In terms of this scheme, we can give the following definition:

> The total or net charge on a body is the sum of the charges on all the electrons and the charges on all the nuclei in the body.

This is not an operational definition, but will serve as a good logical starting point for securing an operational definition of magnitude of charge.

Metals and nonmetals behave quite differently with respect to electric charges. If a piece of metal is brought into contact with a charged rod, the entire surface of the metal becomes charged immediately. Charge can travel easily from one part of a piece of metal to another, and the metal is said to be a *conductor* of electricity. If a piece of nonmetal is brought into contact with a charged rod, some charge will be transferred to the nonmetal at the point of contact; but it will be a long time, if ever,

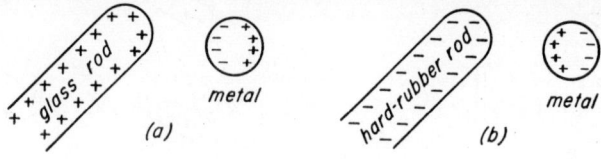

Fig. 2. Induced charges.

before the entire surface of the nonmetal becomes charged. Charge cannot readily travel from one part to another of a nonmetal, which hence is called an *insulator* or *dielectric*. This difference in behavior is explained by the fact that in metals some of the electrons (the valence electrons) are 'free' to wander from atom to atom; in nonmetals the electrons are not, in general, free to leave the atoms to which they belong.

The 'free' electrons in a metal move around inside the metal much like the molecules in a gas. In the neutral or uncharged state of a metal, the electrons are uniformly distributed throughout the volume of the metal. If an uncharged metal object, a ball for example, is brought near a positively charged rod as in Fig. 2(a), the electrons in the ball are attracted by the rod and the positive nuclei in the ball are repelled by it. The mobile free electrons concentrate on the side of the ball near the rod. The nuclei are not free to move and hence suffer only slight elastic displacements. The side of the ball nearer the charged rod acquires a net negative charge; the other side of the ball is left with a deficiency of electrons and hence an *equal* net positive charge. The reverse happens in Fig. 2(b), in which the electrons are repelled by the negatively charged rod. Charges acquired by portions of an uncharged object in this manner are said to be 'induced' by the near-by charged body.

If the metal ball in Fig. 2(a) is made so that the two halves can be separated, one can obtain equal and unlike charges on the two halves by separating them before the charged rod is removed. The sequence of events is shown in Figs. 3(a)–(e), which are intended to be self-explanatory. Instead of a single metal sphere that can be split, two spheres originally in contact can be used as in Figs. 4(a)–(e). The two spheres in Fig. 4(e) have charges that are equal and unlike, since the spheres in Fig. 4(a) were uncharged, and the excess of electrons on the left sphere must exactly equal the deficiency of electrons on the right sphere. These spheres must be held by insulating nonmetallic supports, such as silk threads or glass rods, through which electrons cannot flow.

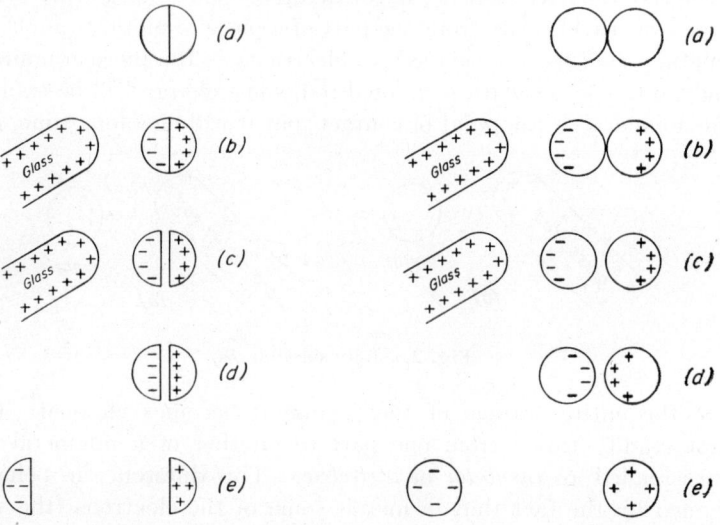

Fig. 3. By induction, equal and opposite charges are obtained on the two halves of a metal sphere.

Fig. 4. By induction, equal and opposite charges are obtained on two metal spheres.

In this way, Coulomb obtained on small spheres charges which he knew were equal and unlike. With his torsion balance he then found that a third charge would exert equal but opposite forces on the equal but unlike charges. In other words, like charges repel each other with the same forces as unlike charges attract, if the charges are numerically equal.

Finally, Coulomb found that the force that either of two charges exerts on the other is proportional to the product of the sizes or magnitudes of the charges. He verified this fact by a technique of splitting a given charge into two, four, or more equal parts that is illustrated in Fig. 5. When the two identical spheres in Fig. 5 are separated, they are found to be equally charged (they exert equal forces on any other charge) as would be expected from symmetry. From our definition of charge in terms of atomic structure, we then conclude that each sphere has half the charge of the original sphere. The charge on one of these spheres can again be divided into two, and so on.

Coulomb found that the force between two charges, denoted by Q_1 and Q_2 (Fig. 6), is proportional to Q_1, to Q_2, and to $1/d^2$; that is,

$$f \propto \frac{Q_1 Q_2}{d^2}. \quad \text{(Coulomb's law)}$$

This experimental law furnishes an *operational definition of magnitude of charge*, once we have selected the proportionality constant in the relation

$$f = \text{const} \times \frac{Q_1 Q_2}{d^2}.$$

The choice of this arbitrary proportionality constant determines the size and dimensions of the unit in which charge is measured. The unit, the *coulomb* (coul), is chosen so that if f is in newtons and d in meters, the proportionality constant will be $10^{-7}c^2$, where c is the speed of light in meters/sec. Hence we write

Fig. 5. By touching a charged metal sphere to an uncharged sphere of the same size, the charge is divided into two equal parts.

$$f = 10^{-7} c^2 \frac{Q_1 Q_2}{d^2}. \quad \begin{cases} f \text{ in nt} \\ c \text{ in m/sec} \\ Q_1, Q_2, \text{ in coul} \\ d \text{ in m} \end{cases} \quad (2)$$

The reason for the occurrence of the speed of light in the value chosen

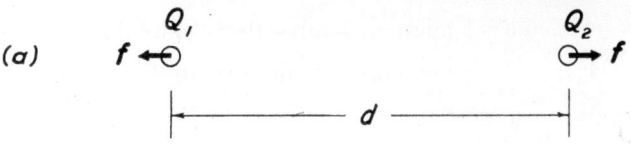

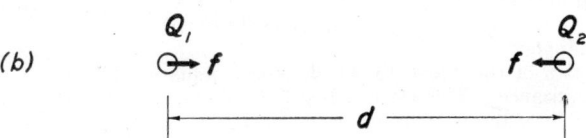

Fig. 6. When Q_1 and Q_2 have like signs, the force f in (2) comes out positive and is to be interpreted as repulsive, as in (a); when Q_1 and Q_2 have unlike signs, f comes ont negative in (2) and is to be interpreted as attractive, as in (b).

for the proportionality constant is discussed in detail in Chap. 41.*

Since the speed of light is $c = 2.99776 \times 10^8$ m/sec, the coefficient occurring in (2) has the value

$$10^{-7}c^2 = 8.9866 \times 10^9 \text{ m}^2/\text{sec}^2. \tag{2a}$$

Since the speed of light is very close to 3×10^8 m/sec, for many purposes it is sufficiently accurate to take the coefficient in (2) as

$$10^{-7}c^2 \approx 9 \times 10^9 \text{ m}^2/\text{sec}^2. \tag{2b}$$

This approximate value may be used in working the problems in this book, and problem answers are given on the basis of this approximation.

According to equation (2), the coulomb is a derived unit defined in terms of the fundamental units of length, mass, and time. If we substitute $Q_1 = Q_2 = 1$ coul, $d^2 = 1$ m^2, and $10^{-7}c^2 = 9 \times 10^9$ m^2/sec^2 in (2), we obtain $f = 9 \times 10^9$ coul^2/sec^2. But by definition, f comes out in nt when Q, d, and c are in these units. Therefore $f = 9 \times 10^9$ nt, and we see that

$$1 \text{ coul}^2/\text{sec}^2 = 1 \text{ nt},$$

or
$$1 \text{ coul} = 1 \sqrt{\text{nt} \cdot \text{sec}}. \tag{3}$$

We note that there are a number of different consistent ways of defining electrical and magnetic quantities in terms of fundamental mechanical units. Of these numerous ways, we choose in this book the particular one that seems most convenient for our purposes. Further discussion of this matter will be found in Sec. 1 of the Appendix.†

The coulomb is chosen to be a unit of convenient size in working with electric currents. From the standpoint of electrostatics it is an enormous unit, and electrostatic charges are usually expressed in terms of the submultiples:

$$1 \text{ } \mu\text{coul} = 1 \text{ microcoulomb} = 10^{-6} \text{ coulomb},$$

or
$$1 \text{ } \mu\mu\text{coul} = 1 \text{ micromicrocoulomb} = 10^{-12} \text{ coulomb},$$

---

* Historically, two different types of systems of electrical and magnetic units were set up. One was an *electrostatic* system in which the above proportionality constant was taken as dimensionless. The other was an *electromagnetic* system in which the fundamental definitions were based on the forces between wires carrying currents, and in which the above constant turned out to involve the square of the speed of light. The basic definitions of the *practical* units that we employ are electromagnetic in nature—hence the occurrence of c^2 in (2). The three systems of units are described in Sec. 1 of the Appendix to this volume.

† In this section of the Appendix we show that equation (3) is quite lacking in *fundamental* significance. The electrical and magnetic quantities are not *fundamentally* expressible in terms of length, mass, and time; rather, one additional electrical dimension must be introduced, just as we introduced temperature as a new dimension in discussing heat. However, any *one* system of electrical and magnetic units *can* be derived from the mechanical units in a *logically consistent* fashion; this we shall do for the *one* system we employ because it will be found that relations such as (3) will be very useful in determining the units of expressions involving the electrical and magnetic quantities.

The positive charge on the hydrogen nucleus (the *proton*) and the negative charge on the electron are the smallest (non-vanishing) charges that have ever been observed. The absolute magnitudes of these charges are universally denoted by the symbol e, where

$$e = 16.020 \times 10^{-20} \text{ coul.}$$

Thus, the charge on the electron is $-e$; that on the proton is $+e$. Experimental evidence to date indicates that all charges are integral multiples of the charges $\pm e$.

In equation (2), a positive value of f is obtained if Q_1 and Q_2 have the same sign; such a value indicates repulsion, as in Fig. 6(a). If Q_1 and Q_2

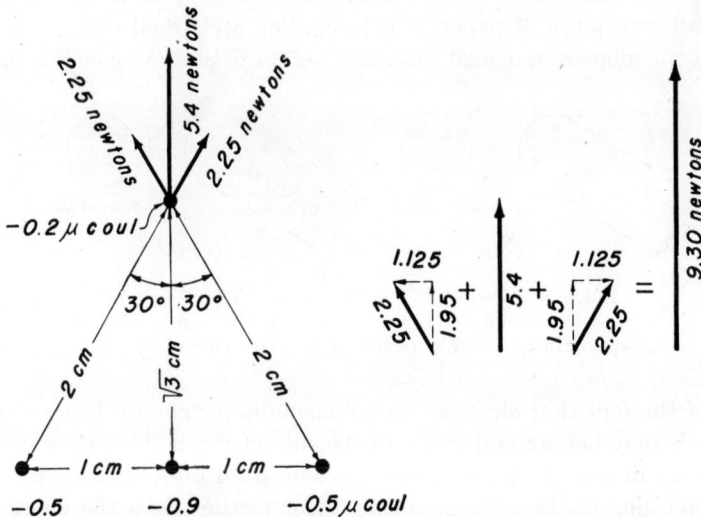

Fig. 7. The resultant electrical force on the -0.2-μcoul charge is the vector sum of the electrical forces arising from each of the other three charges separately.

have unlike signs, a negative value is obtained for f; such a value indicates a force of attraction, as in Fig. 6(b).

We have discussed the force acting between two charges. Where more than two charges are present, the total force acting on one of the charges is the vector sum of the forces arising from each of the other charges individually. Thus, in Fig. 7, where there are four charges, we may compute the total force on the -0.2-μcoul charge by adding vectorially the three forces of repulsion from the other three charges. It can be easily verified from Coulomb's law (2) that these three forces have the magnitudes and directions shown in Fig. 7 and add up vectorially to a total force of 9.30 newtons directed upward.

We are now in a position to see why an *uncharged* metal-coated pith ball is attracted to a charged rod. Looking back to Fig. 2, we see that when the pith ball is brought near the charged rod, equal and opposite charges are induced on the two sides of the pith ball. But the charges of sign unlike the charge on the rod are closer to the rod than are the charges of like sign. Because of this difference in average distance, the force of attraction experienced by the unlike charges is greater than the force of repulsion experienced by the like charges, and the pith ball experiences a net force of attraction. When the pith ball actually touches the rod, some or all of the unlike charges are neutralized by transfer of charge from the surface of the rod to the ball; this leaves a preponderance of like charge to be strongly repelled.

The fact that an uncharged nonmetallic object, such as an uncoated pith ball or a piece of paper, is attracted to a charged rod is associated with a phenomenon called *polarization*, or *dielectric polarization*. In

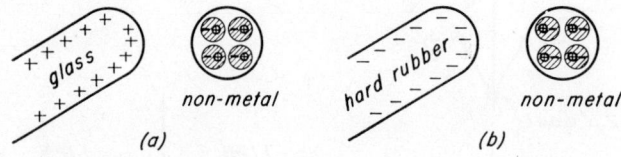

Fig. 8. Dielectric polarization. The cross-hatched circles are intended to represent individual atoms, each with a positive nucleus and a 'cloud' of negative electrons.

spite of the fact that electrons in a nonconductor cannot leave the atom to which they belong and move to the side of the ball, as they do in the conductor of Fig. 2, the electrons in each atom are pulled or pushed so that they lie, on the average, closer to or farther from the charged rod than the positive nucleus. When the charges of the nonmetal (the dielectric) are disturbed thus, it is said to become *polarized*. In Fig. 8(a) the electrons in each atom are on the average closer to the positive charges of the rod than is the positive nucleus. Thus, each atom experiences a net force of attraction toward the rod and the whole ball is attracted toward the rod. A similar effect takes place in Fig. 8(b) with a negative rod. The force of attraction between an uncharged dielectric body and a charged rod is in general much smaller than that between an uncharged conducting (metal) body and the same charged rod. The laws governing dielectric polarization will be considered further in Chap. 32.

The fact that a material medium (even air) becomes polarized in the neighborhood of an electric charge has an influence on the force between two charged bodies immersed in the material medium. Thus, formula (2) is strictly true only in the absence of all other material media, that is, when the charges are in empty space. However, the polarization of air is so slight that for all ordinary purposes formula (2) can be assumed to hold for charges immersed in air.

PROBLEMS

1. Charges of $+20$ and $+30$ μcoul are 3 m apart. What is the force between them? Ans: 0.6 nt repulsion.

2. Charges of $+10$ and -15 μcoul are 6 m apart. What is the force between them?

3. Two small spheres carrying unequal positive charges repel each other with a force of 0.1 nt when 3 cm apart. If the charge on each of the spheres is doubled, and the distance between them is doubled, what is the force of repulsion?

4. In each of the three sketches in Fig. 1, assume that the two strings are of equal length and that the signs of the charges are as indicated. Which of the two strings makes the greater angle with the vertical if
 (a) the charges are equal in magnitude and the balls equal in weight?
 (b) the left-hand charge is greater in magnitude than the right-hand charge and the balls are equal in weight?
 (c) the charges are equal in magnitude but the left-hand ball is heavier than the right-hand one?
 (d) the left-hand charge is greater in magnitude than the right-hand and the left-hand ball is heavier than the right-hand one?
 (Give adequate reasons for your answers to the above questions.)

5. Two small metal-coated pith balls weighing 14 g each are held at the ends of silk threads 70 cm long. The other ends of the threads are fastened at a common point. Charges are placed on the two balls and they come to equilibrium at a distance apart of 10 cm. If the charge on one ball is -0.04 μcoul, what is the charge on the other ball? Ans: -0.273 μcoul.

6. Two small metal-coated pith balls weighing 14 g each are held at the ends of silk threads 70 cm long. The other ends of the threads are fastened at a common point. Equal positive charges are placed on the two balls and they come to equilibrium at a distance apart of 10 cm. Find the charge on each ball.

7. Two charges, of $+10$ and -10 μcoul, are 20 cm apart in air, the $+$ charge being to the left, the $-$ charge to the right. (a) What force does each exert on a $+5$-μcoul charge placed halfway between them? (b) What is the total force on the $+5$-μcoul charge? (c) on the $+10$-μcoul charge? (d) on the -10-μcoul charge?
 Ans: (a) 45 nt to right; (b) 90 nt to right; (c) 22.5 nt to left; (d) 67.5 nt to left.

8. Two charges of $+10$ μcoul each are 10 cm apart. (a) What force does each exert on a $+5$-μcoul charge placed halfway between them? (b) What is the total force on the $+5$-μcoul charge? (c) on one of the $+10$ μcoul charges?

9. Two charges, $+10$ and -5 μcoul, are 10 cm apart. Where must a third charge be placed in order that the resultant force acting upon it should be zero?
 Ans: 24.14 cm from the -5-μcoul charge (in what direction?).

10. Two charges of $+20$ and -5 μcoul are 5 cm apart. Where must a third charge be placed in order that the resultant force acting on it should be zero?

11. Two charges of $+10$ and -10 μcoul are 8 cm apart. Find the magnitude and direction of the total force exerted by these charges on a third charge of $+0.5$ μcoul that is 5 cm distant from each of the two charges.
 Ans: magnitude 28.8 nt (in what direction?).

12. Two charges of $+10$ μcoul each are 8 cm apart in air. Find the magnitude and direction of the total force exerted by these charges on a third charge of $+0.5$ μcoul that is 5 cm distant from each of the two charges.

13. (a) In the normal hydrogen atom, the proton and electron are an average distance of 0.529×10^{-10} m apart. What is the force of attraction at this distance? (b) The electron mass is 9.11×10^{-31} kg. What acceleration (direction and magnitude) does this force of attraction give the electron? (c) Considering the electron as revolving in a circular orbit around the much heavier proton, what is its speed in this orbit? (d) What is its frequency, that is, how many revolutions per second does it make? Ans: (a) 8.23×10^{-8} nt; (b) 9.03×10^{22} m/sec² toward the proton; (c) 2.18×10^6 m/sec; (d) 6.56×10^{15}/sec.

14. How far apart in a vacuum must two electrons be if the force of electrostatic repulsion on each electron is just equal in magnitude to the weight of the electron? (The electron mass is 9.11×10^{-31} kg.)

15. (a) Two bodies attract each other electrically. Are they necessarily both charged?
(b) Two bodies repel each other electrically. Are they necessarily both charged? Explain the reasons for your answers.

3. ELECTRIC FIELD

An *electric field* is said to exist in any region of space in which an electric charge would experience an electrical force. The regions around

Fig. 9. The electric field has the same direction as the force f acting on a small positive test charge $+q$, and has the magnitude f/q.

charged bodies such as the electrodes in a radio tube contain electric fields. The strength or intensity of the electric field at a point is defined in terms of the electrical force f that would be exerted on a very small positive test charge $+q$ placed at the point. The test charge must be so small that it does not appreciably disturb the charges on the bodies that set up the field; that is, it must not cause appreciable redistribution of the charges on conductors or alteration of the polarization of dielectrics in its neighborhood.

The net force f on the test charge $+q$ (see Fig. 9, for example) is the vector resultant of all the forces on q exerted by the various individual charges or elements of charge on the charged bodies in the neighborhood. By Coulomb's law, each of these component forces is proportional to the magnitude of q. Hence, the vector resultant f has a magnitude proportional to q, and we may write

$$f = q\mathcal{E}. \tag{4}$$

In this equation, $\quad\quad\quad\mathcal{E} = f/q, \tag{5}$

the force in newtons per coulomb of test charge, is known as the *electric intensity*.

Electric intensity (electric field strength). The electric intensity at a point is a vector which has the direction of the force which would be exerted on a charged particle placed at the point and a magnitude equal to the quotient of the force divided by the quantity of electricity on the particle. It is assumed that the quantity of electricity on the particle does not affect the electric field.*

From (3) we see that the unit of electric intensity, when expressed in terms of fundamental mechanical units, is

$$1 \text{ nt/coul} = 1 \sqrt{\text{nt}}/\text{sec}.$$

Thus, in an electric field there is a vector $\mathcal{E}$ associated with each point of space. In terms of this vector, equation (4) gives the force on a small charge placed at that point. Equation (4) is valid for negative charges (q negative) as well as for positive charges (q positive). *If the small charge q is positive, the force f has the same direction as $\mathcal{E}$; if the small charge is negative, the force f has the direction opposite to the vector $\mathcal{E}$.*

One of the most important applications of the equation $f = q\mathcal{E}$ is the computation of forces on electrons in vacuum tubes so that the motion of the electrons can be determined. The charge on an individual electron is so very small that this charge does not alter the charge distributions on the electrodes (filament, plate, grids, and so on) which set up the electric field.† Hence (4) can be used to determine the force. For example, in one type of *electron-ray tube* (also called *cathode-ray tube*), used in oscillographs and in television receivers, a beam of electrons is deflected by an amount proportional to the strength of an electric field through which it passes. Deflections of electron beams by electrostatic fields also take place in television iconoscopes, 'magic-eye' tubes, beam power tubes, and electron-multiplier tubes. In an electron-ray tube, the electrons are deflected by a uniform electric field set up between a pair of charged plates as indicated in Fig. 10. The charge on each electron is $q = -e = -16.0 \times 10^{-20}$ coul. In an electric field $\mathcal{E}$, the electron experiences a force

$$f = q\mathcal{E} = -(16.0 \times 10^{-20} \text{ coul}) \, \mathcal{E}.$$

The minus sign indicates that this force is opposite in direction to the electric intensity $\mathcal{E}$. A small positive charge placed between the plates of Fig. 10 would experience a downward electrical force, but a negative charge is repelled by the lower negative plate, attracted toward the upper positive plate, and experiences an upward electrical force.

A typical magnitude for $\mathcal{E}$ in an electron-ray tube (we shall see later how to compute such electric intensities) would be about 30,000 nt/coul.

---

* AIEE definition 05.15.010.
† Under some circumstances a great cloud of electrons will collect in one region of a vacuum tube (resulting in a *space charge*), and the total charge on the cloud will be sufficient to alter the electric field set up by the charges on the electrodes.

If $\mathcal{E}$ has this magnitude and a downward direction, the electrostatic force on each electron would have an upward direction and a magnitude of

$$f = (16.0 \times 10^{-20} \text{ coul})(3.00 \times 10^4 \text{ nt/coul}) = 48.0 \times 10^{-16} \text{ nt}. \quad (6)$$

Of course the force of gravity also acts on these electrons, but since the mass of an electron is only 9.11×10^{-31} kg, the force of gravity (weight of the electron) is only $(9.11 \times 10^{-31} \text{ kg})(9.81 \text{ m/sec}^2) = 8.94 \times 10^{-30}$ nt. The electrostatic force is about 5×10^{14} times as great as the gravitational force! In vacuum tubes the gravitational forces are always extremely small in comparison with the electrical forces and can be entirely neglected.

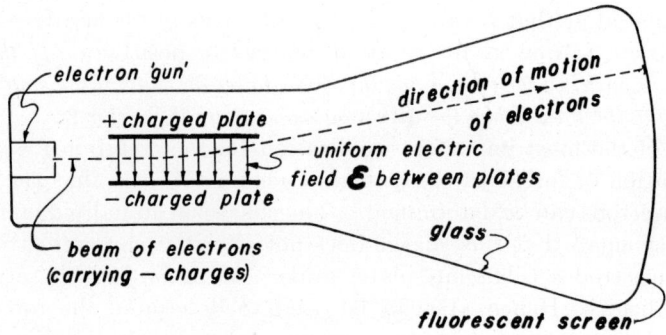

Fig. 10. Deflection of a beam of electrons by a pair of charged plates in an electron-ray tube.

When the electrical force given by (6) acts on an electron of mass 9.11×10^{-31} kg, the electron experiences an upward acceleration of magnitude

$$a = \frac{f}{m} = \frac{48.0 \times 10^{-16} \text{ nt}}{9.11 \times 10^{-31} \text{ kg}} = 5.27 \times 10^{15} \text{ m/sec}^2.$$

This is an enormous acceleration compared with the acceleration of gravity, as must be expected since the electrical force is enormous compared to the force of gravity. Since the electrons in an electron-ray tube move with very high speeds and hence do not spend much time in the electric-field region, even this enormous acceleration does not result in a very large deflection of the electron beam. A reasonable speed for the electrons in an electron-ray tube is about 10^7 m/sec ($= 6200$ mi/sec). The length of path between the plates is exaggerated in Fig. 10 and is actually only 1 or 2 cm, and the electron spends only about 10^{-9} sec in the field.

The problem of computing the deflection of the electron beam as it passes between the plates in Fig. 10 is just like computing the fall of a projectile fired horizontally from a gun at 10^7 m/sec if the acceleration of gravity were increased to 5.27×10^{15} m/sec^2 and imagined to act upward. In time t, the upward distance of travel of the electron is

$$s = \tfrac{1}{2} at^2.$$

With $a \approx 5 \times 10^{15}$ m/sec^2 and $t = 10^{-9}$ sec, we have

$$s \approx \tfrac{1}{2} \times 5 \times 10^{15} \text{ m·sec}^{-2} \times 10^{-18} \text{ sec}^2 = 0.0025 \text{ m}.$$

This is a deflection of 0.25 cm or about 0.1 in when the electron leaves the electric field. Such a deflection produces a much larger displacement of the bright spot on the screen of the tube since the electrons travel many inches along the deflected path before they hit the fluorescent screen.

Now that we have seen an example of the use of the electric-field concept in modern vacuum tubes, we shall turn to a study of the computation of electric intensities. We start with the simplest example, the field in the neighborhood of a single isolated positive point charge of magnitude Q. To measure the field at a distance r from charge Q, we imagine that we place a small test charge $+q$ (Fig. 11) at a distance r (in meters) from the charge Q. At any point on a sphere of radius r drawn around the charge Q, the force on the test charge would be radially outward and of magnitude

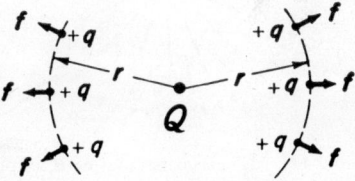

Fig. 11. The field at distance r from Q is determined by the force on a small test charge $+q$. If Q were negative all the force vectors would be reversed in direction.

$$f = 10^{-7} c^2\, Qq/r^2, \quad \text{in nt}.$$

The electric intensity is, then, by definition (5), directed radially outward and of magnitude

$$\mathcal{E} = \frac{f}{q} = 10^{-7} c^2 \frac{Q}{r^2}, \quad \text{in } \frac{\text{nt}}{\text{coul}}. \tag{7}$$

The intensity falls off inversely as the square of the distance from the charge, as indicated by the lengths of the vectors in Fig. 12.

If the charge Q were negative in Fig. 11, the force f on a positive test charge would be directed radially inward rather than outward. Since the direction of the electric field is the direction of the force on a positive test charge, the electric intensity would be directed inward as in Fig. 13. Its magnitude would still be given by (7).

It is convenient to visualize a set of lines, called *lines of force*, whose direction gives at every point in space the direction of the electric-intensity vector at that point.

> A **line of force** is a line whose tangent at each point is in the direction of the electric-intensity vector at that point.

As so defined, lines of force are not intended to give information about the magnitude of the electric field—only about its direction. As a matter of fact, we have already drawn lines of force between two charged plates in Fig. 10. Lines of force about the positive and negative point charges of Figs. 12 and 13 are shown in Figs. 14 and 15. Of course these figures can show only sample lines of force in one plane. Lines of force must be

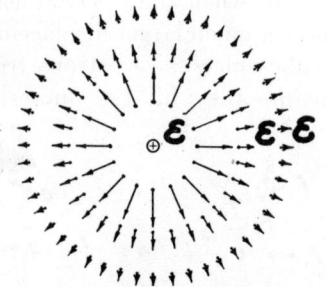

Fig. 12. Electric intensities $\mathcal{E}$ at points near a positive charge.

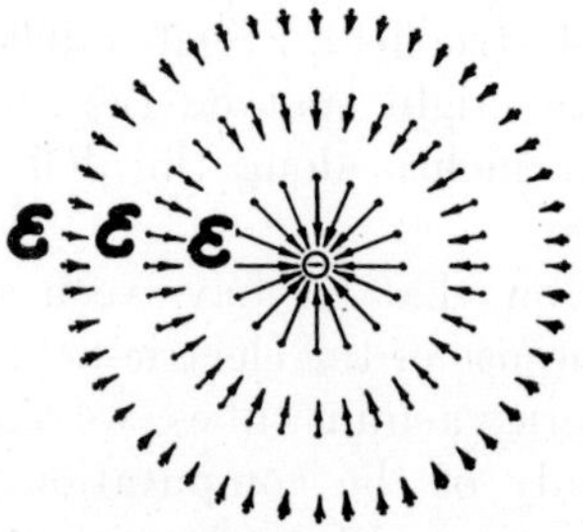

Fig. 13. Electric intensities $\mathcal{E}$ at points near a negative charge.

imagined to bristle out from the charges in every direction in space like the quills of a curled-up porcupine. Only a few lines of force are shown in the sketches. Through every point in space there is a line of force starting at the + charge and going out to infinity, or starting at an infinite distance and ending on the − charge. This description assumes that in

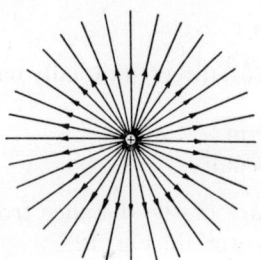 

Fig. 14. Lines of force go radially out from a positive point charge.

Fig. 15. Lines of force go radially into a negative point charge.

the whole of space there is only a single positive charge (Fig. 14) or a single negative charge (Fig. 15). This is obviously an absurd assumption, but the pictures of Figs. 12–15 hold in practice if the charge we are considering is well isolated from all other charges so that the forces exerted on our test charge by other charges are negligible. The lines of force in Figs. 14 and 15 do not really go on indefinitely to infinity but are disturbed as soon as they come near other charges, however there is a certain region near an isolated charge where these pictures are valid and useful.

Now let us see how we would compute the field arising from more than one charge. A simple case is the field of two equal and opposite charges, for example, charges of ± 5 microcoulombs separated by a distance of 1.2 meters as in Fig. 16. Consider the field at point A, which is 0.5 meter from the negative charge and 1.3 meters from the positive charge. We imagine a small test charge $+q$ at this point. The test charge will experience an attractive force $\boldsymbol{f}_1$ toward the negative charge and a repulsive

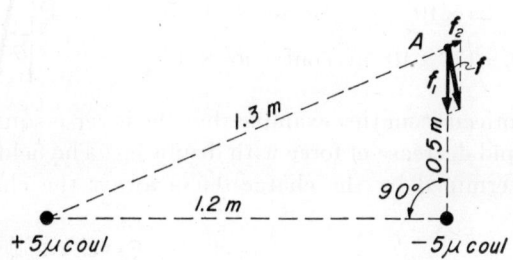

Fig. 16.

force $\boldsymbol{f}_2$ from the positive charge. These two forces must be added vectorially to obtain the total force $\boldsymbol{f}$:

$$\boldsymbol{f} = \boldsymbol{f}_1 + \boldsymbol{f}_2.$$

If we divide each term of this equation by the scalar q, we have

$$\frac{\boldsymbol{f}}{q} = \frac{\boldsymbol{f}_1}{q} + \frac{\boldsymbol{f}_2}{q}.$$

But $\boldsymbol{f}_1/q$ is the electric field $\boldsymbol{\varepsilon}_1$ that the charge -5 microcoulombs would set up alone; $\boldsymbol{f}_2/q$ is the field $\boldsymbol{\varepsilon}_2$ that the charge $+5$ microcoulombs would set up alone; $\boldsymbol{f}/q$ is, by definition, the electric field $\boldsymbol{\varepsilon}$ at this point. Hence, we have

$$\boldsymbol{\varepsilon} = \boldsymbol{\varepsilon}_1 + \boldsymbol{\varepsilon}_2.$$

This important equation states that the electric field arising from two charges is the vector sum of the fields that the two charges would individually contribute. This result can be immediately generalized to the field set up by any number of charges, and shows that

The field arising from any number of individual charges is the vector sum of the fields that the charges would individually contribute.

To return to our example of Fig. 16, instead of working with force vectors $\boldsymbol{f}$, we can work directly with field vectors $\boldsymbol{\varepsilon}$ at point A as shown in

Fig. 17. $\mathcal{E}_1$ and $\mathcal{E}_2$ have the directions shown and magnitudes given by (7) as

$$\mathcal{E}_1 = 9 \times 10^9 \times 5 \times 10^{-6}/(0.5)^2 = 180 \times 10^3 \text{ nt/coul,}$$
$$\mathcal{E}_2 = 9 \times 10^9 \times 5 \times 10^{-6}/(1.3)^2 = 27 \times 10^3 \text{ nt/coul.}$$

These vectors are added to give $\mathcal{E}$, as follows:

$\mathcal{E}_{1x} = 0$	$\mathcal{E}_{1y} = -180 \times 10^3$
$\mathcal{E}_{2x} = 24 \times 10^3$	$\mathcal{E}_{2y} = 10 \times 10^3$
$\mathcal{E}_x = 24 \times 10^3$	$\mathcal{E}_y = -170 \times 10^3$

$$\mathcal{E} = 172 \times 10^3 \text{ nt/coul}; \quad \theta = 8°.1.$$

It will be noticed from this example that the inverse-square law represents a very rapid decrease of force with distance. The field at point A is principally determined by the charge 0.5 m away; the charge of equal

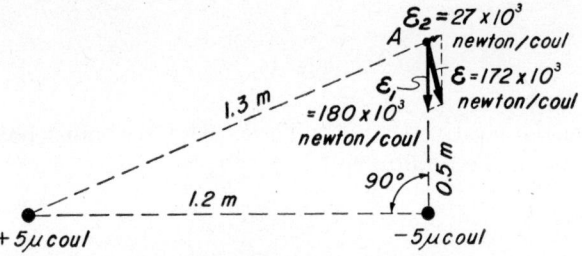

Fig. 17.

magnitude at 1.3 m has a very much smaller effect, so that $\mathcal{E}$ does not differ very much from $\mathcal{E}_1$ in magnitude or direction.

Figures 18, 19, 20, and 21 illustrate the computation of the electric field at four other points in the field of these two charges. The reader should check these computations in detail.

Figure 22 shows the system of lines of force for the field of these two charges. Lines of force through the points A, B, C, D, E of Figs. 17–21 are shown, and a number of other lines of force. All lines of force begin on the positive charge and end on the negative charge. This system of lines shows the direction of the electric field at any point.

Figure 23 shows the corresponding picture of lines of force for two equal positive charges. Here all the lines of force start at the positive charges and go to infinity, or in practice probably end on negative charges they may find on the earth or the walls of the room a long distance outside the picture.

Figure 24 shows the lines of force for a negative charge $-Q$ and a positive charge four times as large, $+4Q$. In this case all the lines of force start on the large positive charge; some end on the small negative charge, and the rest go to infinity.

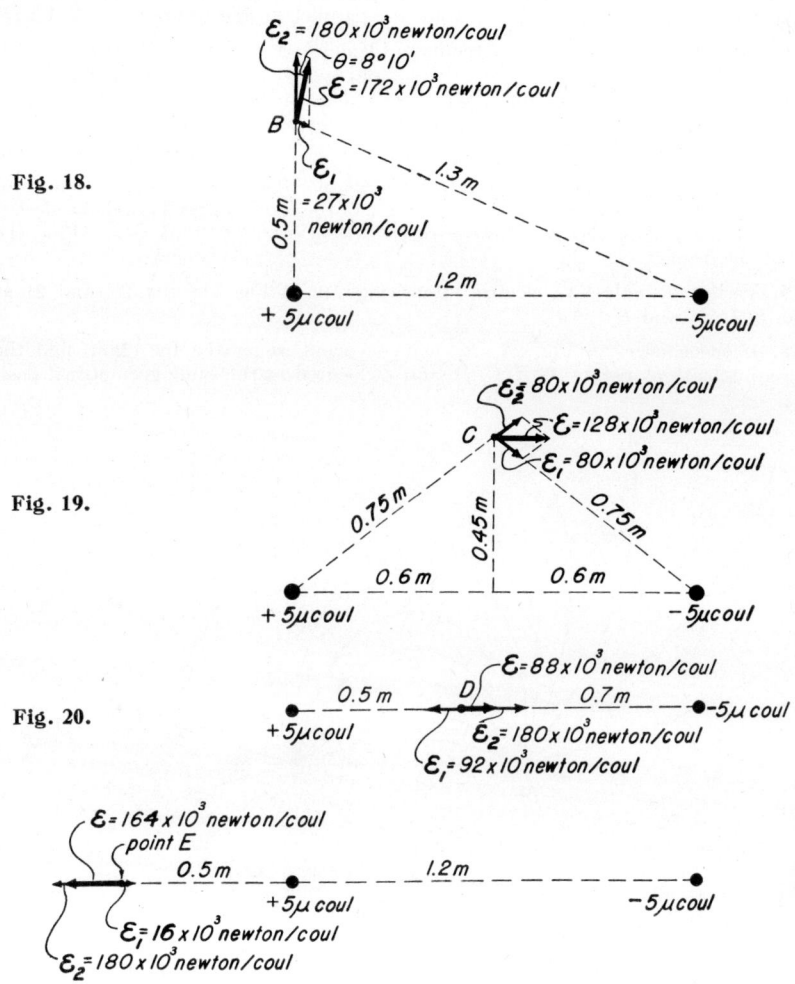

Fig. 18.

Fig. 19.

Fig. 20.

Fig. 21.

PROBLEMS

1. If a charge of $+4$ μcoul experiences a force of magnitude 8 nt at a certain point in an electric field, what is the magnitude of the electric intensity at that point?
Ans: 2×10^6 nt/coul.

2. What are the magnitude and direction of the electric intensity at a point 50 cm from a charge of -200 μcoul?

3. Two charges of $+2$ and -2 μcoul are 16 cm apart. Find the electric intensity at a point distant 10 cm from each of the charges.
Ans: 2.88×10^6 nt/coul; parallel to line from $+$ to $-$ charge.

4. Two charges of -2 μcoul each are 16 cm apart. Find the electric intensity at a point distant 10 cm from each of the charges.

5. Two charges of $+4$ and -2 μcoul are 16 cm apart. Find the electric intensity at a point that is 20 cm from the positive charge and 12 cm from the negative.
Ans: 10.1 nt/coul at angle 44°6 from line parallel to line from $+$ to $-$ charge.

6. Two charges of $+4$ and -2 μcoul are 16 cm apart. Find the electric intensity at a point that is 12 cm from the positive charge and 20 cm from the negative.

7. A charged particle weighing 0.003 gf is held stationary in space by placing it in a downwardly directed electric field of 24×10^4 nt/coul. Find the charge on the particle in μcoul. Ans: -1.23×10^{-4} μcoul.

8. An oil droplet has a net negative charge of $-6e$, representing an excess of 6 electrons. It remains at rest under the action of the force of gravity and the electrical force when it is placed in a downward electric field of 3×10^6 nt/coul. Find the mass of the droplet.

9. Verify the values of electric intensity given in Figs. 18, 19, 20, and 21 at points B, C, D, and E.

10. If the charges of Fig. 23 are each $+5$ μcoul, separated by 1.2 m, find the electric intensity at points A, B, C, D, and E, located at the same geometrical posi-

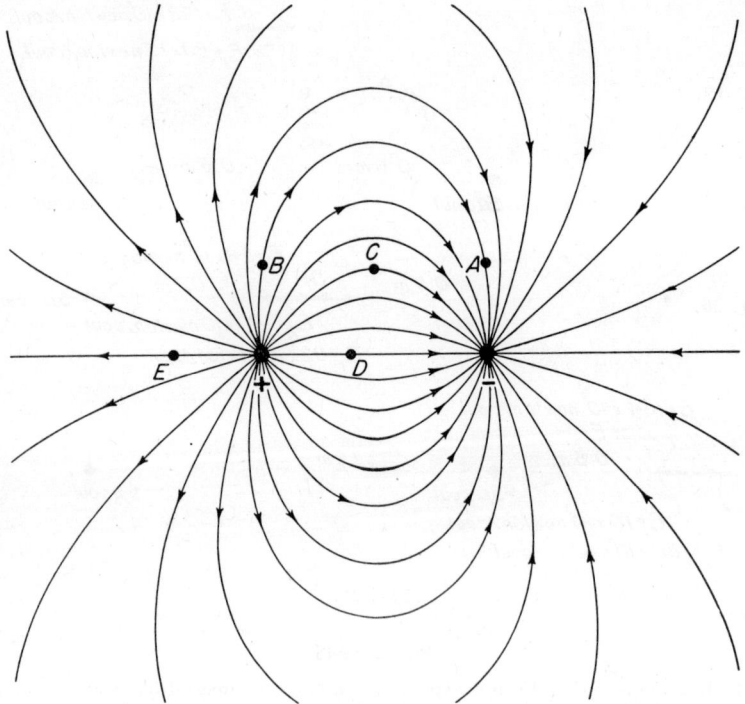

Fig. 22. Lines of force in the vicinity of equal but unlike charges.

tions as in Figs. 17–22. Note that the directions you obtain should agree with the directions of the lines of force shown in Fig. 23.

11. If the charges of Fig. 24 are $+20$ and -5 μcoul and are 1.2 m apart, find the electric intensity at points A, B, C, D, and E, located at the same geometrical posi-

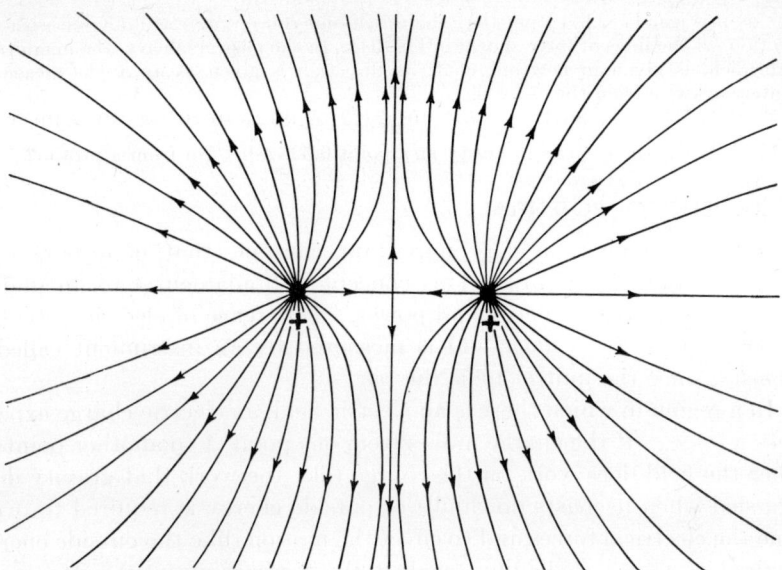

Fig. 23. Lines of force in the vicinity of two equal positive charges.

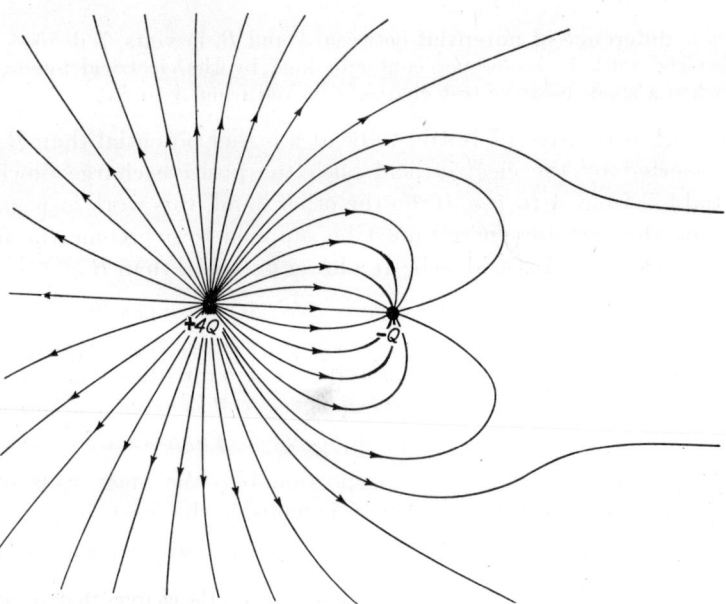

Fig. 24. Lines of force in the vicinity of a negative charge $-Q$ and a positive charge $+4Q$.

tions as in Figs. 17–22. Note that the directions you obtain should agree with the directions of the lines of force shown in Fig. 24. In the answers below, the magnitude of the field is given in newtons/coul; its direction is given as an angle measured counterclockwise from the $+x$-axis. Ans: A, 170×10^3, $-55°.1$; B, 730×10^3, $88°.1$; C, 351×10^3, $24°.2$; D, 812×10^3, $0°$; E, 704×10^3, $180°$.

12. What is the electric intensity at a point 0.528×10^{-10} m from a proton?

4. DIFFERENCE OF POTENTIAL

We now come to a very important concept, that of *difference of potential* (abbreviated DP). This concept is fundamental to an understanding of electrical energy and power. Difference of electric potential is commonly called *voltage* and is measured by an instrument called a *voltmeter*, since the unit of DP is the *volt*.*

In a region in which there is an electric field, an electric charge experiences a force. If the charge moves from one point A to another point B, either the field does work on the charge (like the work that gravity does on a sled when it coasts downhill) or outside energy is required to overcome the electrical forces and to effect the motion (like the outside energy required to pull a sled uphill against the force of gravity). It can be rigorously proved that if the charge is small† *the magnitude of this work is independent of the path taken from A to B*, just as the change in potential energy in motion under the force of gravity is independent of the path. We shall sketch the general proof of this important statement at the end of this section.

> The **difference of potential** between A and B, in volts, is defined as the work in joules per coulomb done by the electrical forces when a small positive test charge is moved from A to B.‡

If this work is positive, A is said to be at a higher potential than B—the forces exerted by the electric field push the positive charge down the potential hill from A to B. If, on the other hand, this work is negative, indicating that outside energy must be supplied to overcome the forces of the electric field, A is said to be at a lower potential than B.

> *In an electric field, the electrical forces tend to move a positive charge from a region of higher to one of lower potential.* Since the electrical force on a negative charge is reversed in direction from that on a positive charge, *the electrical forces tend to move a negative charge from a region of lower potential to one of higher.*

In either case the work done is proportional to the magnitude of the charge, and the magnitude of the DP in volts is the work in joules per

---
* Named for Alessandro Volta (1745–1827), Italian scientist and professor; inventor of the electroscope and the voltaic cell.

† Small enough so that it does not appreciably disturb the charges that are setting up the field, like the small test charge used to measure the electric intensity. The expression 'small test charge' implies 'small' in this sense.

‡ This statement is in agreement with AIEE definition 05.15.025.

coulomb of charge moved. These remarks will be clarified by the study of various examples in the following pages.

We start by returning to our example of the electron-ray tube in Fig. 10. A section of the charged plates of Fig. 10 is reproduced in Fig. 25. Let us imagine a small positive test charge $+q$ to move along a line of force from point A on the positively charged plate to point B on the negatively charged plate. Of course in the electron-ray tube no charge actually moves in this way, but we can imagine one to do so.

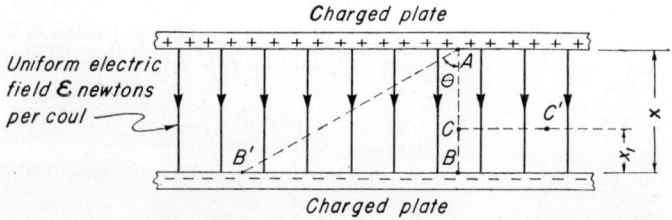

Fig. 25. A section of the charged plates of an electron-ray tube.

At any point along the line AB, the test charge $+q$ experiences a *downward* electrostatic force

$$f = q\mathcal{E}, \quad \text{in nt,}$$

by (4). In the motion from A to B, this force does work

$$W_{A \to B} = f \cdot x = q\mathcal{E} \cdot x, \quad \text{in nt·m or joules.}$$

The work done per coulomb is

$$\frac{W_{A \to B}}{q} = \mathcal{E} \cdot x, \quad \text{in } \frac{\text{nt·m}}{\text{coul}} \text{ or } \frac{\text{joules}}{\text{coul}} \text{ or volts.} \tag{8}$$

By the definition on p. 806, this is the difference of potential between A and B in volts. This DP is usually denoted by $V_A - V_B$ (V for voltage). We have, then,

$$\text{DP} = V_A - V_B = \mathcal{E}x, \quad \text{in volts.} \tag{9}$$

The deflection of the beam in the electron-ray tube was found in Sec. 3 to be proportional to the field strength $\mathcal{E}$; hence, for a given plate spacing x, it is proportional to the difference of potential between the plates and furnishes a measure of this DP. The electron-ray tube acts as a voltmeter to measure the DP between its plates.

From (8), we see that the volt (v) as a unit of DP is really defined by

$$1 \text{ volt} = 1 \frac{\text{newton·meter}}{\text{coulomb}} = 1 \sqrt{\text{nt·m}}/\text{sec,} \tag{10}$$

so

$$1 \frac{\text{volt}}{\text{meter}} = 1 \frac{\text{newton}}{\text{coulomb}} = 1 \sqrt{\text{nt}}/\text{sec,} \tag{11}$$

and *volt/meter* is usually used as the name of the unit of electric intensity in place of *newton/coulomb*. Because of this fact, electric intensity is frequently called *potential gradient;* it is the change of potential per unit of distance. If the DP in Fig. 25 is known, equation (9) shows that the field strength is given by

$$\mathcal{E} = \frac{V_A - V_B}{x}, \quad \text{in } \frac{\text{volts}}{\text{meter}} \text{ or } \frac{\text{newtons}}{\text{coulomb}}, \qquad (12)$$

which is seen to represent change in potential per unit of distance.

To go back to Figs. 10 and 25, if the DP between the plates is 240 volts (240 v) and the distance between the plates is 0.8 cm, the electric intensity is

$$240 \text{ v}/0.008 \text{ m} = 30,000 \text{ v/m},$$

which was the intensity used in the computation of the deflection in Fig. 10.

Now consider the difference of potential $V_A - V_{B'}$ in Fig. 25. We can imagine a small test charge $+q$ to move from A to B' along the straight line AB'. The component of electrostatic force along this line is $q\mathcal{E} \cos\theta$. The distance AB' is $x/\cos\theta$. The work done is

$$q\mathcal{E} \cos\theta \cdot x/\cos\theta = q\mathcal{E}x,$$

and the DP is $\qquad V_A - V_{B'} = q\mathcal{E}x/q = \mathcal{E}x.$

We have obtained the same answer for $V_A - V_{B'}$ that we obtained in (9) for $V_A - V_B$. This identity implies that B and B' are at the same potential: $V_B - V_{B'} = 0$. We can see why this must be so if we imagine moving a charge from B to B' directly, just outside the surface of the plate. Since the motion takes place perpendicularly to the electric field, no work is done by the electrical forces, so $V_B - V_{B'} = 0$. The surface of the plate is said to be an *equipotential surface*.

As a matter of fact, any horizontal plane between the plates is an equipotential surface, since no work is done in moving a charge from one point to another in the same horizontal plane, for example from C to C' in Fig. 25. The potential between the plates may be marked on a whole plane at a time, as illustrated in Fig. 26 for plates 0.8 cm apart at a DP of 240 v. In this case, the electric field $\mathcal{E} = (V_A - V_B)/x = 30,000$ v/m, as we computed above. We see that the DP $V_C - V_B$ is proportional to the distance x_1 shown in Fig. 25, since $V_C - V_B = \mathcal{E}x_1 = 30,000(\text{v/m})x_1$. Hence, the DP increases uniformly with the distance as in Fig. 26.

Because no work is done in moving a charge along an equipotential surface, *the lines of electric intensity must be normal to the equipotential surfaces. The direction of electric intensity is downhill, from higher to lower potential.*

The electron beam of Fig. 10 is deflected upward. This direction is consistent with the fact that electrical forces tend to move a *negative* charge *up* the potential hill, from regions of lower to regions of higher potential.

As a second example of computation of differences of potential, we shall compute the difference of potential between two points in space near

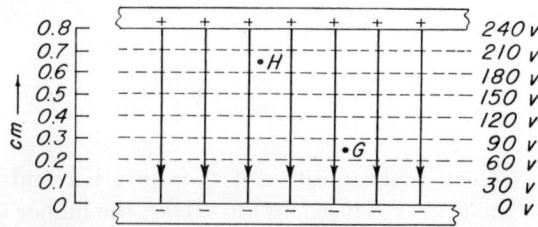

Fig. 26. Equipotential surfaces (broken lines) and lines of force for the plates of Fig. 25, 8 cm apart with a DP of 240 v. The potential of the negative plate is arbitrarily called 0 v, but differences between potential values are the only quantities with physical significance.

a single point charge. The equipotential surfaces are clearly spheres surrounding the charge, as indicated in Fig. 27, since the surface of one of these spheres is everywhere perpendicular to the lines of force, and a test charge may be moved about freely on one of these spheres without the electrostatic forces doing any work. The DP, $V_1 - V_2$, between the sphere

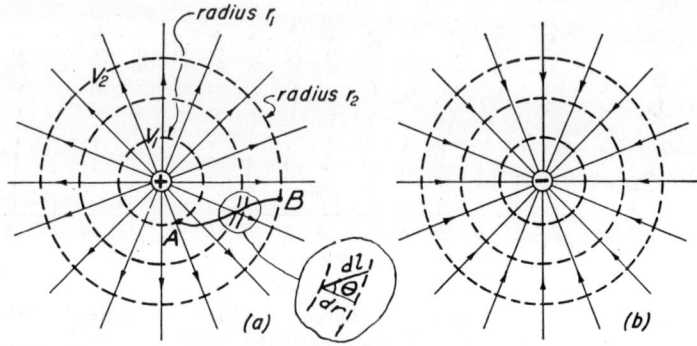

Fig. 27. Equipotential surface (broken lines) are spheres surrounding an isolated point charge Q, positive in (a) and negative in (b).

of radius r_1 and that of radius r_2 in Fig. 27(a) is, by definition, the work in joules per coulomb that would be done by the electrostatic forces on a test charge $+q$ moved from radius r_1 to radius r_2. Let us compute the work required to move a charge $+q$ from A to B in Fig. 27. When the charge q is at radius r, it experiences electrostatic force $f = 10^{-7} c^2 \, Qq/r^2$, radially outward. When the charge moves a distance dl along the path AB, the work done by this electrostatic force (see inset, Fig. 27) is $f\,dl\,\cos\theta = f\,dr = (10^{-7}c^2\,Qq/r^2)\,dr$. The total work done when the charge moves from A to B is

$$W = 10^{-7}c^2 \int_{r_1}^{r_2} \frac{Qq}{r^2}\,dr = 10^{-7}c^2\,Qq \int_{r_1}^{r_2} \frac{dr}{r^2},$$

and the DP is

$$V_1 - V_2 = \frac{W}{q} = 10^{-7}c^2\,Q \int_{r_1}^{r_2} \frac{dr}{r^2} = -10^{-7}c^2\,\frac{Q}{r}\bigg]_{r_1}^{r_2} = 10^{-7}c^2\left(\frac{Q}{r_1} - \frac{Q}{r_2}\right). \quad (13)$$

This quantity is seen to be positive if Q is positive and $r_1 < r_2$. The closer we are to the positive charge in Fig. 27(a), the higher the potential.

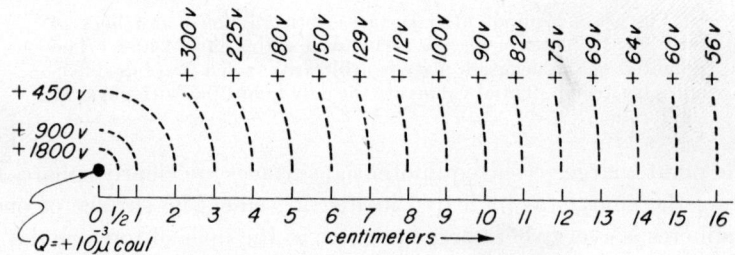

Fig. 28. Potential values near a charge of $+10^{-3}$ microcoulomb with the zero of potential taken at infinity.

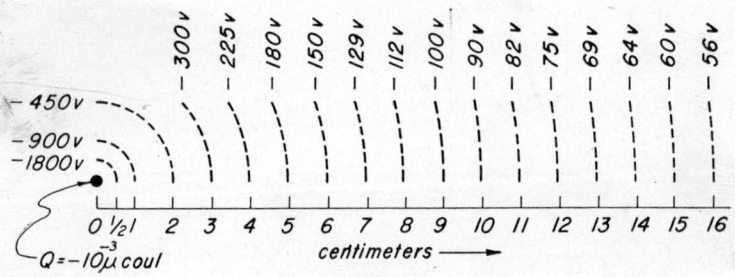

Fig. 29. Potential values near a charge of -10^{-3} microcoulomb with the zero of potential taken at infinity.

If Q is negative in (13), as in Fig. 27(b), $V_1 - V_2$ comes out negative, so that V_2 is higher than V_1; the closer we get to the negative charge, the lower the potential.

The difference of potential between the sphere at r_1 and a sphere at an infinite distance is obtained by setting $r_2 = \infty$ in (13), to get

$$V_1 - V_\infty = 10^{-7}c^2\,Q/r_1. \quad (14)$$

Sometimes it is convenient to arbitrarily call the potential at infinity *zero*.

in which case $V_1 = 10^{-7} c^2 \, Q/r_1$, and, in general,

$$V = 10^{-7} c^2 \, Q/r. \tag{15}$$

In Figs. 28 and 29, the potential values are shown for charges of $\pm 10^{-3}$ μcoul, with this convention. Again we notice that the field tends to move a positive test charge from a region of higher to one of lower potential—away from the positive charge in Fig. 28, toward the negative charge in Fig. 29.

Note that in the above derivation we have rigorously proved that for the field of a single point charge the work done in the motion of a test charge from A to B is independent of the path taken from A to B. This proof is still valid as B moves out to infinity. This is a special case of the general theorem that in any electrostatic field the work done in moving a test charge from one point to another is independent of path. If this general theorem were not true, the definition of DP would not give a unique value. The general theorem can be easily proved by considering that any electrostatic field is the superposition of the fields of a number (actually an enormous number) of point charges (see Prob. 13, below).

PROBLEMS

1. What is the magnitude of the force on a charge of 6 μcoul placed at a point where the potential gradient has a magnitude of 400,000 v/m? Ans: 2.4 nt.

2. What is the magnitude of the force on a charge of -12 μcoul placed at a point where the potential gradient has a magnitude of 30,000 v/m?

3. If the potential at H, Fig. 26, is 195 v and that at G is 75 v, how much work is required to move a positive charge of 6 μcoul from G to H? Ans: 0.00072 joule.

4. If the potential at H, Fig. 26, is 195 v and that at G is 75 v, how much work is required to move one electron from H to G?

5. (a) What is the difference of potential between two points 20 and 40 cm distant from a charge of -120 μcoul? (b) Which point is at the higher potential? (c) How much work must be done on a $+2$ μcoul charge to move it from the point of lower potential to that of higher? Ans: (a) 2.7×10^6 v; (c) 5.4 joules.

6. What is the potential difference between two points 50 and 20 cm from a $+100$-μcoul charge? Which point is at the higher potential? How much work does the field do on a 6-μcoul charge moved from the higher- to the lower-potential point?

7. Two large plane-parallel plates 5 cm apart are held at a potential difference of 12,000 v.
    (a) How much work is necessary to carry 0.3 μcoul of charge from the lower-potential plate to the higher-potential plate?
    (b) What are the magnitude and direction of the force acting on this charge?
    (c) What is the intensity of the electric field between the plates?
          Ans: (a) 3.6×10^{-3} joule; (b) 7.2×10^{-2} nt; (c) 2.4×10^6 nt/coul.

8. Two large parallel plates 2 mm apart are held at a potential difference of 900 v.
    (a) How much work, in joules, is necessary to carry 0.2 μcoul of charge from the lower- to the higher-potential plate?
    (b) What are the magnitude and direction of the force acting on this charge?
    (c) What is the electric intensity between the plates, in nt/coul?
    (d) How much work, in joules, would be necessary to carry a total of 1 coul of

charge from the lower- to the higher-potential plate, the DP being maintained at 900 v?

9. What difference of potential must be maintained between two horizontal plane-parallel plates 3 mm apart if an oil droplet of mass 10^{-12} g and carrying a negative charge of 4 electrons is to be held at rest in the space between the plates with an upward electrostatic force just balancing the force of gravity?   Ans: 45.9 v.

10. In Millikan's oil-drop experiment to determine the electronic charge, a DP of 47.9 v between horizontal plates 3 mm apart furnishes sufficient upward field to balance the weight of a drop of radius 600×10^{-7} cm of oil of density 0.860 g/cm³. What is the charge on the oil drop? How many electrons are missing from the neutral drop?

11. In a vacuum tube, the plate is maintained at a potential 144 v higher than the filament. Electrons are emitted by the filament and accelerated toward the plate by the electric field. The work done by the electrostatic force goes into kinetic energy of the electrons.
(a) What is the kinetic energy of each electron when it hits the plate?
(b) What is the speed of each electron when it hits the plate?   (Mass of electron $= 9.11 \times 10^{-31}$ kg.)   Ans: (a) 2.31×10^{-17} joule; (b) 7.10×10^6 m/sec.

12. The 'electron gun' of the electron-ray tube of Fig. 10 consists of a filament which emits electrons at negligible velocity and a plate at higher potential toward which the electrons are accelerated by the electric field maintained between the filament and the plate. The plate contains a small hole through which streams the high-velocity beam of electrons. What difference of potential (in volts) must be maintained between the filament and the plate in order to give the electrons the speed of 10^7 m/sec assumed in the discussion of Fig. 10? (Mass of electron = 9.11×10^{-31} kg.)

13. Prove the following

THEOREM: *The potential at a point P* (Fig. 30) *in the neighborhood of charges* Q_1, Q_2, Q_3, $\cdots$, *at distances* r_1, r_2, r_3, $\cdots$, *is*

$$V_P = 10^{-7} c^2 \left(\frac{Q_1}{r_1} + \frac{Q_2}{r_2} + \frac{Q_3}{r_3} + \cdots \right),$$

Fig. 30.

when the zero of potential is taken at infinity.

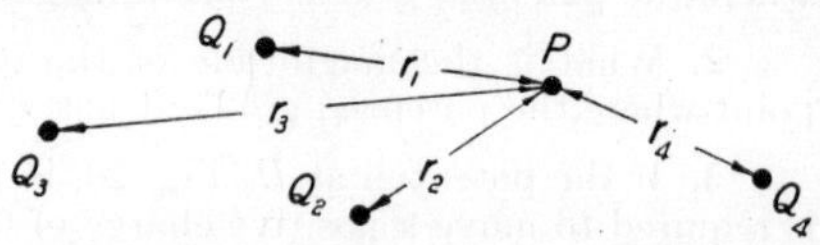

In this theorem, the various Q's can be either positive or negative. In your proof choose an arbitrary path from P to ∞; then show that the work done by the resultant electric field is the sum of the works done by the parts of the electric field resulting from each charge individually, and hence that the potential at P is the scalar sum of the potentials arising from each charge separately.

14. Making use of the theorem of Prob. 13, find the potentials at points A, B, C, D, and E in Figs. 17–21.

15. Making use of the theorem of Prob. 13, find the potentials for charges $+4$ μcoul, -1 μcoul, of Fig. 24 at points A, B, C, D, and E located as in Figs. 17–21.
            Ans: A, 9680 v; B, 6510 v; C, 3600 v; D, 5910 v; E, 6470 v.

5. CHARGES ON CONDUCTORS; SHIELDING

We first note that *in electrostatic problems there can be no electric field within a conductor*. Electrostatics implies that all charges are at rest (static); if there were a field within a conductor, this field would exert a force on the free electrons and would cause them to move. As we shall see later, in current electricity an electric field is continuously maintained within a conductor and the electrons continue to move. But in the static problems that we are considering in this chapter, the electrons in a conductor must have settled down in such a configuration that there is no electric field and therefore no lines of force within the conductor. This settling down takes place very quickly. For example, if a metal sheet is introduced between the plates of Fig. 31, the electric field of the charged

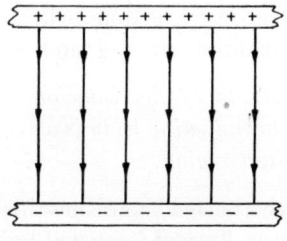

(*a*) Charged plates.

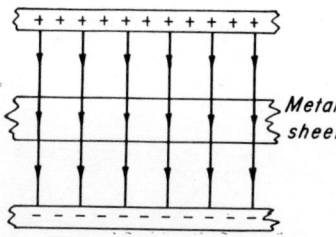

(*b*) Metal sheet introduced between charged plates. Momentarily the field of the charges on the plates acts on the electrons in the sheet.

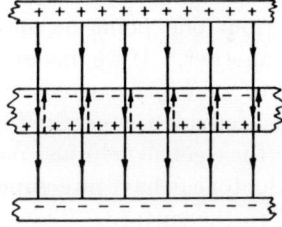

(*c*) This field causes the electrons to move to the top of the sheet. The charges on the sheet then set up a field (broken lines) opposing the original field. When enough electrons have moved so that this field exactly balances the original field . . .

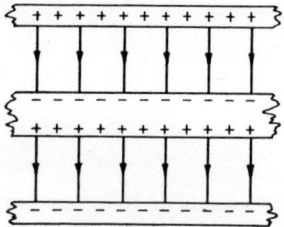

(*d*) . . . there is no longer any force on the electrons in the sheet and we have electrostatic equilibrium with no electric field within the conducting sheet.

Fig. 31. In electrostatic equilibrium there is no electric field within a conductor. The whole process of establishment of equilibrium which is illustrated here takes place in about 10^{-17} sec.

plates pulls electrons to the top of the sheet, leaving a net positive charge on the bottom of the sheet. Within the sheet, these layers of positive and negative charge set up an upward field in opposition to the downward field of the charged plates. When enough electrons have moved so that these two fields balance within the plate, there is no longer any force tending to displace more electrons. This whole process of reaching a static-equilibrium condition when the sheet is inserted between the charged plates or when the metal ball is brought near the charged rod in Fig. 2 takes place in a time of the order of 10^{-17} second.

In electrostatic problems, since no electric field can exist within a conductor, *there can be no difference of potential between two points in the same conductor.* The difference of potential between two points is determined by the work done by the electric field on a test charge moved from one point to the other; and if the two points are within the same conductor, no electric field exists along a path joining the two points and lying entirely within the conductor, so that no work is done when a test charge is moving along such a path.

The whole of the interior of a single conducting body is an equipotential region.

Since the field vanishes inside a conductor, lines of force will begin or end on the surface of a conductor. Because the surface of the conductor is an equipotential surface, no work is required to move a small test charge from one point on the surface to another. If we imagine this motion to take place along a path lying just outside the conductor, we see that the electric field just outside the conductor can have no component parallel to the surface. This statement means that the *lines of force start out perpendicularly from the surface of a conductor* (Fig. 32).

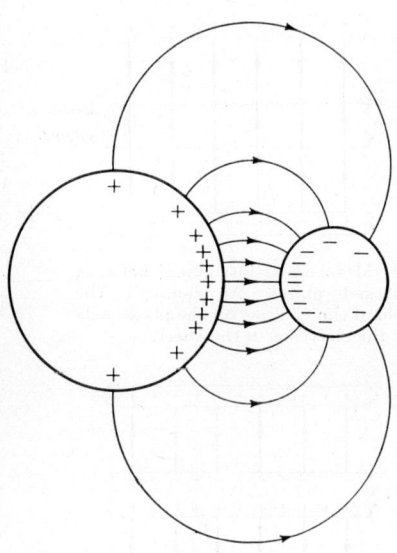

Fig. 32. Lines of force are perpendicular to the surface of a conductor. All the charge on a conductor is on its surface.

It will be proved in Sec. 7 that the absence of electric field within a conductor implies that

All the charge on a conductor lies on its surface.

Only the layers of atoms nearest the surface can have an excess or deficiency of electrons. The atoms in the interior of the conductor must be neutral.

From a positively charged region of the surface of a conductor, lines of force start out; on a negatively charged region, lines of force end. Consider a bundle of lines of force (a *tube of force*) starting from an area A_1 of one conductor and ending on an area A_2 of another (Fig. 33). It will be shown in Sec. 7 that the magnitude of the positive charge in the area A_1 at the beginning of this tube precisely equals magnitude of the negative charge in the area A_2 at its end.

A tube of force has equal charges of opposite sign at beginning and end.

Furthermore, there is a definite relationship between the electric intensities along the tube of force, its area (measured on an equipotential surface perpendicular to the lines of force), and the amount of charge on its ends.

The product of electric intensity by area ($\varepsilon_1 A_1$, $\varepsilon_2 A_2$, or $\varepsilon_3 A_3$) is called the electric flux in the tube:

> The **electric flux** in a tube of force is the product of the electric intensity by the cross-sectional area of the tube.* Electric flux is measured in $(v/m) \cdot m^2$ or $v \cdot m$.

In this definition it is assumed that the cross section of the tube is so small that the electric intensity does not vary appreciably over this cross section. If this is not the case, the definition should be modified to read

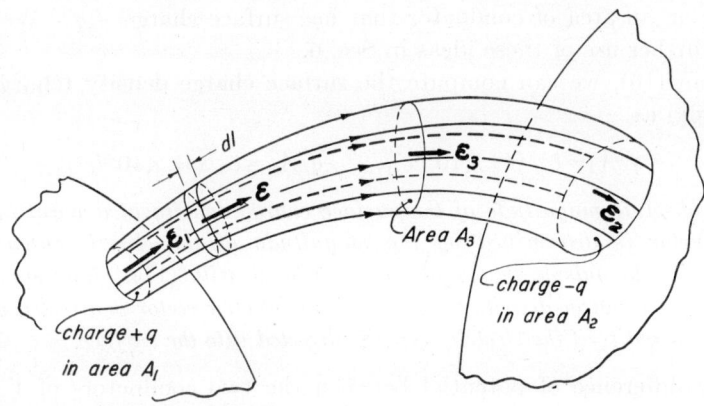

Fig. 33. A tube of force.

'*average* electric intensity,' the average being taken over the cross section of the tube.

The relation between the flux in a tube and the amount of charge at either end is derived in Sec. 7. This relation can be stated:

> *The electric flux in a tube of force is constant along its length and equal to $4\pi \times 10^{-7} c^2$ times the charge at the end of the tube.*

In other words, in Fig. 33,

$$\varepsilon_1 A_1 = \varepsilon_2 A_2 = \varepsilon_3 A_3 = 4\pi \times 10^{-7} c^2 \, q. \tag{16}$$

The quantity εA is sometimes loosely called *the number of lines of force passing through the tube.* The tube is considered to carry

$$N = \varepsilon A$$

---

* We follow the AIEE definition 05.15.015 of *electric flux.* We note that many writers call a different quantity 'electric flux.' The quantity that many writers call electric flux is that defined as 'displacement flux' in AIEE definition 05.30.054. We shall not have occasion to use this quantity in this text.

lines of force. This terminology is somewhat misleading, since there is no limit to the number of different lines of force that we might draw within the tube. However, it is useful to imagine that we symbolize the strength of the tube by drawing just N lines. Since we can write

$$\mathcal{E} = N/A,$$

$\mathcal{E}$ is sometimes called the number of lines of force per square meter. We can symbolize the field strength by drawing $\mathcal{E}$ lines of force through each square meter of an equipotential surface, which is of course a surface perpendicular to the lines of force.

In accordance with (16), we can think of $4\pi \times 10^{-7} c^2\, q$ lines of force starting out from an area of conductor that has surface charge $+q$, and ending on an area of conductor that has surface charge $-q$. We shall make further use of these ideas in Sec. 6.

From (16), we can compute the surface charge density (charge per unit area) as

$$q/A_1 = \mathcal{E}_1/(4\pi \times 10^{-7} c^2), \qquad q/A_2 = \mathcal{E}_2/(4\pi \times 10^{-7} c^2). \qquad (17)$$

The absolute magnitude of the surface charge density at a point on a conductor is determined by the magnitude of the electric intensity immediately outside the point, in accordance with (17). The sign of the surface charge density is positive if the electric vector is directed outward, negative if the electric vector is directed into the surface.

The difference of potential between the two conductors of Fig. 33 is measured by the work that the field would do on a test charge moved along the tube of force from one conductor to the other, divided by the size of the test charge. Let the magnitude of the test charge be denoted by ε. The force on this charge is $\mathcal{E}\varepsilon$. The work done on this charge in moving the distance dl is $\mathcal{E}\varepsilon\, dl$, and the total work is

$$\int \mathcal{E}\varepsilon\, dl = \varepsilon \int \mathcal{E}\, dl,$$

the integration being carried from one conductor to the other. The difference of potential is, then, this integral divided by ε, or

$$V_1 - V_2 = \int \mathcal{E}\, dl. \qquad (18)$$

The difference of potential between two conductors is the integral, along a line of force, of field strength multiplied by the element of length of the line of force.

Or, since we can write $\int \mathcal{E}\, dl = \mathcal{E}_{\text{av}} \int dl$, we can state:

The average electric field along a line of force connecting two conductors equals the difference of potential divided by the length of the line of force.

In general, then, the electric field between two conductors is high where the lines of force are short, low where they are long (note Fig. 32). Since the surface charge density is proportional to the electric field at the surface, this statement means that the charges on oppositely charged conductors tend to congregate on the parts of the surface facing each other where the lines of force are shortest. This effect is illustrated in Fig. 32 and many other figures in this chapter. The extreme example of this congregation is in the case of two large oppositely charged plane-parallel conductors close to each other. Except near the very edges of

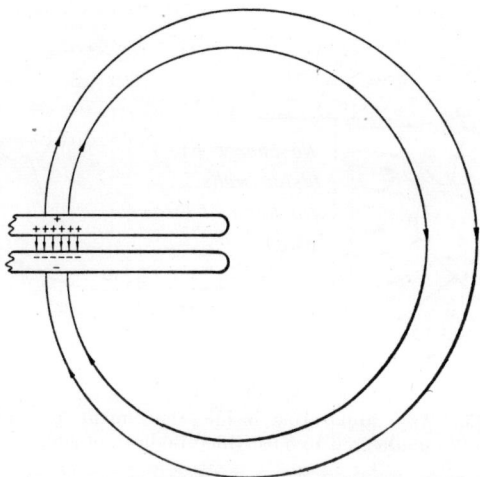

Fig. 34. Schematic diagram of representative lines of force for oppositely charged parallel plates. The constant length of the lines of force between the plates implies a uniform distribution of charge on the facing surfaces. The enormous length of the lines of force connecting charges on the outer faces implies very low charge density on these faces.

the plates, the charge can be considered to be all on the *facing* surfaces, uniformly distributed. This distribution is associated (Fig. 34), with the constant length of lines of force between the plates, which in turn gives rise to constant electric fields and uniform distribution of charge on the facing surfaces, and with the enormous length of lines of force connecting charges on the outer surfaces, which makes for very low electric fields and very low charge densities on these surfaces.

We can now show that

Lines of force always begin and end on electric charges (or on conductors with surface charge). They cannot terminate in free space nor can they form closed curves in free space.

For lines to terminate in free space would violate the theorem of continuity of flux through a tube of force. To see that the lines cannot form closed curves, consider the integral (18) carried entirely around such a closed curve. This integral cannot vanish because $\mathcal{E}$ is everywhere in the direction of the line. But the left side of (18) must vanish because V_1 and V_2 are in this case both at the same point of space. This leads to an absurdity that negates the hypothesis that a line of force can form a closed curve.

The existence of lines of force joining the two conductors in Fig. 32 or Fig. 33 implies that there *must* be a difference of potential between the

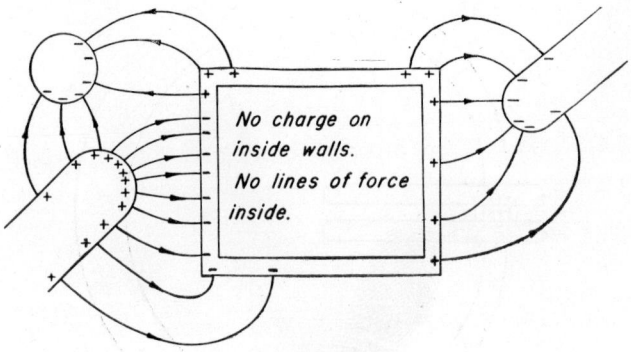

Fig. 35. Any apparatus inside the shield is completely unaffected by electrified bodies outside.

conductors. Hence, they must be *different* conductors not electrically connected, since no difference of potential can exist between two points on the same conductor.

No line of force can begin and end on the same conductor.

This statement furnishes the explanation of the very important phenomenon of *electrostatic shielding*. A closed box made entirely of metal acts as an electrostatic shield. In Fig. 35 there can be no charge on the inside walls of the box and no lines of force in the interior volume. No matter how many charged objects are near the shielded box in Fig. 35, there is no effect in the interior of the box. Why?—because if there were lines of force in the interior of the box they would begin and end on the same conductor, which is forbidden; and if there are no lines of force ending on the inside walls, there are no charges on the walls, by (17).

The shield may be as thin as a sheet of foil or a coat of aluminum paint. It makes no difference. Any apparatus inside the shield is completely unaffected by electrified bodies outside. If a charged metal body is placed inside the shield, an equal and opposite charge is induced on the inner walls of the shield (Fig. 36), but the distribution of charge on the body and on the inner walls is completely unaffected by charges outside the shield. *If now the charged body is electrically connected to the shield, it becomes completely discharged* (Fig. 37), because all the surfaces inside the shield are now at the same potential and no surface charges can exist there. The charge that was on the body has moved to the outside wall of the shield, where it has no effect on the interior.

Shielding is familiar to everyone who has looked inside a radio set. It is designed to keep electric fields originating in other components of

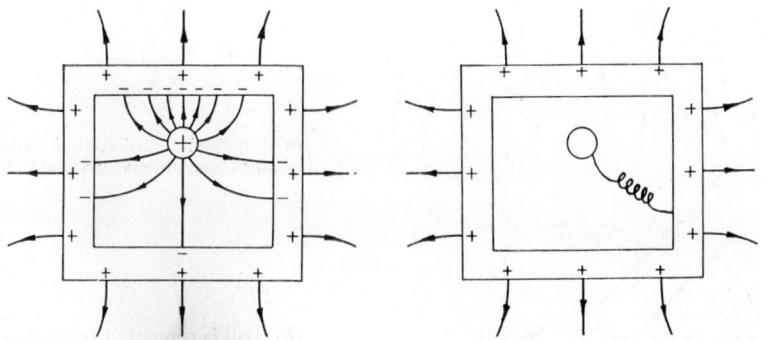

Fig. 36. If a charged conductor is placed inside a shield, an equal and opposite charge appears on the inner wall of the shield.

Fig. 37. If the charged body in Fig. 36 is electrically connected to the shield, it becomes *completely* discharged.

the set, or outside, from interfering with the operation of the various vacuum tubes and other field-sensitive parts.

PROBLEMS

1. What is the electric intensity adjacent to the surface of a sphere uniformly charged with -0.2 μcoul/cm^2?   Ans: 720π nt/coul (in what direction?).

2. A sphere of radius 1.5 cm has a total charge of 9 μcoul uniformly distributed over its surface. (a) What is the electric intensity at the surface of the sphere? (b) What is the total number of lines of force leaving the sphere?

3. Two large plane-parallel plates are 0.4 cm apart and have a DP of 1000 v.
   (a) What is the density of charge, in μcoul/m^2, on each plate?
   (b) How many lines of force start out from a square 5 cm $\times$ 5 cm of the positive plate?   Ans: (a) 2.21 μcoul/m^2; (b) 625.

4. Two large plane-parallel plates are 0.6 cm apart and have a DP of 2000 v.
   (a) What is the electric field strength?
   (b) What is the density of charge in μcoul/m^2 on each plate?

5. Two large plane-parallel plates are 0.4 cm apart and are charged to densities of ± 3 μcoul/m^2.
   (a) What is the electric intensity between the plates?
   (b) What is the DP?   Ans: (a) 3.40×10^5 v/m; (b) 1360 v.

6. Two large plane-parallel plates are 0.6 cm apart and are charged to densities of ± 8 μcoul/m^2.
   (a) What is the electric intensity between the plates?
   (b) What is the DP?

7. Show that in the MKS system the last term of equation (16) is expressed in the same units as the preceding terms.

6. CHARGING BY INDUCTION; THE ELECTROSCOPE*

The ideas about lines of force which were presented in the previous section will help us to understand the phenomena involved in the process

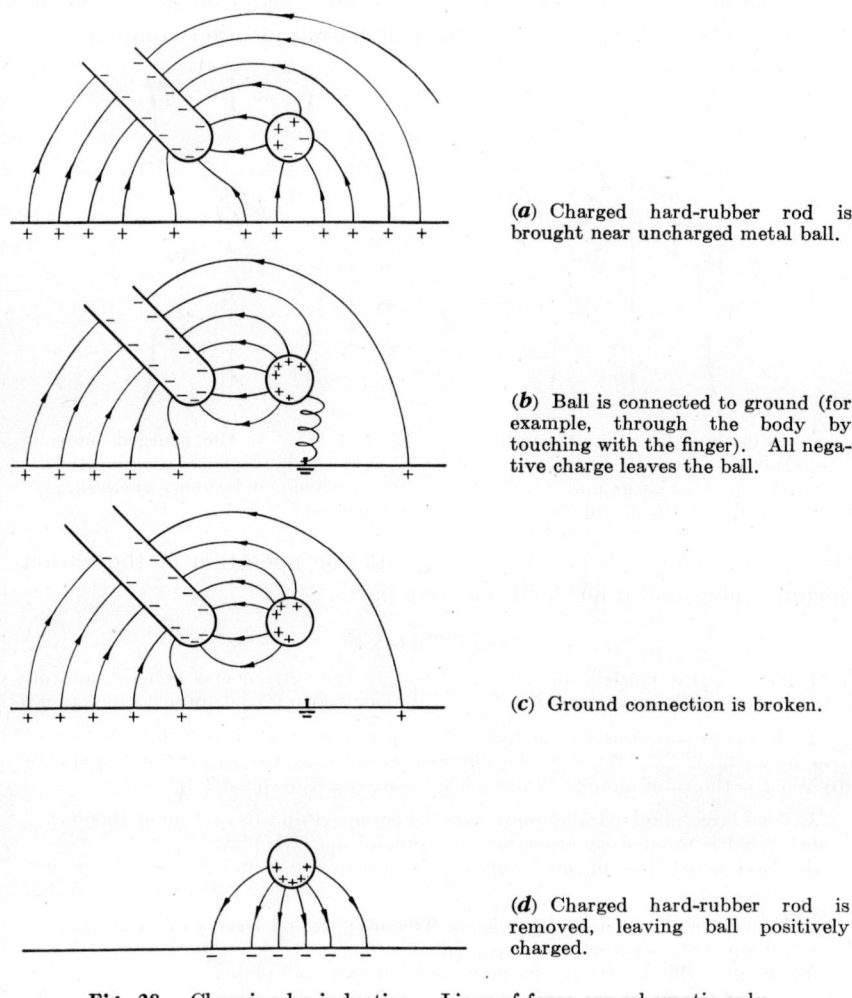

(*a*) Charged hard-rubber rod is brought near uncharged metal ball.

(*b*) Ball is connected to ground (for example, through the body by touching with the finger). All negative charge leaves the ball.

(*c*) Ground connection is broken.

(*d*) Charged hard-rubber rod is removed, leaving ball positively charged.

Fig. 38. Charging by induction. Lines of force are schematic only.

of charging by induction. The steps in the procedure for charging a metal object positively by induction are given in Fig. 38. It will be

* This section may be omitted without loss of continuity. Its topics are given considerable emphasis in classical treatments of electrostatics but are not of first importance in modern science or engineering.

noticed that in this figure all the lines of force that end on the negative charges on the rod are shown beginning either on the ball or on the ground. None of them come from infinity. This is the usual situation when charged objects are near the surface of a very large conductor such as the earth. An equal and opposite charge is induced in the nearby areas of the earth's conducting surface, so that all the lines of force begin or end there. Of course, if a positive charge is induced on a certain area of the earth's surface, equal negative charge must appear elsewhere, but this negative charge is spread out so thinly and is so far away on the other side of the earth-sphere that the fields it sets up are undetectable.

The process of charging by induction should be clear from Fig. 38, with the possible exception of one point, namely, why *all* the negative charge leaves the ball when it is grounded [see Fig. 38(b)]. The answer is that if negative charges did remain on the ball, there would have to be

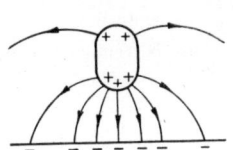 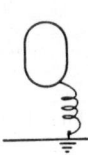 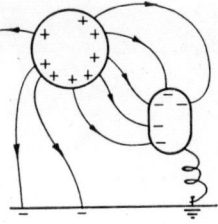

Fig. 39. A charged metal body . . .   . . . loses all of its charge when it is grounded . . .   . . . unless there is an ungrounded charge nearby.

positive charges at the beginnings of the lines of force that ended on these negative charges. But there are no positive charges on the glass rod. Moreover, the positive charges at the other ends of the lines of force could not be on the ball or the earth because these now form one single conductor, and a line of force cannot begin and end on the same conductor. So it is impossible that there should be any negative charges left on the ball after it is grounded. Like a body connected to the inside of a shield, a charged metal body loses all its charge when it is grounded unless there is an ungrounded charge near-by to induce charge on it (Fig. 39).

Note that a body charged by induction acquires a charge opposite in sign to that of the inducing charge. In Fig. 38, a negatively charged rod is used to induce a positive charge on the sphere; a positively charged rod would be used to induce a negative charge.

The *electrophorus*, a familiar piece of demonstration apparatus which permits large charges to be obtained by induction, is shown in Fig. 40. A large, flat, hard-rubber plate is highly charged on its top surface by rubbing with cat's fur. When a grounded metal plate is placed on the hard-rubber plate, the positive charge induced on the metal plate is

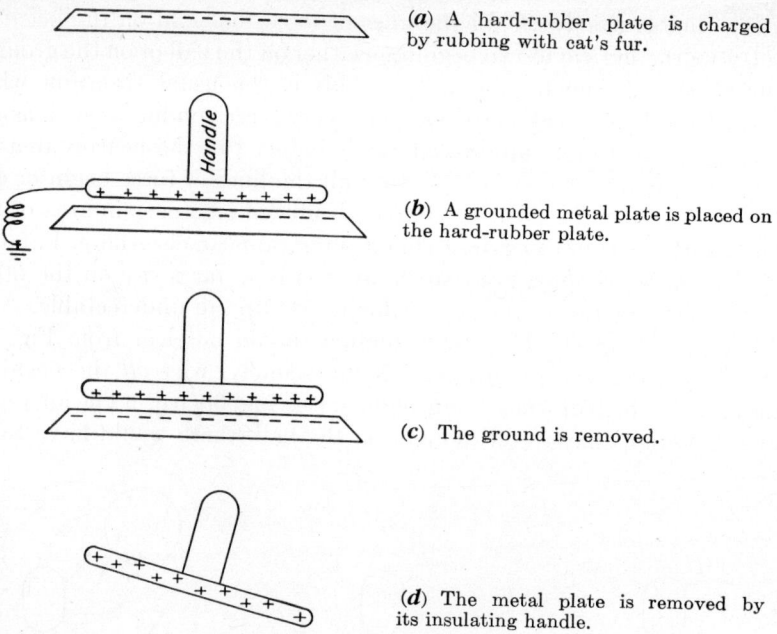

Fig. 40. The electrophorus.

approximately equal to the negative charge on the hard-rubber plate because the metal plate collects most of the lines of force that end on the charges on the hard-rubber plate. This positive charge remains on the metal plate when it is removed in Fig. 40(d). The metal plate may be discharged elsewhere and then recharged by induction repeatedly without recharging the hard-rubber plate. The metal plate does not steal the negative charge from the hard rubber to any appreciable extent because it is actually in intimate contact with the hard rubber in only a very few microscopic spots, and, since this material is nonconducting, the charge on it cannot flow along the surface to the points of contact. The success of this apparatus, like the success of most electrostatic experiments, depends on having the nonconducting surface dry and clean, free from a conducting film of moisture and foreign material.

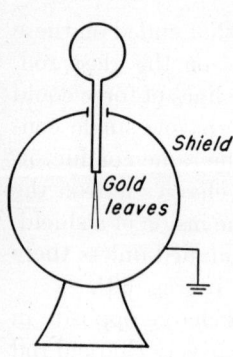

Fig. 41. The electroscope.

The *electroscope* (Fig. 41) is a useful and interesting instrument. It consists of two thin gold leaves fastened to a metal rod commonly terminated by a metal ball or plate. Usually, the leaves are more or less completely surrounded by a grounded metal shield, from which the protruding metal rod is insulated.

If a charged body of either polarity is brought near the ball of the electroscope, the leaves diverge because of the repulsion of the charges induced on the two leaves (Fig. 42).

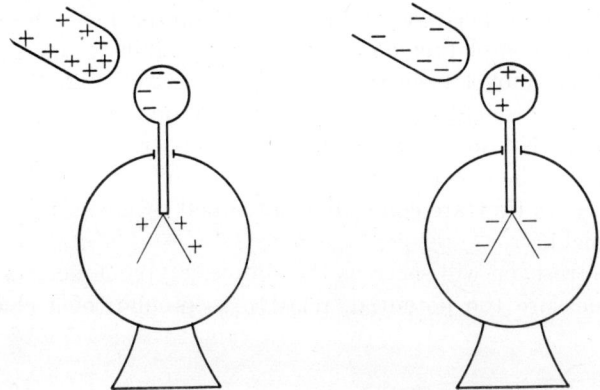

Fig. 42. When a charged body is brought near the ball of an electroscope, the leaves diverge.

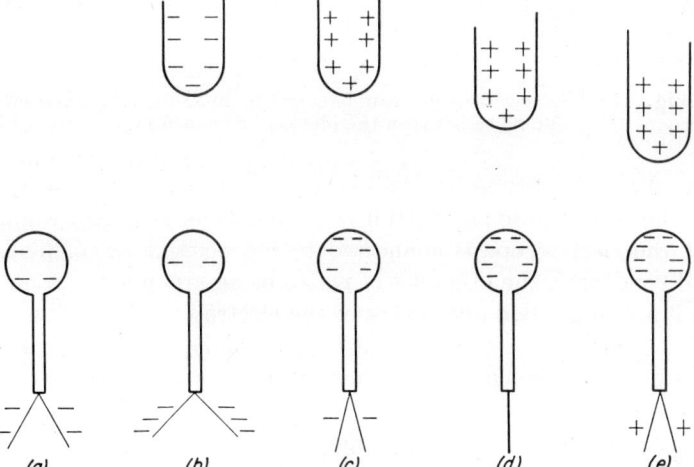

Fig. 43. The effect of an external charge on an already charged electroscope. (The electroscope shield is omitted from these schematic drawings.)

If the electroscope is charged, by touching the ball with a charged body, or by induction, the leaves remain permanently deflected, as in Fig. 43(a). If a negatively charged body is brought near the ball of a negatively charged electroscope, as in Fig. 43(b), the leaves diverge further, because some of the negative charge is driven from the ball into the leaves, giving the leaves a greater negative charge and hence greater repulsion. If a positively charged body approaches the negatively charged electroscope, the leaves draw together because negative charge is drawn from the leaves into the ball as in Fig. 43(c). If the body has a sufficiently strong positive charge, as it approaches still closer the leaves collapse completely and then diverge again as more and more negative charge moves from the leaves into the ball [Fig. 43(d) and (e)].

Note that the shield prevents any direct action of an external charge on the leaves. No lines of force can go directly from an external charge to the leaves. The effect on the leaves is due entirely to charges induced on them because they are connected to the ball by a conductor insulated from the shield.

The electroscope will serve as the simplest type of electrostatic voltmeter to measure the potential, relative to ground, of a charged con-

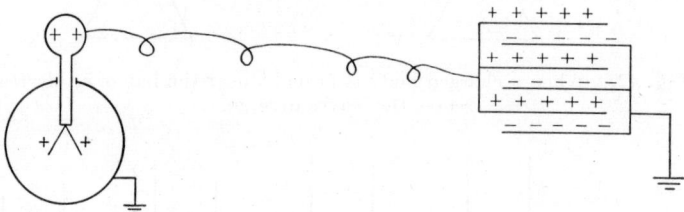

Fig. 44. The electroscope can be used to measure the potential difference between the plates of a condenser.

ductor. For this purpose the ball is connected by a long, fine, insulated wire to the body whose potential it is desired to measure; for example, in Fig. 44 the electroscope is connected to the positive set of plates of a charged condenser, the other set of plates being grounded. Some of the charge flows to the ball and leaves of the electroscope, charging them so that they have the same potential as the condenser plates, since they and the positive condenser plates now form a single conductor. If the amount of charge that flows to the electroscope when it is connected is small compared with the total charge on the plates, the potential of the plates is not appreciably altered by connecting the electroscope. If the amount of charge is not small compared with the total charge, at least the electroscope leaves and the plates come to the same potential, and the electroscope measures the potential that exists after it is connected. We shall now try to explain why *the deflection of the electroscope is a measure of the potential difference between the electroscope leaves and the grounded case.*

When the electroscope is charged positively, as in Fig. 44, each element of surface area of the ball and leaves has a positive charge, and lines of force start out from this surface element and go to the grounded shield or directly to ground (Fig. 45). By (18), the product of the average electric field along any one of these lines of force by the length of the line of force is equal to the potential of the electroscope (relative to ground), and hence to the potential of the body to which the electroscope is connected. Consequently, the average electric field along any line of force in Fig. 45 is proportional to the potential of the electroscope. The charges on the parts of the electroscope, in particular on the leaves, are proportional to the electric field strength near by, in accordance with (17).

Now if the potential of the body and of the electroscope is increased relative to ground, the electric field everywhere in Fig. 45 must increase, and the surface charges must increase. In particular, the charges on the leaves increase, and hence the force between the leaves and the divergence of the leaves increase. If the potential of the body is decreased, the divergence of the leaves is correspondingly decreased. Although the angle of divergence of the leaves is not exactly *proportional* to the potential, it is directly related to the potential and serves to determine it once the electroscope has been properly calibrated. It is to be noted, however, that the electroscope gives the same reading for a negative potential as for the numerically equal positive potential.

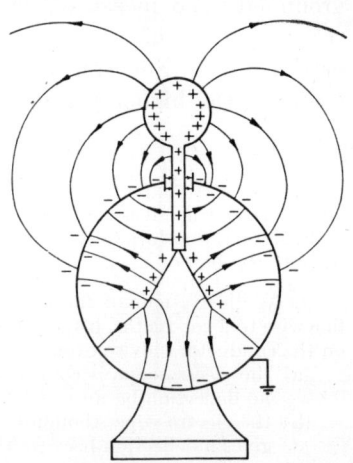

Fig. 45. Schematic representation of lines of force in a charged electroscope.

Fig. 46. Movement of commercial electrostatic voltmeter (*courtesy of Sensitive Research Instrument Corporation*).

These principles are utilized in a more rugged but less sensitive instrument called an *electrostatic voltmeter*, a commercial type of which is illustrated in Fig. 46. In this instrument a set of rotating vanes charged with one polarity is pulled by electrostatic forces into a position between a set of oppositely charged stationary vanes. Rotation of the vanes is resisted by the restoring torque of a spring, and the amount of rotation is a measure of the difference of potential between the two sets of vanes. To measure the DP between a charged conductor and ground, one set of vanes is connected to the conductor, the other grounded. To measure the voltage developed by a battery or generator, one set of vanes is connected to each terminal of the battery or generator. Such an instrument is relatively insensitive and is most useful in the higher voltage ranges (above 500 volts).

PROBLEMS

1. Sketch an experimental scheme for showing that a charged metal body loses all its charge when it is connected to the inside of a closed shield as in Figs. 36 and 37, at least to the accuracy with which the charge could be detected by touching the body to the ball of a sensitive electroscope.

2. As illustrations of the fact that, when an electroscope is connected by a long fine wire to a conductor, it furnishes a measure of the potential rather than the charge on the conductor, devise examples in which
 (a) the electroscope is connected to a positively charged metal sphere and gives no deflection because the sphere is at zero (ground) potential;
 (b) the electroscope, though connected to a metal sphere that has no net charge, gives a deflection because the sphere is not at ground potential.

3. When an electroscope is used to measure the potential of a conductor, why must the electroscope be connected to the conductor by a *long* wire? How could you tell whether the electroscope was *far enough* away from the conductor?

7. GAUSS'S THEOREM*

We have defined in Sec. 5 the electric flux (or number of lines of force) passing through a tube of force as the product of the field intensity by the cross-sectional area of the tube. This definition assumes that the field intensity does not vary across the section of the tube and hence is in general applicable only to tubes of infinitesimal cross section. The electric flux passing through a finite area is to be obtained by an integration over the infinitesimal tubes of force passing through that area. We shall prove the following important theorem concerning electric flux:

GAUSS'S THEOREM: *The electric flux that passes outward through any closed surface equals $4\pi \times 10^{-7}c^2$ times the net charge enclosed within the surface.*

It should be pointed out that the surface contemplated by this theorem is an imaginary mathematical surface, not necessarily coinciding with a physically existing surface.

As illustration of this theorem, which will help us get started on the general proof, let us consider the lines of force that leave an isolated positive point charge Q and pass out through a sphere (Fig. 47). At any point on the sphere of radius R surrounding the charge, the field strength is $\mathcal{E} = 10^{-7}c^2 Q/R^2$ by (7). The electric flux in the infinitesimal tube of

---

* This section, which contains mathematical proofs of many of the statements of Sec. 5, may be omitted without loss of continuity. However, Gauss's theorem is of fundamental importance in the advanced study of electricity.

force shown in Fig. 47 is, then, $\mathcal{E}\, dA = 10^{-7}c^2(Q/R^2)\, dA$. The total flux going outward through the sphere is obtained by integrating this quantity over the surface of the sphere. Since Q/R^2 is constant over the sphere and dA integrates to the surface area $4\pi R^2$, the total flux becomes

$$N = 10^{-7}c^2 \int\!\!\int \frac{Q}{R^2}\, dA = 10^{-7}c^2 \frac{Q}{R^2} \int\!\!\int dA = 10^{-7}c^2 \frac{Q}{R^2} 4\pi R^2 = 4\pi \times 10^{-7}c^2\, Q,$$

in agreement with the theorem. The double-integral sign here is used to indicate integration over an area, which is essentially a two-dimensional integration.

We have thus shown that Gauss's theorem is true for a spherical surface with a point charge at its center. Figure 47 is drawn for a positive charge, and the lines of force pass *outward* through the sphere. If the charge were negative, the lines of force would pass *inward*, the flux would be counted as negative, and the theorem would still be satisfied.

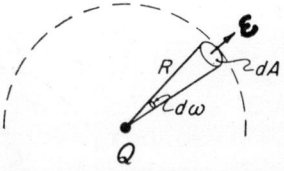

Fig. 47. Computation of the flux through a sphere.

Let us now prove the theorem for a point charge Q and a closed surface of arbitrary shape. Consider first the surface indicated in Fig. 48. Let a tube of force subtending an infinitesimal solid angle $d\omega$ at the charge Q cut an area dS out of the surface at a distance R from the charge. At the surface the field strength is $\mathcal{E} = 10^{-7}c^2\, Q/R^2$, directed away from Q along the radius vector. The flux passing out through the surface in this tube is $\mathcal{E}\, dA$, where dA is the area of the tube measured, not on the surface, but perpendicular to $\mathcal{E}$. By the definition of solid angle, $dA = R^2\, d\omega$. Hence, the number of lines of force in the tube starting from Q in the solid angle $d\omega$ is

$$\mathcal{E}\, dA = 10^{-7}c^2(Q/R^2)R^2\, d\omega = 10^{-7}c^2\, Q\, d\omega.$$

Since in this derivation we used an arbitrary radius R, which canceled out, we conclude that the flux in the tube of force starting from charge Q in solid angle $d\omega$ is equal to $10^{-7}c^2\, Q\, d\omega$ at any distance from Q.

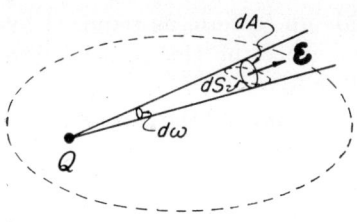

Fig. 48. Computation of the flux through a non-spherical surface.

The total flux (number of lines of force) starting from charge Q in Fig. 48 and passing out through the closed surface is obtained, then, by integrating $d\omega$ over the whole sphere:

$$N = \int\!\!\int 10^{-7}c^2\, Q\, d\omega = 10^{-7}c^2\, Q \int\!\!\int d\omega = 10^{-7}c^2\, Q \cdot 4\pi = 4\pi \times 10^{-7}c^2\, Q.$$

The 4π comes from the fact that the total solid angle in a sphere is 4π.

This result shows that the theorem is satisfied for a point charge and a simple surface like that of Fig. 48. However, the proof of the theorem for a point charge is still not quite complete. We must consider a more complicated surface, such as that in Fig. 49, in which some tubes of force may re-enter the surface after having passed out. If a tube of force such as b cuts the surface three times, its flux $10^{-7}c^2 Q\,d\omega$, which is constant along its length, is counted positively twice, where it passes outward, and negatively once, where it passes inward. Hence, its contribution to the net outward flux is $10^{-7}c^2 Q\,d\omega$, the same as if it had cut the surface

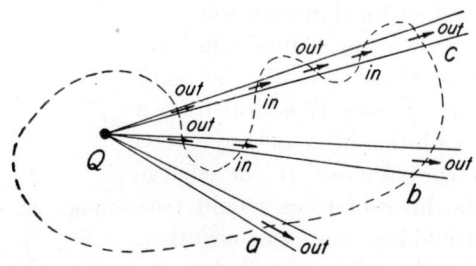

Fig. 49.

only once. Similarly, tube c, which cuts the surface five times, is counted positively three times, negatively twice, and still makes the net contribution $10^{-7}c^2 Q\,d\omega$. The same argument would hold for tubes that cut a more complex surface any number of times. Hence, we conclude that *the theorem is valid for a point charge inside any surface whatsoever.*

Let us now consider a point charge lying *outside* a closed surface, as in Fig. 50. In this case any tube of force from the point charge cuts the surface an *even* number of times. The total outward flux through the surface adds up to zero, as required by the theorem, since the charge inside the closed surface is zero.

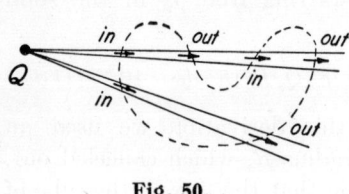

Fig. 50.

Having thus proved the theorem for a single point charge, either inside or outside the surface, we can proceed to prove it for any collection of charges whatever.

We must first learn to write the flux in the tube of force in Fig. 48 in terms of the surface area dS cut off by the tube instead of in terms of the perpendicular area dA. Let $\mathbf{n}$ be a vector normal to the element of area dS and directed outward. In Fig. 51, let the vectors $\mathbf{\varepsilon}$ and $\mathbf{n}$ lie in the plane of the paper so that the area elements dA and dS are perpendicular to the paper and cut the paper in the lines shown in the diagram. The flux in the tube, which is assumed to pass outward through the surface in this diagram, is $\varepsilon\,dA$. But the area dA is the projection of the area dS on a plane making angle θ with the plane of dS, so $dA = dS\cos\theta$. Hence, the strength of the tube may be written as $\mathcal{E}\,dS\,\cos\theta$. But $\mathcal{E}\cos\theta$ is the component $\mathcal{E}_n$ of $\mathcal{E}$ in the direction of the normal $\boldsymbol{n}$. So, finally,

$$\mathcal{E}\,dA = \mathcal{E}\,dS\,\cos\theta = \mathcal{E}_n\,dS \tag{19}$$

is the contribution to the outward flux in Gauss's theorem from a tube passing outward through area dS.

A tube passing inward makes a negative contribution $-\mathcal{E}\,dA$ to the net outward flux, but we can show from Fig. 52 that this contribution can be written again in form (19), the important point being that $\mathcal{E}_n$ is the component of $\mathcal{E}$ along the *outward* normal, which will be a negative number in this case. In Fig. 52, θ is defined as the angle between the

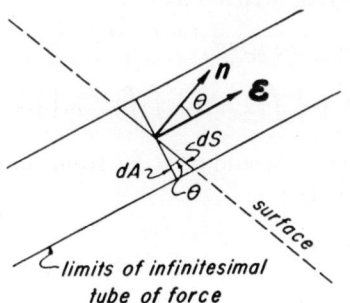
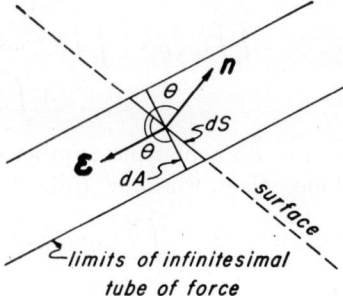

Fig. 51. Tube of force passes *outward* through an imaginary surface.

Fig. 52. Tube of force passes *inward* through an imaginary surface.

vectors $\mathcal{E}$ and $\boldsymbol{n}$, so that $\mathcal{E}_n = \mathcal{E}\cos\theta$. We must now write $dA = -dS\cos\theta$, since $\cos\theta$ is negative. Then the contribution of this tube, which passes *inward*, to the total outward flux in Gauss's theorem is

$$-\mathcal{E}\,dA = \mathcal{E}\,dS\,\cos\theta = \mathcal{E}_n\,dS, \tag{20}$$

just as in (19).

These considerations enable us to state Gauss's theorem in a more useful mathematical form. The total outward flux in all the tubes of force that pass through the closed surface may, in view of (19) and (20), be written as $\iint \mathcal{E}_n\,dS$, integrated over the surface, and *Gauss's theorem* becomes

$$\iint_{\substack{\text{over}\\\text{closed}\\\text{surface}}} \mathcal{E}_n\,dS = 4\pi \times 10^{-7} c^2 \sum_{\substack{\text{over in-}\\\text{terior of}\\\text{surface}}} Q. \tag{21}$$

We can now quickly complete the proof of Gauss's theorem in the form (21). Let the charges in the interior of the surface be Q_1, Q_2, Q_3, $\cdots$. There can be as many such charges as we please—in the last analysis, as many charges as there are electrons and nuclei within the surface. Then let there be charges Q'_1, Q'_2, Q'_3, $\cdots$ outside the surface—

these charges should include all the rest of the electrons and nuclei in the universe.

Now the electric field strength $\mathcal{E}$ at any point on the surface is the vector sum of contributions $\mathcal{E}_1, \mathcal{E}_2, \mathcal{E}_3, \cdots$ from the charges $Q_1, Q_2, Q_3, \cdots$, and contributions $\mathcal{E}'_1, \mathcal{E}'_2, \mathcal{E}'_3, \cdots$ from the charges $Q'_1, Q'_2, Q'_3, \cdots$; that is,

$$\mathcal{E} = \mathcal{E}_1 + \mathcal{E}_2 + \mathcal{E}_3 + \cdots + \mathcal{E}'_1 + \mathcal{E}'_2 + \mathcal{E}'_3 + \cdots.$$

The component of $\mathcal{E}$ in the direction of n is the sum of the components of the vectors that are added to get $\mathcal{E}$:

$$\mathcal{E}_n = \mathcal{E}_{1n} + \mathcal{E}_{2n} + \mathcal{E}_{3n} + \cdots + \mathcal{E}'_{1n} + \mathcal{E}'_{2n} + \mathcal{E}'_{3n} + \cdots.$$

Hence, the integral occurring in (21) may be written as

$$\iint \mathcal{E}_n \, dS = \iint \mathcal{E}_{1n} \, dS + \iint \mathcal{E}_{2n} \, dS + \iint \mathcal{E}_{3n} \, dS + \cdots$$
$$+ \iint \mathcal{E}'_{1n} \, dS + \iint \mathcal{E}'_{2n} \, dS + \iint \mathcal{E}'_{3n} \, dS + \cdots.$$

Now $\iint \mathcal{E}_{1n} \, dS$ is just the number of lines that would pass out from charge Q_1 alone, which we know to be $4\pi \times 10^{-7} c^2 Q_1$:

$$\iint \mathcal{E}_{1n} \, dS = 4\pi \times 10^{-7} c^2 Q_1.$$

Similarly,
$$\iint \mathcal{E}_{2n} \, dS = 4\pi \times 10^{-7} c^2 Q_2,$$
$$\iint \mathcal{E}_{3n} \, dS = 4\pi \times 10^{-7} c^2 Q_3, \quad \cdots.$$

Also, $\iint \mathcal{E}'_{1n} \, dS$ is the net number of lines that would pass outward from charge Q'_1 alone. Since this charge is outside the surface, we have seen (Fig. 50) that this number vanishes:

$$\iint \mathcal{E}'_{1n} \, dS = 0.$$

Similarly,
$$\iint \mathcal{E}'_{2n} \, dS = 0, \quad \iint \mathcal{E}'_{3n} \, dS = 0, \quad \cdots.$$

Finally, then,

$$\iint \mathcal{E}_n \, dS = 4\pi \times 10^{-7} c^2 (Q_1 + Q_2 + Q_3 + \cdots) = 4\pi \times 10^{-7} c^2 \, \Sigma \, Q,$$

where the summation includes only charges interior to the surface.

This completes the proof of Gauss's theorem [equation (21)]. By using this powerful theorem, we can readily prove all the statements that were made without proof in Sec. 5. We shall repeat these statements in italics and follow each with a paragraph showing its proof.

There is no net charge in any volume lying wholly in the interior of a conducting medium.

Consider a closed surface S (Fig. 53) that lies wholly inside a conductor. S is supposed to bound any arbitrary volume whatsoever that lies wholly within a conductor of arbitrary shape. Since by the argument advanced in Sec. 5, the electric field vanishes everywhere within the conductor, it vanishes everywhere on the surface S. Hence, the flux through the surface S vanishes, and by Gauss's theorem the net charge inside S must vanish. Since S bounds an arbitrary volume, the net charge must vanish in any volume* whatsoever, and hence must vanish everywhere inside the conductor. All the charge on a conductor must therefore reside on its surface.

The flux through a tube of force is constant along its length.

Figure 54 represents a section of an infinitesimal tube of force with flux $\mathcal{E}_1\,dA_1$ lines at one point and $\mathcal{E}_2\,dA_2$ lines at another. Apply Gauss's theorem to the surface composed of the areas dA_1, dA_2, and the walls of

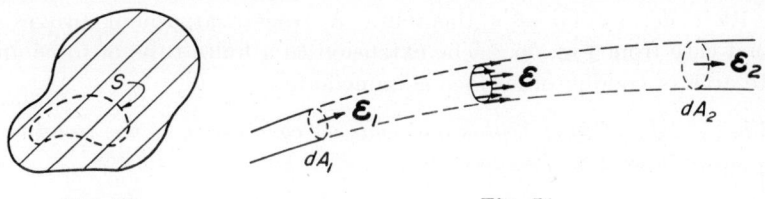

Fig. 53. Fig. 54.

the tube of force connecting these areas. By the definition of a tube of force, the walls of the tube are generated by lines of force; consequently, no lines of force pass into or out of the surface through these walls. $\mathcal{E}_2\,dA_2$ lines pass out at the right end, and $\mathcal{E}_1\,dA_1$ lines pass in at the left end. Since the charge within the surface is zero, the *net number of lines passing outward* must be zero. Hence, we must have $\mathcal{E}_1\,dA_1 = \mathcal{E}_2\,dA_2$. This equation proves the statement for any infinitesimal tube. Since a finite tube can be considered as made up of infinitesimal tubes, we see that the statement must be true also for any finite tube.

When a tube of force begins on a conductor, the flux in the tube equals $4\pi \times 10^{-7} c^2$ times the positive charge at its end; when it terminates on a conductor, the flux in the tube equals $4\pi \times 10^{-7} c^2$ times the absolute magnitude of the negative charge at its end.

These cases are illustrated in Figs. 55 and 56 for infinitesimal tubes. In Fig. 55, apply Gauss's theorem to the surface consisting of the area dA, the walls of the tube between dA and the conductor, and the dotted

---

* To be precise, S must enclose a volume of size large compared to atomic dimensions. It is certainly not true that there is no net charge in a volume large enough to contain just a single nucleus. It is not Gauss's theorem that breaks down when the volume is very small, but rather the statement that the electric field vanishes everywhere inside a conductor. Certainly, large local electric fields exist between the nuclei and the electrons. But the average $\mathcal{E}_n$, averaged over an element of area dS (large compared with atomic dimensions) must be zero, since there is no average motion of electrons in a conductor in electrostatic equilibrium. It is really such an average field that we are talking about in macroscopic electrostatics.

surface inside the conductor. No lines pass through the walls of the tube of force, and no field exists within the conductor. Hence, lines pass out of this surface only through dA, the number being $\mathcal{E}\,dA$, which equals

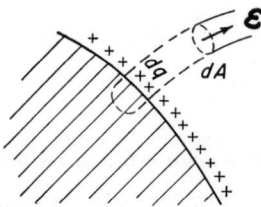

Fig. 55. Tube begins at positive charge dq.

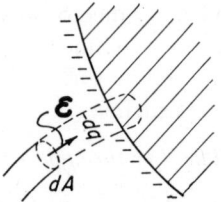

Fig. 56. Tube ends on negative charge $-dq$.

$4\pi \times 10^{-7} c^2\, dq$, by Gauss's theorem. A similar argument proves the second case from Fig. 56. The extension to a finite tube of force and a finite area of conductor surface is immediate.

When a tube of force begins and ends on conductors, it has equal and opposite charges on its two ends.

This theorem follows directly from the previous one and from the fact that the flux in a tube of force is constant along its length.

PROBLEMS

1. Two concentric, thin, metallic spherical shells of radii R_1 and R_2 ($R_1 < R_2$) bear charges Q_1 and Q_2 distributed with spherical symmetry. Using Gauss's theorem, show that
    (a) the electric intensity at radius $r < R_1$ is zero;
    (b) the electric intensity at radius r between R_1 and R_2 is $10^{-7} c^2\, Q_1/r^2$;
    (c) the electric intensity at radius $r > R_2$ is $10^{-7} c^2\, (Q_1 + Q_2)/r^2$.

2. For the system of charges in Prob. 1, show that the potential, relative to a zero at infinity, is
    (a) $10^{-7} c^2\, (Q_1 + Q_2)/r$ for $r > R_2$;
    (b) $10^{-7} c^2\, [Q_1/r + Q_2/R_2]$ for $R_2 > r > R_1$;
    (c) $10^{-7} c^2\, [Q_1/R_1 + Q_2/R_2]$ for $r < R_1$.

3. For the system of charges of Prob. 1, find the charge per unit area on the inner and outer surfaces of each spherical shell. Find the answers in the two different ways given below, and check.
    (a) Use the total charge on each shell, the area of the shell, and the theorem that equal and opposite charges reside at the two ends of a line of force.
    (b) Use the fact that the electric intensity just outside a conductor is $4\pi \times 10^{-7} c^2$ times the charge per unit area. From the electric intensities in Prob. 1, compute the values of the charge per unit area.

4. Charge is *uniformly* distributed throughout the interior of a non-conducting sphere of radius R, the *total* charge being Q. Using Gauss's theorem, show that
    (a) the electric intensity at radius $r > R$ is $10^{-7} c^2\, Q/r^2$;
    (b) the electric intensity at radius $r < R$ is $10^{-7} c^2\, Qr/R^3$.

5. Show that the electric intensity at distance r from an infinite straight fine wire with linear charge density q, in coulombs per meter length, is $2\pi \times 10^{-7} c^2\, q/r$.

CHAPTER 32

CONDENSERS

The most familiar device whose action is entirely electrostatic is the *condenser*, of which a considerable number occur in every radio set or electronic circuit. In such applications, current flows into the terminals of the condenser but does not flow *through* the condenser—it merely piles up as charge on the plates. The relation between the charge on the plates and the DP between the plates is governed by the laws of electrostatics, the charge being at rest. The ratio between the magnitude of charge on either plate and the DP is a constant, called the *capacitance* of the condenser. This capacitance we shall learn how to compute. In more advanced study of electricity, it will be found that many circuit elements that are not actually called condensers behave like condensers and that a consideration of their capacitance is necessary to an understanding of their performance. One example of such a circuit element is the cable discussed in Sec. 1; others are alternating-current power lines, telephone lines, and the metallic elements of any vacuum tube. Although we shall not discuss these other examples in detail in this text, we point them out to emphasize the importance of a basic understanding of condenser action.

1. CAPACITANCE OF A CYLINDRICAL CONDENSER

As a first example, we shall consider a concentric cable and the effect of its capacitance (to be defined on p. 836) on transoceanic telegraphy and telephony. We choose this introductory example because it is one of the earliest instances of impact of a purely electrostatic phenomenon, *capacitance*, on what otherwise should have been purely an advance in the use of current electricity.

The cable (Fig. 1) consists of a conductor inside a cylindrical lead and steel protecting sheath which is in intimate contact with conducting sea water and hence effectively grounded. The essential ideas of telegraphy are the following: A battery is attached at one end of the cable, as shown in Fig. 1, so that when the key is closed the conductor is raised to a certain potential relative to the grounded shield. Because of this potential, a small current (a *current* is a flow of electric charge) passes through the conductor and through the sensitive detecting element, denoted by V (for voltmeter), at the other end. When the key is released, the current stops flowing and the conductor returns to ground potential, since it is connected to ground through the instrument V. Thus, telegraphic signaling takes place.

This scheme presents difficulties where the cable is very long, as in transoceanic work. An appreciable time elapses after the key is closed and current starts into the conductor before the meter registers current at the other end, and an appreciable time elapses after the key is opened before the meter stops registering current. The reason for this behavior is that appreciable time is required merely to charge up the conductor. Current is a flow of charge, and the current at first charges the conductor and is not available to pass through the meter V. Only as the conductor is charged up does the potential appear at the other end. Correspondingly, after the key is opened, the charge on the conductor

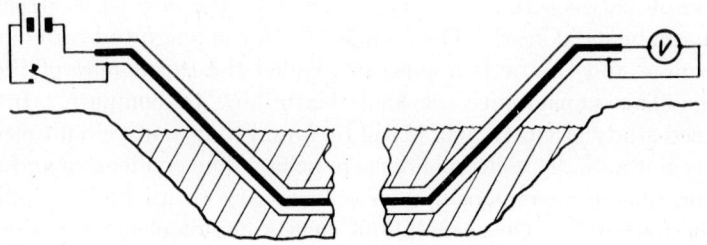

Fig. 1. An underwater telegraph cable.

must flow out through the meter, and only as the conductor is discharged does the potential at V drop to zero.

We cannot go further here into the theory of this type of communication. Suffice it to say that the delayed response of the simple type of cable shown in Fig. 1 renders transoceanic telegraphic communication sluggish and telephonic communication impossible, since in the latter application the current must vary with the high frequency of sound. However, since the electrical *capacitance* of the cable plays a fundamental role in communication theory, we shall define and learn how to compute this capacitance.

We represent the cable by the two long concentric cylindrical conductors illustrated in cross section in Fig. 2, the inner conductor having radius R_1 and the outer grounded conductor, radius R_2. We wish to determine the charge (per meter length) that must be placed on the inner conductor in order to raise it to a potential V above the potential of the outer conductor. If the inner conductor is to be raised to a positive potential, it must acquire a positive charge in order that lines of force will begin on it and go out to the outer conductor. We denote the positive charge per meter length by $+q$. The outer conductor must acquire an equal and opposite charge $-q$ per meter length, since equal and opposite charges lie at the two ends of each tube of force.

By symmetry, the charges must be distributed uniformly around the conductors, and the lines of force must point radially outward. For the moment we shall assume that there is air between the inner conductor and the sheath though in practice there is some insulating dielectric such as rubber. The effect of this dielectric will be discussed in Sec. 4.

In order to compute the difference of potential between the cylinders, we must find the field strength $\mathcal{E}$ as a function of radius R. This we shall do by considering a wedge-shaped tube of force having a small angle $d\theta$ radians between its faces as indicated in Fig. 2, and of length dl along the cable. This tube has at its inner end an amount of charge that equals $q\,dl$ times the ratio of $d\theta$ to the number 2π of radians in a circle. That is, a charge

$$dQ = q\,dl\,d\theta/2\pi$$

must lie at the inner end of this tube of force, with an equal and opposite negative charge at the outer end. The cross-sectional area of the tube, at radius R, equals the width $R\,d\theta$ times the length dl. That is, $dA = R\,dl\,d\theta$. If $\mathcal{E}$ is the field strength at radius R, the flux in the tube is

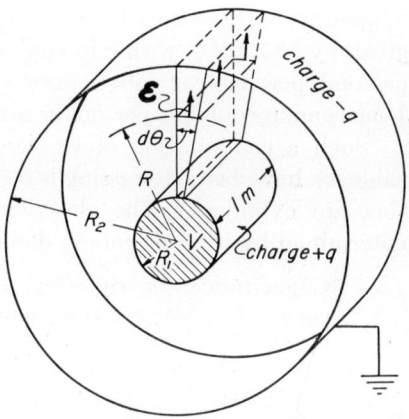

Fig. 2. A 1-meter length of a cylindrical condenser, with charge q.

$$\mathcal{E}\,dA = \mathcal{E}R\,dl\,d\theta.$$

This flux is constant along the tube, and by (16), p. 815, is $4\pi \cdot 10^{-7}c^2$ times the charge at the end of the tube. That is,

$$\mathcal{E}\,dA = \mathcal{E}R\,dl\,d\theta = 4\pi \cdot 10^{-7}c^2\,dQ = 4\pi \cdot 10^{-7}c^2\,q\,dl\,d\theta/2\pi = 2 \cdot 10^{-7}c^2\,q\,dl\,d\theta.$$

Therefore, $$\mathcal{E}R = 2 \cdot 10^{-7}c^2\,q,$$

and $$\mathcal{E} = 2 \cdot 10^{-7}c^2\,q/R. \qquad (1)$$

Equation (1) gives the field strength at any radius R for charges $\pm q$ in coul per m length of the conductors. It will be noticed that the field strength is proportional to q, varies inversely with R, and does not depend on the radii of the conductors. However, the difference of potential between the conductors, which, by (18), p. 816, is the integral of $\mathcal{E}\,dR$ from R_1 to R_2, does depend very much on these radii. This difference of potential is

$$V = \int_{R_1}^{R_2} \varepsilon\, dR = \int_{R_1}^{R_2} 2\cdot 10^{-7} c^2 \frac{q}{R}\, dR = 2\cdot 10^{-7} c^2\, q\, \log_e R \Big]_{R_1}^{R_2}$$

$$= 2\cdot 10^{-7} c^2\, q\, [\log_e R_2 - \log_e R_1],$$

or $\qquad V = 2\cdot 10^{-7} c^2\, q\, \log_e(R_2/R_1).$ \hfill (2)

Equation (2) gives the potential, in volts, to which the conductor of a cable is raised, relative to the sheath, by charge q, in coulombs per meter length. Alternatively, it gives the charge per meter length that must be supplied if the potential is to be raised to V in volts. It will be noticed that charge is proportional to potential. Thus, if $R_2/R_1 = 2.72$, which happens to be e, so that $\log_e 2.72 = 1$, we find that the value of V in volts is given by $18 \times 10^9\, q$, with q in coul/m. In this case, a charge of 1 microcoulomb per meter of cable causes a difference of potential of 18,000 volts; 1 micromicrocoulomb per meter a DP of 0.018 volt.

Such a combination of two conductors is called a *condenser*. The cable we have been discussing is a *cylindrical condenser*, since the conductors are cylinders. The electrical characteristics of a condenser are determined by its *capacitance*, defined as follows:

Capacitance (or capacity) between two conductors. The capacitance between two conductors is equal to the ratio of the charge placed on either conductor to the resulting potential difference, provided the conductors have received equal and opposite charges.*

The capacitance is a measure of the ability of the conductors to store up charge when a potential difference is produced, for instance by a battery. Capacitance $C = Q/V$, the amount of charge per volt of potential difference. Capacitance is measured in coulombs per volt, and the unit, 1 coulomb/volt, is given the name *farad*† (f). In terms of the mechanical units, we find that

$$1\,\text{f} = 1\,\text{coul/v} = 1\,\text{sec}^2/\text{m}. \tag{3}$$

If a cable is of length l, in meters, and has charge q, in coulombs per meter length, its whole charge will be $Q = ql$, and according to (2) its capacitance will be

$$C = \frac{Q}{V} = \frac{ql}{V} = \frac{l}{2\cdot 10^{-7} c^2 \log_e(R_2/R_1)}, \tag{4}$$

in farads with c in m/sec.

Even for a cable crossing the ocean, this capacitance is a small fraction of a farad. The capacitances of all ordinary condensers are always very

---

* A.I.E.E. definition 05.15.060.

† After Michael Faraday (1791–1867), director of the laboratory of the Royal Institution, London, who conceived the idea of representing an electrostatic field by tubes of force and formulated its properties in terms of them, and who discovered electromagnetic induction and the laws of electrolysis.

Sec. 1] CAPACITANCE OF A CYLINDRICAL CONDENSER 837

small fractions of a farad; in other words, a DP of 1 volt stores only a very small fraction of a coulomb. Hence, capacitances are ordinarily specified in *microfarads* (μf) or *micromicrofarads* ($\mu\mu$f):

$$1\ \mu\text{f} = 10^{-6}\ \text{farad} = 1\ \mu\text{coul/volt},$$

$$1\ \mu\mu\text{f} = 10^{-12}\ \text{farad} = 1\ \mu\mu\text{coul/volt}.$$

Thus, the cable with $R_2/R_1 = 2.72$ discussed above will store 1 $\mu\mu$coul per meter length for a DP of 0.018 volt, so that its capacitance per meter length is

$$\frac{1\ \mu\mu\text{coul/m}}{0.018\ \text{volt}} = 55.5\ \mu\mu\text{f/m}.$$

PROBLEMS

1. A condenser has a capacitance of 8 μf. What potential is necessary to charge it to 1600 μcoul? Ans: 200 v.

2. A condenser has a capacitance of 50 $\mu\mu$f. What DP is necessary to give the plates equal and opposite charges of 1 μcoul?

3. A condenser consists of two large metal plates 1 mm apart in air. When it is connected to a 1000-volt battery, each plate becomes charged with 1 μcoul. What is its capacitance in $\mu\mu$f? Ans: 1000 $\mu\mu$f.

4. The plates of a condenser become charged with 0.6 μcoul when a DP of 1200 v is applied. What is the capacitance of the condenser in $\mu\mu$f?

NOTE: The student is reminded that there are three convenient ways of finding logarithms to the base e: first, by using a log-log slide rule; second, by using a table of natural logarithms; third, by using the relation $\log_e N = \log_e 10 \log_{10} N = 2.3026 \log_{10} N$.

5. Find the capacitance per meter length of two concentric cylinders of radii 0.5 cm and 1.0 cm in air. Ans: 80.2 $\mu\mu$f/m.

6. Find the capacitance per meter length of two concentric cylinders of radii 0.5 cm and 2.0 cm in air.

7. The cylinders of Prob. 5 are charged to a DP of 5000 v. Find (a) the charge per meter length; (b) the maximum electric intensity between the cylinders; (c) the minimum electric intensity between the cylinders; (d) the average electric intensity between the cylinders (see the statement in italics on p. 816).
Ans: (a) 0.401 μcoul/m; (b) 14.4×10^5 v/m; (c) 7.22×10^5 v/m; (d) 10×10^5 v/m.

8. The cylinders of Prob. 6 are charged to a DP of 5000 v. Find the same quantities as in Prob. 7.

9. Verify that the left and right sides of equation (1) have the same dimensions. Do the same for equations (2) and (4).

2. THE SPHERICAL CONDENSER

The next example we shall consider is the *spherical condenser*, in which the conductors are spheres. We shall first compute the formula for the capacitance and then give an example of the use of the formula in connection with modern high-voltage 'atom smashers.'

Figure 3 shows two concentric spheres, the inner sphere of radius R_1, in meters, and the outer of radius R_2, in meters, with air or vacuum between. The inner sphere is raised to potential V, in volts, above the potential of the outer grounded sphere. The inner and outer spheres have equal and opposite charges $\pm Q$, in coulombs. By symmetry, the lines of force run radially outward and the charges are uniformly distributed over the surface of the spheres. Thus, since the total solid angle in a sphere is 4π steradians, the charge in any small solid angle $d\omega$ is

$$dq = Q\, d\omega/4\pi.$$

Let the tube of force shown in Fig. 3 subtend a solid angle $d\omega$ and hence begin and end on the charge dq given in the above equation. The area of the tube at radius R is $R^2\, d\omega$. If the field strength is $\mathcal{E}$ at radius R, the strength of the tube is $\mathcal{E}R^2\, d\omega$, and this, by (16), p. 815, must equal $4\pi \cdot 10^{-7} c^2\, dq$. That is,

$$\mathcal{E}R^2\, d\omega = 4\pi \cdot 10^{-7} c^2\, dq$$
$$= 4\pi \cdot 10^{-7} c^2\, Q\, d\omega/4\pi = 10^{-7} c^2\, Q\, d\omega$$

Therefore, $\qquad \mathcal{E}R^2 = 10^{-7} c^2\, Q$

and $\qquad \mathcal{E} = 10^{-7} c^2\, Q/R^2. \qquad (5)$

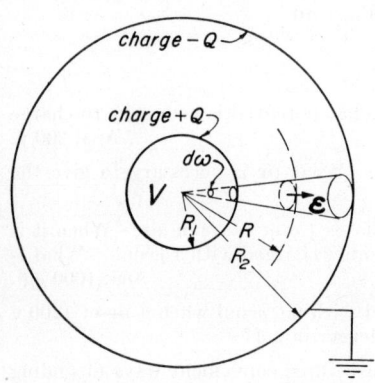

Fig. 3. A spherical condenser.

The field strength between the conductors is the same as the field strength from a point charge Q at the center of the sphere.

Knowing the field strength, we can easily compute the difference of potential between the spheres by integrating the field strength along a line of force:

$$V = \int_{R_1}^{R_2} \mathcal{E}\, dR = 10^{-7} c^2 \int_{R_1}^{R_2} \frac{Q}{R^2}\, dR = -10^{-7} c^2 \frac{Q}{R}\bigg]_{R_1}^{R_2}$$

or $\qquad V = 10^{-7} c^2\, Q \left[\dfrac{1}{R_1} - \dfrac{1}{R_2}\right] = 10^{-7} c^2\, Q\, \dfrac{R_2 - R_1}{R_1 R_2}. \qquad (6)$

Hence, $\qquad Q = \dfrac{V}{10^{-7} c^2} \dfrac{R_1 R_2}{R_2 - R_1}, \qquad (7)$

and the capacitance, by definition, is

$$C = \frac{Q}{V} = \frac{1}{10^{-7} c^2} \frac{R_1 R_2}{R_2 - R_1}, \qquad (8)$$

in farads when c is in m/sec.

It is interesting to see how the capacitance changes as the size of the outer sphere changes. If $R_1 = 9$ cm $= 9 \times 10^{-2}$ m and $R_2 = 18$ cm $= 18 \times 10^{-2}$ m, then $C = 20$ $\mu\mu$f. If now R_2 be decreased to 10 cm, keeping $R_1 = 9$ cm, $C = 100$ $\mu\mu$f. If R_2 be decreased to 9.1 cm, leaving 1 mm air gap, C becomes 910 $\mu\mu$f. If R_2 be further decreased to 9.01 cm, leaving only 0.1 mm air gap, C is increased to 9010 μμf. *The capacitance increases rapidly as the air gap decreases.* On the other hand, if R_2 be increased to 109 cm, keeping $R_1 = 9$ cm, C is decreased to 10.9 μμf. For $R_2 = 1009$ cm, $C = 10.09$ μμf; and as $R_2 \to \infty$, $C \to 10$ μμf. If we go back to (6), we have

$$V = 10^{-7} c^2 \, Q \left[\frac{1}{R_1} - \frac{1}{R_2} \right],$$

and for $R_2 = \infty$, $V = 10^{-7} c^2 \, Q/R_1$ and $C = Q/V = R_1/10^{-7} c^2$, in farads. For $R_1 = 9$ cm $= 9 \times 10^{-2}$ m, this expression gives $C = 10^{-11}$ f $= 10$ μμf, as we found above. When $R_2 = \infty$, we have only one conductor left, and to talk about its capacitance means imagining a second conductor very far away at the other end of the lines of force. With this convention we can say that the capacitance of an isolated sphere of radius R_1, in meters, is

$$C = R_1/10^{-7} c^2, \quad \text{in farads.}$$

An important device for which the formula for the capacitance of a spherical condenser is useful is the Van de Graaff electrostatic generator. This machine, whose principle is illustrated in Fig. 4, represents a fundamental advance in the art of generating high electrostatic potentials (several millions of volts). Though the action of this machine depends only on basic principles that had been known since the early nineteenth century, it was not until 1931 that R. J. Van de Graaff, working at Princeton, developed the device.

A belt is driven by a motor on the floor and passes over an idler pulley inside a large metal sphere carried on insulating supports well away from the walls of the room. The metal idler pulley is connected to the metal sphere. Van de Graaff's first design contemplated the use of a belt composed of small squares of metal insulated from each other. Although later this construction was found unnecessary and was abandoned in favor of a smooth silk or paper belt, it will be easier to explain the principle of operation if we assume for the moment that the belt is composed of such insulated metal squares.

The left side of the belt in Fig. 4 runs upward at high speed. At the bottom of the belt are a set of fingers that contact the metal squares as

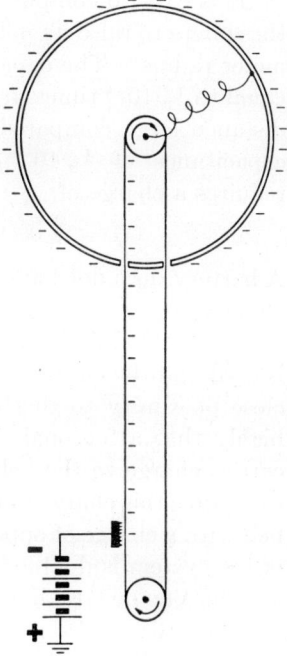

Fig. 4. Schematic diagram of the Van de Graaff electrostatic generator. An actual generator is shown in Fig. 1 of Chap. 34.

they go past. The fingers are kept charged negatively, say by a 1000-volt storage battery. Each metal square acquires a small negative charge which it carries upward into the sphere. When the metal square touches the idler pulley, which is connected to the sphere, all the charge leaves the square and goes to the outside of the sphere, since sphere, pulley, and metal square constitute a single conductor, and all the charge must go to the very outside of this conductor. Thus, the sphere continues to receive more and more charge and to build up to a higher and higher potential, which is limited only by dielectric breakdown when a spark jumps through the air or along the belt to ground.

It is easy to compute the amount of charge that must be supplied to the sphere to raise its potential to, say, $-3{,}000{,}000$ volts for a sphere of 1-meter radius. The capacitance of the sphere in farads is approximately equal to $\frac{1}{9} \cdot 10^{-9}$ times its radius in meters if the walls of the room are at a distance large compared to the radius. For a radius of 1 m, this is a capacitance of $\frac{1}{9} \cdot 10^{-3}$ μf. To raise the potential to -3×10^6 volts requires a charge of

$$Q = CV = (\tfrac{1}{9} \cdot 10^{-3}) \times (-3 \times 10^6) = -333 \ \mu\text{coul}.$$

A battery does not have to work very hard to supply this relatively tiny charge.

In practical designs of this electrostatic generator, a silk or paper belt is used and the charge is 'sprayed' on by using a series of sharp points in close proximity to the belt at the bottom. The points are charged so highly that a 'coronal' discharge takes place which ionizes the air and carries charge to the belt. Satisfactory methods have been worked out to remove this charge in the sphere and even to charge the down-traveling belt with a charge of opposite sign so that the charge-transferring capacity of the system is doubled.

The Van de Graaff generator will work equally well on either polarity, charging the sphere positively or negatively according to the sign of the charge sprayed on the upgoing belt.

The potentials obtained with this generator exceed by a large margin any other constant potentials obtainable in the laboratory. The associated electric fields are capable of giving very high energy to electrons or nuclear ions accelerated along vacuum tubes connected between the sphere and ground. In particular, extremely penetrating X rays can be obtained by connecting an X-ray tube between the sphere and ground.

PROBLEMS

1. Find the capacitance of two concentric spheres of radii 10 cm and 15 cm in air. Ans: 33.3 $\mu\mu$f.

2. Find the capacitance of two concentric spheres of radii 8 cm and 13 cm in air.

3. The spheres of Prob. 1 are charged to a DP of 80,000 v. Find (a) the charge on each sphere; (b) the maximum electric intensity between the spheres; (c) the minimum electric intensity between the spheres; (d) the average electric intensity between the spheres (see statement in italics on p. 816).

Ans: (a) 2.67 μcoul; (b) 2.40×10⁶ v/m; (c) 1.07×10⁶ v/m; (d) 1.60×10⁶ v/m.

4. The spheres of Prob. 2 are charged to a DP of 80,000 v. Find the same quantities as in Prob. 3.

5. A spherical condenser is formed from two concentric spheres of thin metal, one 0.5 m in radius, the other 1 m. The outer sphere is grounded, the inner charged with +3 μcoul. Find the electric intensity and the potential relative to ground at points (a) 0.2 m from the center, (b) just outside the inner sphere, (c) 0.8 m from the center, (d) just inside the outer sphere. Ans: (a) 0 v/m, 27,000 v; (b) 108,000 v/m, 27,000 v; (c) 42,200 v/m, 6750 v; (d) 27,000 v/m, 0 v.

6. Show that the contribution to the potential at a point at radius R from the center of a sphere of radius r, arising from a charge Q uniformly distributed on the surface of the sphere, is

$$10^{-7}c^2 Q/R^2 \quad \text{if} \quad R > r$$
$$10^{-7}c^2 Q/r^2 \quad \text{if} \quad R < r.$$

7. Verify the dimensional correctness of equations (7) and (8).

3. THE PARALLEL-PLATE CONDENSER

As a final and very important example of capacitance, we shall consider the *parallel-plate condenser*. Figure 5 shows two plane plates, each of area A, in m², separated by distance d, in m, charged with equal and

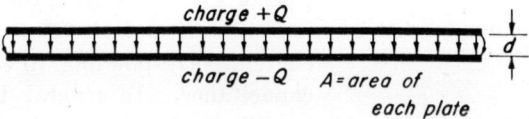

Fig. 5. Parallel-plate condenser.

opposite charges $\pm Q$. The separation d is assumed to be small compared with the linear dimensions of the plates. Under these conditions, the charges are almost entirely on the inside surfaces of the plates, and, except near the edges, the lines of force go perpendicularly from one plate to the other as in Fig. 5.

For plates of size large compared with the separation d, edge effects are negligible, and the charge per m² on each plate is $\pm Q/A$. Then, by (16) p. 815, a tube of force of area dA in cross section has flux $4\pi \cdot 10^{-7}c^2 (Q/A) dA$. Since the flux in this tube is, by definition, the field intensity $\mathcal{E}$ times the area dA, we have

$$\mathcal{E} \, dA = 4\pi \cdot 10^{-7}c^2 (Q/A) \, dA,$$

or
$$\mathcal{E} = 4\pi \cdot 10^{-7}c^2 \, Q/A. \tag{9}$$

Under the conditions above, *the electric field between two parallel plates equals $36\pi \times 10^9$ times the charge density in coul/m² on either plate, independent of the separation of the plates.*

The difference of potential between the plates is

$$V = \mathcal{E}d = \frac{4\pi \cdot 10^{-7} c^2 \, Qd}{A}. \tag{10}$$

Hence, the capacitance of the condenser formed by these plates is

$$C = \frac{Q}{V} = \frac{A}{4\pi \cdot 10^{-7} c^2 \, d}. \tag{11}$$

In this formula, C is in farads when A is in m², d in m, and c in m/sec.

Parallel-plate condensers are frequently made with a stack of plates connected alternately, as in the familiar condensers of variable capacitance used in radio sets. The plates are stacked as in Fig. 6. With the exception of the end plates, each plate carries charges on both sides, at the ends of the lines of force going to both adjoining plates. The condenser of Fig. 6, which has five sets of lines of force, has as much positive and negative charge as five condensers like that of Fig. 5. Hence, for the same potential difference it has five times the charge, corresponding to five times the capacitance. In general, if a condenser has N plates, there are $N-1$ sets of lines of force and the capacitance is $N-1$ times (11), or

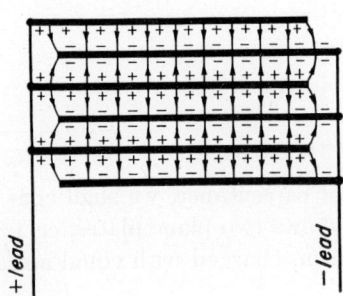

Fig. 6. Illustrating a 6-plate condenser.

$$C = \frac{(N-1) \, A}{4\pi \cdot 10^{-7} c^2 \, d}. \tag{12}$$

In the variable tuning condenser used in radios, the capacitance is varied by moving one mesh of plates into and out of the other mesh, so that the area A of plates facing each other is varied.

PROBLEMS

1. A condenser is made of two parallel plates 15 cm square and 0.2 cm apart in air.
  (a) What is its capacitance in farads and in $\mu\mu$f?
  (b) What is the charge on each plate when the potential difference is 90 volts?
  Ans: (a) 9.97×10^{-11} f, 99.7 $\mu\mu$f; (b) 8.97×10^{-9} coul.

2. A condenser is made of two parallel plates 12 cm square and 1 mm apart in air.
  (a) What is its capacitance in farads and in $\mu\mu$f?
  (b) What is the charge on each plate when the DP is 150 v?

3. What is the maximum capacitance of a radio tuning condenser consisting of 13 fixed plates and 12 movable plates if the effective area of each plate in the interleaved position is 30 cm² and the air gap between fixed and movable plates is 1.8 mm? Express your answer in $\mu\mu$f. Ans: 354 $\mu\mu$f.

4. What is the maximum capacitance of a radio tuning condenser consisting of 11 fixed plates and 11 movable plates if the effective area of each plate in the interleaved position is 22 cm² and the air gaps between fixed and movable plates are 1.5 mm? Express your answer in $\mu\mu f$.

5. The condenser of Prob. 3 is charged with a 144-v battery when it has its maximum capacitance. The battery is disconnected, leaving the condenser charged. The knob is then turned to reduce the effective area to 10 cm². What then is the charge on the condenser and its DP?   Ans: 51,000 $\mu\mu$coul; 432 v.

6. The condenser of Prob. 4 is charged with a 120-v battery when it has its maximum capacitance. The battery is disconnected, leaving the condenser charged. The knob is then turned to reduce the effective area to 5.5 cm². What then is the charge on the condenser and its DP?

7. In order to verify that the parallel-plate condenser formula gives approximate values for curved surfaces when the distance between the surfaces is small compared with the radius of curvature, consider a cylindrical condenser like that in Fig. 2, with $R_1 = 1.95$ cm, $R_2 = 2.05$ cm. Compare the capacitance per m length given by the accurate formula (4) with that obtained from the parallel-plate formula with $d = 1$ mm and $A = 0.04 \pi$ m², the area at mean radius.
   Ans: Parallel-plate formula gives value too large by 0.021%.

8. In order to verify that the parallel-plate condenser formula gives approximate values for curved surfaces when the distance between the surfaces is small compared with the radius of curvature, consider a spherical condenser like that in Fig. 3, with $R_1 = 19.5$ cm, $R_2 = 20.5$ cm. Compare the capacitance given by the exact formula (8) with that obtained from the parallel-plate formula with $d = 1$ cm and $A = 1600 \pi$ cm², the area at mean radius.

4. DIELECTRIC CONSTANT

The discussion of the previous sections assumed that there was air or vacuum between the plates of the condenser. This condition obtains in the case of variable radio tuning condensers, the sphere in the Van de Graaff generator, and the condenser formed by a pair of overhead electric wires in an electrical power distribution system. But in many other cases some insulator other than air fills the space between the plates. Fixed radio condensers use mica or paraffined paper; underground or underwater cables have a rubber compound between the conductor and the sheath or between the two conductors in a two-wire cable; large high-voltage condensers are made with plates of metal foil placed on opposite sides of a sheet of glass.

The reason for using such substances between the plates is not solely *mechanical* convenience. A dielectric between the plates improves the condenser *electrically* in two ways: it increases the capacitance and it permits the use of higher voltages without danger of breakdown or flash-over between the plates. The question of breakdown is discussed in Sec. 7 under the heading *Dielectric Strength*. We turn here to an explanation of the increase in capacitance.

Consider first the effect of inserting a sheet of insulating material that almost completely fills the space between the plates of a plane-plate condenser. Let Fig. 7(a) represent a small section of the condenser with the plates uncharged. By smoothing out the atomic irregularities, we can imagine the dielectric to be composed of uniform distributions of positive and negative charges as indicated. When the condenser plates are charged, as in (b), the dielectric becomes *polarized* as discussed on p. 794. The electrons are not free to leave their own nuclei, but on the

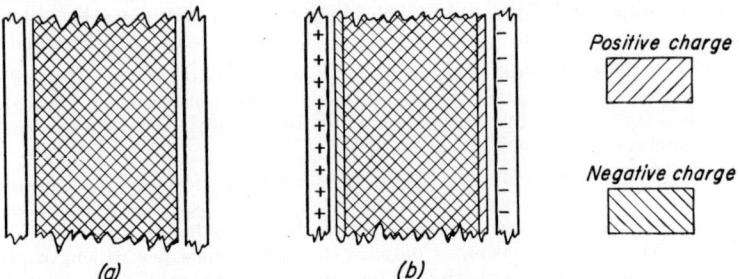

Fig. 7. Illustrating the relative displacement of positive and negative charge when a dielectric becomes polarized.

average there is a slight shift of the negative charge toward the positive plate. This shift results in a very slight relative displacement of the smoothed-out negative- and positive-charge distributions as indicated schematically in Fig. 7(b).

Since the positive and negative charge distributions in the center of the dielectric still neutralize each other, the net effect of this polarization is to leave an unneutralized layer of negative charge on the surface of the dielectric near the positively charged plate and a layer of positive charge near the negatively charged plate, as in Fig. 8. The charges on the plates are called *free charges*, and those on the dielectric surface, *bound charges*, for obvious reasons.

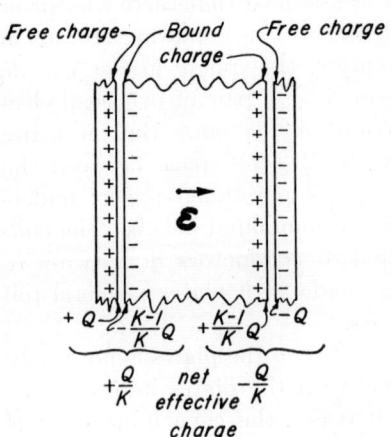

Fig. 8. Bound and free charges for a dielectric constant K.

The negative charge on the dielectric surface is usually almost, but not quite, as large as the positive charge on the plate. Since the dielectric is supposed to be in contact with the plate, these two layers of charge set up the same fields as a single layer with positive charge reduced to a fraction of $+Q$, say to $+Q/K$ (K varies from 2 to 8 for practical condenser dielectrics). As indicated in Fig. 8, the amount of bound charge is $-[(K-1)/K]\,Q$, so that the sum of free and bound charges becomes $+Q/K$:

$$+Q - \frac{K-1}{K} Q = \left(1 - \frac{K-1}{K}\right) Q = +\frac{1}{K} Q.$$

For example, if $K=5$, the bound charge is $-\frac{4}{5} Q$ and the net effective charge is $\frac{1}{5} Q$.

Because of the presence of the dielectric, the net effective charge on each plate is reduced by a factor K. Hence the electric field between the plates and the difference of potential between the plates are also reduced by the factor K, so that in place of (9) and (10) we have

$$\mathcal{E} = \frac{4\pi \cdot 10^{-7} c^2 \, Q}{KA}, \quad V = \frac{4\pi \cdot 10^{-7} c^2 \, Qd}{KA}. \tag{13}$$

The capacitance is increased by a factor K to

$$C = \frac{Q}{V} = \frac{KA}{4\pi \cdot 10^{-7} c^2 \, d}. \tag{14}$$

For an N-plate condenser, as in Fig. 6, with dielectric between all pairs of plates, the capacitance becomes

$$C = \frac{K(N-1)A}{4\pi \cdot 10^{-7} c^2 \, d}. \tag{15}$$

The constant K, which is called the *dielectric constant* or *specific inductive capacity*, is a function of the dielectric material. For a given kind of material it has a given fixed value.

> The **dielectric constant** of a material is the ratio of the capacitance of a condenser with the material between the plates to the capacitance with vacuum between the plates. It is dimensionless in the system of units we are using.

For a given difference of potential, with the dielectric the plates will store K times as much charge as without the dielectric. The reference here is to free charge—the charge that flows through the wires to the plates if they are connected to the two poles of a battery maintaining a given potential difference.

Values of the dielectric constant K for some of the dielectrics of interest are given in Table I. Values are also given for certain gases. It is not strictly true, as we have assumed so far, that the capacitance of an air condenser is the same as that of the condenser evacuated. But the increase of capacitance arising from the polarization of the air is only 6 parts in 10,000, a change that is not of importance for most purposes and that requires apparatus of high precision to detect experimentally.

So far, we have discussed the effect of polarization on the field between parallel plates only. However, if the space between plates of any shape be completely filled with a dielectric, the capacitance of the resulting condenser is increased by a factor of K—the same K as given in Table I,

TABLE I
Typical Values of Dielectric Constant and Dielectric Strength

	K	Dielectric strength (kv/cm)
Insulator porcelains...............	6	100–200
Pyrex glass.......................	4.8	130
Other glasses.....................	5–10	200–400
Rubber, vulcanized................	3.0	160–500
Hard rubber, commercial..........	3.1	100–500
Vulcanized fiber..................	5	90–160
Phenolic insulating materials.......	4.5–7.5	90–450
Transformer oils..................	2.1	50–150
Mica.............................	4.5–7.5	250–2000
Paraffined paper..................	2	400–600
Shellac...........................	2.7–3.7	350
Nitrocellulose plastics.............	6–12	100–400
Dry air at 1 atm..................	1.0006	30
Carbon dioxide at 1 atm..........	1.0010	28

no matter what the shape of the plates. This increase arises from the fact that the polarization of the dielectric along any tube of force results in the appearance of bound charges at the ends of the tube, as in Fig. 9. The result is that the net effective charges, the field strength at any point, and the difference of potential are all reduced by the factor K.

Thus, the formulas (4) and (8) for the capacitances of cylindrical and spherical condensers become, respectively,

$$C = \frac{Kl}{2\cdot 10^{-7} c^2 \log_e(R_2/R_1)} \quad (16)$$

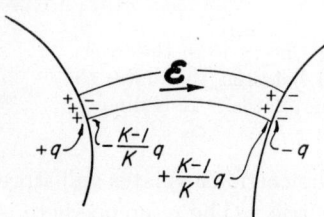

Fig. 9. Bound charges appear at the ends of every tube of force in a dielectric material.

and

$$C = \frac{K R_1 R_2}{10^{-7} c^2 (R_2 - R_1)} \quad (17)$$

when a dielectric of constant K is between the plates.

The fact that a dielectric increases the capacitance of a condenser is usually, but not always, desirable. In radio condensers, where the aim is to store charge in as small a space as possible, the increase is desirable. In telephone and power cables, where storage of charge is wasteful and leads to sluggish operation, the increase is undesirable.

PROBLEMS

1. A 100-plate condenser has plates 40 cm × 30 cm separated by glass plates 3 mm thick of dielectric constant 7.0. Find the capacitance in μf. Ans: 0.246 μf.

2. A condenser is formed from 50 parallel metal plates 20 cm × 20 cm separated by glass sheets ($K = 7.0$) 1.5 mm thick. What is its capacitance in μf?

3. A condenser with air dielectric ($K = 1.00$) is charged by connecting it across a battery. A meter measures the charge that flows to one of the condenser plates as 150 µcoul. Without disconnecting the battery, the condenser is completely immersed in an insulating oil, and an *additional* charge of 225 µcoul flows to the plate. What is the dielectric constant of the oil? Ans: 2.5.

4. A condenser with air dielectric ($K = 1.00$) is charged by connecting it across a 100-v battery. Without disconnecting the battery, the condenser is completely immersed in an insulating oil of $K = 3.00$. As a result of immersion, the charge on each condenser plate *increases* in magnitude by 300 µcoul. What is the capacitance of the condenser with air dielectric?

5. What would be the size of a single pair of square tin-foil plates on glass ($K = 6$) 3 mm thick if the resulting condenser has a capacitance of 1 µf? Ans: 7.5 m square.

6. What would be the number of plates required for a parallel-plate condenser with metal-foil plates of effective area 2 cm × 2 cm and mica dielectric ($K = 6$) 0.1 mm thick, if the condenser is to have a capacitance of 0.02 µf?

7. If a transatlantic cable were built with a central conductor of 0.1-inch diameter and a sheath of 0.75-inch inside diameter filled with material of dielectric constant 3.0, how many coulombs of charge would be stored in 1500 nautical miles of the cable when the conductor is raised to a potential of 100 volts relative to the grounded sheath? (1 nautical mile = 6080 ft.) Ans: 2.31×10^{-2} coul.

8. Find the capacitance per mile (5280 ft) of cable having a conductor of diameter 0.2 inch and a lead sheath of inner diameter 0.6 inch, the space between being filled with rubber of $K = 3$.

9. The small fixed-capacitance condensers used throughout radio sets and other electronic apparatus are frequently constructed as in Fig. 10. An approximate value of their capacitance can be obtained by using the plane-plate formula, since the dielectric is very thin compared with the radius of curvature throughout most of the condenser. Consider such a condenser, rolled as in Fig. 10 from two strips of paper

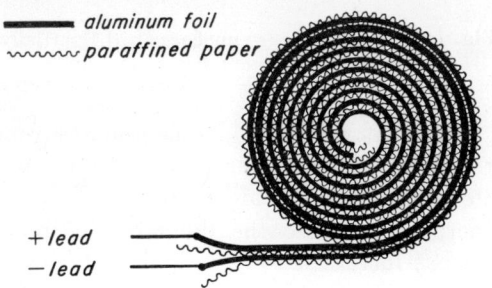

Fig. 10. Illustrating the construction of a commercial paper condenser.

and two strips of aluminum foil. Each strip of foil is 2.5 inches wide. If the foil is 0.0005 inch thick and the paper 0.001 inch thick, with $K = 2$, compute approximately (a) the length of strips required for a 0.5-µf condenser, and (b) the outside diameter of the complete roll. Ans: (a) approx 220 in; approx 0.9 in.

10. Repeat Prob. 5, p. 841, for the case in which the space between the spheres is filled with dielectric of $K = 3$.

5. ENERGY OF A CONDENSER

Energy must be supplied to charge a condenser; and when the condenser is discharged by connecting a wire between its plates, this energy is released in another form such as heat. The heat made available by a condenser discharge is used, for example, to fire detonators in ordnance devices such as mines, torpedoes, and shells. It is important in many uses of condensers to know the amount of energy stored. The computation can be made as follows:

Consider a condenser of capacitance C, in farads, initially uncharged as in Fig. 11(a). We start to charge this condenser by moving electrons, a few at a time, from the right-hand plate to the left. We may imagine that we move the electrons through the space between the plates, although in practice the electrons are usually impelled by a battery or generator through a wire that connects the two plates. This difference is unimportant, since the DP and hence the work is independent of the route followed by the electrons.

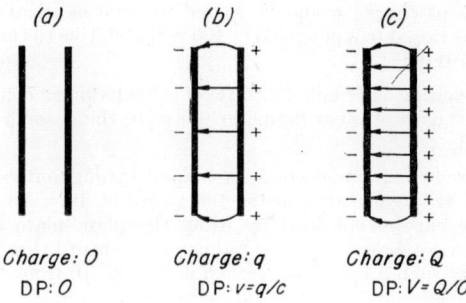

Fig. 11. Condenser: (a) uncharged; (b) partially charged; (c) completely charged.

At first the work that must be done on the electrons to force them from one plate to the other is small, since the difference of potential is low. But as the charge on the plates builds up, the work that must be done on each electron increases because the difference of potential increases. When the charge has increased to q, as in Fig. 11(b), the difference of potential has become $v = q/C$. At this stage the work required to move an additional charge dq is

$$v \, dq = (q/C) dq.$$

The total work required to move all the charges necessary to build up the charge Q of Fig. 11(c) is then obtained by integrating this expression:

$$W = \int_{q=0}^{q=Q} \frac{q}{C} \, dq = \frac{1}{C} \left[\frac{q^2}{2} \right]_0^Q = \frac{1}{2} \frac{Q^2}{C}. \tag{18a}$$

Since $V = Q/C$, we can write this equation as

$$W = \tfrac{1}{2} QV, \tag{18b}$$

or, since $Q = CV$, we get the third alternative form

$$W = \tfrac{1}{2} CV^2. \tag{18c}$$

In these expressions, *Q is in coulombs, V in volts, C in farads, and W in joules.*

The above derivation will apply to a condenser with plates of any shape, not merely to the plane-plate condenser illustrated in Fig. 11. The reason for the occurrence of the factor $\tfrac{1}{2}$ in (18) is easily understood. The first bit of charge is moved between the plates when there is no difference of potential; hence, no work is required to move this bit of charge. As more and more charge is transferred, the potential increases, and more and more work is required to move each bit of charge. Finally, the last bit of charge is moved through practically the full difference of potential V and requires work $V \cdot dq$. The charge Q is transferred across a DP that starts at 0 and ends at V, averaging $\tfrac{1}{2} V$. Hence the work is $Q \cdot \tfrac{1}{2} V$ as in (18b).

When a charged condenser is discharged by connecting a wire across its plates, this electrostatic energy disappears. It is transformed into heat in the wire. As we shall see later, whenever current flows in a wire, heat is generated. When a wire is connected between the plates of a charged condenser, the first passage of the electrons from the negative to the positive plate does not usually generate enough heat to take up all the energy of the condenser. Rather, like the oscillations of a pendulum, the flow of electrons overshoots, making the positive plate negative; then the flow reverses. Charge oscillates back and forth from one plate to the other until all the energy has been used up in heating the wire.

This type of oscillation is fundamental to the oscillating circuits of radio which we shall discuss later.

PROBLEMS

1. What is the energy in joules in a 6-μf condenser charged to 1200 v?

Ans: 4.32 joules.

2. A condenser of 50-μf capacitance is charged to a DP of 80 v. Calculate the energy stored in joules.

3. How many joules are stored in a 0.50-μf condenser charged with 0.0125 coul?

Ans: 156.2 joules.

4. A condenser consists of two large parallel plates 0.5 mm apart in air. Its capacitance is 200 μf. It is charged to 600 v by means of a battery.
  (a) What is its energy?
  (b) The charged condenser is disconnected from the battery. The plates are so mounted that they will remain parallel and insulated when a glass rod is used to push them 3 mm apart. What is the energy of the condenser after this separation is made? What is the source of the extra energy?

6. CONDENSERS IN PARALLEL AND SERIES

If a number of condensers are connected in *parallel* as in Fig. 12 and placed in a (real or imaginary) box, at the terminals on the box they appear indistinguishable from a single condenser of capacitance equal to the sum of the capacitances of the individual condensers. The reason for this result is that the DP across each condenser is the same (their positive plates form a single conductor and their negative plates a single conductor) and is equal to the DP across the terminals. But the charge

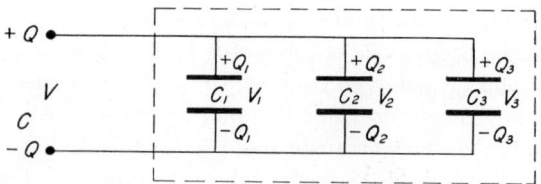

Fig. 12. Condensers in parallel.

that must flow in or out through the terminals on charge or discharge is the sum of the charges on the several condensers. More formally, referring to Fig. 12,

$$V_1 = V_2 = V_3 = V,$$
$$Q_1 = C_1 V, \quad Q_2 = C_2 V, \quad Q_3 = C_3 V,$$
$$Q = Q_1 + Q_2 + Q_3 = (C_1 + C_2 + C_3) V.$$

Hence,
$$C = Q/V = C_1 + C_2 + C_3. \qquad \text{(parallel)} \quad (19)$$

This formula may be easily generalized to the case of any number of condensers in parallel.

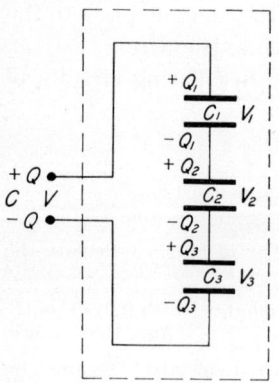

Fig. 13. Condensers in series.

If a number of condensers are connected in *series* as in Fig. 13 and placed in a (real or imaginary) box, the determination of the resultant capacitance is somewhat more complicated than in the parallel case. By *resultant capacitance* we mean the capacitance of a single condenser that could replace the series combination in the box with no detectable difference in behavior as observed at the terminals of the box.

We first note that the DP's of the individual condensers are not the same as V, but rather that they add up to V:

$$V_1 + V_2 + V_3 = V.$$

Fundamentally, this relation expresses the fact that as a test charge is moved from one terminal to the other through the wire and through the three condensers, work is done on the test charge in three steps as it passes through the three condensers, and the total work is the same as if the test charge were moved directly from one terminal to the other.

On the other hand, in the series case, the charge on each condenser is the same. Consider what happens when a battery is connected to the initially uncharged group of condensers. The charge $-Q$ represents the quantity of electrons that flows out of the negative terminal of the battery; all of these electrons appear as $-Q_3$ on condenser 3. Hence, $Q = Q_3$. The top plate of condenser 3 and the bottom plate of condenser 2 form one conductor of net charge zero. The charge $-Q_2$ represents a movement of electrons to condenser 2, which leaves behind an equal and opposite positive charge $+Q_3$, so that $Q_2 = Q_3$, and so on. Hence,

$$Q = Q_1 = Q_2 = Q_3.$$

Having established these relations between voltages and charges, we derive the formula for the resultant capacitance as follows:

$$V_1 = \frac{Q}{C_1}, \quad V_2 = \frac{Q}{C_2}, \quad V_3 = \frac{Q}{C_3},$$

$$V = V_1 + V_2 + V_3 = Q\left(\frac{1}{C_1} + \frac{1}{C_2} + \frac{1}{C_3}\right),$$

and
$$\frac{V}{Q} = \frac{1}{C} = \frac{1}{C_1} + \frac{1}{C_2} + \frac{1}{C_3}. \qquad \text{(series)} \quad (20)$$

Hence, the reciprocal of the resultant capacitance equals the sum of the reciprocals of the individual capacitances of the condensers in series. It is best to leave the formula in this form, first computing $1/C$ and then C. This formula can be directly generalized to the case of any number of condensers in series.

PROBLEMS

1. Show that the capacitance of a number of condensers in parallel is *larger* than that of any one of the condensers, and that the capacitance of a number of condensers in series is *smaller* than that of any one of the condensers.

2. Three condensers of respective capacitances 1, 1.5, and 3 μf are connected in *parallel* across a 120-volt battery. Find
   (a) the resultant capacitance from formula (19);
   (b) the charge that flows from the battery, using the capacitance obtained in (a);
   (c) the total energy in joules stored in the condenser combination, using the results of (a) or (b);
   (d) the charge on each condenser, comparing the total with (b);
   (e) the energy of each condenser, comparing the total with (c).

3. Three condensers, of respective capacitances 1, 1.5, and 3 μf, are connected in *series* across a 120-volt battery. Find
   (a) the resultant capacitance from formula (20);
   (b) the charge that flows from the battery, using the capacitance obtained in (a);
   (c) the total energy in joules stored in the condenser combination, using the results of (a) or (b);
   (d) the voltage across each condenser, checking the total;
   (e) the energy of each condenser, comparing the total with (c).

4. (a) Two condensers, of 2-μf and 4-μf capacitance, are connected in series and charged from a 120-volt battery. What are the charge, DP, and energy for each condenser?

(b) If these two condensers are now disconnected without discharging and are then connected to each other, + plate to + plate and − to −, what are the new values of charge, DP, and energy for each condenser?

5. If a 1-μf condenser charged to 100 volts and a 2-μf condenser charged to 200 volts are connected in parallel, + plate to + plate, find the resulting DP, the charge on each condenser, and the loss of energy.

Ans: 167 v; 167, 333 μcoul; ⅓×10⁻² joule.

6. If a 1-μf condenser charged to 100 volts and a 2-μf condenser charged to 200 volts are connected, + plate of each to − plate of the other, find the resulting DP, charge on each condenser, and the loss of energy.

7. Condensers A, B, and C of respective capacitances 4, 3, and 2 μf are connected as shown in Fig. 14. Before the switch is closed, A is charged to a potential difference of 100 volts, B and C are uncharged. What will be the charge and DP of each condenser after the switch is closed?

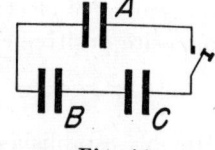

Fig. 14.

Ans: $V_A = 76.9$ v, $V_B = 30.8$ v, $V_C = 46.1$ v; $Q_A = 308$ μcoul, $Q_B = Q_C = 92.3$ μcoul.

8. Condensers A, B, and C of respective capacitances 4, 3, and 2 μf are connected as shown in Fig. 14. Before the switch is closed, B and C are each independently charged to a DP of 100 volts, the left-hand plate being positive in each case. A is uncharged. What will be the charge and DP of each condenser after the switch is closed?

7. DIELECTRIC STRENGTH*

As we have previously mentioned, when an electric field exists within an insulating dielectric material in a condenser of any type, the electrons become slightly displaced relative to the nuclei but still remain bound to the nuclei. This situation obtains so long as the electric intensity is sufficiently low, but there is a certain value of electric intensity that is sufficient actually to pull electrons away from the atoms to which they belong. When this separation occurs in a gaseous or a liquid material, the material becomes ionized; when it occurs in a solid material, the material becomes ruptured or broken or punctured. Exceeding the critical electric intensity usually results in disruptive discharge of the condenser by sparks that pass through the dielectric material, although the discharge may take place quietly in air in the form of the corona that is observed around lightning rods or high-tension wires.

The critical electric intensity at which breakdown will take place is called the *dielectric strength:*

> **Electric strength (dielectric strength).** The electric strength of a dielectric material is the maximum potential gradient that the material can withstand without rupture.†

Dielectric strength must not be confused with dielectric constant. They are essentially unrelated. The dielectric constant determines how much charge a given condenser will store up with a given potential differ-

---

* This section may be omitted without loss of continuity.
† AIEE definition 05.30.105.

ence; dielectric strength determines how much voltage this condenser will stand without breaking down.

Dielectric strength is usually expressed in volts/cm or kilovolts/cm. Typical values of dielectric strength are given in Table I on p. 846. It will be noticed that the dielectric strengths of most solid and liquid insulators are higher than that of air. Thus a parallel-plate condenser composed of plates 1 mm (0.1 cm) apart in air would break down at a potential difference of about 3.0 kv (3000 volts), since the electric intensity would then be

$$\frac{3.0 \text{ kv}}{0.1 \text{ cm}} = 30 \frac{\text{kv}}{\text{cm}},$$

which is the value of dielectric strength given in Table I. This same condenser immersed in transformer oil would stand between 5 and 15 kv, depending on the type of oil. With mica between the plates, the condenser would withstand a potential difference of from 25 to 200 kv, depending on the quality of the mica.

In the case of condensers other than plane-plate, where the electric intensity is not constant, breakdown will usually occur if the intensity at any point exceeds the dielectric strength. An interesting application occurs in attempts to increase the potentials obtainable by electrostatic machines of the Van de Graaff type by controlling the atmosphere surrounding the collecting sphere. In order to accomplish this objective, the machine is built inside an outer tank-like shell as in Fig. 15.

The largest electric intensity (potential gradient) in Fig. 15 will occur just outside the inner sphere at the upper part where it is closest to the tank wall. To a good approximation this potential gradient will be the same as that for a spherical condenser charged to the same voltage.

We see from equation (5) that the electric intensity just outside the inner sphere is

$$\mathcal{E} = 10^{-7} c^2 \, Q/K R_1^2, \qquad (21)$$

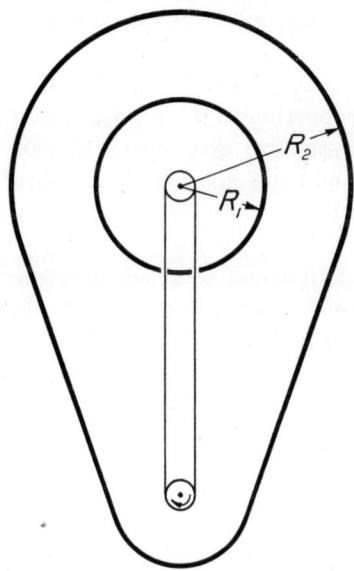

Fig. 15. 'High-pressure' type of Van de Graaff generator.

where Q is the charge on the sphere and K is the dielectric constant of the dielectric gas. K is introduced in the denominator in accordance with the discussion of p. 846. From the value of the capacitance in equation (17), we find that

$$Q = \frac{KV}{10^{-7}c^2} \frac{R_1 R_2}{R_2 - R_1}, \qquad (22)$$

where V is the difference of potential between the spheres. Substitution of (22) into (21) shows that the relation between the maximum potential gradient $\mathcal{E}$ and the potential difference V is independent of K and is given by

$$\mathcal{E} = V \frac{R_2}{R_1(R_2 - R_1)}.$$

This formula gives $\mathcal{E}$ in volts/m if V is in volts and R_1 and R_2 are in meters; it will also give $\mathcal{E}$ in volts/cm if R_1 and R_2 are in cm.

Let us consider an example in which $R_1 = 1$ m (100 cm) and $R_2 = 2$ m (200 cm). Then

$$\mathcal{E} = \frac{V \cdot 200}{100 \cdot 100} = \frac{V}{50} \text{ (in volts/cm)},$$

or
$$V = 50 \, \mathcal{E}. \qquad (23)$$

The maximum potential difference (in volts) that can be reached before sparkover is 50 times the maximum field strength (in volts/cm) that the dielectric can withstand, or 50 times the dielectric strength in volts/cm.

If the dielectric is ordinary air of dielectric strength 30,000 volts/cm, this maximum potential is 1,500,000 volts.

It turns out that if the pressure of air is increased to values above 1 atm, the dielectric strength increases in proportion to the pressure, so if the air is at 5 atm pressure, the dielectric strength goes up to 150,000 volts/cm, and the electrostatic machine would not spark over below a potential of 7,500,000 volts. Air at elevated pressure has been used in a number of electrostatic machines.

Another way of increasing the potential that can be reached before sparkover is to change from air to a gas of higher dielectric strength. An admixture of Freon in air has been used for this purpose.

PROBLEMS

1. How thick must the mica dielectric be in a parallel-plate condenser built to withstand 10,000 v if the mica has dielectric strength 900 kv/cm? Ans: 0.111 mm.

2. At what voltage will a parallel-plate condenser with dielectric of dry air 1.5 mm thick break down?

3. What are the approximate relative volumes of condensers made of stacked parallel plates with the following dielectrics?
  (a) air, $K = 1$, dielectric strength 30 kv/cm;
  (b) paraffined paper, $K = 2$, dielectric strength 500 kv/cm;
  (c) mica, $K = 6$, dielectric strength 900 kv/cm.
The condensers are to have the same capacitance and the same breakdown voltage. Neglect the thickness of the metal plates in your computation. Ans: 5400 : 9.7 : 1.

4. To what potential can a single isolated sphere 1 m in diameter in dry air be raised before breakdown occurs?

5. To what potential can a single isolated sphere 1 cm in diameter in dry air be raised before breakdown occurs? Ans: 15,000 volts.

CHAPTER 33

DIRECT ELECTRIC CURRENTS

In this chapter we develop the laws that govern the flow of constant currents, ordinarily known as *direct currents* (DC). Development of the laws governing varying and alternating currents (AC) will be postponed until after the subjects of electromagnetism and electromagnetic induction have been studied.

1. CURRENT ARISING FROM A CONDENSER DISCHARGE

An electroscope or electrostatic voltmeter connected across the charged condenser of Fig. 1 will serve to measure the difference of potential between the condenser plates, as explained previously on p. 824.

If now a short, thick wire be connected across the condenser plates, the plates will be discharged almost instantaneously, as indicated by the sudden collapse of the electroscope leaves. But if a very long and very fine wire be connected across the condenser plates, the electroscope leaves will collapse gradually over a period of seconds or minutes; the longer and finer the wire, the longer the time required for the condenser to discharge. Although any wire connected across the condenser plates permits electrons to flow from the negative to the positive plate, a long, fine wire appears to offer more 'resistance' to the flow than a short, thick wire.

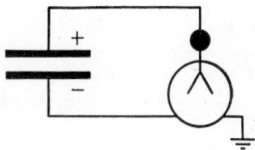

Fig. 1. Electroscope measures the DP of a condenser.

Furthermore, wires made of certain metals such as nichrome (a nickel-chromium alloy often used in commercial resistors) offer much more resistance to the flow than wires of the same size made of other metals such as copper.

In Fig. 2, the conventional symbol for 'resistor' is used to indicate that the wire connected across the condenser plates presents resistance.

During the period in which the condenser is discharging, electrons move from the negative plate through the resistor to the positive plate. A *current* is said to exist. However, by an unfortunate convention originated by Ampère before the days of the electron theory, the *current* is said to have the direction *opposite* to that in which the electrons really move. This convention is so firmly established that no attempt is being made to change it. *We must always specify the direction of current as the direction* in which positive charges would move if the charge were transferred by means of positive charges rather than by means of electrons. Thus, the current in Fig. 2 is directed from the positive plate of the condenser to the negative.

From the rate of change of potential in Fig. 2 and the known capacitance of the condenser, it is easy to compute the rate at which charge is being transferred from one plate to the other by flow through the resistor. Thus, if

Q = charge on either plate in coulombs,

C = capacitance of condenser in farads,

V = DP of condenser in volts,

we have, at any instant, $\qquad Q = CV,$

and, differentiating, $\qquad \dfrac{dQ}{dt} = C\,\dfrac{dV}{dt}.$

The rate of decrease of charge in coul/sec equals C times the rate of decrease of potential in v/sec. But this rate of decrease of charge must

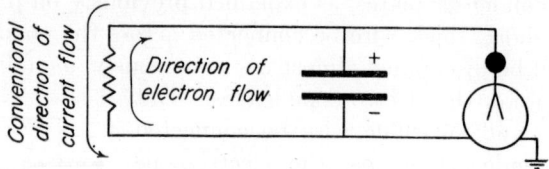

Fig. 2. Rate of decrease of DP indicates magnitude of current flow.

represent the rate of flow of charge in coul/sec through the resistor. The *rate of flow of charge,* in coul/sec, is called the *current* through the wire in amperes (amp)* and is denoted by the symbol I.

> **A current of one ampere** in a wire represents a flow of charge at a rate of one coul/sec past any point. The direction of the current is opposite to the direction in which the electrons in the wire actually move.

In terms of the mechanical units, since, by (3), p. 792, 1 coul = 1 $\sqrt{\text{nt}}\cdot$sec,

$$1 \text{ amp} = 1 \text{ coul/sec} = 1\ \sqrt{\text{nt}}. \qquad (1)$$

An instrument called an *ammeter* may be connected into the circuit to measure the current in amperes. It usually measures the current by means of the magnetic effects of the current which we shall study in the next chapter.

* After André Marie Ampère (1775–1836), French physicist who formulated the fundamental laws of the magnetic effects of electric currents.

2. CONSTANT CURRENTS

The currents considered in the preceding section were *transient currents* in that charge flowed only during the period required for the condenser to discharge. If it is desired to keep a *constant current* for an indefinite period, some means must be found for keeping the condenser continuously charged, that is, for renewing the supply of electrons on the negative plate as fast as they flow around through the wire. Energy must be supplied to move these electrons from the positive to the negative plate through the difference of potential existing between these plates. This energy could be supplied and the potential difference maintained by an electrostatic generator of some type, but there are more practical and convenient means. In discussing this question, *let us agree to ignore our knowledge that in most cases it is negative electrons, rather than positive charges, that move, and speak as if it were only positive charges that move.*

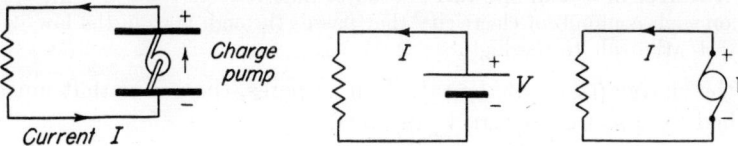

Fig. 3. In order to maintain a continuous current flow, a 'charge pump' is needed.

Fig. 4. The most common sources of constant EMF (charge pumps) are the electric battery and the direct-current electric generator

This procedure will lead to no essential error and will avoid much confusion because it is consistent with the conventional current direction as historically established.

What we need, then, is a 'charge pump' that will pump charge up the 'potential hill' from the negative plate of the condenser to the positive plate, as illustrated in Fig. 3, as fast as the charge runs back downhill through the resistor. This charge pump must do work of amount V, in joules per coulomb of charge moved, if a difference of potential of V, in volts, is to be maintained (see p. 806). If the current is I, in amperes, charge must be pumped at the rate I, in coul/sec, and the power that must be supplied is IV, in joules/sec or watts. In Fig. 3, the pump must supply energy at the rate

$$P = IV, \quad \text{in watts.} \tag{2}$$

This energy must be supplied to the charges by some outside means; it reappears as heat in the resistor as the charges flow back down the potential hill through the resistor.

A 'charge pump,' which converts some other form of energy to electrical potential energy by moving charges against an electric field is called a *source of electromotive force*. The first source of *electromotive force*

(EMF) suitable for the production of continuous currents was discovered by Volta in 1799 and called the galvanic pile or voltaic *battery*. This source was the prototype of our modern dry cells and storage batteries, which obtain their power from stored *chemical energy*. A second type of source of EMF, based on the discovery of electromagnetic induction by Faraday and Joseph Henry (independently) in 1831, converts *mechanical energy* into electrical energy. The modern direct-current electric generator is of this type. These sources of EMF are illustrated in the circuits of Fig. 4, where of course we can now dispense with the condenser and hook our wires directly to the plates of the battery or to the terminals of the generator.

The operation of sources of electromotive force will be discussed in detail in later chapters. For the present, we need only understand that EMF is measured in volts and that:

A source of EMF of one volt is a source that does one joule of work on each coulomb of electricity that passes through it from the low potential side to the high.

If the charge passes at the rate I, in amperes, the power that must be furnished by a source of EMF V, in volts, is

$$P = VI, \text{ in watts.} \tag{2}$$

PROBLEMS

1. What is the magnitude of the constant current in a wire if it is found that 2400 coulombs of charge flow through the wire in 2 min? Ans: 20 amp.

2. An electroplating tank requires 180,000 coulombs per hour. What current must be fed to the tank?

3. How many coulombs are delivered by a storage battery in 24 hr if it is supplying current at the rate of 2 amp? Ans: 1.728×10^5 coul.

4. In 8 hr, how many coulombs pass through a light bulb drawing 0.3 amp?

5. Within limits, the total amount of charge that a storage battery will deliver before it goes 'dead' is independent of the rate at which the charge is delivered. A typical automobile battery is guaranteed for 80 ampere-hours, which means that it will deliver 1 amp for 80 hr, or 2 amp for 40 hr, and so on.
(a) How many coulombs is it guaranteed to deliver?
(b) How many amperes will it deliver for 5 hr?
(c) If the starter draws 500 amp, how long would a fresh battery drive the starter? Ans: (a) 2.88×10^5 coul; (b) 16 amp; (c) 9.6 min.

6. Why is a coulomb sometimes called an *ampere-second?* How many coulombs are there in an *ampere-hour?*

7. If a storage battery is supplying 20 amp and has an EMF of 6 v, what power is it delivering? Ans: 120 watts.

8. A 120-v generator delivers 50 kw to an electric furnace. What current is the generator supplying?

9. What voltage should a generator have if it is to supply a 50-kw furnace with a current of 200 amp? Ans: 250 volts.

10. What current must a 6-v battery deliver if it is to supply 2 hp to an automobile starter?

11. What horsepower must a steam engine have if it is to drive a 3300-v electric generator capable of supplying 150 amp, if the generator converts 90 per cent of the mechanical energy supplied to it into electrical energy? *Ans*: 738 hp.

12. If a water turbine delivers 900 hp to an electric generator of 95 per cent efficiency, what current will the generator deliver at 1400 v?

13. Verify the dimensional correctness of equation (2).

3. RESISTANCE; OHM'S LAW

Whenever there is a DP between the ends of a wire, there is a current through it. The current is caused by the electric field (potential gradient) in the wire. If the DP is continuously maintained by a source of EMF, the current is continuous. The current meets resistance in its flow which causes generation of heat, just as liquid flowing through a pipe meets frictional and viscous resistance which causes generation of heat. Just as the magnitude of the current of liquid (in ft³/sec) that will flow downhill through a pipe depends on the difference in elevation of the ends of the pipe, on the diameter, length, and internal roughness of the pipe, and on the temperature (viscosity effect), so does the magnitude of the electric current through a wire depend on the potential difference between the ends of the wire, its diameter, length, and material, and the temperature. The laws determining the dependence of the magnitude of the current on these various factors are simple and will be discussed in order.

The dependence of current on DP is expressed by *Ohm's law*, discovered experimentally by Ohm* in 1826, which states:

For a given conductor at given temperature, the current is directly proportional to the difference of potential between the ends of the conductor.

(OHM'S LAW)

If, in Fig. 5, V is the DP in volts between the ends of a conductor R as measured by a voltmeter V, and I is the current in amperes through the conductor as measured by the ammeter A, and if the temperature is kept constant, Ohm's law states that the current is proportional to V:

$$I \propto V. \quad \text{(Ohm's law)}$$

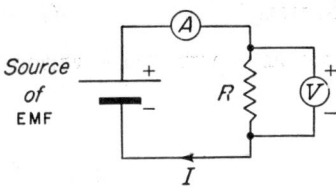

Fig. 5. Voltmeter V measures the DP between the ends of resistor R. Ammeter A measures the current I through the resistor.

The proportionality constant is called the *conductance G* in *mhos*:

$$I = GV.$$

The reciprocal of the conductance G in mhos is the *resistance R* in *ohms*:

$$R = \frac{1}{G}; \quad G = \frac{1}{R}; \quad I = \frac{V}{R}. \tag{3}$$

* Georg Simon Ohm (1787–1854), German physicist.

In terms of mechanical units,

$$1 \text{ ohm} = 1 \text{ v}/1 \text{ amp} = 1 \text{ m/sec}. \tag{4}$$

The value of R depends on the size, shape, material, and temperature of the conductor, but within wide limits it does not depend on the DP V. This rule is true for metals but is not obeyed very accurately by non-metals (see Sec. 6). R is called the *resistance* because the DP, $V = RI$, required to force a certain current I through a wire becomes greater as the value of R becomes greater. A wire of greater resistance requires a greater voltage and hence greater power for a given current.

To repeat, Ohm's law states that *if* we write

$$V = RI \tag{5}$$

for the DP necessary to force current I through a given conducting body at a given temperature, *then* R is a constant independent of I within wide limits.

Since the difference of potential V represents the work in joules done by the electrical forces per coulomb of charge passing through the wire, and since all of this work appears as heat in the wire, we have, from (5), the following important relation:

When a wire of resistance R carries current I, a quantity IR (*in joules*) of heat is generated for each coulomb of charge that is transported through the wire. $\tag{6}$

To get the power expended in the resistor, which is the same as the rate of heat generation, in watts or in joules/sec, we merely multiply the energy per coulomb $(V = IR)$ by the number of coulombs per second (I). The expression for power can then be written in several convenient forms:

$$P = IV = I^2 R = V^2/R, \quad \text{in watts}. \tag{7}$$

The amount of heat generated in t seconds can then be written in various ways:

$$W = Pt = IVt = I^2 Rt = V^2 t/R, \quad \text{in joules}. \tag{8}$$

This value in joules may be changed into kilocalories or BTU by using the equivalents:

$$1 \text{ kilocalorie} = 4186 \text{ joules},$$
$$1 \text{ BTU} = 1055 \text{ joules}.$$

It must be emphasized that the symbol V in (7) and (8) represents the difference of potential between the two ends of the wire whose resistance is R, as would be measured by a voltmeter connected as in Fig. 5. This V will in general be *less* than the battery voltage because of resistance in the leads, internal resistance in the battery, etc. These points will be discussed in succeeding sections.

RESISTANCE, OHM'S LAW

Electrical energy is usually measured and paid for in kilowatt-hours, rather than in joules (watt-seconds). The kilowatt-hour (kwh) is the amount of energy delivered in a period of one hour if it is being delivered at the rate of one kilowatt. In other words, we get energy in kwh from the formula $W = Pt$ if P is expressed in kw and t in hours. We note that

$$1 \text{ kwh} = (1 \text{ kw}) \cdot (1 \text{ hr}) = (1000 \text{ w}) \cdot (3600 \text{ sec}) = 3.6 \times 10^6 \text{ joules}.$$

This is a unit of energy of a size convenient for commercial purposes; it usually retails for somewhere between 1 cent and 6 cents.

PROBLEMS

NOTE: The symbol ω (or Ω) is frequently used as an abbreviation for the word *ohms*. We shall follow this convenient usage.

1. The DP between the ends of a wire is 18 v and the current is 2 amp. What is the resistance of the wire? Ans: 9 ω.

2. The resistance of a wire is 5 ω. What current flows when the DP between its ends is 120 v?

3. A flashlight bulb has a resistance of 5 ω, and the battery produces a DP of 1.5 v. Calculate the current through the bulb. Ans: 0.3 amp.

4. A lamp takes 0.5 amp when connected to 120-v DC mains. What is its resistance?

5. What power is expended in a 110-ω resistor connected across a 220-v DC line? Ans: 440 w.

6. A 110-v flatiron has a resistance of 8 ω. Calculate the power expended in it.

7. What is the resistance, when hot, of a 100-w bulb in a 110-v DC line? Ans: 121 ω.

8. A 1000-w electric iron is designed to operate from 120-v DC mains. What must be the resistance of its heating element at operating temperature?

9. A current of 5 amp flows through a resistance of 50 ω for 1 hr. How much heat is generated in joules? in kcal? Ans: 4.5×10^6 joules; 1075 kcal.

10. If a 5-ω wire is connected across 110 v for 1 hr, how much heat is generated, in joules? in kcal?

11. What is the resistance of an immersed coil of wire that heats a liter of water from 19° C to 99° C in 5 min when attached to 110-v DC mains? Ans: 10.9 ω.

12. It is required to generate 1 kcal of heat per minute in a resistor connected to 110 v. What must be the resistance?

13. At 4 cents per kwh, what is the cost of operating fifteen 40-w lamps for 8 hr? Ans: 19.2 cents.

14. At 3 cents per kwh, what is the cost of operating a 5-hp motor for 12.5 hr?

15. The coil of a powerful electromagnet is made of copper tubing and is cooled by water flowing through the tubing. The current is 500 amp and the resistance 0.24 ω, and 0.6 ft³/min of water flows through the coil. Find the temperature rise of the water on the assumption that all the heat generated is carried away by the water stream. Ans: 91.0 F deg.

16. It is desired to provide a water-cooled electromagnet in which the windings carry 350 amp, with a DP of 220 v. What flow of cooling water, in ft³/min, is required to carry off all the heat if the water is to enter at 50° F and leave at 170° F?

17. Verify the dimensional agreement of all terms in equation (7) and in equation (8).

4. RESISTIVITY

Now let us consider the dependence of resistance on length and cross-sectional area of a wire. Consider first the dependence of resistance on length, other things being equal. Figure 6 shows three wires, identical except for their lengths, which are l, $2l$, $3l$. If we denote by v the DP required to force a certain current I through the shortest wire, it is clear that a DP of $2v$ will be required to force the same current I through the second, since each half of the second is identical with the first and each half must have a DP of v for current I. Similarly, each third

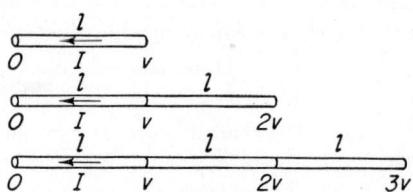

Fig. 6. For a given current, DP is proportional to length of wire.

of the longest wire is identical with the shortest, so that if current I is to flow, each third must have a DP of v and the total DP must be $3v$. Since the resistance of a piece of wire equals the DP between its ends divided by the current, we see that the resistances of the three pieces in Fig. 6 are, respectively, v/I, $2v/I$, $3v/I$; and that in general the resistance varies in direct proportion to the length of the wire:

$$R \propto l. \qquad (9)$$

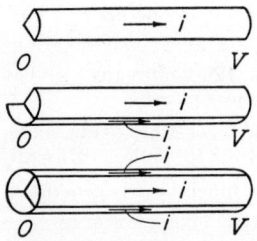

Fig. 7. For a given DP, current is proportional to cross-sectional area A.

Now, consider the dependence of resistance on cross-sectional area A, length being constant. Figure 7 shows three wires of the same length but with cross-sectional areas in the ratios $1:2:3$. The second and third wires are equivalent, respectively, to two and three of the first wires, and will carry two and three times the current with the same DP. Hence, if the current in the first wire is called i, that in the second will be $2i$ and in the third $3i$ for the same DP V. Hence, the resistances of the wires will be V/i, $V/2i$, $V/3i$, respectively, and we see that the resistance goes down as the area goes up; in general, the resistance is inversely proportional to the cross-sectional area:

$$R \propto 1/A. \qquad (10)$$

Putting (9) and (10) together, we see that for wires of given materials and temperature,

$$R \propto l/A.$$

TABLE I
Resistivity and Temperature Coefficient of Common Metals and Alloys

Alloy	Specification	Resistivity at 20° C		Temperature coefficient (per C deg at 20° C)
		(ohm·m)	(ohms per mil ft)	
Copper.........	Pure (99.999%)	1.673×10^{-8}	10.06	4.05×10^{-3}
	International Standard-annealed (~99.91%)	1.724	10.37	3.93
	Hard-drawn	1.77	10.6	3.8
Aluminum......	Pure (99.96%)	2.655	15.97	4.03
	AIEE Standard hard-drawn (99.5%)	2.828	17.01	4.03
Iron...........	Pure (99.99%)	9.71	58.4	5.76
	Commercial wire	11–13	66–78	5.5
	Cast (typical)	60	360	5
Steel..........	Rail	14–22	84–130	4
Nichrome......	60% Ni, 15% Cr, 25% Fe	112	675	0.16
Manganin......	4% Ni, 12% Mn, 84% Cu	48	290	<0.01
Monel.........	69% Ni, 28% Cu	44	268	1.96
German silver..	18% Ni, 65% Cu, 17% Zn	29	175	0.27
Constantan.....	45% Ni, 55% Cu	49	294	<0.01
Silver.........	Pure	1.630	9.80	3.75
Gold..........	Pure	2.44	14.7	3.4
Tungsten.......	Pure	5.50	33.1	4.7
Platinum.......	Pure (99.99%)	10.6	64	3.64

The proportionality constant, usually written as ρ, is called the *resistivity*:

$$R = \rho \, l/A. \tag{11}$$

Of course the resistivity ρ depends on the material of which the wire is made, and on the temperature.

The numerical value of the resistivity ρ will depend on the units used for l and A. In the metric system, l and A are expressed in m and m²; and since

$$\rho = RA/l,$$

the unit in which ρ is expressed is the ohm·meter.

In a system convenient for engineering calculations, particularly with round wires, l is expressed in feet and A in circular mils. A circular mil is defined as the area of a circle one mil (0.001 inch) in diameter. The area of a circular wire of diameter d, in mils, is $A = d^2$, in circular mils. In this system the unit of ρ is ohm·circ mil/ft. This unit is commonly written as *ohm per mil ft;* we shall use this designation in spite of the fact that it is *dimensionally incorrect.* With these units we can write the resistance of a *round* wire as

$$R = \rho\, l/d^2. \quad \begin{cases} R \text{ in ohms} \\ \rho \text{ in ohms per mil ft} \\ l \text{ in ft} \\ d \text{ in mils} \end{cases} \quad (12)$$

Table I gives the value of resistivity ρ in both systems for various metals and commercial alloys at a temperature of 20° C. The resistivity

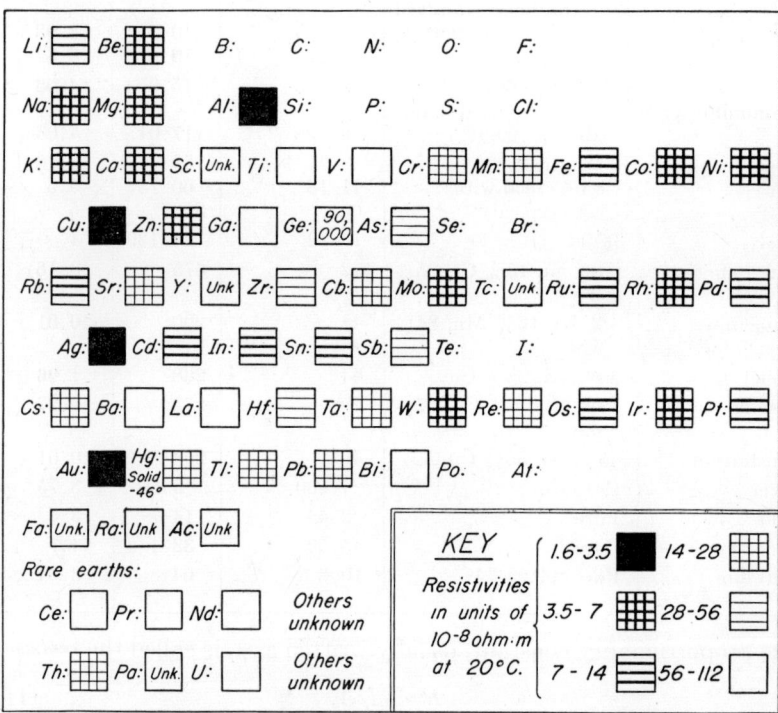

Fig. 8. Resistivities of the metallic elements in the periodic table. Hydrogen and the rare gases have been omitted. The elements not followed by a box are non-metals. Source of data: NATIONAL BUREAU OF STANDARDS CIRCULAR C447 (1943).

in ohms per mil ft, which is the resistance of a circular wire one foot long and 0.001 inch in diameter, is of course much larger than the resistivity in ohm·m, which is the resistance of a one-meter cube, but the ratio is constant at 6.015×10^8, as may readily be computed.

Figure 8 shows in graphical form the resistivities of the pure metallic elements. In this periodic chart the best conductors are represented by the blackest squares. It is seen that there is a periodicity of electrical

TABLE II (WIRE TABLE)
Properties of International Standard-annealed Copper Wire and Hard-drawn Aluminum Wire (AIEE Standard) According to American Wire Gauge (Brown and Sharpe Wire Gauge) Number

Gauge No.	Diameter in mils	Area in circ mils	Copper		Aluminum	
			Ohms per 1000 ft at 20° C	Pounds per 1000 ft	Ohms per 1000 ft at 20° C	Pounds per 1000 ft
0000	460.0	211,600	0.04901	640.5	0.0804	195.
000	409.6	167,800	0.06180	508.0	.101	154.
00	364.8	133,100	0.07793	402.8	.128	122.
0	324.9	105,500	0.09827	319.5	.161	97.0
1	289.3	83,690	0.1239	253.3	.203	76.9
2	257.6	66,370	0.1563	200.9	.256	61.0
3	229.4	52,630	0.1970	159.3	.323	48.4
4	204.3	41,740	0.2485	126.4	.408	38.4
5	181.9	33,100	0.3133	100.2	.514	30.4
6	162.0	26,250	0.3951	79.46	.648	24.1
7	144.3	20,820	0.4982	63.02	.817	19.1
8	129.5	16,510	0.6282	49.98	1.03	15.2
9	114.4	13,090	0.7921	39.63	1.30	12.0
10	101.9	10,380	0.9989	31.43	1.64	9.55
11	90.74	8,234	1.260	24.93	2.07	7.57
12	80.81	6,530	1.588	19.77	2.61	6.00
13	71.96	5,178	2.003	15.68	3.29	4.76
14	64.08	4,107	2.525	12.43	4.14	3.78
15	57.07	3,257	3.184	9.858	5.22	2.99
16	50.82	2,583	4.016	7.818	6.59	2.37
17	45.26	2,048	5.064	6.200	8.31	1.88
18	40.30	1,624	6.385	4.917	10.5	1.49
19	35.89	1,288	8.051	3.899	13.2	1.18
20	31.96	1,022	10.15	3.092	16.7	0.939
21	28.46	810.1	12.80	2.452	21.0	0.745
22	25.35	642.4	16.14	1.945	26.5	0.591
23	22.57	509.4	20.36	1.542	33.4	0.468
24	20.10	404.0	25.67	1.223	42.1	0.371
25	17.90	320.4	32.37	0.9699	53.1	0.295
26	15.94	254.1	40.81	0.7692	67.0	0.234
27	14.20	201.5	51.47	0.6100	84.4	0.185
28	12.64	159.8	64.90	0.4837	106	0.147
29	11.26	126.7	81.83	0.3836	134	0.117
30	10.02	100.5	103.2	0.3042	169	0.0924
31	8.928	79.70	130.1	0.2413	213	0.0733
32	7.950	63.21	164.1	0.1913	269	0.0581
33	7.080	50.13	206.9	0.1517	339	0.0461
34	6.305	39.75	260.9	0.1203	428	0.0365
35	5.615	31.52	329.0	0.0954	540	0.0290
36	5.000	25.00	414.8	0.0757	681	0.0230
37	4.453	19.82	523.1	0.0600	858	0.0182
38	3.965	15.72	659.6	0.0476	1080	0.0145
39	3.531	12.47	831.8	0.0377	1360	0.0115
40	3.145	9.89	1049	0.0299	1720	0.0091

resistivity similar to the periodicity of other properties of the elements. In particular, the three best electrical conductors are Ag, Cu, Au—the three elements that occupy column I-b of the periodic table. Next comes Al. The resistivities of these four elements will be found in Table I.

In scientific work, the conductivity σ is frequently used in place of the resistivity ρ. These quantities are reciprocal,

$$\sigma = 1/\rho,$$

so that the conductance [compare equation (3)]

$$G = \sigma A/l.$$

In the metric system, the unit of σ is the mho/m.

Table II gives useful data on the characteristics of standard round copper and aluminum wires. Wires larger than #0 are usually specified by giving the area in circular mils rather than a gauge number. A stranded wire of a certain gauge is made up of strands of smaller wire such that the total area adds up to the correct value for the given gauge. The entries in Table II are divided into groups of three to emphasize certain properties of the American Wire Gauge. The ratio of diameters of two adjacent gauge numbers is $\sqrt[6]{2}$, very closely, so the ratio of areas, resistances, and weights for two adjacent gauges is $\sqrt[3]{2} = 1.26$, very closely. This ratio means that we must move three gauge numbers to double or halve the resistance of a wire. For example, #13 wire has twice the resistance and half the area of #10; and #16 wire has 4 times the resistance, ¼ the area, and ½ the diameter of #10. Four strands of #16, eight of #19, or 16 of #22 would make #10 stranded. If we remember that #10 copper wire is almost exactly 0.1 inch (100 mils) in diameter and has a resistance of almost exactly 1 ohm per thousand feet, we shall be able to carry out approximate computations on wire-gauge diameters and resistances mentally in the absence of a wire table.

PROBLEMS

1. At 20° C, what is the resistance of a Standard aluminum bus bar ½ cm × 2 cm in section and 20 m long? Ans: 5.66×10^{-3} ω.

2. At 20° C, what is the resistance of an annealed copper bus bar ½ cm × 2 cm in section and 20 m long?

3. From the resistivity of annealed copper in Table I, compute the resistance of 1000 ft of #10 wire (101.9 mils in diameter), at 20° C. Compare your answer with that given in Table II.

4. What is the resistance of 5000 ft of #10 silver wire (101.9 mils diameter) at 20° C?

5. If 150 ft of round nichrome resistance wire is to have a resistance of 10 ohms at 20° C, what diameter of wire should be used? Ans: 101 mils.

6. If 150 ft of round nichrome resistance wire is to have a resistance of 90 ohms at 20° C, what diameter of wire should be used?

7. Magnet wire is sometimes made of square cross section to obtain closer packing. What is the cross-sectional area in circular mils of wire 102 mils square? To what wire gauge is this approximately equivalent in terms of area and resistance?
Ans: 13,200 circ mils; #9.

8. What size of square wire has the same resistance as #10 round wire?

9. Show that for a square wire of a given effective gauge number (the effective gauge being determined by the resistance), the side of the square is very close to the diameter of round wire of the next larger gauge number.

10. From the definitions of the units, show that

$$1 \text{ ohm} \cdot \text{m} = 6.015 \times 10^8 \text{ ohms per mil ft.}$$

NOTE: The density at 20° C of Standard annealed copper is 8.89 g/cm^3; that of hard-drawn aluminum is 2.70 g/cm^3; and that of silver is 10.5 g/cm^3. These values should be used in Probs. 11 and 12.

11. If 1000 ft of Standard annealed copper wire has diameter d_{Cu}, weight w_{Cu}, and resistance R, what are the diameters d_{Ag}, d_{Al} and the weights w_{Ag}, w_{Al} of 1000 ft of silver and hard-drawn aluminum wire having the same resistance?
Ans: 0.972 d_{Cu}, 1.28 d_{Cu}; 1.12 w_{Cu}, 0.499 w_{Cu}.

12. (a) What are the ratios $R_{Ag}:R_{Cu}:R_{Al}$ of the resistances of silver, annealed copper, and hard-drawn aluminum wires of the same length and the same *diameter?* Which is the best and which the poorest conductor of the three, volume for volume?

(b) What are the ratios $R_{Ag}:R_{Cu}:R_{Al}$ of the resistances of silver, annealed copper, and hard-drawn aluminum wires of the same length and the same *weight?* Which is the best and which the poorest conductor of the three, weight for weight?

5. TEMPERATURE COEFFICIENT OF RESISTANCE

We turn now to a consideration of the dependence of resistance (or resistivity) on temperature. The resistance of a pure metal increases rapidly with temperature, the temperature effect being so pronounced that it must be taken into account in most engineering applications. Figure 9 shows, for example, how the resistivity of copper varies with temperature. The reason for the rapid variation with temperature is that the whole resistance of a metal to electron flow arises from the thermal agitation of the metallic ions that comprise the lattice structure of the metal. This agitation increases rapidly with increasing temperature. These ideas are confirmed by the fact that the resistance of all metals seems to approach zero as the absolute temperature approaches zero. In fact, in the phenomenon known as *superconductivity*, which is the outstanding macroscopic phenomenon not yet explained by atomic theory, the resistance of many metals drops entirely to zero at a temperature still a few degrees above absolute zero, so that when a current is once started in a metal ring below such temperature it continues to flow indefinitely without necessity of an EMF to maintain it and hence without causing any heating of the material. The presence of such a persistent current can be detected by means of the magnetic field it sets up, as we shall see later.

Over a wide range of the temperatures of practical interest, the resistivity of a metal can be represented by a linear curve. The data of Fig. 9

show this statement to be accurately true for copper for temperatures from $-200°$ C to $+300°$ C, and approximately true for still higher temperatures. It is customary to use the resistivity ρ_{20} at 20° C as a reference value, since 20° C = 68° F is usually taken as the specification of 'room temperature.' The resistivity ρ_T at temperature T (Centigrade) is written in the form

$$\rho_T = \rho_{20} + \text{const} \times (T - 20°),$$

which is the equation of a straight line for ρ_T as a function of T; the line passes through the point $\rho_T = \rho_{20}$, $T = 20°$. The constant is usually

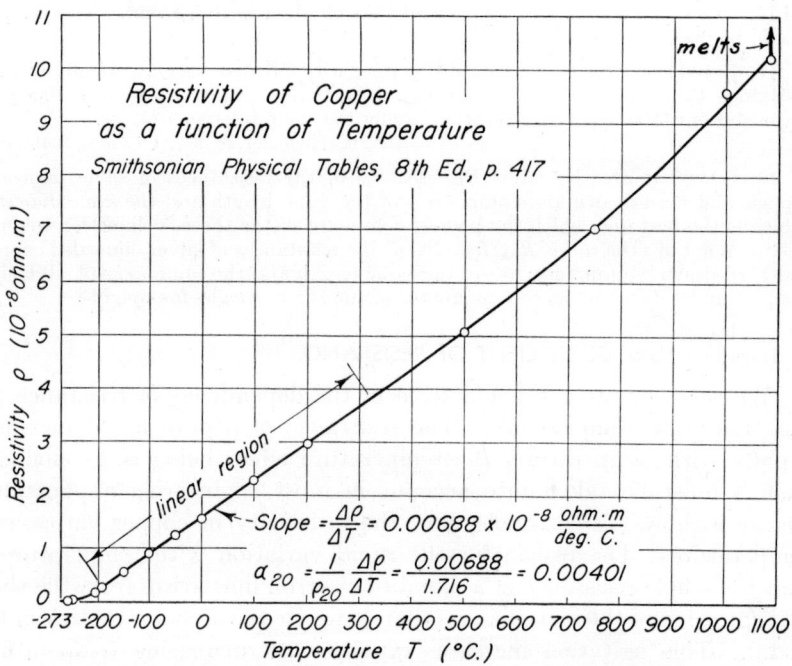

Fig. 9. Typical data on the resistivity of copper of high purity.

written as $\alpha_{20}\rho_{20}$, so that the equation takes the convenient form

$$\rho_T = \rho_{20} + \alpha_{20}\rho_{20}(T - 20°), \tag{13}$$

or
$$\rho_T = \rho_{20}\,[1 + \alpha_{20}(T - 20°)]. \tag{14}$$

The constant α_{20} is called the *temperature coefficient of resistance* referred to 20° C.

Since we can write (13) in the form

$$\alpha_{20} = \left(\frac{\rho_T - \rho_{20}}{\rho_{20}}\right) \bigg/ (T - 20°),$$

we see that the value α_{20} is independent of the units used for the resistivity ρ; it has the same value whether ρ is in ohm·m or ohms per mil ft. α_{20} is the *relative* change in resistivity per C degree change in temperature. As seen in Table I, α_{20} has a magnitude of about 0.004 per C degree for most metals. This value corresponds to an increase in resistivity of about 0.4 per cent per C degree rise in temperature, or 100 per cent for a 250 C degree rise. Such an increase is very large compared, for example, with linear expansion, where the length increases only about 0.001 per cent per C degree.

Because changes in physical dimensions are only about $\frac{1}{400}$ the change in resistivity with temperature, we can neglect changes in dimensions in discussing the change in resistance of a conductor of given size and shape. If we multiply (14) on both sides by l/A, where l is the length and A the cross-sectional area of a conductor, we obtain

$$\frac{\rho_T l}{A} = \frac{\rho_{20} l}{A}[1+\alpha_{20}(T-20°)],$$

or, by (11),
$$R_T = R_{20}[1+\alpha_{20}(T-20°)]. \tag{15}$$

This very useful equation expresses the resistance of any conductor at temperature T in terms of its resistance at temperature 20° C.

Since the change in resistance of a conductor as the temperature changes is large enough to be easily measured, the resistance of a conductor can be used as a thermometer—the so-called *resistance thermometer*. In particular, refractory metals like tungsten can be used to measure very high temperatures in this way. One type of electronically controlled electric blanket employs a pure nickel wire, which zigzags back and forth in the blanket, as a resistance thermometer to measure the average blanket temperature and to control the current in the heating wires, which are separate from the resistance-thermometer wire.

For construction of laboratory apparatus, such as resistance boxes, it is desirable to have a material of very low temperature coefficient so that the resistance will not change when the resistor is heated by current through it. This requirement has been met by certain alloys that have been developed specifically for the purpose—notably manganin and constantan (see Table I).

PROBLEMS

1. The resistance of a coil of pure copper wire at 20° C is 48.0 ohms. What will be the resistance of the coil at 50° C?   Ans: 53.7 ohms.

2. The resistance of a copper wire is 4.90 ohms at 20° C. What is it at 80° C?

3. Find the resistance at 30° C of 1000 ft of #19 copper wire.   Ans: 8.37 ohms.

4. The resistance of a conductor is 50.3 ohms at 20° C and 55.9 ohms at 50° C. Calculate the temperature coefficient of resistance of the material.

5. The resistance of the copper field coils of a generator is measured when the room temperature is 25° C and is found to be 225 ohms. What will be the resistance of these coils at the operating temperature of 90° C?   Ans: 281 ohms.

6. What is the resistance at 20° C of the tungsten filament of a lamp bulb which operates at 2000° C and 100 watts on 110 volts DC?

7. The primary coils of a transformer have a resistance of 5.48 ohms at 20° C. When the transformer is operating at full load, the resistance is 6.32 ohms. What is the operating temperature?   Ans: 59.0° C.

8. What will the resistance of a silver wire be at −20° C, if its resistance at 15° C is 19.5 ohms?

9. To prevent insulation damage, it is specified that the field coils of a certain type of motor should not exceed 105° C when it is running continuously under full load. The field coils of a particular motor were found to have a resistance of 6.38 ohms at 20° C and 8.26 ohms during a full-load run. Did the motor meet this specification?

10. A platinum wire has a resistance of 254 ohms at 20° C. When it is placed in a furnace, its resistance is 1630 ohms. What is the temperature of the furnace?

11. Show that the resistances of a conductor at temperatures T and T' are related by the equation
$$R_{T'} = R_T \frac{1+\alpha_{20}(T'-20°)}{1+\alpha_{20}(T-20°)}.$$

12. The temperature coefficient α_t referred to temperature t is defined by the equation
$$R_T = R_t[1+\alpha_t(T-t)].$$

(a) Show that
$$\alpha_t = \frac{\alpha_{20}}{1+\alpha_{20}(t-20°)}.$$

(b) Show that if α_t and $\alpha_{t'}$ refer to any two base temperatures t and t', then
$$\alpha_{t'} = \frac{\alpha_t}{1+\alpha_t(t'-t)}.$$

13. In terms of the definitions of Prob. 12, compute α_0, α_{40}, and α_{100} for standard-annealed copper. Explain in terms of the curve of Fig. 9 why α_t decreases as t increases.   Ans: 4.27, 3.64, 3.02×10⁻³ (C deg)⁻¹.

6. RESISTANCE OF INSULATORS, SEMICONDUCTORS, AND LIQUIDS*

The resistance of nonmetallic solids (insulators) is not really infinite—there is some extremely slight conductivity. But the resistance of an insulator is enormous compared with that of a metal; it is greater by a factor of about 10^{20}, and for most practical purposes the resistance can be considered infinite. Typical values of resistivity are

Glass: 10^{12} ohm·m,
Rubber: 10^{16} ohm·m,
Mica: 10^{15} ohm·m,
Shellac: 10^{14} ohm·m,
Sulfur: 10^{15} ohm·m.

These numbers are intended only to give the correct order of magnitude, because the resistivity varies from sample to sample, decreases with increasing potential gradient so that Ohm's law is not obeyed, and decreases very sharply with increasing temperature.

* This section may be omitted if desired.

The above values apply to current conducted through the body of the material. It is to be noted that, with exposed insulators, the leakage of current over the surface is usually much greater than the current flow through the body of the material. Particularly when the surface is wet or dusty, the leakage over the surface of transmission-line insulators can be very troublesome, whereas the body leakage is entirely negligible. It is for this reason that such insulators are corrugated to increase the length of surface leakage path or are even made with 'skirts' to keep part of this path dry.

Carbon is one nonmetal that is a fairly good electrical conductor. Its resistivity is about 3500×10^{-8} ohm·m at 20° C. Unlike metals, it has a negative temperature coefficient of resistance of about -0.0005 per C deg. Its resistivity drops to 2700×10^{-8} ohm·m at 500° C, 2100×10^{-8} at 1000° C, and 1100×10^{-8} at 2000° C. Carbon is used in 'brushes' of electrical machinery, in the carbon-button microphone, and in the carbon-pile rheostat. Carbon was the only material available for incandescent-lamp filaments before it was discovered how to draw tungsten wire; all other commercial conducting materials soften or melt at too low a temperature. It is used for one electrode in a dry cell.

There is a class of materials called *semiconductors* that is assuming increasing technical importance. These materials are principally the oxides and sulfides of certain metals, for example, CuO, ZnO, and PbS (galena). Semiconductors have a feeble electronic conductivity which increases rapidly in exponential fashion with increasing temperature. For example, CuO has resistivity about 1×10^3 ohm·m at 20° C but only one-tenth this resistivity at 70° C. The explanation of this behavior is that these materials have no free electrons at absolute zero of temperature, but as the temperature rises, more and more electrons are 'boiled off' from their parent atoms and become free to wander about in the material and to conduct electricity. Since at ordinary temperatures the number of free electrons is very low compared with the number in a metal, the resistivity is still very high.

The most important application of a semiconductor is the copper-oxide rectifier. A thin layer of CuO is formed on one side of a sheet of copper. If the type of contact between the copper oxide and the copper is just right, it is found that electrons will flow freely from the copper into the copper oxide but not in the reverse direction. Hence, when this sheet is placed in a circuit as indicated in Fig. 10, current will flow through it in only one way and an alternating potential will give a rectified unidirectional current. A rough explanation is that a large current of electrons can pass from the metal into the semiconductor, greatly supplementing the supply of free electrons in the semiconductor and hence permitting the passage of current through it. In the reverse direction the electron current is necessarily very small, since there are very few free electrons in the semiconductor and a supply cannot enter from the external wire because contact conditions at this junction do not satisfy the critical conditions necessary to permit their entry. The cat's-whisker and galena-crystal type of radio rectifier furnishes a similar example of rectification at the boundary between a metal and a semiconductor.

Certain liquid solutions of acids, bases, and salts are fairly good conductors because they contain ionized atoms or radicals that are free to move and carry the current. Even some pure liquids such as water and alcohol are slightly ionized, so that their resistivity is much lower than that of a good insulator. Distilled water has a resistivity of about 5000 ohm·m. The resistivity of sea water is about 0.2 ohm·m. With most good electrolytes (acids, bases, or salts), aqueous solutions can be

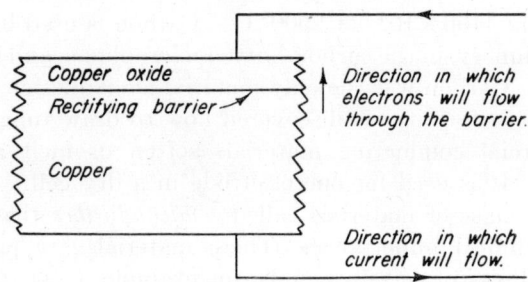

Fig. 10. The copper-oxide rectifier.

made with resistivities as low as 0.01–0.1 ohm·m. Such solutions of electrolytes have a negative temperature coefficient of resistance, the resistance dropping by a factor of about 3 when the temperature is increased from 20° C to 100° C. Some organic liquids are very good insulators; for example, the resistivity of transformer oil (petroleum) is about 2×10^{14} ohm·m.

PROBLEMS

1. A condenser is made by placing sheets of metal foil on the two sides of a glass plate 1 mm thick, of dielectric constant $K = 8.0$. The foil area is 0.25 m² on each side. The condenser is charged to 1000 volts and then disconnected from the source of DP.

(a) Find the current conducted through the glass if $\rho = 10^{12}$ ohm·m.

(b) If this current were the only source of leakage, how long would it take the DP to drop by 10 volts? Ans: (a) 0.25 microamp; (b) 0.71 sec.

2. Show that the time required for the DP to drop 1 per cent in a charged condenser constructed like that of Prob. 1 is $8.84 \times 10^{-14} \, K\rho$, in sec, with ρ in ohm·m, and that this time is independent of the thickness of the plate, the area of the foil, and the voltage.

3. A metal sphere 20 cm in diameter and charged to 1000 volts is supported on a glass rod 1 cm in diameter and 15 cm long.

(a) What magnitude of current is conducted through the glass rod to a grounded metal base?

(b) If this current were the only source of leakage, how long would it take the DP to drop by 10 volts?

7. TERMINAL VOLTAGE OF GENERATORS, MOTORS, AND BATTERIES

We have defined a source of EMF V as a device that will do work of amount V, in joules, on each coulomb of charge passing through it, deriving the energy from a mechanical, chemical, or other source. This statement regarding the work done is true if charges pass through the source of EMF in a particular direction, from what is called the *negative terminal* to what is called the *positive terminal*. This situation is illustrated in Fig. 11, in which the source of EMF does work of amount V, in joules, on each coulomb of charge passing *through it from the $-$ terminal to the $+$ terminal*. This work raises the potential (potential energy per coulomb) of the $+$ terminal by amount V above that of the $-$ terminal.*

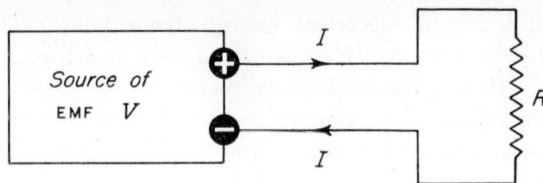

Fig. 11. A source of EMF supplies electrical energy which in turn heats a resistor.

This DP V across the resistance R causes current in the external circuit from the $+$ terminal to the $-$ terminal, the energy furnished by the source reappearing as heat in the resistor. The magnitude of the current is $I = V/R$, in amperes or coulombs/second. Since each coulomb has been given energy of amount V, in joules, the rate of energy delivery is $VI = V^2/R$, in joules/sec, or watts, in agreement with (7).

When current I passes through a resistance R *in either direction*, electrical energy is converted into heat at the rate I^2R, in watts, as given by (7).

But only when current passes through a source of EMF *from the $-$ terminal to the $+$ terminal* is energy of some other form changed into electrical energy at the rate V, in joules per coulomb. If, by employing a higher EMF in the external circuit, current is forced *backward* through the source of EMF as in Fig. 12 (in at the $+$ terminal, through the source from $+$ to $-$, and out at the $-$ terminal) electrical energy is changed into energy of the other form, and each coulomb passing through the source loses energy of amount V, in joules. *A source of EMF represents a reversible device for changing from electrical energy to some other form of*

---

* In this introductory paragraph we are neglecting a correction, arising from resistance internal to the source of EMF itself, that will be discussed a few pages later.

energy. If current is sent backward through a battery, electrical energy is converted into stored chemical energy—in a useful form if the battery is a storage battery, in a form mostly useless if the battery is a dry cell. Send current backward through a generator and you have a motor. There is no difference in principle between a DC generator and a DC motor. All such machines are called *dynamos* and will operate either as generators or motors. If a generator turned at a certain speed in a certain direction changes mechanical energy to electrical energy at the rate V, in joules per coulomb of charge passing through it, then if current is forced through it backward, the generator will turn, as a motor, in the same direction; and when sufficient current is supplied to bring the dynamo up to the same speed, it will convert electrical energy into mechanical energy at the rate V, in joules per coulomb passed through it.

In contrast, a resistor is a device that converts electrical energy into heat no matter what the direction of current; it is not possible to reverse the process and regain electrical energy from heat. The potential always *drops* by an amount IR as we traverse a resistor *in the direction* of the current. Hence, the DP across a resistor is called an IR-*drop*.

A battery, or a dynamo turning in a certain direction, has one terminal that can be permanently labeled $+$ and one that can be permanently labeled $-$. When no charge flows, the $+$ terminal has a potential V_e (*e* for EMF) above that of the $-$ terminal. When current flows, chemical or mechanical energy is converted to electrical energy at the rate V_e, in joules per coulomb of charge, when charge flows through the source of EMF from $-$ to $+$. When charge flows in the other direction, the same amount of energy, V_e, in joules per coulomb, is converted from electrical to mechanical or chemical form. The $+$ terminal would always be at potential V_e above the $-$ except for the fact that all dynamos and batteries have *internal* resistance in the internal current path *between* their terminals. As a result of internal resistance, there is a conversion of some energy to heat inside the battery or dynamo, no matter which direction the current has. The copper-wire and carbon-brush path through a dynamo, or the metal-plate and electrolyte path through a battery, has a certain resistance R_i (*i* for *internal*), so that, for current I in *either* direction, energy is converted into heat at the rate IR_i, in joules per coulomb of charge passing [compare with (6)].

Because of internal resistance, the difference of potential V_t between the *terminals* of a battery or dynamo when charge flows is not exactly the same as the EMF V_e, which is the DP when no charge flows, although the difference is usually small for a *good* battery or dynamo. We must distinguish two cases:

Generator, or battery on discharge. Internal current passes from $-$ to $+$ as in Fig. 11. Each coulomb of charge gains energy V_e from mechanical or chemical energy but loses energy IR_i in heat. Net gain is $V_e - IR_i$, in joules/coulomb. Hence, the DP V_t between the $+$ and $-$ terminals is

$$V_t = V_e - IR_i. \qquad \left\{\begin{array}{l}\text{Terminal voltage of generator, or of battery on}\\ \text{discharge}\end{array}\right\} \quad (16)$$

Multiplication of this equation by I gives an equation that expresses the power balance:

$$V_t I = V_e I - I^2 R_i. \qquad (17)$$

$\left\{\begin{array}{l}\text{Electrical power}\\ \text{delivered by the}\\ \text{source of EMF}\end{array}\right\} = \left\{\begin{array}{l}\text{electrical power}\\ \text{generated in the}\\ \text{source of EMF}\end{array}\right\} - \left\{\begin{array}{l}\text{electrical power converted into heat in the source of EMF}\end{array}\right\}$

Motor, or battery on charge. Internal current passes from $+$ to $-$ as in Fig. 12. Each coulomb of charge loses energy V_e that is changed to

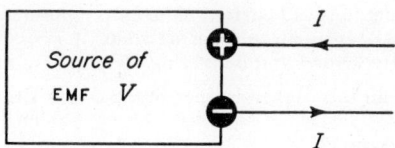

Fig. 12. When a current is forced backward through a source of EMF, electrical energy is converted into mechanical or chemical energy.

mechanical or chemical energy *and* energy IR_i in heat. Total loss is $V_e + IR_i$, in joules per coulomb. Hence, in this case the $+$ terminal is at higher potential than the $-$ by

$$V_t = V_e + IR_i. \qquad \left\{\begin{array}{l}\text{Terminal voltage of motor, or of battery on charge}\end{array}\right\} \quad (18)$$

Multiplication of this equation by I gives an equation that expresses the power balance:

$$V_t I = V_e I + I^2 R_i. \qquad (19)$$

$\left\{\begin{array}{l}\text{Electrical power delivered to the motor, or to the battery on charge}\end{array}\right\} = \left\{\begin{array}{l}\text{electrical power converted to mechanical or chemical energy}\end{array}\right\} + \left\{\begin{array}{l}\text{electrical power converted into heat in the motor, or in the battery on charge}\end{array}\right\}$

In the case of a motor, the quantity V_e, which gives the mechanical energy developed in joules per coulomb of charge passing, is commonly called the *back*-EMF, since it is a voltage in a direction opposing the flow of current.

PROBLEMS

1. Consider a 6-v storage battery, with internal resistance of 0.01 ω, delivering a current of 50 amp.
   (a) What is the terminal voltage?
   (b) What is the rate of conversion of chemical to electrical energy?
   (c) What is the rate of heat generation in the battery?
   (d) What is the power delivered? *Ans:* (a) 5.5 v; (b) 300 w; (c) 25 w; (d) 275 w.

2. Answer the questions (a)–(d) of Prob. 1 for a 1.5-v dry cell, with internal resistance of 0.1 ω, delivering 1.3 amp.

3. Consider a 6-v storage battery, with internal resistance of 0.01 ω, when it is being charged with a current of 50 amp.
(a) What is the terminal voltage?
(b) At what rate is electrical energy being delivered to the battery?
(c) At what rate is heat being developed in the battery?
(d) At what rate is electrical energy being changed into chemical energy?
Ans: (a) 6.5 v; (b) 325 w; (c) 25 w; (d) 300 w.

4. Answer the questions (a)–(d) of Prob. 3 for a 110-v bank of storage batteries, consisting of 55 two-volt cells in series, *each cell* having an internal resistance of 0.008 ω, when the bank is being charged with a current of 25 amp.

5. The terminal voltage of a generator is 120 v at no load (no current output). The internal resistance is 0.2 ω. What will its terminal voltage be when it is rotating at the same speed and has the same field excitation (in which case it has the same generated EMF) but is delivering 40 amperes? Ans: 112 v.

6. The terminal voltage of a generator of 0.2 ω internal resistance is 115 v when the generator is delivering full-load current of 40 amp. Assuming the same generated voltage, what will be its terminal voltage (a) when it is overloaded and delivering 60 amp? (b) when lightly loaded and delivering 20 amp? (c) at no load?

7. A DC motor has an internal resistance of 0.2 ω. It draws 40 amp at full load from 120-v lines.
(a) What is the back-EMF?
(b) What is the power drawn by the motor?
(c) What is the heat generated in the internal resistance?
(d) What is the mechanical power developed?
(e) Note that not all of the mechanical power computed in (d) appears as useful work at the shaft. Some of it is reconverted to heat within the motor because of friction, windage, and the so-called *iron-losses* (from hysteresis and eddy currents). The amount of mechanical energy reconverted to heat can be determined approximately by a measurement of current drawn at no load, when there is no mechanical output at the shaft. If this motor draws 3 amp from 120-v lines at no load, what is the back-EMF at no load, and what is the mechanical energy developed at no load?
(f) Assuming that the mechanical losses are the same at full load and no load, so that the 358.2 w computed in (e) are to be subtracted from the 4480 w of (d) to get the actual mechanical output at the shaft, compute the over-all efficiency of this motor when running at full load, and the mechanical output in horsepower.
Ans: (a) 112 v; (b) 4800 w; (c) 320 w; (d) 4480 w; (e) 119.4 v, 358.2 w; (f) 85.9%, 5.52 hp.

8. Make the same computations as in Prob. 7 for the case of a motor of 0.1-ω internal resistance that draws 150 amp from 240-v lines at full load and 4 amp from 240-v lines at no load.

8. SIMPLE CIRCUITS; RESISTORS IN PARALLEL AND IN SERIES

The simplest type of electric circuit is illustrated in Fig. 13. Here the terminal voltage of the generator or battery, given by (16), is applied across the resistor and causes current to flow through it:

$$V_t = IR.$$

Since the terminal voltage itself depends on the current flowing, this gives an algebraic equation to be solved for I: substituting from (16),

$$V_e - IR_i = IR,$$

or
$$I = \frac{V_e}{R+R_i}. \tag{20}$$

The current is determined by the EMF and the total resistance in the circuit, both internal and external.

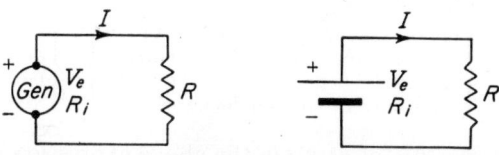

Fig. 13. A resistor connected across a generator or battery.

Energetically, the above equation, which may be written as

$$V_e = IR_i + IR,$$

expresses the fact that the chemical or electrical energy V_e given to each coulomb equals, in accordance with (6), the sum of the heat generated by each coulomb in flowing through the internal resistance and that generated in flowing through the external resistance.

A more complicated single-mesh network, in which a battery is being charged by a generator through wires having different resistances, is shown in Fig. 14. The EMF's and internal resistances of the generator and battery are denoted by V_g, R_g and V_b, R_b. In this case each coulomb that flows around the circuit gains energy V_g in the generator, and loses V_b to chemical energy in the battery and $IR_g + IR_1 + IR_b + IR_2$ to heat. Since gain must equal loss,

$$V_g = V_b + I(R_g + R_1 + R_b + R_2),$$

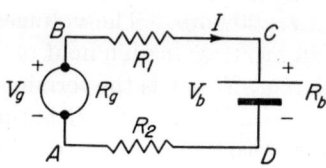

Fig. 14. A generator charging a battery.

hence
$$I = \frac{V_g - V_b}{R_1 + R_2 + R_g + R_b}. \tag{21}$$

Alternatively, equation (21) may be derived by considering that the terminal voltages V_{gt} and V_{bt} of the generator and battery oppose each other and that it is only their difference that is available to force current through the external resistances R_1 and R_2. Hence, we write

$$(V_{gt} - V_{bt}) = I(R_1 + R_2). \tag{22}$$

But, from (16),
$$V_{gt} = V_g - IR_g,$$
and, from (18),
$$V_{bt} = V_b + IR_b.$$

When these expressions are substituted in (22), we obtain

$$V_g - IR_g - V_b - IR_b = I(R_1 + R_2),$$

which, when solved for I, gives (21) directly.

It will be readily seen that any simple single-mesh circuit can be solved at once by a generalization of (21). The rule is:

$$\begin{Bmatrix} \text{Current} \\ \text{clockwise} \\ \text{around the} \\ \text{circuit} \end{Bmatrix} = \begin{Bmatrix} \textit{algebraic} \text{ sum of EMF's counted posi-} \\ \text{tive if they tend to force current} \\ \text{clockwise, negative if they tend to} \\ \text{force current counterclockwise} \end{Bmatrix} \div \begin{Bmatrix} \text{sum of all resist-} \\ \text{ances in the circuit,} \\ \text{both internal and} \\ \text{external} \end{Bmatrix}$$

If the algebraic sum of EMF's in the above expression comes out negative, the clockwise current also comes out negative; the negative sign indicates that the current is counterclockwise instead of clockwise.

It will be instructive to consider the DP's between various points in the circuit of Fig. 14 in detail for the numerical example given in Fig. 15.

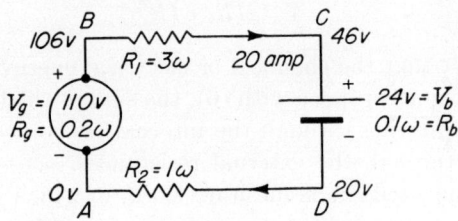

Fig. 15. A numerical example, showing the potentials at points B, C, D, if point A is arbitrarily assigned the potential 0.

For the constants in this example, (21) gives $I = 20$ amp. The voltages indicated at points A, B, C, D are based on an arbitrary assignment of 0 volts as the potential of A. The voltage difference $B - A$ is the terminal voltage of the generator as given by (16). The difference $B - C$ is the IR-drop in R_1. The difference $C - D$ is the terminal voltage of the battery on charge as given by (18). Finally, the difference $D - A$, which brings us back to 0, is the IR-drop in R_2. Any one of these voltage differences represents the reading of a voltmeter connected between the two points mentioned, whereas a voltmeter connected between B and D would read $106 - 20 = 86$ volts, and one connected between C and A would read 46 volts.

Single-mesh circuits can always be solved by the methods given above. Networks containing more than one mesh will in general need the application of Kirchhoff's laws, which are given in the next section. However some networks can be reduced to a single-mesh circuit by the device of replacing a set of pure resistances in parallel by a single equivalent resistance. Suppose that between two points in a circuit, such as A and B

in Fig. 16, three resistors are connected in parallel. The DP across each resistor is the same, V_{AB}. Hence,

$$I_1 = V_{AB}/R_1, \quad I_2 = V_{AB}/R_2, \quad I_3 = V_{AB}/R_3.$$

The current flowing in the external circuit is the sum of these:

$$I = I_1 + I_2 + I_3 = V_{AB}\left(\frac{1}{R_1} + \frac{1}{R_2} + \frac{1}{R_3}\right).$$

The ratio V_{AB}/I is defined as the effective resistance R of the parallel circuit, so that

$$\frac{I}{V_{AB}} = \frac{1}{R} = \frac{1}{R_1} + \frac{1}{R_2} + \frac{1}{R_3}.$$

R, as given by this formula, is the single resistance that will carry the same current with the same voltage as the parallel combination, will

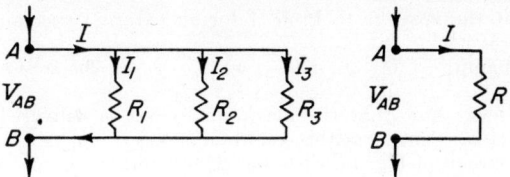

Fig. 16. Resistors in parallel are equivalent to a single resistor of resistance R given by (23).

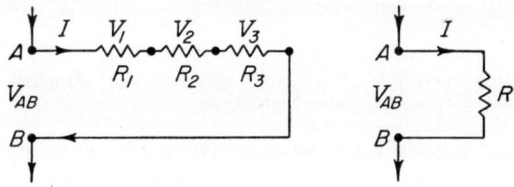

Fig. 17. Resistors in series are equivalent to a single resistor with $R = R_1 + R_2 + R_3$.

generate the same heat, and in general can replace the parallel combination with no effect on the rest of the circuit. For any number n of resistors in parallel, the effective resistance is similarly given by

$$\frac{1}{R} = \frac{1}{R_1} + \frac{1}{R_2} + \cdots + \frac{1}{R_n}. \quad \left\{\begin{array}{l}\text{Resistors}\\\text{in parallel}\end{array}\right\} \quad (23)$$

In the same way, one can replace a number of resistors in series as in Fig. 17 by a single equivalent resistance

$$R = R_1 + R_2 + \cdots + R_n. \quad \left\{\begin{array}{l}\text{Resistors}\\\text{in series}\end{array}\right\} \quad (24)$$

To derive this, note that the current is the same through each resistor; the potential drops are $V_1 = IR_1$, $V_2 = IR_2$, $\cdots$; the total potential drop will be $V_{AB} = V_1 + V_2 + \cdots = I(R_1 + R_2 + \cdots)$; and the effective resistance V_{AB}/I will be $R_1 + R_2 + \cdots$.

PROBLEMS

1. Consider the circuit of Fig. 13, with EMF $V_e = 6$ v and internal resistance $R_i = 0.5\ \omega$. Compute
  (a) the current,
  (b) the terminal voltage,
  (c) the generated electrical power,
  (d) the power lost in internal heat in the generator or battery,
  (e) the power delivered by the generator or battery and used in heating the external resistance,
for the following values of external resistance R:
  (1) $R = 9.5\ \omega$.   Ans: (a) 0.6 amp; (b) 5.7 v; (c) 3.6 w; (d) 0.18 w; (e) 3.42 w.
  (2) $R = 1.0\ \omega$.   Ans: (a) 4 amp; (b) 4 v; (c) 24 w; (d) 8 w; (e) 16 w.
  (3) $R = 0.5\ \omega$.   Ans: (a) 6 amp; (b) 3 v; (c) 36 w; (d) 18 w; (e) 18 w.
  (4) $R = 0.1\ \omega$.   Ans: (a) 10 amp; (b) 1 v; (c) 60 w; (d) 50 w; (e) 10 w.

2. Show that the answers to Prob. 1 for an external resistance of $R = r\ \omega$ are given by the expressions
  (a) $6/(r+\tfrac{1}{2})$ amp;   (c) $36/(r+\tfrac{1}{2})$ w;   (e) $36r/(r^2+r+\tfrac{1}{4})$ w.
  (b) $6r/(r+\tfrac{1}{2})$ v;   (d) $18/(r^2+r+\tfrac{1}{4})$ w.
From these answers, show that the maximum power is delivered to the external circuit when $R = \tfrac{1}{2}\ \omega$. Note that this condition makes $R = R_i$. In analogous fashion, show that in the circuit of Fig. 13, with *any* given values of V_e and R_i, the maximum heat is developed in an external resistance R if R is chosen so that $R = R_i$.

3. In Fig. 15, verify the given values of current and of the potentials at B, C, D. Compute
  (a) the generated electrical power;
  (b) the heat loss in the generator;
  (c) the heat developed in R_1;
  (d) the heat developed in the battery;
  (e) the heat developed in R_2;
  (f) the rate of creation of chemical energy.
Verify that (a) = (b) + (c) + (d) + (e) + (f).
  Ans: (a) 2200 w; (b) 80 w; (c) 1200 w; (d) 40 w; (e) 400 w; (f) 480 w.

4. In Fig. 14, take $V_g = 24$ v, $V_b = 6$ v, $R_g = 0.4\ \omega$, $R_b = 0.2\ \omega$, $R_1 = 1\ \omega$, $R_2 = 2\ \omega$. Compute I. Letting the potential V_A at point A equal 0, compute the potentials V_B, V_C, V_D. Also compute all the quantities asked for in parts (a)–(f) of Prob. 3.

5. In Fig. 15, to what value would R_2 have to be changed to drop the battery-charging current to 10 amp?   Ans: 5.3 ω.

6. In Fig. 15, to what value would R_1 have to be changed to increase the battery-charging current to 30 amp?

7. In Fig. 16, let $R_1 = 1\ \omega$, $R_2 = 2\ \omega$, $R_3 = 6\ \omega$, and $V_{AB} = 12$ v.
  (a) Compute R.
  (b) Compute I from V_{AB} and R.
  (c) Compute the total power from V_{AB} and R.
  (d) Find I_1, I_2, and I_3, and verify that the sum is I.
  (e) Compute the power developed in R_1, R_2, and R_3 individually, and verify that the sum agrees with (c).
Ans: (a) 0.6 ω; (b) 20 amp; (c) 240 w; (d) 12 amp, 6 amp, 2 amp; (e) 144 w, 72 w, 24 w.

8. Answer the same questions as in Prob. 7 for $R_1 = 100\ \omega$, $R_2 = 20\ \omega$, $R_3 = 10\ \omega$, and $V_{AB} = 120$ v in Fig. 16.

9. In Fig. 17, let $R_1 = 1\ \omega$, $R_2 = 2\ \omega$, $R_3 = 6\ \omega$, and $V_{AB} = 12$ v.
(a) Compute R.
(b) Compute I from V_{AB} and R.
(c) Compute the total power from V_{AB} and R.
(d) Find V_1, V_2, and V_3, and verify that the sum is V_{AB}.
(e) Compute the power developed in R_1, R_2, and R_3 individually, and compare the sum with (c). Ans: (a) 9 ω;
(b) 1.333 amp; (c) 16 w; (d) 1.333 v, 2.667 v, 8 v; (e) 1.778 w, 3.556 w, 10.667 w.

10. Answer the same questions as in Prob. 9 for $R_1 = 100\ \omega$, $R_2 = 40\ \omega$, $R_3 = 10\ \omega$, and $V_{AB} = 120$ v in Fig. 17.

11. Prove that the effective resistance of a parallel combination of resistors is **less** than any one of the individual resistances, and that the effective resistance of a series combination is greater than any one of the individual resistances.

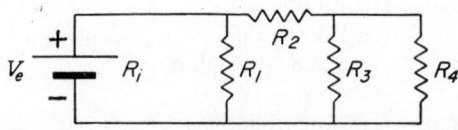

Fig. 18.

12. In Fig. 18, let $V_e = 12$ v, $R_i = 0.2\ \omega$, $R_1 = 4\ \omega$, $R_2 = 0.5\ \omega$, $R_3 = 2\ \omega$, and $R_4 = 3\ \omega$.
(a) Find the currents I_b, I_1, I_2, I_3, and I_4 through the battery and each of the resistors.
(b) Find the voltages V_t, V_1, V_2, V_3, and V_4 across the battery and each of the resistors.
(c) Find the power P_t delivered by the battery and the amounts of power P_1, P_2, P_3, and P_4 absorbed in each of the resistors. Verify that $P_t = P_1 + P_2 + P_3 + P_4$.

13. Answer the questions in Prob. 12 for the case $V_e = 105$ v, $R_i = 0.5\ \omega$, $R_1 = 20\ \omega$, $R_2 = 5\ \omega$, $R_3 = 20\ \omega$, and $R_4 = 60\ \omega$ in Fig. 18. Ans: (a) 10, 5, 5, 3.75, 1.25 amp; (b) 100, 100, 25, 75, 75 v; (c) 1000, 500, 125, 281.25, 93.75 w.

9. ELECTRICAL NETWORKS; KIRCHHOFF'S LAWS

In this section we shall consider electrical networks more complex than those treated in the previous section. There is a straightforward procedure for solution of such networks. We shall explain the method by using the two-mesh network of Fig. 19 as an example.

In this example the two unknowns are the charging current I of the battery and the back-EMF V_e of the motor. We are given that the motor current is 5 amp; hence, we can represent the current delivered by the generator as $I + 5$ amp. This statement is an illustration of

KIRCHHOFF'S FIRST LAW: *At any junction in the circuit the total current flowing toward the junction must equal the total current flowing away.*

Kirchhoff's two laws do not state any new principles, but they do give the two principles that must be systematically applied in the solution of electrical networks. The second law can be stated as follows:

KIRCHHOFF'S SECOND LAW: *If we start at any point and 'walk' around any closed loop back to our starting point, we must also arrive back at the* same electrical potential. *So if, as we walk, we note the different changes in electrical potential arising from* EMF'S, *IR-drops, and IR-rises* (which occur when we happen to walk through a resistance against the current), *and add them all up keeping proper algebraic signs, we must get zero when we have completed our tour of the loop.*

In Fig. 19, if we start at point A and walk clockwise around mesh 1 of the net, we encounter successively the following changes in potential in volts:

$+120$ v	(EMF of generator)
$-(0.3\,\omega)(I+5$ amp$)$	(IR-drop in generator; we walk with the current)
$-(0.5\,\omega)(I+5$ amp$)$	(IR-drop in line)
$-V_e$	(back-EMF of motor, representing a drop in potential as we walk through it)
$-(0.4\,\omega)(5$ amp$)$	(IR-drop in motor)
$-(0.5\,\omega)(I+5$ amp$)$	(IR-drop in line)

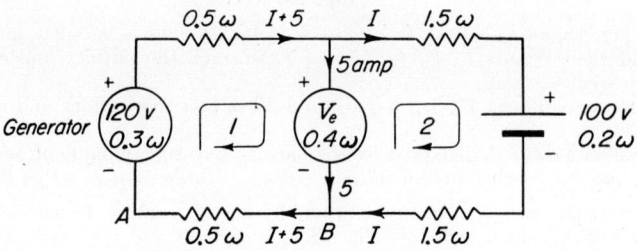

Fig. 19. A generator charges a 100-v battery and drives a motor that draws 5 amp.

The sum must be zero. This gives the equation

$$120\text{ v} - (0.3\,\omega)(I+5\text{ amp}) - (0.5\,\omega)(I+5\text{ amp}) - V_e - (0.4\,\omega)(5\text{ amp})$$
$$- (0.5\,\omega)(I+5\text{ amp}) = 0,$$

or, simplifying, $\qquad 111.5\text{ v} - (1.3\,\omega)I - V_e = 0. \qquad (25)$

This single equation cannot be solved for the two unknowns, but we can get a second equation from the second mesh. Starting at point B and walking clockwise around mesh 2, we encounter the following changes in potential in volts:

$+V_e$	(this time the back-EMF of the motor represents an increase of potential in the direction we are walking)
$+(0.4\,\omega)(5$ amp$)$	(an IR-rise, since we are walking against the current)
$-(1.5\,\omega)I$	(IR-drop in line)
-100 v	(drop in potential arising from generated EMF of battery)
$-(0.2\,\omega)I$	(IR-drop in battery)
$-(1.5\,\omega)I$	(IR-drop in line)

Setting the sum equal to zero gives us

$$V_e + (0.4\,\omega)(5\text{ amp}) - (1.5\,\omega)I - 100\text{ v} - (0.2\,\omega)I - (1.5\,\omega)I = 0,$$

or
$$-98\text{ v} - (3.2\,\omega)I + V_e = 0. \tag{26}$$

Equations (25) and (26) can be solved simultaneously for I and V_e. Adding (25) and (26) gives

$$13.5\text{ v} - (4.5\,\omega)I = 0,$$

or
$$I = 3\text{ amp}. \tag{27}$$

Substitution in (25) then gives

$$V_e = 107.6\text{ v}. \tag{28}$$

These values of I and V_e check when substituted in (26).

There is a third equation which could have been used in place of either (25) or (26), or which can be used as a check on the work. It is derived by walking around the whole outside of the circuit from A clockwise back to A. Let us use it as a check on the current values of $I = 3$ amp through the battery and $I + 5$ amp $= 8$ amp delivered by the generator. When we walk around the outside of meshes 1 and 2 combined, we encounter the following changes in potential in volts:

$+120$ v	(EMF of generator)
$-(0.3\,\omega)(8\text{ amp})$	(IR-drop in generator)
$-(0.5\,\omega)(8\text{ amp})$	(IR-drop in line)
$-(1.5\,\omega)(3\text{ amp})$	(IR-drop in line)
-100 v	(drop arising from EMF of battery)
$-(0.2\,\omega)(3\text{ amp})$	(IR-drop in battery)
$-(1.5\,\omega)(3\text{ amp})$	(IR-drop in line)
$-(0.5\,\omega)(8\text{ amp})$	(IR-drop in line)

The sum of these numbers of volts is

$$120 - 2.4 - 4 - 4.5 - 100 - 0.6 - 4.5 - 4 = 0,$$

which checks.

By a procedure similar to the above, a set of simultaneous equations may be found that will solve any network, provided the number of unknowns is not greater than the number of meshes in the network. The unknowns may be values of current, EMF, terminal voltage, or resistance. By a *mesh*, we mean one of the separate areas into which the circuit diagram is divided; thus, Fig. 15 has one mesh; Fig. 18, three; Fig. 19, two; and Fig. 20, four. The *loop* contemplated in Kirchhoff's second law is any closed path in the circuit, for example, any path indicated by the fine lines of Fig. 20.

The general procedure for applying Kirchhoff's laws to the solution of networks may be outlined as follows:

1. Draw the circuit diagram, and label all known currents, voltages, and resistances. Put $+$, $-$ signs on all sources of EMF to show the high- and low-potential sides.

2. Assign letters to all unknown EMF's and to all unknown resistances. However, in case both the EMF and the internal resistance of a source of EMF are unknown, it will be impossible to solve for both unknowns, and one should work directly with the terminal voltage, assigning a letter to the terminal voltage if it is unknown.

3. For all branches of the circuit in which the current is unknown, assign a current direction. Frequently it will be impossible to guess the correct direction of the current, but this uncertainty is not important. Guess a *definite* direction; and if you have guessed incorrectly, the computed magnitude of the current will merely come out negative in the final solution.

4. Assign symbols to all unknown currents, but in making these assignments keep the number of symbols to a minimum by taking full advantage of Kirchhoff's first law at each current junction. Thus, in Fig. 19, there are two unknown currents; but if the current through the battery is called I, the current delivered by the generator must be $I+5$ amp, so that only one unknown *symbol* need be introduced.

5. Now apply Kirchhoff's second law to a number of loops equal to the number of meshes in the circuit. You need not use the individual meshes exclusively, but you cannot hope to get more independent equations than there are individual meshes. The loops you choose must altogether traverse each circuit element at least once. Thus, in the four-mesh circuit symbolized in Fig. 20, we must use

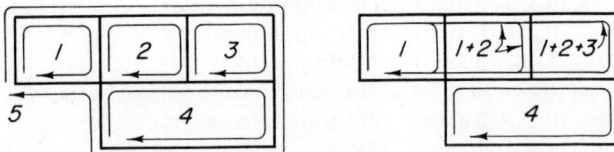

Fig. 20. Various circuit loops can be used in writing Kirchhoff's laws for this four-mesh circuit, as discussed in the text.

four loops. These could be the loops labeled 1, 2, 3, and 4, which are the meshes themselves; or any *one* of these loops could be omitted and replaced by the outside loop 5. Another alternative would be to choose the loops labeled 1, $1+2$, and $1+2+3$, along with loop 4. Various other combinations are possible. Now walk around each loop, either clockwise or counterclockwise, back to your starting point. In walking, write down each EMF (or terminal voltage), positive if it represents a rise of potential as you walk, negative if it represents a drop. Also write down the IR-drop or -rise associated with each resistance. If you walk through a resistance in the assumed direction of the current, there is a drop in potential which is called negative. If you walk against the assumed direction of the current there is a rise of potential, called positive. When the walk is completed, the algebraic sum of all these changes in potential is equated to zero.

6. Solve the resulting set of linear equations for the unknowns by addition and subtraction.* Draw a new diagram, or use a colored pencil, to show the

---

* The method of solution of a set of linear equations by determinants, which is given in all books on algebra, is fundamental to theoretical discussions, but it is not

numerical current values and corrected directions of current flow. Check this final solution against Kirchhoff's first law at each junction, and check also by applying the second law to some circuit loops not previously used.

NOTE: In place of the rule given in paragraph 5 in which you write down each voltage change as you walk around a loop and equate the sum to zero, you may prefer to use an alternative rule based on the equation

$$\sum \text{EMF} = \sum IR,$$

in which EMF's appear on the left side, IR-drops on the right. In applying this rule, walk around the loop in a definite direction; write all EMF's on the left side of the equation, $+$ or $-$ according to whether they *tend* to cause current flow *in* the direction of walking or *against* the direction of walking; and write the values of IR for all resistors on the right side, $+$ or $-$ according to whether you are walking *with* or *against* the *current*. In this form, *IR-drops* appear with a $+$ sign on the *right* side of the equation, since an IR-drop occurs if you are walking with the current. This result is equivalent to having an IR-drop appear with a $-$ sign on the *left* side of the equation, as in the rule of paragraph 5. The equations obtained from either rule are algebraically equivalent.

This procedure is best illustrated by an example somewhat more complex than that of Fig. 19. We shall work through the example of Fig. 21(a). Here we have a generator and a battery, of known EMF and internal resistance, connected in parallel to a motor drawing a known current. In addition to the ordinary leads there is a single low-resistance lead from the motor back to the generator. The unknowns are the terminal voltage of the motor and two unknown currents, in terms of which all other currents may be expressed by using Kirchhoff's first law.

Let us assume that since the battery EMF is lower than the generator EMF, the generator will furnish a charging current to the battery as well as furnishing the motor current. Call the battery charging current I_1 and the generator current I_1+12 amp, as in the figure. At the junction below the motor, the motor current splits in an unknown proportion. If we call the current in one wire I_2, the other wire will carry 12 amp $-I_2$, as indicated. All the other currents are now determined, and Kirchhoff's first law is satisfied at each junction, as indicated in Fig. 21(a).

Now that we have labeled all wires with the current directions and magnitudes, we proceed to apply Kirchhoff's second law to each of the three meshes of the network. The student should carefully check each term in the following equations.

Mesh 1:

$115 \text{ v} - (0.5 \text{ } \omega)(I_1+12 \text{ amp}) - (0.6 \text{ } \omega)(I_1+12 \text{ amp}) - 110 \text{ v} - (0.1 \text{ } \omega)I_1$
$\qquad - (0.6 \text{ } \omega)(I_1+I_2) = 0.$

---

usually the most expeditious procedure in numerical computations. In general, the use of determinants is much more tedious than the method of successive elimination of unknowns by multiplication, addition, and subtraction. The latter method should always be used in numerical computations.

Mesh 2: $110 \text{ v} + (0.1 \text{ } \omega)I_1 - 2.4 \text{ v} - V_t - (0.2 \text{ } \omega)I_2 = 0.$

Mesh 3: $(0.6 \text{ } \omega)(I_1 + I_2) + (0.2 \text{ } \omega)I_2 - (0.25 \text{ } \omega)(12 \text{ amp} - I_2) = 0.$

These three equations simplify to

$$-8.2 \text{ v} - (1.8 \text{ } \omega)I_1 - (0.6 \text{ } \omega)I_2 = 0, \qquad (a)$$

$$107.6 \text{ v} + (0.1 \text{ } \omega)I_1 - (0.2 \text{ } \omega)I_2 - V_t = 0, \qquad (b)$$

$$-3.0 \text{ v} + (0.6 \text{ } \omega)I_1 + (1.05 \text{ } \omega)I_2 = 0. \qquad (c)$$

We can easily eliminate I_1 by multiplying the last equation by three,

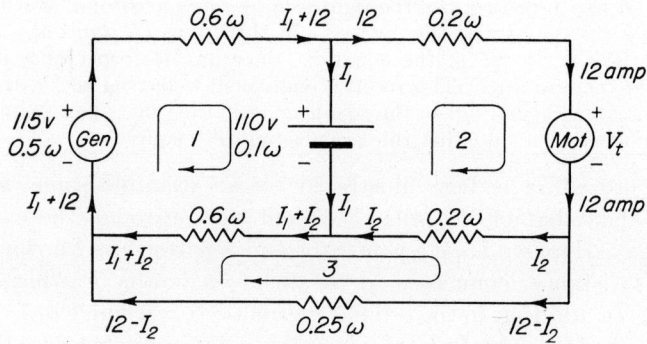

Fig. 21(a). Three-mesh-network problem.

which gives $\qquad -9.0 \text{ v} + (1.8 \text{ } \omega)I_1 + (3.15 \text{ } \omega)I_2 = 0,$

and by adding this to (a), to get

$$-17.2 \text{ v} + (2.55 \text{ } \omega)I_2 = 0,$$

or $\qquad \boxed{I_2 = 6.75 \text{ amp.}}$

When this value is substituted in (c), we find

$$-3.0 \text{ v} + (0.6 \text{ } \omega)I_1 + 7.09 \text{ v} = 0,$$
$$(0.6 \text{ } \omega)I_1 + 4.09 \text{ v} = 0,$$

or $\qquad \boxed{I_1 = -6.82 \text{ amp.}}$

(We guessed the direction of I_1 incorrectly.) Finally, V_t is obtained by substitution in (b):

$$107.6 \text{ v} - 0.68 \text{ v} - 1.35 \text{ v} - V_t = 0,$$

$$\boxed{V_t = 105.57 \text{ v.}}$$

The currents that occur in the various other conductors of Fig. 21(a) are

$$I_1 + 12 \text{ amp} = 5.18 \text{ amp},$$
$$12 \text{ amp} - I_2 = 5.25 \text{ amp},$$
$$I_1 + I_2 = -0.07 \text{ amp}.$$

We guessed the directions incorrectly, both of the battery current and of the current through the lower 0.6-ω lead. Both the generator and battery furnish current to the motor, and a small part of the battery

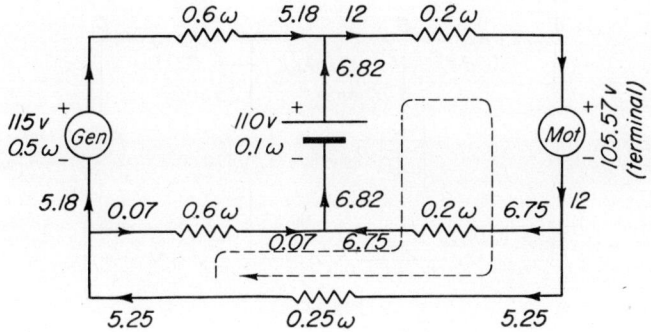

Fig. 21(*b*). Solution to the problem of Fig. 21(a).

current, as well as all the generator current, prefers to return by way of the 0.25-ω lead. When the current directions are corrected and numerical values are entered, we get the solution shown in Fig. 21(b).

A little mental arithmetic shows that this solution satisfies the first law at each junction. As an additional check we shall try writing Kirchhoff's second law for the loop indicated by the broken arrow in Fig. 21(b). For this loop we obtain the following equation (in volts):

$$-0.07(0.6) + 110 - (6.82)(0.1) - 12(0.2) - 105.57 - 5.25(0.25) = 0$$
or
$$-0.04 + 110 - 0.68 - 2.40 - 105.57 - 1.31 = 0$$
or
$$0.00 = 0,$$

a satisfactory check. As a second check we might walk around the whole outside of the circuit beginning at the lower left, to get, in volts,

$$115 - 5.18(0.5) - 5.18(0.6) - 12(0.2) - 105.57 - 5.25(0.25) = 0$$
or
$$115 - 2.59 - 3.11 - 2.40 - 105.57 - 1.31 = 0$$
or
$$0.02 = 0,$$

a check within the rounding-off error of the computation.

PROBLEMS

1. In Fig. 19, if the motor is loaded so that the motor current is increased to 10 amp, no other constants being changed, what is the charging current of the battery and the back-EMF of the motor? Ans: $I = 1.556$ amp, $V_e = 100.98$ v.

2. In Fig. 19, if the motor is loaded so that the motor current is increased to 20 amp, no other constants being changed, what is the charging current of the battery and the back-EMF of the motor?

3. Two generators G_1 and G_2 supply currents to two loads I and II, as in Fig. 22. Calculate the currents in AB, BC, and CD and the DP's V_I and V_{II} across the two loads.

Ans: $64\frac{1}{3}$ amp from A to B; $5\frac{2}{3}$ amp from C to B; $80\frac{2}{3}$ amp from D to C; $V_I = 114.6$ v; $V_{II} = 115.1$ v.

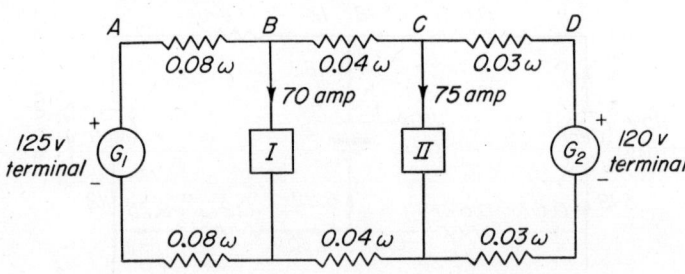

Fig. 22.

4. In Fig. 22, if the current to load I is 30 amp instead of 70 amp, with no other change, calculate the currents in AB, BC, and CD and the DP's across loads I and II.

5. The two generators shown in Fig. 23 have nominal ratings of 120 v. Together they supply 100 amp to a transmission line. V_{e1}, the EMF of generator 1, is exactly 120 volts. The EMF of generator 2 may be varied by making variations in the exciting field current, in order to make it carry more or less of the load, as indicated by an ammeter measuring I_2. Compute the exact value of V_{e2} if generator 2 is to supply

(a) half the line current;
(b) one-quarter of the line current;
(c) none of the line current (this is the condition to which the power-station attendant would adjust before he pulled a switch to disconnect generator 2 from the line, leaving generator 1 to carry the whole load);
(d) all of the line current.
(e) What happens if the EMF of generator 2 is raised to 150 v?

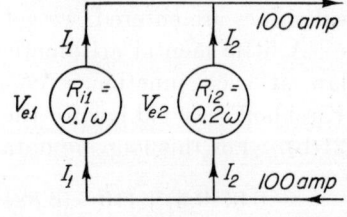

Fig. 23.

Ans: (a) 125 v; (b) 117.5 v; (c) 110 v; (d) 140 v; (e) $I_2 = 133$ amp, of which 100 amp go into the line and 33 amp go backward through generator 1 to drive it as a motor.

6. In Fig. 23, if $V_{e1} = 120$ v and $V_{e2} = 130$ v, find the currents I_1 and I_2, the voltage across the line, and the effective resistance of the load connected across the line, assuming that this is a pure resistance load, such as a lighting load.

7. *Wheatstone bridge.* This convenient circuit for the measurement of an unknown resistance is shown in Fig. 24. One of the resistances, say R_1, is unknown. The others are variable but known resistances, which are adjusted until the galvanometer indicates zero current, when the bridge is said to be balanced. (A galvanometer is a current-measuring instrument that is electrically equivalent to a fixed resistance R_G.) By applying Kirchhoff's laws show that when the bridge is balanced,

the resistances are in the ratio
$$\frac{R_1}{R_2} = \frac{R_3}{R_4},$$
from which R_1 may be computed if the other three are known.

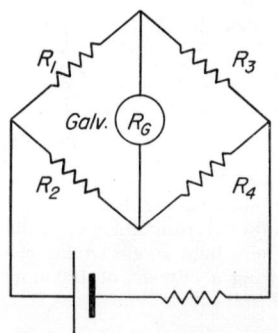

Fig. 24. The Wheatstone bridge.

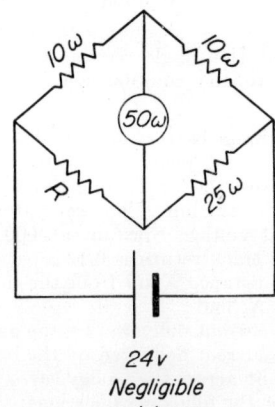

Fig. 25. A Wheatstone-bridge circuit.

8. If the bridge of Fig. 25 is balanced for the resistance values shown, what is the value of the unknown resistance R?

9. A two-wire underwater power cable runs across a bay and is 52,000 ft long. Each wire is #0. One wire develops a ground to the lead sheath at some point. A Varley-loop test is applied by connecting the two wires together at the far end and setting up a bridge circuit at the near end as shown in Fig. 26. The bridge is balanced with $R_1 = 15.00\ \omega$, $R_2 = 7.63\ \omega$. Which section of the cable should be pulled up to look for the defect? (The resistance of the grounded circuit through the sheath may be assumed negligible.)   Ans: the section 35,000 ft from the near end.

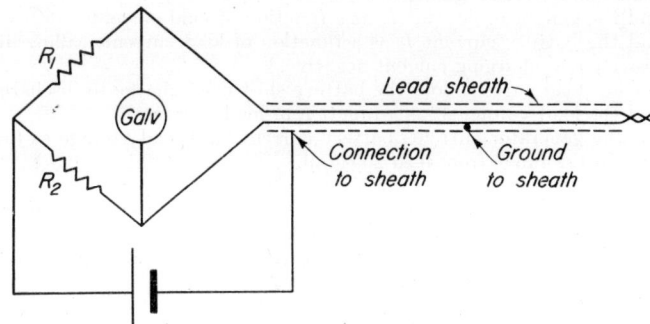

Fig. 26. Varley-loop test.

10. If the bridge of Fig. 26, used as in Prob. 9, is balanced for $R_1 = 6.00\ \omega$ and $R_2 = 29.7\ \omega$, approximately where is the defect?

11. Compute the current through the 50-ω galvanometer in the Wheatstone bridge of Fig. 25 when the bridge is *unbalanced*, with $R = 20\ \omega$. The + side of the battery is at the left.   Ans: 0.0202 amp upward.

12. Compute the current through the 50-ω galvanometer in the Wheatstone bridge of Fig. 25 when the bridge is *unbalanced*, with $R = 30\,\omega$. The $+$ side of the battery is at the left.

13. Find the single resistance that is equivalent to the combination shown in Fig. 27. Ans: 4.84 ω.

14. Find the single resistance that is equivalent to the combination shown in Fig. 28.

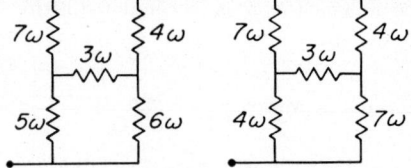

Fig. 27.   Fig. 28.

15. A storage battery of 550 volts EMF, with an internal resistance of 0.20 ω, is 'floated' across the far end of a 10-mi trolley line in order to help maintain the voltage at that end of the line. The generator at the near end is so regulated as to maintain its terminal voltage constant at 600 v. The combined resistance of trolley wire, feeder, and track return is 0.12 ω per mile. Let there be a single trolley car on the track at a distance X mi from the near end, drawing a current of 100 amp. As a function of X, find

(a) the current delivered by the generator;
(b) the current delivered by the battery;
(c) the DP across the trolley car.

Also answer the following questions:

(d) What is the maximum charging current of the battery?
(e) What is the maximum current delivered by the battery?
(f) What is the minimum voltage across the car and at what point of the track does it occur?
(g) If there were no floating battery, what would be the minimum voltage across the car? Ans: (a) $135.7 - 8.57X$ amp; (b) $8.57X - 35.7$ amp; (c) $600 - 16.3X + 1.03X^2$ v; (d) 35.7 amp; (e) 50.0 amp; (f) 536 v at 7.92 mi; (g) 480 v.

16. A load that draws current I is fed from a 120-volt generator through leads that have a total resistance of 0.2 ohm. A 110-volt battery is also floated across the load. The internal resistance of the battery and the resistance of the battery leads total 0.05 ohm. The load current I varies from 0 to 200 amp. The generator charges the battery when the load is light, and the battery takes over part of the load and helps to maintain voltage regulation when the load is heavy.

(a) Find the generator current I_g as a function of load current.
(b) Find the battery current I_b as a function of load current, calling discharging current positive and charging current negative.
(c) At what load current does the battery shift from charge to discharge?
(d) Find the load voltage V as a function of load current.
(e) Plot the generator current, battery current, and load voltage as functions of load current, in the range from 0 to 200 amp.
(f) What generator capacity, in kilowatts, is required?
(g) With the battery disconnected, so that the generator supplies the whole load current, what generator capacity would be required? For this case, plot the load voltage on the same graph as in (e). Note the great improvement in regulation resulting from the floating battery.

CHAPTER 34

ELECTROCHEMISTRY

Much of this chapter can be omitted, if desired, without loss of continuity. We shall meet again the important modern unit of energy, the electron-volt, which is discussed in Sec. 1. Secs. 2–6, on electrochemistry, may be a review of material already studied in a course in chemistry, with perhaps a different emphasis. In these sections we confine ourselves to deriving EMF's from heats of reaction and reversible heats, without going into the thermodynamics of 'free energy.' We do not state in detail *where* the differences of potential in an electrolytic cell occur. The simple picture given in many books which puts all the DP between the electrodes and the electrolyte is not correct. Unfortunately, the correct picture which puts most of the DP at the contact between dissimilar metals, outside the cell, is too difficult to understand at the level of this course. It involves a detailed discussion of electronic energy levels in metals and ions, and of potential barriers, and makes a difficult distinction between the electrostatic potential on the one hand and the potential energy of electrons in the metal and ions in the solution on the other. These details are admirably presented in *Ions in Solution* by R. W. Gurney (Cambridge University Press, 1936), to which we refer the interested reader. Finally, Sec. 7 describes the batteries of present technical importance.

1. THE ELECTRON-VOLT (EV) AS A UNIT OF ENERGY

The unit of energy most widely used in modern atomic and nuclear physics is the 'electron-volt.' It must be emphasized at the outset that the electron-volt is simply a unit of energy like the calorie or joule. Moreover the fact that an energy is expressed in electron-volts does not imply that we are talking about electrons. The electron-volt is defined in such a way as to be of convenient size for specification of the energy of a single electron, atom, molecule, nucleus, photon, or cosmic-ray particle, and in such a way as to simplify the computation of the work done when a particle bearing a multiple of the electronic charge moves through a difference of potential.

> The electron-volt is a unit of energy equal to the work done by the electric field when a charge equal to the electronic charge moves through a DP of one volt.

Just as 1 joule = 1 coul × 1 volt, 1 electron-volt = 1 electronic charge × 1 volt. We can compute the number of joules in an electron-volt by multiplying the magnitude of the charge on the electron in coulombs by a

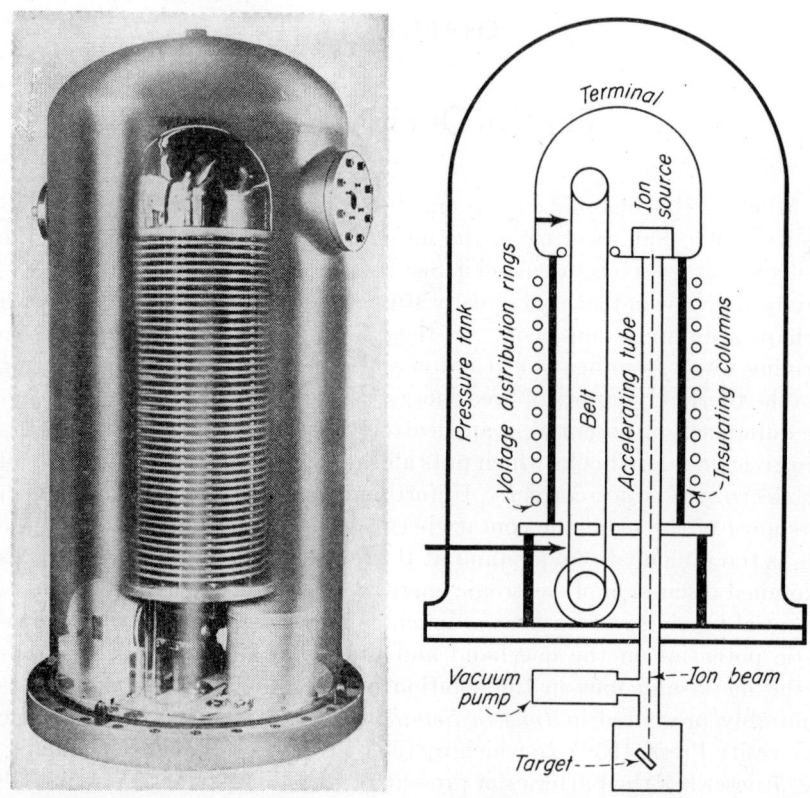

Fig. 1. Van de Graaff positive-ion accelerator (*courtesy of High Voltage Engineering Corporation, Cambridge, Mass.*). In this form of generator, the terminal is maintained at a steady positive potential above ground. The rings help to maintain a uniform potential gradient between the high-voltage terminal and the ground plane. Within the terminal is a capillary containing a DC arc in hydrogen or deuterium. Positive H or D ions emerge from a small opening in the capillary into the evacuated accelerating tube, along which they are accelerated through the full DP between the terminal and ground.

difference of potential of one volt in accordance with the relation $W = QV$. We thus find

$$1 \text{ ev} = 16.020 \times 10^{-20} \text{ coul} \times 1 \text{ volt} = 16.020 \times 10^{-20} \text{ joule.} \qquad (1)$$

This unit of energy is particularly convenient in considering the energy of charged particles accelerated by electric fields in a vacuum. For example, the Van de Graaff generator (see p. 839) is usually built with an evacuated tube down which particles are accelerated between one electrode at high positive or negative potential and one at ground potential, as in Fig. 1. If the high-potential electrode is at $+V$, in volts (for example, 2.5 million volts = 2.5 Mv) and the accelerated particles are protons, the work done by the electric field on each proton is V, in electron-volts (for example, 2.5 million electron-volts = 2.5 Mev), since the charge on each proton is the electronic charge. All this work goes into increasing the kinetic energy of the proton, so that if it is accelerated from rest, its kinetic energy when it reaches the negative electrode is just V, in electron-volts (for example, 2.5 Mev). If deuterons (the nuclei of the hydrogen isotope of atomic weight 2) are used as the bombarding particles, their kinetic energy is again V, in electron-volts, since the charge is the same; but of course the speed of deuterons is only $1/\sqrt{2}$ times as great as that of protons of the same energy because their mass is twice as great, and kinetic energy is proportional to mv^2. On the other hand, if α-particles (helium nuclei) are accelerated through potential V, the work done on each particle is $2V$, in electron-volts, since the charge on each particle is *twice* the electronic charge.

In general, *if a charge ne, where e is the electronic charge, moves through a difference of potential of V, in volts, work nV, in electron-volts, is done.*

PROBLEMS

1. Find the speed, in m/sec, of each of the following particles when they are accelerated from rest through a DP of 12,000 v: (a) protons; (b) deuterons; (c) alpha-particles; (d) electrons. (Charges and masses of these particles may be found in Sec. 2 of the Appendix.) Do this by computing first the kinetic energy in electron-volts, converting to joules by (1), and equating this result to $\frac{1}{2}mv^2$. Ans: (a) 1.52×10^6 m/sec; (b) 1.07×10^6 m/sec; (c) 1.08×10^6 m/sec; (d) 6.50×10^7 m/sec.

2. By the method sketched in Problem 1, find the speeds, in m/sec, of protons, deuterons, and α-particles accelerated through a DP of 2.5 Mv.

3. What is the energy in joules of a singly ionized oxygen atom (O^+) accelerated through a difference of potential of 1 Mv? Ans: 1.60×10^{-13} joule.

4. What is the energy in joules of a hydrogen molecular ion (H_2^+) accelerated through a DP of 1 Mv?

2. ATOMIC WEIGHT; AVOGADRO'S NUMBER; THE MOLE; THE FARADAY; THE KILOCALORIE/MOLE

Since we have arrived at a point where we need to use atomic weights, we again (see p. 370) point out that there are now two atomic-weight scales, called the 'physical' and the 'chemical.' Chemists developed a convenient scale to represent the *relative masses* of the different elements. The mass of the oxygen atom was taken as exactly 16 units, and this was called the *atomic weight* of oxygen. The atomic weight of hydrogen then came out 1.008, that of silver 107.88, and so on. After the discovery of isotopes by physical methods and in particular the discovery that oxygen has 3 isotopes, of masses in the ratio 16:17:18 approximately, it was realized that the chemists' atomic weight of 16 did not refer to a definite atomic species but to the average of a mixture of three different isotopes of oxygen as they occur in nature. The natural abundances are in the ratio $O^{16}:O^{17}:O^{18} = 2500:1:5$ approximately. Physicists began to measure the relative masses of different *individual* isotopes, and to do so with such accuracy that the ratio of the mass of H^1 (the hydrogen isotope of mass about 1) to O^{16} (the oxygen isotope of mass about 16) is known to an accuracy of 1 part in 100,000, and the ratios of C^{12} and N^{14} to O^{16} are known to 1 part in 300,000. These accuracies are greater than those that have been achieved by chemical methods and much greater than the accuracy with which the relative concentrations of oxygen isotopes in natural oxygen are known. Thus, physical methods of determining mass ratios are now more accurate than chemical methods.

Because of these developments, physicists need an atomic-weight scale that refers to a definite isotope as a standard rather than to a mixture. They have adopted a *physical scale* in which the mass of the isotope O^{16} is taken as 16 exactly. On this scale the average mass of the atoms in the naturally occurring oxygen mixture is 16.0044, whereas it is 16 exactly on the *chemical scale*, in which the average mass of the oxygen isotopes in the natural mixture is taken as 16. Atomic masses on the physical scale are thus greater than those on the chemical scale by 3 parts in 10,000, and each of the quantities named in the title of this section has two values differing in this ratio according to which scale is used.*

We shall state all values on the physical scale in this book.

Average atomic weights of the natural elements are given in Sec. 4 of the Appendix. These are on the physical scale. The difference between the physical scale and the chemical scale is negligible for many purposes.

We now define *Avogadro's number:*

Avogadro's number is the number of oxygen atoms in 16 grams of O^{16} atoms.

Because the masses of individual atoms are proportional to the atomic weights, Avogadro's number is also the total number of oxygen atoms in 16.0044 g of natural oxygen; the number of hydrogen atoms in 1.008 grams of natural hydrogen; the number of silver atoms in 107.91 grams of natural silver; and in general the number of atoms of any element in a quantity whose mass in grams equals the atomic weight. It is equally well the number of molecules of any compound in a quantity whose mass in grams equals the molecular weight. *Avogadro's number*, which we shall denote by $\mathfrak{N}$, has the value

$$\mathfrak{N} = 6.025 \times 10^{23}. \tag{2}$$

This is an enormous number—but then, atoms are really very small!

* For further details see R. T. Birge, REVIEWS OF MODERN PHYSICS **13**, 233 (1941).

We now define a *mole:*

> A mole of any kind of particle is a quantity containing $\mathfrak{N}$ such particles.

This is a generalization of the standard usage of the chemists, who talk about a mole of atoms or of molecules but not about a mole of electrons. However, we shall find this extended definition highly useful in the case of electrons. We can make immediate use of it in defining the *faraday:*

> The faraday is the absolute magnitude of the charge carried by a mole of electrons.

That is, the faraday is a unit of positive charge such that the charge carried by a mole of electrons is -1 faraday. We obtain the size of the faraday in coulombs by multiplying $\mathfrak{N}$, Avogadro's number, by e, the magnitude of the electronic charge.

$$1 \text{ faraday} = \mathfrak{N}e = 6.025 \times 10^{23} \cdot 16.020 \times 10^{-20} \text{ coul},$$

or
$$1 \text{ faraday} = 96,520 \text{ coulombs}. \qquad (3)$$

The faraday is a very convenient unit of charge for treating problems in electrolysis, since it is the absolute magnitude of the charge carried by a mole of monovalent ions of any type. Before we proceed to such problems, it will be advisable to discuss another energy unit.

When hydrogen burns and the resulting steam is condensed to form liquid water, according to the equation

$$H_2 + \tfrac{1}{2} O_2 \rightarrow H_2O_{\text{liq}}, \qquad (4)$$

the heat of reaction*, determined calorimetrically, is usually expressed in *kilocalories per mole* of water molecules formed when one mole of hydrogen molecules reacts with one-half mole of oxygen molecules. This heat of reaction is 69 kcal/mole.

When one mole of water molecules in liquid form is decomposed electrolytically, an equal energy must be supplied from electrical sources. In discussing this topic later, we shall find it desirable to know the reaction energy per *molecule* of water. A suitable and convenient energy unit for

---

* In determining a heat of reaction (for example, in a bomb calorimeter), the products of the reaction are allowed to cool to the initial temperature of the substances entering the reaction. Thus the heat of reaction represents the difference of internal energy (including chemical energy) between the substances on the left and right of the reaction equation at the same temperature. In the case of gaseous reactions, the heat of reaction will also depend on whether the reaction takes place at constant volume or at constant pressure. It is customary to specify heats of reaction for the case where all substances in the equation are at NTP, or at normal pressure and some other specified temperature.

expressing the energy of a molecule is the electron-volt. In order to tie together a physical discussion of energies per molecule with chemical data on heats of reaction, we need to know how many kcal/mole correspond to 1 ev/molecule. We can determine this relationship as follows. By (1),

$$1 \text{ ev/molecule} = 16.020 \times 10^{-20} \text{ joule/molecule}.$$

If this value is multiplied by $\mathfrak{N}$, we obtain the corresponding number of joules/mole:

$$1 \frac{\text{ev}}{\text{molecule}} = 16.020 \times 10^{-20} \frac{\text{joule}}{\text{molecule}} \times 6.025 \times 10^{23} \frac{\text{molecules}}{\text{mole}} = 96{,}520 \frac{\text{joules}}{\text{mole}}.$$

Since 4186 joules = 1 kcal, we divide the above value by 4186 to get

$$1 \text{ ev/molecule} = 23.06 \text{ kcal/mole}. \tag{5}$$

This relation means that if we supply 1 electron-volt of energy to each molecule, we supply 23.06 kcal of energy to a mole, which contains $\mathfrak{N}$ molecules. The heat of the reaction (4) is measured calorimetrically as 69 kcal/mole. Hence, if we wish to *reverse* the reaction by electrolysis, we must *supply* 69 kcal/mole or 3.0 ev/molecule.

3. CHARGE TRANSPORT IN ELECTROLYSIS

As we remember from the study of chemistry, the molecules of an acid, base, or salt in water solution are more or less completely dissociated into positively and negatively charged *ions**. It is the availability of these ions to carry the current that enables such a solution to conduct electricity. The ions play the role that free electrons play in metallic conduction. An ionized solution is called an *electrolyte* because it will conduct electricity.

In the process of *electrolytic conduction*, electric current enters and leaves a solution at metallic plates called *electrodes*. The combination of electrodes and electrolyte constitutes an *electrolytic cell*. At the electrodes some type of chemical reaction takes place, resulting usually in deposition or solution of solid material or evolution of gas from decomposition of solvent or solute. These chemical changes are said to result from *electrolysis* of the solution.

Let us consider the reactions that take place in the electrolysis of pure water by current that enters and leaves through chemically inert platinum electrodes. Pure water is only weakly ionized, but it does contain in each mole a definite number of hydrogen† ions, H^+, and the same number of hydroxyl ions, OH^-. The number of ions of each type per mole of water molecules is 9×10^{14}, which at first sight looks like a very large num-

---

* From the Greek for 'going.'

† Hydrogen ions are always attached to a neutral water molecule so that the actual ions are $(H_3O)^+ = H^+ + H_2O$, but this detail is unimportant to our discussion.

ber but is actually *very small* compared with Avogadro's number, so that only about one in 10^9 of the water molecules is ionized. With this degree of ionization, pure water is a poor conductor compared with other electrolytes, but it has some conductivity and will carry a feeble current and electrolyze slowly. The ionization, and hence the conductivity, is greatly increased by the addition of a small amount of acid. In the case of sulfuric, perchloric, and some other acids, the net result of electrolysis is decomposition of the water into hydrogen and oxygen, just as in the case of the electrolysis of pure water. While electrolytic generation of hydrogen and oxygen would normally be carried out in acidulated water, it will be simplest if we discuss the phenomena occurring in pure water.

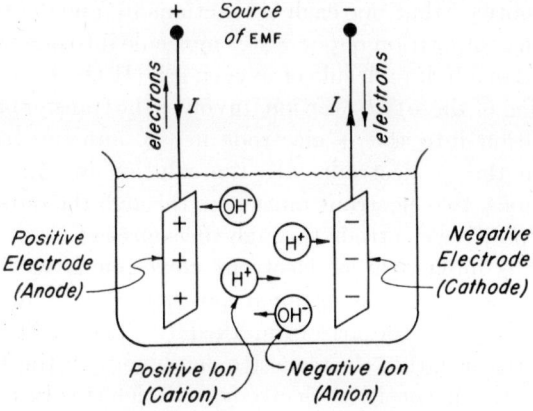

Fig. 2. Electrolysis of water.

Figure 2 shows two platinum electrodes immersed in water and connected to a source of EMF. The Greek names of the positive and negative electrodes and ions shown on Fig. 2 were given by Faraday and are still in common use.* The source of EMF sets up an electric field in the space between the electrodes. The H^+ ions slowly drift down the field toward the negative cathode. Those that reach the negative cathode

---

* The *anode* (Greek for "the way which the sun rises," according to Faraday, *Experimental Researches in Electricity*), is the electrode at which current enters the cell (AIEE definition 60.05.040). The *cathode* (Greek for "the way which the sun sets") is the electrode at which the current leaves (AIEE definition 60.05.045). *Anions* are negatively charged ions; *cations* are positively charged ions. Anions move toward the anode, cations toward the cathode, in carrying current through the cell. This notation becomes annoyingly confusing when applied to a reversible battery cell, because the current direction changes and hence the electrodes exchange names when conditions change from charge to discharge. For a stabilizing battery floated across a line, an ammeter is required to tell even the names of the plates. Hence, in discussing batteries, we shall prefer to talk about positive and negative ions and positive and negative electrodes, the positive electrode being the one at higher potential whether the battery is charging or discharging. These designations are not capricious.

pick up negative electrons from it and form hydrogen gas in accordance with the equation (we use ε^- as the chemical symbol for an electron)

$$2H^+ + 2\varepsilon^- \rightarrow (H_2)_{gas}. \qquad (-\text{electrode}) \qquad (6)$$

The OH^- ions are attracted to the positive anode. On reaching it, they give up their electrons to the electrode and form oxygen gas and water in accordance with the equation

$$2OH^- \rightarrow 2\varepsilon^- + H_2O + \tfrac{1}{2}(O_2)_{gas}. \qquad (+\text{electrode}) \qquad (7)$$

New H^+ and OH^- ions are continuously generated within the water to keep up the ionic concentration at all points, in accordance with the laws of ionic equilibria, which the student should review in his chemistry text.

It will be noticed that one each of reactions (6) and (7) together correspond to the decomposition of one water molecule into one molecule of hydrogen gas and one-half molecule of oxygen gas ($H_2O \rightarrow H_2 + \tfrac{1}{2}O_2$). Also, the combination of these two reactions involves the transfer of two electrons from the solution into the $+$ electrode in (7), and the transfer of two electrons from the $-$ electrode into the solution in (6). To maintain steady conditions, two electrons must pass through the outside metal circuit from the positive electrode through the source of EMF to the negative electrode. This movement of electrons corresponds to the flow of an equivalent quantity of conventional positive charge in the opposite direction, as shown by the arrows marked I. The 2 electrons enter the electrolyte at the negative electrode (to combine with the H^+) and leave the electrolyte at the positive electrode. Under steady conditions, the same amount of net negative charge must cross each plane in the electrolyte (from right to left in Fig. 2); otherwise, the net charge of the electrolyte on one side of the plane would increase and that on the other side would decrease. Hence, under steady conditions the same current flows across each plane of a closed circuit that includes the electrolytic cell of Fig. 2. The current is carried by electrons in the metallic parts of the circuit; in the electrolyte it is carried by both positive and negative ions.

A nice electrostatic balance will guarantee that, after the process is started, *exactly the same number of reactions (6) and (7) will occur*. We have in Fig. 2 an electrolyte which is normally neutral (no *net* electric charge) and a metal circuit, comprising the plates and the connections through the source of EMF, which is also normally electrically neutral. Suppose that when the electrolysis starts, more of reactions (6) occur than of (7). This inequality results in a net removal of positive charges from the electrolyte, leaving it with a net negative charge, and a net removal of electrons from the metal circuit, leaving the metal with a net positive charge. This difference will set up local fields near the electrodes, as sketched in Fig. 3. These fields are superposed on the field set up by the source of EMF, and are in a direction to help attract negative ions to the

+ electrode and hence speed up reaction (7), and to reduce the attraction of positive ions to the − electrode and hence retard reaction (6). If more of reactions (7) were to take place than of (6), local fields of exactly the reverse type would be set up. In any case, a very little net charge transfer from electrolyte to metal will set up sufficient local fields to restore equilibrium between reactions (6) and (7), and it is seen that this equilibrium will be automatically and stably maintained. This is the process that guarantees equality of charge transfer at anode and cathode in any type of electrolysis.

Since reactions (6) and (7) must go on at the same rate, and since two electrons are required for decomposition of each water molecule, we see that two moles of electrons (corresponding to two faradays of charge) must flow through the circuit for every mole of hydrogen gas and half mole of oxygen gas generated. Thus, 2 faradays $= 2 \times 96{,}500$ coul $= 193{,}000$ coul of charge are required to decompose one mole (18 grams) of water into one mole of H_2 gas (2 grams or 22.4 liters at NTP) and one-half mole of O_2 gas (16 grams or 11.2 liters at NTP).

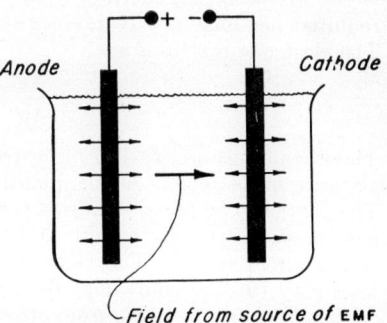

Fig. 3. Illustrating local fields that hinder the progress of positive ions toward the cathode and aid the progress of negative ions toward the anode (cf. Fig. 2).

In any electrolysis, the proportionality between charge and mass of material electrolyzed is *exact*. The proportionality factor can be easily obtained by an argument similar to the above as soon as equations corresponding to (6) and (7) for the reactions at the electrodes have been written down. We give two other examples:

Copper plating. Both electrodes are copper in a solution of $CuSO_4$, which ionizes to Cu^{++} and SO_4^{--}. (Even if copper is being plated onto a cathode of some other metal, both electrodes are effectively copper as soon as the process is under way and a thin layer of copper has been deposited.) At the anode, metallic copper is dissolved and goes into solution as Cu^{++}:

$$Cu_{metal} \rightarrow 2\varepsilon^- + Cu^{++}, \qquad (+ \text{ electrode})$$

the two electrons of course going up the wire. At the cathode, the Cu^{++} ions take up two electrons (which come down the wire) and are deposited as metallic copper:

$$Cu^{++} + 2\varepsilon^- \rightarrow Cu_{metal}. \qquad (- \text{ electrode})$$

Thus, copper metal dissolves from the anode, is transported through the electrolyte, and deposits on the cathode. *One mole of copper atoms moves from anode to cathode for each two faradays of charge that flow through the circuit.* The SO_4^{--}

ions really play no role in these reactions, and any other soluble salt of copper would give the same effect. The SO_4^{--} ions help carry the current. When their concentration near the + electrode, to which they are attracted, gets too high for ionic equilibrium, they combine with Cu^{++} to form $CuSO_4$. This compound can diffuse back toward the negative electrode, where it can ionize again because of the deficiency of SO_4^{--}.

This is the commercial method of purifying copper for electrical purposes, since impurities are in general left behind in this process. Something over a million tons annually of copper is refined electrolytically at such places as Niagara Falls where cheap electrical power is available. A single electrolysis from crude copper gives copper of purity better than 99.9 per cent. Copper of such high purity is needed for electrical use, since very small quantities of impurity greatly increase the electrical resistance.

The silver coulometer. The previous example involved bivalent Cu^{++} ions, and two faradays were required to deposit one mole of copper. If silver electrodes are used in a solution of silver nitrate ($AgNO_3$), only one faraday will be required per mole of silver, since the silver is monovalent and forms Ag^+ ions. The electrode reactions are

$$Ag_{metal} \rightarrow \varepsilon^- + Ag^+, \qquad (+ \text{ electrode})$$

$$Ag^+ + \varepsilon^- \rightarrow Ag_{metal}. \qquad (- \text{ electrode})$$

These reactions are used in an instrument called a *coulometer*, designed for very accurate measurement of the quantity of electricity that flows through a circuit. The charge to be measured flows through what amounts to a small silver-plating bath in series with the circuit, and the amount of silver dissolved or deposited is accurately weighed. The charge that flows is determined from the fact that 1 faraday (96,520 coul) deposits 1 mole (107.91 g) of silver. Less satisfactory coulometers can be made from other metals. An *iodine* coulometer is found to give high accuracy and is used in the determination of the magnitude of the faraday.

The laws relating the amount of material deposited, or gas generated, in electrolysis were first determined by Faraday:

Faraday's laws

(1) *The quantity of material undergoing chemical reaction at an electrode is in direct proportion to the quantity of electricity passing.*

(2) *The quantity of a given element dissolved or released from solution at an electrode by a given quantity of electricity is proportional to the ratio of the atomic weight of the element to its valence. This ratio is called the equivalent weight of the element, and 96,520 coulombs of charge are required per gram-equivalent weight.*

The reason for these laws is clear from the atomic-ionic picture given above. However, before the knowledge of the electron, the reason why it is 96,520 coulombs that deposits one mole of a monovalent metal or one-half mole of a bivalent metal was not understood in terms of the more fundamental quantities occurring in the computation of (3).

In the case of solution or deposition of a metal, we can summarize Faraday's laws by the formula

$$m = \frac{Q}{96{,}520} \frac{w}{n},$$

where

m = mass of metal deposited or dissolved, in grams,
Q = quantity of electricity passing through the cell, in coulombs,
w = atomic weight of the metal,
n = valence of the metal—specifically, the number of positive electronic charges carried by the metallic ion in the electrolyte.

In this formula the ratio w/n is called the equivalent weight. The expression $w/96{,}520n$ is sometimes called the *electrochemical equivalent* and denoted by z. Values of z will be found listed in handbooks. In terms of z, the above equation takes the compact form $m = zQ$.

Faraday's laws apply directly to ideal, simple situations. In practical electrolytic processes the actual reactions that occur are frequently so complex that Faraday's laws, as stated in the simple form given above, are not directly applicable.

PROBLEMS

1. The cathode of a silver coulometer increased 0.2105 g in mass during an electrolysis. How many coulombs of electricity passed? Ans: 188.

2. How many coulombs are required to purify 1 kg of electrolytic copper? If an average current of 125 amp is used, how long will it take?

3. Dilute sulfuric acid ionizes to give H^+ and SO_4^{--} ions. On electrolysis with platinum electrodes, hydrogen gas is given off at the cathode and oxygen gas at the anode. Write down the electrode reactions and show that the amount of gas of each type, per faraday, is the same as in the electrolysis of pure water.

4. A current of 0.3 amp passes successively through solutions of hydrochloric acid (HCl), sulfuric acid (H_2SO_4), and phosphoric acid (H_3PO_4) via platinum electrodes. Calculate the weight of hydrogen liberated in each case.

5. What volumes of H_2 and O_2 gas (at NTP) are liberated if 0.05 amp passes through dilute sulfuric acid for 20 min? Ans: 6.97 cm^3; 3.48 cm^3.

6. Chlorine and caustic soda are prepared commercially by electrolyzing a solution of common salt (NaCl), using inert electrodes. At the cathode, caustic soda (NaOH) is formed in solution, with hydrogen evolution. At the anode, chlorine gas (Cl_2) is evolved. Write down the electrode reactions. How many liters of chlorine gas at NTP are evolved per faraday? of hydrogen gas?

7. When a ferric-chloride ($FeCl_3$) solution is electrolyzed by using platinum electrodes, chlorine gas is generated at the anode but iron is not plated out at the cathode. Rather, the solution starts changing to one of ferrous chloride ($FeCl_2$) in the neighborhood of the cathode. Write the electrode reactions.

8. Three electrolytic cells with platinum electrodes are connected in series. The first cell contains Ag^+ and NO_3^- ions; the second, Fe^{++} and Cl^-; the third, K^+ and I^-. In 1 hr, 100 g of silver are deposited. In the same time, how many grams of oxygen are released, iron deposited, chlorine released, and iodine deposited? Compare the number of liters of O_2 and of Cl_2 at NTP.

4. VOLTAGE NECESSARY FOR ELECTROLYSIS

When voltage is applied between platinum electrodes in pure water or in a dilute acid solution that electrolyzes to form H_2 and O_2, almost no charge flows so long as the DP between the electrodes is below 1.7 volts. Higher applied voltages result in a current proportional to the difference between the applied voltage and 1.7 volts. When charge is flowing, the electrolytic cell seems to have a back-EMF of 1.7 volts, which, according to what we have learned in the previous chapter, must be related to a change of electrical energy into chemical energy. In fact, a chemical reaction is taking place:

$$H_2O \rightarrow H_2 + \tfrac{1}{2}O_2,$$

which, as we saw on p. 895, requires 69 kilocalories of energy per mole of water decomposed, or 3 electron-volts of energy per molecule of water. For each molecule of water decomposed, a charge of 2 electrons passes through the cell; and in order to furnish 3 ev of energy to a charge of 2 electrons, the charge must pass through a DP of 1.5 volts. This figure is in substantial agreement with the back-EMF of 1.7 volts given above.*

In the case we have been considering, charge does not start to flow until we apply a potential of 1.7 volts to furnish the energy absorbed in the reaction that accompanies the flow. Above this voltage the amount of current will be governed by the terminal voltage and by the internal resistance just as in the case of a battery on charge considered in the previous chapter.

In electrolysis in which copper is being plated from a copper anode to a copper cathode, no chemical energy need be supplied, since for each pair of electrons that traverses the cell, one molecule of solid copper is dissolved, but also one molecule of solid copper is plated, so there is no *net* chemical change. In this case charge will flow with the smallest voltage, and to a certain approximation the current is proportional to the voltage, since there is no back-EMF. Since the energy supplied per coulomb is proportional to the voltage, the energy per kg of copper plated is also proportional to the voltage. To save energy, electrolytic refining is done with low voltages (a fraction of a volt). Large areas of copper plate are used to keep the internal resistance low and the current high.

Now suppose that we arrange a cell so that copper will be dissolved and zinc plated out. This process, which seems at first sight to be impossible, actually is accomplished in the old Daniell cell, which was used almost universally in the early days of telegraphy. In this cell, illustrated in Fig. 4, solutions of $CuSO_4$ and $ZnSO_4$ are separated by a porous partition through which diffusion of the solutions is very slow.

If we apply sufficient external EMF to drive current through the cell in the direction marked 'charge,' the electrode reactions put copper in solution and plate out zinc, one atom of each for every two electrons, according to

* We should expect only approximate agreement between observed EMF's and those computed from chemical heats of reaction, as is made clear by the discussion in Sec. 6 of the reversible-heat effect.

$$\left.\begin{array}{c}\text{Cu}_{\text{metal}} \rightarrow \text{Cu}^{++} + 2\varepsilon^-, \\ \text{Zn}^{++} + 2\varepsilon^- \rightarrow \text{Zn}_{\text{metal}}.\end{array}\right\} \quad \text{(charge)} \quad (8)$$

A minimum external voltage of 1.09 volts is required to bring about this reaction. Hence, it must be that a minimum energy of 2.18 ev/molecule or 50.1 kcal/mole is required to make Cu displace Zn in solution, since the net result of the above reactions is

$$\text{Cu}_{\text{metal}} + \text{Zn}^{++} \rightarrow \text{Cu}^{++} + \text{Zn}_{\text{metal}}. \tag{9}$$

The reverse reaction, Zn displacing Cu in solution, should then release energy at the rate of 50.1 kcal/mole. The heat of this reaction,

$$\text{Zn}_{\text{metal}} + \text{Cu}^{++} \rightarrow \text{Cu}_{\text{metal}} + \text{Zn}^{++}, \tag{10}$$

can be measured calorimetrically, because it can be made to take place by merely stirring up flakes of zinc metal in $CuSO_4$ solution. Each zinc

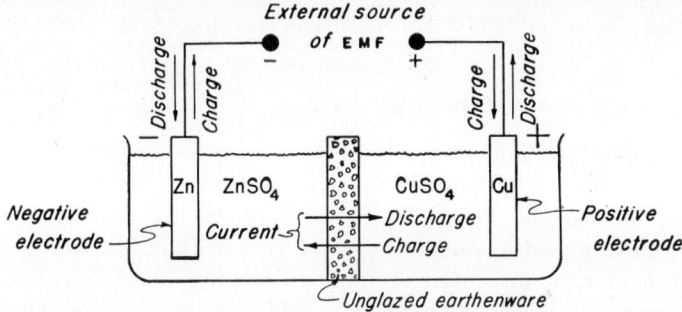

Fig. 4. Schematic diagram of the Daniell cell. Arrows show directions of conventional current in charge and discharge. The cell was usually made with the zinc electrode and $ZnSO_4$ inside a porous cup. This cup was in turn immersed in a glass jar containing $CuSO_4$. A cylindrical copper electrode surrounded the porous cup.

flake will start to dissolve from one portion of its surface, while copper plates out on another portion of the surface of the flake (atom for atom, to keep the flake electrically neutral), until we are left with a collection of copper flakes and all the zinc in solution. When the heat generated in this reaction is measured, it is found to be exactly 55.2 kcal/mole. The reason for the difference between this figure and 50.1 is explained in Sec. 6.

In Figure 2, when the voltage of the source of EMF drops below 1.7 volts, the current drops abruptly and water ceases to be electrolyzed because sufficient energy cannot be supplied. The cell of Fig. 4 behaves differently. In Fig. 4, as the voltage of the external source of EMF falls to 1.09 volts, the charging current falls to zero right enough, but when the external voltage falls below 1.09 volts, the current *reverses* and the cell begins to discharge. Charge is now moving through the cell in the reverse direction to that discussed above, the reactions (8) are proceeding in the reverse direction, copper is being plated, and zinc is being dissolved. The net reaction is now (10) instead of (9). Reaction (10) *releases* chemical energy which in this case does not appear as heat, as in the zinc-flake experiment described above, but principally as electrical energy of 2.18 ev per atom, representing an increase of potential energy of $+$ charges moved from the negative to the positive electrode through the cell. *The cell is acting as a source of* EMF. Transformation of 2.18 ev of chemical energy into electrical energy for each 2 electronic charges moved represents an EMF of 1.09 volts.

To discuss the action of the cell on discharge in another way, we may start by noting that the reaction (10) will go by itself, with release of chemical energy. But in the arrangement of the Daniell cell (Fig. 4), the reaction (10) has no opportunity to take place by itself because there are no copper ions in contact with the zinc plate. This net reaction can take place, however, via two electrode reactions, the reverse of (8):

$$\left. \begin{array}{l} Zn_{metal} \rightarrow Zn^{++} + 2\varepsilon^-, \\ Cu^{++} + 2\varepsilon^- \rightarrow Cu_{metal}. \end{array} \right\} \quad \text{(discharge)} \quad (11)$$

But *this pair of reactions can take place only as fast as an external circuit carries the electrons left behind in the zinc plate around to the copper plate to combine with the copper ions*. If the reactions tried to go faster than this, the zinc plate would acquire a negative charge that would prevent, by electrostatic forces, any more Zn^{++} from leaving, and the copper plate would acquire a positive charge that would prevent any more Cu^{++} from approaching. The current is carried through the barrier by diffusion through it of Zn^{++} ions in one direction and SO_4^{--} ions in the other.

The fundamental difference in behavior between this cell, which will act as a source of EMF, and the cell of Fig. 2, which will not, is that reactions (8) and (11) are essentially reversible, whereas reactions (6) and (7) are not. In practice, the Daniell cell cannot be successfully charged because the solutions are only imperfectly separated by the porous partition. On discharge, zinc is dissolving and copper is plating out, and there is no tendency for zinc to plate out on the copper even if some Zn^{++} ions get into the copper sulfate, because the reaction (9) does not proceed by itself but requires a large energy to make it go. On the other hand, if we attempt to charge the cell, dissolving Cu and plating out Zn, we do well enough with freshly poured solutions before Cu^{++} ions have had a chance to diffuse through the partition and encounter the Zn plate. But as soon as any Cu^{++} ions do encounter the zinc plate, they will immediately plate out on the zinc, with zinc going into solution, according to (10), which will go by itself with release of heat energy. This reaction not only wastes energy but also soon spoils the battery by creating two copper plates. With the cell on charge, the electric fields within the cell, corresponding to the IR-drop of the internal resistance, are in a direction to help pull Cu^{++} ions through the partition and to accelerate the above detrimental process. On discharge, the internal electric fields tend to move positive ions toward the copper plate and to retard the diffusion of Cu^{++} ions into the $ZnSO_4$. The Daniell cell is never allowed to stand on open circuit. When the cell is not in use, the external circuit is always closed with a resistance of about 100 ohms, so that a small current will continually flow in the direction that prevents Cu^{++} ions from getting into the $ZnSO_4$. As remarked above, no harm results from Zn^{++} ions getting into the $CuSO_4$. Used in this way, the cell lasts until either the zinc plate is eaten away or all the Cu is plated out of the $CuSO_4$, which is started as a saturated solution.

The Daniell cell is mostly of historical and theoretical interest. Cells of importance in modern technology, some of which are truly reversible, are discussed in Sec. 7.

PROBLEMS

1. Assuming that there is adequate $CuSO_4$, how many ampere-hours will a Daniell cell deliver before a 400-g zinc cathode is all dissolved? Ans: 328.

2. The solubility of $CuSO_4$ is 140 g per liter of solution. If a Daniell cell starts with ½ liter of saturated $CuSO_4$ solution and adequate zinc, how many ampere-hours will it deliver before the $CuSO_4$ is used up?

5. THE ELECTROCHEMICAL SERIES

The metals can be arranged in a list (Table I) called the *electrochemical series* (or the *electromotive series*) such that each metal will tend to displace from solution any metal occurring below it in the list. Thus, in an experiment described above, zinc dust shaken into $CuSO_4$ solution was dissolved and an equal number of atoms of copper metal were precipitated. This shows that the reaction (10),

$$Zn_{metal} + Cu^{++} \rightarrow Cu_{metal} + Zn^{++},$$

must proceed with release of energy. If now Zn and Cu electrodes are arranged in a suitable cell (the Daniell cell) such that the reaction (10) can only take place when current flows externally, an EMF of 1.09 volts, which is directly related to the heat of the reaction (10), is measured, with the Zn electrode negative and the Cu positive.

If now any two bivalent metals A and B are such that the reaction

$$A_{metal} + B^{++} \rightarrow B_{metal} + A^{++}$$

represents a decrease in chemical energy, A will tend to displace B from solution; A will stand above B in the electrochemical series; and a suitable cell made from metals A and B will have an EMF related to the heat of the above reaction with A negative and B positive. If A and B are monovalent, the reaction in question is

$$A_{metal} + B^+ \rightarrow B_{metal} + A^+,$$

whereas if A is monovalent and B bivalent, or vice versa, 2 atoms of A displace one of B, or vice versa, as follows:

$$2A_{metal} + B^{++} \rightarrow B_{metal} + 2A^+$$

or

$$A_{metal} + 2B^+ \rightarrow 2B_{metal} + A^{++}.$$

The electrochemical series is given in Table I.* A number in volts is given opposite each metal such that *the EMF of an ideal cell composed of any two metals will be the difference between these voltages, the metal lower in the table furnishing the positive electrode.*† These EMF's are additive in the sense that the EMF of a Zn-Ni cell plus the EMF of a Ni-Cu cell will be the EMF of a Zn-Cu cell.

In this table, the voltages are referred to hydrogen as zero. The metals above hydrogen will displace hydrogen from acid with release of energy; those below hydrogen will not. The EMF's can actually be measured relative to a clever 'hydrogen electrode' consisting of spongy platinum which adsorbs hydrogen strongly and is kept 'soaked' with hydrogen gas while immersed in a solution containing hydrogen ions. If one is careful never to draw more than minute currents while measuring the EMF, this device behaves like a reversible metal electrode.

We can now see from Table I why electrolytically refined copper is so very pure. With the exception of silver, all the metals commonly occurring as impurities in crude copper lie above Cu in the electrochemical series. Hence, these metals tend to displace copper in solution, or tend to remain in solution in preference to letting copper remain in solution. The voltages used in electrolyzing copper are deliberately kept very low so that the energy necessary to plate out these elements at the expense of copper is not available. This energy is like that which we discussed in connection with plating out zinc and dissolving copper in charging the Daniell cell. The valuable silver impurity is removed from solution, as fast as silver ions enter solution, by the addition to the $CuSO_4$ electrolyte of a small amount of common salt (NaCl) to form a very insoluble precipitate of AgCl.

TABLE I
ELECTROCHEMICAL SERIES

Li	−2.96 volts
Rb	−2.93
K	−2.92
Ca	−2.76
Na	−2.71
Zn	−0.76
Fe	−0.44
Cd	−0.40
Tl	−0.34
Ni	−0.23
Sn	−0.14
Pb	−0.12
H	0
Cu	+0.34
Ag	+0.80
Hg	+0.80
Au	+1.36

* From the *International Critical Tables* (McGraw-Hill, New York, 1926).

† The EMF of an actual cell will differ from the value obtained in this way if the electrolysis involves other chemical reactions in addition to the simple solution and deposition of the metals.

PROBLEMS

1. From Table I, determine the EMF of the Daniell cell. Ans: 1.10 v.

2. A cell is made with Zn and Ni electrodes in a solution of $NiCl_2$ containing Ni^{++} ions. What is the EMF, and which electrode is positive?

6. THE REVERSIBLE-HEAT EFFECT*

We have been noticing small but definite discrepancies between measured EMF's and those computed from chemical-reaction energies. The reason is that not all of the chemical energy that disappears when a cell is discharging is turned into electrical energy; a definite small portion of the energy appears as heat. Chemical reactions occur at the electrodes. All the chemical energy would go into electrical energy if it happened that the products of the reaction were left with just such random thermal energy as to have the same temperature as the particles entering the reaction. But usually this does not happen, and the reaction products are left with slightly more than this thermal energy; then the cell tends to become warmer. (*The heat we are discussing is in addition to, and to be sharply distinguished from, any I^2R-heating, and has a direct influence on the generated* EMF, *or open-circuit voltage, measured by drawing only an infinitesimal current.*) If heat is thus generated, its amount must be subtracted from the chemical energy released to get the electrical energy—in accordance with the law of conservation of energy. The equation is

$$H = nV + h \qquad \text{(discharge)} \qquad (12)$$

where V = generated EMF, in volts,
n = number of electrons transferred per molecular reaction,
nV = electrical energy generated, in ev per molecular reaction,
H = chemical energy released, in ev per molecular reaction,
h = heat generated, in ev per molecular reaction.

For reasons we shall explain presently, h is called the *reversible heat*.

For the Daniell cell, the chemical energy released is 56.0 kcal/mole, so that $H = 56.0/23.1 = 2.43$ ev/molecule. The quantity h can be determined calorimetrically by putting the cell in a calorimeter and carefully separating the reversible heat, which is directly proportional to the current, from the I^2R-heat which varies as the square of the current; or h can be obtained from the temperature coefficient of EMF, as we shall explain below. For the Daniell cell, $h = 0.25$ ev/molecule. Hence, $nV = 2V = 2.43 - 0.25 = 2.18$ ev, and $V = 1.09$ volts, as observed. In this case some 10 per cent of the chemical energy is changed into heat h, 90 per cent into electrical energy.

Now this whole process is exactly reversible. If we charge a Daniell cell, the EMF does not change, so that 2.18 ev of electrical energy is con-

---

* This section may be omitted without loss of continuity.

verted to chemical energy (per molecule). But 2.43 ev of chemical energy is gained. The difference, 0.25 ev, must be taken out of thermal energy, and the cell tends to cool correspondingly. This is why h is called *reversible heat*. If some of the chemical energy is changed into heat on discharge, an equal amount of heat is changed into chemical energy on charge. On charge we have the same equation

$$H = nV + h \qquad \text{(charge)} \qquad (13)$$

with reversed meaning for all terms:

H = chemical energy created,
nV = electrical energy that disappears,
h = thermal energy that disappears.

In some cells, h is a *negative* number in equations (12) and (13). In this case, heat disappears on discharge and *more* electrical energy is generated than the amount of chemical energy released; conversely, on charge, heat is generated from a portion of the electrical energy supplied. This situation obtains for the lead-acid cells in the ordinary automobile storage battery. At an electrolyte density of 1.200 g/cm³, the EMF of this cell is 2.05 volts. In the reaction [equations (15), (16), (17) of the next section], $n=2$, so that $nV = 4.10$ ev. The energy of the reaction (17) is 91.2 kcal/mole so $H = 91.2/23.1 = 3.95$ ev/molecule. From (12) or (13) we must, then, have

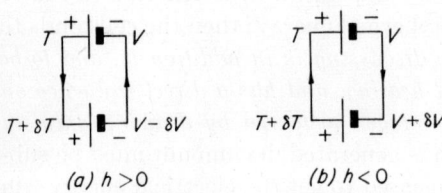

Fig. 5. Illustrating the Gibbs-Helmholtz equation.

$$h = -0.15 \text{ ev/molecule},$$

meaning that in the discharge, 4 per cent of the energy is supplied from heat.

We are now in a position to see, from the principle of Le Châtelier-Braun, that a cell with positive h will have a negative temperature coefficient of EMF; that is, that dV/dT will be negative and the voltage will decrease with rise in temperature. Conversely, a cell with negative h will have a positive temperature coefficient of EMF, as does the lead storage cell. Consider two *identical* cells connected in parallel, + to + and − to − as in Fig. 5. If the cells are at the same temperature, no current will flow. If now the temperature of the lower cell in the diagram is raised slightly, current will flow in such a direction as to try to restore the temperature equality, that is, so as to cool the lower cell and heat the upper. In Fig. 5(a), with $h > 0$, the upper cell is heated by discharging [compare equation (12)], and the lower cell is cooled by charging [compare equation

(13)], so that current must flow in the direction indicated. But for current to flow in this direction, the EMF of the lower cell must have dropped slightly below that of the upper cell. We see that the EMF must go down when the temperature goes up; that is,

$$\text{if} \quad h > 0, \quad dV/dT < 0.$$

Similar arguments applied to Fig. 5(b) show that

$$\text{if} \quad h < 0, \quad dV/dT > 0.$$

The exact relation between h and dV/dT, derived from thermodynamic principles, is

$$h = -nT\, dV/dT, \quad \text{(Gibbs-Helmholtz relation)} \quad (14)$$

where h, n, and V are the same as in (12) and (13), and T is the *absolute* temperature. The unit used for absolute temperature is arbitrary, since T occurs in the numerator and dT in the denominator.

This equation is very important because it enables the chemical energy of the reactions occurring in a cell to be determined completely by a measurement of voltage and temperature coefficient of voltage. If V and dV/dT are measured and h is computed from (14), we have all the data necessary to determine H in (12). For example, for the Daniell cell at 15° C, $dV/dT = -0.00043$ v/C deg. Therefore, from (14),

$$h = -2(288)(-0.00043) = +0.25 \text{ ev/molecule},$$

in agreement with the value given above. For the lead-acid cell, dV/dT is measured as $+0.00023$ v/C deg at 25°C, so that

$$h = -2(298)(0.00023) = -0.14 \text{ ev/molecule},$$

in agreement with the value -0.15 found above from the reaction energy determined thermochemically. Alternatively, these values of h together with the voltage V will determine the reaction energy H in (12). This electrolytic method of determining the energy of a chemical reaction has important applications.

7. CELLS IN CURRENT USE

Many different cells have been devised and used in the past. These cells fall into three types, which may be designated as *standard cells*, *primary cells*, and *storage cells*. Of each type, only one or two examples, which have proven superior to all others, still remain in use. These examples, which will be described in this section, are the following:

(a) *Standard cells:*   Weston cadmium cell
(b) *Primary cells:*   The dry cell
(c) *Storage cells:*   The lead-acid storage cell
            The Edison cell

(a) *Standard cells.* A standard cell is not intended as a source of energy but for use as a secondary standard of voltage. It is always used in a voltage-comparison circuit such as the potentiometer which will be described in Sec. 9 of Chap. 42. It is designed to maintain a very constant voltage over a long period of time, provided no appreciable current is ever drawn from the cell. Therefore, the circuit in which it is used must be so designed that no current of over about $\frac{1}{10000}$ amp ever passes through the cell. Under these conditions, the voltage of the Weston cadmium cell, which is about 1.018 v, can be trusted to remain constant to about 1 part in 100,000, so that this cell furnishes an admirable secondary standard of voltage for use in laboratory calibrations of voltmeters and other instruments.

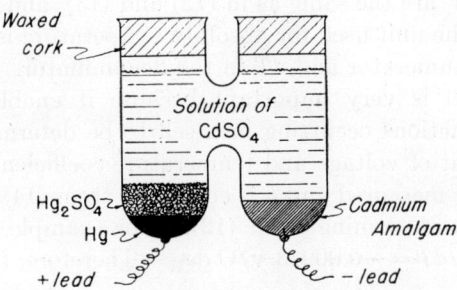

Fig. 6. The Weston standard cell.

The Weston cell (Fig. 6) has as its positive electrode liquid mercury on which floats a paste of mercurous sulfate, Hg_2SO_4, which is an almost insoluble compound. The negative electrode is an amalgam, 10 to 15 per cent of cadmium dissolved in mercury. The electrodes are held in place in the legs of an H-shaped glass vessel by porous porcelain retainers; the construction is delicate and will not permit rough handling. The electrolyte is a solution of $CdSO_4$, either almost saturated or kept saturated by the presence of crystals of solid $CdSO_4$.

The electrode reactions are accurately reversible so long as the current is kept extremely low. On discharge, at the negative electrode cadmium goes into solution as Cd^{++}:

$$Cd_{metal} \rightarrow 2\varepsilon^- + Cd^{++}. \qquad \text{(negative electrode)}$$

At the positive electrode, neutral mercury is released from the Hg_2SO_4, the SO_4 going into solution:

$$Hg_2SO_4 + 2\varepsilon^- \rightarrow 2\ Hg_{liq} + SO_4^{--}. \qquad \text{(positive electrode)}$$

Actually, this last reaction must take place in two steps. Since the solubility of Hg_2SO_4 is small but finite, there will be some Hg^+ ions in solution. Two of these ions pick up electrons from the mercury surface and deposit as liquid mercury, and their removal from solution permits another molecule of Hg_2SO_4 to dissolve.

(b) *Primary cells.* A primary cell is one that cannot be 'charged,' because the cell reactions are not reversible or not efficiently reversible in practice. All of the energy that the cell will ever deliver is put in as chemical energy when the cell is made; when this energy is exhausted, the cell is dead. The only cell of this type in general use is the common dry cell, which of course is not really 'dry.' It is merely *unspillable* because the electrolyte is soaked up in sawdust, blotting paper, gelatin, flour, plaster of Paris, or the like, and is tightly sealed in with tar to prevent evaporation.

The negative electrode of a dry cell (Fig. 7) is the zinc can itself. The positive electrode is a large stick of carbon, which is inert and does not enter the chemical reaction. The carbon electrode is made with a large

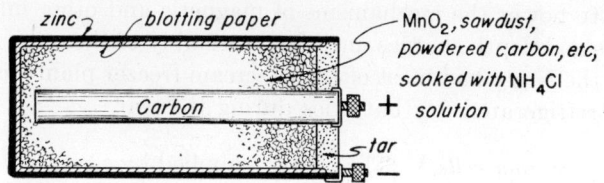

Fig. 7. The dry cell.

surface area so as to keep down the internal resistance of the cell. The electrolyte is a strong solution of sal ammoniac (NH_4Cl). The space between the carbon electrode and the can is filled with a mixture of inert material to absorb the electrolyte, manganese dioxide (MnO_2) to absorb the generated hydrogen, and powdered carbon to further reduce the internal resistance. This mixture is mechanically separated from the zinc can by several layers of blotting paper.

When this cell delivers current, zinc goes into solution at the negative electrode. At the inert carbon electrode, NH_4^+ ions are discharged, releasing free ammonia and hydrogen:

$$2\ NH_4^+ + 2\varepsilon^- \rightarrow 2\ NH_3 + H_2.$$

The ammonia, NH_3, is readily soluble and remains dissolved in the electrolyte. The free hydrogen gas, which would quickly spoil the action of the cell if allowed to collect around the carbon electrode (a phenomenon called, for some reason, *polarization*), is taken up and oxidized by the manganese dioxide:

$$H_2 + 2\ MnO_2 \rightarrow H_2O + Mn_2O_3.$$

A dry cell, when new, gives an EMF of slightly over 1.5 volts. The EMF is of course completely independent of the battery size. The internal resistance is comparatively high, varying from something less than 0.1 ohm for the large No. 6 cell to well over 1 ohm for the small cells used in B-batteries. If a cell is short-circuited, the internal resistance rapidly rises and the current drops because of polarization—the MnO_2 does not take up the hydrogen as fast as it is generated under these conditions.

The 'fuel' for this cell is essentially metallic zinc, which is consumed to form zinc ammonium chloride. As the cell is used, the zinc can is eaten up until it begins to leak and the cell becomes worthless. Because of local action caused by impurities in the zinc and other materials, the cell deteriorates even when it is standing on the shelf with no current drawn, and becomes worthless in a matter of a couple of years. The rate of deterioration is accelerated by high temperatures and can be reduced by refrigeration. During World War II, the Navy found it desirable to ship to its tropical bases large refrigerators in which to store the batteries used to power the mechanisms of magnetic and other influence-actuated mines and depth charges until final assembly of these devices for use. In fact, the Navy had most of the ice-cream freezer plants in Honolulu filled with refrigerated dry batteries during the war.

(c) *Storage cells.** The energy supplied by a primary cell is in general very expensive compared with energy obtained by burning coal. Zinc to 'burn' is extremely expensive compared with coal to burn. A *storage* cell employs completely reversible chemical reactions so that the chemical energy used up in discharge can be restored by charging. Aside from the initial cost of the cell, which is high, the energy is obtained substantially at the cost of the electrical energy used to charge the cell. When the cell is charged from power lines, this energy is obtained from coal or water-power. The automobile storage battery is charged by energy obtained by burning gasoline in the internal-combustion engine. These are all relatively inexpensive ways of obtaining energy as compared with consuming zinc.

Two types of storage cells are used now: (1) the lead-acid cell, whose electrodes are lead and lead peroxide in a sulfuric acid solution, and (2) the Edison akaline cell, whose electrodes are nickel and iron in various stages of oxidation, and whose electrolyte is a solution of the alkali, potassium hydroxide (caustic potash, KOH).

The lead-acid battery has the advantage of extremely low internal resistance, which enables it to supply extremely large currents for short periods of time. It is the only battery suitable for motor starting. Starting an automobile motor on a winter day at 0° F requires a current of about 300 amp. A 3-cell, 6-volt automobile battery has an internal

* An excellent reference is the book *Storage Batteries*, by G. W. Vinal (3d ed., Wiley, New York, 1940).

resistance of about 0.003 ohm, or only 0.001 ohm per cell, and when fully charged is capable of supplying a current of 300 amp steadily for about 3 min when the battery is at 0° F.

The disadvantages of the lead-acid battery are that it is heavy, weak structurally, and comparatively short-lived. The active materials are in the form of pastes of gray spongy lead and brown lead peroxide held in a grid of lead-antimony alloy. The grid is itself structurally weak and tends to sag or buckle, and the pastes tend to flake off with repeated charging and discharging and to sink to the bottom of the jar. These disadvantages are less pronounced in batteries having large-sized cells using very heavy plates in installations where weight is no consideration.

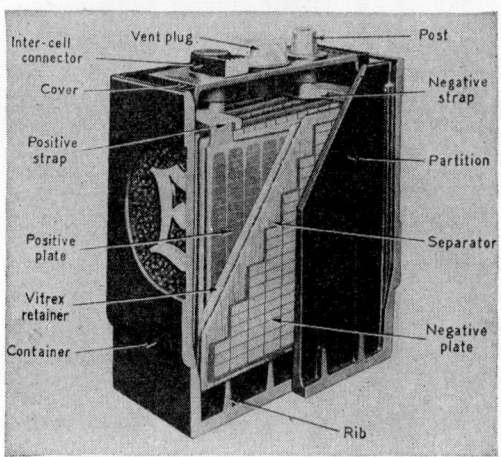

Fig. 8. The lead-acid cell. (*Courtesy of the Electric Storage Battery Co.*)

The Edison alkaline battery, developed in the Thomas A. Edison laboratory, is lighter in weight and structurally much stronger and more durable than the lead-acid cell. Its lightness (less than half the weight of the lead-acid cell for the same ampere·hour capacity) makes it advantageous for propulsion of vehicles such as industrial tractors and lift trucks. It is constructed entirely of nickel-plated steel, except for the active materials, which are contained in finely perforated steel tubes or cells. Its high internal resistance (about 10 times that of a comparable lead battery) makes it unsuitable for motor-starting service and is disadvantageous in other applications.

In the lead-acid battery, the active material of the negative plate is metallic lead in a spongy condition so that a large surface area is exposed to the sulfuric-acid electrolyte. On discharge, the metallic lead changes to solid lead sulfate which remains on the surface and in the pores of the

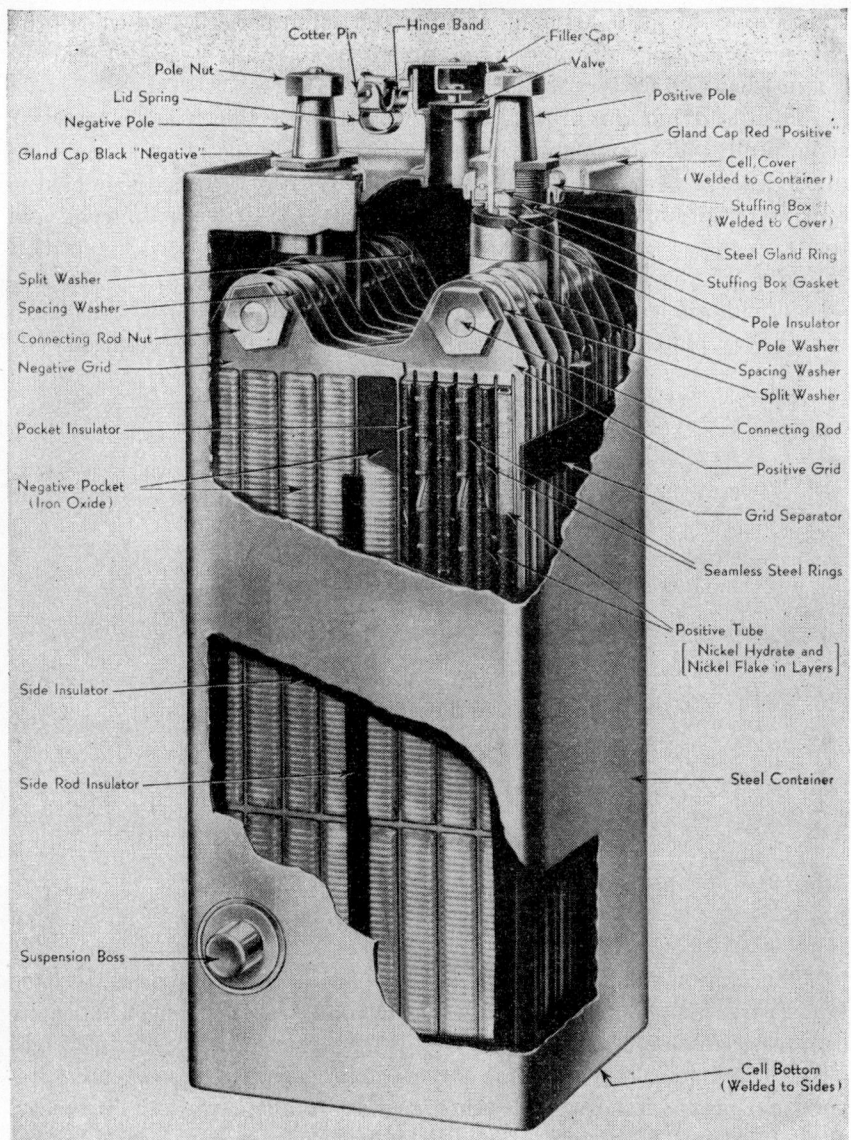

Fig. 9. The Edison alkaline cell. *(Courtesy of Thomas A. Edison, Inc.)*

spongy-lead electrode. The reaction is

$$Pb_{metal} + SO_4^{--} \xrightarrow{discharge} 2\varepsilon^- + (PbSO_4)_{solid}. \quad \binom{negative}{electrode} \quad (15)$$

At the positive plate the reaction is more complex. The active material is lead peroxide, PbO_2, in which the lead is quadrivalent. Two electrons arriving at the positive plate apparently reduce the valence of the Pb and permit one molecule of PbO_2 to combine with one of H_2O and pass into solution as a bivalent lead ion and four OH^- ions, so that a net charge of 2 electrons is carried into solution to compensate the net charge of 2 electrons that leaves the solution at the negative plate in (15). This reaction is

$$(PbO_2)_{solid} + 2\ H_2O + 2\varepsilon^- \xrightarrow{discharge} Pb^{++} + 4\ OH^-. \quad \left(\begin{array}{c}\text{positive}\\\text{electrode}\end{array}\right) \quad (16a)$$

But the Pb^{++} ion immediately combines with an SO_4^{--} ion to form insoluble $PbSO_4$ on the surface or within the pores of the lead-peroxide paste:

$$Pb^{++} + SO_4^{--} \xrightarrow{discharge} (PbSO_4)_{solid}; \quad (16b)$$

and the OH^- ions combine with H^+ ions to form water:

$$4\ OH^- + 4\ H^+ \xrightarrow{discharge} 4\ (H_2O)_{liq}. \quad (16c)$$

The secondary reactions (16b) and (16c) do not involve any transfer of charge to or from the electrode.

The net result of (15) and (16) is that, for each two electrons that flow, one molecule of lead peroxide is changed to lead sulfate at the positive electrode, one atom of lead is changed to lead sulfate at the negative electrode, and two molecules of H_2SO_4 disappear from solution and are replaced by two molecules of water. The over-all reaction is

$$PbO_2 + Pb + 2\ H_2SO_4 \xrightarrow{discharge} 2\ PbSO_4 + 2\ H_2O, \quad (17)$$

with a requirement of two faradays of charge transfer if (17) is in moles.

Exactly the reverse of (15), (16), and (17) takes place on charge.

The density of the sulfuric-acid solution will decrease as discharge progresses, since heavy sulfuric-acid molecules are replaced by lighter water molecules, according to (17). Hence, the density of the electrolyte furnishes an indication of the state of charge, and lead-acid batteries can be 'tested' with a hydrometer. Such batteries are ordinarily used in an operating range between densities of 1.285 g/cm³ (fully charged) and 1.150 g/cm³ (time to recharge).

The energy released in the chemical reaction (17) varies with the concentration of the sulfuric acid, because of variations in the large heat of solution of H_2SO_4 in water; hence, the EMF of the cell will also vary with charge condition and will furnish an indication of the state of charge. At 25° C and a density of 1.285 g/cm³, the EMF is 2.13 volts; whereas at a density of 1.150 g/cm³, the EMF has dropped to 2.01 volts.

The reactions in the Edison nickel-iron cell are less simple than those in the lead cell. Nickel and iron form many oxides and hydroxides of different valences, and it is possible that under various conditions various mixtures of Ni, NiO, Ni_2O_3, Ni_3O_4, $Ni(OH)_2$, and $Ni(OH)_3$ are found on the positive plate, with mixtures of Fe, FeO, and $Fe(OH)_2$ on the negative plate. In any case, the chemical energy during discharge is furnished by oxidation (increase in valence), of the iron and a corresponding reduction (decrease in valence) of the nickel. The action of the cell can be explained if we suppose that the over-all cell reaction is given by the simple equation

$$NiO_2 + Fe \xrightarrow{discharge} NiO + FeO. \qquad (18)$$

The electrolyte does not enter into this over-all reaction as it does in the corresponding over-all reaction (17) for the lead-acid cell. On this account, the electrolyte concentration does not change with state of charge, and the cell voltage is independent of the electrolyte concentration. The cell voltage does, however, depend on the state of oxidation of the material of the electrodes. The open-circuit voltage drops from about 1.48 volts for a freshly charged cell to about 1.35 volts after the cell has been standing unused for a day or two, probably because of spontaneous reduction of NiO_2 to Ni_2O_3 with the evolution of oxygen gas, which can be observed.

Although the electrolyte, KOH dissolved in H_2O, does not enter the overall equation (15), it is of course needed to carry the charge which permits a reaction to go on between NiO_2 on one plate and Fe on the other. The electrode reactions whose net result is (18) would be

$$(NiO_2)_{solid} + 2K^+ + 2\varepsilon^- + H_2O \xrightarrow{discharge} (NiO)_{solid} + 2 KOH, \quad \binom{positive}{plate}$$

$$Fe + 2 OH^- \xrightarrow{discharge} FeO + H_2O + 2\varepsilon^-. \quad \binom{negative}{plate}$$

The reactions on charge would be exactly the opposite.

PROBLEMS

1. (a) How many coulombs are there in 1 amp·hr?
   (b) How many ampere-hours are there in 1 faraday?
   Ans: (a) 1 amp·hr = 3600 coul; (b) 1 faraday = 26.8 amp·hr.

2. (a) In the lead-acid cell, how many grams of PbO_2 are changed to $PbSO_4$ on the positive plate for each faraday (that is, for each 26.8 amp·hr) of charge delivered?
   (b) How many grams of lead are converted to $PbSO_4$ on the negative plate for each faraday?
   (c) By how many grams does the mass of the electrolyte decrease for each faraday?

3. The capacity of a lead-acid cell in ampere-hours is limited by the amount of PbO_2 on the positive plate. Before *all* the PbO_2 is converted to $PbSO_4$, the voltage of the cell has dropped and the internal resistance has increased to the point where it is desirable to recharge. A cell with a rated useful capacity of 50 amp·hr has 500 g of PbO_2 on the positive plates. What would be the capacity of this cell if *all* the PbO_2 were converted to $PbSO_4$? Ans: 112 amp·hr.

4. Why does a lead cell 'gas' when it is 'overcharged'? What gas is given off at the positive electrode? at the negative electrode? Why must rooms in which lead storage batteries are charged be well ventilated to avoid an explosion hazard? A

moderate amount of overcharging does not damage the battery; in fact, it is good to overcharge a lead battery occasionally until all cells are gassing freely, to be sure that both plates are fully formed. This procedure is known as 'equalization.' After an overcharge, what needs to be added to bring the electrolyte back to its normal fully charged density? Explain.

5. From the principle of Le Châtelier-Braun, using an argument similar to that employed in connection with Fig. 5, show that because concentration of electrolyte in a lead-acid cell increases on charge and decreases on discharge, the cell voltage must increase with increase in electrolyte concentration.

6. A lead cell of EMF 2.05 v is connected in parallel to a lead cell of EMF 2.10 v. Assuming an internal resistance of 0.001 ω per cell, what current will flow initially? Why does the current decrease with time and approach zero?

CHAPTER 35

THERMOELECTRICITY

A number of different thermoelectric effects occur in metals. These effects involve direct reversible interchange between thermal and electrical energy, and certain other types of interactions between temperature gradients and potential gradients. While thermoelectric effects have played an important role in connection with our understanding of the electronic and atomic structure of metals, detailed discussion, linked as it is with the details of the thermal distribution-in-energy of electrons in metals, is beyond the scope of this book. However, since one of these effects, the *Seebeck effect*, is utilized in the thermocouple, a thermometer of great practical importance, it and its inverse, the *Peltier effect*, will be described here.

1. THERMOELECTRIC EFFECTS

About 1834, Jean Charles Athanase Peltier, in Paris, discovered that if current flows through a circuit composed of two dissimilar metals, one of the junctions between the metals tends to become warmer and the other junction tends to become cooler. These temperature changes are a result of heat generation at the warm junction and heat absorption at the cool junction. The rate of heat generation or absorption is proportional to the current. When the current is reversed, the roles of the two junctions are reversed. The temperature changes associated with this *Peltier effect* appear in addition to temperature increases resulting from the normal I^2R-heating. The I^2R-heating depends on the square of the current and is independent of current direction. By use of low-resistance pieces of metal, it is possible, in spite of the I^2R-heating, to get one of the junctions to cool below room temperature.

The dependence of the effect on current direction in the case of the metals Cu and Ni is shown in Fig. 1.

The *Seebeck effect*, discovered in 1821 by Thomas Johann Seebeck in Berlin, is the inverse of the Peltier effect. Here (Fig. 2), holding the two junctions at different temperatures causes a current to flow when no other source of EMF is present. The direction of the flow shown in Fig. 2 is related to the direction in Fig. 1 by the principle of Le Châtelier-Braun, which always governs the relation between an effect and its inverse. The current in Fig. 2 flows in such a direction as to *try* to

THERMOELECTRIC EFFECTS

equalize the temperature discrepancy. With the current direction shown, we note from Fig. 1 that the hot junction tends to cool and the cold junction to warm up, in accordance with the principle. The circuit of Fig. 2 is a heat engine which absorbs heat at the hot junction, converts some of the heat into electrical energy, and rejects the rest of the absorbed heat at the cold junction.

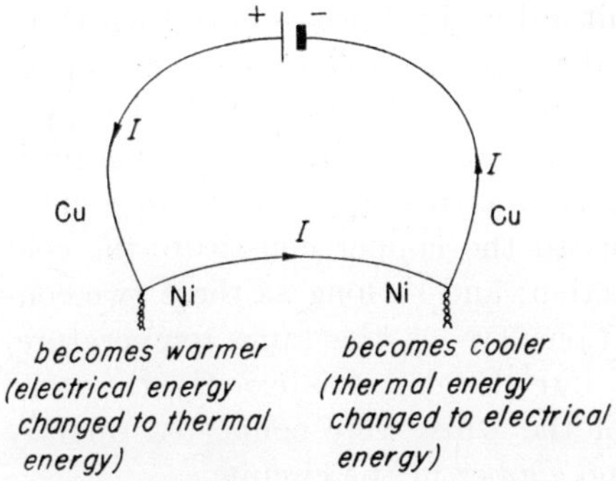

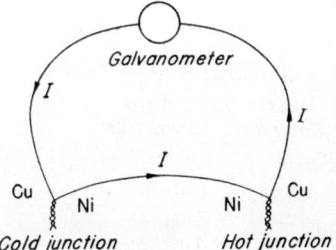

Fig. 1. Peltier effect for copper and nickel. When current is forced through the circuit, one of the junctions emits heat, the other absorbs heat.

Fig. 2. Seebeck effect. The thermocouple.

2. THE THERMOCOUPLE

When used as a thermometer, the circuit of Fig. 2 is called a *thermocouple*. The value of the thermocouple as a thermometer depends on the fact that the net EMF developed is directly related to the temperature difference between the junctions. For small temperature differences, it is approximately proportional to the temperature difference. Although the net EMF is small (of the order of 10 to 40 microvolts per C deg of temperature difference), a sensitive galvanometer can be calibrated to read temperature differences to an accuracy of $\frac{1}{1000}$ deg. For precise work, the cold junction is placed in ice water to furnish a constant reference temperature. One advantage of the thermocouple is that the hot junction can be in an inaccessible location, for example in the wheat in the middle of a grain elevator, where it would be impossible to read a mercury thermometer.

The proportionality between EMF and temperature difference does not hold over a very wide temperature range. In fact, for some metal pairs the EMF goes to a maximum and then decreases again as the hot-junction temperature is raised; but metals can be selected in which this reversal does not occur, and temperatures can be read accurately from a calibration curve.

Thermocouples in which the two metals are copper and constantan,*

* Constantan is an alloy of 45 per cent Ni, 55 per cent Cu.

or iron and constantan, are widely used in the lower temperature ranges. For higher temperatures, noble metals of high melting point and low chemical activity must be used; the most satisfactory combination employs platinum as one metal and a rhodium-platinum alloy as the other. Such a couple furnishes a satisfactory thermometer up to a temperature of about 1600° C (2900° F).

In practice, a thermocouple circuit ordinarily consists of at least three metals—the two metals constituting the thermocouple proper, and copper leads to the galvanometer and copper galvanometer windings. The wiring is arranged as in Fig. 3. The two connections to the copper constitute the cold junction; and so long as these two connections are at the same temperature, the EMF developed is exactly the same as if the wires were connected directly together at the cold junction, with no copper in the circuit.

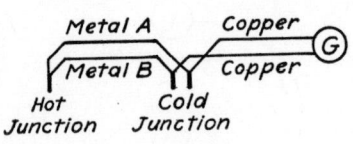

Fig. 3.

Thermocouples furnish one of the most sensitive devices for the detection and measurement of radiant energy. The junctions are made small, so as to have low thermal capacity, and blackened. The radiant energy to be measured is focused by a mirror on one of the junctions. A sensitive galvanometer can detect the small temperature rise associated with the absorption of very small quantities of radiant energy. Such an instrument is used for the mapping of spectra in the infrared beyond the limits of the photographic plate. It is also used in connection with reflecting telescopes for measuring the total amount of radiation of all wavelengths received from a star. One form, which has several cold and several hot junctions in series so that the EMF's are additive, and is arranged so that the radiation falls on all the hot junctions, is called a *thermopile*. This instrument is the basis of the *radiation pyrometer*, designed to be pointed at a hole in a furnace and to determine the furnace temperature by measuring the total radiant energy emitted.

The thermoelectric effect is not an unmixed blessing. In any electrical apparatus in which the circuits contain different metals or even different grades of the same metal, temperature differences arising from any cause will set up small 'thermal EMF's' and 'thermal currents,' as they are called. In sensitive apparatus these spurious thermal effects can cause a good deal of trouble, and sometimes great pains are taken to construct whole pieces of equipment of exactly the same grade of copper in order to eliminate them.

PROBLEMS

1. In a nickel-iron thermocouple, the EMF is in such direction as to send current from the nickel to the iron at the hot junction. Apply the principle of Le Châtelier-

Braun to decide whether current flowing in a nickel-iron circuit will cause heating or cooling at the junction where the current flows from nickel to iron, because of the Peltier effect.

2. When current flows in a lead-zinc circuit, there is a Peltier heating at the junction where the current flows from the zinc to the lead, with cooling at the other junction. From the principle of Le Châtelier-Braun, determine which way the current would flow in a lead-zinc thermocouple.

3. In Fig. 3, if metal A is replaced by a copper wire of the same resistance, the galvanometer reads a current I_1; if metal B is replaced by a copper wire of the same resistance, the galvanometer reads a current I_2. Show that for the actual circuit of Fig. 3, the galvanometer will read I_1+I_2.

4. For given hot- and cold-junction temperatures, the *thermoelectric power* of a given metal A is defined as the voltage developed in the circuit of Fig. 3 per degree temperature difference when metal B is lead. If, when the hot junction is at 100° C and the cold junction at 10° C, the thermoelectric power of platinum is 4 μv/C deg and that of nickel is 20 μv/C deg (EMF in the same sense) what will be the voltage developed by a Pt-Ni thermocouple with the junctions at these temperatures. Explain your reasoning carefully.

5. If the thermoelectric power of iron is -12 μv/C deg under the conditions of Prob. 4, what will be the magnitude of the EMF of a Ni-Fe thermocouple with junctions at 100° and 100° C?   Ans: 2.88 mv.

CHAPTER 36

MAGNETIC EFFECTS OF ELECTRIC CURRENTS

The word *magnetism* comes from the ancient Greek name for certain naturally occurring iron-oxide stones that possess distinctive properties. These stones, called *lodestones*, have the property of exerting forces on each other and on bits of iron or steel. They also have the power of imparting their own distinctive properties to pieces of steel that they touch. A piece of steel (for example, a steel needle) that has thus acquired the properties of the lodestone is said to be *magnetized*, and is called a *magnet*.

It was later discovered that a lodestone or a steel magnet experiences a torque that tends to orient it in a particular direction on the earth. This led to the important invention, sometime before the 12th century A.D., of the mariner's compass.

In 1820, Hans Christian Oersted discovered that forces exist between a lodestone or a steel magnet and a wire carrying electric current. In the same year, Ampère found that related forces exist between two wires carrying electric currents. Ampère suggested that the forces between steel magnets arise from the presence of circulating currents ('Amperian whirls') within the magnets. Modern research has shown this hypothesis to be correct, the circulating currents consisting of electrons in motion around the positive atomic nuclei or 'spinning' on their own axes.

Since the forces between currents are fundamental, we begin the study of magnetism with a description of these forces in this chapter, applications involving magnetized materials being left for the two succeeding chapters. Study of magnetic forces between currents is known as *electromagnetism*, as distinguished from the older *magnetostatics*, which considered only magnetized materials. Ampère's hypothesis makes magnetostatics a branch of electromagnetism, and we shall so consider magnetostatics in this text.

A good knowledge of the magnetic effects of electric currents is extremely important because it is fundamental to an understanding of electrical machinery of all types. Electric meters, motors, generators, transformers, relays, lifting magnets, and loudspeakers are all electromagnetic devices. *Electrostatics* by itself would have led to very little technical development of electricity. *Electromagnetism*, together with electrostatics and such subjects as electrochemistry and thermoelectricity, made possible all the present applications of electricity except those depending on twentieth-century developments in *electronics* (use of vacuum tubes).

1. INTRODUCTION

As Ampère first discovered, wires carrying currents exert on each other forces proportional to the currents, in addition to any electrostatic forces that may exist between the wires. Since a wire carrying a current can usually be considered as electrostatically neutral—the negative electrostatic charge on the moving electrons being exactly equal and opposite to the fixed positive charge in the wire—these additional forces must be associated with the *motion* of electric charges. In addition to the electrostatic forces between charges, there is another distinct system of forces associated with the motion of the charges; these are called *magnetic forces*. Magnetic forces exist between two charges only if both charges are in motion, the magnitude of the force being proportional to the product of the speeds of the charges.

Magnetic forces are forces associated with the *motion* of charges.

The existence of magnetic forces between parallel wires carrying current can be easily demonstrated with the apparatus sketched in Fig. 1. Here two stiff wires hang with their lower ends dipping into a pool of mercury so that the lower ends are free to move. If currents are sent through the two wires in opposite directions as in Fig. 1(b), the wires are mutually repelled; if currents are sent through the two wires in the same direction as in Fig. 1(c), the wires are mutually attracted.

That these forces are fundamentally forces between charges in motion can be easily demonstrated by replacing the left-hand wire of Fig. 1 (whose upward current corresponds to *electrons moving down*) by an electron-ray tube in which a beam of electrons moves down through a vacuum. According to the direction of the current in the fixed parallel wire, the beam of electrons is transversely deflected in the direction corresponding to the motion of the wire in Fig. 1. This experiment is sketched in Fig. 2, the three parts of this figure corresponding to the three parts of Fig. 1.

The forces between two *parallel* currents constitute a particularly simple case of a fairly complex system of forces which we need to study in detail. These forces are best expressed in terms of the *magnetic-field strength* $\mathcal{B}$.* The procedure is similar to the determination of electrostatic forces in terms of the electric-field strength $\mathcal{E}$. In the electrostatic

---

* We must here depart slightly from standard AIEE terminology. There are two vectors associated with a magnetic field; these are universally denoted by the symbols $\mathcal{B}$ and $\mathcal{H}$ (or B and H). For purely historical reasons, associated with the

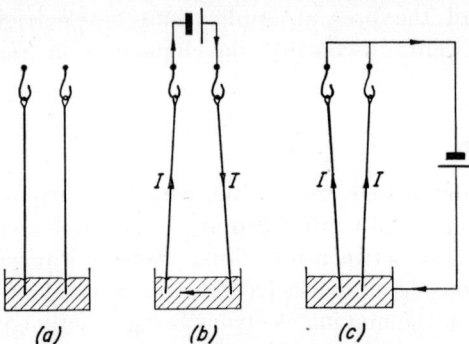

Fig. 1. (a) Two stiff wires dipping into a pool of mercury . . .
(b) . . . repel each other when they carry currents in opposite directions;
(c) . . . attract each other when they carry currents in the same direction.

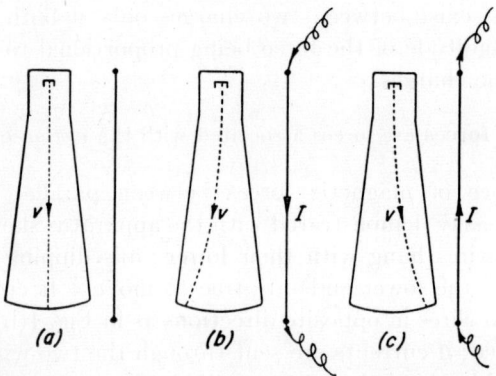

Fig. 2. A stream of electrons in an electron-ray tube is attracted or repelled by a parallel electric current. In (b), the motions of the electrons in the tube and of the electrons in the wire are in opposite directions, and the force is repulsive as in Fig. 1(b). In (c), the motions are in the same direction and the force is attractive, as in Fig. 1(c).

case we proceeded in two steps. We first learned to compute the electric-field strength $\mathcal{E}$ from the distribution in space of electrostatic charges.

earlier development of magnetostatics and the later development of electromagnetism, $\mathcal{H}$ has been considered as the fundamental vector in most engineering treatments. Actually, as we shall see when we define it in Chap. 38, $\mathcal{H}$ has no fundamental physical significance, but is merely an auxiliary vector that is extremely useful in computations involving magnetic materials. The AIEE defines a magnetic field as a vector field of $\mathcal{H}$; we define it as a vector field of $\mathcal{B}$. Except for the different size of units used to measure $\mathcal{B}$ and $\mathcal{H}$, these two fields agree in magnitude and direction everywhere except in the interior of magnetic materials. The AIEE calls $\mathcal{H}$ the 'magnetizing force,' 'magnetic intensity,' or 'magnetic force.' We shall call $\mathcal{H}$ the *magnetizing force*. The AIEE calls $\mathcal{B}$ the 'magnetic induction' or 'magnetic-flux density.' We shall call $\mathcal{B}$ the *magnetic-field strength* or simply the *magnetic vector*. We shall define magnetic flux in the same way as the AIEE, and $\mathcal{B}$ will be the *magnetic-flux density*.

Similarly, we shall learn to compute the magnetic-field strength $\mathcal{B}$ from the distribution in space of electric currents. Then as a second step, the force on an electrostatic charge was determined by the magnitude and direction of $\mathcal{E}$ at the location of the charge. Similarly the magnetic force on a current element (a short length of the wire carrying current, or a single moving charge) is determined by the magnitude and direction of $\mathcal{B}$ at the location of the current element.

The student is warned, however, that the laws for computing the magnetic field and for computing magnetic forces are much more complex than the corresponding laws in electrostatics. The fundamental reason for this complexity is that a current element is a vector quantity, having magnitude and direction, whereas an electric charge is a scalar quantity, having only magnitude.

2. DEFINITION OF THE DIRECTION OF THE MAGNETIC VECTOR; MAGNETIC LINES

Logically, before we can ask about the magnetic field set up by a system of currents, we must *define* magnetic field. This we shall do operationally by specifying a method of measuring the magnetic-field-strength vector $\mathcal{B}$ at a point of space. In this section we shall define the *direction* of the magnetic vector; in the next section, its *magnitude*.

A magnetic field (for example, the earth's magnetic field, the field in the vicinity of magnetized iron, or that in the vicinity of conductors carrying current) can be explored by means of either a small magnet mounted as in Fig. 4 so that it is free to rotate about an axle perpendicular to the magnet, or a small current-carrying coil consisting of many turns of wire mounted as in Fig. 3 so that it is free to rotate about an axle in the plane of the coil. These devices must be carefully balanced so that they will not tend to rotate because of gravitational forces, particularly when the axle is horizontal. The magnet of Fig. 4, when the axle is vertical, is the prototype of the familiar compass needle.

At any point in a magnetic field, either the magnet or the coil will tend to orientate in a certain direction. We specify the orientation of the magnet by means of a vector M along the axis of the magnet pointing in the direction from the south-seeking end toward the north-seeking end, as in Fig. 5. We specify the orientation of a coil by a vector M lying along the *axis* of the coil (not to be confused with the *axle* of Fig. 3) and pointing in the direction in which a right-hand screw would advance if its head were turned in the direction of the current flow in the coil, as in Fig. 5. A vector in this direction, and of a magnitude to be defined presently, is called the *magnetic moment* of the small magnet or the small coil. The *right-hand rule*, given above, for determining the direction of the magnetic moment of the coil, is most conveniently applied as follows:

Let the fingers of your right hand curl around in the direction of the current flow in a small coil; then the thumb of this hand will point out in the direction of the magnetic-moment vector of the coil.

With these specifications for the direction of the magnetic-moment vector, it is found experimentally that the small coil and the small magnet behave exactly alike; at a given point in a magnetic field, either will tend

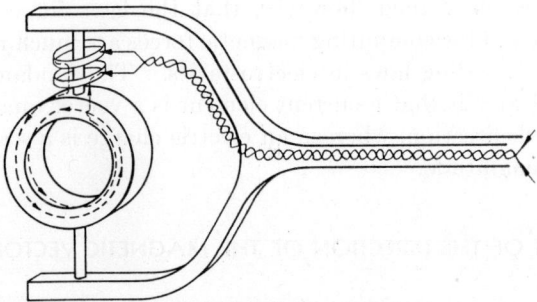

Fig. 3. A small current-carrying coil mounted so as to be free to turn about an axle.

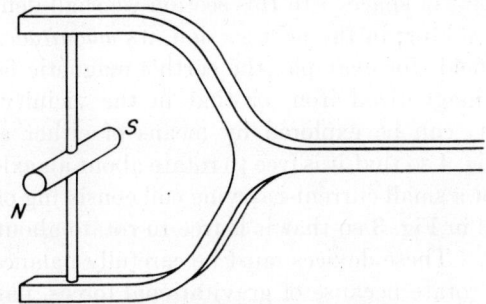

Fig. 4. A small magnet behaves like a small coil.

to turn so that its magnetic-moment vector is pointing in a certain particular direction.

> **The direction of the magnetic vector $\mathcal{B}$** at a point of space is defined as the direction in which the magnetic-moment vector of either a small coil or a small magnet tends to orientate when the small coil or magnet is placed at that point of space.

In this definition, one should think of the size of the small coil or of the small magnet used to explore the field as infinitesimal. Also, *one should think of the coil or magnet as somehow cleverly mounted so that the magnetic-moment vector is free to turn in every direction.* In the practical mounting of Figs. 3 and 4, the magnetic-moment vector can only rotate in one plane and define the direction of the component of the magnetic vector in that plane. With such a mounting, successive tests with the axle in various orientations will determine the direction of the magnetic vector in space.

Thus, at a point in the vicinity of a long straight wire carrying a heavy current (so that the magnetic field of this current is large compared to that of the earth), the small coil or magnet tends to turn so that its magnetic moment has a direction perpendicular to the wire and perpendicular to the radius from the wire to the point. Thus, the magnetic field set up by the current in the wire is found to have the direction shown by the magnetic-moment vectors in Fig. 6.

Just as we defined electric lines of force as directed lines that are everywhere in the direction of the electric field, we define *magnetic lines* as directed lines whose tangent is in the direction of the magnetic field $\mathcal{B}$. From the observed directions given by Fig. 6, we see that the magnetic lines in the vicinity of a long straight wire are circles surrounding the wire, as in Fig. 7.

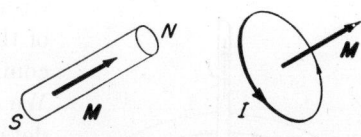

Fig. 5. Direction of the magnetic moment *M* of a magnet and of a coil.

The experimental results of Figs. 6 and 7 also determine the sense of the magnetic vector along the circular magnetic lines, in relation to the

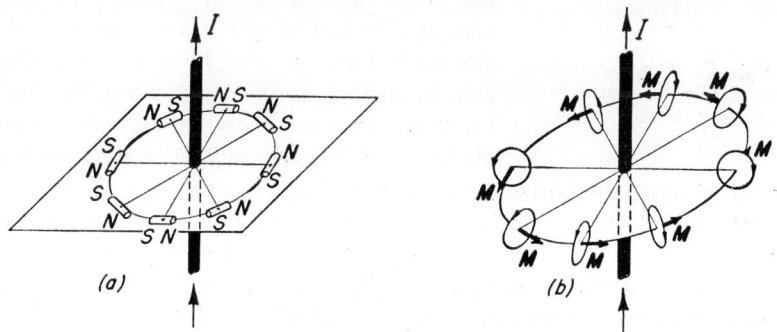

Fig. 6. Exploration of the field near a long straight wire by means of (a) a small magnet, (b) a small coil.

current direction. This sense, as shown in Fig. 7, is given by a right-hand rule of the following type:

> Point the thumb of your right hand in the direction of the current in the wire, and your curled fingers will point in the direction the magnetic vector points along the circular magnetic lines.

According to this rule, if the direction of the current is reversed in Fig. 7, the direction of the magnetic vector and of the magnetic lines will reverse at each point. By turning Fig. 7 upside down, one can see that this reversal of direction certainly occurs.

The earth has a magnetic field which, over most of the inhabited surface of the earth, has its horizontal component pointing generally northward.* Hence, we define the north-seeking end of a magnet (marked N in Figs. 4, 5, and 6) as the end that tends to point northward when the magnet is mounted like a compass needle. The earth's field also has a strong downward component throughout most of the Northern Hemisphere, a strong upward component throughout most of the Southern. We shall consider the earth's field in more detail in the next chapter, but we can discuss here the determination of its direction. The field near San Francisco, for example, has a northward component, an eastward component, and a large downward component, so that the actual vector $\mathcal{B}$ points in the direction shown in Fig. 8(a). The direction of this field could be determined by a small magnet mounted so as to be free to rotate in all directions, but a perfectly balanced, sufficiently frictionless, gimbaled mounting of this type has never been achieved. Rather, the direction of this and of any other magnetic field is determined in two steps, by the use of a single-axle mounting of the type shown in Fig. 4. First a *compass needle*, mounted to rotate about a vertical axle only, is used to determine the direction of the horizontal component $\mathcal{B}_H$ of the field, as in Fig. 8(b). To assure that the needle moves in a horizontal plane, an accurate compass needle is floated, like a ship's card, on the horizontal surface of a liquid. Then a second needle, called a *dipping needle*, which rotates in perfect gravitational balance about a horizontal axis, is used as indicated in Fig. 8(c). The horizontal axis is aligned perpendicular to the horizontal component of the field so that the needle swings accurately in the plane determined by $\mathcal{B}_H$ and $\mathcal{B}_V$, which plane contains the vector $\mathcal{B}$ itself. This needle then points along $\mathcal{B}$ and gives the *dip* of the magnetic field below the horizontal. For example, at San Francisco, the horizontal component points 18° east of north, and the dip is 62°, as indicated in Fig. 8.

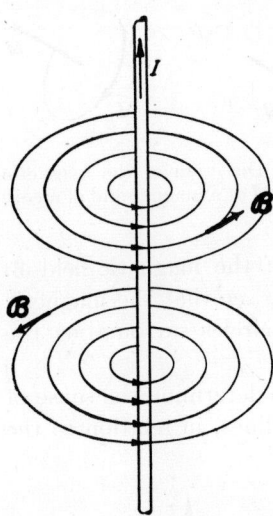

Fig. 7. Representative lines of the magnetic field set up by a long straight wire.

---

* The direction of the horizontal component is shown in Fig. 9 of Chap. 37.

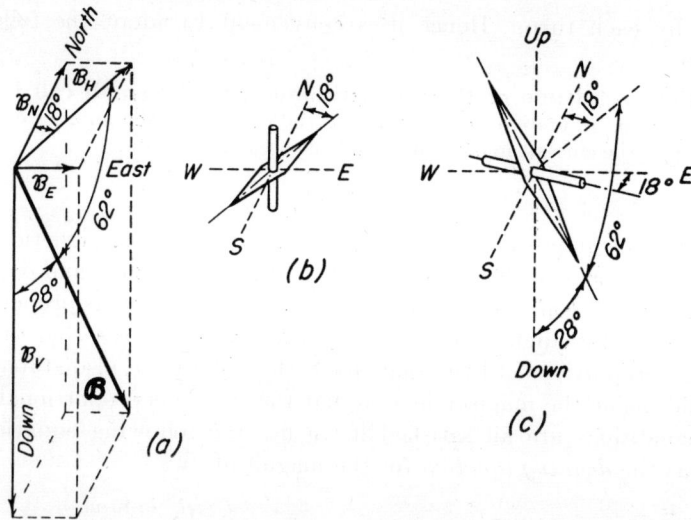

Fig. 8. (a) The direction of the earth's field at San Francisco. (b) A compass needle determines the direction of the horizontal component. (c) A dipping needle determines the angle of dip.

3. STRENGTH OF A MAGNETIC FIELD; FORCE ON A CURRENT ELEMENT

Since a small magnet or a small coil tends to turn so that its magnetic-moment vector M lines up with the magnetic-field vector $\mathcal{B}$, there must be a torque acting to turn the vector M into $\mathcal{B}$ when these are not aligned. *This torque is found experimentally to be proportional to the sine of the angle between the two vectors* (see Fig. 9). A measurement of the amount

Fig. 9. The torque L that tends to turn M into $\mathcal{B}$ is proportional to $\sin\theta$.

of this torque, for example by mounting a small magnet on a torsion fiber, will furnish a measure of the *strength of the magnetic field*, which is taken as *proportional to the torque on a given small magnet*. This method is used directly in a certain type of *magnetometer* that consists of small magnets mounted on quartz torsion fibers and is designed to make a continuous record of the fluctuations in the earth's magnetic field.

Different small magnets or small coils in the same magnetic field will experience different torques. It will be shown in Sec. 4 that in a given magnetic field, the torque on a small coil is proportional to the number N of turns, to the current I in each turn, and to the area A of the circuit formed by each turn. Hence it is convenient to adopt the following definition:

The magnitude of the magnetic moment of a small coil is measured in amp·m², and defined as the product of the number of turns, the current in each turn, and the area of the circuit.

Thus
$$M = NIA. \tag{1}$$

We are now in position to define the magnitude of the magnetic vector $\mathcal{B}$. We have defined the direction of $\mathcal{B}$ and the magnitude and direction of M for a small coil. We have observed that the torque is proportional to the sine of the angle θ between $\mathcal{B}$ and M, and have asserted that the torque is proportional to the magnitude M. We have also stated that we would define the magnitude $\mathcal{B}$ so that the torque is proportional to $\mathcal{B}$. These conditions are all satisfied if we use the following equation for torque as the *defining equation* for the magnitude $\mathcal{B}$:

$$L = M\mathcal{B}\sin\theta. \qquad \begin{cases} L \text{ in nt·m} \\ M \text{ in amp·m}^2 \\ \mathcal{B} \text{ in weber/m}^2 \end{cases} \tag{2}$$

The unit of magnetic-field strength defined by this equation is given the name *weber per square meter*. We shall later wish to consider magnetic-field strength as magnetic-flux density; the name weber* is given to the unit of magnetic flux and hence weber/m² to the unit of flux density. According to (2):

One weber per square meter is the strength of a magnetic field that will exert a torque of one newton·meter on a coil of magnetic moment one ampere·meter² placed with its axis perpendicular to the direction of the magnetic vector.

Formula (1) gives the correct value for the magnetic moment to be used in (2) no matter the shape of the coil: the coil may be wound on a circular frame as in Fig. 3, on a rectangular frame, or on a frame of any other shape. If the different turns of the coil have different areas, A is to be taken as the average area.

We should also like to have equation (2) applicable to the case of a small magnet by giving a suitable definition of the magnetic moment of the magnet. The following definition accomplishes this purpose:

The magnetic moment of a small magnet is equal to the magnetic moment of a small coil that would experience the same torque when placed in the same orientation at the same location in the same magnetic field.

The magnetic moment of a magnet is thus measured in amp·m². This unit will seem more reasonable when we see later on how the magnetic

---

* After Wilhelm Edward Weber (1804–1891), German physicist who, along with Karl Friedrich Gauss (1777–1855), German mathematician, devised the absolute systems of electric and magnetic units.

moment of the magnet actually arises from the presence of currents circulating within the substance of the magnet.

For dimensional check of (2) and succeeding equations, we note that the unit of $\mathcal{B}$ can be written as

$$1 \frac{\text{weber}}{\text{m}^2} = 1 \frac{\text{nt}}{\text{amp} \cdot \text{m}} = 1 \frac{\sqrt{\text{nt}}}{\text{m}}, \qquad (3)$$

while the unit of M is $\quad 1 \text{ amp} \cdot \text{m}^2 = 1 \sqrt{\text{nt}} \cdot \text{m}^2$.

The torque on a small coil in a magnetic field arises from forces on the different elements of length of the current-carrying conductors that compose the coil. We now turn to consideration of the forces on such current elements.

By a current element $I\,dl$, in ampere-meters, we mean a piece of conductor of length dl carrying current I. The force on such a current element is determined by the magnetic field at the location of the current element. The whole force on a conductor is obtained by integrating the forces on the current elements. We proceed to state the formulas for force on a current element; these formulas are derived from (1) and (2) in Sec. 4.

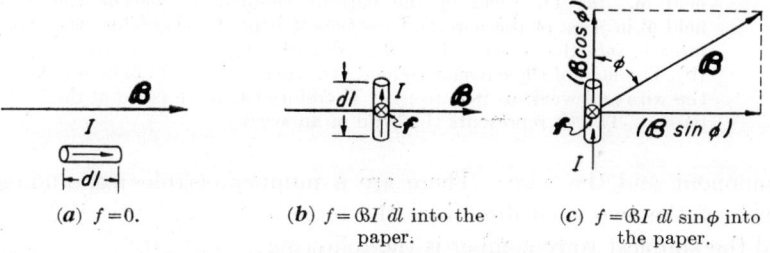

(a) $f = 0$. (b) $f = \mathcal{B}I\,dl$ into the paper. (c) $f = \mathcal{B}I\,dl \sin\phi$ into the paper.

Fig. 10. The force on a current element in a magnetic field. (The $\otimes$ represents the tail of an arrow.)

The following three statements are illustrated by the corresponding parts of Fig. 10:

(a) *A current element parallel to the magnetic vector experiences no force.*

(b) *A current element perpendicular to the magnetic vector experiences the force*

$$f = \mathcal{B}I\,dl, \quad \text{in newtons,} \qquad (4a)$$

in a direction perpendicular to both the magnetic vector and the current element, in the sense shown in Fig. 10(b).

(c) *When a current element makes an angle ϕ with the magnetic vector, the magnetic vector may be resolved into two components: One component* is of magnitude $\mathfrak{B}\cos\phi$ and parallel to the current; according to (a) *this component occasions no force.* The other component is of magnitude $\mathfrak{B}\sin\phi$ and perpendicular to the current; according to (b) *this component gives rise to the force*

$$f = \mathfrak{B} I\, dl\, \sin\phi \tag{4b}$$

in the direction determined by (b).

The force is determined by the component of the magnetic field perpendicular to the wire, and is in turn perpendicular to both this field

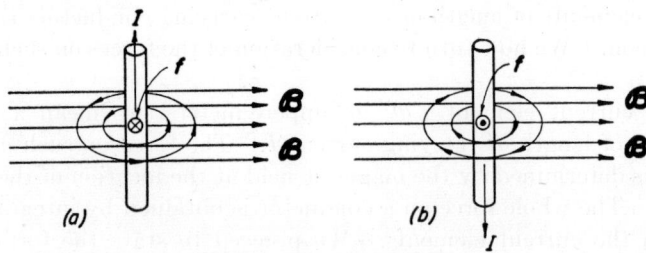

Fig. 11. Illustrating the rule for determining the direction of the force on a current element placed in an external magnetic field $\mathfrak{B}$. (a) The field of the current element *strengthens* the field $\mathfrak{B}$ in *front* of the wire and *weakens* it behind. Therefore the force is *into* the paper. The $\otimes$ represents the tail of an arrow. (b) The field of the current element strengthens the field $\mathfrak{B}$ behind the wire and weakens it in front. Therefore the force is *out of* the paper. The $\odot$ represents the head of an arrow.

component and the wire. There are a number of rules for finding in which of the two such directions the force acts. The rule the writers find the simplest to remember is the following:

Apply the right-hand rule as in Fig. 7 to find the sense of the circular magnetic field set up by the field of the wire itself. This field (see Fig. 11) will be in the same direction as, and will strengthen, the applied field on one side of the wire. It will be in the direction opposite to, and hence tend to weaken, the applied field on the opposite side of the wire. *The force on the wire is a vector directed from the side on which the field is strengthened toward the side on which it is weakened.*

As an example of these rules regarding direction of the force, let us reconsider the two parallel wires of Fig. 1. Each of the wires is in a magnetic field, like that of Fig. 7, set up by the other wire; and the direction of this field determines, according to the above rule, the direction of the force. This example is illustrated in detail in Fig. 12.

We can now discuss the principle of the DC electric motor in terms of the simple prototype illustrated in Figs. 13 and 14. Figure 13 shows a single rectangular loop arranged so that it can rotate about a horizontal axle as indicated by the curved arrow in the sketch. The axle carries a commutator arranged to reverse the direction of current in the loop each time the plane of the loop passes through the vertical plane. The necessity for this commutation can be seen by investigating the direction of the torque as the loop turns. In this simple example we assume the rectangular loop to be in a uniform magnetic field. The forces on the sides of length l are then in a direction to give a resultant clockwise torque at any angle except $\theta = 0$ in Fig. 14. The forces on the ends of length w can be seen from Fig. 14 to be perpendicular to the plane of the drawing in Fig. 14. They tend to push the ends together or apart in the direction

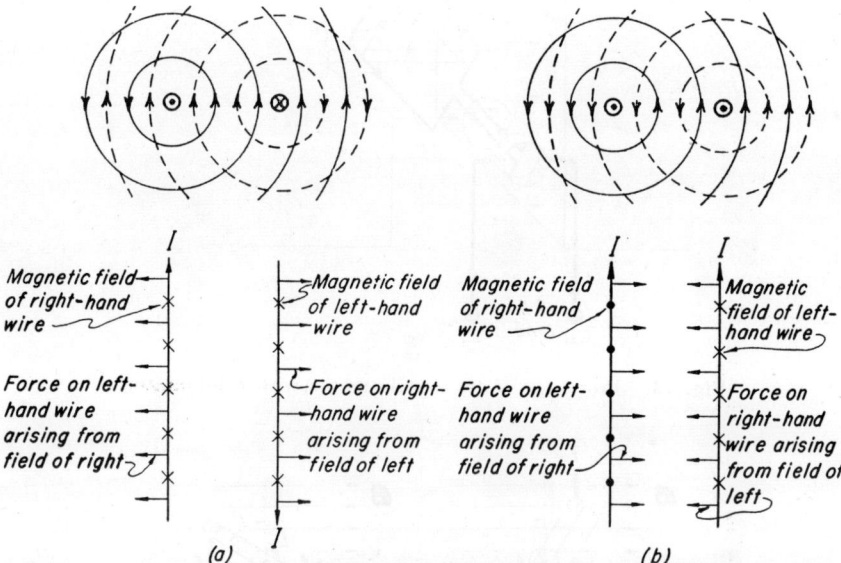

Fig. 12. The forces between parallel wires carrying current arise from the fact that each wire is in the magnetic field of the other. The top view illustrates particularly well that the experimental results of Fig. 1 are in agreement with the rule that the magnetic force is 'from the strengthened toward the weakened part of the field.'

of the axle but do not contribute to the torque about this axle. We see from Fig. 14 that by reversing the current direction in the loop every half revolution, the torque will always have the same sense.

The magnitude of any one of the forces f in Fig. 14 is $\mathcal{B}lI$, obtained from (4a) by replacing dl by l since the field is uniform. With respect to the axle, this force has a lever arm $\tfrac{1}{2}w \sin\theta$, so that the total torque of the two forces in Fig. 14 is

$$L = \mathcal{B}lwI \sin\theta, \quad \text{in nt·m,} \tag{5}$$

always in the clockwise sense.

The torque (5) vanishes when the plane of the coil is normal to the magnetic field and is at a maximum when the plane of the coil is parallel to the magnetic field. The torque of such a one-turn motor would come in spurts, and the motor would depend on inertia to carry it through the no-torque position. An actual motor contains a number of turns arranged at various angles so that only one turn at a time passes through the

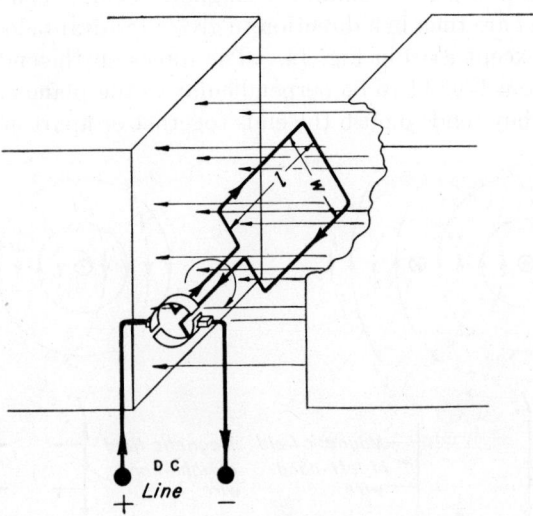

Fig. 13. Prototype of DC electric motor with commutator.

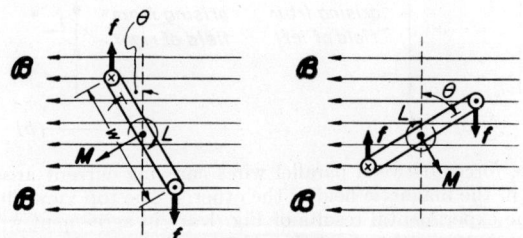

Fig. 14. Two positions of the rotating conductor of Fig. 13, showing how the commutator reverses the current as the plane of the conductor passes through the dotted center line so that the conductor to the left of this line always has current into the paper and force upward; the conductor to the right always has current out of the paper and force downward; the torque always has the same sense.

no-torque position. Such a motor then delivers mechanical energy at a fairly constant torque but requires a complex commutation system to reverse the current in each turn as it passes the no-torque position. Many segments are required in the commutator of any DC motor to do this switching properly.

The torque formula (5) can also be derived from (2). Formula (2) gives the torque on a small coil, the condition of smallness being that the magnetic field should not change appreciably in magnitude or direction over the size of the coil. In a *uniform* magnetic field, the formula will apply to as large a coil as we please, in particular to the coil of Figs. 13 and 14. According to (1), the magnetic moment of this single turn is of magnitude $M = IA = Ilw$, and has the direction shown in Fig. 14. The torque of Fig. 14 is in the proper direction to turn $\boldsymbol{M}$ into $\mathcal{B}$. Since the sine of the angle between $\boldsymbol{M}$ and $\mathcal{B}$ is $\sin\theta$, formula (2) gives the same answer as in (5).

PROBLEMS

1. If a straight horizontal conductor carrying 50 amp from south to north passes through the magnetic field of a large cyclotron magnet such as in Fig. 7 of Chap. 38, the magnetic field being 1.5 webers/m² vertically upward over a length of 1.2 m of the wire, what is the force on the wire in magnitude and direction?

Ans: 90.0 nt toward the east.

2. If 25 cm of a straight conductor is at right angles to a uniform magnetic field of 0.7 weber/m², what current must flow in the conductor in order that the force on this section be 4 nt?

3. In a region where the earth's magnetic field has a downward component of 1.00×10^{-4} weber/m², a northward component of 0.20×10^{-4} weber/m², and no east-west component, what is the force on a meter length of wire carrying 100 amp: (a) horizontally, from S to N? (b) horizontally, from W to E? (c) vertically upward?

Ans: (a) 0.0100 nt toward the west; (b) 0.0102 nt, northward and upward at an angle of 11°.3 above the horizontal; (c) 0.0020 nt toward the west.

4. In a region where the northward component of the earth's field is 0.25×10^{-4} weber, what current would a #10 aluminum conductor running E and W have to carry in order that the upward magnetic force should equal the downward gravitational force?

5. When the single-turn coil of Fig. 14 is carrying 40 amp and the dimensions of the coil are $l = 20$ cm, $w = 12$ cm, what are the torques on the coil at $\theta = 0°$, 30°, 60°, and 90°, if the magnetic field strength is 0.5 weber/m²?

Ans: 0, 0.240, 0.416, 0.480 nt·m.

6. If the coil of Fig. 14 is made of 40 concentrated turns, each carrying 10 amp, with dimensions $l = 20$ cm, $w = 12$ cm, in a field of 0.6 weber/m², what will be the torque on the coil at $\theta = 0°$, 30°, 60°, and 90°?

7. Prove that the single-turn coil of Figs. 13 and 14, when turning at n revolutions per second, has a mechanical power output of $4n\mathcal{B}lwI$, in watts if l and w are in meters.

SUGGESTION: Integrate $L\,d\theta$ from $\theta = 0$ to π to get the energy output in joules in ½ revolution. Multiply this result by $2n$ to get the energy output per second.

8. Show that the period of oscillation of a compass needle, when it is performing small oscillations about the direction of the horizontal component of the earth's magnetic field, is

$$T = 2\pi \sqrt{I/M\mathcal{B}}, \text{ in sec,}$$

where
I is the moment of inertia in kg·m²,
M is the magnetic moment in amp·m²,
$\mathcal{B}$ is the horizontal field component in weber/m².

A measurement of T in a known field will determine I/M for a compass needle; this needle of known I/M can then be used in the same way to determine the horizontal component of an unknown field.

4. DISCUSSION OF THE MAGNETIC MOMENT OF A COIL AND OF THE FORCES ON A CURRENT ELEMENT*

We wish first to show that the magnetic moment of a small coil is proportional to number of turns, current, and area, as in (1). We note first that the magnetic moment is to be defined as proportional to the torque on the coil when it is oriented with its plane parallel (magnetic moment perpendicular) to a particular magnetic field. In terms of this definition, it is clear that the magnetic moment of an N-turn coil is N times that of a single-turn coil, since each turn will experience the same

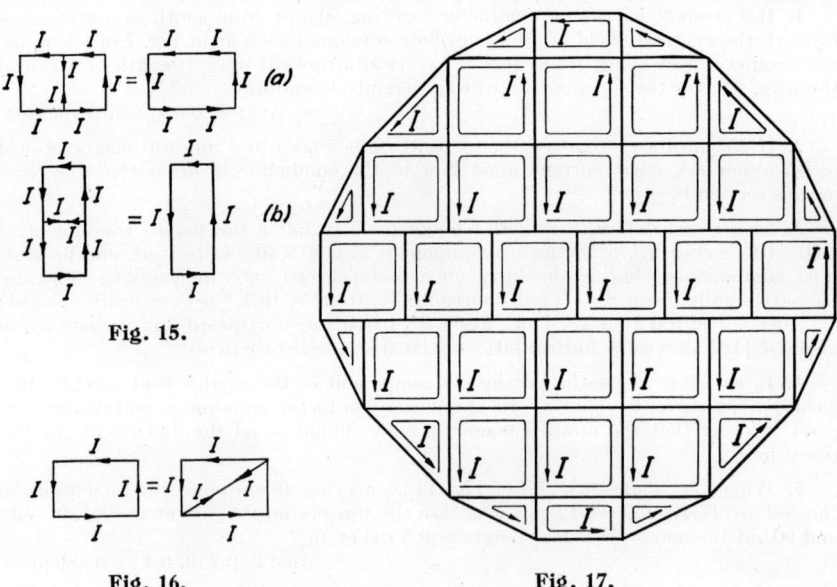

Fig. 15.

Fig. 16.   Fig. 17.

torque and the N turns will experience a torque N times as great as a single turn. It is also clear that the magnetic moment will be proportional to I, because a coil of N concentrated turns each carrying current I is equivalent to a coil of a single turn carrying current NI (consider the N turns as the N strands of a stranded wire). Hence, a single turn having current NI has N times the magnetic moment of a single turn having current I.

The proof that the torque, and hence the magnetic moment, is proportional to the area and independent of the shape is almost as easy. Consider the two single-turn coils at the left of Fig. 15(a). Since

---

* This section may be omitted without loss of continuity. In it we discuss, from a somewhat advanced standpoint, the logical reasoning underlying the development of the formulas given in the preceding section.

they are identical in size, shape, and current, they have the same magnetic moment and experience equal torques in a uniform magnetic field. But placed together, with a side of one coincident with a side of the other, the currents in the coincident sides cancel and are equivalent to no current, so that the two coils together are completely equivalent to the rectangular coil of twice the area shown at the right of Fig. 15(a). The coil at the right will thus experience as much torque as both the coils at the left, or twice as much as either coil. Thus, the coil at the right has twice the magnetic moment of either coil at the left—doubling the area has doubled the magnetic moment. In Fig. 15(b) we have placed the same two coils together in a different manner and obtained at the right an equivalent coil of the same area and the same magnetic moment as the coil at the right of Fig. 15(a), but of quite different shape. Thus, continuing this argument, we prove that any rectangular coil has a magnetic moment that is proportional to its area and independent of its shape.

By showing (Fig. 16) that a rectangular coil is equivalent to two identical triangular coils, each of half the area and the same current, we may extend the rule $M \propto A$ to triangles of any shape. Finally, any plane circuit (Fig. 17) can be approximated as closely as we please by rectangular and triangular circuits, carrying the same current, with all currents canceling out except around the boundary, so the rule that M is proportional to area, for given current, can be extended to an arbitrarily shaped circuit.

This completes the proof that the magnetic moment to be used in (2) should be defined as equal to the quantity in (1) or to a multiple of this quantity.

We now proceed to a derivation of the force on a current element in a magnetic field, starting from the formulas (1) and (2) for the torque on a small coil. We first note that

(a) *the force on a current element must reverse when the magnetic vector reverses,*

because the sum of two equal and opposite magnetic fields is no field, gives no torque on a coil, and must give no force on a current element—hence, equal and opposite magnetic fields must give equal and opposite forces; and

(b) *the force on a current element must reverse when the current reverses,*

because superposed equal and opposite currents equal no current and must experience no force.

From these statements we can draw two conclusions:

(1) *There is no force on a current element parallel to the field.*

Suppose there were a force F in some direction, as in Fig. 18(a). Now look at Fig. 18(a) upside down, as in Fig. 18(b). By merely changing our point of view we have reversed both the current direction and the field direction, which from successive application of statements (a) and (b) above should leave the force direction unchanged, but the force direction has reversed—a contradiction which is resolved only if the force vector is zero.

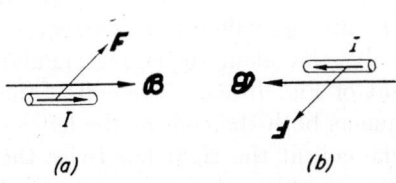

Fig. 18.

(2) *When I is perpendicular to $\mathcal{B}$, F is perpendicular to both.*

Let F_1, F_2, F_3 in Fig. 19(a) represent the three components of the force vector in this case. Look at Fig. 19(a) upside down as in Fig. 19(b). Both I and $\mathcal{B}$ are reversed from this point of view, so F should be unchanged. However, F_1 and F_2 are reversed, so they must vanish. F_3 is unchanged and is the only component that may exist.

Having shown that force must be perpendicular to both current and field, we easily derive formula (4a) from formula (2) applied to the rectangular single-turn coil in Fig. 20. The coil has $M = I\,dl\,dw$, with $M \perp \mathcal{B}$; therefore, the torque must be

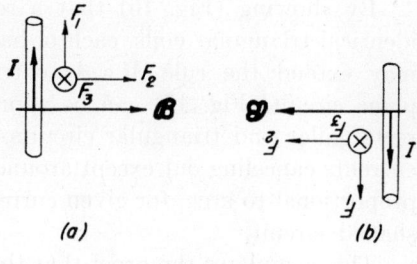

Fig. 19.

$$L = \mathcal{B} I\, dl\, dw$$

in the sense shown. By the preceding arguments, the force on the top and bottom edges of the coil must be zero; the forces on the left and right edges must be equal and opposite and normal to the plane of the paper. The correct sense of the torque is obtained only if we give f the direction shown in Fig. 20, and the correct magnitude is obtained only if we give f the magnitude $\mathcal{B} I\,dl$, as in (4a).

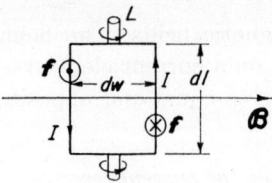

Fig. 20.

5. MAGNETIC FIELDS SET UP BY ELECTRIC CURRENTS

Now that we have defined the magnitude and direction of the magnetic field and learned to measure it* in terms of the forces it exerts on current-

---

* We have not given the most convenient practical methods of measuring magnetic

carrying conductors, we turn to the question of the magnitude and direction of the field set up by a given system of electric currents. First, let us look at some pictures of the field. We have already seen Fig. 7, which gives the magnetic lines around a long straight conductor. Figure 21 shows the lines of force around a circular turn of wire. Figure 56(c) on p. 963 shows the field around a solenoid. We notice one thing in common in these pictures, and this is true of all magnetic fields:

Magnetic lines never begin or end but form continuous closed curves, each curve linking at least some of the current that sets up the field, the sense of the linkage being given by the right-hand rule.

There is no magnetic stuff on which magnetic lines can begin or end in the way in which electric lines begin and end on electric charges.

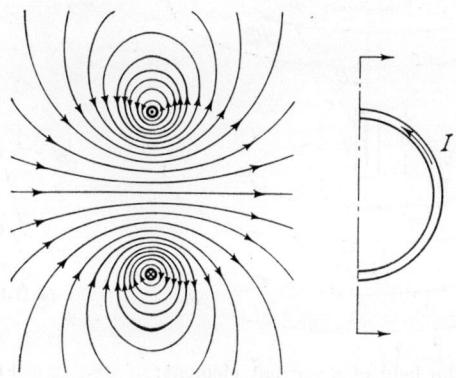

Fig. 21. Lines of force around a circular turn of wire.

Magnetic lines are always associated with electric currents, and they wrap themselves *around* the currents in the direction of curl of the fingers of the right hand if the thumb points in the direction of the current.

To compute the field of a current, we use Ampère's law, which gives the contribution of a current element to the field. The field arising from any circuit can then be obtained by integrating the contributions of the elements of the circuit. The integration is frequently very complicated because each contribution is a little vector, not a scalar, and the contributions must be added vectorially.

Ampère's law gives the contribution $d\mathcal{B}$ that a current element $I\,dl$ makes to the field at a point P (see Fig. 22). It states that $d\mathcal{B}$ has a direction perpendicular to the current element and perpendicular to the line joining the current element and P, and has the magnitude

---

field strength. These will have to wait until we have studied electromagnetic induction. But in principle we know how to measure the field.

$$d\mathcal{B} = \frac{I\,dl}{10^7\,r^2}\sin\theta. \qquad \begin{Bmatrix} \mathcal{B} \text{ in weber/m}^2 \\ I \text{ in amp} \\ l,\, r \text{ in m} \end{Bmatrix} \qquad (6)$$

Ampère's law is based on experimental observation. It gives a value of $d\mathcal{B}$ which, when integrated, gives agreement with the observed field of any system of currents. Advanced treatments show how the form of (6) can be logically deduced from certain simple experimental observations; this discussion is somewhat beyond the mathematical level of the present text.

As a first application of Ampère's law, we compute the field contribution at the point P (Fig. 23) of a piece of straight wire of length L carrying

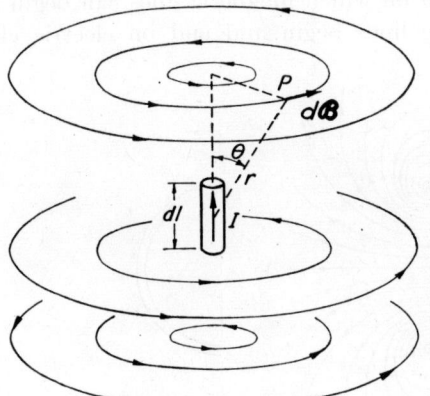

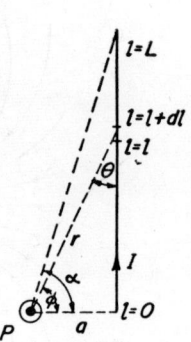

Fig. 22. The field of a current element:

$$d\mathcal{B} = \frac{I\,dl}{10^7\,r^2}\sin\theta.$$

Fig. 23.

$$\mathcal{B}_P = \frac{I}{10^7\,a}\sin\alpha.$$

current I, P being opposite one end of the wire and at a distance a from it. The contribution of all current elements is in the same direction (out of the paper at P). We obtain the field at point P by integrating the contributions (6) to obtain

$$\mathcal{B}_P = \int_0^L \frac{I\sin\theta}{10^7\,r^2}\,dl.$$

This integral is most easily evaluated in terms of the variable angle ϕ, which runs from 0 to α. By use of the substitutions

$$\sin\theta = \cos\phi, \quad r = a/\cos\phi, \quad l = a\tan\phi, \quad dl = a\sec^2\phi\,d\phi,$$

the integral becomes

$$\mathcal{B}_P = \frac{I}{10^7\,a}\int_0^\alpha \cos\phi\,d\phi = \frac{I}{10^7\,a}\Big[\sin\phi\Big]_0^\alpha = \frac{I\sin\alpha}{10^7\,a}. \qquad (7)$$

From this equation, we can easily get the formulas for the general case, when P is not opposite one end of the wire, that are given under Figs. 24 and 25. In Fig. 24 we have added together the contributions, computed from (7), of two pieces of wire, one subtending an angle α and the other an angle β at P. In Fig. 25, we have subtracted what would be the contributions of a piece of wire subtending angle β from the contribution of a piece subtending angle α to get that of the remaining piece.

By using the formulas given with Figs. 24 and 25, we can find the field of any circuit composed entirely of straight runs of wire. As an

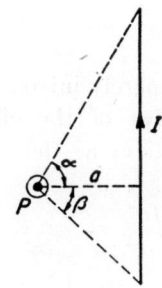

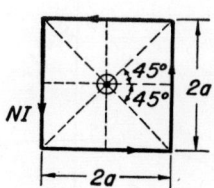

Fig. 24.
$$\mathfrak{B}_P = \frac{I}{10^7\, a}\, (\sin\alpha + \sin\beta).$$

Fig. 25.
$$\mathfrak{B}_P = \frac{I}{10^7\, a}\, (\sin\alpha - \sin\beta).$$

Fig. 26. Field at the center of a square coil of N turns is
$$\mathfrak{B} = \frac{4\sqrt{2}\, NI}{10^7\, a}.$$

example, the field at the *center* of the square coil of N turns shown in Fig. 26 is obtained from (7), with $\alpha = 45°$, taken 8 times over, as

$$\mathfrak{B} = \frac{8\, NI\, (\sqrt{2}/2)}{10^7\, a} = \frac{4\sqrt{2}\, NI}{10^7\, a}.$$

The field of a straight infinite wire is obtained from Fig. 24 with $\alpha = \beta = 90°$. This gives

$$\mathfrak{B} = \frac{2I}{10^7\, a}. \qquad \text{(infinite straight wire)} \quad (8)$$

From this equation we see that the field of Fig. 7 falls off inversely with distance a from the wire. Of course no infinite wire really exists, but we notice from Fig. 24 that so long as a is very small compared to the distance of P from the ends of the wire, α and β will be approximately $90°$, and formula (8) will be closely realized.

As a next application of Ampère's law, we shall compute the field at any point on the axis of a circular turn of radius a (Fig. 27). In this case the current element $I\, dl$ makes a field contribution of

$$d\mathfrak{B} = \frac{I\, dl}{10^7\, r^2}$$

(the angle corresponding to θ in Fig. 22 is 90°), in a direction perpendicular to r, in the axial plane as shown in Fig. 27. This field has a component $d\mathcal{B}\sin\phi$ along the axis and a component $d\mathcal{B}\cos\phi$ normal to the axis. We show in Fig. 27 the field elements $d\mathcal{B}^{(1)}$ and $d\mathcal{B}^{(2)}$ arising from equal lengths dl on opposite sides of the circle to show how the components normal to the axis cancel out in pairs all the way around the circle, so that the result of integration around the circle is a field in the axial direction.

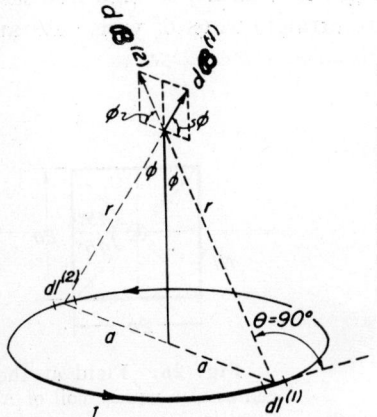

Fig. 27. Field on the axis of a circular turn is directed along the axis and has magnitude

$$\mathcal{B} = \frac{2\pi I a^2}{10^7 \, r^3}.$$

Since $\sin\phi = a/r$, the axial component arising from dl is

$$d\mathcal{B}_{\text{axial}} = \frac{I\,a}{10^7\,r^3}\,dl.$$

Summation over dl merely introduces the circumference $2\pi a$ of the circle in place of dl and gives as the total field

$$\mathcal{B} = \frac{2\pi I a^2}{10^7 \, r^3},$$

in the axial direction. The maximum value of this field is obtained when r takes on its smallest value, $r = a$, at the center of the coil. The field at the center of a circular coil of N turns has the value

$$\mathcal{B} = \frac{2\pi N I}{10^7 \, a}, \quad \text{(center of circular coil)}$$

slightly greater than the field (Fig. 26) at the center of a square coil of half side a.

The computation of the field of a square coil at points off the axis involves only the use of the results in Figs. 24 and 25, and a certain amount of geometry and trigonometry. The computation of the field of a circular coil at points off the axis involves complex integrals (elliptic integrals) beyond the scope of a first course in calculus. The magnetic lines for this case are plotted in Fig. 21. It will be seen that all lines of force link the current.

As a last example, we shall compute the field on the axis of a solenoid of circular section. A *solenoid* (from Greek *solen*, meaning 'tube') is a single layer of wire wound as in Fig. 28 on the surface of a cylinder, not necessarily circular. The wire may be slipped off the cylinder after winding, or the cylinder may remain in plane if it is of nonferromagnetic material.

It is usually satisfactory to consider that the solenoid has the same magnetic effects as though it were a sheet of current flowing around the cylinder. If the solenoid has n turns per meter length and each turn carries current I, the current around a meter length of the cylinder will be nI, and the current in a length $d\lambda$ will be $nI\,d\lambda$, as indicated in Fig. 29.

Solenoids play an important role in magnetic experimentation because a solenoid provides a very uniform field over its whole central section to within about one 'diameter' from the end (see Fig. 33). We shall consider the fields of solenoids in more detail in Sec. 10, but the treatment below will show where the end effects begin to come in along the axis.

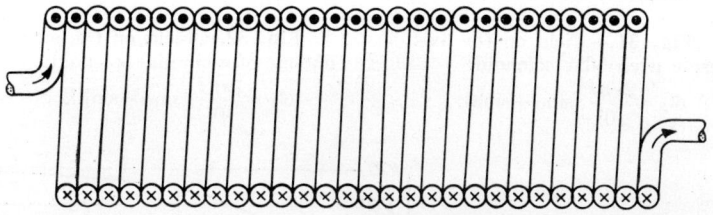

Fig. 28. Cross-section of a solenoid with n turns per meter length, each turn carrying current I.

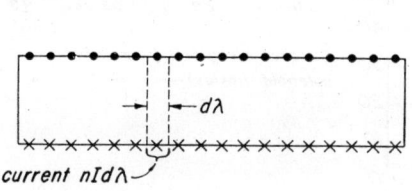

Fig. 29. A current sheet of nI amp/m or $nI\,d\lambda$ amp in a length $d\lambda$ is equivalent to the solenoid of Fig. 28.

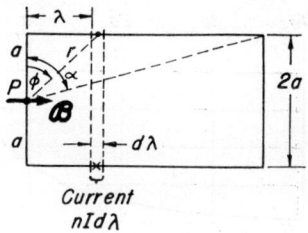

Fig. 30. Field on the axis at the end of a circular solenoid of n turns/m:

$$\mathcal{B}_P = \frac{2\pi nI}{10^7}\sin\alpha.$$

We shall start by computing the field on the axis at the very end of a circular solenoid; then, by superpositions analogous to those that led from Fig. 23 to Figs. 24 and 25, we can obtain the field for any point on a solenoid axis. In Fig. 30, the field at point P arising from the current $nI\,d\lambda$ in the strip of width $d\lambda$ is given by Fig. 27 as

$$d\mathcal{B} = \frac{2\pi(nI\,d\lambda)a^2}{10^7\,r^3}.$$

This value is to be integrated over the length of the solenoid. The best integration variable is ϕ, which runs from 0 to α. We can write

$$r = a/\cos\phi, \quad \lambda = a\tan\phi, \quad d\lambda = a\sec^2\phi\,d\phi,$$

to get $$\mathcal{B} = \frac{2\pi nI}{10^7}\int_0^\alpha \cos\phi\, d\phi = \frac{2\pi nI}{10^7}\Big[\sin\phi\Big]_0^\alpha = \frac{2\pi nI}{10^7}\sin\alpha.$$

The arguments that lead to the formulas under Figs. 31 and 32 are now similar to those we have used before. We note that on the axis

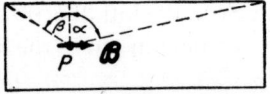

Fig. 31. Field on the axis inside a circular solenoid:
$$\mathcal{B}_P = \frac{2\pi nI}{10^7}(\sin\alpha + \sin\beta).$$

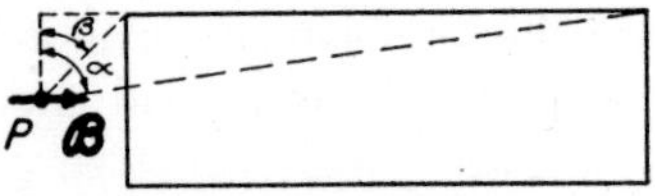

Fig. 32. Field on the axis outside of a circular solenoid:
$$\mathcal{B}_P = \frac{2\pi nI}{10^7}(\sin\alpha - \sin\beta).$$

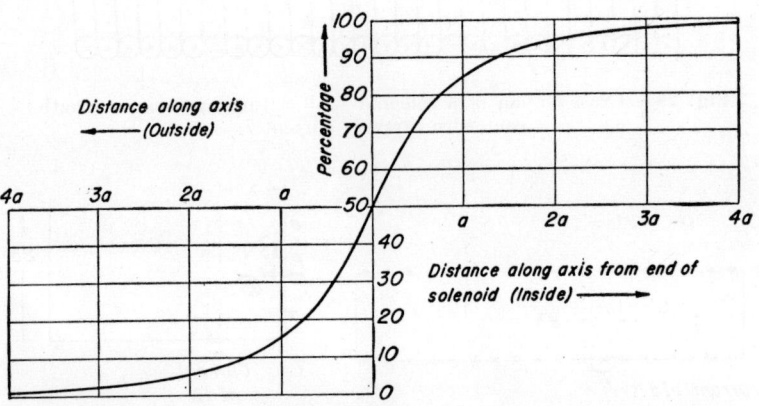

Fig. 33. Field on the axis near the end of a long circular solenoid. Ordinates are percentage of the field $4\pi nI/10^7$ given by the solenoid formula. Abscissas are distances from the end of the solenoid in terms of the solenoid radius a. The left end of the solenoid lies at the central vertical line of this chart.

inside and well away from the ends of a long solenoid, where we may take $\beta = \alpha = \tfrac{1}{2}\pi$ in Fig. 31, we have

$$\boxed{\mathcal{B} = \frac{4\pi nI}{10^7}.} \qquad \begin{pmatrix}\text{SOLENOID}\\ \text{FORMULA}\end{pmatrix} \quad (9)$$

We shall show later that *this formula gives the field in the interior of a long solenoid of any cross-sectional shape, at any point that is well away from the ends.*

The field on the axis near the end of a long circular solenoid falls off as in Fig. 33. This plot is made by taking $\alpha = 90°$ in Fig. 31 or Fig. 32 and plotting $\mathcal{B}$ against distance from the end of the solenoid expressed in units of the radius a. The field is expressed as percentage of the field inside the solenoid as given by (9). It will be noticed that the field at the end of the solenoid is just half the full field, in accordance with the formula of Fig. 30, whereas the field is up to 95 per cent of its full value one diameter ($2a$) inside the solenoid, and down to 5 per cent one diameter outside. The general characteristic of a solenoid is that the field is large inside, small outside. We shall return to this point later.

We note that in all the formulas of this section we must use the same system of units as in (6), with $\mathcal{B}$ in weber/m², I in amp, lengths in m, and n in turns/m.

PROBLEMS

1. What is the field strength in weber/m² at a distance of 1 cm from an infinite straight wire carrying 120 amp? At 2 cm? 3 cm? 4 cm?

Ans: 24, 12, 8, 6×10^{-4} weber/m².

2. What current must flow in an infinite straight wire in order that the field at a distance of 2 cm be 0.025 weber/m²?

3. What current must flow in a circular coil of 100 turns and 10 cm radius to give a field of 0.001 weber/m² at the center? Ans: 1.59 amp.

4. What current must flow in a square coil of 100 turns and 10 cm half side to give a field of 0.001 weber/m² at the center?

5. Show that the field at the center of a rectangular coil of sides a and b, in m, is $8NId/10^7 ab$, in webers/m², where d is the length of the diagonal. Find the field at the center of a rectangular coil of 100 turns with sides 10 cm and 40 cm long, carrying 5 amp. Ans: 0.00412 weber/m².

6. Find the magnitude and direction of the field at points A, B, C, D, and E in the plane of the square coil of Fig. 34, composed of 100 turns carrying 5 amp.

7. In Fig. 34, change the two dimensions marked with an asterisk (*) to 5 cm, so that the coil becomes rectangular, 10 cm high by 20 cm wide. If this coil is composed of 100 turns carrying 5 amp, find the magnitude and direction of the field at the points A, B, C, D, and E in the plane of the coil.

Ans: 4470, 4940, -789, -208, -46 μweber/m².

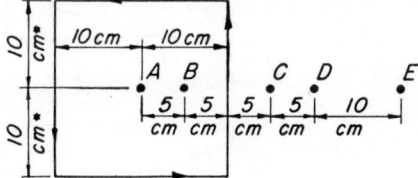

Fig. 34.

8. Show that the force between two very long parallel wires separated by a distance a, in m, and carrying currents I and I' is

$$\frac{2II'}{10^7 a}, \text{ in } \frac{\text{newtons}}{\text{meter length}}, \qquad (10)$$

attractive if the currents are in the same direction, repulsive if in opposite directions.

9. From (10) find the force per meter length between two parallel wires each carrying 250 amp, 1 cm apart. Ans: 1.25 nt/m.

10. Find the current that a bare #20 aluminum wire must carry in order that when the aluminum wire is 1 cm away from a horizontal insulated copper wire carrying 1000 amp, the magnetic force between the wires will be sufficient to support the aluminum wire against the force of gravity when it is parallel to and vertically above the copper wire. Use (10).

11. In the notation of Fig. 35, show that the field at any point on the axis of a square turn carrying current I is

$$\mathcal{B} = \frac{8Ia^2}{10^7 \, r^2 \sqrt{r^2+a^2}}.$$

12. Show that at a large distance, the field of Prob. 11 on the axis of a square coil can be written as $\mathcal{B} = 2M/10^7 r^3$, where M is the magnetic moment of the coil.

13. Show that the field on the axis of the circular coil of Fig. 27 can be written as $\mathcal{B} = 2M/10^7 r^3$, where M is the magnetic moment of the coil.

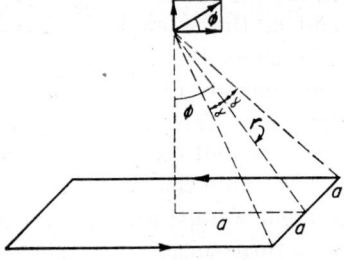

Fig. 35.

14. Let Fig. 30 represent a square solenoid instead of a circular solenoid, with a and r defined as in Prob. 11 and Fig. 35. Carry out an integration of the field given by the formula of Prob. 11 from $\phi = 0$ to $\phi = \frac{1}{2}\pi$, to show that the field on the axis at the end of a very long square solenoid is $2\pi nI/10^7$, the same as for a circular solenoid. Hence, show that the solenoid formula (9) holds for a square solenoid as well as for a circular solenoid.

15. For testing magnetic mines during World War II, large square solenoids were constructed, 3 or 4 ft square and 20 or 30 ft long, which could be used to apply a uniform field to the entire mine case. The solenoids were wound with 2 turns/inch length. From the solenoid formula (9), compute the field in webers/m² per ampere current. Ships' fields are usually specified in a unit called the milligauss (1 milligauss $= 10^{-7}$ weber/m²). Show that the solenoid constant you have computed is very close to 1 milligauss/milliampere, a very convenient value for test purposes.

16. The particular arrangement of two coaxial circular coils of radius a with planes separated by distance a shown in Fig. 36 is known as a pair of *Helmholtz coils*. This particular coil system is useful because it gives an almost constant field over a

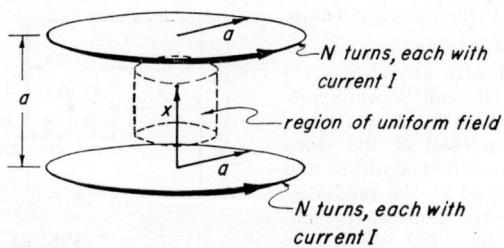

Fig. 36. Helmholtz coils.

fairly large volume at the center as indicated in Fig. 36. Let x denote the distance from the plane of the lower coil to any point on the axis.

(a) Compute the field at the center ($x = 0.5\,a$).
(b) Compute the field at $x = 0.4\,a$, $0.6\,a$.
(c) Compute the field at $x = 0.3\,a$, $0.7\,a$.
(d) Compute the field at $x = 0.2\,a$, $0.8\,a$.
(e) The reason for the slow variation of the field in the neighborhood of $x = 0.5\,a$ is that with this particular spacing, with distance a between the coils, not only is $d\mathcal{B}/dx = 0$ at $x = 0.5\,a$, but also $d^2\mathcal{B}/dx^2 = 0$ at $x = 0.5\,a$. Prove this statement. The second derivative vanishes halfway between the coils only for this particular coil spacing.

17. For design work on the 'degaussing' of ship models at various latitudes, a pair of Helmholtz coils (Fig. 36) were constructed 10 ft in radius, to give a field at the center of approximately 1 gauss (10^{-4} weber/m²) per ampere current. How many turns of wire were used in each coil? Ans: 339.

18. Figure 37 is an accurate plot of the magnetic lines in a plane perpendicular to two long parallel wires carrying equal currents in opposite directions. For the case in which the wires are 2 m apart, each carrying current I, find the magnitude and direction of ℬ at points A, B, C, D, and E, which lie on a ½-m square grid having the wires as grid points.

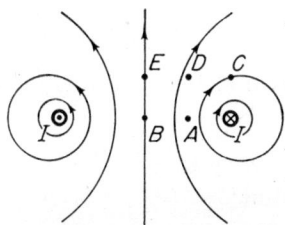 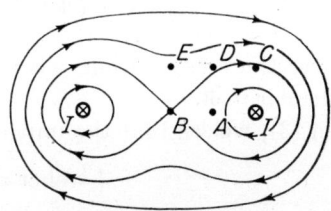

Fig. 37. Magnetic lines near two parallel infinite wires with equal currents oppositely directed.

Fig. 38. Magnetic lines near two parallel infinite wires with equal currents in the same direction.

19. Figure 38 is a plot of the magnetic lines in a plane perpendicular to two long parallel wires carrying equal currents in the same direction. For the case in which the wires are 2 m apart, each carrying current I, find the magnitude and direction of ℬ at points A, B, C, D, and E, which lie on a ½-m square grid having the wires as grid points. In the answers, the magnitudes of ℬ are in weber/m²; the angles are measured clockwise from the horizontal axis. Ans: A, $2.67 \times 10^{-7} I$, 90°; B, 0; C, $4.34 \times 10^{-7} I$, $-12°.5$; D, $2.53 \times 10^{-7} I$, 18°.4; E, $1.60 \times 10^{-7} I$; 0°.

20. Show that the left and right sides of equations (6), (8), and (9) are in the same units.

6. MAGNETIC FLUX

A *magnetic tube* is an imaginary tube whose generators are magnetic lines (see Fig. 39). A magnetic tube is *always* a region topologically equivalent to a doughnut.

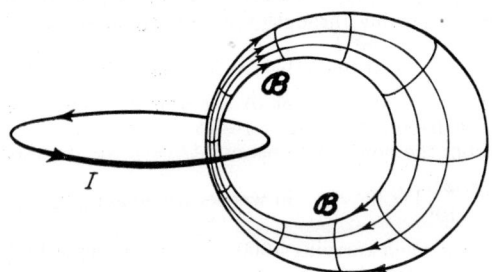

Fig. 39. A magnetic tube in the field of a circular current.

The product of field strength ℬ by the cross-sectional area A of the tube is called the *flux through the tube*. The flux is usually denoted by

Φ, and is measured in *webers:*

$$\Phi = \mathcal{B}A, \quad \text{in webers.} \tag{11}$$

Since $\mathcal{B} = \Phi/A$, $\mathcal{B}$ is frequently called the *flux density*. If $\mathcal{B}$ cannot be considered as constant over the cross section of the tube, we must define Φ as the surface integral

$$\Phi = \iint \mathcal{B}\, dA,$$

taken over the cross section, where dA is an element of area of surface perpendicular to $\mathcal{B}$.

From (3), we see that the unit of flux,

$$1 \text{ weber} = 1 \sqrt{\text{nt}\cdot\text{m}}.$$

A fundamental theorem that is proved in more advanced texts is:

The flux through a magnetic tube is constant along the length of the tube.

The concept of magnetic flux will prove to be very important when we come to study electromagnetic induction, electric generators, transformers, and similar topics. Some problems for practice in the computation of flux are given below.

PROBLEMS

1. It can be shown that the flux density is uniform across the cross section of a long solenoid, so long as we are well away from the ends, and is given by (9) no matter the shape of the cross section. Hence, the flux through such a solenoid is

$$\Phi = \frac{4\pi n I A}{10^7}, \quad \text{in webers,} \tag{12}$$

where n is the number of turns per m, and A is the cross-sectional area in m^2. What is the flux through a circular solenoid 5 cm in radius and 100 cm long wound with 1200 turns of wire carrying 2 amp? Ans: 23.7 μweber.

2. What is the flux through a long solenoid 3 ft square wound with 2 turns/inch carrying 4 amp? Use (12).

3. In Figs. 13 and 14, p. 934, if $l = 60$ cm, $w = 30$ cm, $\mathcal{B} = 0.6$ weber/m^2, what is the flux linking (that is, passing through) the rectangular conductor when (a) $\theta = 0°$, (b) $\theta = 30°$, (c) $\theta = 60°$, (d) $\theta = 90°$? Ans: (a) 0.108 weber; (b) 0.0935 weber; (c) 0.0540 weber; (d) 0.

4. Two telephone wires are parallel to a power wire carrying current I. The telephone wires are at distances r_1 and r_2, respectively, from the power wire. Show that the total flux from the power wire passing *between* the telephone wires is

$$\Phi = \frac{2I}{10^7} \log_e(r_2/r_1), \quad \text{in webers per meter length.}$$

5. Two power wires, each carrying 1000 amp but in opposite directions, are 1 m apart on the crossbar of telephone poles. On the same poles, on a crossbar 5 m below, are two telephone wires also 1 m apart, each directly below a power wire. From the formula in Prob. 4, compute the magnetic flux from the power circuit that links the telephone circuit, per kilometer of line. NOTE: Telephone wires would never be strung just this way. Such magnetic linkage would be highly undesirable because currents would be induced in the telephone circuit whenever the current in the power circuit changed. We shall see in Chap. 39 that the magnitude of the induced current depends directly on the flux linkage you have computed.

Ans: 0.00784 weber/km.

7. THE POLE CONCEPT; FORCES ON THIN SOLENOIDS AND THIN MAGNETS*

We now introduce a useful concept: that of the *magnetic pole*. A magnetic pole is conceived to be made of some magnetic stuff on which a magnetic field exerts forces, just as an electric field exerts forces on electric charges. *There really is no such magnetic stuff.* A magnetic field exerts forces only on currents, or moving charges, and hence exerts torques on coils in which currents are flowing. A steel magnet is equivalent to a large collection of small coils, each coil consisting of the electrons

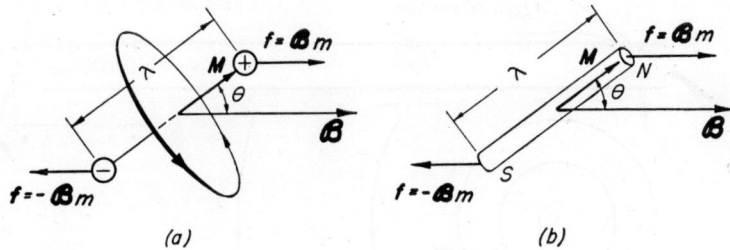

Fig. 40. The torque on a small coil or a small magnet can be computed from the forces on two fictitious magnetic poles on the axis, of strengths $\pm m$, separated by a distance λ such that $M = m\lambda$. The coil shown in (a) is not necessarily circular, but may have any shape.

of a single iron atom. These electrons move in orbits around the nucleus and 'spin' on their own axes, as discussed on p. 970. The resultant magnetic moments of the atoms are systematically oriented so that most of them are pointing along the axis of the magnet. The torque on the magnet is the cumulative effect of the torque on each of the atoms.

Nevertheless, the pole concept plays a useful role in the development of magnetic theory and in the visualization of magnetic effects.

The manner in which the torque on a small coil or a small magnet can be expressed in terms of forces on magnetic poles is illustrated in Fig. 40. We suppose that a pole of strength m experiences a force

$$f = m\mathcal{B}, \quad \text{in newtons,} \tag{13}$$

the force vector being in the direction of the field $\mathcal{B}$ if m is positive, in the opposite direction if m is negative. Then equal and opposite poles $\pm m$ separated by a short distance λ along the magnetic-moment vector as in Fig. 40 would experience equal and opposite forces, forming a couple with

---

* Sections 7, 8, and 10, which employ the concept of magnetic poles, may be omitted without loss of continuity.

the torque
$$L = \mathfrak{B} m \lambda \sin\theta,$$
which agrees with (2): $L = \mathfrak{B} M \sin\theta$, provided that
$$M = m\lambda. \tag{14}$$

In the case of a small coil, λ can be chosen arbitrarily, but it should be comparable to the diameter or distance across the coil; m is then fixed by (14) and the formula (1): $M = NIA$. In the case of a small magnet, it is customary to take λ as the length of the magnet, as in Fig. 40; m is then determined by (14) if the magnetic moment M of the small magnet is known.

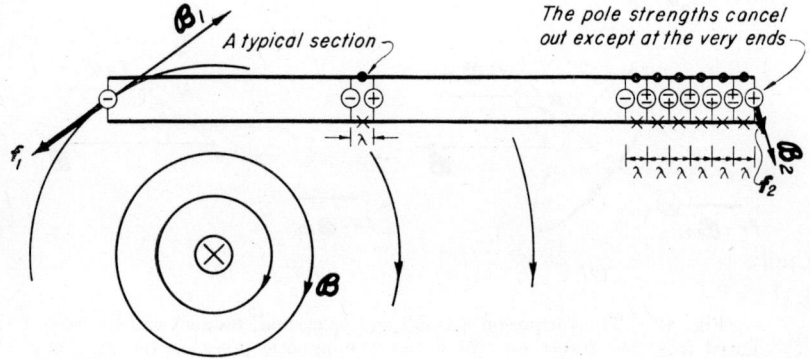

Fig. 41. A thin solenoid in the field of an infinite straight wire is acted on by a force system that is equivalent to a force $f_1 = -m\,\mathfrak{B}_1$ at the left end and a force $f_2 = m\,\mathfrak{B}_2$ at the right end. Here $\mathfrak{B}$ is the field set up by the current in the straight wire, and $m = nIA$, where I is the solenoid current.

Since M is measured in amp·m², we see from (14) that m is measured in amp·m.

By using the pole concept, it is easy to compute the forces on a long thin solenoid in a magnetic field. The solenoid is to be so thin that the variation of the magnetic field over the cross section of the solenoid is negligible, but the variation over the length of the solenoid may be as large as we please.

Such a thin solenoid is sketched in Fig. 41; in this example the solenoid is placed in the magnetic field of a long straight wire. We shall show from the pole concept given above that the whole system of forces acting on this solenoid can be reduced to a force $f_2 = m\mathfrak{B}_2$ on a pole of a certain strength m at the right end of the solenoid where the field of the wire is of strength $\mathfrak{B}_2$ and a force $f_1 = -m\mathfrak{B}_1$ on a pole $-m$ at the left end of the solenoid where the field of the wire is $\mathfrak{B}_1$.

Consider a short section of the solenoid of length λ. This section can be considered as a small coil carrying current $nI\lambda$ (Fig. 29) with magnetic moment $M = nI\lambda A$, where A is the cross-sectional area of the solenoid. The forces on this small coil can be represented by the forces on a pair

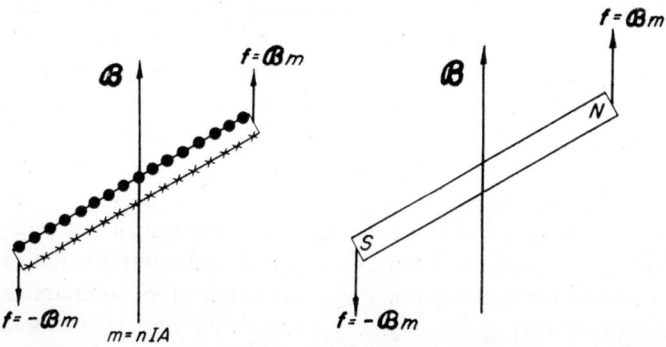

Fig. 42. Forces on a solenoid and a thin magnet in a uniform field as given by the pole picture.

of poles separated by the distance λ, and of strength $\pm m$, with, according to (14),

$$m = nIA. \qquad (15)$$

This is the strength of the poles indicated by $\oplus$ and $\ominus$ signs in Fig. 41. Now if, as indicated at the right of Fig. 41, we slice the whole solenoid into strips of length λ, with a view to computing the forces on each strip from the forces on $+$ and $-$ poles on its right and left faces, then so far as the net forces on the whole solenoid are concerned, the poles cancel all down the line except at the ends, where we are left with poles of strength $\pm nIA$. Note that this value is independent of the thickness λ chosen for the strips. The net force system acting on the solenoid, considered as a rigid body, is then equivalent to just the two forces obtained by imagining the solenoid to have a $+$ pole at one end and a $-$ pole at the other, these poles being acted on by the external magnetic field in accordance with (13). The pole strength is given by (15), and the $+$ or N end of the solenoid is determined by the right-hand rule that gives the direction of the magnetic-moment vector.

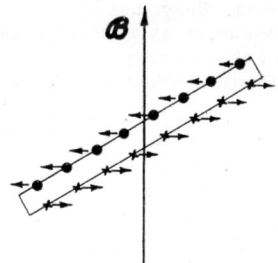

Fig. 43. Actual system of forces on a solenoid in a uniform magnetic field.

Note that in Fig. 41 the solenoid experiences a resultant force as well as a torque.

A long thin magnet, such as a magnetized steel knitting needle, behaves exactly like a long thin solenoid; the forces in a magnetic field can be considered as arising from poles of strength $+m$ on its N end and $-m$ on its S end.

Thus, there is complete similarity of behavior between a thin solenoid and a thin magnet. In a uniform field, such as that of the earth, each behaves as if it were acted on by equal and opposite forces on its two ends, which result in a torque tending to turn it into the direction of the field (Fig. 42). It must be emphasized that this is not at all the system of forces that really exists. The real system consists of forces to the right on all current elements going into the paper in Fig. 43, and forces to the left on all current elements coming out of the paper. The forces are to be computed from (4). The actual computation of the net torque from the force system of Fig. 43 is much more complex than from the pole picture of Fig. 42, which by the above arguments is known to give the correct answer.

By using the pole concept, we have proceeded from formula (1), which gives the torque on a coil so small that the applied field does not vary appreciably over the size of the coil, to a method of computing the forces on a thin solenoid where the field variation over the thickness of the solenoid is negligible but the variation over its length is not. In Sec. 11 we shall extend this argument to the forces on a solenoid not necessarily thin. But first we shall see that the pole picture is also useful in computing the field set up by a solenoid or magnet.

PROBLEMS

1. Show that if the solenoid of Fig. 43 is of length l, and has rectangular cross-section of width w in the plane of the paper and height h perpendicular to the plane of the paper, then the force system of Fig. 43 has the same torque as that given by the pole picture of Fig. 42.

2. Show that if the external applied field is uniform, the pole picture gives a force system on a solenoid in which the resultant force vanishes and the torque is that given by (2) with $M = NIA$, where N is the total number of turns on the solenoid.

3. A thin magnet 15 cm long experiences a torque of 0.030 newton·cm when placed perpendicular to a uniform field of 0.045 weber/m². What is the pole strength of the magnet? *Ans:* $m = 0.0444$ amp·m.

4. What is the pole strength of a thin solenoid of area 0.6 cm², length 15 cm, wound with a total of 500 turns carrying 0.2 amp?

5. If the magnet of Prob. 3 is placed in the same plane as an infinite straight wire carrying 100 amp, perpendicular to the wire, with its N end 5 cm from the wire and its S end 20 cm from the wire, what is (a) the net force acting on the magnet and (b) the net torque about the center of the magnet?
Ans: (a) 1.33×10^{-5} nt; (b) 1.67×10^{-6} nt·m.

6. If the thin solenoid of Prob. 4 is placed in the same plane as an infinite straight wire carrying 100 amp, perpendicular to the wire, with one end 5 cm from the wire and the other end 20 cm from the wire, what is (a) the net force acting on the solenoid and (b) the net torque about the center of the solenoid?

8. EXTERNAL FIELDS OF SOLENOIDS AND MAGNETS

We have seen that the torque on a small coil can be attributed to forces on a pair of fictitious poles arranged as in Fig. 40. The pole concept has, however, more useful applications than this. It can be shown that the field of any small coil is, at distances large compared to the size of the coil, the same as the field which would be computed by an inverse-square law, like Coulomb's law, from the pair of fictitious poles shown in Fig. 40. In the inverse-square law we must, of course, use a different constant from that used in the electrostatic case. We must take the field at distance r from a pole of strength m as

$$\mathcal{B} = \frac{m}{10^7 \, r^2}. \qquad (16)$$

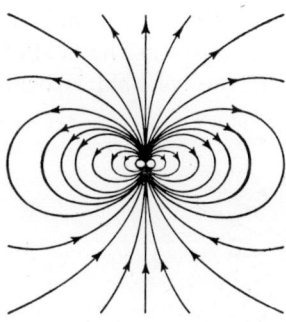

Fig. 44. Field of a magnetic dipole or an infinitesimal coil, with magnetic-moment vector pointing upward.

The magnetic-field lines computed in this way for a pair of poles of strengths $+m$ and $-m$ (called a *magnetic dipole*) are shown in Fig. 44. This picture is the same as Fig. 21 but reduced in size so that the coil has become infinitesimal and hence invisible at the center of the picture. So far as the visible parts of Fig. 44 are concerned, we have a correct picture of the field of an infinitesimal coil. However, we know that the picture is incorrect right at the center, because the lines of force of a pair of poles start at one pole and end at the other, whereas magnetic lines actually are endless and thread through the coil as in Fig. 21.

From the equivalence of the field of a dipole and a small coil everywhere except in the immediate vicinity, we can easily compute the field *outside* a solenoid, such as that of Fig. 41, that is thin in comparison with its length. The external field of each typical section is that of a pair of poles of strength $\pm m = \pm nIA$. In getting the whole external field of the solenoid, the $+$ and $-$ poles cancel out, just as in Fig. 41, except at the ends. Hence, *the field of the whole solenoid, external to the solenoid and at a distance from the end large compared with the thickness of the solenoid, is the field computed from* (16) *for a pole of strength* $m = nIA$ *at one end and a pole of strength* $-m$ *at the other.*

The external field of a thin magnet is exactly like that of a thin solenoid.

Since both the external fields of, and the forces on, thin solenoids and thin magnets are given correctly by the pole concept, with equal and opposite poles at the ends, we see that such solenoids and magnets interact just as if they had poles on their ends that interact by the inverse-square law, the rest of the solenoid or magnet merely furnishing a rigid mechanical connection between the poles. On this picture the force between two poles m and m' is to be taken as

$$f = \frac{mm'}{10^7 \, r^2}, \quad \text{in newtons,}$$

with r in meters. The force is repulsive if the poles have like sign, attractive if they have unlike sign.

The magnetic lines external to a thin solenoid or magnet are illustrated in Fig. 45. These lines are the same as those of Fig. 22, p. 804, for the electrostatic field of a pair of equal and opposite charges.

An argument similar to the above will show that if the solenoid is curved as in Fig. 46, its external field is still representable as the field of $+$ and $-$ poles of strength nIA at its ends. If the solenoid is bent

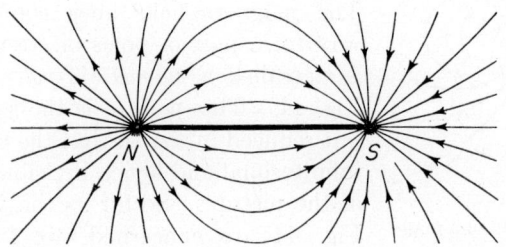

Fig. 45. External field of a thin magnet or solenoid.

through 360° and closed, to form a toroid as in Fig. 47, the *external* field entirely disappears, since the poles that give the field of each typical section are canceled by the poles of the adjoining sections, *all the way around*. Hence, *the external field of a toroid* is represented by the field of *no* poles, and *is zero*.

It must be emphasized that the arguments of this section apply only to the field outside the solenoid, since the field *close* to the poles representing a typical section is not given at all correctly by the pole picture. If we are inside a solenoid, we are close to some of the poles representing typical sections, and the field there cannot be obtained from the pole picture. We can, however, compute the flux through the solenoid. A certain amount of flux leaves the $+$ pole and makes its way outside the solenoid around to the $-$ pole. Since flux tubes do not actually begin and end on these fictitious poles but are continuous, all this flux must thread *through* the solenoid *inside*, from the $-$ end to the $+$ end.

We can compute the flux that leaves a $+$ pole in the same way that we computed the electric flux leaving a $+$ charge in Chap. 31. At a distance r from a $+$ pole of strength nIA, the flux density is $\mathcal{B} = nIA/10^7 r^2$.

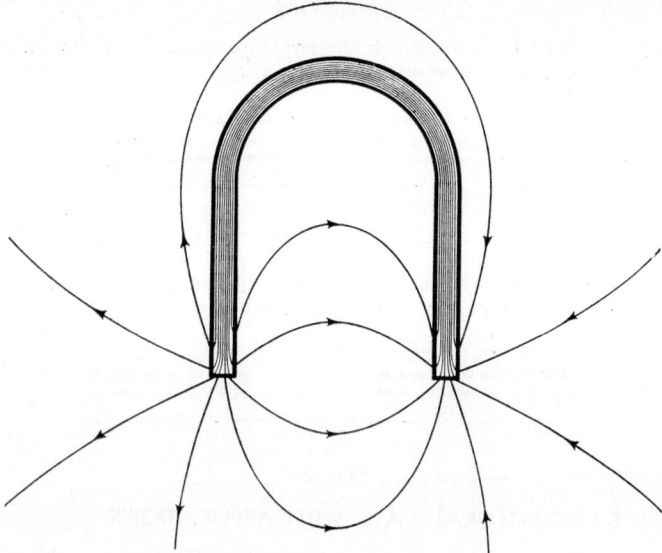

Fig. 46. The external field of a thin curved solenoid is the field of a pair of poles of strength $\pm nIA$ at its ends and is hence represented by the same magnetic lines between these poles as in Fig. 45, regardless of the contour of the curved solenoid between these poles. The return circuit for all the lines is inside the solenoid.

This flux passes normally through the sphere of radius r and area $4\pi r^2$, so that the total flux through the sphere is $\Phi = 4\pi r^2 \mathcal{B} = 4\pi nIA/10^7$. This is the amount of flux that leaves the $+$ end of a thin solenoid and passes externally around to the $-$ end. Hence, the amount of flux threading through a thin solenoid is

$$\Phi = \frac{4\pi nIA}{10^7}, \quad \text{in webers.} \quad (17)$$

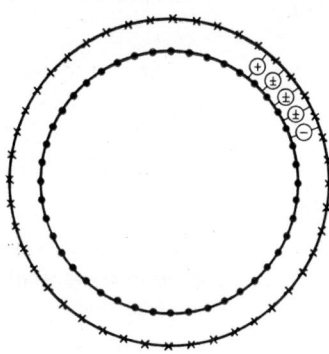

Fig. 47. A toroid has *no* external field.

This is the same value as in (12), but we have derived the formula by a rigorous argument here.

We see, then, that in the curved solenoid of Fig. 46, this flux Φ passes externally between the poles and returns internally by following the contour of the solenoid, as indicated schematically in this figure.

PROBLEMS

1. Find the total force with which the two thin solenoids of Fig. 48 repel each other if each solenoid has a cross-sectional area of 0.5 cm². Ans: 6.25 μnt.

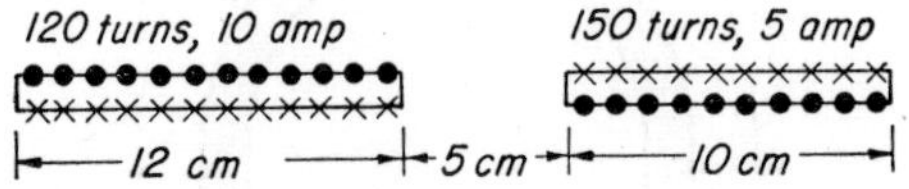

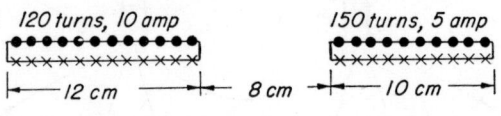

Fig. 48.

2. Find the total force with which the two thin solenoids of Fig. 49 attract each other if each solenoid has a cross-sectional area of 0.5 cm².

Fig. 49.

9. AMPERE'S LINE-INTEGRAL LAW, WITH APPLICATIONS

We have seen that the magnetic lines (Fig. 7) around a long straight conductor are circles, with field strength $\mathcal{B} = 2I/10^7 a$ from equation (8), where a is the radius of the circle. If we multiply the field strength on any circle by the circumference $2\pi a$ of the circle, we get

$$\oint \mathcal{B}\, dl = 4\pi I/10^7, \qquad (18)$$

where we have written the product of field strength by circumference in more complicated fashion as the integral around the closed magnetic line (indicated by the symbol for contour integration: $\oint$) of $\mathcal{B}$ times the element of length dl along the path. Since $\mathcal{B}$ is constant along the path,

$$\oint \mathcal{B}\, dl = \mathcal{B} \oint dl = \mathcal{B} \cdot 2\pi a.$$

Equation (18) is written as a contour integral because it is a special case of a more general theorem, applying to a line integral once around any magnetic line, along which $\mathcal{B}$ may not be constant—an integral around any magnetic line of Fig. 21, 37, 38, or 56(c), for example. The theorem, which is proved in more advanced texts, is

The integral $\oint \mathcal{B}\, dl$ once around any magnetic line equals $4\pi I/10^7$, where I is the current that links the magnetic line, that is, the net total current in all conductors that thread through the magnetic line.

(AMPÈRE'S LINE-INTEGRAL LAW)

Thus, the integral around any magnetic line of Fig. 21 or 37 is $4\pi I/10^7$. The integral around any magnetic line of Fig. 38 is either $4\pi I/10^7$ or $2 \cdot 4\pi I/10^7$, according to whether the line links one or both conductors. The integral around any line of Fig. 56(c) is $4\pi NI/10^7$, where N is the number of turns of the solenoid linked by the particular line in question.

Equation (18), for a long straight conductor, is a special case of this theorem. We can use the theorem immediately, however, to obtain more information about this particular field. Equation (8) is derived on the assumption of a *line current*, which is equivalent to a conductor of zero radius. For a real conductor, which does not have zero radius, (8) might be expected to hold only at a distance large compared to the thickness of the conductor. Actually, we can show that for a circular conductor of radius R, (8) holds for any $a > R$, as close to the conductor as we please. By symmetry, the magnetic lines close to the conductor must

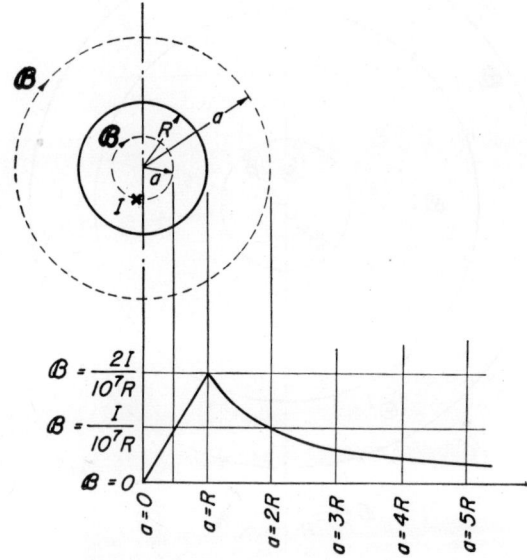

Fig. 50. Magnetic field of a long straight circular conductor of radius R carrying current I, as a function of distance a from the center.

still be circles, with equal field at all azimuths. By Ampère's law, the line integral of $\mathcal{B}$ must be $4\pi I/10^7$, so that $\mathcal{B}$ must be this line integral divided by the circumference $2\pi a$:

$$\mathcal{B} = 2I/10^7 a. \qquad (a > R) \qquad (19a)$$

We can go on to investigate the field *inside* the circular conductor, assumed to be of nonferromagnetic material. By symmetry, the magnetic lines must still be circles, with $\mathcal{B}$ independent of azimuth, but now (Fig. 50), the magnetic line no longer links the whole current I. For constant current, the flow of electrons is uniform throughout the cross section of a conductor. Consequently, within a circle of radius $a < R$ there is only the fraction a^2/R^2 (the ratio of the area of a circle of radius a to one of radius

R) of the whole current. Hence, a magnetic line of radius a links current $(a^2/R^2)I$, and the line integral of $\mathcal{B}$ around such a line is $4\pi(a^2/R^2)I/10^7$. $\mathcal{B}$ is again the line integral divided by the circumference $2\pi a$; hence, *inside a conductor of radius R*,

$$\mathcal{B} = \frac{2aI}{10^7 R^2}. \qquad (a<R) \quad (19b)$$

The field (19a) outside a conductor carrying a constant current varies inversely as the radius a of the magnetic line. The field (19b) inside the

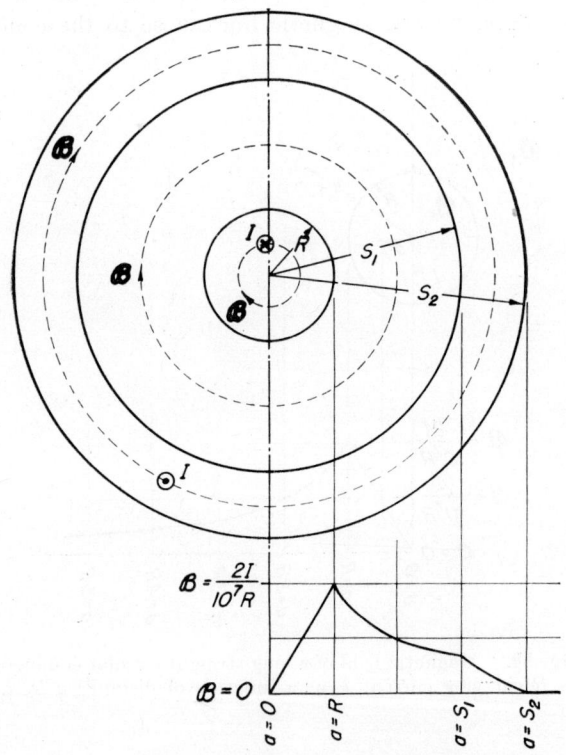

Fig. 51. Field of coaxial cable.

conductor varies directly as the radius a, is zero at $a=0$, and is the same as the external field at $a=R$. The field magnitude is plotted in Fig. 50.

As a second application, we shall consider the field of the coaxial line of Fig. 51, in which the current flows one way in the central conductor and returns in the surrounding sheath. In this case the line-integral law applied to a magnetic line within the central conductor gives the same result as (19b), and in the space between conductor and sheath it gives the same result as (19a), because in the line-integral law only currents threading through the *inside* of the closed magnetic line are considered.

For a circular magnetic line in the region $S_1 < a < S_2$, the central current I is canceled by part of the return current in the opposite direction, so that the field falls off faster than in (19a). The derivation of the exact formula for this case will be assigned as a problem at the end of this section. Outside the sheath, a magnetic line (if it existed) would, by symmetry, be circular; but the *net* current threading a circle of radius $a > S_2$ is zero, so that $\mathcal{B} = 0$ outside the sheath. The complete formulas for this case are

$$\mathcal{B} = \frac{2aI}{10^7 R^2}, \qquad (0 \leq a \leq R) \quad (20a)$$

$$\mathcal{B} = \frac{2I}{10^7 a}, \qquad (R \leq a \leq S_1) \quad (20b)$$

$$\mathcal{B} = \frac{2I}{10^7 a}\left(\frac{S_2^2 - a^2}{S_2^2 - S_1^2}\right), \qquad (S_1 \leq a \leq S_2) \quad (20c)$$

$$\mathcal{B} = 0. \qquad (S_2 \leq a) \quad (20d)$$

As a final application of Ampère's line-integral law, we compute the field of a toroid, not necessarily thin and not necessarily of circular cross section, but of circular contour. We assume that the toroid (Fig. 52) is

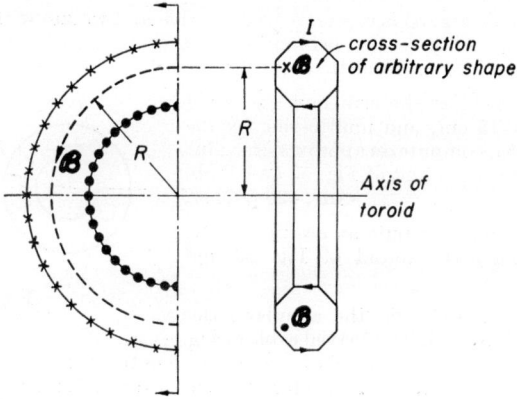

Fig. 52. A toroid of arbitrary cross-section. Only half of the toroid is shown in this drawing.

wound with N turns of wire, uniformly spaced around the circle, so that the whole current flowing around the toroid is NI, in amp. We assume that the current flows in a uniform sheet, neglecting any fine structure the field may have because of the discrete wires. Because of the completely axisymmetrical character of this arrangement and because the magnetic lines must be closed loops linking current, they must be circles as shown in Fig. 52. Furthermore, they must be circles confined to the region within the toroid, since a circle anywhere outside of the toroid would link no current.

If we take a circle of circumference $2\pi R$ within the toroid, the integral occurring in Ampère's law becomes $2\pi R\mathcal{B}$. Since all N turns link such a circle, the current linkage is NI, and Ampère's law gives

$$2\pi R\mathcal{B} = 4\pi NI/10^7,$$

$$\mathcal{B} = \frac{2NI}{10^7 R}. \tag{21}$$

This is the field inside the toroid. It varies slightly from point to point in accordance with the variation in distance R from the axis. *The field outside the toroid is zero.*

If the toroid is thin, so that R is substantially constant over the cross section, we can consider the toroid to have a 'length' $2\pi R$ and to be wound with $n = N/2\pi R$ turns per meter length. In this case, by substituting $2\pi n$ for N/R in (21), we get, for a *thin toroid*,

$$\mathcal{B} = 4\pi nI/10^7. \tag{22}$$

This is the same as the solenoid formula (9).

PROBLEMS

1. Derive formula (20c).

2. The toroid of Fig. 53 is of square cross section and wound with 900 turns each carrying 35 amp. What is the field inside the toroid at 10, 15, and 20 cm from the axis?

3. Using the field at the center of the toroid cross section ($R = 15$ cm) and multiplying by the cross-sectional area, compute an approximate value of the flux through the toroid of Fig. 53 and Prob. 2. Ans: 420 μweber.

4. By integration, compute an accurate value of the flux through the toroid of Fig. 53 and Prob. 2.

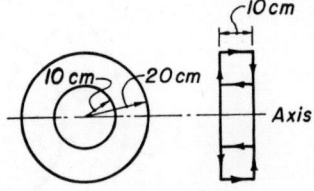

Fig. 53.

5. Show that the flux in the annular space between $a = R$ and $a = S_1$ in the coaxial cable of Fig. 51 is $\Phi = (2I/10^7) \log_e(S_1/R)$, in webers per meter length (compare Prob. 4, p. 948). This result is needed in obtaining the formula for the self-inductance of such a cable (Chap. 39).

6. Show that the total flux surrounding a meter length of an infinitely long straight conductor of radius R is infinite. This nonphysical result is associated with the fact that no such conductor exists. Discuss the conditions under which formula (19a) is physically useful and show that these conditions will break down when a is too large, so that an integration that carries a to infinity is physically unrealistic.

7. In Fig. 21, one exceptional magnetic line does not close but goes along the axis from $-\infty$ to $+\infty$. This line may be considered to close at ∞, where the field is zero anyway. Using the field formula given with Fig. 27, show that $\int_{-\infty}^{\infty} \mathcal{B}\, dl$, along this line, equals $4\pi I/10^7$. This result agrees with Ampère's line-integral law.

8. Repeat Prob. 7 for the exceptional line on the axis of the square coil, Fig. 35.

9. If the conductors of Fig. 37 are not mathematical lines but circular conductors, show that the field values of Fig. 37 are still valid at all points lying outside the conductors, provided we place the centers of the conductors at the positions of the line currents in Fig. 37.

10. If the conductors of Fig. 37 are each 1 cm in diameter with centers separated by 2 cm, and each carry 1000 amp, make a plot of the magnetic-field strength along the horizontal center line of Fig. 37 that contains the centers of the conductors. Pay particular attention to the field within the conductors.

10. FIELD OF A SOLENOID*

We have seen in Sec. 8 how the external field of a thin solenoid may be obtained as the field of poles $\pm nIA$ at its ends. We continue this argument here and investigate not only the external but also the internal field of a solenoid of any cross section.

Given (Fig. 54) a solenoid of cross-sectional area A, idealized to a current sheet of strength nI, in amp per m length; the solenoid may in

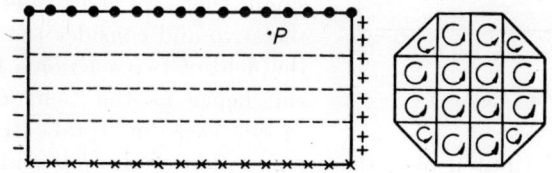

Fig. 54. The external field of a solenoid may be obtained as the field of a sheet of $+$ poles on one end and of $-$ poles on the other.

imagination be 'sliced' longitudinally into thin solenoids of infinitesimal area that resemble shoestring potatoes. If, as indicated at the right of Fig. 54, the same current is imagined to flow around each of these thin solenoids, the currents will cancel wherever two solenoids adjoin, leaving just the original current sheet. Thus, the original solenoid is physically equivalent to the sum of all these infinitesmal shoestring solenoids, and the field of the original solenoid will be the sum of the fields of all the infinitesimal solenoids.

Now consider one of the thin solenoids of area dA. Its external field will be the field of poles $\pm nI\, dA$ at its ends. The poles of the various thin solenoids will altogether constitute two sheets of poles on the ends of the original solenoid. Since each area dA will have poles of strength $\pm nI\, dA$, the poles will be uniformly distributed with pole density $\pm nI$ per unit area, or a pole strength $\pm nIA$ altogether. Thus we see that

The external field of any solenoid is the field arising from a sheet of poles of total strength nIA uniformly distributed over one end of the solenoid, and a sheet of total strength $-nIA$ uniformly distributed over the other end.

---

* This section may be omitted without loss of continuity. The figures will be of interest whether or not the text is studied.

Since we have obtained this result by dividing the solenoid into *infinitesimal* pieces, the result will be good as close to the solenoid as we please, just so we are definitely outside the current sheet that represents the winding and outside the imaginary plane across the end of the solenoid where we put the imaginary pole sheet.

We may now readily extend this treatment to find the internal field of the solenoid. To find the field at point P (Fig. 54), cut a thin strip out of the solenoid by means of planes on either side of point P, as in Fig. 55. The field at P is then the field of two solenoids, to both of which P is external, plus the field of the current $nI\lambda$ in the strip of thickness λ. As $\lambda \to 0$, the current in this strip goes to zero and hence the field it sets up goes to zero. By considering λ as very small, then, we can neglect the field of the strip and consider the field at P as the field of two solenoids BC and DA, and hence as the field of four pole sheets each of total strength $\pm nIA$ uniformly distributed over the cross section of the solenoid at B, C, D, and A.

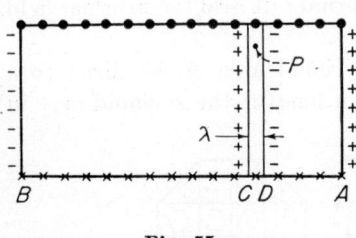

Fig. 55.

The magnetic field at P arising from the two very close pole sheets at C and D may be readily computed, since it is like the electric field between the plates of the plane-plate condenser that was considered in Chap. 32. In (9), p. 841, we saw that the electric field between two sheets of electric charge is given by $\mathcal{E} = 4\pi \times 10^{-7} c^2 q$, where $\pm q$ are the charges per unit area on the two plates. The magnetic field $\mathcal{B}$ from a distribution of poles, $\pm m$ per unit area, is given by a similar formula, but we must take account of the different constants in the formulas for electric field of a charge and magnetic field of a pole. According to (7), p. 799, the electric field of a unit charge is $10^{-7} c^2/r^2$, whereas according to (16) above, the magnetic field of a unit pole is $10^{-7}/r^2$; hence, any formula for electric field from a charge distribution must be divided by c^2 to get the formula for the magnetic field of an equal pole distribution. In this way we see that the field between two close sheets of poles, of density $\pm m$ per unit area, is

$$\mathcal{B} = 4\pi \times 10^{-7} \, m.$$

Since our pole density in the two sheets close to P in Fig. 55 is $m = nI$, the field set up by these two sheets is

$$\mathcal{B}_0 = 4\pi nI/10^7 \tag{23}$$

from left to right in Fig. 55. Note that this is the field given by the solenoid formula (9).

The field at any point P *inside* the solenoid is then obtained by super-

(a) 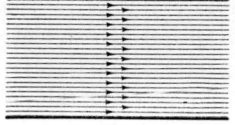 $\mathcal{B}_0$

(b) 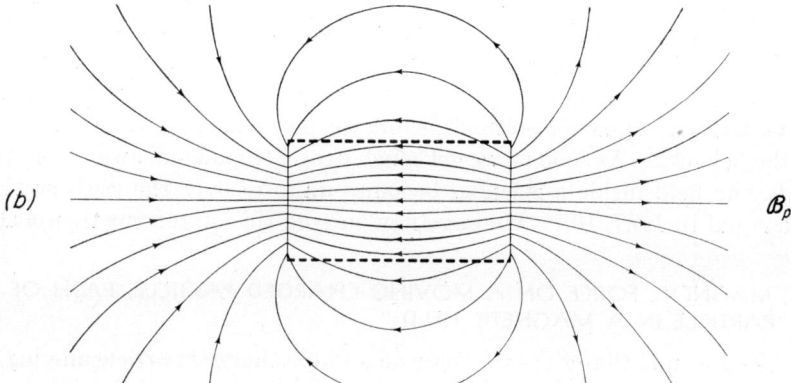 $\mathcal{B}_p$

(c) 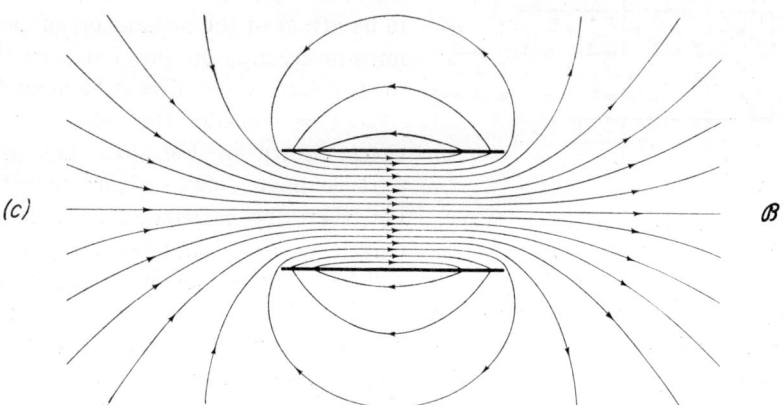 $\mathcal{B}$

Fig. 56. The field of a solenoid, whose lines are shown in (c), may be computed by superposing the fields of (a) and (b).

posing, on the uniform field $\mathcal{B}_0$ (from left to right in Fig. 55) given by the solenoid formula (23), the field $\mathcal{B}_p$ of the pole sheets on the ends of the solenoid. In general, this latter field is from right to left in Fig. 55 and tends to reduce the field below the value given by the solenoid formula.

The field outside the solenoid is just $\mathfrak{B}_p$. These two fields are shown in Fig. 56, together with the resultant field $\mathfrak{B} = \mathfrak{B}_0 + \mathfrak{B}_p$, for a short solenoid of circular section.

Remember that the employment of the pole picture and the splitting of the field $\mathfrak{B}$ into these two parts is completely artificial and is just a useful computational trick. The $\mathfrak{B}$ obtained this way is the same as would be obtained by an integration over all current elements of the solenoid, using Ampère's law (6). However, such an integral is much more difficult to set up than the computation we have sketched.

We see that within a long solenoid, at a distance x from one end, $\mathfrak{B}_p \sim nIA/10^7 x^2$. When $x^2 \sim A$, $\mathfrak{B}_p \sim nI/10^7 \sim \frac{1}{12}\mathfrak{B}_0$, so that we need not go far from the ends of a solenoid before the pole field $\mathfrak{B}_p$ is small compared to the field $\mathfrak{B}_0$. As soon as we get much over a 'diameter' away from the ends, the field inside a solenoid becomes uniform over the cross section and equal to $4\pi nI/10^7$. We have now proved this statement rigorously.

11. MAGNETIC FORCE ON A MOVING CHARGED PARTICLE; PATH OF A PARTICLE IN A MAGNETIC FIELD

The formula that gives the force on a single charged particle moving in a magnetic field is of great importance in modern atomic and nuclear research. We can derive this formula by considering that a beam of moving particles constitutes a current, and that the total force on all the particles in length dl of the stream of particles must be given by our previous formulas for the force on a current element.*

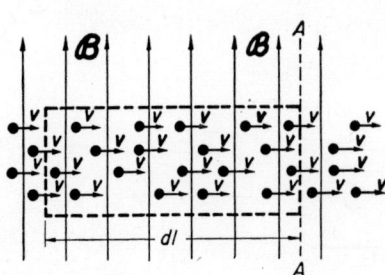

Fig. 57. A beam of charged particles.

Let us consider the beam of particles shown in Fig. 57. Let each particle have charge q and speed v. Let there be p particles per meter length of the beam, so that there will be $p\, dl$ particles in the length dl. Counting from the instant at which Fig. 57 is drawn, all these $p\, dl$ particles will cross the plane AA in the time required for the leftmost particles to go a distance dl, that is, in a time $dt = dl/v$. The charge carried across the plane AA in this time is the charge on $p\, dl$ particles, or $qp\, dl$, in coulombs. The current then is

$$I = \frac{qp\, dl}{dt} = \frac{qp\, dl}{dl/v} = pqv. \qquad (24)$$

---
* Actually, formula (25) below, for the force on a single moving particle, is the more fundamental formula from which formula (4) for the force on a current element could be derived. We have chosen the historical approach.

MAGNETIC FORCE ON A MOVING CHARGED PARTICLE

This important formula gives the current represented by a beam containing p particles per unit length of beam, each having charge q and traveling with speed v.

Now the formula
$$\mathcal{B} I\, dl = \mathcal{B} pqv\, dl$$
gives the total force on length dl of the current in (24), when the particles are moving perpendicular to a magnetic field as in Fig. 57. This is the total force on the $p\, dl$ particles in dl. Hence, the force on each particle may be obtained by dividing this expression by $p\, dl$, to get

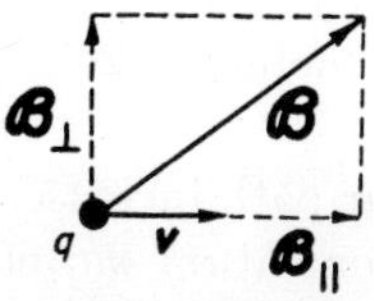

$$f = \mathcal{B} qv, \quad \text{in newtons.} \tag{25}$$

Fig. 58. The force on charge q moving in the magnetic field $\mathcal{B}$ is $f = \mathcal{B}_\perp qv$, and is perpendicular to both $\mathcal{B}$ and v.

This is the force on a single particle of charge q, in coulombs, moving with speed v, in meters/second, perpendicular to a magnetic field of strength $\mathcal{B}$, in webers/meter². The direction of the force is perpendicular to both $\mathcal{B}$ and v, the choice of the two such directions being made by considering the direction of the equivalent current. Thus, in Fig. 57, if q is positive, the current direction is to the right, and f is out from the paper; if q is negative, the conventional current is toward the left, and f is into the paper.

If $\mathcal{B}$ is not perpendicular to v, the force is determined, as in the case of ordinary currents, entirely by the magnitude and direction of the component of $\mathcal{B}$ perpendicular to v (see Fig. 58).

These considerations are fundamental to the theory of the cyclotron, which will be discussed in Chap. 45; of the electron microscope, which will be discussed in Chap. 43, of the mass spectrograph, which will be discussed in Chap. 45; and of various other types of vacuum tubes and electron-ray tubes. In preparation for these applications we need to learn about the path of a charged particle in a uniform magnetic field.

Consider (Fig. 59) a particle of positive charge q and mass m moving at a particular instant with speed v toward the top of the paper in a uniform magnetic field $\mathcal{B}$ directed into the paper. The magnetic force on this particle will be

$$f = \mathcal{B} qv$$

to the left. This force will give the particle an acceleration

$$a = f/m = \mathcal{B} qv/m$$

to the left.

Since this acceleration is perpendicular to v, it does not result in a change in magnitude of v but merely changes its direction, that is, the path of the particle curves to the left.

Now consider the particle a little later, when it has reached the position indicated by broken lines. Since the force on the particle and its acceleration are still perpendicular to its velocity, there is still no tendency to change the magnitude of the velocity. Since the field is uniform, the acceleration has the same magnitude as before. Motion at constant speed with a constant acceleration always at right angles to the velocity is known, from mechanics, to be motion in a circle of such radius R that $a = v^2/R$, or, in our case,

$$R = \frac{v^2}{a} = \frac{v^2}{\mathscr{B}qv/m} = \frac{mv}{\mathscr{B}q}, \quad \text{in meters.} \quad (26)$$

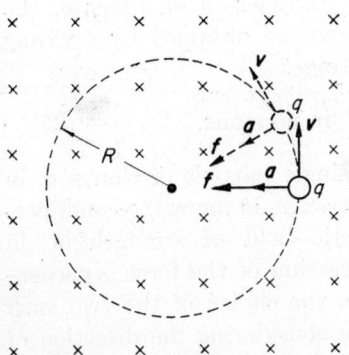

Fig. 59. A positively charged particle moving normally to a uniform magnetic field describes a circular path. A negative particle would curve the other way. The field is directed into the paper, as indicated by ×'s.

The radius of the circular path increases in proportion to the momentum mv of the particle and varies inversely as the magnetic-field strength and the charge on the particle. A negative particle would have its force and acceleration vectors reversed relative to those of a positive particle. Hence, if q were negative in Fig. 59, the path would curve to the right instead of to the left.

Figures 60 and 61 are Wilson cloud-chamber photographs showing paths of charged particles in a magnetic field directed into the paper just as in Fig. 59. Such photographs can be used to determine the momentum of the particle and the sign of the charge.

As we shall see later, the whole operation of the cyclotron depends on an interesting property of an orbit such as that of Fig. 59, namely, that the time it takes a particular type of particle to go once around the orbit and return to its starting point is quite independent of the speed v of the particle. A particle of high speed travels rapidly around an orbit of large radius, and one of low speed travels slowly around an orbit of small radius; but since, according to (26), the distance traveled, $2\pi R$, is directly proportional to the speed, the times taken are equal. The time of revolution is $T = 2\pi R/v$; from (26), $R/v = m/\mathscr{B}q$; so that

$$T = 2\pi m/\mathscr{B}q, \quad (27)$$

independent of the speed v.

One other comment. In Fig. 59 we have considered a particle moving perpendicular to a uniform magnetic field. If the particle also has a velocity component along the field direction, that component remains unchanged, since there is no force in the direction of the field. Hence, superposed on the motion of Fig. 59 is a uniform velocity in the direction

Sec. 11] MAGNETIC FORCE ON A MOVING CHARGED PARTICLE

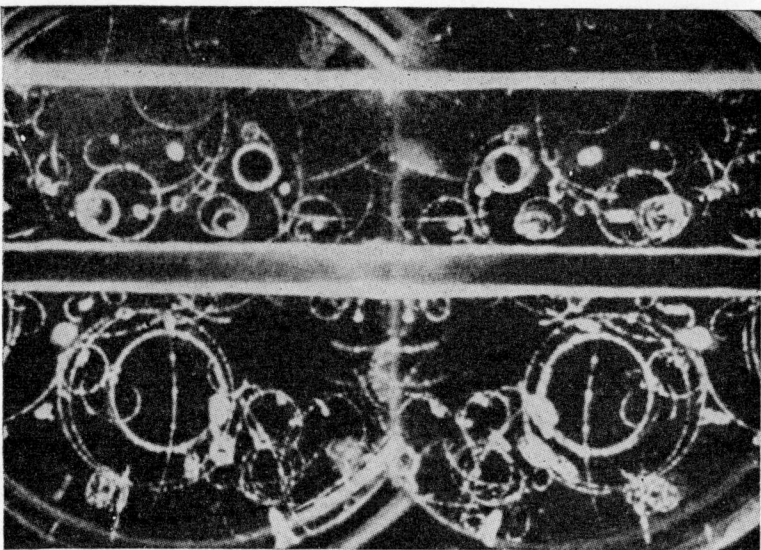

Fig. 60. Cloud chamber photograph showing tracks of particles known to be electrons. The larger the circle the faster the speed in accordance with (26): $v = R(\mathcal{B}q/m)$. (From Rasetti, *Elements of Nuclear Physics*, Prentice-Hall, 1937.)

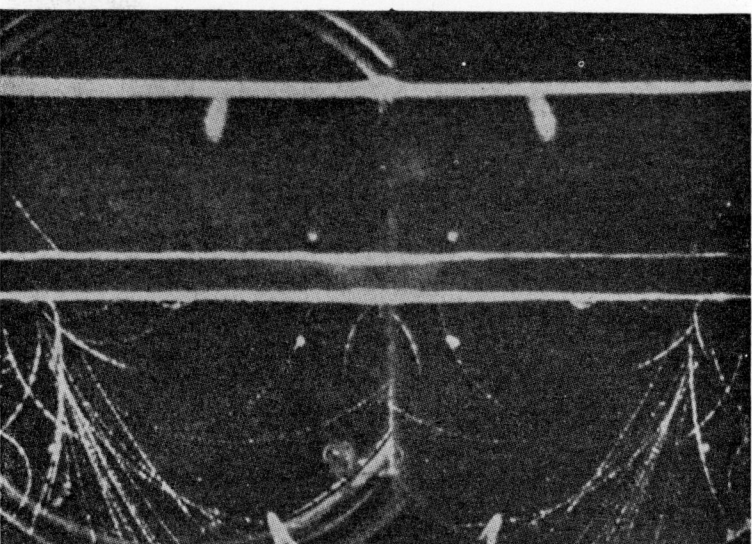

Fig. 61. Cloud-chamber stereoscopic photograph of cosmic-ray tracks. The particles are known to be traveling from top to bottom in this photograph. Hence the tracks curving to the right in the direct view are those of positively charged particles, the tracks curving to the left those of negatively charged particles. The left view is the direct view; the right is a mirror image. (From Rasetti, *Elements of Nuclear Physics*, Prentice-Hall, 1937.)

of the field. The whole path is thus a perfect helix, with the axis of the helix in the direction of the field. A cloud-chamber photograph of a charged particle traversing a path of this type is shown in Fig. 62.

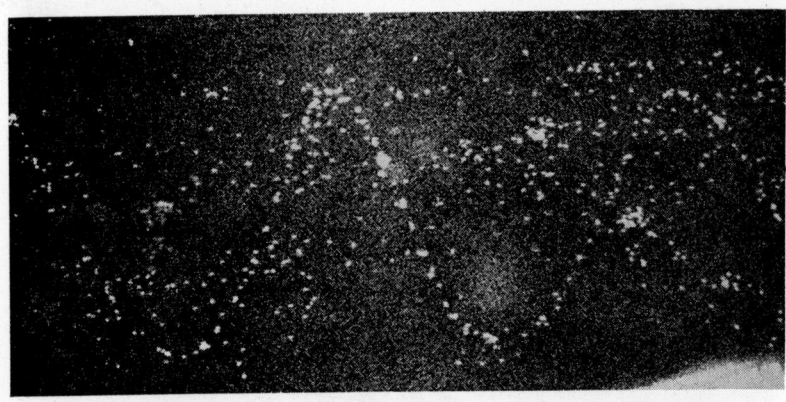

Fig. 62. Cloud-chamber photograph of an electron having velocity components both perpendicular and parallel to the field direction. The magnetic field runs from left to right, parallel to the paper. The electron has a helical path, which appears as a sine curve when viewed from the side. (*Courtesy of Dr. Carl Nielsen of the Ohio State University.*)

PROBLEMS

1. If an electron is traveling at 10^6 m/sec perpendicular to a magnetic field of 0.0015 weber/m², what is the radius of curvature of its path?   Ans: 3.79 mm.

2. If a proton is traveling at 10^5 m/sec perpendicular to a magnetic field of 0.015 weber/m², what is the radius of curvature of its path?

3. What field strength is required to cause an electron traveling at 10^4 m/sec to follow a path of 1 cm radius?   Ans: 5.66×10^{-6} weber/m².

4. What field strength is required to deflect a proton traveling at 10^5 m/sec into a path of 10 cm radius?

5. It is desired to deflect a beam of protons emerging from a 1-Mv Van de Graaff generator through an angle of 90° by means of a magnetic field of 0.5 weber/m². For what radius of path curvature must the magnet be designed?   Ans: 28.7 cm.

6. If a beam of deuterons has energy 2.5 Mev and it is desired to make them move in a circle of 30 cm radius, what magnetic field is required? (A deuteron is a nucleus of heavy hydrogen, H², of charge $+1e$ and mass 2.014 amu.)

CHAPTER 37

FERROMAGNETISM; PERMANENT MAGNETS; THE EARTH'S FIELD

All matter is composed of atoms with positive nuclei and negative electrons. Since the negative electrons are in continual motion and hence constitute microscopic electric currents, all matter responds more or less to the presence of a magnetic field.

In the absence of an applied magnetic field, the microscopic currents ordinarily have sufficiently random orientation that, though they set up large local magnetic fields on the microscopic (atomic) scale, the net current and the net magnetic moment in any microscopic volume vanish and no physically observable macroscopic magnetic field is set up by the matter. An exception occurs in the case of a 'permanent magnet.'

When matter is placed in a magnetic field from some external source, magnetic forces on the moving electrons will cause some type of reorientation of electron orbits in atoms and of current paths of free electrons in metals, so that the matter will itself set up a macroscopic magnetic field. This field may be either in the same direction as the applied field, in which case the matter is said to be *paramagnetic*, or in the opposite direction, in which case the matter is said to be *diamagnetic*.

However, except for those substances described below as *ferromagnetic*, these effects are always very small; the field set up by matter is of the order of 10^{-7} (for gases) or 10^{-6} (for liquids or solids) of the applied field—always a very small fraction of the applied field. Such paramagnetism and diamagnetism have little or no technical importance and can be completely neglected in most magnetic computations. Unlike the case in electrostatics, where all materials except gases have a sufficiently large dielectric constant to have a profound electrical effect when placed in an electric field, *all except the few ferromagnetic materials can, for technical purposes, be treated as magnetically inert and can be considered to behave no differently from a vacuum in the presence of a magnetic field.*

Thus, for all practical purposes, the field of a solenoid may be considered the same whether its core is vacuum, air, brass, or wood. But if the core is ferromagnetic, the core may set up a field hundreds, thousands, or even hundreds of thousands of times greater than the field of the winding itself. *Ferromagnetism* is thus of tremendous technical importance and will occupy our attention in this and the following chapter.

The study of the paramagnetism or diamagnetism of non-ferromagnetic substances has great scientific importance in connection with the development of the understanding of the electrical structure of matter. However, we shall leave detailed discussion of these subjects to more advanced texts.

1. FERROMAGNETISM

The electrons in matter set up local magnetic fields on a microscopic scale for two reasons. First, because the charged electron in its orbital motion around the atomic nucleus constitutes a little circulating current that has a magnetic moment. Second, because the electron has an intrinsic magnetic moment associated with an intrinsic angular momentum called the electron *spin*. The necessity of giving the electron a 'spin' in order to account for observed atomic properties was first pointed out by Uhlenbeck and Goudsmit in 1925. Later work has amply confirmed the correctness of this postulate. The electron behaves as if it is spinning about its own axis like a top. It has an intrinsic angular momentum of 5.271×10^{-35} kg·m²/sec (this value is $h/4\pi$, where h is Planck's constant which we defined in Chap. 30). As would be expected from the picture of a charged body spinning like a top, there is a magnetic moment associated with this angular momentum. The magnetic moment vector points in the direction opposite to the angular momentum vector because the charge is negative. The intrinsic magnetic moment of each electron has the magnitude 9.274×10^{-24} amp·m² (this value is $eh/4\pi m$, where e and m are the charge and mass of the electron). A magnetic moment of this magnitude is called one *Bohr magneton*.

The Bohr magneton furnishes a quantum unit of magnetic moment for electrons, for not only is the spin magnetic moment one Bohr magneton, but the magnetic moment arising from orbital motion of each electron in an atom is a small integral number of Bohr magnetons (0, 1, 2, or 3 Bohr magnetons in the case of atoms in their normal states). The total magnetic moment of an atom is the vector sum of the spin moments and the orbital moments of all the electrons. The total magnetic moment is a small rational, but not necessarily integral, number of Bohr magnetons. It can be measured by observing the effect of a magnetic field on the spectrum of an atom (Zeeman effect), and can be correctly predicted by modern atomic theory.

The discussion so far has applied particularly to free individual atoms such as occur in a monatomic gas. The individual atoms of most elements have sufficient magnetic moment so that if they retained this magnetic moment when put together to form a solid, and if the atomic magnetic moments were all orientated in the same direction, they would set up a very large macroscopic magnetic field (this field is estimated for iron in Prob. 1, p. 976). Actually, in only a very few materials is any appreciable orientation possible. This surprising fact was not explained satisfactorily until 1928. Only in the few substances called *ferromagnetic* do the electrons ever set up anything but an extremely tiny macroscopic magnetic field. The ferromagnetic substances are *iron, cobalt,* and *nickel,* some but not all alloys of these three metals with each other and with other metals, certain oxides of these metals, one rare earth (*gadolinium*), and one type of alloy, called a *Heusler alloy,* containing no iron, cobalt, or nickel, but rather about 15 per cent aluminum, 61 per cent copper, and 24 per cent manganese.

These constitute all the substances having ferromagnetic properties at ordinary temperatures. Certain other substances acquire these properties at very low temperature. The list is very restricted because there is a peculiarity in structure that is necessary for a substance to be ferromagnetic. Let us try to get a rough understanding, in the case of solids and liquids, of the conditions necessary for ferromagnetism.

The electrons in an atom occur in 'shells' of different 'radii.' In most elements, all electrons except the 'valence' electrons are in 'complete' shells. The different shells, as we progress outward from the nucleus, may contain at most 2, 8, 18, · · · electrons. When a shell contains all the electrons that are permitted, it is said to be 'complete,' which really means *full;* that is, there is no room for any more passengers; it is *complet* like a Parisian omnibus.

When a shell is complete, the vector sum of the magnetic moments of the electrons in the shell is zero. A complete shell does not set up an external magnetic field, neither does it respond in any way to any external magnetic field. Irrevocably, it is magnetically inert.

Hence, for most materials, only the magnetic moments of the valence electrons would be available to be oriented by an external magnetic field so that they can set up an appreciable macroscopic field of their own. But in a solid or liquid, the valence electrons play an essential role in the cohesive binding that holds the atoms together. As a result, *the valence electrons in a solid or liquid cannot contribute significantly to a microscopic magnetic field.* The valence electrons may move from one atom to an adjoining atom to form magnetically inert complete shells in both resulting ions (ionic binding, like NaCl); the valence electrons from two adjoining atoms may pair to form a magnetically inert homopolar bond in the space between the atoms (like C in diamond and in organic compounds); or the valence electrons become free, as in a metal. In the metallic case, the valence electrons are no longer moving in little orbits with magnetic moments, and it also turns out that in any small region of the metal the spin magnetic moments add up to a vector resultant of zero. In no type of cohesive binding do we get appreciable magnetic effects from the valence electrons. The presence of an externally applied magnetic field does have a slight effect on the valence electrons that gives rise to a weak paramagnetism or diamagnetism.

How then do we get any ferromagnetism if it cannot arise from valence electrons and cannot arise from electrons in complete shells? Clearly it must arise from electrons that are neither valence electrons nor in complete shells. Such electrons occur in the 'transition elements,' of which Fe, Co, Ni, Pd, Pt, Rh, and the rare earths are examples. In these elements we have *two* incomplete shells, with one so well buried in the atom that its electrons do not contribute to cohesive binding and remain free to be oriented by a magnetic field. The electronic structure of Fe, Co, and Ni is shown in Fig. 1. The M and N shells are both incomplete. But only the electrons of the outer incomplete shell (the N shell) are valence electrons that take part in chemical or metallic binding. The inner incomplete shell (the M shell) remains undisturbed even in the solid metal, and the electronic moments in this shell can be oriented by an external magnetic field.

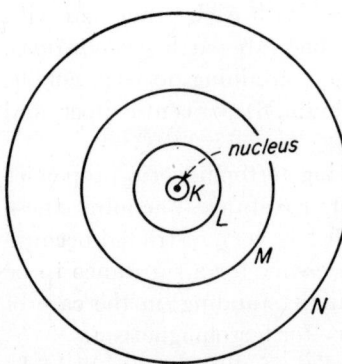

Fig. 1. Electronic structure of iron, cobalt, and nickel:

The K-shell has 2 electrons. It is complete and hence magnetically inert.

The L-shell has 8 electrons. It is complete and hence magnetically inert.

The M-shell has 14,15,16 electrons in Fe, Co, Ni. It is incomplete since it will hold 18 electrons. The electrons of this shell are responsible for the ferromagnetism.

The incomplete N-shell has 2 electrons that are responsible for the binding forces in the solid.

But this exposition still does not explain why only Fe, Co, Ni, and Gd are *strongly* magnetic; we might expect the other transition elements to be ferromagnetic also. A clue to the explanation is found when one considers that *permanent* magnets can be made of ferromagnetic materials— once magnetized, they tend to retain their magnetism permanently. Consequently, when the atomic magnetic moments in a ferromagnetic material are once orientated, there must be strong interatomic forces tending to maintain this orientation in spite of the thermal agitation that tends to disarrange the orientation. This fact was realized quite early. Wilhelm Weber, in 1852, first proposed that each atom is a permanent magnet capable of orientation; and Sir Alfred Ewing, in 1890, first pointed out the necessity for strong interatomic forces to account for the observed phenomena. The shell structure of the atomic electrons and the fact that the inner incomplete shell is responsible for ferromagnetism were recognized in the period following the fundamental work of Niels Bohr (1913). But not until quantum mechanics was formulated in 1925 was a satisfactory theory of atomic processes, which permitted computation of interatomic forces, available. In the years following 1928, Werner Heisenberg and others computed the magnitudes of the forces between the magnetic moments of adjacent atoms. These computations showed that in the case of Fe, Co, and Ni the atomic properties and the spacing of the atoms in the crystalline lattice are such that there are strong interatomic forces tending to keep the magnetic moments of adjacent atoms lined up parallel to one another, whereas in the case of other transition elements the interatomic forces actually tend to prevent the magnetic moments from lining up and hence prevent these elements from being strongly magnetic. Thus, quantum mechanics finally gave an answer to the old question of why only three common* elements of the periodic table are ferromagnetic.

PROBLEM

1. Atomic theory tells us that the electrons responsible for ferromagnetism move in circular orbits around the nucleus with angular momentum h/π. Assume that the radius of the orbit is $r = 10^{-10}$ m; this radius is not accurately known. Compute literal and numerical values of the speed v of the electron, the equivalent current I (the charge passing any point in the orbit per second), and the orbital magnetic moment M (defined as I times the area of the orbit). Note that, independent of the value assumed for r, the magnetic moment turns out to be 2 Bohr magnetons.

Ans: $v = h/\pi mr = 2.32 \times 10^6$ m/sec; $I = eh/2\pi^2 mr^2 = 5.90 \times 10^{-4}$ amp; $M = 2(eh/4\pi m) = 18.5 \times 10^{-24}$ amp·m².

2. PERMANENT MAGNETS

Once the microscopic magnetic moments of the electrons in a ferromagnetic material have been oriented by application of a magnetic field, they tend to a greater or lesser degree to remain orientated and to continue to set up a macroscopic field of their own. In a material like pure soft iron or mild steel, little of the systematic orientation remains after removal of the applied field. Such a material is said to be *magnetically soft;* it approaches the ideal magnetic material we shall study in Chap. 38, and is suitable for use in transformers, dynamos, relays, and similar equipment. In contrast, the hard alloy steels, particularly the aluminum-nickel-cobalt steels (Alnico) are *magnetically hard*. Once such steel has been magnetized by application of an external field, it retains most of the magnetism indefinitely and constitutes a *permanent magnet*. In this section we shall discuss permanent magnets as such, apart from the question of how they became magnetized.

---

* The ferromagnetic properties of the rare element gadolinium were not discovered until 1935. Quantum-mechanical theory accounts satisfactorily for the ferromagnetism of this rare earth and also for the ferromagnetism of the transition element manganese, which occurs just before iron in the periodic table, when the manganese atoms are separated by abnormally large distances as they are in the Heusler alloys.

The basic physical quantity used to describe the state of magnetization of a material is the *magnetic moment per unit volume*. Consider a cube small in size compared with dimensions of physical interest but large enough to contain many billions of atoms. When the material is unmagnetized, the electron moments (those that are magnetically effective) are orientated with sufficient randomness so that if their magnetic moments were summed vectorially for the whole volume dV, we should get an answer close to zero. This situation is indicated schematically at the left of Fig. 2, in which the microscopic magnetic moments are represented by equivalent current loops.* When the material is magnetized, the magnetic moments are orientated with a preference for a particular direction, as shown at the right of Fig. 2. In this case the vector sum of the atomic magnetic moments would give a resultant magnetic moment

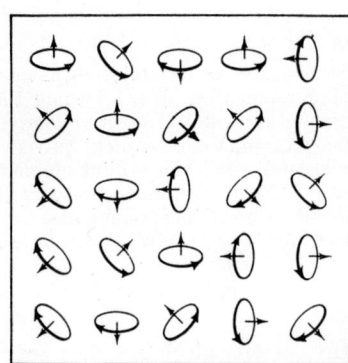
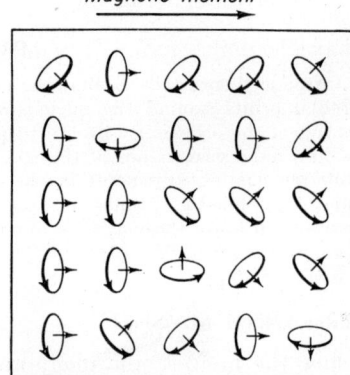

Unmagnetized

Magnetized, with resultant magnetic moment to the right.

Fig. 2. A schematic representation of the orientation of the microscopic magnetic moments of unmagnetized and magnetized material.

M for the volume dV. The magnetic moment M would be proportional to the volume dV, and by dividing the resultant magnetic moment by the volume, we can define a *magnetic moment per unit volume*, which we denote by the vector $\mathfrak{M} = M/dV$. The total magnetic moment of the volume dV is $M = \mathfrak{M}\, dV$. $\mathfrak{M}$ is usually called the *intensity of magnetization*.

Macroscopically (that is, averaged over the violent microscopic irregularities), the field set up by the magnetized cube of Fig. 3 will be the same as the field of a current (flowing around the edge of the cube in the

---

* Discussion of the domain structure of ferromagnetic materials is omitted from this text. Actually, because of the interatomic forces discussed in the preceding section, whole blocks of atoms ($\sim 10^{-6}$ mm³ in volume) have their magnetic moments uniformly orientated, even in an unmagnetized sample; and each 'atom' of Fig. 2 should be thought of as representing such a block or 'domain.'

direction shown) that has the same magnetic moment. The magnetic moment of such a current I would be $I\,dl^2$, since the area of the circuit is dl^2. This quantity is equal to the magnetic moment $\mathfrak{M}\,dV$:

$$I\,dl^2 = \mathfrak{M}\,dl^3, \quad \text{or} \quad I = \mathfrak{M}\,dl.$$

We need a total current $\mathfrak{M}\,dl$ around the cube, or current $I/dl = \mathfrak{M}$ per unit width in the current sheet.

We are now prepared to calculate the field of a permanent bar magnet uniformly magnetized in the direction of its length, with magnetic moment $\mathfrak{M}$ per unit volume. The macroscopic field of each volume element is the field of the current sheet of Fig. 3. In a slice of length dl across the magnet, these currents will be equivalent to a single current $\mathfrak{M}\,dl$ around the periphery, as indicated in Fig. 4. Hence, the whole field of the bar magnet, inside and outside, will be exactly like the field of a solenoid with current $nI = \mathfrak{M}$ per meter length. The external field will be the coulomb field of $+$ poles of total strength $\mathfrak{M}A$

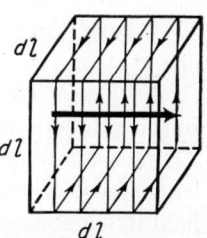

Fig. 3. The magnetic moment $\mathfrak{M}\,dV$ indicated by the heavy arrow sets up the same field as current $\mathfrak{M}\,dl$ in the direction shown by the light arrows.

spread across the area A of the N end of the bar, with equal and opposite negative poles at the S end of the bar. The internal field will be

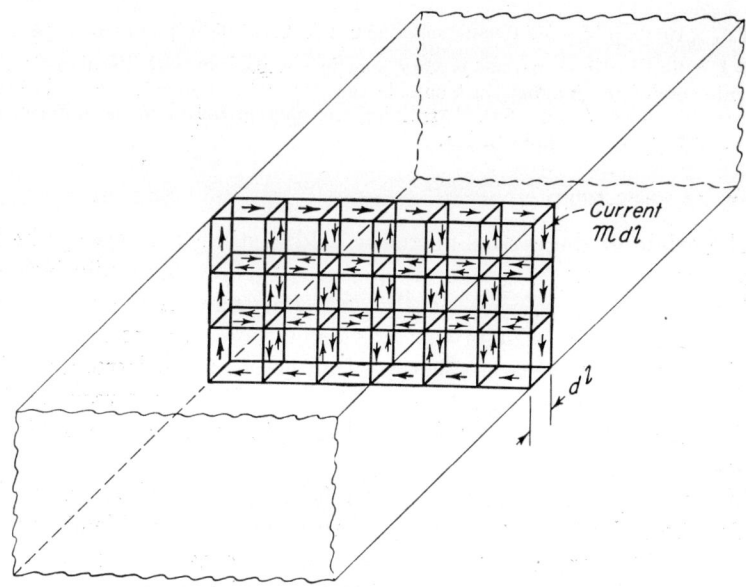

Fig. 4. Part of a uniformly magnetized bar magnet.

$\mathfrak{B} = 4\pi\mathfrak{M}/10^7$ at points well away from the ends. The diagram of Fig. 56, p. 963, will apply, with the correlation $nI = \mathfrak{M}$. These considerations are independent of the shape of the cross section of the bar.

This section justifies our simultaneous treatment of bar magnets and solenoids in the previous chapter.

A permanently magnetized horseshoe magnet will have a field much like that of Fig. 46, p. 955.

An actual bar magnet will not necessarily be uniformly magnetized, so the magnetic moment per unit volume will not necessarily be constant. There is usually some tendency for the magnetic moment per unit volume to decrease toward the ends of the bar. Such a magnet would have a field like a solenoid whose turns are wound more densely near the center than near the ends.

PROBLEMS

1. (a) If iron has a density of 7870 kg/m^3, how many atoms are there per cubic meter?

(b) If each atom of iron in a bar magnet has a resultant magnetic moment of 1 Bohr magneton, and these magnetic moments are all orientated in the direction of the length of the magnet, what is the value of $\mathfrak{M}$, the magnetic moment per cubic meter?

(c) What is the field strength $\mathfrak{B} = 4\pi\mathfrak{M}/10^7$ in the center of a long bar magnet magnetized as in (b)?

(d) The saturation magnetization (the maximum field strength that can arise from the oriented atomic moments of the material) of iron is observed to be 2.15 weber/m^2. To what magnetic moment, in Bohr magnetons per atom, does this value correspond? Ans: (a) 8.49×10^{28};
(b) 7.87×10^5 amp/m; (c) 0.989 weber/m^2; (d) 2.17 Bohr magnetons per atom.

2. A cylindrical bar magnet is very long in comparison with its diameter. On the centerline of the magnet, just outside the end of the magnet, the field strength is measured as 0.457 weber/m^2. Assuming the magnetization to be uniform, compute the intensity of magnetization.

3. THE EARTH'S FIELD

The origin of the earth's magnetic field is still a mystery. The field is presumed to arise from macroscopic currents flowing around inside the earth rather than from permanently magnetized materials: at the temperatures that probably exist in the interior of the earth, iron, cobalt, and nickel are no longer ferromagnetic. Iron ceases to be ferromagnetic at 770° C, Ni at 358° C, and Co at 1120° C. This temperature, above which a material is no longer ferromagnetic, is known as the *Curie point* of the material.

In general, the earth's magnetic field consists of magnetic lines running from the Southern Hemisphere to the Northern Hemisphere, so it would arise from currents in the earth running from east to west. From the gross structure of the field as observed near the surface, it can be determined that the currents that set up the field lie almost entirely within the earth and not in the earth's atmosphere.

The field is much like that of a magnetic dipole at the center of the

Sec. 3] THE EARTH'S FIELD

earth. The field of such a dipole, mapped by means of iron filings, is shown in Fig. 5.

The unit we shall use in describing the strength of the earth's field is the one commonly used in considerations of terrestrial magnetism. It is known as the *gamma*:

$$1 \text{ gamma} = 10^{-9} \text{ weber/m}^2.$$

The earth's field is of the order of some tens of thousands of gammas. The field is not constant, but has fluctuations that are normally of the

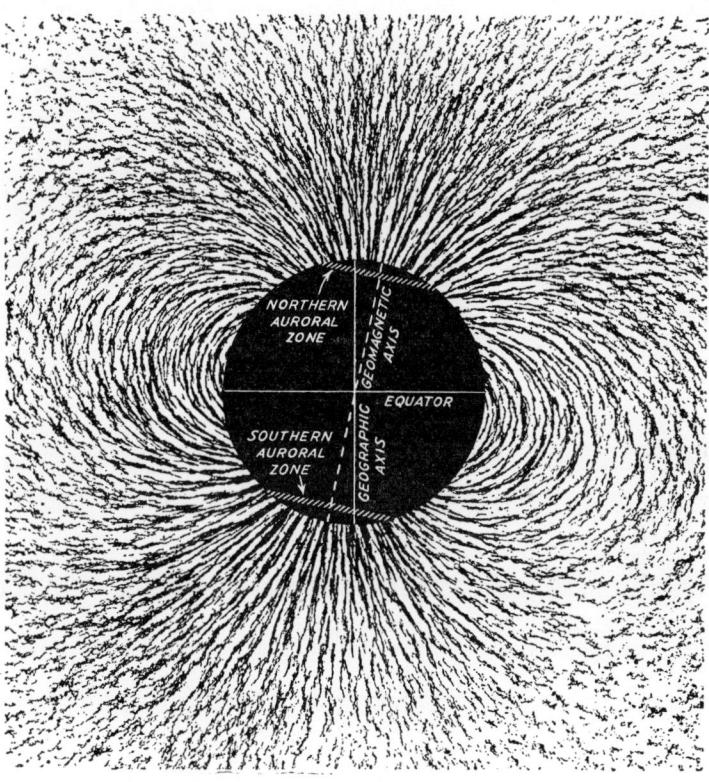

Fig. 5. The magnetic field of the earth. (From *Terrestrial Magnetism and Electricity*, edited by J. A. Fleming, Dover Publications, Inc.)

order of some tens of gammas, and a gradual change with time of the order of magnitude 100 gammas per year.

The earth's field is approximately symmetrical about an axis, called the *geomagnetic axis*, that is tilted 12° with respect to the geographic axis. The great circle in a plane normal to the geomagnetic axis is called the *geomagnetic equator*. From the geomagnetic equator one can measure a geomagnetic latitude. Plots of the earth's field are simpler if given in

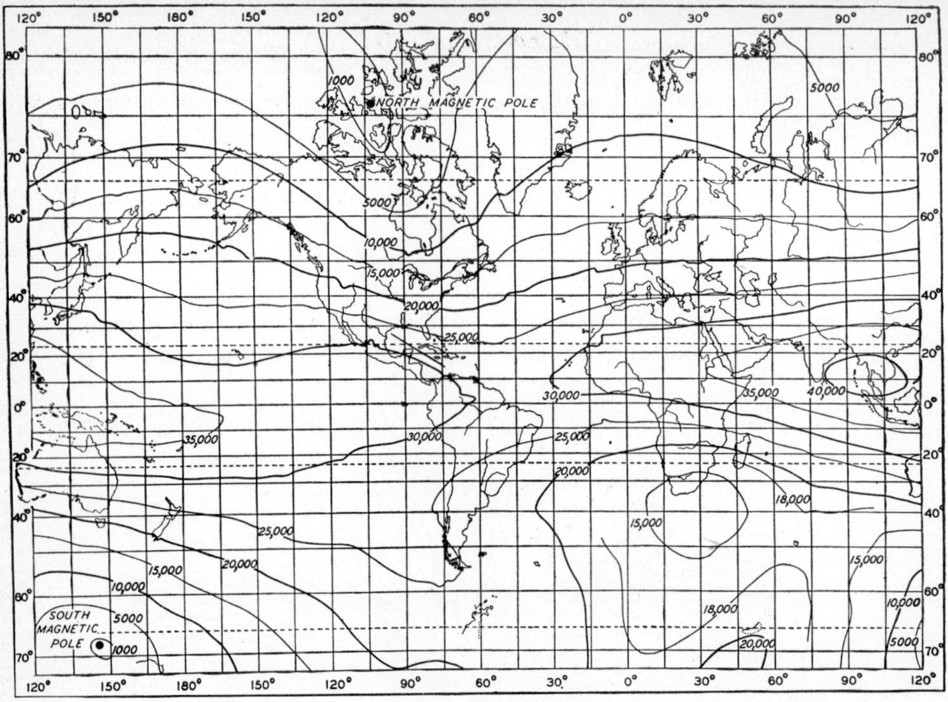

Fig. 6. The magnitude in gammas of the horizontal component of the earth's magnetic field. (*Figures 6, 7, and 8 courtesy of the Department of Terrestrial Magnetism, Carnegie Institution of Washington.*)

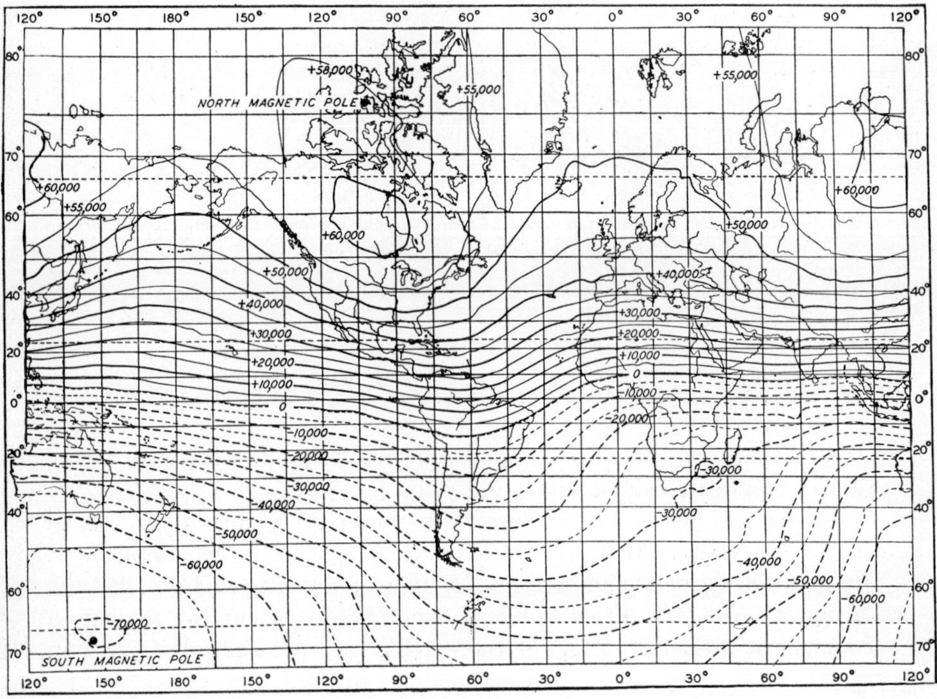

Fig. 7. The magnitude in gammas of the vertical component of the earth's magnetic field.

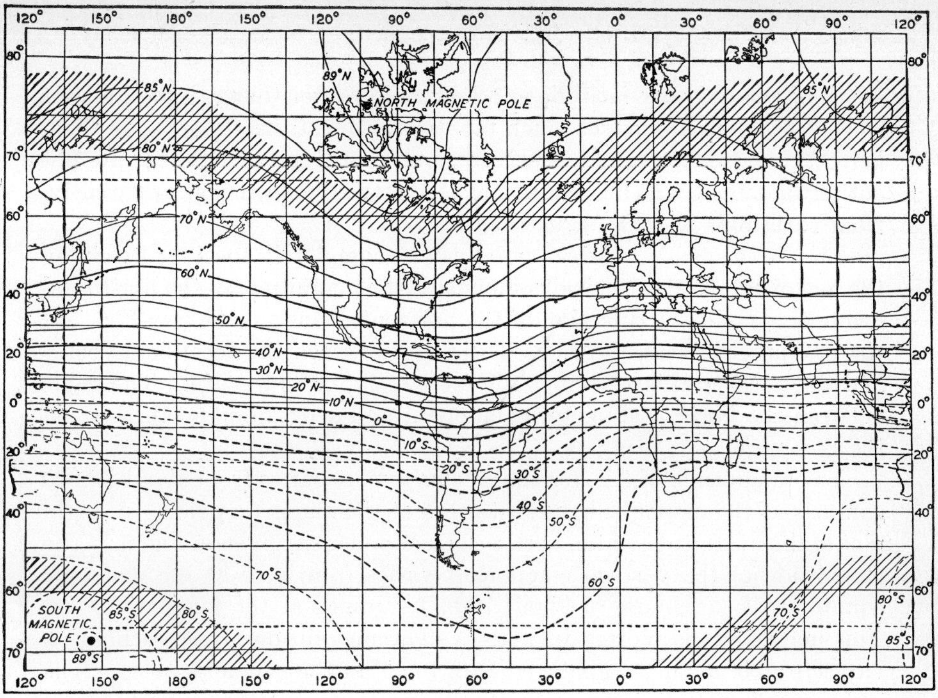

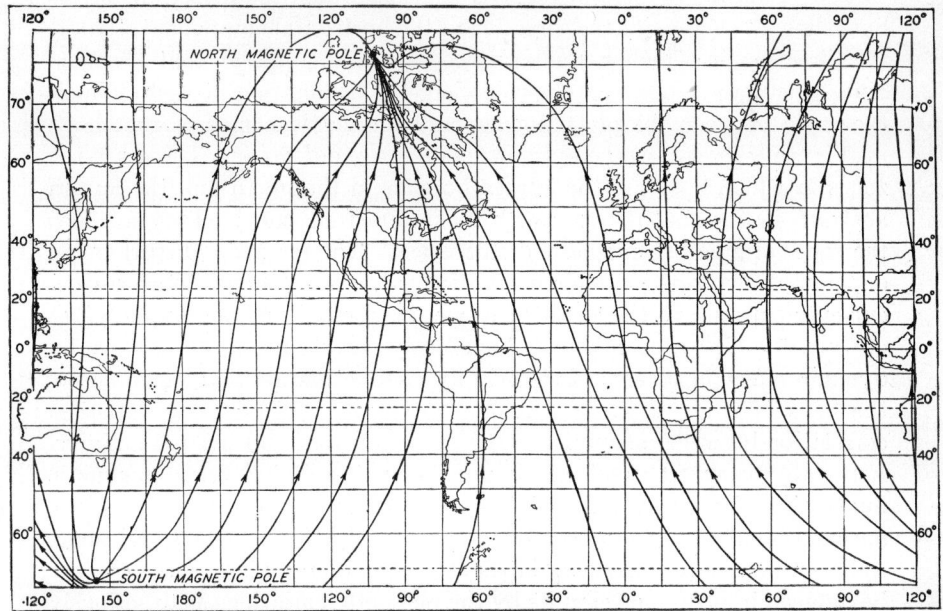

Fig. 8. The inclination (or dip) of the earth's magnetic field (the angle between the field vector and the horizontal). The hatched areas represent the zones in which auroras are observed on over 80 per cent of the nights.

Fig. 9. Lines (called *magnetic meridians*) whose tangents show the direction of the horizontal component of the earth's magnetic field, that is, the direction in which a compass needle will point.

terms of geomagnetic latitude and longitude rather than geographic; but since such plots are not of much practical interest, we do not give them here. Even when plotted in geomagnetic coordinates, the fields are not entirely symmetrical but show localized variations arising, apparently, from variations in earth structure.

The earth's field at a given point can be completely specified by giving the magnitude of the vertical component, the magnitude of the horizontal component, and the direction of the horizontal component (see Fig. 5 of the previous chapter, p. 929). The angle between the total field vector and the horizontal is known as the *inclination*, or as the *dip*. The angle between the horizontal vector component and geographic north is called the *declination*.

The magnitude of the horizontal component varies from about 35,000 gammas at the magnetic equator to zero at the magnetic poles. A world plot of the magnitude of the horizontal component is given in Fig. 6. The magnitude of the vertical component varies from zero at the magnetic equator to a maximum of about 70,000 gammas at the magnetic poles. This magnitude is plotted in Fig. 7. The magnitude of the inclination varies from 0° at the magnetic equator to 90° at the magnetic poles. The inclination is plotted in Fig. 8. The declination can have any value from 0° to 180°, either east or west. It is 180° at points north of the North Magnetic Pole, where the horizontal component of the field points due south. Instead of plotting lines of constant declination, which are difficult to visualize, we give in Fig. 9 a chart in which the directions of the lines show at each point the direction of the horizontal component, that is, the direction in which a compass needle would point at that location. Since this map is a Mercator projection, the declination at each point is the angle between the plotted curve and the vertical lines on the chart.

Figure 8 shows two belts known as the *auroral zones*. These are the zones in which auroras (the aurora borealis in the north and the aurora australis in the south) occur with maximum frequency. They are also the zones of greatest magnetic disturbance. The magnetic disturbances, or fluctuations in the earth's magnetic field, can be shown to arise from currents external to the earth's surface, presumably in the ionized gases of the very high atmosphere. Apparently these currents are set up by dynamo effect in masses of electrically conducting air that move across the lines of force of the earth's magnetic field. There is a statistical correlation between magnetic disturbances, auroras, and sunspot activity. Especially near times of maximum sunspot activity, large magnetic fluctuations known as *magnetic storms* may occur. At these times, the aurora borealis will be observed far to the south of the auroral zone, radiocommunication may be interrupted, and such large voltages may be induced in telephone circuits by the magnetic variations as to seriously hamper long-distance telephone service. In the vicinity of New York or

Chicago, such a magnetic storm will cause the earth's field to vary by as much as 100 gammas in a minute. During World War II, a very detailed study of magnetic fluctuations was made by the Department of Terrestrial Magnetism of the Carnegie Institution of Washington for the United States Navy. Such fluctuations impose a natural limit to the sensitivity of magnetic mines.

The light of the aurora, green or less frequently red, arises from certain definite transitions in neutral oxygen atoms and neutral nitrogen molecules in the rarefied gases of the high upper atmosphere. The origin of the excitation of these spectral lines is not well understood.

CHAPTER 38

IDEAL MAGNETIC MATERIALS; THE MAGNETIC CIRCUIT; REAL MAGNETIC MATERIALS

In Chap. 36 we considered the magnetic field arising from a system of currents. These currents could be either 'free' currents in wires or the 'bound' currents that represent the magnetization of a material and which were considered in some detail in Chap. 37. If we have a solenoid with an iron core, the total magnetic field is the resultant of the field set up by the current in the winding and that set up by the currents that represent the magnetization of the core. But we have not yet learned to answer the very practical question: What intensity of magnetization in the core will result from a given current in the winding? To learn to answer that question is in essence the aim of this chapter.

Computations involving magnetic materials are extremely complex. We shall be able to treat only very simple cases—we cannot even treat the problem of the solenoid mentioned in the preceding paragraph, which turns out to be a difficult one. Courses in electrical engineering devote considerable attention to computations involving magnetic materials. Our principal aim here will be to acquire an understanding of the basic physical principles involved in such computations.

1. DEFINITIONS OF MAGNETIZING FORCE $\mathcal{H}$, IDEAL MAGNETIC MATERIAL, PERMEABILITY

For purposes of specification of the properties of magnetic materials and of computations where magnetic materials are involved, it is desirable to define a vector called the *magnetizing force* $\mathcal{H}$. In the general case, the physical significance of this vector is obscure, and its mathematical treatment is well beyond the scope of the present course. Hence, the accurate general definitions given in this section will seem somewhat abstract. Their usefulness will be illustrated by the special examples treated later in this chapter.

A magnetic material will have at any point a definite value of the vector $\mathcal{M}$, which is the magnetic moment per unit volume. This is a macroscopic quantity obtained in principle by adding up the atomic magnetic-moment vectors in a macroscopic volume and dividing by the volume, as discussed in the previous chapter. Correspondingly, at each point there will be a vector $\mathcal{B}$, which is the macroscopic magnetic field. This is an average of the detailed microscopic field over a macroscopic volume. This field $\mathcal{B}$ will arise partly from the magnetic moments of the magnetized material and partly from ordinary currents in conductors near the material.

The magnetizing force $\mathcal{H}$ is *defined* as the vector difference between two vectors:

$$\mathcal{H} = \frac{10^7}{4\pi} \mathcal{B} - \mathcal{M}. \tag{1}$$

The unit of $\mathcal{H}$, defined in this way, is called the *ampere-turn per meter*.

We note that at any point where $\mathcal{M} = 0$, that is, at any point in a vacuum (or, to ordinary accuracy, at any point in any material except a ferromagnetic material) $\mathcal{H}$ and $\mathcal{B}$ are vectors in the same direction and with magnitudes differing by the factor $10^7/4\pi$:

$$\mathcal{H} = \frac{10^7}{4\pi} \mathcal{B} \quad \text{except in ferromagnetic materials.} \tag{2}$$

Because of this relation, the formulas of Chap. 35 for the magnetic effects of electric currents will give $\mathcal{H}$ instead of $\mathcal{B}$ if they are multiplied by a factor of $10^7/4\pi$, provided that no ferromagnetic materials are present.

An *ideal magnetic material* is one in which the magnetization $\mathcal{M}$ is in the same direction as the field $\mathcal{B}$ and is proportional to $\mathcal{B}$. For such a material we can write

$$\mathcal{M} = \chi \frac{10^7}{4\pi} \mathcal{B},$$

where χ is a constant for a given material. Such a material is said to be magnetically 'soft.' $\mathcal{M}$ vanishes when $\mathcal{B}$ vanishes and reverses when $\mathcal{B}$ reverses; we shall see that it is impossible to make a permanent magnet of such a material. Good iron-silicon alloys used in transformers approximate ideal magnetic materials very closely if $\mathcal{B}$ is not too large (less than 1 weber/m²). It is the properties of such ideal materials that we shall study first.

If we substitute $\chi \frac{10^7}{4\pi} \mathcal{B}$ for $\mathcal{M}$ in (1), we find

$$\mathcal{H} = \frac{10^7}{4\pi} \mathcal{B} - \frac{10^7}{4\pi} \chi \mathcal{B} = \frac{10^7}{4\pi}(1-\chi)\mathcal{B},$$

or

$$\mathcal{B} = \frac{4\pi}{10^7}\left(\frac{1}{1-\chi}\right)\mathcal{H}.$$

Thus we see that, for an ideal magnetic material, $\mathcal{H}$ is a vector in the same direction as $\mathcal{B}$ and is proportional to $\mathcal{B}$. It is customary to denote $1/(1-\chi)$ by μ and to call μ the *permeability*. Then we can write

$$\mathcal{B} = \frac{4\pi}{10^7} \mu \mathcal{H}. \tag{3}$$

This equation can be taken as the definition of permeability μ. We consider the permeability as a *dimensionless* number.

We note that for nonmagnetic materials $\mathfrak{M}=0$; therefore, $\chi=0$ and $\mu=1$ [compare (2)]. For good magnetic materials, χ can be shown to be close to, but definitely less than, one; in this case $\mu=1/(1-\chi)$ can become a fairly large number, of the order of some thousands or more. The significance of the permeability μ is best illustrated by the examples to which we now turn.

2. MAGNETIZATION OF A TOROID WITH DISTRIBUTED WINDING

Fundamental experiments on the magnetic properties of ferromagnetic materials are usually done by using a thin toroidal ring of the

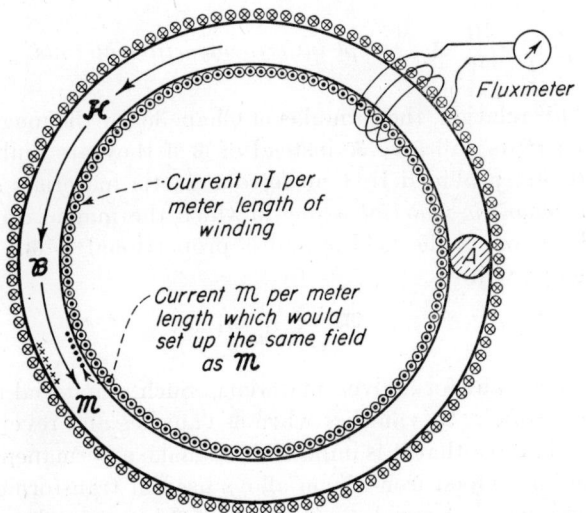

Fig. 1. A toroid with a core of ferromagnetic material.

material with a winding applied completely around the outside, as in Fig. 1. The variation in the flux density $\mathfrak{B}$, or rather in the flux $\Phi = \mathfrak{B}A$, is measured as the current I in the winding is varied. This determination of the flux in an iron ring without cutting into the ring sounds very mysterious at the moment. Actually, there is an instrument called a *fluxmeter*, which, when linked to the ring with a few turns of wire (called a *secondary coil*), will accurately record, in webers, all changes in flux that occur inside the ring. The operation of the fluxmeter depends on the phenomenon of electromagnetic induction, which we shall study later. The fluxmeter will be described in detail in Chap. 42.

The flux density $\mathfrak{B}$ in the ring is made up of two parts—that arising directly from the field of the winding and that arising from the magnetization of the material.

From formula (22), p. 960, the part of the field in the thin toroid arising from current nI per meter length of winding is $4\pi nI/10^7$.

The ferromagnetic core will have a magnetic moment $\mathfrak{M}$ per unit volume which, by symmetry, will be in the circumferential direction shown in Fig. 1, will be the same all the way around the toroid, and for a thin toroid can be assumed constant across the cross section. Such a distribution of magnetic moments will, by the argument of Sec. 2, Chap. 37, and Fig. 4, p. 975, set up the same field as a current $\mathfrak{M}$ per meter length around the surface of the core, as indicated in Fig. 1.

This fictitious current, from which the field set up by the magnetization of the toroid can be computed, is exactly like the current in the winding of a toroid itself, so it sets up the field $4\pi\mathfrak{M}/10^7$.

The total magnetic field in the toroid is the sum of these two contributions:

$$\mathfrak{B} = \frac{4\pi nI}{10^7} + \frac{4\pi\mathfrak{M}}{10^7},$$

or
$$\frac{10^7}{4\pi}\mathfrak{B} = nI + \mathfrak{M}. \tag{4}$$

Now from the definition (1) of $\mathfrak{K}$, we see that the magnetizing force has the magnitude

$$\mathfrak{K} = \frac{10^7}{4\pi}\mathfrak{B} - \mathfrak{M}$$

or
$$\mathfrak{K} = nI. \tag{5}$$

The direction of $\mathfrak{K}$ is the same as the direction of $\mathfrak{B}$ and $\mathfrak{M}$, as indicated in Fig. 1. If the core is considered to be of ideal magnetic material, we can define a permeability μ as in (3) and write

$$\mathfrak{B} = \frac{4\pi}{10^7}\mu\mathfrak{K} = \mu\frac{4\pi}{10^7}nI, \tag{6}$$

or
$$\mathfrak{B} = 1.257 \times 10^{-6}\,\mu\mathfrak{K} = 1.257 \times 10^{-6}\,\mu\,nI. \tag{6a}$$

If the core had been nonmagnetic, we should have had $\mathfrak{B} = 1.257 \times 10^{-6}\,nI$. *The presence of the magnetic core increases the flux density by a factor μ.*

Since $\mathfrak{K}$ in (5) is obtained by taking (turns/meter length) $\times$ (current), the unit of $\mathfrak{K}$ is called the *ampere-turn/meter*. Actually, as will be seen from (1), the units of $\mathfrak{K}$, $\mathfrak{B}$, $\mathfrak{M}$ are fundamentally the same, although they are given different names:

$$1\text{ amp-turn/m} = 1\text{ weber/m}^2 = 1\text{ amp/m} = 1\ \sqrt{\text{nt}}/\text{m}.$$

A closed path of magnetic material (such as this toroid) is called a *magnetic circuit*, since the magnetic flux runs through the magnetic material like the electric current in an electric circuit. This analogy explains the terminology of some of the following definitions.

If N is the total number of turns in the winding and l is the average length of the core or winding in meters (the length of bar required to make the toroid if an iron bar is bent into a circle and welded), then $n = N/l$. We can write the formula for the total flux as

$$\Phi = \mathcal{B}A = \mu \frac{4\pi}{10^7} nIA = \frac{4\pi\mu A}{10^7 l} NI, \quad \text{in webers,}$$

or
$$\Phi = \frac{NI}{10^7 \, l/4\pi\mu A}.$$

The numerator of this expression is called the *magnetomotive force:*

$$\text{MMF} = NI, \quad \text{in ampere-turns.} \tag{7}$$

The denominator is called the *reluctance* of the magnetic circuit:

$$\mathcal{R} = \frac{10^7 \, l}{4\pi\mu A}, \quad \text{in } \frac{\text{ampere-turns}}{\text{weber}}. \tag{8}$$

With these notations the formula for flux through the magnetic circuit can be written in the form

$$\Phi = \frac{\text{MMF}}{\mathcal{R}}, \tag{9}$$

in exact analogy with the electric-circuit formula $I = \text{EMF}/R$.

Note that from (5), $\quad \mathcal{H} = nI = \dfrac{NI}{l} = \dfrac{\text{MMF}}{l},$

so that the relation between MMF and $\mathcal{H}$ is

$$\text{MMF} = \mathcal{H} \, l. \tag{10}$$

Although *the formulas of this section apply only to the particular case of a uniform toroid with distributed winding as in Fig. 1*, they do illustrate why it is convenient to define $\mathcal{H}$ by the general formula (1) with the particular factor $10^7/4\pi$ multiplying $\mathcal{B}$. In this particular case, this procedure makes $\mathcal{H}$ come out simply nI, the number of ampere-turns per meter, and $\text{MMF} = \mathcal{H}l = NI$, the total number of ampere-turns. The current in the winding causes the flux in the core. Since the flux is proportional to nI in the case of an ideal magnetic core, it is reasonable to call $\mathcal{H}$ the *magnetizing force*.

The example of Fig. 2 will illustrate the use of these formulas. In this case the core is a mild-steel casting. Such a core approximates an ideal magnetic material of permeability $\mu = 1000$ up to a magnetizing force $\mathcal{H}$ slightly greater than 1000 ampere-turns/meter. We have, in Fig. 2,

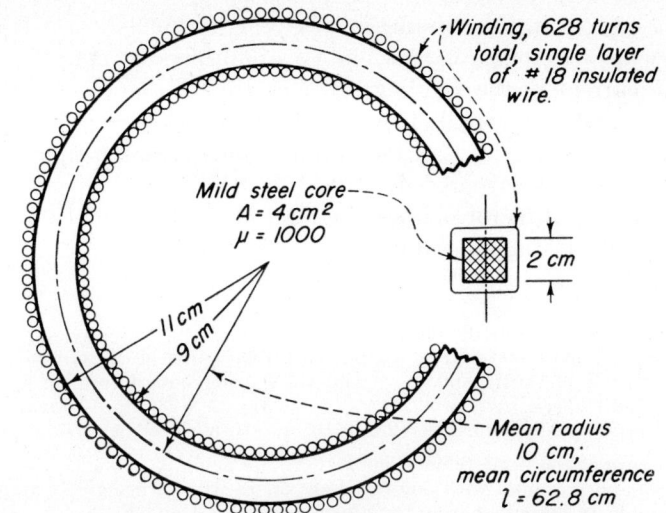

Fig. 2.

$N = 628$ turns.

The mean circumference is $l = 0.628$ m,

so $n = N/l = 1000$ turns/m.

If we take $I = 1$ amp,

we get $\mathcal{H} = nI = 1000$ amp-turn/m.

For this magnetizing force, (6) gives

$$\mathcal{B} = \frac{4\pi}{10^7} \mu \mathcal{H} = 1.257 \times 10^{-6} \times 10^3 \times 10^3 = 1.257 \text{ weber/m}^2.$$

The core area of 4 cm² is 4×10^{-4} m², so that

$$A = 4 \times 10^{-4} \text{ m}^2,$$

Hence, $\Phi = \mathcal{B}A = 1.257 \times 4 \times 10^{-4} = 5.028 \times 10^{-4}$ weber.

Alternatively, we can compute Φ from (9) by using the MMF and the reluctance. From (7),

$$\text{MMF} = NI = 628 \text{ amp-turn},$$

or, from (10), $\text{MMF} = \mathcal{H}l = 628$ amp-turn.

From (8), $\mathcal{R} = \dfrac{10^7 l}{4\pi\mu A} = \dfrac{10^7 \times 0.628}{4\pi \times 10^3 \times 4 \times 10^{-4}} = 0.125 \times 10^7 \dfrac{\text{amp-turn}}{\text{weber}}.$

Hence, $\Phi = \dfrac{\text{MMF}}{\mathcal{R}} = \dfrac{628}{0.125 \times 10^7} = 5.027 \times 10^{-4}$ weber,

which agrees with the previous value.

If the current in the winding is x amp instead of 1 amp, where $x<1$, the above answers for $\mathcal{H}$, $\mathcal{B}$, MMF, and Φ are multiplied by x; $\mathcal{R}$ is unchanged.

If the current in the winding becomes greater than 1 amp, the mild steel begins to depart rapidly from an ideal material because it approaches a saturated state in which all the atomic moments are completely orientated. Even if the current is increased to 10 amp, and hence $\mathcal{H}$ and MMF are increased by a factor of 10, $\mathcal{B}$ and Φ will not be so much as doubled (see Sec. 6, Real Magnetic Materials).

PROBLEMS

1. If a core of the same dimensions as Fig. 2 is made of laminated annealed sheet steel of permeability 5000 and is wound with 1000 turns of No. 19 wire carrying 0.15 amp, find $\mathcal{H}$, $\mathcal{B}$, MMF, and $\mathcal{R}$. Compute Φ from both formulas: $\Phi = \mathcal{B}A$ and $\Phi = \text{MMF}/\mathcal{R}$, and check. Ans: $\mathcal{H} = 239$ amp-turn/m; $\mathcal{B} = 1.50$ weber/m²; MMF $= 150$ amp-turn; $\mathcal{R} = 2.50 \times 10^5$ amp-turn/weber; $\Phi = 6.00 \times 10^{-4}$ weber.

2. If a core of the same dimensions as Fig. 2 is made of wrought iron of permeability 8000 and is wound with 500 turns of No. 18 wire carrying 0.15 amp, find $\mathcal{H}$, $\mathcal{B}$, MMF, and $\mathcal{R}$. Compute Φ from both formulas: $\Phi = \mathcal{B}A$ and $\Phi = \text{MMF}/\mathcal{R}$, and check.

3. A toroid is made by bending a circular rod of 3 cm diameter and 1 m length into a circle and welding the ends. The material is mild steel of permeability 1100. It is wound with 150 turns uniformly distributed. What current is necessary to set up a flux density of 1.2 webers/m²? Ans: 5.79 amp.

4. A cast-iron toroid is made by casting a doughnut shape. The mean radius of the toroid is 12 cm, the radius of the section is 1.5 cm. The permeability is 400. It is wound with 400 turns uniformly distributed. What current is necessary to set up a flux density of 0.3 weber/m²?

5. In Prob. 3, what current is necessary to set up a flux of 6×10^{-4} weber? Ans: 4.09 amp.

6. In Prob. 4, what current is necessary to set up a flux of 1.5×10^{-4} weber?

3. A MAGNETIC CIRCUIT OF UNIFORM CROSS SECTION AND PERMEABILITY

If the distributed turns on the highly permeable toroid of Fig. 1 or 2 are collected into a concentrated coil as indicated in Fig. 3, it is an experimental fact that the flux lines continue to follow the toroid around, and the total flux Φ remains unchanged if the total number of ampere-turns remains unchanged.

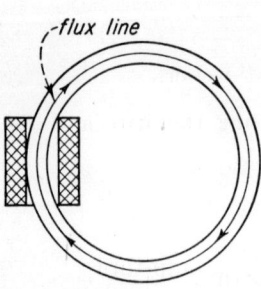

Fig. 3.

If the core were made of wood or brass, the flux patterns of the concentrated winding of Fig. 3 would be entirely different from that of the distributed winding of Fig. 1, and the presence of the toroidal core in Fig. 3 could be completely ignored. But with a core of permeability 1000, the flux in the core of Fig. 1 is 1000 times the flux arising from the winding alone; $999/1000$ of the flux arises from the magnetization of the core. And, so long as the core permeability is large compared to unity, the magnetization of the core in Fig. 3 can be shown, experimentally and theoretically, to be the same as the magnetization of the core of Fig. 1, for the same total ampere-turns. Since the bulk of the flux arises from the core magnetization and only a trivial part directly from the current in the winding, most of the flux will follow the iron circuit as indicated on Fig. 3 and the flux will have the same magnitude as for the case of Fig. 1 if the number of ampere-turns in the winding is the same.

All the formulas of the previous section that apply to Fig. 1 can be applied to Fig. 3 except those involving n, the number of turns per unit length, which is meaningless for Fig. 3. The best set of formulas to use for Fig. 3 is the following: Let

N = total turns,
I = current in each turn in amp,
l = length of 'iron' path in m,
A = cross section of 'iron' path in m^2,
μ = permeability of core.

Then

$\text{MMF} = NI$, in ampere-turns,

$$\mathcal{R} = \frac{10^7 \, l}{4\pi\mu A}, \quad \text{in } \frac{\text{ampere-turns}}{\text{weber}},$$

$$\Phi = \frac{\text{MMF}}{\mathcal{R}} = \frac{4\pi NI\mu A}{10^7 \, l}, \quad \text{in webers},$$

$$\mathcal{B} = \frac{\Phi}{A} = \frac{4\pi NI\mu}{10^7 \, l}, \quad \text{in } \frac{\text{webers}}{\text{m}^2},$$

$$\mathcal{H} = \frac{\mathcal{B}}{4\pi \times 10^{-7}\,\mu} = \frac{NI}{l}, \quad \text{in } \frac{\text{ampere-turns}}{\text{meter}}.$$

Alternatively,

$$\mathcal{H} = \frac{\text{MMF}}{l} = \frac{NI}{l}, \quad \text{in } \frac{\text{ampere-turns}}{\text{meter}}.$$

This same set of formulas will apply to a core of any arbitrary shape but constant cross section, with any type of concentrated or distributed winding, if l is the mean length of 'iron' path. For example, the formulas will apply to a good approximation to the transformer core of Fig. 4 if l is taken as the length of the broken line, 0.44 m.

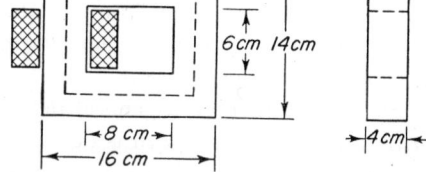

Fig. 4. A transformer core. The mean length of the core is the length of the broken line, $l = 12+12+10+10 = 44$ cm $= 0.44$ m.

PROBLEMS

1. If the core of Fig. 4 has permeability 5000 and the winding contains 60 turns carrying 0.5 amp, compute MMF, $\mathcal{R}$, $\mathcal{B}$, $\mathcal{H}$, and Φ. Ans: 30 amp-turn; 4.38×10^4 amp-turn/weber; 0.428 weber/m^2; 68.2 amp-turn/m; 6.85×10^{-4} weber.

2. If the core of Fig. 4 has permeability 1000 and the winding contains 120 turns carrying 0.2 amp, compute MMF, $\mathcal{R}$, $\mathcal{B}$, $\mathcal{H}$, and Φ.

3. If the iron toroid of Fig. 3 has a mean length of 30 cm, a cross section of 2 cm², and a permeability of 500, how many ampere-turns are required in the winding to set up a flux density of 0.5 weber/m²? *Ans: 239.*

4. If the permalloy toroid of Fig. 3 has a mean length of 70 cm, a cross section of 6 cm², and a permeability of 15,000, and the winding contains 500 turns, how many milliamperes of current are required to set up a flux of 2.4×10^{-4} weber?

4. LINE-INTEGRAL LAW FOR $\mathcal{H}$

In the previous sections we have seen that for the case of either a concentrated or a distributed winding,

$$\text{MMF} = \mathcal{H}\, l = NI,$$

where l is the length of ferromagnetic path and N is the total number of turns.

This equation is a special case of a theorem known as *the line-integral law for $\mathcal{H}$*, which can be rigorously proved from the formal definition of $\mathcal{H}$ in Sec. 1 and the line-integral law for $\mathcal{B}$ which was stated on p. 956. The proof is omitted here because it is somewhat difficult mathematically. The theorem is:

If we follow any closed path and take the integral of $\mathcal{H}_l\, dl$, where dl is an element of length along the path, and $\mathcal{H}_l$ is the component of $\mathcal{H}$ in the direction we are moving along the path, then

$$\oint \mathcal{H}_l\, dl = NI, \tag{11}$$

where the integral is extended completely around the closed path and N is the number of turns, each carrying free current I, that are linked by the path.

In this law *only the free currents in wires occur*, whereas in Ampère's line-integral law for $\mathcal{B}$ all currents must be considered, both the free currents in wires and the bound currents in magnetized material media. The fact that $\mathcal{H}$ obeys such a law involving only free currents makes the vector $\mathcal{H}$ very useful from the standpoint of computation. Equation (11) is completely general; no assumption of ideal magnetic material is involved in its derivation.

We can now give a general definition of magnetomotive force. The MMF around a closed path is defined as

$$\text{MMF} = \oint \mathcal{H}_l\, dl, \tag{12}$$

which, from (11), gives $\quad\text{MMF} = NI. \tag{13}$

5. SERIES MAGNETIC CIRCUITS

By a *series magnetic circuit* we mean a closed highly permeable path such as that of Fig. 5, which may be made up of pieces of different lengths, different cross-sectional areas, and different permeabilities. A good approximation to the flux in such a circuit may be obtained by the following method.

Most of the flux will follow around the ferromagnetic path, because of its high permeability, and it will be satisfactory to consider that *all* the flux follows around this path. Since flux tubes are closed and of constant strength throughout, the flux must be the same in all parts of the circuit, say

$$\Phi_1 = \Phi_2 = \Phi_3 = \Phi_4 = \Phi,$$

where subscripts 1, 2, 3, and 4 refer to the four legs of the circuit in Fig. 5. Then

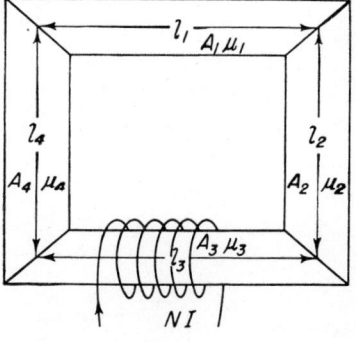

Fig. 5.

$$\mathfrak{B}_1 A_1 = \mathfrak{B}_2 A_2 = \mathfrak{B}_3 A_3 = \mathfrak{B}_4 A_4 = \Phi,$$

so that $\quad \mathfrak{B}_1 = \Phi/A_1, \quad \mathfrak{B}_2 = \Phi/A_2, \quad \mathfrak{B}_3 = \Phi/A_3, \quad \mathfrak{B}_4 = \Phi/A_4.$

Now, the line integral occurring in (12) has the value

$$\text{MMF} = \mathfrak{IC}_1 l_1 + \mathfrak{IC}_2 l_2 + \mathfrak{IC}_3 l_3 + \mathfrak{IC}_4 l_4 = NI.$$

In this equation we substitute the following expressions obtained from equation (3):

$$\mathfrak{IC}_1 = \frac{10^7}{4\pi\mu_1} \mathfrak{B}_1 = \frac{10^7}{4\pi\mu_1} \frac{\Phi}{A_1}, \qquad \mathfrak{IC}_2 = \frac{10^7}{4\pi\mu_2} \mathfrak{B}_2 = \frac{10^7}{4\pi\mu_2} \frac{\Phi}{A_2},$$

$$\mathfrak{IC}_3 = \frac{10^7}{4\pi\mu_3} \mathfrak{B}_3 = \frac{10^7}{4\pi\mu_3} \frac{\Phi}{A_3}, \qquad \mathfrak{IC}_4 = \frac{10^7}{4\pi\mu_4} \mathfrak{B}_4 = \frac{10^7}{4\pi\mu_4} \frac{\Phi}{A_4},$$

to obtain

$$\text{MMF} = \frac{10^7}{4\pi\mu_1} \frac{\Phi}{A_1} l_1 + \frac{10^7}{4\pi\mu_2} \frac{\Phi}{A_2} l_2 + \frac{10^7}{4\pi\mu_3} \frac{\Phi}{A_3} l_3 + \frac{10^7}{4\pi\mu_4} \frac{\Phi}{A_4} l_4 = NI.$$

This equation can be solved for the flux Φ:

$$\Phi = \frac{NI}{\dfrac{10^7 l_1}{4\pi\mu_1 A_1} + \dfrac{10^7 l_2}{4\pi\mu_2 A_2} + \dfrac{10^7 l_3}{4\pi\mu_3 A_3} + \dfrac{10^7 l_4}{4\pi\mu_4 A_4}}. \tag{14}$$

This expression can be written more concisely if we define the reluctances of the various parts of the circuit, in analogy with (8), by

$$\mathfrak{R}_1 = \frac{10^7 l_1}{4\pi\mu_1 A_1}, \quad \mathfrak{R}_2 = \frac{10^7 l_2}{4\pi\mu_2 A_2}, \quad \mathfrak{R}_3 = \frac{10^7 l_3}{4\pi\mu_3 A_3}, \quad \mathfrak{R}_4 = \frac{10^7 l_4}{4\pi\mu_4 A_4}.$$

Formula (14) then becomes

$$\Phi = \frac{\text{MMF}}{\mathcal{R}_1 + \mathcal{R}_2 + \mathcal{R}_3 + \mathcal{R}_4} = \frac{\text{MMF}}{\mathcal{R}}, \tag{15}$$

where $\text{MMF} = NI, \quad \mathcal{R} = \mathcal{R}_1 + \mathcal{R}_2 + \mathcal{R}_3 + \mathcal{R}_4.$

Similar formulas apply, of course, to magnetic circuits composed of any number of pieces of magnetic material in series. They will also apply to the case of a magnetic circuit with a *short* air gap. By a *short* gap we mean one whose length (in the direction of the flux lines) is considerably less than its width in either of the other directions.

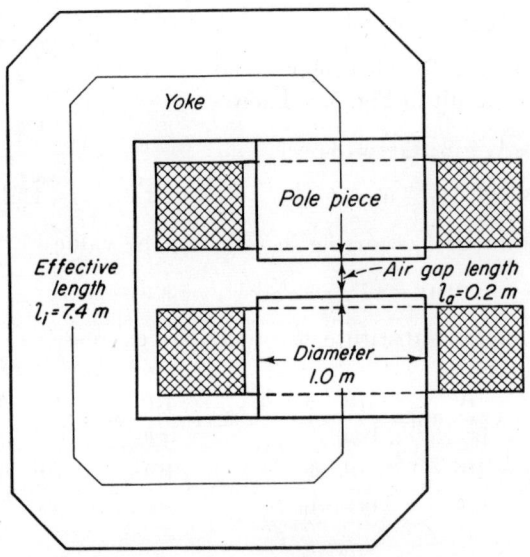

Fig. 6. Prototype cyclotron magnet.

As an example of a circuit with an air gap, consider the prototype cyclotron* magnet of Fig. 6. The dimensions here are typical of a cyclotron designed to produce a beam of protons with an energy of about 3 million electron-volts. A field of about 1 weber/m^2 in the air gap is desired, and a permeability of about 500 may be assumed for the iron. Let us assume that in Fig. 6 the effective length of path in the iron is 7.4 m and that the effective cross-sectional area of the iron is constant around the circuit and is equal to the area $\tfrac{1}{4}\pi$ m^2 of the circular pole pieces of one meter diameter. Let us compute the number of ampere-turns required in the winding in order to set up a field of 1 weber/m^2.

* The cyclotron is a particle accelerator which will be discussed in Chap. 45.

The reluctance of the iron part of the circuit (length $l_i = 7.4$ m, area $A_i = \frac{1}{4}\pi$ m², permeability $\mu_i = 500$) is

$$\mathcal{R}_i = \frac{10^7 l_i}{4\pi\mu_i A_i} = \frac{10^7 \times 7.4}{500\,\pi^2} = 15{,}000\,\frac{\text{amp-turn}}{\text{weber}}.$$

Since the air gap is short compared with its horizontal dimensions, we can use a similar formula to compute the reluctance of the air gap. Such a formula assumes that the flux lines go straight across the gap so that the length of the flux path is just the gap length ($l_a = 0.2$ m in our case) and the area of the flux path is just the area of the pole pieces ($A_a = \frac{1}{4}\pi$ m²). These assumptions are analogous to those involved in the derivation of the parallel-plate condenser formula in electrostatics. They neglect the 'fringing' of the flux at the edges of the poles and are valid only for short gaps. In our case, with $\mu_a = 1$ for air, we have, for the reluctance of the air gap,

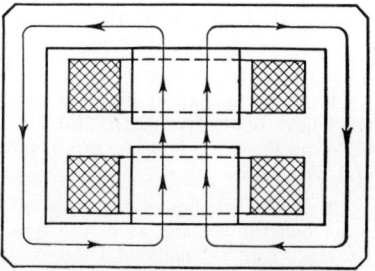

Fig. 7. Actual cyclotron magnet in which the flux path is split in the yoke as indicated by typical magnetic lines.

$$\mathcal{R}_a = \frac{10^7 l_a}{4\pi\mu_a A_a} = \frac{10^7 \times 0.2}{\pi^2} = 203{,}000\,\frac{\text{amp-turn}}{\text{weber}}.$$

The total reluctance of the circuit is

$$\mathcal{R} = \mathcal{R}_i + \mathcal{R}_a = 15{,}000 + 203{,}000 = 218{,}000 \text{ amp-turn/weber}.$$

It will be noticed that most of the reluctance is in the air gap.

The total flux desired is

$$\Phi = \mathcal{B}A = (1 \text{ weber/m}^2) \times \tfrac{1}{4}\pi \text{ m}^2 = 0.785 \text{ weber}.$$

Thus, the MMF required is

$$\text{MMF} = \Phi\mathcal{R} = 0.785 \times 218{,}000 = 171{,}000 \text{ amp-turn}.$$

Such an enormous number of ampere-turns is usually supplied by coils that surround the pole pieces as in the figure. The coils are wound of heavy copper tubing carrying a very heavy current, and water flows through the tubing to carry off the I^2R-heat.

For mechanical reasons, cyclotron magnets are not made in the shape of Fig. 6 but in the more symmetrical shape shown in Fig. 7. In Fig. 7, the yoke splits the flux path so that half the flux goes around each way. This is an example of a *parallel magnetic circuit*. We shall not discuss parallel circuits in general. In Fig. 7 it is clear that if each side of the yoke has half the area of the yoke of Fig. 6, so that the total area available for flux is the same as in Fig. 6, then the computations of Fig. 6 will apply equally well to Fig. 7. Actually, when this condition of equal areas is met, the average length of flux path in Fig. 7 will be slightly less than that in Fig. 6, so that the reluctance is cut and some iron is saved. This economy is one of the advantages of the design of Fig. 7. The principal advantage, however, is concerned with mechanical support of the upper pole piece and the upper part of the yoke.

PROBLEMS

1. If the air gap of Fig. 6 is decreased to 0.1 m, with a corresponding increase in the length of the iron path, and the permeability of the iron is 500, as in the computation in the text, find the number of ampere-turns required to set up a flux density of 1 weber/m^2. Ans: 91,600.

2. If the air gap of Fig. 6 is filled with a block of iron of permeability 100, all other constants being as in the text, compute the number of ampere-turns required to set up a flux density of 1 weber/m^2.

3. In the computation in the text for the magnet of Fig. 6, how many ampere-turns would be required if the yoke were made of better iron, of permeability 1000? Ans: 165,000.

4. In a magnet of the type shown in Fig. 6, if the air gap is of length 0.1 m and cross section 1 m^2, the pole pieces each of length 0.75 m, cross-section 1 m^2, and permeability 100, and the yoke of effective length 5.8 m, effective cross section 0.7 m^2, and permeability 500, what flux density is set up in the air gap with 90,000 ampere-turns in the windings?

5. In the magnet shown in Fig. 7, if the air gap is 3 cm long with an area of 1600 cm^2, the pole pieces each have area 1600 cm^2, length 25 cm, and permeability 200, and each of the parallel paths in the yoke has effective area 500 cm^2, effective length 150 cm, and permeability 500, find the flux density in the air gap that will be set up by 15,000 ampere-turns in the windings. Ans: 0.506 weber/m^2.

6. REAL MAGNETIC MATERIALS*

If we take a ring specimen of a magnetic material with a toroidal winding as in Fig. 1, we can increase the value of $\mathcal{H} = NI/l$ in small steps by increasing the value of the current I in small steps. For each change in $\mathcal{H}$, we can measure the change in flux, and hence the change in $\mathcal{B}$, by means of the fluxmeter. Hence, we can plot a curve of $\mathcal{B}$ against $\mathcal{H}$. If

---

* We are indebted to the excellent article on *Magnetism* by R. M. Bozorth, in REVIEWS OF MODERN PHYSICS, January 1947, for much of the data in this section. In Bozorth's article, as well as in most of the older scientific treatments of magnetism that do not employ the MKS system of electric and magnetic units of this text, the flux density $\mathcal{B}$ is measured in a unit called the *gauss:*

$$1 \text{ gauss} = 10^{-4} \text{ weber/m}^2;$$

and the magnetizing force $\mathcal{H}$ is measured in a unit called the *oersted:*

$$1 \text{ oersted} = \frac{1000}{4\pi} \frac{\text{ampere-turns}}{\text{meter}}.$$

Bozorth's permeability has the same numerical value as ours, both being defined so that the permeability of nonmagnetic material equals unity. In Bozorth's units, the permeability is just the ratio of $\mathcal{B}$ in gauss to $\mathcal{H}$ in oersteds.

we start with an unmagnetized specimen, a curve obtained in this way is known as a *magnetization curve*. A magnetization curve for annealed iron is shown in Fig. 8. It will be noticed that this real material corresponds only roughly to the useful concept of an ideal material which we have been discussing in the preceding sections. For an ideal material, we assumed that the ratio

$$\mu = \frac{10^7 \, \mathcal{B}}{4\pi \, \mathcal{3C}} \qquad (16)$$

is a constant. In the actual case of annealed iron, we see that μ starts with a value of about 200, determined by the slope of the line marked μ_0 in Fig. 8, which is known as the *initial permeability* μ_0. As the magnetizing force increases, the ratio $\mathcal{B}/\mathcal{3C}$ at first increases, reaching its maximum at about $\mathcal{B} = 1$ weber/m², as indicated by the slope of the line marked μ_m in Fig. 8. The *maximum permeability* μ_m in this case is 5000. The ratio $\mathcal{B}/\mathcal{3C}$ then decreases, and $\mathcal{B}$ approaches the *saturation magnetization* $\mathcal{B}_s$, which in this case is 2.15 weber/m².

A plot of permeability against magnetizing force for the material of Fig. 8 is given in Fig. 9.

For many applications of magnetic materials, high flux densities are desired at very low values of magnetizing force. For such applications, which include low-current transformers, low-current relays, inductive 'loading' of telephone cables, and sensitive detectors of small field changes (as in magnetic mines), the best material is the one of highest initial permeability or of highest maximum permeability, depending on the particular application. A great deal of effort* has gone into the development of materials of increased permeability during the past few decades, and tremendous progress has been achieved as indicated in the following tabulation, which lists type of material, heat-treatment, year of introduction, and presently attainable magnetic characteristics:

Iron, 99.9%, annealed at 900° C, *1890*, $\mu_0 = 200$, $\mu_m = 5000$, $\mathcal{B}_s = 2.15$ weber/m².

Silicon-iron, 3.3% Si, 96.6% Fe, cold-rolled, then annealed at 800° C, *1900*, $\mu_0 = 600$, $\mu_m = 10,000$, $\mathcal{B}_s = 2.0$ weber/m².

78 permalloy, 78% Ni, 21% Fe, heat-treated at 1050° C with rapid cool, *1913*, $\mu_0 = 8,000$, $\mu_m = 100,000$, $\mathcal{B}_s = 1.0$ weber/m².

4-79 permalloy, 79% Ni, 4% Mo, 16% Fe, heat-treated at 1100° C, *1921*, $\mu_0 = 20,000$, $\mu_m = 80,000$, $\mathcal{B}_s = 0.87$ weber/m². (*Mumetal*, 75% Ni, 2% Cr, 5% Cu, 18% Fe, has almost identical properties.)

1040 alloy, 72% Ni, 14% Cu, 3% Mo, 11% Fe, heat-treated in hydrogen at 1100° C, *1934*, $\mu_0 = 40,000$, $\mu_m = 100,000$, $\mathcal{B}_s = 0.6$ weber/m².

Supermalloy, 79% Ni, 5% Mo, 15% Fe, heat-treated in hydrogen at 1300° C, *1944*, $\mu_0 = 100,000$, $\mu_m = 800,000$, $\mathcal{B}_s = 0.8$ weber/m².

* Largely at the Bell Telephone Laboratories, where the permalloys were developed.

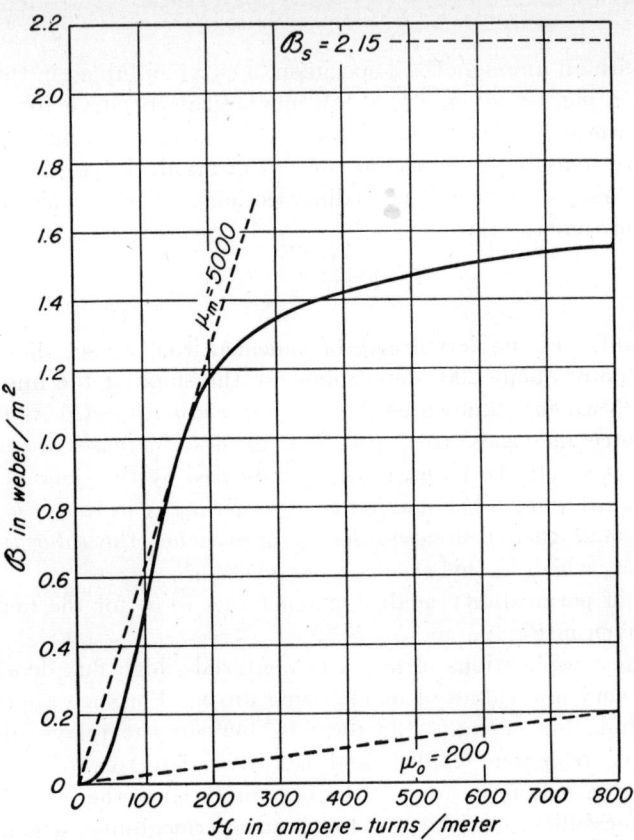

Fig. 8. Magnetization curve for annealed iron of high purity.

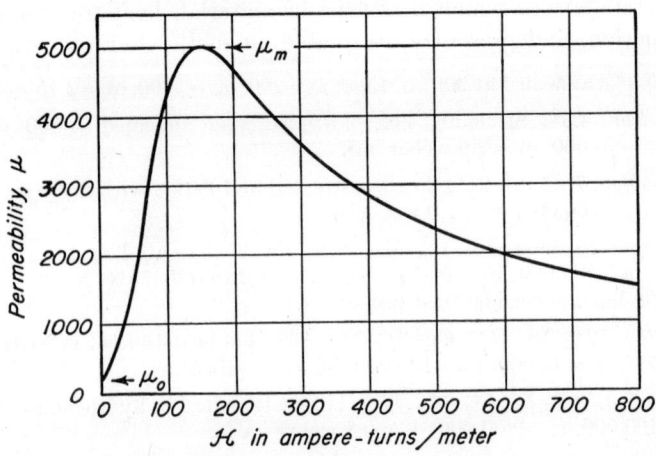

Fig. 9. Permeability *vs* magnetizing force for the material of Fig. 8.

The permeability of any of the above materials will be drastically lowered if they are deformed beyond the elastic limit after heat-treatment. Consequently, such materials are fabricated in final size and shape before heat treatment. After heat-treatment, they are assembled directly into apparatus for use or test, without bending and without undue shock.

If we take an initially unmagnetized sample of iron that has the magnetization curve of Fig. 8, increase the magnetizing force to 160 amp-turn/m so that the flux density becomes 1 weber/m², and then start decreasing the magnetizing force, the flux density does not decrease along the same curve but decreases along the curve shown in Fig. 10. When the magnetizing force has dropped to zero (no current in the winding), we still have a *residual flux* of density $\mathcal{B}_r$, which in this case is about 0.7 weber/m². Not until the magnetizing force has assumed the negative value of about -60 amp-turn/m (known as the *coercive force* $\mathcal{H}_c$) does the flux density become zero. If the magnetizing force is repeatedly varied between the limits of $+160$ and -160 amp-turn/m, the flux density follows around the closed curve of Fig. 10, which is called a *hysteresis loop*. For higher or lower maximum values of cyclically applied magnetizing force, the flux density follows around correspondingly larger or smaller hysteresis loops.

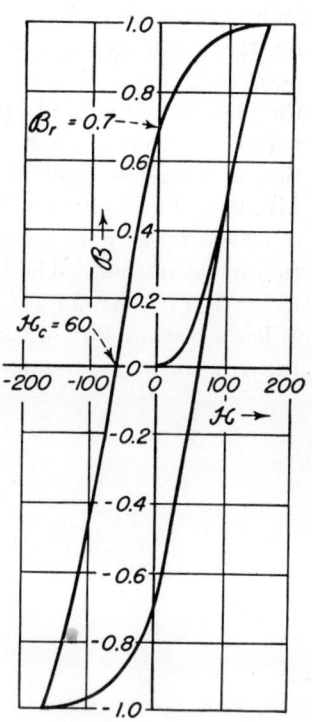

Fig. 10. Typical hysteresis loop for the material of Fig. 8.

A magnetic material with a high residual flux and a high coercive force is a very good permanent magnet material but a very bad material for a transformer or a motor where the flux varies continuously. The reason for the latter part of this statement is that the energy of self-inductance expended in setting up the magnetic field (see Chap. 40) is not completely recovered when the field decreases to zero if there is hysteresis. Rather, there is an energy loss in each cycle, if an alternating current is applied, that is proportional to the area of the hysteresis loop on a plot such as that of Fig. 10. Hence, for materials subjected to cyclic magnetization, a very narrow hysteresis loop is highly desirable. For transformers and armatures, silicon iron alloys are ordinarily used, but for very-high-frequency transformers, nickel-iron alloys like permalloy are employed.

For permanent magnets, a high value of residual flux is desired if the magnet is to have a strong field. Also, a high value of coercive force is desired if the magnet is not to be easily demagnetized and is still to have high residual flux when there is an air gap. From the line-integral law for $\mathcal{H}$ we can see that in the case of a permanent magnet with a high positive $\mathcal{H}$ in the air gap, a *negative* magnetizing force must exist within the magnet material itself. Characteristics of permanent-magnet material have continuously improved from the time of the first introduction of tungsten steel in 1855. This material (6% W, 0.7% Cr, 0.3% Mn, 93% Fe) had a residual flux of 1.05 weber/m^2 and a coercive force of 5200 amp-turn/m for the hysteresis loop corresponding to magnetization to saturation. The latest of the Alnicos (Al-Ni-Co steels), Alnico V (8% Al, 14% Ni, 24% Co, 3% Cu, 51% Fe), was introduced in 1940. It has a residual flux of 1.25 weber/m^2 and a coercive force of 44,000 amp-turn/m, for magnetization to saturation.

CHAPTER 39

ELECTROMAGNETIC INDUCTION

We have stated earlier that an electric generator changes mechanical energy into the electrical energy associated with an electric current, and that if current is forced through the generator in the opposite direction, the same machine will act as a motor, changing electrical energy into mechanical energy. We have described the action of the DC motor in Chap. 36, Sec. 3, but we have not yet described the action of the generator.

The action of the motor depends on the fact that a wire carrying current in a magnetic field experiences a force and tends to move. The generator action must be the reverse; the motion of a wire in a magnetic field must set up an EMF that tends to cause a current to flow. The latter phenomenon is a case of what is known as *electromagnetic induction*, which we shall study here.

The fact that an EMF is set up in a wire moving in a magnetic field was discovered in 1831 independently by Faraday in London and by Henry[*] in America. These men were the first to change mechanical energy directly into the energy of current electricity.

1. MAGNITUDE AND DIRECTION OF THE INDUCED EMF

Consider a wire, Fig. 1, a length l of which lies in a magnetic field $\mathcal{B}$ and moves with velocity v. The wire, field, and velocity are all three mutually perpendicular.

Although the wire as a whole is macroscopically neutral, each individual microscopic charge q in the wire is acted on by a force, in the direction shown, of magnitude

$$f = \mathcal{B}qv$$

in newtons. This expression is the formula for force on a charge moving in a magnetic field, equation (25), p. 965.

Unlike the positive nuclei, the electrons are free to move and will move to the left. If the ends of the wire are open, the movement of the electrons will cause the left end of the wire to become negatively charged and the right end to become positively charged. Motion of the electrons

---

[*] Joseph Henry (1797–1878), instructor at Albany Academy, Albany, N. Y., where he made this discovery; then professor of natural philosophy at Princeton College, Princeton, N. J.; later the first secretary of the Smithsonian Institution, Washington.

continues until the ends of the wire reach such different potentials that the force exerted by the resulting electric field on the electrons exactly balances the force f that acts on the electrons because of the motion of the wire. Since the force on a charge q in an electric field $\mathcal{E}$ is $\mathcal{E}q$, this requires that an electric field of magnitude $\mathcal{E} = \mathcal{B}v$ be set up in the part of the wire located in the magnetic field. The electric field must be

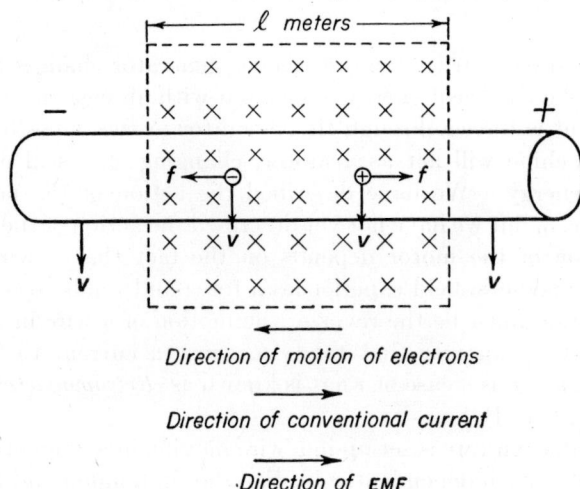

Direction of motion of electrons

Direction of conventional current

Direction of EMF

Fig. 1. Forces on the free electrons and positive nuclei in a wire moving downward through a magnetic field directed into the paper. The direction of EMF indicated is in accordance with the conventional definition—it is the direction of motion of positive charges in which work would be done *on* the charges *if* it were the positive charges that moved. It is analogous to the direction from − plate to + plate through a battery.

from right to left to balance the magnetic force f. An electric field $\mathcal{E}$, in volts per meter, acting over the length l, in meters, corresponds to a difference of potential

$$V = \mathcal{E}l = \mathcal{B}vl, \qquad (1)$$

in volts. Hence *the wire of Fig. 1, if open-circuited, acquires a* DP *of magnitude $\mathcal{B}vl$ between its ends; the right end being at the higher potential.*

On the other hand, suppose the circuit to be closed externally between the ends of the wire. A current will then flow in the direction indicated in Fig. 1. During the passage of the current through the section of wire moving in the magnetic field, work will be done *by* the magnetic forces *on* the charges since the magnetic forces are *in* the direction of motion of the charges. The amount of work will be $fl = \mathcal{B}qvl$ on a charge q. By definition, the EMF is the work in joules per coulomb of charge, or

$$\boxed{\text{EMF} = V_e = \mathcal{B}vl, \text{ in volts.}} \qquad (2)$$

Equation (2) is the fundamental formula for EMF generated in a wire moving in a magnetic field. It is the same as the DP (1) between the ends of the wire in the open-circuit case, but not necessarily the same as the DP between the ends of the wire in the closed-circuit case because there may be an IR-drop in the wire.

Let us now verify that in the case where the circuit is closed by an external resistance, as in Fig. 2, the heat generated in the resistance exactly equals the mechanical work we must do to push the stiff wire through the magnetic field at constant speed. Let us assume that in

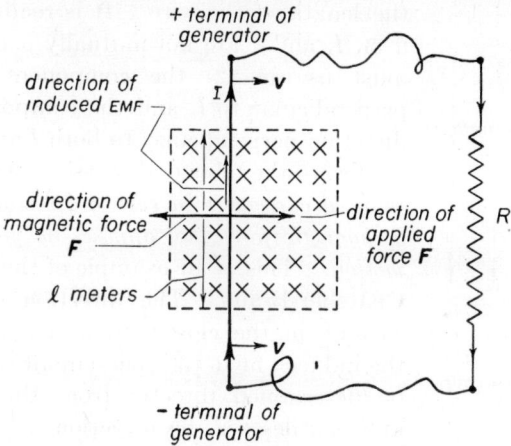

Fig. 2. A simplified electric generator.

Fig. 2 the resistance of the straight wire and flexible leads is negligible compared to the external resistance R.

The EMF (2) will cause current

$$I = \mathcal{B}vl/R$$

to flow through R. This current will develop heat in the resistance at the rate

$$I^2R = \mathcal{B}^2v^2l^2/R, \text{ in watts,} \qquad (3)$$

by dissipation of electrical energy. This dissipated energy must come from mechanical energy expended to push the wire. The need for expenditure of mechanical energy is clear if we note that we now have a wire carrying current in a magnetic field and that therefore there is a magnetic force normal to the wire in the direction opposite to the motion as indicated in Fig. 2. The magnitude of this force is

$$F = \mathcal{B}lI = \mathcal{B}^2vl^2/R, \quad \text{in newtons.}$$

Since the wire has no acceleration, the net force on it must be zero; consequently, our applied force in the direction of motion must have the same magnitude F as this magnetic force. The applied force F then does work at the rate

$$Fv = \mathcal{B}^2v^2l^2/R, \quad \text{in watts,}$$

which is the same as the rate of development of heat in the resistor as given by (3).

Formula (2) is derived for the case where $\mathcal{B}$, l, and v are mutually perpendicular. Here l represents a vector along the length of the wire. It is readily shown that if $\mathcal{B}$, l, and v are not mutually perpendicular, we must use in (2) the component of v that is perpendicular to l, and the component of $\mathcal{B}$ in a direction perpendicular to both l and v.

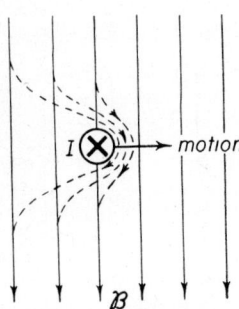

Fig. 3. View of Fig. 2 looking from the bottom toward the top of the page.

From the above discussion we see that *the induced current is in such a direction as to produce a magnetic force that opposes the force causing the motion.* This is an example of the principle of Le Châtelier-Braun. The direction of the induced current in the closed-circuit case, and hence of the induced DP in the open-circuit case, can readily be determined directly from this rule and the known rules for the direction of magnetic force. Alternatively, a very convenient scheme based on Fig. 3 can be used to determine this direction:

Imagine the magnetic lines to be like rubber bands so that they stretch and bend around the wire as it is pushed through them. Then if the fingers of the right hand are curled around the wire, pointing in the same direction as the magnetic lines wrapped around the wire, the thumb will point in the direction of the induced current.

PROBLEMS

1. A stiff piece of wire 2.4 m long is moved vertically upward in the earth's magnetic field, whose horizontal northward component is 2×10^{-5} weber/m². The wire is horizontal, points east and west, and moves at 50 m/sec. What is the DP between the ends, and which end is positive? *Ans:* 0.0024 v; west end.

2. If the wire of Prob. 1 moves horizontally toward the north at the same speed, and the vertical component of the earth's field is 9×10^{-5} weber/m² downward, what is the DP between the ends, and which end is positive?

Sec. 1] MAGNITUDE AND DIRECTION OF THE INDUCED EMF 1003

3. With what speed must a piece of wire 1 m long move through a field of 1 weber/m² in order to acquire a DP of 1 volt?

4. How strong a magnetic field is required to generate an EMF of 1 volt in a wire 1 m long moving at a velocity of 1 m/sec perpendicular to the field?

5. In Fig. 2, if $l=0.6$ m, $v=3$ m/sec, $\mathcal{B}=1.5$ weber/m², and $R=5$ ohms:
(a) What is the generated EMF?
(b) What is the current?
(c) What is the power expended in heating the resistor?
(d) What is the magnitude of the magnetic force? of the applied force?
(e) What is the rate at which the applied force does work?
 Ans: (a) 2.7 v; (b) 0.54 amp; (c) 1.46 w; (d) 0.486 nt; (e) 1.46 w.

6. In Fig. 2, if $l=0.6$ m, $\mathcal{B}=0.8$ weber/m², $R=9$ ohms, and $F=0.2$ nt, find (a) the current, (b) the EMF, (c) the speed, (d) the rate of doing work, and (e) the rate of heat generation.

2. THE RELATION BETWEEN EMF AND RATE OF CHANGE OF FLUX

There is another very useful way of writing the EMF generated in the closed circuit of Fig. 2. Let the symbol Φ stand for the flux in webers that is *linking* the closed circuit of Fig. 2. Φ then stands for the amount of flux *to the right* of the straight wire in this figure and decreases in time as the wire moves. We want to compute $d\Phi/dt$, which is of course a negative quantity. In time dt, let the wire move to the right a distance dx, so that $dx/dt = v$. Then during the time interval dt, Φ decreases by the amount of flux in an area $l\,dx$. This amount of flux is $\mathcal{B}l\,dx$, so that we can write

$$d\Phi = -\mathcal{B}l\,dx.$$

A more analytical derivation of this formula is given in the legend of Fig. 4. If we divide through by dt, we get

$$\frac{d\Phi}{dt} = -\mathcal{B}l\frac{dx}{dt} = -\mathcal{B}lv$$

for the rate of change of flux. But the expression on the right is just the negative of the generated EMF as given by (2). Hence

$$\boxed{V_e = -\frac{d\Phi}{dt}.} \qquad (4)$$

The magnitude of generated voltage equals the magnitude of the rate of change of flux linking the closed circuit, in webers/sec. Equation (4) can be used to determine the direction of the induced EMF in accordance with the following convention: The flux linking the circuit of Fig. 4 has a direction into the paper. Associate a positive sense of V_e around the closed circuit with the direction of Φ through the circuit in accordance with the right-hand rule (point thumb in direction of Φ; curled fingers will point in positive sense of V_e). Then in the case illustrated in Fig. 4,

$d\Phi/dt$ on the right side of (4) is a negative number (the flux is decreasing), therefore V_e is in the sense called positive. If the wire moves to the left instead of to the right, Φ is increasing, $d\Phi/dt$ is positive, and $V_e = -d\Phi/dt$ is negative. Therefore V_e, and hence the current, is in the opposite direction to that discussed above.

This sign convention is somewhat tedious. Usually it is convenient to use equation (4) to determine the absolute magnitude of V_e and to determine its direction separately by a rule known as *Lenz's law*. This law, which is a special case of the principle of Le Châtelier-Braun, can be stated as follows:

LENZ'S LAW: *When the flux linking a closed circuit is changing, the flux set up by the induced current is in such a direction as to tend to prevent the change in the flux linkage.*

Thus, in Fig. 4, the flux Φ linking the circuit is into the paper and decreasing in time. The induced current will be in such a direction that the flux it produces is into the paper through the circuit and therefore tends to keep the total flux linking the circuit from decreasing. The current, and hence the induced EMF, will be clockwise around the circuit. If v be reversed, Φ will be increasing. Since the induced current must now set up a flux out of the paper to try to prevent Φ from increasing, it must be counterclockwise. These directions are seen to be consistent with those we determined in Sec. 1 from fundamental considerations.

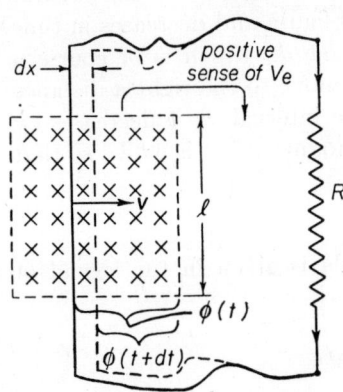

Fig. 4. The same circuit as Fig. 2. The computation of $d\Phi$ may be made as follows:

$$d\Phi = \Phi(t+dt) - \Phi(t).$$

But $\quad \Phi(t) = \Phi(t+dt) + \mathfrak{B}l\,dx,$

so $\quad \Phi(t+dt) - \Phi(t) = -\mathfrak{B}l\,dx.$

Therefore $\quad d\Phi = -\mathfrak{B}l\,dx.$

The great convenience of equation (4) and Lenz's law is that they can be shown to apply *whenever* the flux through a closed circuit is changing. For example, in Fig. 5, a single loop of wire is moved toward the north pole of a permanent magnet. The flux Φ through the loop is to the right. The amount of flux is increasing. An EMF is induced whose magnitude is $d\Phi/dt$. The direction of the EMF is determined by Lenz's law. The flux to the right is increasing. The induced current tends to prevent the increase by setting up its own flux *to the left*. Hence, the current must be counterclockwise when viewed from the left as indicated in Fig. 5.

If the loop of Fig. 5 moves to the right, the flux is decreasing; consequently, the induced current is in the opposite direction, tending to set up a flux to the right.

If, in Fig. 5, the loop is stationary and the magnet is moved to the right, exactly the same EMF is induced as when the magnet is stationary and the loop is moved to the left at the same speed, because the rate of change of flux through the loop is the same in the two cases.

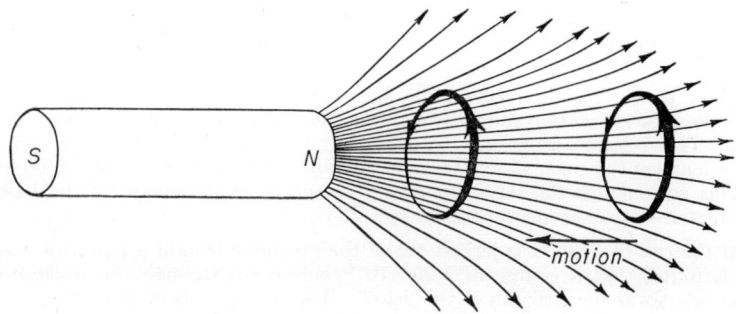

Fig. 5. Motion of a loop of wire in the vicinity of a permanent magnet induces a current in the direction shown.

If the single loop is replaced by a coil wound with N turns and connected into an external circuit as indicated in Fig. 6, the EMF in each of the N turns in series is $-d\Phi/dt$, and the whole EMF is

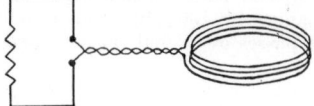

$$V_e = -N \frac{d\Phi}{dt}. \qquad (5)$$

Fig. 6. An N-turn coil.

Equations (4) and (5) also apply to cases in which the flux through a loop or a coil is changing with no apparent motion. A case of this type is a coil placed in the field between the poles of an electromagnet when the exciting current is changing. The flux through the coil changes as the current in the windings of the electromagnet changes, and an EMF is generated in the coil. Equation (5) gives the magnitude of this EMF, and Lenz's law gives its direction. If the coil is wound around the iron yoke of a magnet, or around an iron toroid as in Fig. 3, p. 988, these same relations are applicable, and the voltage generated in the coil can be made the basis for a determination of the rate of change of flux within the solid ferromagnetic material.

PROBLEMS

1. A 25-turn coil of the type shown in Fig. 6 has an area of 1 cm². If this coil is moved toward a magnet as in Fig. 5 in such a way that the mean flux density through the coil changes at the rate of 0.3 weber/m²·sec, what voltage is induced in the coil?

Ans: 0.75 mv.

2. A 'harbor loop' is a coil of wire of extensive area laid out on the floor of a harbor entrance to detect the entrance of submarines by means of the voltage induced by the submarine's natural magnetism.

(a) If the flux through the loop changes at the maximum rate of 0.008 weber/sec as the submarine passes over the near side of the loop, what is the maximum voltage induced in a 50-turn loop?

(b) If the earth's vertical field may be expected to vary as fast as 0.3×10^{-9} weber/m²·sec, what is the maximum area the harbor loop can have if the voltage generated by fluctuations in the earth's field is to be less than 1% of the voltage generated by the submarine in (a)?

3. Show that if the flux linking the coil of Fig. 6 changes in any manner from Φ_1 to Φ_2, then the *charge* that flows through the resistor R is given by $Q = N(\Phi_2 - \Phi_1)/R$, in coul. This relation is derived by integrating $I\,dt$ and involves no assumption as to the shape of the curve of flux *vs* time in the period during which the flux is changing. This equation is the basis for measurement of flux changes by the ballistic galvanometer—a charge-measuring device.

4. If the coil of Prob. 1 is jerked out of the magnetic field of a powerful magnet and it is found that a charge of 1.25×10^{-4} coul passes through the resistance of 40 ohms, what was the strength of the field? (Use the formula of Prob. 3.)

5. The 'search coil' of a magnetic mine is a long permalloy rod of 4 cm² cross-sectional area, wound with 50,000 turns of wire. When the external field component parallel to the rod changes by x weber/m², the average flux density in the rod changes by $5000\,x$ weber/m², provided the externally applied field is sufficiently small—a condition adequately satisfied by the earth's field and by ships' fields. When a ship passes over the mine, the field component parallel to the rod changes by 5×10^{-7} weber/m² during a period of 25 sec. Find the average voltage induced in the search coil during this period.

Ans: 2.00 mv.

6. If the rod of the magnetic mine of Prob. 5 is wound with 100,000 turns of wire and if the field component parallel to the rod changes by 150×10^{-7} weber/m² during a period of 10 sec when a high-speed battleship passes over, find the average induced voltage during this period.

3. HOMOPOLAR DC DYNAMOS

It is easy to see how to generate an alternating EMF, for example by moving the wire of Fig. 2 back and forth, or by rotating a coil in a magnetic field. Direct EMF's are usually produced by generating an alternating EMF in individual conductors and then employing a commutator as a switching arrangement to make proper connections to the external circuit. But there is one type of generator, known as a *homopolar generator*, that accomplishes the trick of moving a conductor continuously at constant speed in a constant magnetic field, and hence generates a truly constant direct EMF. This type of generator, which has occasionally been used for special purposes to generate large direct currents at low voltages, is illustrated in Fig. 7. The operation of the homopolar dynamo of Fig. 7, both as generator and motor, is very easy to understand because of its simple design. We shall discuss this operation in some detail because the fundamental relations we derive will be directly applicable to more complicated machines.

In Fig. 7 the *stator* (the part of any dynamo that stands still) is an iron electromagnet provided with a cylindrical air gap. The flux is radially inward all around this gap as shown in section AA. The *rotor* (rotating part) consists of two rings, mounted on suitable bearings and connected by heavy copper bars that move through the flux of the air gap. Current flows through the bars from one ring to the other, and connections to the external circuit are made through stationary brushes bearing on the rings.

Let us assume that the generator of Fig. 7 is turned at such a speed that the bars move with speed v, in m/sec, and that the average flux

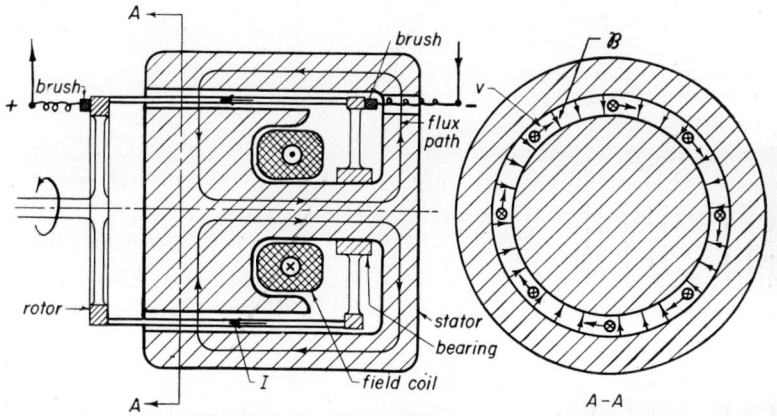

Fig. 7. Schematic diagram of a homopolar dynamo. The diagram is drawn for the dynamo operating as a generator. The *only* change needed for operation as a motor is to reverse the current direction.

density is $\mathcal{B}$, in webers/m², over an effective length l, in m, of each bar. Then the voltage generated in each bar is, by (2),

$$V_e = \mathcal{B}lv. \tag{6}$$

Since the bars are all in parallel, this is the EMF of the machine and, on open circuit, the DP between terminals. The student should verify, by comparison with Fig. 3, the correctness of the polarity indicated on Fig. 7 and of the direction of current flow that is indicated (for a closed-circuit condition).

The voltage of this machine is usually under 100. The greatest practicable $\mathcal{B}$ is about 2 webers/m². In the case of a rotor of radius 30 cm turning at 3000 rev/min = 50 rev/sec = 314 rad/sec we find that $v = 0.3 \times 314 = 94$ m/sec. If $l = 0.5$ m and $\mathcal{B} = 2$ webers/m²,

$$V_e = 2 \times 0.5 \times 94 = 94 \text{ volts}.$$

A smaller machine would generate less voltage.

If the internal resistance of the machine is R_i, in ohms (this is the resistance, between terminals, of leads, brushes, and rotor bars), the terminal voltage when the machine is delivering current I is

$$V_t = V_e - IR_i.$$

This formula was derived and discussed in Chap. 33. In particular, we obtained a power equation by multiplication by I:

$$IV_t = IV_e - I^2 R_i,$$

which was interpreted as

$$\left\{\begin{array}{c}\text{electrical}\\ \text{power}\\ \text{delivered}\end{array}\right\} = \left\{\begin{array}{c}\text{mechanical power}\\ \text{changed to}\\ \text{electrical power}\end{array}\right\} - \left\{\begin{array}{c}\text{electrical}\\ \text{power lost}\\ \text{in machine}\end{array}\right\}.$$

We can now verify that we have to supply mechanical power IV_e to turn the machine (in addition to power needed for mechanical losses such as bearing friction). Mechanical work must be done against the magnetic forces on the conductors carrying current. The magnetic force on each conductor is in a circumferential direction opposite to its velocity, as can be seen from the current and field directions shown in Fig. 7. The current I, and hence the force f, is split up among the conductors, but the total force (circumferential and opposite in direction to the velocity) on all conductors is

$$f = \mathcal{B}lI, \quad \text{in newtons.}$$

To move the conductors against this force, we do work at the rate

$$fv = \mathcal{B}lvI, \quad \text{in watts,}$$

which, from (2), is IV_e, the rate of generation of electrical energy.

Thus, if the electrical load is a resistance load and the prime mover that drives the generator is governed to constant speed, V_e does not change when we decrease the value of the resistance, because nothing changes in (6); therefore, I increases. With increase of I, the magnetic forces increase, hence the prime mover must do more work to supply the increased electrical energy.

Now let us see how the dynamo of Fig. 7 operates as a *motor*. We replace the prime mover by a mechanical load. If we want the motor to turn in the direction indicated in Fig. 7, we supply current in the opposite direction to that indicated in the figure, because now we want the magnetic force to be *in* the direction of the velocity, not opposite as it was before. We accomplish this change in current direction by connecting the $+$ and $-$ terminals to the $+$ and $-$ sides of a DC power line of voltage V_t. The magnetic forces will accelerate the rotor until the conductors reach a certain steady speed v. *At this speed there will be an induced voltage in the conductors, of magnitude*

$$V_e = \mathcal{B}lv. \tag{7}$$

The direction of this EMF is the same as for the case of operation as a generator, but now it opposes the current flow, rather than causing the current flow. Hence, it is called the *back*-EMF or the *counter*-EMF. The magnitude of current flow will be determined by the difference between the terminal voltage V_t and the back-EMF V_e, divided by the internal resistance R_i:

$$I = \frac{V_t - V_e}{R_i},$$

or
$$V_e = V_t - IR_i \qquad (8)$$

We are already acquainted with this equation and its significance in terms of power when multiplied by I:

$$\underbrace{IV_e}_{\substack{\text{mechanical power} \\ \text{developed}}} = \underbrace{IV_t}_{\substack{\text{electrical} \\ \text{power input}}} - \underbrace{I^2 R_i}_{\substack{\text{electrical} \\ \text{losses}}} \qquad (9)$$

To see that IV_e is really the rate at which the magnetic forces do work, notice that the total magnetic force (circumferential) is $\mathcal{B}lI$; the rate at which it does work is $\mathcal{B}lIv = IV_e$.

Equations (7), (8), and (9) enable us to answer all possible questions about the performance of the motor, as illustrated by the plots of Fig. 8 for the special case of a motor with $R_i = 0.2$ ohm operated from 100-volt lines. Against I as abscissa are plotted (left-hand scale) terminal voltage V_t, internal IR_i-drop, and back-EMF V_e, which is the difference (8). The motor turns at such a speed as to *generate* the voltage V_e, that is, at a speed $v = V_e/\mathcal{B}l$ proportional to V_e. Also plotted (right-hand scale) are the electrical input IV_t, the electrical energy $I^2 R_i$ changed to heat in the conductors, and the mechanical power developed, which is the difference (9).

Looking at Fig. 8, let us see how the motor behaves. First suppose it is unloaded. It still has to develop enough mechanical power to overcome friction and other losses. Let us exaggerate this no-load power as 0.5 kw. The motor then draws 5 amp. It runs at such speed that V_e is 99 volts—almost equal to V_t, since only 1 volt is required to send 5 amp through 0.2 ohm.

Now let us load the motor by applying a mechanical torque to the shaft—imagine a brake on the shaft or the connection of a lathe or drill press to the shaft. When the load is applied, the motor tends to slow down. The decrease in speed causes a small drop in V_e, which immediately causes a large increase in current and power output. For example, if the speed drops 1 per cent, V_e drops 1 per cent, from 99 to 98 volts; the current increases 100 per cent, from 5 amp to 10 amp; and the mechanical output increases 100 per cent, from 0.5 kw to 1 kw. Thus, only a small drop in speed is needed to pick up a large mechanical load. In Fig. 8, if the load is increased from 0.5 kw to 4.5 kw, a factor of 9, V_e drops from 99 v to 90 v, a drop of 9 per cent, and the speed also drops 9 per cent.

Even this speed drop is exaggerated in Fig. 8, because an actual 5-kw motor would never have an internal resistance as high as 0.2 ohm.

All the formulas we have given above apply equally well to a commutated DC dynamo, except for the relation $V_e = \mathcal{B}lv$. However, for a commutated dynamo, whose construction we shall discuss later, V_e is still proportional to the speed v of the conductors, or to the rate of rotation

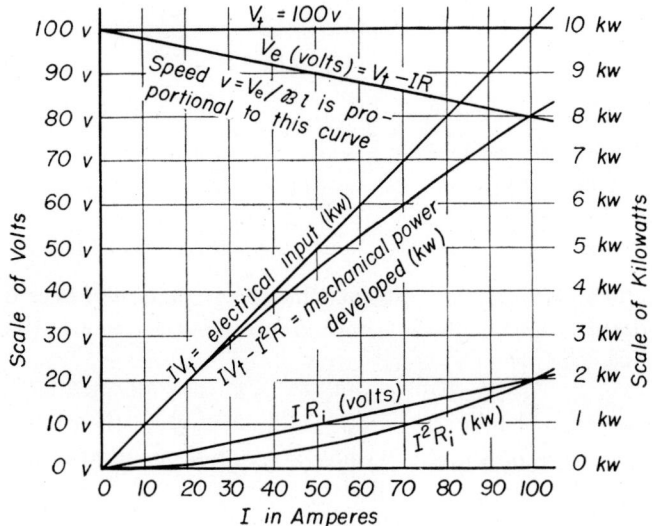

Fig. 8. Voltage, power, and current relationships for a DC motor of 0.2-ohm internal resistance operating on 100 volts.

n in rev/min. It is also proportional to the average field $\mathcal{B}$ in which the conductors move, or, better, proportional to the flux Φ set up by each pole. Hence, in the general case, we can write

$$V_e = Kn\Phi,$$

where K is some constant.

It is of interest to discuss one more question. Suppose the motor of Fig. 8 is running at $I = 50$ amp and is delivering 4.5 kw of mechanical power, but that we should like to raise the speed by 10 per cent—back to the no-load speed—without changing its power output. We could effect this speed increase by increasing the line voltage V_t, but this is not usually convenient. In practice we raise the speed by *decreasing* $\mathcal{B}$. It is easy to decrease $\mathcal{B}$ by a rheostat in the circuit supplying current to the field coils. If we decrease $\mathcal{B}$ by 10 per cent, v goes up 10 per cent, and none of the curves plotted in Fig. 8 changes at all. It may seem strange that $\mathcal{B}$ *is decreased to increase v*, but that is the situation. Both the generated voltage $V_e = \mathcal{B}lv$ and the mechanical power $fv = \mathcal{B}lIv$ depend on $\mathcal{B}$ and v only through the product $\mathcal{B}v$. Hence, if $\mathcal{B}$ is dropped, v will rise and nothing else will change; if $\mathcal{B}$ is increased, v will drop and nothing else will change. Similarly, for a commutated DC motor, we *decrease* the field current to decrease Φ in order to *increase* the number of rev/min in the same proportion. This property makes speed variation of a DC motor very simple and convenient, in contrast to an AC motor, whose speed cannot readily be varied.

PROBLEMS

1. In the homopolar dynamo of Fig. 7, if the conductors have an effective length of 30 cm in a field of 1.2 weber/m² and are placed at a radius of 20 cm from the axis, find the generated voltage when the rotor is turning at 3500 rev/min.   Ans: 26.4 v.

2. How fast would the rotor of Prob. 1 have to turn in order to generate 100 v?

3. If the dynamo of Prob. 1 is connected to a 13.2-v battery and is unloaded, at what speed does it run as a motor in the ideal frictionless case?   Ans: 1750 rev/min.

4. If the dynamo of Prob. 1 is connected to a 25-v battery and is unloaded, at what speed does it run as a motor in the ideal frictionless case?

5. If the motor of Prob. 3 has an internal resistance of 0.005 ohm and is developing 1.5 hp of mechanical energy, what current does it draw? At what speed is it running? What is the electrical power input?   Ans: 87.6 amp; 1690 rev/min; 1160 w.

6. If the motor of Prob. 4 has an internal resistance of 0.01 ohm and is developing 2 hp of mechanical energy, what current does it draw? At what speed is it running? What is the electrical power input?

7. If the motor of Prob. 3 has an internal resistance of 0.005 ohm and is connected to a brake that exerts a retarding torque of 8.5 nt·m, at what speed does it run when connected to a 13.2-v battery? What are the electrical power input, the I^2R_i-loss, and the mechanical power output? Neglect friction in the motor.
    Ans: 1650 rev/min; 1540 w; 70.3 w; 1470 w.

8. If Fig. 8 refers to a homopolar motor with a rotor radius of 30 cm, a conductor length of 0.5 m, and a field of 2 weber/m², plot a curve showing mechanical torque in nt·m as a function of current.

9. For the motor of Fig. 8, what is the maximum mechanical power that could be developed (assuming that the motor could handle the necessary current without burning out)? What would be the current and the ratio of speed to no-load speed under these conditions?   Ans: 12.5 kw; 250 amp; ½.

10. To what value must the magnetic field be changed if the motor of Prob. 6 is to run 10% faster and still develop 2 hp? Does the current or the input power change?

11. To what value must the magnetic field be changed if the motor of Prob. 5 is to run 10% slower and still develop 1.5 hp? Does the current or the input power change?   Ans: 1.32 weber/m²; no.

4. AC AND DC GENERATORS

Without going into technical details, we shall explain briefly the principles of construction of the usual forms of AC and DC generators.

Such generators are made with two, four, six, or more poles, usually at least four. A schematic cross section of a four-pole generator is shown in Fig. 9; this sketch will apply equally well to a DC or an AC generator. The yoke and pole pieces are of mild steel, and the armature is built up of laminated steel sheets; the reason for the laminations will be discussed later. The magnetic field is excited by a direct current in the field coils. The magnetic flux paths are indicated in the figure. The copper conductors on the armature are buried in slots to decrease the air gap and hence reduce the number of ampere-turns required to maintain the magnetic field, in order to keep to a minimum the energy lost as heat in the field coils. We ignore the slots in Fig. 9 and the following discussion, since they have no effect on the computation of the generated EMF.

Consider now the EMF generated in a single conductor as the armature revolves. This EMF will alternate in direction as the conductor passes under successive poles, since the magnetic fields of adjacent poles are in opposite directions. Since we want an AC generator to generate a sinu-

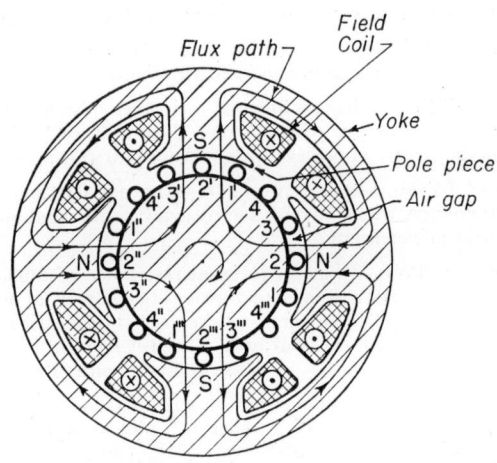

Fig. 9. Schematic cross section of a four-pole generator. The central rotating part (the rotor) is called the *armature*.

soidal EMF, the aim in designing an AC generator is to generate a sinusoidal EMF in each conductor by so shaping the pole pieces that the flux density in the air gap varies sinusoidally with angle around the machine. In this case the EMF in a single conductor will vary sinusoidally in time as in Fig. 10. This accurate sinusoidal variation is of no importance in a DC generator; however we shall use this same curve in discussing both cases.

The simplest machine to discuss is the AC generator. Consider conductors *1, 1′, 1″, 1‴* in Fig. 9. These conductors are 90° apart on the armature. Conductor *1″* is always moving in exactly the same field as *1*, and hence has exactly the same EMF as a function of time. Conductors *1′* and *1‴* are always moving past poles of polarity opposite to the polarity of the poles under which *1* and *1″* are moving, and hence have EMF's equal and opposite to those of *1* and *1″*. If just these four conductors were connected to each other and to a pair of slip rings in the manner shown in Fig. 12, the total EMF at the leads *AB* would at each instant be just four times the EMF generated in conductor *1*, since the connections are made so the four EMF's, of equal magnitude, superpose in the same direction so far as the external circuit is concerned. If the curve of Fig. 10 represents the EMF of conductor *1*, then this same curve, multiplied by 4, would represent the EMF in the line in Fig. 12.

Now consider the phase relation between the EMF's in conductors *1, 2, 3, 4*. These EMF's can be represented by the curves marked *1, 2, 3, 4*

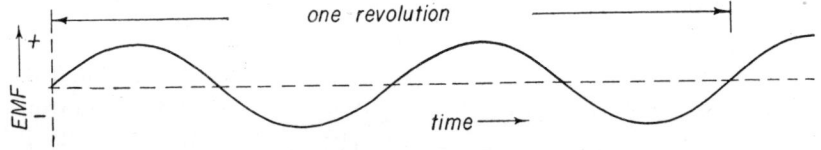

Fig. 10. The EMF in a single conductor of Fig. 9, as a function of time, will be a sinusoidal curve if the pole pieces are shaped so that the flux density varies sinusoidally with angle.

in Fig. 11. Each is a sine wave, but the EMF in *2* lags $1/16$ revolution *behind* that in *1*, since there are 16 equally spaced conductors on the armature. By 'lags behind,' we mean that the curve *2* in Fig. 11 is the same as curve *1* but is moved to *later* times by the time taken for the armature to turn $1/16$ rev. The maximum voltage in *1* occurs when it is opposite the center of a pole; the armature must turn $1/16$ rev farther before *2* is opposite the center of the same pole and has its maximum

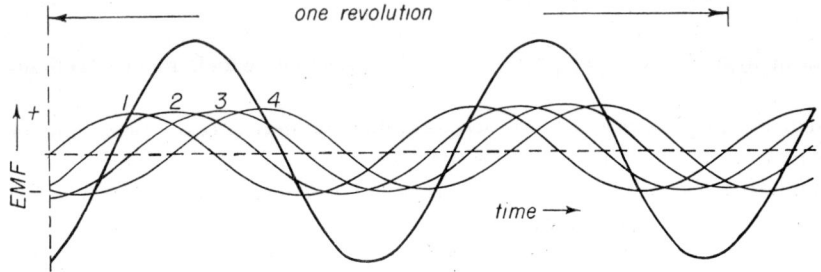

Fig. 11. The sum of the sinusoidal curves *1, 2, 3, 4*, is the heavy sinusoidal curve.

EMF. The EMF in *1* is zero when it is exactly between two poles; the EMF in *2* becomes zero $1/16$ rev later when it is between the same two poles, and so forth. Similarly the EMF in *3* lags $1/16$ revolution behind that in *2* and the EMF in *4* lags $1/16$ revolution behind that in *3*.

The sum of the EMF's in *1, 2, 3,* and *4* is represented as a function of time by the heavy curve in Fig. 11. This sum turns out also to be a sinusoidal curve, as can be readily proved by trigonometric relations.

It is now easy to see how the 16 conductors of Fig. 9 can be connected to each other and to a pair of slip rings so that the EMF at the slip rings will be four times the heavy curve of Fig. 11. Start by making all connections of Fig. 12 except for the final connection from the front of $1'''$ to the slip ring connected to B. In the circuit between A and the front of $1'''$, we get four times the EMF of curve 1 in Fig. 11. Now connect the front of $1'''$ to the front of 2, the back of 2 to the back of $2'$, $2'$ to $2''$ in front, and $2''$ to $2'''$ in back. Then between A and the front of $2'''$ we have EMF given by four times the sum of curves 1 and 2 in Fig. 11. Continue by connecting $2'''$ to 3 in front, 3 to $3'$ in back, $3'$ to $3''$ in front, $3''$ to $3'''$ in back, $3'''$ to 4 in front, 4 to $4'$ in back, $4'$ to $4''$ in front, $4''$ to $4'''$ in back, and finally $4'''$ in front to the slip ring connected to B. It is now apparent that between A and B we have an EMF four times as large as the EMF indicated by the heavy curve of Fig. 11.

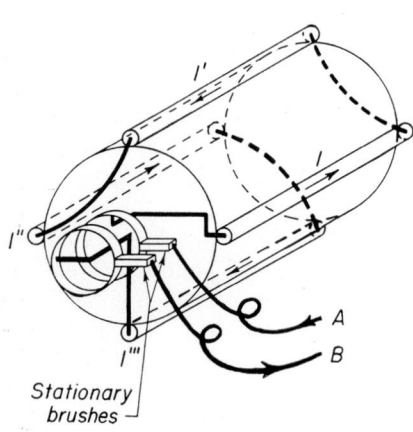

Fig. 12. Showing how four conductors 90° apart on the rotating armature of Fig. 9 can be connected to a pair of rotating slip rings so that their EMF's are additive at every instant.

This discussion covers the basic ideas involved in the generation of AC voltages. A four-pole machine such as the one we have been discussing gives two complete cycles (two complete sine waves of voltage) per revolution. Hence, if we wish to generate 60 cycles/sec, which means 60 complete sine waves per second, we turn the armature at 30 rev/sec, or 1800 rev/min. If the prime mover is essentially slow, as is a water turbine, we can still get 60 cycles/sec by increasing the number of poles. It is not uncommon to use 24 or more poles in such cases. A 24-pole machine would give 12 cycles per revolution, so that we should need only 5 rev/sec, or 300 rev/min, to generate 60 cycles/sec. The *frequency* of the generated AC voltage is fixed by the speed; the amplitude can be varied by varying the field current and hence the field strength, since the voltage in each conductor is proportional to the ℬ in the expression ℬlv. The field current must be a direct current supplied from an external source of DC.

Let us now turn to a brief discussion of the generation of DC voltages. The voltage in a single conductor of Fig. 9 is represented by the sinusoidal curve of Fig. 10. If the connection of this single conductor into the external circuit could be reversed each time it passed an interpole position of zero voltage, its contribution to the voltage observed in the external circuit would be always in the same direction and would be represented by the rectified curve of Fig. 13. The process of changing an alternating voltage into a voltage that is always in the same direction is called *rectification;* the curve shown in Fig. 13 is called the *rectified-voltage curve.*

Now let curve *1* of Fig. 14 represent the rectified voltage in conductor *1.* Then curve *2* of Fig. 14 will represent the rectified voltage in conductor *2,* as can be seen by comparison with curve *2* of Fig. 11. Similarly, curves *3* and *4* of Fig. 14 represent the rectified voltages in conductors *3* and *4.* The sum of the rectified voltages in *1, 2, 3,* and *4* is given by the heavy curve of Fig. 14.

The *rectified* voltages in *1, 1', 1", 1'''* are all identical. The same statement is true of *2, 2', 2", 2'''; 3, 3', 3", 3'''*; and *4, 4', 4", 4'''*. Hence, if a switching arrangement called a *commutator* can be devised so that

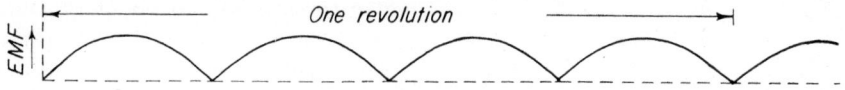

Fig. 13. Rectified sinusoidal EMF.

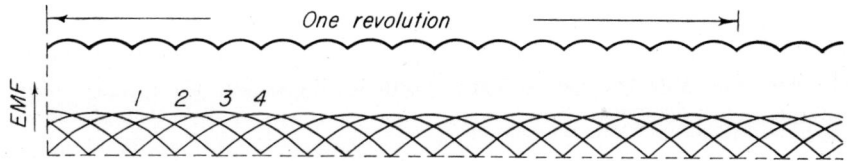

Fig. 14. The sum of the rectified sinusoidal curves *1, 2, 3, 4,* is the heavy curve.

each conductor at every instant makes a *positive* contribution to the voltage in the external circuit, this external voltage would be represented by four times the heavy curve of Fig. 14. This value represents an almost constant voltage with, however, a certain amount of 'commutator ripple.' It turns out that the necessary switching required for this task can be accomplished by a multisegment commutator and a single pair of brushes. Connections between the conductors at the back of the machine, and between the conductors and the commutator bars at the front of the machine, can be made in such a way that each time a conductor passes a zero-field interpole position, the brushes move from one commutator bar to the next, with the result that the connection of this particular conductor into the external circuit is reversed. We shall not give any further discussion of the complex connections required to accomplish this commutation; the connections are described in detail in every engineering text on DC machinery. The method of commutating the output to secure rectification in the simple case of two poles and two conductors can be seen from the diagram in Fig. 13, p. 934.

In an actual DC generator, with a large number of conductors and a large number of commutator bars, the generated voltage resembles that of Fig. 14 except that the commutator ripple, which represents a variation of voltage with the frequency with which commutator bars pass the brushes, becomes very small, of the order of only one per cent of the average voltage.

The voltage of a DC generator is seen to be proportional to the speed at which it is rotating (because of the v in $V_e = \mathcal{B}lv$) and to the field strength $\mathcal{B}$. The voltage can be varied by varying the speed, but it is common to drive generators at a fixed speed and to regulate the voltage by changing the current in the field coils and hence the field $\mathcal{B}$.

DC generators are commonly *self-excited* as in Fig. 15; that is, the current for the field coils is produced by the generator itself. When the generator is first started, there is no current in the field coils, but there is some residual magnetic field in the iron stator, left over from previous excitation. Because of this residual field, a small voltage is generated in the conductors; this voltage sends a small current through the field coils, which increases the field, which increases the voltage, and so on. The voltage rapidly *builds up* to a steady operating value. If it is desired to increase the generated voltage when the generator is running steadily, the field resistance is decreased; this decrease in resistance increases the field current, the field, and hence the generated voltage.

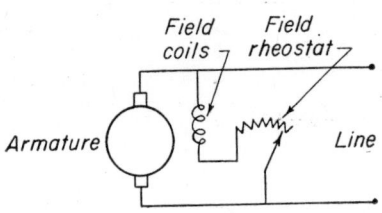

Fig. 15. A self-excited DC generator. This diagram will equally well represent a shunt-wound DC motor.

PROBLEMS

1. If the 60-cycle AC generator represented in Figs. 9–12 has 16 conductors at 20 cm from the axis, each of effective length 50 cm in a magnetic field of 1.2 weber/m² maximum and varying sinusoidally with angle, what is the maximum value of the generated AC voltage? Ans: 236 v.

2. Show that the average value of the rectified sinusoidal voltage of Fig. 13 is $(2/\pi)$ times the maximum value of this voltage. Hence, determine the average value of the voltage of the generator of Fig. 9 when it is operated as a commutated DC machine so that the generated voltage is four times the heavy curve of Fig. 14. Take the speed as 1800 rev/min, and assume that the conductors are 20 cm from the axis, each of effective length 50 cm in a magnetic field of 1.2 weber/m² maximum and varying sinusoidally with angle.

3. Make the same computation as in Prob. 2 for the case of a smaller 16-conductor, 4-pole generator turning at 3600 rev/min, with conductors 10 cm from the axis, each of effective length 25 cm in a magnetic field of 1.5 weber/m² maximum.
Ans: 144 v.

4. Suppose that after the self-excited generator of Fig. 15 has been running and is shut down, the prime mover is reversed and the generator is started up in the reverse direction of rotation.
   (a) Will the voltage build up?
   (b) What would you have to do to get the voltage to build up?

5. DC MOTORS

A DC motor does not differ in construction from a DC generator, except that in addition to the *shunt-wound* DC motor illustrated by Fig. 15, some DC motors are made with very-low-resistance, high-current, field coils connected in series with the armature as in Fig. 16. These are called *series-wound* motors or series motors. In either case there is generated in the armature a back-EMF that is proportional to the speed of rotation and to the magnetic field. The discussion of Sec. 3 applies.

At the instant of starting a motor, the back-EMF is zero. Since the resistance of the motor is very low, an external current control (starting

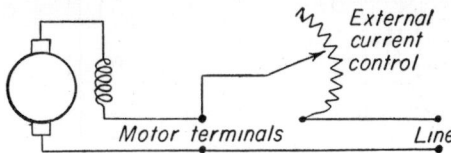

Fig. 16. A series-wound DC motor with external current control.

rheostat) must be used to limit the current to tolerable values until the motor speed and back-EMF can build up to limit the current. This starting resistance is completely cut out as the motor builds up speed.

The speed of a shunt motor is controlled by varying the resistance in the field circuit in a manner similar to that described at the end of Sec. 3. Series motors are never started except under load. They are used in applications where the load is constantly connected, as in streetcars and rolling mills. If the load were completely removed from a series motor, it would be liable to 'run away' and 'blow up.' As the load on a series motor is decreased, the speed and back-EMF increase. This increase causes the current to drop, which, in turn, causes a field drop. The drop in field results in an increase in speed to generate the requisite back-EMF. If very much load is removed, this process goes on in unstable fashion and results in excessive speed.

The torque of a DC motor is proportional to armature current and field strength (force on a conductor $= \mathcal{B}lI$). For a shunt motor, then, the torque varies as the first power of the line current; but for a series motor, if it is assumed that $\mathcal{B}$ is proportional to the field current, the torque varies as the *square* of the line current. Hence, in starting the motor under load, if it is permissible to use, say, six times the normal full-load operating current, a shunt motor will give 6 times as much starting torque as operating torque, but a series motor will give 36 times as much starting torque. Hence, series motors are used in applications where they must start under load and where very high starting torques are desirable to overcome starting friction in the apparatus being driven.

6. EDDY CURRENTS; AC MOTORS

Suppose that we have a solid metal cylinder, Fig. 17, rotating in a magnetic field. Consider the longitudinal elements of this cylinder, parallel to the axis of rotation. These elements are conductors moving in a magnetic field. The elements in the left portion of the cylinder are moving up in the magnetic field, and hence an EMF is induced in these ele-

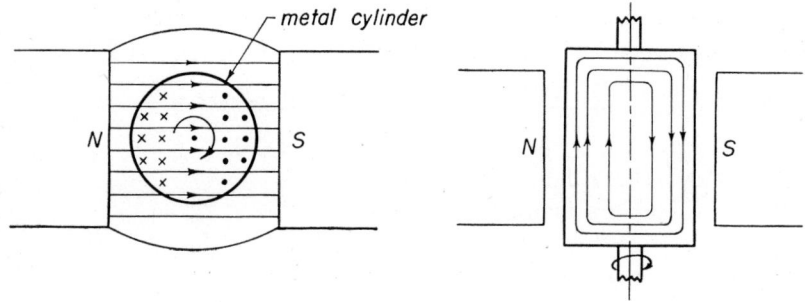

Fig. 17. Cross-section of a solid metal cylinder rotating in a magnetic field. Crosses and dots represent the direction of the eddy currents whose paths are shown in Fig. 18.

Fig. 18. Top view of Fig. 17, in cross-section, showing eddy-current paths (schematic).

ments that tends to drive current in the indicated direction (into the paper in Fig. 17). Conversely, the elements on the right side are moving down in the magnetic field, and an EMF is induced in these elements that tends to drive current in the opposite direction (out of the paper). As a result of these EMF's, a system of circulating currents flows in the metal, as shown in Fig. 18. These currents are called *eddy currents* because they form closed loops within the metal like eddies within a fluid.

Like the currents in the conductors of an armature, these currents are normal to the magnetic field and experience magnetic forces in the direction opposing the rotation of the cylinder. If the cylinder is spinning freely and the magnetic field is brought around it, the magnetic forces on the resulting eddy currents will stop the rotation very quickly, the kinetic energy of rotation going into heat created by the eddy currents. If the cylinder is driven at constant speed in the magnetic field, mechanical power equal to the heat produced by the eddy currents must be supplied. For a given magnetic field, this power can be shown to vary as the square of the speed: (EMF) ∝ (speed); (current) ∝ (EMF); (heat generated in the form of I^2R losses) ∝ (current)^2; and hence (power) ∝ (speed)^2. Or, from an equivalent point of view, (current) ∝ (EMF) ∝ (speed); (force on current element) ∝ (current); hence, (torque) ∝ (current) ∝ (speed); and (power) ∝ (torque) × (speed) ∝ (speed)^2.

Such eddy currents and eddy-current losses would occur in the armature (of a motor or generator) if it were a solid-iron cylinder. The losses would be so large as to be intolerable. By constructing the armature from steel sheets or laminations only a few hundredths of an inch thick, as shown in Fig. 19, the eddy-current losses can be kept to a negligible magnitude. Lamination of the armature has little effect on the magnetic flux since the flux lines pass through the sheets 'edge-wise' and do not need to cross from one lamination to the next. The steel laminations are electrically insulated from each other, either by shellac or by nonconducting iron oxide, so that the eddy currents are confined to circulation within each individual steel sheet. Two factors contribute to the reduction in losses. First, the length of conductor moving perpendicular to the magnetic field is now just the thickness of the lamina, so that the EMF generated is very small. Second, the resistance of the eddy-current path is very large because this path is of small cross-sectional area.

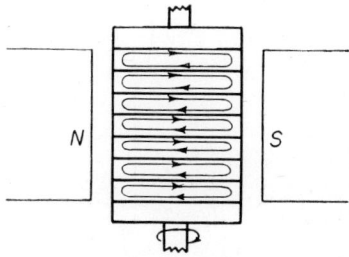

Fig. 19. Eddy-current paths in an armature like that of Fig. 18, only laminated. The laminations in an actual armature are only a few hundredths of an inch thick. The stack of laminations is held together by bolts that run through them in a direction parallel to the axis of rotation.

This is just one example of a large class of phenomena connected with eddy currents. In general, *if there is relative motion between a piece of metal and a magnetic field, eddy currents will be set up in the metal in such a direction that the resulting magnetic forces on the eddy-current elements will tend to stop the relative motion.*

As another example, consider the eddy-current brake of Fig. 20. Such a brake is used in every watt-hour meter (see Chap. 42) to produce a definite torque opposing the rotation of the meter element and to stop rotation quickly when power ceases to flow through the meter. In this case, an EMF directed from center to rim is induced in each radial element of the disk as it moves through the magnetic field. This EMF sets up the system of eddy currents sketched. The magnetic force on these currents in the magnetic field opposes the rotation.

In Fig. 20 we see that we get a counterclockwise torque opposing the clockwise rotation of the metal disk. We should get exactly the same counterclockwise torque on the disk if the disk were standing still and the magnet were rotated counterclockwise about the same axis, because the same eddy-current pattern would be set up. The eddy-current forces oppose the *relative* motion of disk and magnet. If the disk is stationary and the magnet moving around, the disk tends to follow it around.

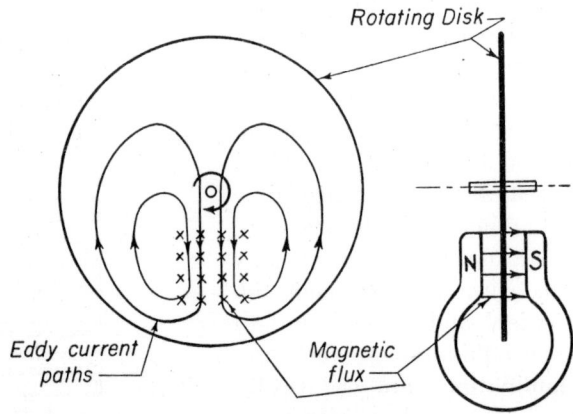

Fig. 20. An eddy-current brake designed to oppose rotation of a circular disk.

Also, in the case of Fig. 20, with the disk rotating, the elements of the disk lying in the field experience a force to the right. By Newton's third law, the magnet setting up the field experiences a force to the left. The magnet tends to be dragged around with the disk. This principle is made use of in some automobile speedometers, where a disk rotating at a speed proportional to car speed exerts a force on a magnet which is used to control the position of the speedometer needle.

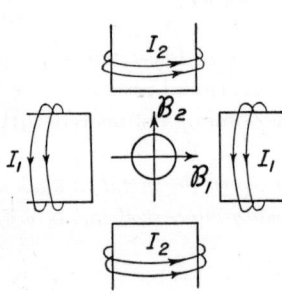

Fig. 21. Superposition of two alternating fields at right angles. This figure defines the positive directions of I_1, I_2, $\mathcal{B}_1$, $\mathcal{B}_2$, as used in Fig. 22.

The same idea furnishes the principle of operation of the most common type of AC motor, the *induction motor*. Consider what would happen in Fig. 17 if the metal cylinder were standing still but the pole pieces were rotating counterclockwise, so that there was the same relative motion of cylinder and field. Then the same system of eddy currents would be set up in the cylinder, the same counterclockwise torque would be felt by the cylinder, and the cylinder would tend to rotate with the field.

In an induction motor the poles are not actually rotated, but, by exciting two or more windings with currents out of phase, the field is made to rotate just as it would if the poles were rotated. The two-phase (or single split-phase) case is illustrated in Fig. 21. There are four poles.

Sec. 6] EDDY CURRENTS; AC MOTORS 1021

An alternating current I_1 sets up an alternating horizontal field $\mathfrak{B}_1$. An alternating current I_2 sets up an alternating vertical field $\mathfrak{B}_2$. As shown in Fig. 22, if the currents I_1 and I_2 are ¼ cycle out of phase the vector

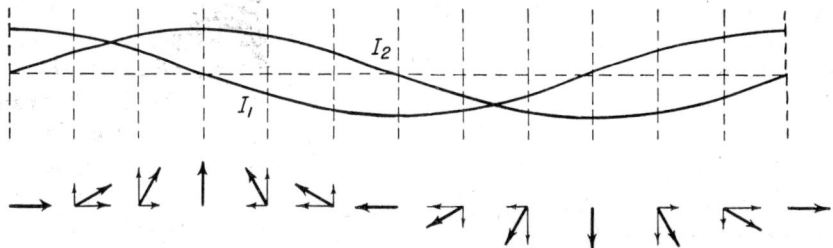

Fig. 22. The *resultant* of a horizontal magnetic field proportional to I_1 and a vertical magnetic field proportional to I_2 is a magnetic field of constant magnitude, rotating one revolution per cycle of the AC. The vectors show the fields $\mathfrak{B}_1$ and $\mathfrak{B}_2$ of Fig. 21, and the resultant field, at various instants of time.

resultant of the two fields is a rotating field of constant magnitude, exactly the same as the field of a single pair of poles carrying DC but rotating around the armature with the frequency of the AC.

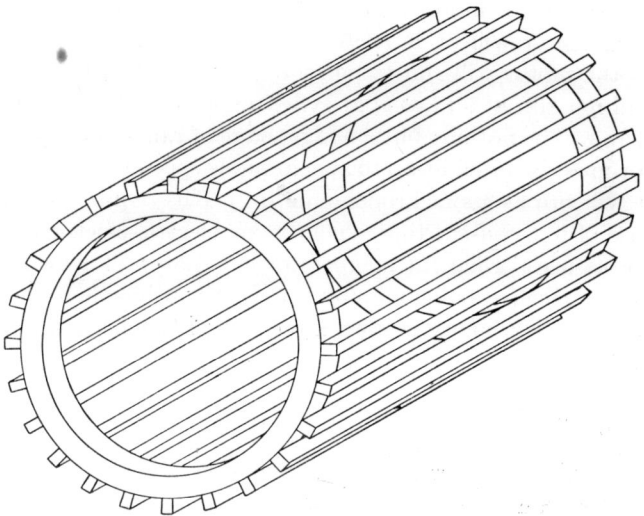

Fig. 23. The 'squirrel-cage' of the rotor of an induction motor.

In an induction motor, a 'squirrel cage' (Fig. 23) of heavy copper bars joined at the ends by low-resistance copper rings is used instead of a solid metal cylinder. The bars of the squirrel cage are embedded in slots in a laminated-iron rotor to keep down the reluctance of the flux path. For the two-phase motor of Fig. 22, the squirrel-cage rotor will run almost but not quite up to synchronous speed (60 rev/sec for 60-cycle AC): At exactly 60 rev/sec there would be no torque on the rotor because there would be no motion of conductors relative to field, and no eddy currents. At rotor speeds below 60 rev/sec the eddy-current system and the torque we have been discussing are set up. The slower the speed, the greater is the relative motion and hence the greater is the torque tending to increase the rotor speed. The motor will run at such a speed below 60 rev/sec that the torque will be sufficient to turn the load. This is ordinarily only a few per cent under 60 rev/sec.

Most modern induction motors are three-phase, rather than two-phase. They employ three currents, mutually out of phase by ⅓ cycle, and a minimum of six poles. The three currents are furnished directly by three-phase power lines. The principle of operation is exactly the same as in the simpler two-phase case we have sketched.

We shall not discuss the AC *synchronous motor* in detail. It is essentially the generator of Figs. 9–12 run as a motor, with DC in the field, AC in the armature. It runs at synchronous speed, which is such speed that the AC in each conductor reverses each time the conductor passes the gap between two poles, that is, the same speed as the generator must turn to generate 60 cycles/sec, if we are talking about 60-cycle AC. It is not hard to see that once this motor is turning at synchronous speed, the current in each conductor will be in such a direction as to maintain the speed, and that the motor will run synchronously with good torque. But the motor will not run at all *except* at synchronous speed, since at any other speed there will be nothing but a hodgepodge of random torques. Hence, the motor must be brought up to synchronous speed by some other means before it will run as a synchronous motor. This requirement is familiar in the case of non-self-starting synchronous electric-clock motors. Such clock motors use permanent magnets rather than DC for field excitation. Those that are self-starting employ some other principle for starting and only run as synchronous motors after they have been brought up to synchronous speed.

7. MUTUAL INDUCTANCE

Consider the transformer windings of Fig. 24. Let the iron circuit be an ideal magnetic circuit, so that it can be assigned a constant reluctance $\mathcal{R}$. Also neglect leakage flux, so that all flux in the circuit can be assumed to thread both coils.

Current I_1 in coil 1 will set up MMF $= N_1 I_1$ and flux

$$\Phi = \frac{N_1 I_1}{\mathcal{R}}.$$

If I_1 is changing at the rate dI_1/dt, Φ will change at the rate

$$\frac{d\Phi}{dt} = \frac{N_1}{\mathcal{R}}\frac{dI_1}{dt}.$$

If Φ is changing, an EMF will be induced in coil 2, of magnitude

$$V_{e2} = N_2 \frac{d\Phi}{dt} = \frac{N_1 N_2}{\mathcal{R}}\frac{dI_1}{dt}.$$

The EMF in coil 2 is proportional to the rate of change of current in coil 1. The coefficient is known as the *coefficient of mutual inductance* M_{12}:

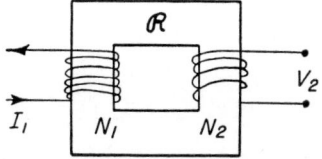

Fig. 24.

$$V_{e2} = M_{12}\frac{dI_1}{dt}, \qquad (10)$$

where $\quad M_{12} = \dfrac{N_1 N_2}{\mathcal{R}}, \quad$ in henrys. $\quad(11)$

The unit of mutual inductance is given the name *henry*, after Joseph Henry. As we see from (10), the henry is the same as the volt·sec/amp or the ohm·sec. In our system of expressing electrical units in the MKS system, the henry is just the meter. Thus

$$1 \text{ henry} = 1 \text{ ohm·sec} = 1 \text{ m}.$$

By similar reasoning, we see that if the current in coil 2 is changing there will be an EMF in coil 1 given by

$$V_{e1} = M_{12}\frac{dI_2}{dt}, \qquad (12)$$

with the *same* coefficient M_{12} as in (11).

Equations (10) and (12) can be used to define a coefficient of mutual inductance for any pair of coils, whatever their geometrical configuration and no matter whether or not they are linked by a ferromagnetic circuit. If some of the flux set up by one coil links the second, then a rate of change of current dI_1/dt in the first will produce an EMF V_{e2} in the second, M_{12} being defined as $V_{e2}/(dI_1/dt)$. Reciprocally, a rate of change of current dI_2/dt in the second will produce an EMF V_{e1} in the first. It can be shown rigorously that where no magnetic materials, or only ideal magnetic materials, are involved in the flux paths, then $V_{e1}/(dI_2/dt) = V_{e2}(dI_1/dt) = M_{12}$, so that one obtains the same value for the coefficient of mutual inductance, no matter which coil is considered to be the primary (the coil in which the current changes) and which the secondary (the coil in which EMF is induced). The coefficient of mutual inductance is always taken as a positive quantity. The directions of currents and induced voltages must then be assigned in accordance with Lenz's law.

The action of the transformer, which depends on the phenomenon of mutual inductance, will be discussed in detail in Chap. 40.

PROBLEMS

1. If the mutual inductance of the transformer of Fig. 24 is 0.5 henry, find the expression for the voltage induced in the secondary when the primary carries the alternating current $I_1 = 0.6 \sin 120\pi t$ amp. Ans: $V_{e2} = 36\pi \cos 120\pi t$ volts.

2. If the transformer of Fig. 24 has 200 turns on the primary, 50 turns on the secondary, and a reluctance of 2×10^5 amp-turn/weber, what is the mutual inductance in henrys?

3. If the transformer of Fig. 24 has 200 turns on the primary, 50 turns on the secondary, and an iron path of mean length 110 cm, cross section 10 cm $\times$ 10 cm, and permeability 1300, what is the mutual inductance? Ans: 0.149 henry.

4. A small permalloy toroid has a cross-sectional area of 1 cm², a mean circumference of 10 cm, and a permeability of 50,000 so long as the flux density is small. It has a primary winding of 50 turns and a secondary winding of 1000 turns of very fine wire. What is the mutual inductance? If the primary current changes at the rate of 1 milliamp/sec, what voltage is induced in the secondary?

5. A *long* air-core solenoid has a cross-sectional area of 400 cm² and is wound with 30 turns per cm. Around the center of the solenoid is wound a secondary coil of 150 turns of wire.
(a) What is the mutual inductance between the solenoid winding and the secondary coil?
(b) If the solenoid current changes at the rate of 1 amp/sec, what voltage is generated in the secondary winding?
(c) If the secondary winding is connected to a source of current and the current in this winding changes at the rate of 1 amp/sec, what voltage is induced in the solenoid winding? Ans: (a) 22.6 millihenrys; 22.6 mv; 22.6 mv.

6. Design a long solenoid, with a concentrated secondary winding around its central section, that will serve as a 1-millihenry mutual-inductance standard.

7. Note that the mutual inductance between the windings of solenoids such as described in Probs. 5 and 6 is determined by geometry alone. This fact is of importance in connection with the setting up of electrical standards, as we shall discuss in Chap. 42. Show that if two such solenoids differ in size but are *geometrically similar* in all respects, including wire size and wire spacing, then the mutual inductances are just proportional to the linear dimensions, in accordance with the fact that the henry has the dimensions of the meter.

8. What is the mutual inductance per kilometer length between the power lines and the telephone lines of Prob. 5, p. 948?

9. An induction coil such as is used to set off the spark in an automobile spark plug consists of a primary coil, and a secondary coil of very many more turns of finer wire, both wound around a straight iron core. The primary normally carries a current, which is broken at each instant that a spark is desired. If the primary winding has 200 turns and normally carries a current of 5 amp, and if this current falls to zero in 0.002 sec when the circuit is broken, what must be the mutual inductance if an average of 20,000 v is to be induced in the secondary? If this current sets up a total flux in the core of 10^{-3} weber, how many turns are required on the secondary? Ans: 8 henrys; 40,000.

8. SELF INDUCTANCE

Consider again coil 1 of Fig. 24. If the current I_1 is changing, an EMF is induced not only in coil 2 but also in coil 1 itself, since the flux through coil 1 is changing. We have

$$\Phi = N_1 I_1 / \Re,$$

hence
$$V_{e1} = -N_1 \frac{d\Phi}{dt} = -\frac{N_1}{\Re} \frac{dI_1}{dt}.$$

The coefficient here is called the *self inductance* in henrys, and denoted by $-L_1$:

$$V_{e1} = -L_1 \frac{dI_1}{dt}. \tag{13}$$

The minus sign indicates that the generated EMF is in a direction to oppose the change of current. If the current is increasing, the EMF is in a direction opposite to the current, tending to retard it; if the current is decreasing, the EMF is in the direction of the current, tending to keep it flowing.

In the same way any circuit, even a simple circuit such as that of Fig. 25(a), has self inductance. In Fig. 25(a) a single loop of wire is connected to an AC generator so that the wire carries a varying current. When the

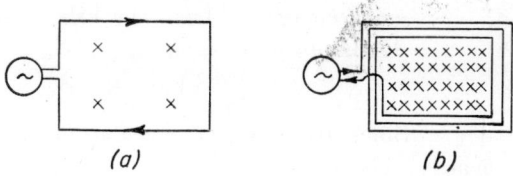

Fig. 25. Even a simple circuit (a) has self inductance, but the self inductance is greatly increased if (b) the circuit is an N-turn coil.

current I has the direction shown, there is a flux linking the circuit in the direction shown. When I increases, Φ increases, and an EMF

$$V_e = -d\Phi/dt$$

is generated in the direction opposing the increase of current. Since the flux Φ is proportional to the current I, $d\Phi/dt \propto dI/dt$, so that we can write $V_e \propto -dI/dt$, or

$$V_e = -L \frac{dI}{dt}. \tag{14}$$

This equation defines the self inductance L, in henrys. Self inductance is measured in the same units as mutual inductance.

The self inductance of a simple circuit like Fig. 25(a) is very small—often negligibly small. The self inductance is greatly increased if the circuit is an N-turn 'coil' as in Fig. 25(b). For a given current, each turn of this coil sets up the same flux as in Fig. 25(a), so that the total flux is multiplied by N. Hence, for given rate of change of current, the EMF generated in *each turn*, $-d\Phi/dt$, is N times as great as in Fig. 25(a). But the EMF's in the N turns are additive so, for a given rate of change of current in Fig. 25(b), the generated EMF is N^2 times that in Fig. 25(a). consequently, the self inductance of Fig. 25(b) is N^2 times that in Fig. 25(a). The self inductance of the coil of Fig. 25(b) would be further greatly increased if the coil were placed around an iron or steel core, because of the great increase in flux.

While the self inductance of coils is particularly significant, it must be remembered that all circuits have a certain amount of self inductance. The coefficient of self inductance plays a fundamental role in the study of alternating currents, which we shall take up in Chap. 40. In particular, we shall need equation (15), derived below, in this study.

We shall now set down carefully the expression for the DP between terminals of a coil or other part of a circuit having self inductance L and resistance R, and carrying a varying current I. Let Fig. 26 define the positive senses of these quantities. Then each coulomb that moves through the circuit from the $+$ to the $-$ terminal loses energy IR to heat but gains energy V_e from the EMF of self inductance. So the *drop* in potential V_t is

$$V_t = IR - V_e.$$

Since, from (14), $V_e = -L\, dI/dt$, we have

$$V_t = IR + L\frac{dI}{dt}. \tag{15}$$

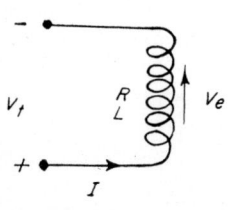

Fig. 26. Defining the positive senses of current, I, generated EMF, V_e, and terminal DP, V_t, for a circuit element having resistance R and self inductance L. With these definitions, equation (15) applies.

We can verify the signs in this equation by considering the case where I is positive and increasing (dI/dt positive). Then we must apply to the terminals *more* voltage than is required to overcome the IR-drop, since we must also overcome the EMF of self inductance, which is a back-EMF in this case, opposing the current flow (V_e is negative in the convention of Fig. 26).

PROBLEMS

1. What is the self inductance of the primary winding of the transformer described in Prob. 3, p. 1024? Of the secondary winding? Ans: 0.594, 0.0371 henry.

2. What is the self inductance of the primary winding of the transformer described in Prob. 2, p. 1024? Of the secondary winding?

3. Show that if the total flux linking the coil of Fig. 25(b) is Φ when the current is I, then $L = N\Phi/I$ henrys.

4. If a current of 5 amp in a 120-turn concentrated coil sets up a total flux of 5×10^{-4} weber linking the coil, find the self inductance of the coil.

5. Show that an N-turn coil wound on an ideal magnetic circuit of reluctance $\mathcal{R}$ has self inductance $L = N^2/\mathcal{R}$.

6. Consider two coils of self inductances L_1 and L_2, and mutual inductance M_{12}. Show that if these two coils are connected in series, the self inductance of the resulting circuit is either $L_1 + L_2 + 2M_{12}$ or $L_1 + L_2 - 2M_{12}$, according to the manner in which the connection is made. Since L_1, L_2, and M_{12} are defined so as to be positive, and since by the principle of Le Châtelier-Braun the resulting self inductance cannot be negative, show that $M_{12} \leq \frac{1}{2}(L_1+L_2)$. Show that if the two coils of Fig. 24 have the same numbers of turns and there is no flux leakage, then $M_{12} = \frac{1}{2}(L_1+L_2)$. Show that if there is flux leakage, or if numbers of turns are different, then $M_{12} < \frac{1}{2}(L_1+L_2)$.

9. ENERGY OF SELF-INDUCTANCE

Multiply equation (15) by I to obtain the equation

$$IV_t = I^2R + LI\frac{dI}{dt}. \qquad (16)$$

$$\left\{\begin{array}{c}\text{power}\\\text{delivered}\\\text{to circuit}\end{array}\right\} = \left\{\begin{array}{c}\text{power}\\\text{appearing}\\\text{as heat}\end{array}\right\} + \left\{\begin{array}{c}\text{power being}\\\text{stored in}\\\text{circuit}\end{array}\right\}$$

The last term in this equation must represent a rate at which energy is being stored in the circuit, since this amount of power is being delivered to the circuit and is not appearing as heat (or as mechanical work). This energy is of some electromagnetic form, and one usually thinks of it

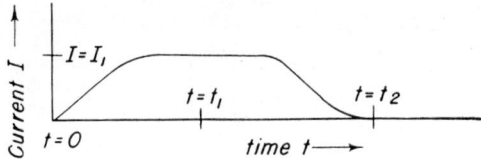

Fig. 27.

as stored in the magnetic field, just as it is possible to think of the energy of a charged condenser as stored in the electric field. Note that energy is being stored in the magnetic field only when the current and hence the magnetic field strength are changing with time.

Now let us consider the energy balance for a current that increases from 0 at $t=0$ to I_1 at $t=t_1$ and back to 0 at $t=t_2$ as in Fig. 27. If we multiply (16) by dt and integrate from $t=0$ to $t=t_1$, we find that

$$\int_0^{t_1} IV_t\, dt = \int_0^{t_1} I^2R\, dt + \int_0^{t_1} LI\frac{dI}{dt}\, dt.$$

The last term has the value

$$\int_0^{t_1} LI\frac{dI}{dt}\, dt = L\int_0^{I_1} I\, dI = \tfrac{1}{2}LI_1^2,$$

so that

$$\int_0^{t_1} IV_t\, dt = \int_0^{t_1} I^2R\, dt + \tfrac{1}{2}LI_1^2. \qquad (17)$$

$$\left\{\begin{array}{c}\text{energy}\\\text{supplied}\\\text{to circuit}\end{array}\right\} = \left\{\begin{array}{c}\text{heat de-}\\\text{veloped}\end{array}\right\} + \left\{\begin{array}{c}\text{energy}\\\text{stored in}\\\text{circuit}\end{array}\right\}$$

The energy supplied to the circuit is greater than the heat developed by $\tfrac{1}{2}LI_1^2$, which represents the energy stored in the magnetic field when

$I = I_1$. Since I_1 is an arbitrary current value, we conclude that at any current I,

$$\text{energy stored in self inductance} = \tfrac{1}{2}LI^2. \quad \begin{cases} \text{energy in joules} \\ L \text{ in henrys} \\ I \text{ in amperes} \end{cases} \quad (18)$$

This energy is recovered when the current drops back to zero, because if we integrate (16) from t_1 to t_2 (Fig. 27), we find that

$$\int_{t_1}^{t_2} IV_t\, dt = \int_{t_1}^{t_2} I^2 R\, dt + \int_{t_1}^{t_2} LI \frac{dI}{dt}\, dt.$$

The last term now has the value

$$\int_{t_1}^{t_2} LI \frac{dI}{dt}\, dt = L \int_{I_1}^{0} I\, dI = -\tfrac{1}{2}LI_1^2,$$

so

$$\int_{t_1}^{t_2} IV_t\, dt = \int_{t_1}^{t_2} I^2 R\, dt - \tfrac{1}{2}LI_1^2. \quad (19)$$

$$\begin{Bmatrix} \text{energy} \\ \text{supplied} \\ \text{to circuit} \end{Bmatrix} = \begin{Bmatrix} \text{heat de-} \\ \text{veloped} \end{Bmatrix} - \begin{Bmatrix} \text{energy that had} \\ \text{previously been} \\ \text{stored in circuit} \end{Bmatrix}$$

In this case the heat developed is greater that the energy supplied to the circuit, the difference being the energy of self inductance that had previously been stored in the circuit.

The fact that energy is stored in a circuit containing self inductance when a current flows is fundamental to a study of oscillating circuits, such as radio oscillators, and to the study of AC circuits.

PROBLEMS

1. How much energy, over and above that expended in heat, is required to set up a current of 15 amp through a coil of self inductance 0.4 henry? Ans: 45.0 joules.

2. How much energy, over and above that expended in heat, is required to set up a magnetic field of 2 weber/m² in the circular pole pieces of diameter 1.1 m of a cyclotron magnet (see Fig. 7, p. 993), if a current of 50 amp in the winding is required, and the winding has a total of 200 turns?

3. In Fig. 26, let $R = 2$ ohms, $L = 1$ henry. Suppose that it is desired to have the current rise from 0 to 5 amp at a uniform rate over an interval of 5 sec, and then decrease to 0 at a uniform rate over the next 5 sec, so that the current curve is given by $I = t$ for t between 0 and 5 sec, and $I = 10 - t$ for t between 5 and 10 sec. Compute the form of the voltage curve V_t that must be applied to the circuit in order to give this type of current variation. Compute each of the terms in equations (17) and (19), with $t_1 = 5$ sec, $t_2 = 10$ sec, and verify the correctness of these equations.
Ans: $V_t = 1 + 2t$ volts from $t = 0$ to 5 sec; $V_t = 19 - 2t$ volts from $t = 5$ to 10 sec.

10. GROWTH AND DECAY OF CURRENT IN INDUCTIVE CIRCUITS*

Self inductance gives every circuit a certain degree of sluggishness in the sense that current changes do not instantaneously follow changes in

* This section may be omitted without loss of continuity.

voltage. Consider the battery of voltage V in Fig. 28, which can be connected to the coil by closing switch S_1. With switch S_1 closed and S_2 open, equation (15) gives

$$V = IR + L\, dI/dt, \qquad (20)$$

which must hold at any instant. The final value of I is V/R, but I cannot suddenly jump to this value when the switch is closed, because a sudden jump in I would represent an infinite rate of change dI/dt which would set up an infinite back-EMF. Rather, at the instant the switch is closed ($t=0$, say), $I=0$, the first term on the right of (20) is zero, and

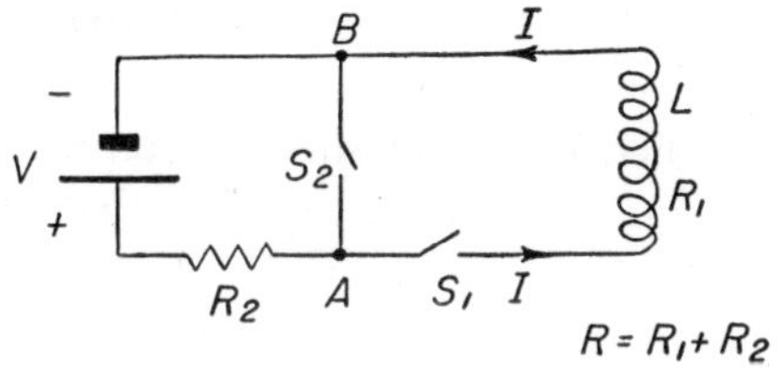

Fig. 28. Switch S_1 is closed to establish current in the coil. Later switch S_2 is closed to short out the coil.

$$V = L\frac{dI}{dt}, \qquad \frac{dI}{dt} = \frac{V}{L}. \qquad (t=0) \quad (21)$$

The larger the value of L, the slower does the current start increasing at the instant of closing the switch. At later instants, the current increases still less rapidly, since as the IR term in (20) grows, the $L\, dI/dt$

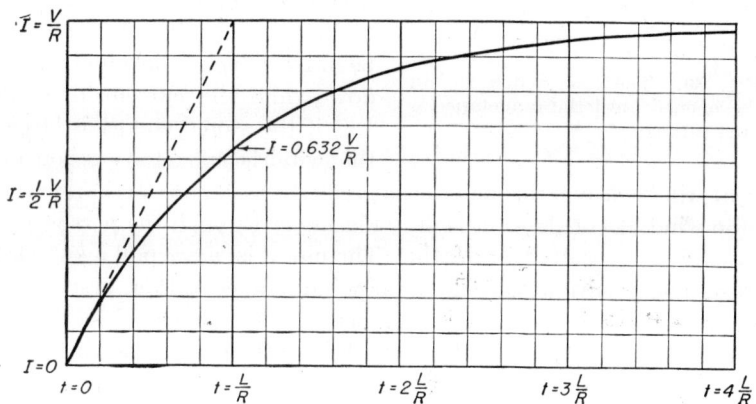

Fig. 29. Growth of current in an inductive circuit.

term must decrease. As I approaches the final value V/R, IR approaches V, so that dI/dt approaches zero, and the current reaches its final value only asymptotically, as in Fig. 29.

As is shown by the broken line in Fig. 29, if the current were to go on increasing at its initial rate $dI/dt = V/L$, in amp/sec, it would take a time L/R, in sec, to reach its final value V/R. The time L/R is known as the *time-constant* of the circuit,

$$\text{time-constant} = \tau = L/R, \qquad (22)$$

since it gives a measure of the order of magnitude of the build-up time.

Actually, the curve of Fig. 29 is

$$I = \frac{V}{R}(1 - e^{-t/\tau}), \qquad (23)$$

with τ defined by (22). It is easily verified by direct substitution that this function satisfies the differential equation (20), and also that it satisfies the conditions that $I=0$ when $t=0$ and $I \to V/R$ as $t \to \infty$. Actually, at $t=\tau$, the current has reached only 63.2% ($=1-e^{-1}$) of its final value. It reaches 95% of its final value at $t=3\,\tau$, 99% at $t=4.6\,\tau$, and 99.9% at $t=6.9\,\tau$.

Now suppose that after a long time, when the current has reached its final value, say

$$I_1 = V/R,$$

we try to interrupt the current by opening the switch S_1 in Fig. 28. The current cannot instantly drop to zero—in fact, any attempt to make the current drop rapidly will set up whatever voltages, enormous if necessary, are required to keep the current flowing until the stored energy $\frac{1}{2}LI_1^2$ is dissipated as heat. Ordinarily, what will happen is that across the terminals of the switch S_1 an arc will be drawn which maintains the current flow while the current dies down. But if the stored energy is large and the switch is pulled too vigorously, the current will flash over through the path of least resistance, perhaps puncturing the windings of the coil itself. Flashover through the person pulling the switch has resulted in death. The moral is, *never* pull a switch that breaks a heavy current through a large inductance; rather, first shunt the inductance through a suitable resistance. In Fig. 30 *first* close the shunting switch S, *then* open the line switch, and the current flowing in L can continue to flow through R' until the stored energy is harmlessly dissipated.

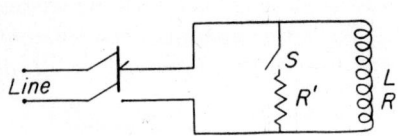

Fig. 30. The line switch should not be opened until the inductance is shunted through R'.

Let us return to Fig. 28, with current I_1 flowing, and see the effect of closing switch S_2. Closing this switch is supposed to introduce a perfect short from A to B, so that the DP across AB becomes 0. The terminal voltage V_t in Fig. 26 and equation (15) now is zero, so that in Fig. 28,

$$0 = IR_1 + L\,dI/dt. \qquad (24)$$

Let us take $t=0$ as the instant of applying the short. At this instant $I = I_1$, and therefore the initial rate of decrease of current is

$$\frac{dI}{dt} = -\frac{R_1}{L}I_1. \qquad (t=0)$$

Again, if the current continued to decrease at this rate, it would drop to zero in a time

$$\tau_1 = L/R_1, \text{ in sec,}$$

which is known as the *time-constant for decay*.

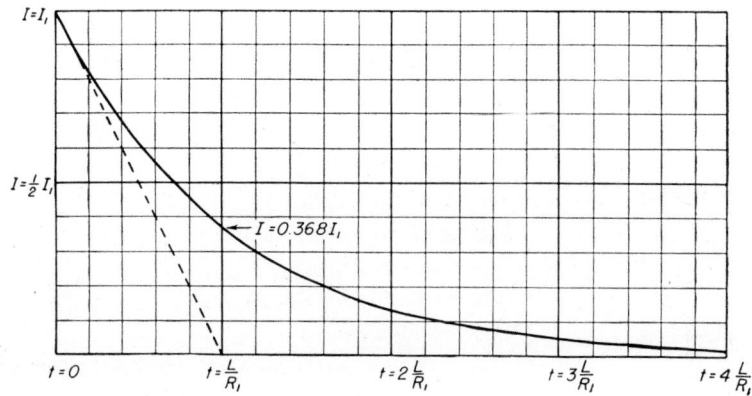

Fig. 31. Decay of current in an inductive circuit.

The actual decay of the current is shown in the curve of Fig. 31, which has the equation

$$I = I_1 e^{-t/\tau_1}. \tag{25}$$

This equation is seen to satisfy the differential equation (24) and the conditions $I = I_1$ when $t = 0$, $I \to 0$ when $t \to \infty$. The curve of Fig. 31 is just the curve of Fig. 29 upside down.

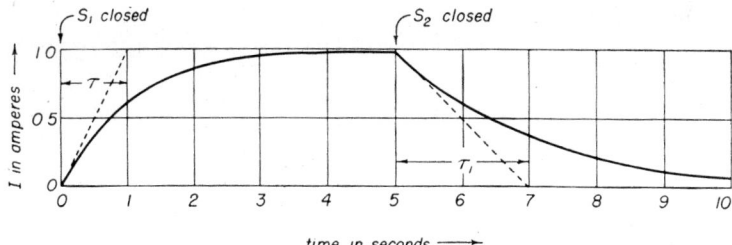

Fig. 32. Growth and decay of current in the inductive circuit of Fig. 28 with $L = 120$ henrys, $R_1 = 60 \, \omega$, $R_2 = 60 \, \omega$, $V = 120$ v.

If, in Fig. 28, $L = 120$ henrys, $R_1 = 60 \, \omega$, $R_2 = 60 \, \omega$, $R = R_1 + R_2 = 120 \, \omega$, and $V = 120$ v, we see that $I_1 = V/R = 1$ amp, $\tau = L/R = 1$ sec, and $\tau_1 = L/R_1 = 2$ sec. If then the switch S_1 is closed at $t = 0$; the shorting switch S_2 closed 5 sec later at $t = 5$ sec, the current builds up with a time constant of 1 sec to 0.99 amp, almost its full value, and decays with a time constant of 2 sec. The curve of current against time is shown in Fig. 32.

PROBLEMS

1. In Fig. 28, if $R_1 = 2$ ohms, $R_2 = 0.5$ ohm, and $L = 0.8$ henry, what is the time constant for current growth? What is the time constant for decay?

Ans: 0.32 sec; 1.6 sec.

2. In Fig. 28, if $R_1 = 50$ ohms, $R_2 = 1$ ohm, and $L = 100$ henrys, what are the time constants for current growth and decay?

3. In Fig. 30 with S closed, show that the current through the inductance decays according to equation (25) when the line switch is pulled, with I_1 equal to the initial current through the coil and $R_1 = R + R'$.

4. Continuing Prob. 3, show that the voltage across the coil, the instant after the line switch is pulled, is $I_1 R'$, and that therefore R' must be chosen small enough that this voltage will not be dangerous or damage the coil.

5. In the above discussion, the time constant L/R has been assigned the dimensions of seconds. Show that this follows from the fundamental MKS dimensions of L and R.

CHAPTER 40

ALTERNATING-CURRENT CIRCUITS

Having studied electromagnetic induction, we are now in a position to determine the current in circuits containing resistance, inductance, and capacitance when alternating voltages are applied. Our study of AC circuits will be applicable not only to ordinary power circuits but also to circuits carrying audio and radio frequencies in connection with telephone, radio, and various other applications of electronics.

1. THE VECTOR DIAGRAM

In simple AC-circuit theory we are concerned entirely with currents and voltages that vary sinusoidally with time at a definite fixed frequency

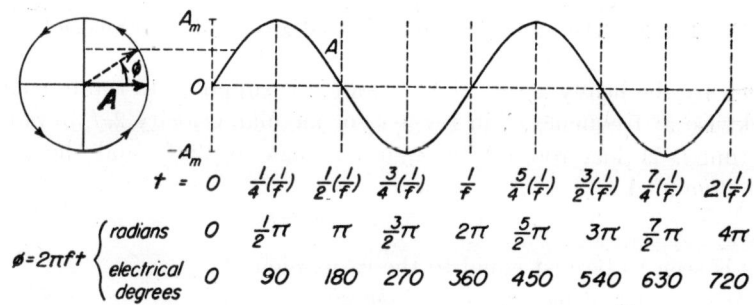

Fig. 1. Representation of the sinusoidally varying quantity in equation (1).

f. For ordinary commercial AC in the United States, the usual value is $f = 60$ sec^{-1}, commonly expressed as $f = 60$ cycles/sec or $f = 60 \sim$. If the function $A(t)$ represents such a current or voltage, it will vary with time according to

$$A(t) = A_m \sin 2\pi f t \qquad (1)$$

where A_m represents the maximum value of A. For $f = 60 \sim$, this expression becomes $A_m \sin 377 t$.*

A plot of the curve (1) is given in Fig. 1. A complete oscillation occurs in the time $1/f$ ($\frac{1}{60}$ sec for $60 \sim$).

---

* The coefficient 377 is actually accurate to about five significant figures because $120 \pi = 376.991$.

In (1), it is customary to think of $2\pi ft$ as an angle in radians, whose sine must be looked up. It is useful to express the equivalent angle in degrees; one speaks in this case of 'electrical degrees.' The various times are expressed in *electrical degrees* as indicated on Fig. 1, and we shall follow the custom of marking the abscissas of our plots only with electrical degrees, the understanding being that these are really plots against time, with the time interval $(1/f)$ representing 360 electrical degrees. This usage is very convenient.

Another useful aid in dealing with such sinusoidally varying quantities as $A(t)$ in (1) is to note that $A(t)$ can be thought of at any instant as the *vertical projection* of the rotating vector A drawn at the left of Fig. 1. The vector A here is drawn of length equal to A_m. A is in the position

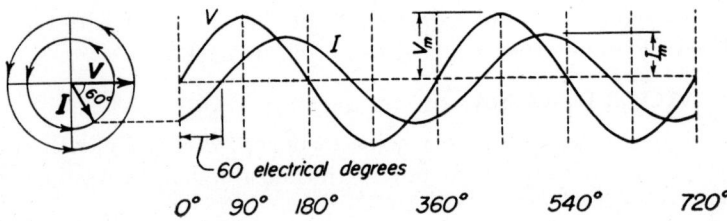

Fig. 2. The current *lags* 60 electrical degrees behind the voltage.

shown by the heavy arrow at $t=0$, and it is supposed to rotate counterclockwise at frequency f, in rev/sec, or angular velocity $2\pi f$, in rad/sec. At time t, A has rotated through an angle $\phi = 2\pi ft$, and the *vertical projection* of A is

$$A_m \sin\phi = A_m \sin 2\pi ft.$$

This is seen to be just equal to the expression (1).

At any instant the ordinate of the sine curve of Fig. 1 is equal to the vertical projection of the rotating vector at the left of Fig. 1.

In AC circuits the sine curves representing current and voltage are ordinarily *out of phase*, and the *phase angle* (in electrical degrees) by which the current leads or lags behind the voltage is an important quantity. Figures 2 and 3 will explain the meanings of the terms used in the preceding sentence. In Fig. 2 are plotted the voltage and current curves:

$$\left. \begin{array}{l} V(t) = V_m \sin 2\pi ft, \\ I(t) = I_m \sin(2\pi ft - \tfrac{1}{3}\pi). \end{array} \right\} \begin{pmatrix} \text{current} \\ \text{lagging} \end{pmatrix}$$

The current is said to *lag behind* the voltage by $\tfrac{1}{3}\pi$ rad, or by a *phase angle* of 60 electrical degrees, because the current reaches its positive maximum $\tfrac{1}{6}$ cycle *later* than the voltage, passes through zero $\tfrac{1}{6}$ cycle *later*, reaches its negative maximum $\tfrac{1}{6}$ cycle *later*, and so on. At the left of Fig. 2 we place, at $t=0$, a vector V like that in Fig. 1 and a vector

I, of length I_m, 60° *behind* V. If we imagine that both these vectors rotate at frequency f, then at any instant the ordinate of the V curve is the vertical projection of the vector V and the ordinate of the I curve is

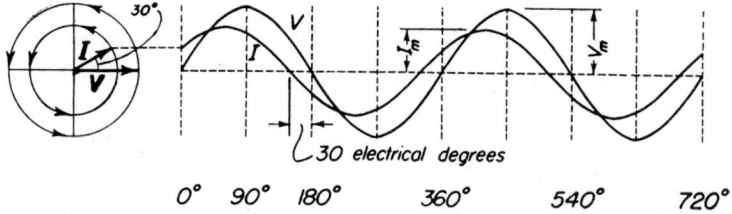

Fig. 3. The current *leads* the voltage by 30 electrical degrees.

the vertical projection of the vector I. Similarly, in Fig. 3 we give plots and vector diagrams of

$$V(t) = V_m \sin 2\pi ft,$$
$$I(t) = I_m \sin(2\pi ft + \tfrac{1}{6}\pi),$$

$$\left.\begin{matrix}\\\\\end{matrix}\right\} \begin{pmatrix}\text{current}\\\text{leading}\end{pmatrix}$$

in which the current *leads* the voltage by $\tfrac{1}{6}\pi$ rad, or by a phase angle of 30 electrical degrees.

The diagrams at the left of Figs. 1, 2, and 3 are known as *vector diagrams*. Properly interpreted, these vector diagrams contain all the information contained in the plots at the right or in the equations of the text, except that the frequency of rotation of the vectors must be specified.

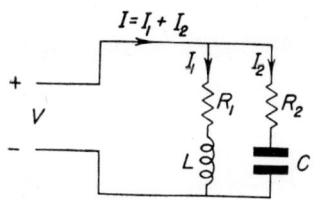

Fig. 4. A parallel AC circuit. The arrows and + and − signs do not give the actual directions of current flow and voltage, which are alternating, but define the directions and polarity for which I_1, I_1, I, and V are to be considered as positive.

Perhaps the greatest advantage of using the vector diagram is that it leads to a very convenient way of carrying out the arithmetic involved in the trigonometric addition of two sinusoidal curves of different amplitudes and different phases. As a concrete example which will come up later, consider the circuit of Fig. 4. Let the alternating voltage be

$$V(t) = 160 \sin 377t \text{ volts}, \qquad (2)$$

corresponding to 60 ~. As we shall see later, the current in an inductive path will in general lag behind the voltage, so let

$$I_1(t) = 3 \sin(377t - \tfrac{1}{6}\pi) \text{ amp}, \qquad (3)$$

corresponding to a phase lag of 30°. Generally, the current in a capacitive path will lead the voltage, so let

$$I_2(t) = 4 \sin(377t + \tfrac{1}{3}\pi) \text{ amp}, \tag{4}$$

corresponding to a lead angle of 60°.

The problem is to find the amplitude and phase of the line current I, which at every instant is the sum of I_1 and I_2:

$$I(t) = I_1(t) + I_2(t).$$

This problem can be solved by pure trigonometry, but it is much more convenient to use an argument from the vector diagram. The student should learn to understand the following procedure thoroughly before proceeding to later sections because we shall frequently omit plotted curves and merely give vector diagrams. He must clearly visualize the meaning of the vector diagram: that the vectors are drawn to represent the situation at a particular instant ($t=0$), that the vectors rotate coun-

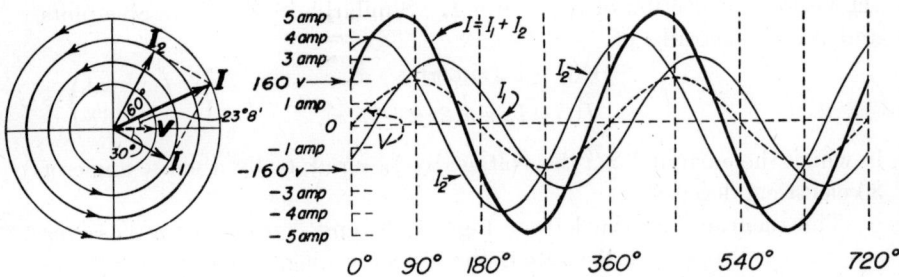

Fig. 5. The sum of two sinusoidal curves of the same frequency is a sinusoidal curve whose representative rotating vector is the vector sum of the representative vectors of the two curves.

terclockwise with frequency f, in rev/sec, and that at any instant the magnitude of each quantity is given by the *vertical projection* of its representative vector.

In Fig. 5 are plotted V, I_1, and I_2 as given by the above equations. The sum I of the curves I_1 and I_2 is also plotted. On the left are shown the positions at $t=0$ of the rotating vectors whose vertical projections give the values of I_1 and I_2. We shall show that *the sum of I_1 and I_2 is represented by a rotating vector **I** that is the vector sum of the rotating vectors I_1 and I_2*. If we consider the vectors $\mathbf{I}_1$, $\mathbf{I}_2$, and $\mathbf{I}$, where

$$\mathbf{I} = \mathbf{I}_1 + \mathbf{I}_2, \tag{5}$$

and if these vectors all rotate together, equation (5) will be true at every instant. Since the vertical projection of the vector sum of two vectors is the sum of their vertical projections, we shall have at every instant

$$I_y = I_{1y} + I_{2y}.$$

But it is just these vertical projections that represent the current values I, I_1, and I_2 at each instant; consequently,

$$I = I_1 + I_2,$$

which proves the statement in italics above.

In our case, then, we find the vector representing I by taking the vector sum of $\boldsymbol{I}_1$ and $\boldsymbol{I}_2$:

$$I_{1x} = 3 \cos 30° = 2.598 \qquad I_{1y} = -3 \sin 30° = -1.500$$
$$I_{2x} = 4 \cos 60° = 2.000 \qquad I_{2y} = 4 \sin 60° = 3.464$$
$$I_x = 4.598 \qquad I_y = 1.964$$

whence, magnitude of $\boldsymbol{I} = 5.000$,

direction of $\boldsymbol{I} = 23°.1$ above x-axis.

If we want to write the equation for I, the magnitude of $\boldsymbol{I}$ appears as the coefficient of the sine, and the angle of $23°.1 = 0.404$ rad appears as a lead angle, so

$$I = 5.000 \sin(377t + 0.404) \text{ amp.} \tag{6}$$

This type of reasoning gives a very simple and straightforward scheme for finding the sum of two sinusoidal curves:

> The rotating vector that represents the sum of two sinusoidal curves is the vector sum of the rotating vectors that represent the two curves individually.

2. CIRCUIT ELEMENTS CONTAINING CAPACITANCE AND RESISTANCE

It is possible for a circuit such as that of Fig. 6 to carry an alternating current. No constant DC could flow in Fig. 6, because charge cannot move through the condenser, but with an alternating current in the lines to the condenser, an alternating charge can pile up on the condenser plates, with the voltage across the plates varying sinusoidally.

Our problem is to find the voltage V required to drive a given alternating current I in the circuit of Fig. 6. This we shall do in two steps, first finding the alternating voltage V_C across the condenser, then the alternating voltage V_R across the resistor. The alternating voltage V will be at any instant the sum

$$V = V_C + V_R.$$

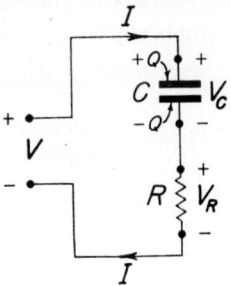

Fig. 6. Circuit containing capacitance and resistance. Arrows and $+$ and $-$ signs define positive senses.

We shall have to tackle the problem of determining V_C in slightly roundabout fashion. Let us suppose that the charge on the condenser varies according to the formula

$$Q = Q_m \sin(2\pi f t - \tfrac{1}{2}\pi),$$

as in Fig. 7. The phase angle is arbitrarily chosen as $-\frac{1}{2}\pi$ here in order to make the subsequent discussion more convenient. Then the voltage V_C across the condenser will be

$$V_C = Q/C = (Q_m/C)\sin(2\pi ft - \tfrac{1}{2}\pi),$$

or, if we write $V_C = V_{Cm}\sin(2\pi ft - \tfrac{1}{2}\pi)$, we have

$$V_{Cm} = Q_m/C$$

as the maximum value of the voltage across the condenser.

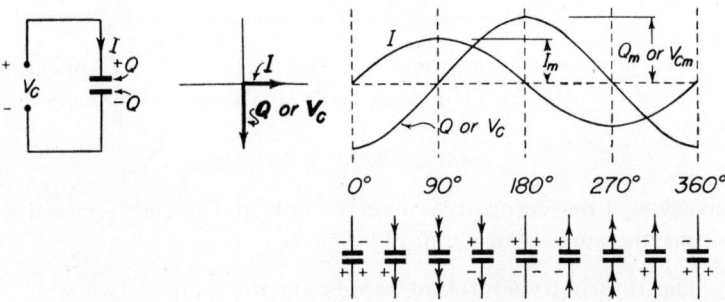

Fig. 7. Current and voltage across a condenser. Note that the circuit diagram on the left merely defines the positive senses of I, Q, and V_C, while the little diagrams below give actual directions of I and signs of Q at various phases.

Now the current I entering the condenser equals the rate dQ/dt at which charge is building up. Therefore,

$$I = dQ/dt = 2\pi f Q_m \cos(2\pi ft - \tfrac{1}{2}\pi) = 2\pi f Q_m \sin 2\pi ft$$

since, by elementary trigonometry, $\cos(2\pi ft - \tfrac{1}{2}\pi) = \sin 2\pi ft$. If we write the above expression as

$$I = I_m \sin 2\pi ft, \tag{7}$$

we have
$$I_m = 2\pi f Q_m = 2\pi f C V_{Cm}. \tag{8}$$

Thus, if the current in Fig. 7 is $I = I_m \sin 2\pi ft$, the voltage across the condenser will be

$$V_C = V_{Cm}\sin(2\pi ft - \tfrac{1}{2}\pi). \tag{9}$$

The current through a condenser leads the voltage across the condenser by 90 electrical degrees.

The relation between I_m and V_{Cm} is given by (8):

$$V_{Cm} = \left(\frac{1}{2\pi fC}\right) I_m. \tag{10}$$

This relation between V_{Cm} and I_m is analogous to Ohm's law. The factor $(1/2\pi fC)$ is called the *capacitive reactance* and is denoted by X_C. If we write

$$X_C = \frac{1}{2\pi fC}, \quad \text{in ohms,} \tag{11}$$

then
$$V_{Cm} = X_C I_m. \tag{12}$$

That it is reasonable for the current to *lead* the voltage by 90° can be seen from the set of little diagrams below the plotted curves in Fig. 7. These diagrams indicate schematically the actual magnitudes and directions of the current and of the charge or voltage at various times. Evidently, the current must be positive during the whole period in which the charge on the upper plate goes from its maximum negative to its maximum positive value. The current is zero when the charge is a maximum because at this instant the charge is not changing. The current reaches its positive maximum 90° before the charge does because it is then that the charge is increasing most rapidly, even though at this instant the charge itself is zero.

Now we can return to Fig. 6 and complete the determination of the relation between current I and voltage V. For current given by (7), the voltage V_C across the condenser will be given by (9) and (12), and the voltage V_R across the resistance will be given by

$$V_R = IR = RI_m \sin 2\pi ft. \tag{13}$$

The maximum voltage across the resistance, V_{Rm}, is given by

$$V_{Rm} = RI_m. \tag{14}$$

At any instant, the line voltage V is

$$V = V_C + V_R.$$

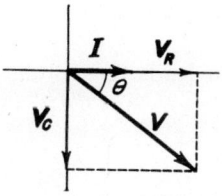

Fig. 8. Vector diagram for the circuit of Fig. 6.

The determination of V involves the addition of two out-of-phase sinusoidal curves for V_C and V_R. This addition is accomplished in the vector diagram of Fig. 8.

Since the length of a voltage vector in a vector diagram is the maximum value of the voltage curve, we see from Fig. 8 that V_m, the maximum value of V, is given by

$$V_m = \sqrt{V_{Cm}^2 + V_{Rm}^2}, \tag{15}$$

and that the angle by which the current I leads the voltage V is

$$\theta = \arctan(V_{Cm}/V_{Rm}). \tag{16}$$

Putting into (15) and (16) the values of V_{Cm} and V_{Rm} given by (12) and (14), we find that

$$V_m = \sqrt{X_C^2 I_m^2 + R^2 I_m^2} = \sqrt{X_C^2 + R^2}\, I_m; \qquad (17)$$

$$\theta = \arctan(X_C/R) = \text{angle of lead}. \qquad (18)$$

It is customary to write
$$V_m = Z I_m, \qquad (19)$$

where Z is known as the *impedance* of the circuit. In this case

$$Z = \sqrt{X_C^2 + R^2}, \quad \text{in ohms}. \qquad (20)$$

The capacitive reactance X_C given by (11) depends inversely on both capacitance C and frequency f. It decreases if C increases or if f increases. For example, the reactance of a 1-μf condenser is

$$\left.\begin{array}{l} X_C = 26{,}500 \text{ ohms} \quad \text{at} \quad 6 \sim, \\ X_C = 2{,}650 \text{ ohms} \quad \text{at} \quad 60 \sim, \\ X_C = 265 \text{ ohms} \quad \text{at} \quad 600 \sim. \end{array}\right\} \qquad (21)$$

A 2-μf condenser would have one-half these reactances.

If a 1-μf condenser is connected in series with $R = 2000$ ohms, the impedance of the circuit, by (20), is

$$\left.\begin{array}{l} Z = 26{,}600 \text{ ohms} \quad \text{at} \quad 6 \sim, \\ Z = 3{,}330 \text{ ohms} \quad \text{at} \quad 60 \sim, \\ Z = 2{,}020 \text{ ohms} \quad \text{at} \quad 600 \sim. \end{array}\right\} \qquad (22)$$

The impedance at $6 \sim$ is almost entirely due to the reactance of the condenser, with $Z \approx X_C$, whereas the impedance at $600 \sim$ is almost entirely due to the resistance, with $Z \approx R$.

From (18), we see that for this example the current leads the voltage by

$$\left.\begin{array}{l} \theta = 86° \quad \text{at} \quad 6 \sim, \\ \theta = 53° \quad \text{at} \quad 60 \sim, \\ \theta = 7°\!.5 \quad \text{at} \quad 600 \sim. \end{array}\right\} \qquad (23)$$

Again, at low frequencies the circuit appears largely capacitive, with lead angle close to 90°, whereas at high frequencies it appears largely resistive, with lead angle close to zero.

As $f \to 0$, $X_C \to \infty$, and $Z \to \infty$. The formulas for an AC circuit reduce to those for a DC circuit as $f \to 0$, and the infinite impedance is consistent with the fact that a circuit containing a condenser will not permit the passage of a direct current.

PROBLEMS

1. (a) What is the reactance of a 1-μf condenser at $6 \sim$? at $60 \sim$? at $600 \sim$?

(b) What is the impedance of a 1-μf condenser in series with a 2000-ω resistor at $6 \sim$? at $60 \sim$? at $600 \sim$?

(c) What is the maximum value of the alternating current that flows through the circuit of (b) when an alternating voltage of 2000 v maximum is applied, with $f = 6 \sim$? $60 \sim$? $600 \sim$?

(d) What is the angle of lead of the current in each case in (c)?

(e) Write the equation of the current in each case in (c), if $V = 2000 \sin 2\pi ft$ volts.
  Ans: (a) see (21); (b) see (22); (c) 0.0752, 0.600, 0.990 amp; (d) see (23);
(e) $I = 0.0752 \sin(37.7t + 1.50)$, $I = 0.600 \sin(377t + 0.925)$, $I = 0.990 \sin(3770t + 0.131)$ amp.

  2. (a) What is the reactance of a 2-$\mu\mu$f condenser at $10^4 \sim$? at $10^5 \sim$? $10^6 \sim$?
  (b) What is the impedance of a 2-$\mu\mu$f condenser in series with a 1-megohm resistor, at $10^4 \sim$? at $10^5 \sim$? at $10^6 \sim$?
  (c) What is the maximum value (in microamperes) of the alternating current that flows through the circuit of (b) when an alternating voltage of 150 v maximum is applied, with $f = 10^4 \sim$? $10^5 \sim$? $10^6 \sim$?
  (d) What is the angle of lead of the current in each case in (c)?
  (e) Write the equation of the current in each case in (c) if $V = 150 \sin 2\pi ft$ volts.

  3. Consider a 1-μf condenser in series with a 10-ohm resistance. Compute the reactance Z at $f = 10^2$, 10^3, 10^4, 10^5, and 10^6 cycles/sec. At each frequency compute the current maximum I_m for an impressed voltage with $V_m = 1$ volt. Compute also the angle of lead, θ, at each frequency. Plot I_m in milliamperes and θ in degrees against frequency, using a logarithmic scale for frequency. (Either use semi-log paper or plot against $\log_{10} f$.) Compute additional values at intermediate frequencies if necessary to get a good curve. Note that this combination acts like a crude 'high-pass filter,' passing relatively small currents for low-frequency voltages but passing currents of 100 milliampere per volt of high-frequency voltage. What is the 'cutoff frequency,' if this is arbitrarily defined as the frequency at which the current is just 50 milliamp/volt—half its high-frequency value?
  Ans: $Z = 1590$, 160, 18.8, 10.1, 10.0 ω; $I_m = 0.628$, 6.27, 53.2, 98.8, 100 mamp; $\theta = 89°.6$, $86°.4$, $57°.9$, $9°.0$, $0°.9$; cutoff frequency $= 9190 \sim$.

3. CIRCUIT ELEMENTS CONTAINING INDUCTANCE AND RESISTANCE

Let us now consider the circuit element of Fig. 9, containing self inductance L henrys and resistance R ohms. R is the total resistance,

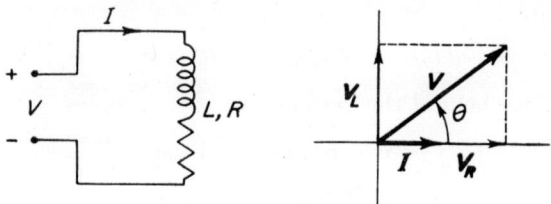

Fig. 9. Circuit containing inductance and resistance.

including the resistance of the coil and any external resistance that may be in series with the coil.

According to the fundamental equation (15), p. 1026, we must have at every instant
$$V = IR + L(dI/dt). \tag{24}$$

It will be convenient to consider the two terms on the right of this equation separately, defining
$$\left. \begin{array}{c} V = V_R + V_L, \\ V_R = IR, \quad V_L = L(dI/dt). \end{array} \right\} \tag{25}$$
where

Let us suppose that the current varies sinusoidally as in (7):

$$I = I_m \sin 2\pi ft. \tag{26}$$

This current is represented by the vector $\boldsymbol{I}$ in Fig. 9.

Then $\qquad V_R = IR = RI_m \sin 2\pi ft;$

or $\qquad V_R = V_{Rm} \sin 2\pi ft,$

with $\qquad V_{Rm} = RI_m. \tag{27}$

Here V_{Rm} is the maximum value of V_R. Note that V_R is in phase with I.

Also, $\quad V_L = L(dI/dt) = (2\pi fL)I_m \cos 2\pi ft = (2\pi fL)I_m \sin(2\pi ft + \tfrac{1}{2}\pi);$

or $\qquad V_L = V_{Lm} \sin(2\pi ft + \tfrac{1}{2}\pi), \tag{28}$

with $\qquad V_{Lm} = (2\pi fL)I_m = X_L I_m \tag{29}$

as the maximum value of V_L. We define the *inductive reactance* by

$$X_L = 2\pi fL, \quad \text{in ohms}, \tag{30}$$

so that $V_{Lm} = X_L I_m$. The voltage V_L leads the current by 90° and so is represented by the vector $\boldsymbol{V}_L$ drawn in Fig. 9, 90° ahead of the current, and of length $V_{Lm} = X_L I_m$.

In accordance with (25), V is represented by the vector sum of $\boldsymbol{V}_R$ and $\boldsymbol{V}_L$. Hence, we have

$$V_m = \sqrt{V_{Lm}^2 + V_{Rm}^2} = \sqrt{X_L^2 I_m^2 + R^2 I_m^2} = \sqrt{X_L^2 + R^2}\, I_m.$$

Again we write $\qquad V_m = ZI_m, \tag{31}$

where Z is the *impedance:* $\quad Z = \sqrt{X_L^2 + R^2}. \tag{32}$

The current lags behind the voltage by

$$\theta = \arctan(V_{Lm}/V_{Rm}),$$

or $\qquad \theta = \arctan(X_L/R). \tag{33}$

It is not hard to see why V_L, the out-of-phase component of the voltage, should lead the current by 90°. This component is the part $L(dI/dt)$ of the voltage required to overcome the EMF of self inductance. At $t=0$, the current is zero but is increasing at its maximum rate. Hence, we need the maximum positive value of V_L to overcome the back-EMF that tends to prevent this current increase. One quarter cycle (90°) later, the current has reached its maximum value but is no longer changing, so that V_L is zero. Thus, V_L has its maximum 90° ahead of the current maximum.

From (30), (32,) and (33), we see that as $f \rightarrow 0$, $X_L \rightarrow 0$, $Z \rightarrow R$, $\theta \rightarrow 0$, consistent with the fact that self inductance has no effect on the flow of a steady direct current. On the other hand X_L increases in pro-

INDUCTANCE AND RESISTANCE

portion to the frequency, so that a coil of large self inductance can be used as a 'choke coil' to prevent the passage of AC, because of its large reactance, but permit the passage of DC; or it can be used to choke off high-frequency AC and permit the passage of low-frequency AC. One scheme of ringing telephone bells on a two-party line has an appropriate condenser in series with the bell in one phone and a choke coil in series in the other phone. To ring one phone an AC voltage is used, which passes current through the condenser but very little current through the choke coil. To ring the other bell, a DC voltage is used, which will not pass current through the condenser but will pass current readily through the choke coil.

Let us consider a coil of inductance 1 henry and resistance 377 ohms. This has

$$\left. \begin{array}{lll} X_L = \ 38 \text{ ohms}, & Z = \ 379 \text{ ohms}, & \text{at} \quad 6 \sim, \\ X_L = \ 377 \text{ ohms}, & Z = \ 534 \text{ ohms}, & \text{at} \ 60 \sim, \\ X_L = 3770 \text{ ohms}, & Z = 3790 \text{ ohms}, & \text{at} \ 600 \sim. \end{array} \right\} \quad (34)$$

The corresponding angles by which the current lags behind the voltage are, from (33),

$$\left. \begin{array}{l} \theta = \ 6° \quad \text{at} \quad 6 \sim \\ \theta = 45° \quad \text{at} \ 60 \sim \\ \theta = 84° \quad \text{at} \ 600 \sim. \end{array} \right\} \quad (35)$$

This angle approaches zero as the frequency goes down and approaches 90° as the frequency goes up.

PROBLEMS

1. (a) What is the inductive reactance of a 1-henry coil of 377-ohm resistance at 6 $\sim$? at 60 $\sim$? at 600 $\sim$?
(b) What is the impedance of this coil at 6 $\sim$? at 60 $\sim$? at 600 $\sim$?
(c) What is the maximum value of the alternating voltage required to send current $I = 0.1 \sin 2\pi ft$ amp through this coil, for $f = 6 \sim$? for $f = 60 \sim$? for $f = 600 \sim$?
(d) What is the angle of lag of the current in each case in (c)?
(e) Write the equation for the voltage in each case in (c).
Ans: (a), (b) see (34); (c) 37.9, 53.4, 379 volts; (d) see (35); (e) $V = 37.9 \sin(37.7t + 0.105)$, $V = 53.4 \sin(377t + 0.785)$, $V = 379 \sin(3770t + 1.47)$.

2. (a) What is the inductive reactance of a 1-millihenry coil of 1-megohm resistance, at $10^7 \sim$? at $10^8 \sim$? at $10^9 \sim$?
(b) What is the impedance of this coil at these frequencies?
(c) What is the maximum value (in microamperes) of the alternating current that flows through this coil when an alternating voltage of 150 v maximum is applied, at $10^7 \sim$? at $10^8 \sim$? at $10^9 \sim$?
(d) What is the angle of lag of the current in each case in (c)?
(e) Write the equation of the current in each case in (c) if $V = 150 \sin 2\pi ft$ volts.

3. A circuit containing a 15-μf condenser and a 10-ohm resistance is connected across a pair of lines. In parallel with this circuit, across the same pair of lines, is a circuit containing a coil of 0.1-henry inductance and 24-ohm resistance.

(a) How much current flows through each of these parallel circuits when 24 v DC is applied to the lines?

(b) What is the maximum value of the current that flows through each of these parallel circuits when AC of 24 v maximum, at 500 $\sim$, is applied to the lines?

Ans: (a) 0, 1 amp; (b) 1.02, 0.076 amp.

4. Two circuits are in parallel across a pair of leads in a radio set. One circuit has capacitance 0.1 μf and resistance 50,000 ohms; the other has inductance 5 henrys and resistance 35 ohms. The first circuit is designed to 'pass' both audio and radio frequency, the second circuit to 'choke out' radio frequency.

(a) If an audio-frequency signal of 50 v maximum at 1000 $\sim$ is impressed, what is the maximum current in microamperes that flows in each of the two circuits?

(b) If a radio-frequency signal of 50 v maximum at 1000 kilocycles/sec is impressed, what is the maximum current in microamperes that flows in each of the two circuits?

5. Consider a 1-millihenry inductance with 50 ohms of resistance. Compute the reactance Z at $f = 10^2$, 10^3, 10^4, 10^5, and 10^6 $\sim$. At each frequency compute the current maximum I_m for an impressed voltage with $V_m = 1$ v. Compute also the angle of lag, θ, at each frequency. Plot I_m in milliamperes and θ in degrees against frequency, using a logarithmic scale for frequency. (Either use semilog paper or plot against $\log_{10} f$.) Compute additional values at intermediate frequencies if necessary to get a good curve. Note that this circuit acts like a crude 'low-pass filter,' passing relatively small currents for high-frequency voltages but passing currents of 20 milliamperes per volt of low-frequency voltage. What is the 'cutoff frequency,' if this is arbitrarily defined as the frequency at which the current is just 10 milliamperes per volt—half its low-frequency value?

Ans: $Z = 50.0$, 50.4, 80.3, 630, 6280 ω; $I_m = 20.0$, 19.8, 12.5, 1.59, 0.159 mamp; $\theta = 0°.7$, 7°.2, 51°.5, 85°.5, 89°.5; cutoff frequency $= 1.38 \times 10^4$ $\sim$.

6. A coil having an inductance of 1.5 henrys and a resistance of 150 ohms is in series with a resistor of 900 ohms. A 60-$\sim$ voltage of 500 v maximum is applied to the combination.

(a) What current flows and what is its angle of lag?

(b) What is the voltage across the coil, and by what angle does it lead the current?

(c) What is the voltage across the resistor, and by what angle does it lead the current?

(d) Show current, coil voltage, resistor voltage, and total voltage on a single vector diagram.

7. A coil having an inductance of 0.6 henry and a resistance of 50 ohms is in series with a resistor of 300 ohms. A 60-$\sim$ voltage of 160 v maximum is applied to the combination.

(a) What current flows and what is its angle of lag?

(b) What is the voltage across the coil, and by what angle does it lead the current?

(c) What is the voltage across the resistor, and by what angle does it lead the current?

(d) Show current, coil voltage, resistor voltage, and total voltage on a single vector diagram.

Ans: (a) 0.384 amp max, 32°.9; (b) 88.9 v max, 77°.5; (c) 115 v max, 0°.

4. SERIES CIRCUITS CONTAINING RESISTANCE, INDUCTANCE, AND CAPACITANCE; SERIES RESONANCE

We are now in a position to consider the general series circuit of Fig. 10. For a given current I of maximum value I_m and frequency f, the required voltage V will be the sum of three parts:

$$V = V_R + V_L + V_C. \qquad (36)$$

The voltage V_R is in phase with the current and has a maximum value given by
$$V_{Rm} = RI_m.$$

The voltage V_L, necessary to overcome the self inductance, is 90° ahead of the current and has a maximum value given by
$$V_{Lm} = X_L I_m = 2\pi fL\, I_m.$$

The voltage V_C across the condenser is 90° behind the current and has a maximum value given by
$$V_{Cm} = X_C I_m = \left(\frac{1}{2\pi fC}\right) I_m.$$

These three sinusoidal voltages can be added by adding the rotating vectors at the right of Fig. 10. Two cases arise, according to whether $X_L > X_C$ or $X_C > X_L$. In the first case we have $V_{Lm} > V_{Cm}$ and the vector

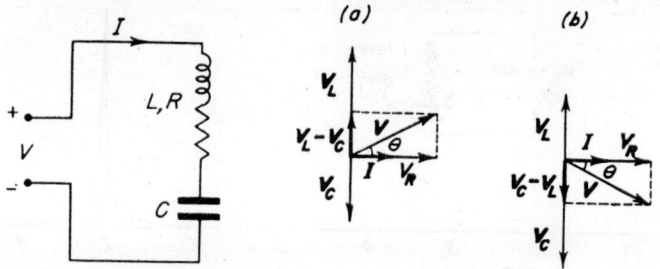

Fig. 10. The general series circuit.
(a) Vector diagram for circuit predominantly inductive, $V_{Lm} > V_{Cm}$; current lags behind voltage.
(b) Vector diagram for circuit predominantly capacitive $V_{Cm} > V_{Lm}$; current leads voltage.

diagram (a) of Fig. 10, with current lagging behind voltage (**V** ahead of **I**), applies; in this case the inductance is said to predominate. In the second case $V_{Cm} > V_{Lm}$ as in (b), with current leading voltage (**V** behind **I**); capacitance is said to predominate.

In either case we see from Fig. 10 that
$$V_m = \sqrt{V_{Rm}^2 + (V_{Lm} - V_{Cm})^2} = \sqrt{R^2 I_m^2 + (X_L I_m - X_C I_m)^2}$$
or
$$V_m = \sqrt{R^2 + (X_L - X_C)^2}\, I_m.$$

If we write
$$V_m = Z I_m, \tag{37}$$

where Z is the *impedance* of the circuit, we have
$$Z = \sqrt{R^2 + (X_L - X_C)^2} = \sqrt{R^2 + \left(2\pi fL - \frac{1}{2\pi fC}\right)^2}. \tag{38}$$

Also from Fig. 10, we see that

if $X_L > X_C$, current *lags* by angle $\quad \theta = \arctan \dfrac{V_{Lm} - V_{Cm}}{V_{Rm}} = \arctan \dfrac{X_L - X_C}{R};$

if $X_C > X_L$, current *leads* by angle $\quad \theta = \arctan \dfrac{V_{Cm} - V_{Lm}}{V_{Rm}} = \arctan \dfrac{X_C - X_L}{R}.$ $\quad$ (39)

In deriving these formulas, we have assumed a value for the current and derived the required voltage. The more usual application occurs the other way around; given V_m, we wish to find I_m and the phase of the current relative to the voltage. I_m is found by dividing V_m by Z, in accordance with (37) and the phase is found from (39).

The series circuit is said to be *resonant* if $X_L = X_C$. The reason for the word *resonant* will be explained in the next section. We shall see here that the resonance condition $X_L = X_C$ occupies a distinctive position with regard to voltage and current relationships.

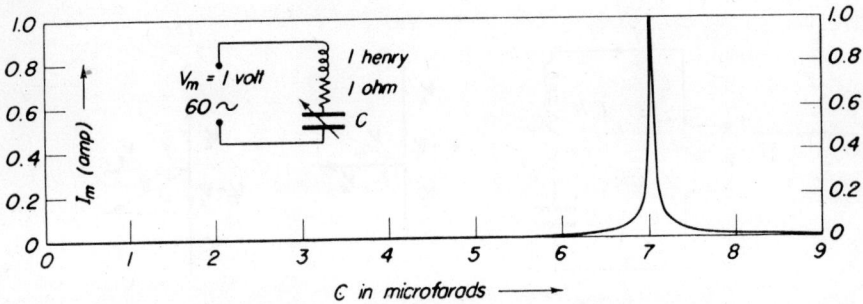

Fig. 11. Current in a series circuit as a function of capacitance, illustrating series resonance at the value of C that makes $X_C = X_L$.

First we note that *in the case of resonance, the current is in phase with the voltage, and $Z = R$, so that at the terminals the circuit behaves exactly as if it had no capacitance or inductance, but merely a pure resistance R.*

The other distinctive properties of the resonant condition can best be illustrated by a specific example. Let us consider the circuit of Fig. 10 with fixed values

$$f = 60 \sim, \quad V_m = 1 \text{ volt}, \quad R = 1 \text{ ohm}, \quad L = 1 \text{ henry}, \quad X_L = 377 \text{ ohms},$$

but with variable capacitance C. Let us compute the current I_m in amperes as a function of the capacitance C in microfarads. The results of this straightforward computation are plotted in Fig. 11. The value of C for resonance is given by the following computation:

$$X_C = X_L, \quad \frac{1}{377C} = 377, \quad C = \frac{1}{(377)^2} = 7.04 \times 10^{-6} \text{ f} = 7.04 \text{ μf}.$$

We notice that in the immediate neighborhood of resonance the current is very large compared with the current for values of C away from resonance, because the impedance Z has its minimum value R at resonance and increases rapidly as the term $X_L - X_C$ in (38) departs from zero either positively or negatively. The sharpness of the peak of a curve such as Fig. 11 depends on the relative values of R and X_L—the smaller the ratio R/X_L, the sharper the peak.

The phenomenon we have just been discussing is familiar to everyone in the tuning of the antenna circuit of a radio to an impressed voltage of a given frequency arising from the radio waves broadcast by a given station. The capacitance of a variable condenser is adjusted until maximum current flows in the antenna circuit. Of course with radio

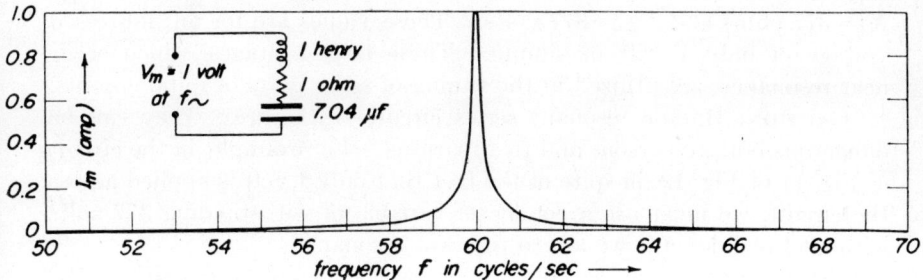

Fig. 12. Current in a series circuit as a function of frequency, illustrating series resonance at the frequency that makes $X_C = X_L$.

frequencies, which are of the order of 100–1000 kilocycles/second, very much smaller inductances and capacitances are used than those we have been discussing in connection with 60-$\sim$ frequency, since L and C enter all formulas in terms $2\pi fL$ and $2\pi fC$.

To see how the antenna circuit of a radio discriminates between stations of different frequency, it is interesting to plot a curve for a circuit like that of Fig. 11, except that C is fixed and f varied. We shall keep to the region of commercial AC frequencies, leaving the discussion of radio frequencies to the problems at the end of this section.

Let us fix C at 7.04 μf, L at 1 henry, R at 1 ohm. These values give resonance at 60 $\sim$. Now let us consider the current when an AC voltage with $V_m = 1$ volt is applied, for various values of the frequency $f \sim$ of the applied voltage.

The equation (38) for impedance becomes

$$Z = \sqrt{1 + \left(6.28f - \frac{22{,}600}{f}\right)^2} \text{ ohms.}$$

This impedance has its minimum value when the parenthesis vanishes, at $f = 60.0$. At this frequency, $Z = 1$ ohm and $I_m = V_m/Z = 1$ amp. At any other frequency, Z is greater than 1 ohm and I is less than 1 amp. Figure 12 shows the curve of I_m as a function of f for a frequency range from 50 to 70 cycles/sec, in the neighborhood of the resonance at 60 $\sim$. This plot also shows a sharp resonance.* In connection with the tuned antenna circuits we were discussing above, the same argument shows that if the circuit is tuned to a station of one frequency, the response to stations of other frequencies is greatly attenuated.

Near resonance, the voltage across part of a series circuit can become very much larger than the line voltage because, in the vector diagram of Fig. 10, if the vectors $\boldsymbol{V}_L$ and $\boldsymbol{V}_C$ are approximately equal in length, they can both be very much larger than the line voltage $\boldsymbol{V}$. To illustrate this point, consider the circuit of Fig. 11 or Fig. 12 at resonance, when $I_m = 1$ amp. Then $X_C = 377$ ohms, so that $V_{Cm} = X_C I_m = 377$ volts. Also, $X_L = 377$ ohms and $V_{Lm} = 377$ volts. These values are for an impressed voltage of only 1 volt maximum. These large voltages, which occur near resonance, are utilized in the tuning of some parts of radio circuits.

CAUTION: Handle resonant series circuits with care. They can be dangerous both to persons and to apparatus. For example, in the circuit of Fig. 11 or Fig. 12, in spite of the fact that only 1 volt is applied across the circuit, we must use a condenser capable of withstanding 377 volts without breakdown if we are to tune for resonance.

Any problem involving voltages across portions of AC circuits can be readily solved by computing V_{Rm}, V_{Lm}, and V_{Cm} from I_m, R, X_L, and X_C and combining these voltages by the vector diagram. A number of problems of this type are given below.

PROBLEMS

1. Consider the circuit of Fig. 10, with $X_L = 3$ ohms, $X_C = 1.5$ ohms, and $R = 0.8$ ohm. Compute I_m for $V_m = 24$ volts, and compute the angle of lag or lead.

Ans: 14.1 amp; current lags by $61°.9$.

2. Consider the circuit of Fig. 10, with $X_L = 3$ ohms, $X_C = 4.5$ ohms, and $R = 2.4$ ohms. Compute I_m for $V_m = 24$ volts, and compute the angle of lag or lead.

3. An inductor (a coil having self inductance and resistance), a resistor, and a capacitor (a condenser) are in series. The inductor has self inductance of 0.5 henry

---

* It is convenient to have a quantitative measure of the sharpness of the resonance peak. A quantity called the 'Q' of the circuit is generally used. This quantity is defined as $Q = 2\pi f_r L/R$, where f_r is the resonance frequency; hence $Q = X_L/R$ at resonance frequency. Let Δf represent the departure from resonance frequency at which the current has dropped to half its resonance value. In a plot such as Fig. 12, Δf is called the 'half-width of the peak at half maximum,' and in Fig. 12, the current would be 0.5 amp at $f = f_r \pm \Delta f$. It can be shown that when $Q \gg 1$, $f_r/\Delta f = (2/\sqrt{3}) Q = Q/0.866$; $\Delta f = 0.866\, f_r/Q$. For a given circuit, Q is a dimensionless constant. The higher the value of Q, the narrower is the resonance peak in comparison with the resonance frequency itself, and the 'sharper' the 'tuning.' For the circuit of Fig. 12, $Q = 377$ and $\Delta f = 0.866 \times 60/377 = 0.14 \sim$, so the current has dropped to half maximum at 60.14 $\sim$ and 59.86 $\sim$.

Sec. 4] RESISTANCE, INDUCTANCE, AND CAPACITANCE 1049

and resistance of 100 ohms. The resistor has 80 ohms of resistance and the capacitor has 8 μf of capacitance. An applied 60-∼ voltage causes 1 amp maximum to flow through the series circuit.

(a) Compute the total impedance Z.

(b) From Z and the current, compute the maximum total voltage, V_m, required, and the phase angle between the voltage and the current.

(c) Compute the maximum, V_{im}, of the voltage across the terminals of the inductor; the maximum V_{rm} of that across the terminals of the resistor; and the maximum V_{Cm} of that across the terminals of the capacitor. In each case obtain the phase angle between these voltages and the current.

(d) Plot the three voltages V_i, V_r, and V_C on a vector diagram. Add these vectorially to obtain the total voltage vector V, and check the agreement of this voltage in magnitude and phase with the result obtained in (b).

Ans: (a) 230 ω; (b) 230 v, 38°.5 behind current; (c) V_{im} = 213 v, 62°.1 ahead of current; V_{rm} = 80 v, in phase with current; V_{Cm} = 332 v, 90° behind current.

4. Repeat Prob. 3 for the case where the inductor has 5 millihenrys of self inductance and 9 ohms of resistance, the resistor has 8 ohms of resistance, the capacitor has 40 μf of capacitance, and an applied 500-∼ voltage causes 1 amp maximum to flow.

5. What is the resonant frequency for the series circuit of Prob. 3? What voltage is required to cause 1 amp maximum to flow at the resonant frequency?

Ans: 79.6 ∼; 180 v.

6. What is the resonant frequency for the series circuit of Prob. 4? What voltage is required to cause 1 amp maximum to flow at the resonant frequency?

7. In the circuit of Fig. 12, if the capacitance and resistance are fixed at 7.04 μf and 1 ohm, but the self inductance is adjustable, what value of self inductance will bring the circuit into resonance for a 50-∼ applied voltage? Ans: 1.44 henry.

8. In the circuit of Fig. 12, if the capacitance and resistance are fixed at 7.04 μf and 1 ohm but the self inductance is adjustable, what value of self inductance will bring the circuit into resonance for a 70-∼ applied voltage?

9. Consider the circuit of Fig. 11, with $C = 7.5$ μf.

(a) Compute X_L, X_C, and Z; is the circuit inductive or capacitive?

(b) Compute I_m and the angle by which the current lags or leads.

(c) Assuming that the 1-ohm resistance is all contained in the coil winding, find the maximum voltage V_{im} across the terminals of the inductor. Find the angle by which this voltage leads the current.

(d) Find the maximum voltage V_{Cm} across the terminals of the condenser and the angle by which this voltage lags behind the current.

(e) Make a single vector diagram showing I, V, V_i, and V_C, together with the magnitudes of all angles between them. Ans: (a) 377, 354, 23.4 ω; inductive; (b) 0.0428 amp, 87°.5 lag; (c) 16.1 v, 89°.8; (d) 15.1 v, 90°.

10. Consider the circuit of Fig. 11, with $C = 6.5$ μf, and answer the same questions as in Prob. 9.

11. Consider the circuit of Fig. 11, with C exactly 7 μf, and answer the same questions as in Prob. 9. Ans: (a) 377, 379, 2.19 ohms; capacitive; (b) 0.456 amp, 62°.8 lead; (c) 172 v, 89°.8; (d) 173 v, 90°.

12. Show that the curve of Fig. 11 applies to a radio antenna circuit if we let the ordinates represent microamperes instead of amperes, the abscissas μμf instead of μf, and change L to 10 millihenrys, R to 100 ohms, V_m to 0.1 millivolt, and f to 600 kilocycles/sec.

13. Show that the curve of Fig. 12 applies to a radio antenna circuit if we let the ordinates represent microamperes instead of amperes, the abscissas kilocycles/sec instead of cycles/sec, leave L at 1 henry, and change R to 1000 ohms, C to 7.04 μμf, and V_m to 1 millivolt.

5. POWER IN SERIES CIRCUITS; EFFECTIVE VALUES OF VOLTAGE AND CURRENT

Let us start by considering an alternating current

$$I = I_m \sin 2\pi ft$$

flowing in a pure resistance R. At any instant the voltage across the resistance will be

$$V_R = R\,I = R\,I_m \sin 2\pi ft = V_{Rm} \sin 2\pi ft,$$

with $V_{Rm} = R\,I_m$. At any instant, the rate at which energy is being supplied to the resistance, which in turn is the rate at which heat is being developed, is the product of the two expressions above:

$$V_R\,I = V_{Rm}\,I_m \sin^2 2\pi ft, \tag{40}$$

a quantity which is never negative.

Since (40) represents instantaneous power, we can get the whole amount of energy supplied during one cycle by multiplying (40) by dt and integrating from $t=0$ to $t=1/f$, which is the time occupied by one cycle. This gives

$$\text{energy per cycle} = \int_0^{1/f} V_{Rm}\,I_m \sin^2 2\pi ft\, dt = V_{Rm}\,I_m \int_0^{1/f} \sin^2 2\pi ft\, dt$$

$$= \frac{V_{Rm}\,I_m}{2f}, \tag{41}$$

as may readily be verified by calculus formulas. The whole energy supplied per second, which we call the *power* and denote by P, is then obtained by multiplying (41) by f, the number of cycles per second. This operation gives

$$P = \frac{V_{Rm}\,I_m}{2} = \frac{I_m^2\,R}{2} = \frac{V_{Rm}^2}{2R}. \tag{42}$$

Note that the power does not come smoothly but in $2f$ spurts per second, as indicated by (40); P in (42) represents a time-average power.

The occurrence of the 2 in the denominator of (42) makes these formulas look different from the corresponding DC formulas. To make the AC power formulas similar in form to the DC, it is customary in specifying AC voltages or currents to give so-called *effective* values rather than maximum values.

Effective voltage V_0 and effective current I_0 are defined by

$$V_0 = \frac{V_m}{\sqrt{2}}, \qquad I_0 = \frac{I_m}{\sqrt{2}}, \tag{43}$$

for any AC voltage or current.

In our particular case, $V_{R0} = V_{Rm}/\sqrt{2}$. The $\sqrt{2}$ is introduced into these

POWER IN SERIES CIRCUITS

definitions so that the power formulas (42) become

$$P = V_{R0} I_0 = I_0^2 R = V_{R0}^2 / R, \tag{44}$$

exactly the form of the DC formulas.

When AC voltages and currents are specified without qualification, it is always effective values that are implied. Thus, when we say that the power company supplies 120 volts AC, we always mean 120 volts effective: $V_0 = 120$ volts; $V_m = 120\sqrt{2}$ volts = 170 volts. Hence, a 120-volt, 60-$\sim$ power circuit has instantaneous voltage

$$V = 170 \sin 377t.$$

The fact that the maximum voltage is 170 shows why a 120-volt AC circuit is more dangerous and will give a greater shock than a 120-volt DC circuit; it will send a greater maximum current through the body.

The formula $V_{Rm} = R I_m$ becomes $V_{R0}/\sqrt{2} = R I_0/\sqrt{2}$, or simply

$$V_{R0} = R I_0. \tag{45}$$

Hence, a 40-watt, 120-volt lamp bulb, which has a resistance of 360 ohms, will draw ⅓ amp DC on 120 volts DC or ⅓ amp *effective* AC on 120 volts *effective* AC, taking 40 watts of power in either case. By using effective values in the AC case, we make the ratings of purely resistive circuits, such as lamp bulbs, completely interchangeable between DC and AC.

From now on, we shall usually employ effective values in place of maximum values. In accordance with (43), all our previous formulas can be expressed in terms of effective values by the substitution

$$V_m = \sqrt{2}\, V_0, \qquad I_m = \sqrt{2}\, I_0,$$

for all AC voltages and currents. The equation $V_m = Z I_m$ becomes just

$$V_0 = Z I_0,$$

so that the impedance we have derived can be used to compute effective voltages and currents directly. Furthermore, we can plot vector diagrams in which the lengths of the vectors are effective rather than maximum values. These diagrams are identical with those we have previously plotted except that they are geometrically reduced in the ratio $1/\sqrt{2}$. The process of vector addition is unchanged if effective rather than maximum values are used throughout. This is common electrical-engineering practice.

For the general circuit of Fig. 10, power considerations are somewhat more involved. The instantaneous power supplied by the line is IV, where

$$I = \sqrt{2}\, I_0 \sin 2\pi f t,$$
$$V = \sqrt{2}\, V_0 \sin(2\pi f t \pm \theta). \qquad \left\{ \begin{matrix} \text{inductive} \\ \text{capacitive} \end{matrix} \right\}$$

The curve IV is shown in Fig. 13 for the particular case of an inductive circuit with $\theta = \frac{1}{3}\pi$ or 60 electrical degrees. We note that part of the time IV is negative, indicating that during these periods of time (cross hatching in Fig. 13) *energy is being delivered to the line* rather than being received from it. The same phenomenon occurs in a capacitive circuit with current leading. In each case during part of the cycle energy that has previously been stored in the inductance or capacitance is being delivered back to the line.

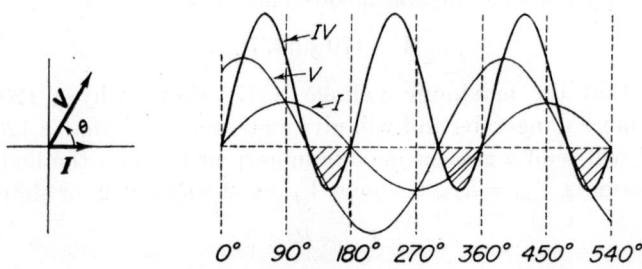

Fig. 13. The product IV of two sinusoidal curves. This is itself a sinusoidal curve of double frequency with axis of ordinates displaced.

We can integrate the curve IV by straightforward trigonometry and calculus to obtain the average power, but it is easier and more instructive to do the computation as follows: Write

$$V = V_R + V_L + V_C$$

as in (36). Then $\qquad VI = V_R I + V_L I + V_C I,$

and the energy supplied in one cycle is

$$\int_0^{1/f} VI\,dt = \int_0^{1/f} V_R I\,dt + \int_0^{1/f} V_L I\,dt + \int_0^{1/f} V_C I\,dt. \qquad (46)$$

Now both V_L and V_C are 90° out of phase with I, and a glance at Fig. 14 shows that the integral of the product of two sinusoidal curves 90° out of phase vanishes over any cycle, or for that matter, over any half-cycle. Hence, the last two integrals in (46) vanish, indicating that the average power all goes into heat in the resistance. This heat is represented by the first integral, which we have just evaluated in (40) and (41), as

$$\text{energy per cycle} = \frac{V_{Rm} I_m}{2f} = \frac{V_{R0} I_0}{f}.$$

This value, when multiplied by the number of cycles per second, gives the average power

$$P = V_{R0} I_0. \qquad (47)$$

To express this in terms of line voltage V_0, we notice, from the vector diagram of Fig. 10, that for either an inductive or capacitive circuit,

$$V_{Rm} = V_m \cos\theta;$$

therefore

$$V_{R0} = V_0 \cos\theta,$$

and

$$P = V_0 I_0 \cos\theta, \quad \text{in watts.} \tag{48}$$

The factor $\cos\theta$ is called the *power factor*. It is the factor by which $V_0 I_0$ (in volt-amperes) must be multiplied in order to get power in watts. As we shall see in Chap. 42, a wattmeter measures actual power P, so power factor can be determined by a simultaneous reading of a wattmeter, an ammeter, and a voltmeter. This determination is done automatically by a *power-factor meter*.

A watt-hour meter integrates the product VI, so its reading represents actual energy used. However, a power company will charge a commercial user more per kwh for power delivered at a low power factor than for power delivered at a high power factor. Suppose one user draws an average of 100 amp at 240 v through a resistive load of power factor unity ($\cos\theta = 1$, $\theta = 0°$). He is drawing 24 kw. Let another user be consuming 24 kw at 240 v with a highly inductive load, such as an induction motor, at a power factor of $\frac{1}{3}$ ($\cos\theta = \frac{1}{3}$, $\theta = 70°.5$). He will require 300 amp. For him, the power company must provide lines and generator capacity to carry 300 amp instead of 100 amp, must stand I^2R-loss in the lines for 300 amp, and so on. Hence, the power company will reasonably make an extra charge for his energy because of the low power factor.

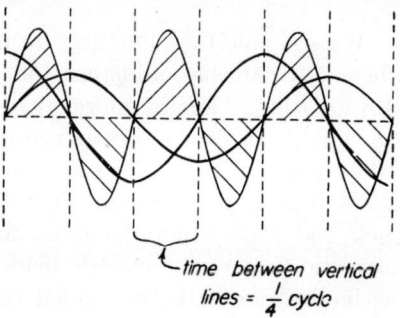

Fig. 14. The product of two sinusoidal curves 90° out of phase is a pure sinusoidal curve of double frequency.

The reason for the negative parts of the power curve, Fig. 13, is that energy is alternately stored and released, twice per cycle, in the condenser and in the inductance.

In the case of *series resonance*, the circuit operates at power factor unity, with current in phase with voltage and with all the instantaneous power going into heating the resistance. There is appreciable energy $\frac{1}{2}LI^2$ of self-inductance, and appreciable energy $\frac{1}{2}CV_C^2$ stored in the condenser. Since these energies have no effect on the external circuit, they must be just handed back and forth from inductance to capacitance. This transfer must occur twice per cycle, since $\frac{1}{2}LI^2$ is zero each time I is

zero, and $\tfrac{1}{2}CV_C^2$ is zero each time V_C is zero. To verify the validity of this argument, let
$$I = I_m \sin 2\pi ft.$$
Then $$\tfrac{1}{2}LI^2 = \tfrac{1}{2}LI_m^2 \sin^2 2\pi ft;$$
or, since $X_L = 2\pi fL$, we see that
$$\text{energy in inductance} = \frac{X_L}{4\pi f} I_m^2 \sin^2 2\pi ft. \tag{49}$$

Also, from (8), (9), and (12),
$$V_C = X_C I_m \sin(2\pi ft - \tfrac{1}{2}\pi) = -X_C I_m \cos 2\pi ft,$$
so that $$\tfrac{1}{2}CV_C^2 = \tfrac{1}{2}CX_C^2 I_m^2 \cos^2 2\pi ft.$$

Since $CX_C = 1/2\pi f$, we can write this as
$$\text{energy in condenser} = \frac{X_C}{4\pi f} I_m^2 \cos^2 2\pi ft. \tag{50}$$

We see now that (49) has its maxima at phases $\phi = 2\pi ft = 90°$, $270°$, when (50) vanishes, and that (50) has its maxima at $\phi = 0°$, $180°$, when (49) vanishes. Furthermore, at resonance, when $X_L = X_C$, these maxima are equal. In fact, at resonance the sum of (49) and (50) is a constant, independent of time, since $\sin^2\phi + \cos^2\phi = 1$. This series of calculations shows that in the resonant case the stored energy is precisely handed back and forth from the inductance to the capacitance, or from the magnetic field to the electric field, just as the energy of a pendulum or mechanical oscillator is handed back and forth from kinetic energy of motion to potential energy of position. The term *electrical resonance* is applied to this case because of the analogy with mechanical resonance.

PROBLEMS

NOTE: AC voltages and currents given without qualification are *effective* values.

1. Write the equation for the instantaneous voltage across 220-v, 60-$\sim$ lines.
    Ans: $V = 311 \sin 377t$ volts.

2. Write the equation for the instantaneous voltage of a 100-mv, 1000-$\sim$ oscillator.

3. Write the equation for the instantaneous current if 10 milliamperes flow into an antenna at 500 kilocycles/sec.   Ans: $I = 14.1 \sin(3.14 \times 10^6 \, t)$ mamp.

4. Write the equation for the instantaneous current flowing into a motor that draws 120 amp at 60 $\sim$.

5. A current of 10 amp, lagging by 30°, flows in an AC circuit when 110 volts are applied. What is the power factor? What is the power?   Ans: 0.866; 953 w.

6. A current of 0.5 amp, leading by 60°, flows in an AC circuit when 24 volts are applied. What is the power factor? What is the power?

7. What is the power in the circuit of Fig. 12 at resonant frequency? What is the maximum energy stored in the self-inductance? in the capacitance?
    Ans: 0.5 w; 0.5 joule; 0.5 joule.

8. A series circuit has self inductance, capacitance, and resistance. A fixed AC voltage is applied and the capacitance adjusted until maximum current flows. The maximum current is found to be 2 amp effective. What power is being supplied to the circuit if the total resistance is 15 ohms?

9. In Prob. 1, p. 1048, compute the power factor and the power.

Ans: 0.471; 80 w.

10. In Prob. 2, p. 1048, compute the power factor and the power.

6. PARALLEL AC CIRCUITS; PARALLEL RESONANCE; OSCILLATING CIRCUITS

We are now in a position to find the various currents and voltages in a parallel circuit such as that of Fig. 4. If we take $V_m = 120$ volts, $R_1 = 34.64$ ohms, $X_L = 20$ ohms, $R_2 = 15$ ohms, and $X_C = 25.98$ ohms, we get just the vector diagram of Fig. 5 to compute the current. The procedure is as follows:

Represent V, which is common to both circuits, by a vector of zero phase as in Fig. 5. Compute the impedance $Z_1 = \sqrt{R_1^2 + X_L^2} = 40$ ohms. Hence, $I_{1m} = V_m/40 = 3$ amp, lagging the voltage by $\theta_1 = \arctan(X_L/R_1) = \arctan 0.577 = 30°$. The vector representing I_1 is plotted in Fig. 5. Also, $Z_2 = \sqrt{R_2^2 + X_C^2} = 30$ ohms, so that $I_{2m} = V_m/30 = 4$ amp, leading the voltage by $\theta_2 = \arctan(X_C/R_2) = \arctan 1.732 = 60°$. I_2 is also plotted in Fig. 5. The remainder of the computation consists in the addition of I_1 and I_2 to obtain the value (6) of the total current I, as was done in discussing Fig. 5.

The power in a parallel circuit is of course the sum of the powers in each branch. In our case, in accordance with formula (48),

$$P_1 = \tfrac{1}{2} V_m I_{1m} \cos\theta_1 = 155.9 \text{ watts},$$

$$P_2 = \tfrac{1}{2} V_m I_{2m} \cos\theta_2 = 120.0 \text{ watts},$$

so that $P = P_1 + P_2 = 275.9$ watts.

We can also get P from the voltage and total current, which is $I_m = 5$ amp at $\theta = 23°.1$ lead. In the expression

$$P_1 + P_2 = \tfrac{1}{2} V_m (I_{1m} \cos\theta_1 + I_{2m} \cos\theta_2),$$

$I_{1m} \cos\theta_1$ is the x-component of I_1, $I_{2m} \cos\theta_2$ is the x-component of I_2, their sum is the x-component of I, which can be written as $I_m \cos\theta$. Thus,

$$P = \tfrac{1}{2} V_m I_m \cos\theta = \tfrac{1}{2} \cdot 120 \cdot 5 \cdot \cos 23°.1 = 275.9 \text{ watts}.$$

The formula $\qquad P = \tfrac{1}{2} V_m I_m \cos\theta = V_0 I_0 \cos\theta \qquad (51)$

holds for any type of circuit if V_0 is the voltage across the leads, I_0 the current through the leads, and θ the angle between the vectors representing V and I. The factor $\cos\theta$ is called the *power factor* in every case.

To approach the subject of *parallel resonance*, let us consider an idealized parallel circuit in which the resistance is assumed negligible, as in Fig. 15. If we assume X_L a little larger than X_C, so that I_L is a little smaller than I_C, we get current curves of the type shown. It will be noted that in this case, where X_L and X_C are only slightly different, the currents I_C and I_L are almost equal and opposite at each instant. When current flows upwards in the condenser circuit, it flows downward in the inductance, and vice versa. Only a little current flows in the line. We can look on the current flow as a large oscillating current in the closed LC-loop (as it is called), alternately charging and discharging the condenser through the inductance, thus transferring energy back and forth from the electric field of the condenser to the magnetic field of the

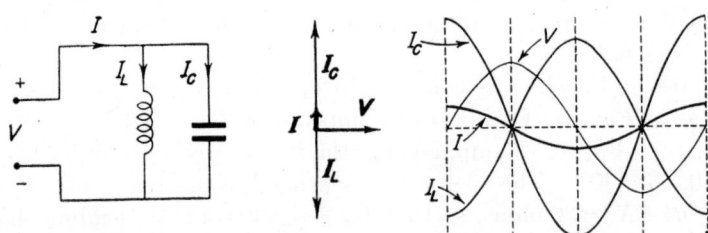

Fig. 15. A parallel circuit of negligible resistance, with X_L slightly larger than X_C.

coil. Only a little current flows in and out through the leads to make up for the fact that X_L differs a little from X_C so that these energies do not quite balance.

If we now shift the frequency of the applied voltage closer and closer to the resonance value given by

$$X_L = X_C, \qquad 2\pi f L = \frac{1}{2\pi f C}, \qquad f = \frac{1}{2\pi \sqrt{LC}}, \qquad (52)$$

the line current I becomes smaller and smaller, until at resonance in this idealized circuit we have a current circulating around the LC-loop given by

$$I_{Lm} = I_{Cm} = V_m/X_L = V_m/X_C,$$

with line current $I = 0$.

Since in an actual circuit we always have some resistance, we always need some in-phase line current to supply the energy for heating the resistance, but it is not difficult to keep the resistances so small that the line current is very small compared to the current circulating in the LC-loop.

Now suppose we have set up the circulating current at resonance frequency and then pull the line switch. In the ideal resistanceless case, the LC-loop goes on oscillating indefinitely at resonance frequency, since there is no energy loss. In the practical low-resistance case, the LC-loop oscillates for very many cycles at this frequency, the amplitude of oscillation gradually decreasing as energy is absorbed in the resistance.

The frequency f given by (52) is the only one at which we can completely shift energy back and forth between the condenser and the coil, as shown by (49) and (50); it is called the *natural frequency* of the LC-loop. In Fig. 16, if the condenser is initially charged and we close the switch, if the circuit resistance is low the condenser will discharge in oscillatory fashion back and forth through the inductance with the natural frequency $f = 1/2\pi \sqrt{LC}$.

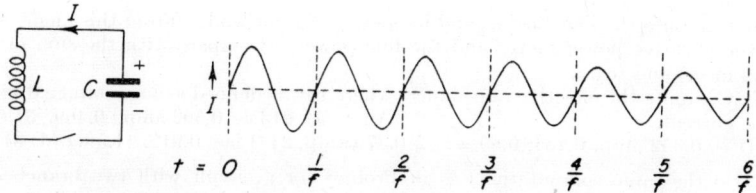

Fig. 16. If the condenser is initially charged, closing the switch results in an oscillatory discharge of frequency $f = 1/2\pi \sqrt{LC}$. For a circuit of very low resistance, the amplitude of the current curve dies down very gradually as indicated at the right, where the switch is closed at $t = 0$.

In fact, if R is negligible in Fig. 16, we have at every instant

$$V_c = L(dI/dt).$$

But the charge on the condenser is $Q = CV_c$, so that

$$(Q/C) = L(dI/dt).$$

Now $\qquad I = -dQ/dt, \quad dI/dt = -d^2Q/dt^2.$

Hence, $\qquad Q/C = -L\, d^2Q/dt^2$

or
$$\frac{d^2Q}{dt^2} = -\frac{1}{LC} Q. \tag{53}$$

Equation (53) is like the differential equation for mechanical simple harmonic motion. It has a solution of the form

$$Q(t) = Q_m \cos 2\pi ft.$$

Direct substitution of this expression in the differential equation (53) gives
$$-4\pi^2 f^2 Q_m \cos 2\pi ft = -(1/LC) Q_m \cos 2\pi ft$$
or
$$4\pi^2 f^2 = 1/LC,$$
$$f = 1/2\pi \sqrt{LC},$$

the natural frequency as defined above.

These considerations are fundamental to the theory of all the oscillating circuits used in radio and many other high-frequency applications.

PROBLEMS

NOTE: In the following problems, use effective values throughout the computations; plot vector diagrams and carry out vector addition in terms of effective values.

1. A circuit has two branches in parallel across 120-v, 60-∼ lines. Branch A has an inductor of 0.5-henry self inductance and 100-ohm resistance. Branch B has 80 ohms of resistance and 8 μf of capacitance.

   (a) Compute the impedance, the current, the power factor, and the power in branch A.

   (b) Compute the impedance, the current, the power factor, and the power in branch B.

   (c) Compute the line current and its angle of lag or lead. From this angle compute the effective power factor and the line power. Compare with the sum of the powers in (a) and (b).

   (d) Compute the effective impedance, where this is defined as line voltage divided by line current. Ans: (a) 213 ω, 0.562 amp, 0.469, 31.6 w; (b) 341 ω, 0.352 amp, 0.234, 9.89 w; (c) 0.379 amp, 24°.1 lag, 0.912, 41.5 w; (d) 317 ω.

2. Do the same computations as in Prob. 1 for a circuit with two branches in parallel across 25-v, 500-∼ lines. Branch A has an inductor of 5-millihenry self inductance and 9-ohm resistance. Branch B has 8 ohms of resistance and 40 μf of capacitance.

3. In Fig. 15, if V_0 is 100 volts, X_L 25 ohms, and X_C 20 ohms, find I_{C0}, I_{L0}, I_0, and Z, where Z is the effective impedance defined as V_0/I_0. Ans: 5, 4, 1 amp, 100 ohms.

4. Repeat Prob. 3, with X_C changed to 30 ohms.

5. In the circuit of Fig. 15, show that the effective impedance Z, defined as V_0/I_0, is given by

$$Z = \frac{X_L X_C}{X_L - X_C} \quad \text{or} \quad Z = \frac{X_L X_C}{X_C - X_L},$$

according to whether $X_L > X_C$ or $X_C > X_L$. Note that the impedance of this ideal resistanceless circuit becomes infinite at resonance.

6. At what frequency will the circuit of Fig. 16 oscillate if $L = 1$ henry, $C = 1$ μf?

7. At what frequency will the circuit of Fig. 16 oscillate if $L = 1$ millihenry, $C = 1$ μμf? Ans: 5030 kilocycles/sec.

8. It is desired to make an oscillator whose basic circuit is that of Fig. 16 and whose frequency is variable from 500 to 1000 kilocycles/sec. A fixed 1-millihenry inductor is used with a variable condenser. Over what capacitance range must the condenser be variable?

9. It is desired to make an oscillator whose basic circuit is that of Fig. 16 and whose frequency is variable from 500 to 1000 cycles/sec. A fixed 1-μf condenser is used with a variable inductor. Over what inductance range must the inductor be variable? Ans: from 0.0253 to 0.101 henry.

7. THE TRANSFORMER*

We are now in position to discuss the theory of the transformer, a simple device with no moving parts which enables one to step AC voltages up and down at will with good efficiency. It is the transformer

---

* This section may be omitted without loss of continuity.

that makes possible the long-distance transmission of electrical power. When the power is transmitted at very high voltages, 100–300 kv (1 kv = 1000 volts), currents can be kept very small. Hence, IR-drops and I^2R-losses in the lines can be kept small even for very long lines which necessarily have comparatively high R. Since electrical energy can neither be generated nor consumed at such high voltages, transformers are necessary to step the voltage up and down. Because no DC counterpart of the transformer exists, long-distance transmission of DC is at present entirely impractical.

The transformer has two windings on a common laminated-steel core, as in Fig. 17. The primary winding, of N_P turns, is where electrical energy is put into the transformer; the secondary winding, of N_S turns, is where the energy is taken out. The ratio

$$r = N_S/N_P \tag{54}$$

gives the ratio of output voltage to input voltage, as we shall see. This ratio is greater than unity for a step-up transformer, less than unity for a step-down transformer. The winding with the greater number of

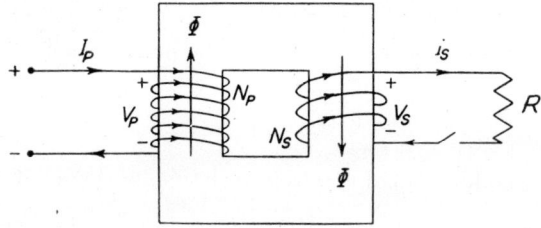

Fig. 17. Diagram of transformer with arrows and + and − signs to indicate positive senses of currents, voltages, and flux.

turns can be made of finer wire than the other, since, being the high-voltage winding, it has to carry less current for the same power. The same transformer will work equally well as a step-up or a step-down transformer, according to which winding is taken as primary, which as secondary.

We shall consider the ideal case of a transformer with no losses. In an actual transformer the losses can be kept well under one per cent of the power transmitted, so that the actual transformer differs very little in operation from the ideal one. In the ideal case, the windings have zero resistance (no I^2R-losses); the magnetic material is assumed ideal (flux Φ directly proportional to MMF, hence no hysteresis losses); eddy currents in the core are assumed negligible; and leakage flux is neglected, so that the same flux may be assumed to thread both windings at any instant.

To simplify the discussion of the operation of the transformer as much as possible, we shall assume a *purely resistive load*, as in Fig. 17.

At the instant when primary and secondary currents are I_P and I_S, the core flux Φ will be the sum of the contributions from the two windings:

$$\Phi = \frac{N_P I_P - N_S I_S}{\mathcal{R}}. \tag{55}$$

Here the numerator represents the MMF, the denominator the reluctance, in the formula $\Phi = \text{MMF}/\mathcal{R}$ of Chap. 38. The minus sign comes from the fact that for the particular winding direction shown in Fig. 17, a positive I_S sets up a negative flux.

At any instant, the generated EMF's (of self and mutual inductance) in the two windings will be

$$V_P = N_P \frac{d\Phi}{dt}, \qquad V_S = N_S \frac{d\Phi}{dt}, \tag{56}$$

where the signs are seen to be correct in accordance with Lenz's law for the conventions of Fig. 17. Hence, at every instant,

$$\frac{V_S}{V_P} = \frac{N_S}{N_P} = r. \tag{57}$$

Since we are neglecting resistance in the primary winding, the applied voltage V is at every instant equal to V_P:

$$V = V_P. \tag{58}$$

Since the secondary load is purely resistive, we have, at every instant,

$$V_S = R I_S. \tag{59}$$

By combining (59), (58), and (57), we see that V, V_P, V_S, and I_S are all in phase, with

$$V_P = V, \qquad V_S = rV, \qquad I_S = rV/R. \tag{60}$$

Since these equations hold at every instant, the same relations must obtain between either the maximum values V_m, V_{Pm}, V_{Sm}, and I_{Sm} or the effective values V_0, V_{P0}, V_{S0}, I_{S0} of the AC voltages and currents. Equations (60) enable us to obtain all quantities of interest except the primary current I_P.

To obtain the primary current, notice that in the ideal resistanceless case the rate of change of flux must *always* be such as to furnish a back-EMF $N_P \, d\Phi/dt$ just equal to V_P, as in (56). The primary current will always change in such a way as to guarantee this.

With the secondary circuit *open*, we have the case of pure self inductance that we have already studied, and the primary current will have the effective value

$$I_{P0}^o = V_0/X_P, \tag{61}$$

lagging the voltage V by 90°. The alternating no-load primary current I_P^o sets up an alternating flux Φ given by (55) as

$$\Phi = N_P I_P^o / \mathcal{R}. \tag{62}$$

When an alternating current I_S is drawn from the secondary, this current trends to modify the flux in accordance with (55). But the flux must be the same alternating function of time whether the secondary is loaded or unloaded. Hence the flux must always be the function (62). The primary current I_P will so adjust itself that this is true.

Equating (62) for the no-load case to (55) for the case in which a secondary current exists, we see that

$$N_P I_P^o = N_P I_P - N_S I_S$$

or
$$I_P = I_P^o + r I_S.$$

This relation must be true at every instant. On the vector diagram, therefore,

$$\boldsymbol{I_P = I_P^o + r I_S}. \tag{63}$$

This equation determines the primary current in terms of the no-load primary current (61) and the secondary current (60).

As an example, let us consider a step-down transformer (such as sits on a post in the middle of every block in a city) designed to step the power-line voltage of $V_0 = 600$ volts effective down to $V_{s0} = 120$ volts effective for distribution to the houses. We shall shift over to the usual electrical-engineering practice of plotting effective rather than maximum values in our vector diagrams. This shift does not change the geometrical relationships of the vectors in these diagrams because it merely amounts to a uniform reduction in scale by a factor of $\sqrt{2}$. The vectors representing the primary and secondary voltages are plotted at the top of Fig. 18, with

$$r = \frac{V_S}{V} = \frac{120}{600} = 0.2, \tag{64}$$

according to (60).

Let us further assume that our particular transformer has $2\pi f L_P = 377 L_P = X_P = 300$ ohms, which corresponds to a reasonable value of L_P, and that our lighting and heating load is equivalent to a resistance of $R = 2.4$ ohms. This gives $I_{s0} = 50$ amp and, since I_S and V_S are in phase, a power output

$$P_S = 120 \times 50 = 6000 \text{ w} = 6 \text{ kw}. \tag{65}$$

Such a figure would represent a fairly light load rather than the maximum load for a block of houses.

Now to find the primary current, we first compute the current I_P^o that would flow in the primary with the secondary circuit open. With the secondary circuit open, the secondary coil has no influence; the primary current is the same as if the secondary winding were removed entirely from the core of Fig. 17. Consequently, the effective primary current with open secondary is

$$I_{P0}^o = V_0/X_P = 2 \text{ amp}, \quad (66)$$

lagging the voltage V by 90° [pure inductance without resistance: $\theta = 90°$ in (33)]. This current is represented by the vector in the middle diagram of Fig. 18, marked 'no-load currents.'

The vector addition (63) that determines I_P is accomplished in the diagram at the bottom of Fig. 18. On this diagram, I_P^o is copied from the diagram above; the vector I_S representing 50 amp effective is plotted in phase with V; the vector rI_S of 10 amp is along the same line. The vector resultant of I_P^o and rI_S gives I_P, of magnitude

$$I_{P0} = 10.2 \text{ amp},$$

lagging the voltage V by

$$\theta = \arctan 2/10 = 11°.3.$$

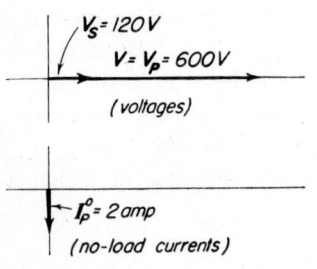

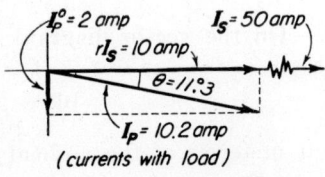

Fig. 18. Vector diagrams for the transformer of Fig. 17. Numerical values are *effective* values.

The power furnished to the primary is

$$P_P = V_0 I_{P0} \cos\theta = 600(10.2)(10/10.2) = 6000 \text{ watts}$$

—exactly the same as the power (65) delivered by the secondary.

We can now discuss the current and power relations for the general case of the transformer of Fig. 17 with a resistive load. The primary and secondary voltages and the secondary current will be given by (60); these are all in phase with the applied voltage V. The power delivered by the secondary will be

$$P_S = V_{S0} I_{S0} = r^2 V_0^2 / R.$$

The primary current at no load will be

$$I_{P0}^o = V_0/X_P = V_0/2\pi f L_P,$$

lagging V by 90° as in Fig. 18. When the secondary is loaded, the primary current is the vector sum of this no-load current, which represents no power input, and an in-phase current of magnitude rI_{S0}, as in Fig. 18. This primary current will lag V by angle θ. The power input to the primary is

$$P_P = V_0 I_{P0} \cos\theta.$$

But, as in Fig. 18, $I_{P0}\cos\theta = rI_{S0}$; hence

$$P_P = V_0\, rI_{S0} = r^2\, V_0^2/R,$$

equal to the secondary power output.

A similar discussion can be given for the cases in which the secondary is loaded inductively or capacitively. Drawing a current from the secondary tends to cause an alteration in the magnetic field which tends to alter the induced voltage in the primary. This in turn alters the primary current in such a way that the flux and the induced voltage do not change. The power input to the primary exactly equals the power output of the secondary in the ideal case and exceeds it only slightly in the actual case.

Thus, a bell-ringing transformer installed in a home draws an appreciable primary current at no load, but it draws this current so nearly at 90° phase to the primary voltage that the power at no load is too small to turn the kilowatt-hour meter that records energy consumption.

PROBLEMS

1. A transformer has 50 turns on the primary and 1000 on the secondary. When the primary is connected to 110-v AC mains, what is the voltage of the secondary?

Ans: 2420 v.

2. A bell-ringing transformer is designed to step 120 volts down to 4 volts. If the secondary has 12 turns, how many turns should the primary have?

3. A toy transformer for operating an electric train has an input current to the primary of 0.9 amp lagging 15° behind the input voltage of 120 v. The terminal voltage of the secondary is 6.0 v. The load on the secondary has a power factor of 0.707. Under these conditions the actual efficiency of the transformer is 95%. Find the secondary current.
Ans: 18.2 amp.

4. A large step-down transformer has a primary input of 5000 kw at 3300 v. The transformer is 99% efficient. The secondary feeds into a load of power factor 0.850 at 550 v. Find the secondary current.

5. Consider an ideal no-loss transformer feeding into a resistive load of 55 ohms, as in Fig. 17. The primary has 20 turns, the secondary 100 turns. The reluctance of the core is 10,000 ampere-turns/weber. The primary is connected to 110-v, 60-∼ lines. Find the secondary voltage, the secondary current, the primary current and its angle of lag, and the power.   Ans: 550 v; 10.0 amp; 50.5 amp, 8°3; 5500 w.

6. Consider an ideal no-loss transformer feeding into a resistive load of 0.55 ohm, as in Fig. 17. The primary has 240 turns, the secondary 40 turns. The reluctance of the core is 2000 ampere-turns/weber. The primary is connected to 3300-v, 60-∼ lines. Find the secondary voltage, the secondary current, the primary current and its angle of lag, and the power.

CHAPTER 41

THE FUNDAMENTAL ELECTRICAL UNITS

Up to this point we have defined the various electrical units in the most convenient fashion in the order in which they were introduced. None of our definitions has been incorrect, but they were not given in the most logical order. Our original definition of the coulomb (p. 791) involved a constant which we arbitrarily chose as 10^{-7} times the square of the speed of light. In terms of this coulomb we defined the ampere as one coulomb per second. We then stated certain experimental formulas for magnetic forces between currents given in amperes. *Alternatively*, the ampere can be independently defined in terms of forces between currents, in which case the coulomb is defined as one ampere·second and the proportionality constant occurring in Coulomb's law of force becomes experimentally determinable. In this alternative scheme this proportionality constant proves, both experimentally and theoretically (on the basis of Maxwell's electromagnetic theory of light), to be related to the square of the speed of light in the manner of our original definition of the coulomb.

The alternative scheme, in which the ampere is defined in terms of forces between currents and the coulomb is defined as one ampere·second is the most convenient for absolute determinations of the ampere and the coulomb, and is by international agreement taken as fundamental.

In this chapter we shall redefine the basic electrical and magnetic quantities in the particular manner that is taken as fundamental by the International Committee of Weights and Measures and is used in the establishment and maintenance of the electrical standards by the various national standardizing laboratories, such as the

>National Bureau of Standards, United States;
>National Physical Laboratory, Great Britain;
>Laboratoire Central d'Électricité, France;
>Physikalisch-Technische Reichsanstalt, Germany;
>Electrotechnical Laboratory, Japan;
>Department of Weights and Measures, U.S.S.R.

In the following sections we shall begin by defining the fundamental electrical units in an order consistent with the definitions internationally adopted.* Then we shall discuss the manner in which these units are

* The present definitions became effective on Jan. 1, 1948. Older books will have

established and maintained at the National Bureau of Standards, and the manner in which instruments are calibrated in terms of them.* After a résumé of this material we shall conclude with a recapitulation of the defining equations for all the electrical and magnetic quantities and of the dimensions of their units.

1. DEFINITION OF THE AMPERE

We *postulate* that magnetic field in webers/m² in an iron-free region can be computed from current in amperes by integrating the vector contribution $d\mathcal{B}$ whose magnitude is $10^{-7} I \, dl \, \sin\theta / r^2$ and whose direction is normal to both dl and r as discussed on p. 940. We further *postulate* that the force on a current element $I \, dl$ in a magnetic field can be computed from the formula $f = \mathcal{B} I \, dl$ newtons, where $\mathcal{B}$ is the field component normal to the wire (p. 931).

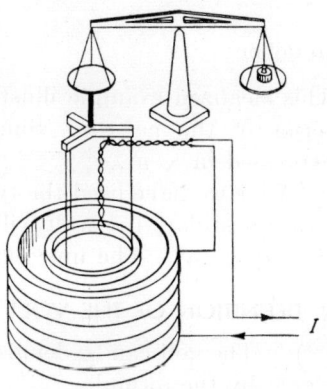

Fig. 1. Schematic diagram of *current balance*.

These two postulates together enable us to compute the magnetic force in newtons between any two current elements $I \, dl$ and $I' \, dl'$ in terms of I, I', and geometrical lengths and angles. By integration, they enable us to compute the whole force in newtons between two coils such as those of Fig. 1. If the two coils are connected in series as in Fig. 1, so that the currents in the two coils have the *same* value I, these two postulates enable us to compute the force in newtons as a function of the current I. Hence, we can use these postulates to define the unit of current, the ampere, since a measurement of the force in Fig. 1 determines the current I in amperes. Such a measurement determines a current in amperes in terms of fundamental mechanical units, the meter and the newton.

The fundamental measurement of current is made in this way by measuring the force between two accurately constructed coils carrying the same current. Such a measurement can be made at the National Bureau of Standards with an accuracy of 1 or 2 parts in a million, using the apparatus of Fig. 1, which is known as a *current balance*.

---

a completely different set of definitions for the so-called 'International Units,' which are now entirely obsolete. The present units are known as the 'absolute units.' Official announcement of the adoption of the absolute units in the United States was made in Circular of the National Bureau of Standards C459 (1947).

* The best reference to this type of material is H. L. Curtis, *Electrical Measurements, Precise Comparisons of Standards and Absolute Determinations of the Units*, McGraw-Hill Book Company, Inc., New York, 1937.

The absolute unit of current, the ampere, is defined by the formulas that give the magnetic force between wires carrying currents.

This definition may seem to be a little vague because the formulas referred to are geometrically complicated and not succinctly repeatable in the definition. However, the definition, using the formulas given by the two postulates at the beginning of this section, is nonetheless precise. If it were practical to measure the force per meter length between two infinite parallel wires spaced distance a apart and carrying the same current I, one could make use of the formula (10), p. 945:

$$f = \frac{2I^2}{10^7 a} \qquad \left\{\begin{array}{l} f \text{ in nt/m} \\ a \text{ in m} \\ I \text{ in amp} \end{array}\right\} \qquad (1)$$

to define
$$I = \sqrt{10^7 af/2}. \qquad (2)$$

This idealized example illustrates the way in which current is defined in terms of the newton. Since af is expressed in nt, I is seen to be expressed in $\sqrt{\text{nt}}$.

After we have used the two postulates together to define the ampere, either postulate by itself will serve to define the unit of magnetic field, the weber/m². The unit of flux, the weber, follows at once.

2. DEFINITION OF THE VOLT

The volt can be defined in terms of the ampere and the watt by the formula
$$P = IV \qquad (3)$$

for the rate in watts at which heat is generated by current I passing through a resistor. Alternatively, the volt can be defined by the formula
$$V = d\Phi/dt \qquad (4)$$

for the EMF induced in a wire cutting flux.

In employing the second definition, the flux is computed from the currents that set up a magnetic field in an iron-free region. These two definitions are logically consistent, since the second formula can be derived from the first and from the definition of current given in Sec. 1.

Although (3) and (4) are logically satisfactory as *definitions*, no method of high accuracy has been devised for an absolute measurement of voltage in terms of either of these definitions. In the case of the first definition the limitation on accuracy arises from the fact that the power must be measured calorimetrically, and the mechanical equivalent of heat is not known with high precision.

Since the ohm, which we define next, *can* be measured to high accuracy, accurate absolute measurements of voltage are made by comparison with the IR-drop across an accurately determined resistance.

3. DEFINITION OF THE OHM

The ohm is defined in terms of the volt and the ampere by the relation
$$R = V/I. \tag{5}$$

There are several methods for absolute measurement of the resistance of a wire to an accuracy of a few parts in a million. One method which has been extensively used is illustrated in simplified fashion in Fig. 2. Here a current I sets up a magnetic field $\mathcal{B} = 4\pi nI \times 10^{-7}$ in a long solenoid

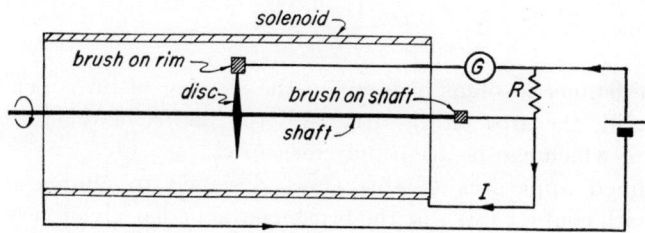

Fig. 2. Homopolar-generator apparatus for absolute measurement of the ohm. This apparatus determines the resistance R in ohms quite independently of the battery voltage or the value of the current I. The dimensions of the solenoid and the disk and the speed of revolution need, however, to be known with precision.

with n turns per meter. A disk rotating in this field has an EMF induced between center and rim, as in the Faraday disk dynamo, of magnitude $V = \Phi/T$, where Φ is the flux cut by a radius of the disk in one revolution, and T is the period of revolution. Φ is just the flux contained in a circle of area equal to the area of the disk, which we denote by A. Hence, $\Phi = \mathcal{B}A = 4\pi nIA \times 10^{-7}$, and

$$V = \Phi/T = (4\pi nIA/T) \times 10^{-7}. \tag{6}$$

The resistance R to be determined is included in the circuit as shown, and a galvanometer G is used to indicate whether or not current is flowing through the disk.

Consider first the situation with the disk at rest so that $V=0$. The battery current splits, part going down through R and part down through the disk. These currents reunite and the whole battery current goes through the solenoid winding. Now let the disk start turning in such a direction that the induced EMF is from shaft to rim, opposing the flow of current from the battery. As the disk speeds up, there will be less and less current through G, until a speed is reached at which the current through G is exactly zero. When this condition is attained, the rotational speed is accurately measured; we denote the time for one revolution of the disk by T. Under these conditions all the solenoid current I flows through R; and by applying Kirchhoff's second law to the loop containing R, G, and the disk, we see that

$$IR = V,$$

where V is the generated EMF. Substituting the expression (6) for V in this equation, we have

$$IR = (4\pi n IA/T) \times 10^{-7}.$$

The important point is that in this equation the current I cancels, giving the equation

$$R = \frac{4\pi n A}{T} \times 10^{-7},$$

for the resistance in ohms in terms of the number of turns per meter on the solenoid, the area of the disk, and the period of revolution of the disk, all of which can be accurately measured.

A refined apparatus of this type, designed to eliminate possible trouble with contact EMF's at the brush contacts, has given very accurate measurements of resistance. Another method for absolute determination of resistance balances, in somewhat similar fashion, the DP produced by a current in the resistance against the EMF induced in the secondary of a standard mutual inductance. A third method, slightly more accurate, employs a standard self inductance. These latter methods, which employ either commutated or sinusoidal currents and voltages, will not be described here in detail. In them, as in the homopolar-generator method we have described, current magnitude cancels and resistance is determined by a value of inductance and a frequency. It is noted that self and mutual inductance of nonferrous coils can be computed from geometry alone; hence, the standards of inductance used in these methods are accurately constructed coils whose inductances have been computed.

4. DEFINITION OF THE COULOMB; THE PROPORTIONALITY CONSTANT IN COULOMB'S LAW

The coulomb is defined in terms of the ampere and the second by the equation

$$Q = It. \tag{7}$$

This definition of Q makes the proportionality constant γ in Coulomb's law for the force between two charges at distance r,

$$f = \gamma \frac{Q_1 Q_2}{r^2} \qquad \begin{cases} f \text{ in nt} \\ Q \text{ in coul} \\ r \text{ in m} \end{cases}$$

(p. 791), a matter for experimental determination. Since (7) gives Q the dimensions of amp·sec = $\sqrt{\text{nt·sec}}$, γ is seen to have the dimensions m²/sec², the square of a speed. In Chap. 31, we gave γ the value $10^{-7}c^2 \approx 9 \times 10^9$ m²/sec², where $c \approx 3 \times 10^8$ m/sec is the speed of light. This is the value that is found experimentally. It is also the value required by the theory of the speed of propagation of an electromagnetic wave. The details of this theory are beyond the scope of this text, but the result it gives for the magnitude of the speed of an electromagnetic wave (light or radio wave in vacuum) is

$$c = \sqrt{10^7 \gamma},$$

from which

$$\gamma = 10^{-7} c^2.$$

Thus, there are two ways of determining γ: by direct electrostatic-force measurement, and by measurement of the speed of light and application of the theory of electromagnetic waves.

The electrostatic determination of γ is made most accurately, not by a direct measurement of the force between charges, but rather by measurement of the capacitance of a condenser, since the same constant γ ($= 10^{-7}c^2$) occurs in all formulas for capacitance of a condenser in Chap. 32. Thus, formula (11), p. 842, for the capacitance of a parallel-plate condenser with vacuum dielectric is

$$C = \frac{1}{\gamma} \frac{A}{4\pi d}.$$

Such a condenser can be accurately constructed, and its capacitance can be measured in terms of the definition $Q = It$ of charge by a method that repeatedly charges the condenser to a known voltage and permits it to discharge a large but known number of times per second through a current-measuring instrument. At potential V, the condenser acquires charge CV. If it is discharged n times per second, the charge that flows in the leads per second is

$$I = nCV,$$

the discharge current in amperes. This discharge current can be measured by a galvanometer calibrated in terms of the definition of the ampere. Thus, C is measured in terms of the ampere and the volt. By putting the measured capacitance C in the above formula, γ is determined.

The most accurate value of γ determined by measuring the capacitance of a condenser is

$$\gamma = (2.9978)^2 \times 10^9 \text{ m}^2/\text{sec}^2.$$

This value is in excellent agreement with the value determined from the measured speed of light:

$$\gamma = 10^{-7} c^2 = (2.99776)^2 \times 10^9 \text{ m}^2/\text{sec}^2.$$

The perfect agreement between these two values is overwhelming evidence for the validity of the electromagnetic theory of light.

5. MAINTENANCE OF THE UNITS AT THE NATIONAL BUREAU OF STANDARDS

A highly accurate measurement of a current or resistance by the method of Fig. 1 or Fig. 2 or by one of the alternatives is not a routine procedure. Rather, it is an exacting and time-consuming task which is performed only at intervals of a decade or so, to measure or check the values of *concrete standards* of resistance and voltage that are the actual standards in terms of which calibrations are made by comparison methods. By a *concrete* standard is meant one that can be physically stored away in a vault for future reference, as can the standard meter and the standard kilogram.

The concrete standard of resistance at the N.B.S. consists of ten 1-ohm coils of manganin wire, whose resistance has been measured from time to time by an absolute method to an accuracy of a few parts in a million. In the years between measurements, the average resistance of the ten coils is assumed, with good justification, to remain constant.

A concrete standard of current cannot be maintained, but a concrete standard of voltage can, in the form of the Weston standard cell. Currents can then be determined by comparison of the voltage drop across a standard resistor with the concrete standard of voltage. Curtis (*op. cit.*, 1937) states:

> "At the National Bureau of Standards the unit of electromotive force has been maintained by a group of about twenty Weston saturated cells, with an even larger number in reserve. All these cells have been maintained at constant temperature, usually 28° C. Occasionally a cell in the standard group will show a decided change in its electromotive force as compared to the mean of the group. It is then replaced by a cell from the reserve group. However the present primary group of twenty cells contains fifteen cells that have been members of the group since 1906, more than a quarter of a century."

The voltage of these cells has been measured from time to time to an accuracy of a few parts in a million by measuring with the current balance the current required to set up an IR-drop in the standard ohm equal to the EMF of the cell. The instrument used is the *potentiometer*, which will be described in the next chapter.

All electrical and magnetic quantities can be readily measured in terms of the volt, the ohm, the meter, the kilogram, and the second. Consequently, the concrete standards of resistance and voltage, together with the mechanical standards, furnish the primary standards used for calibration purposes at the N.B.S. Secondary concrete standards of capacitance, self inductance, and mutual inductance are also maintained by means of standard capacitors and inductors.

6. RÉSUMÉ

We have discussed three separate items in this chapter: fundamental definitions of electrical and magnetic units, fundamental measurements designed to establish the units in terms of these definitions, and concrete standards for maintenance of the units. The definitions of ampere, volt, ohm, and coulomb are interrelated in such a way that fundamental measurements and concrete standards of only two of them are needed. The two that are chosen for fundamental measurements are not the same as the two chosen for concrete standards; the choices are dictated by practical considerations. We shall summarize here the definitions of the units, the fundamental measurements for establishing the units, and the concrete standards for maintenance of the units.

Definitions

The *ampere* is defined in terms of the newton by the formulas of Chap. 36 which enable the magnetic force between coils carrying the same current to be computed. In particular, and purely theoretically, one could define the ampere as that current which when flowing in each of two infinite parallel wires one meter apart would result in a magnetic force of 2×10^{-7} newton per meter length.

The *volt* is defined as the DP across a resistor when one ampere of current generates one watt of heat.

The *ohm* is defined as the resistance such that a current of one ampere requires a DP of one volt.

The *coulomb* is defined as the amount of charge passing a point per second when a current of one ampere is flowing.

Other units, such as those of electric and magnetic fields, capacitance, and inductance, are defined in terms of the above fundamental units. The defining equations for these units are collected in the following Sec. 7. In Sec. 1 of the Appendix to this volume will be found a discussion of other systems of electrical and magnetic units that are in use.

Fundamental measurements for establishment of the units

Absolute measurement of current in amperes can be made by means of the current balance of Fig. 1.

Absolute measurement of resistance in ohms can be made by means of the apparatus of Fig. 2 which employs an accurately constructed solenoid, or by means of apparatus mentioned in Sec. 3 which employs an accurately constructed self or mutual inductance.

Absolute measurement of voltage is made by using a potentiometer (Chap. 42) to compare the voltage with the IR-drop across a resistance that has been measured absolutely, the current being measured by means of a current balance.

Absolute measurement of charge, and hence of capacitance, is made by repeatedly discharging a condenser that has been charged to known voltage through a galvanometer that has been calibrated in terms of the absolute ampere, and measuring the average discharge current.

Maintenance of the units

The following concrete standards are used to maintain the units and to serve for calibration of all electrical measuring instruments in terms of the absolute units:

Standard resistors, whose resistances have been absolutely measured.

Standard cells, whose EMF's have been absolutely measured.

Standard capacitors, whose capacitances have been absolutely measured or computed from their geometry once the proportionality constant in Coulomb's law has been experimentally determined.

Standard inductors, whose self or mutual inductances have been computed from their geometry in accordance with theory.

Calibration of instruments of all types is effected in terms of these concrete standards by use of various circuits. Some of these circuits are described in the following chapter, and all of them are discussed in detail in books such as Curtis's.

7. DEFINING EQUATIONS AND DIMENSIONS OF THE ELECTRICAL AND MAGNETIC UNITS

In this section we shall list a set of equations that can be used to define the various electrical and magnetic quantities, and give the units in which these quantities are measured, both in terms of other electrical units and in terms of the fundamental mechanical units.* The relations between the units follow directly from the defining equations that are given.

Current I [force per unit length between parallel wires as in (1) and (2)]

$$f = 2I^2/10^7 a \qquad I = \sqrt{10^7 af/2}$$

$$1 \text{ amp} = 1 \sqrt{\text{nt}}$$

Charge Q

$$Q = It$$

$$1 \text{ coul} = 1 \text{ amp·sec} = 1 \sqrt{\text{nt}}\text{·sec}$$

DP or EMF V [work done on charge]

$$W = QV \qquad V = W/Q$$

$$1 \text{ volt} = 1 \text{ joule/coul} = 1 \text{ watt/amp} = 1 \sqrt{\text{nt}}\text{·m/sec}$$

---

* As is pointed out in Sec. 1 of the Appendix to this volume, expressing the electrical and magnetic units entirely in terms of mechanical units is quite lacking in fundamental significance, since it can be done in various ways depending on the system of equations adopted for defining the units. The treatment we give in this text is consistent and *very convenient* so long as one adheres to a *single system* of electrical and magnetic units, as we do. Fundamentally however one must consider *one* of the electrical units, say that of current or of charge, as basic and *not* expressible in terms of mechanical units. All physical quantities can be expressed in terms of *five* fundamental units: those of *length, mass, time, temperature,* and *electric current*.

Sec. 7] DEFINING EQUATIONS AND DIMENSIONS 1073

Resistance R; reactance X_L, X_C; impedance Z

$$R = V/I; \quad X_L = V_{L0}/I_0; \quad X_C = V_{C0}/I_0; \quad Z = V_0/I_0$$

1 ohm = 1 volt/amp = 1 watt/amp^2 = 1 m/sec

Electric intensity $\mathcal{E}$ [force on charge or potential gradient]

$$\mathcal{E} = f/Q \quad \text{or} \quad \mathcal{E} = dV/dx$$

1 nt/coul = 1 volt/m = 1 nt/amp·sec = 1 $\sqrt{\text{nt}}$/sec

Capacitance C

$$C = Q/V$$

1 farad = 1 coul/v = 1 amp^2·sec/watt = 1 sec^2/m

Self inductance L; mutual inductance M

$$V = L \, dI/dt; \qquad V_2 = M \, dI_1/dt$$

1 henry = 1 volt·sec/amp = 1 ohm·sec = 1 joule/amp^2 = 1 meter

Magnetic field strength $\mathcal{B}$ [force on wire]

$$f = \mathcal{B}lI \qquad \mathcal{B} = f/lI$$

1 weber/m^2 = 1 nt/amp·m = 1 $\sqrt{\text{nt}}$/m

Magnetic flux Φ

$$\Phi = \mathcal{B}A$$

1 weber = 1 volt·sec = 1 joule/amp = 1 $\sqrt{\text{nt}}$·m

Magnetic moment M [current loop or torque on magnet]

$$M = IA \quad \text{or} \quad L = M\mathcal{B}\sin\theta$$

1 amp·m^2 = 1 nt·m^3/weber = 1 $\sqrt{\text{nt}}$·m^2

Magnetization $\mathfrak{M}$ [magnetic moment per unit volume]

$$\mathfrak{M} = dM/dV$$

1 amp/m = 1 $\sqrt{\text{nt}}$/m

Magnetomotive force MMF

$$\text{MMF} = NI$$

1 ampere-turn = 1 $\sqrt{\text{nt}}$

Magnetizing force $\mathcal{H}$ [line-integral law]

$$\int \mathcal{H} \, dl = \text{MMF} = NI$$

1 amp-turn/meter = 1 $\sqrt{\text{nt}}$/m

Reluctance $\mathcal{R}$

$$\Phi = \text{MMF}/\mathcal{R} \qquad \mathcal{R} = \text{MMF}/\Phi$$

1 amp-turn/weber = 1 henry^{-1} = 1 amp^2/joule = 1 meter^{-1}

Dielectric constant K is dimensionless

Permeability μ is dimensionless.

CHAPTER 42

ELECTRICAL MEASURING INSTRUMENTS

In this chapter we shall describe the most familiar types of instruments for laboratory and service measurement of electric current, voltage, power, and energy. We shall also discuss in some detail the theory of the potentiometer, mentioned in the preceding chapter as the instrument used for accurate comparison of voltages, and of the fluxmeter, which was referred to in Chap. 38 as the most convenient instrument for measurement of flux changes. Other types of instruments will be mentioned briefly.

1. THE D'ARSONVAL GALVANOMETER

The essential element of DC ammeters and voltmeters is a moving-coil galvanometer of the type shown in Fig. 1. The coil of this galvanom-

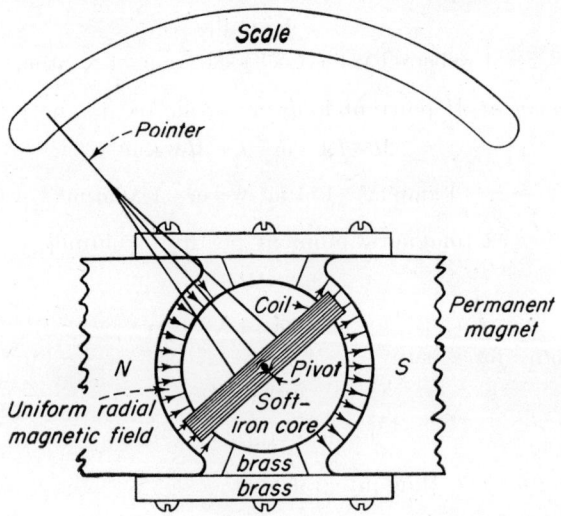

Fig. 1. Schematic drawing of galvanometer coil and magnets. The drawing is distorted in that the coil and pole pieces would ordinarily be much smaller in comparison with the length of the pointer and the length of the scale.

eter is supported on hardened steel pivots turning in jeweled bearings. Its rotational motion is restrained by a pair of springs (not shown in Fig. 1), one above and one below the coil, which also serve as current leads to the coil. The position of coil and pointer in Fig. 1 is intended to represent the equilibrium position as determined by the springs, with no current in the coil. In use, current flows in the coil, into the paper on the right in Fig. 1, and out of the paper on the left, so that the magnetic forces of these currents in the uniform radial magnetic field create a clockwise torque. The coil moves clockwise until the resisting counterclockwise spring torque equals the clockwise magnetic torque. Since the magnetic torque is proportional to the current in the coil and since the spring torque is proportional to the angle of rotation from the equilibrium position, the angle of rotation is proportional to the current in the coil. The straightforward development of the relation between current and angle is left to the reader as an exercise in Prob. 1.

The galvanometer elements of ordinary commercial ammeters and voltmeters have a coil of resistance of the order of magnitude of 1 ohm, and give full-scale deflection with a current of 1 milliampere or less.

Pivoted galvanometers of the type shown in Fig. 1 can be purchased that give full-scale deflection on a current as low as 1 microampere; greater sensitivity than this cannot be achieved because of friction in the bearings. To achieve sensitivity, the spring torque constant must be made very low, but the spring torque must still be large compared to the frictional torque in the bearings if the instrument is to perform properly. To avoid friction and to achieve a very low torque constant, more sensitive instruments, designed to measure currents in the range 10^{-6} to 10^{-10} amperes, are of the *suspended-coil* type, with the coil suspended from a fiber of phosphor bronze, silver, or quartz. Such a suspended-coil instrument is not usually portable. It is read by means of a lamp and scale, with the light beam reflected from a small mirror attached to the top of the coil.

The combination of coil and spiral springs or fiber in a galvanometer forms a torsion pendulum. Such a pendulum would perform harmonic oscillations about its equilibrium position, making the instrument very inconvenient to use, if a special provision were not made to damp out these oscillations. To provide damping, the coil is wound on a light frame, usually of aluminum, which forms a short-circuited turn. When this *damping frame* rotates in the magnetic field, an EMF, and hence a current, is set up in it by the same action as in a generator. As we have observed in connection with the discussions of generators and of eddy currents, the current in the damping frame is in such a direction as to experience a magnetic force opposing the rotation. The thickness and resistance of the frame are made such as to introduce enough damping to prevent overshooting and harmonic oscillations, but not enough to make the motion of the pointer unduly sluggish. The *damping frame* has no effect on the position of equilibrium because when the coil has come to rest there is no current in the frame and hence no magnetic force on the frame.

When a galvanometer is connected into an external circuit of comparatively low resistance, damping is also furnished by the generator action of the swinging coil. When the coil rotates, currents are induced in such a direction that the magnetic forces tend to oppose the rotation of the coil—effectively kinetic energy of rotation is changed into electrical energy and I^2R heat. The damping frame of suspended-coil galvanometers usually does not provide adequate damping to make the galvanometer conveniently usable. The manufacturer specifies an external critical-damping resistance, say of 100 ohms. When the resistance of the external circuit is 100 ohms this galvanometer is just critically damped; that is, the galvanometer coil will rotate into its final steady position, when a current is applied or removed, in the shortest possible time without overshooting (see p. 288). With more resistance the galvanometer will be underdamped and will oscillate about its final position; with less resistance it will be overdamped and its motion may be excessively sluggish. Such a galvanometer should always be used in an external circuit of resistance in the neighborhood of that specified for critical damping.

PROBLEMS

1. In Fig. 1, let

N = number of turns in coil,
$\mathcal{B}$ = strength of radial magnetic field (weber/m²),
l = effective length of wires in the field (m),
r = radius from axis of rotation to coil wires in the magnetic field (m),
θ = angle of rotation of coil, measured from no-current equilibrium position (rad),
K = torque constant of springs (nt·m/rad),
I = current in each turn of coil (amp).

Show that
$$I = \frac{K\theta}{2N\mathcal{B}lr}. \qquad (1)$$

2. A galvanometer coil of wound of No. 30 copper wire. Each turn requires 4 inches of wire. What spring torque constant must be used if, in the notation of Prob. 1, $\mathcal{B} = 0.3$ weber/m², $l = 2.5$ cm, $r = 1$ cm, and the meter is to give full-scale (60°) deflection on 1 milliampere and have 1 ohm resistance at 20° C?

3. A galvanometer is wound of No. 33 copper wire. Each turn requires 4 inches of wire. What spring torque constant must be used if, in the notation of Prob. 1, $\mathcal{B} = 0.5$ weber/m², $l = 2.5$ cm, $r = 1$ cm, and the meter is to give full-scale (60°) deflection on 1 microampere and have 30 ohms resistance at 20° C?

Ans: 1.04×10^{-7} nt·m/rad.

2. THE DC VOLTMETER

A DC voltmeter consists of a d'Arsonval galvanometer with an added series resistor called a *multiplier*. The *galvanometer* is characterized by its resistance R_G and the current I_G or voltage V_G required for *full-scale* deflection, where $V_G = I_G R_G$. If now we want full-scale deflection of the *voltmeter* for voltage V_F, where $V_F > V_G$, we must add enough resistance R_M so that with voltage V_F across the terminals, we get only current I_G

through the galvanometer as indicated in Fig. 2. Since

$$I_G(R_G+R_M) = V_F$$

and

$$I_G R_G = V_G,$$

we find, by division, that

$$\frac{R_G+R_M}{R_G} = \frac{V_F}{V_G}. \qquad (2)$$

Thus, if $R_G = 1$ ohm, $I_G = 1$ ma,* $V_G = 1$ mv, and we want V_F to be 200 volts full scale, we find, from (2), that

$$\frac{1\ \omega + R_M}{1\ \omega} = \frac{200}{0.001} = 200{,}000,$$

so that

$$R_M = 199{,}999\ \omega.$$

The total resistance R of this voltmeter would be $R = R_G + R_M = 200{,}000\ \omega$.

A voltmeter must have a very high resistance if it is to serve its purpose because it is intended to measure the difference of potential between two points in a circuit without disturbing the currents in the circuit. No voltmeter, except one of the electrostatic type, actually does this because the voltmeter actually does draw a minute current. The current drawn, and hence the deflection of the galvanometer, is proportional (Fig. 2) to the voltage across the terminals. Only if this current is very small compared to the current flowing in the circuit under consideration has the voltmeter accomplished its purpose. The voltmeter always reads the difference of potential between its own terminals, and hence the difference of potential that exists between the two points to which it is connected after it is connected. If the voltmeter draws negligible current, this DP will be the same as the DP between the same two points before it was connected.

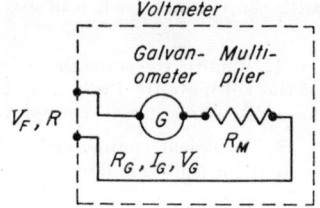

Fig. 2. A DC voltmeter. The symbols V_F, I_G, V_G refer to *full-scale* deflection.

Note that (2) can be rewritten in the form

$$\frac{R}{V_F} = \frac{R_G}{V_G} = \frac{1}{I_G} \quad \text{in} \quad \frac{\text{ohms}}{\text{volt}},$$

where R is the total resistance of the voltmeter. Hence, any voltmeter made from a certain galvanometer, characterized by definite values of R_G, V_G, I_G, will have a definite ratio of resistance to full-scale voltage. The ratio for the instrument considered above is 1000 ohms/volt. The higher this ratio, the better the voltmeter from the standpoint of avoid-

---

* For convenience we are writing 'ma' instead of 'mamp' for *milliampere*. This is the most common abbreviation.

ing disturbance of the circuit. Commercial voltmeters of high quality are ordinarily considerably better than the instrument we have discussed; they usually have a ratio of 30,000 ohms/volt, and employ a galvanometer element of higher current sensitivity (lower I_G for full-scale deflection) than in our example.

PROBLEMS

1. A commercial voltmeter reads 150 volts full scale. The basic element is a d'Arsonval galvanometer of 100 ohms resistance that gives full-scale deflection on 20 mv. Find the resistance of the multiplier.   Ans: 749,900 ohms.

2. A commercial voltmeter reads 10 volts full scale. The basic element is a d'Arsonval galvanometer of 50 ohms resistance that gives full scale deflection on 0.1 ma. Find the resistance of the multiplier.

3. A laboratory that possesses the instrument of Prob. 1 desires to convert it to one reading 450 volts full scale. The laboratory writes to the meter-manufacturing company and orders a ×3 external multiplier for this particular instrument. The manufacturer sends a box with two binding posts which is to be connected in series with the voltmeter when in use. What is in the box?
    Ans: An accurate 1.5-megohm resistance.

4. What is the resistance of the external multiplier that will multiply the readings of the voltmeter of Prob. 2 by 20, converting it to 200 volts full-scale. (See Prob. 3 for a discussion of an external multiplier.)

5. A typical commercial voltmeter is rated at 30,000 ohms/volt. What is the current for full-scale deflection of the galvanometer element?   Ans: $\frac{1}{30}$ ma.

6. It is possible to purchase a commercial voltmeter with a rating of 1,000,000 ohms/volt. What is the current required for full-scale deflection of such an instrument?

7. A commercial multirange voltmeter has a dial switch on the panel that permits settings of 2, 10, 50, or 200 volts full-scale. It has a resistance of 10,000 ohms/volt, and a galvanometer resistance R_G of 150 ohms. Draw a circuit diagram for this instrument, showing the resistances in the various steps of the multiplier.
    Ans: Multiplier has resistances of 19,850, 80,000, 400,000, and 1,500,000 ohms in series, appropriately connected to the various contacts available for the arm of the dial switch.

8. A 100,000-ohm/volt voltmeter has $R_G = 250$ ohms and a dial switch giving choice of 0.05, 0.1, 0.5, 1, 5, or 10 volts full-scale. Draw a circuit diagram for this instrument, showing the resistances connected in series and tapped to the various steps of the dial switch.

3. THE DC AMMETER

A DC ammeter consists of a galvanometer with an added shunt resistance as in Fig. 3. If we want full-scale deflection with current I_F, where $I_F > I_G$, we must use a shunt resistance low enough that with current I_F flowing in at the terminals, only current I_G will flow through the galvanometer. Since current $I_F - I_G$ flows through the shunt, we have, from Kirchhoff's second law,

$$(I_F - I_G)R_S = I_G R_G$$

or
$$\frac{R_S}{R_G} = \frac{I_G}{I_F - I_G}. \qquad (3)$$

Thus, if $I_G = 1$ milliampere and $R_G = 1$ ohm, and we want an ammeter with $I_F = 10$ amp, we must have

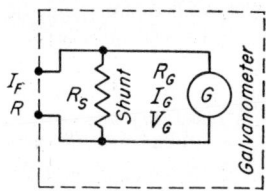

$$R_S = 1\ \omega \times \frac{0.001 \text{ amp}}{9.999 \text{ amp}} = 0.00010001\ \omega.$$

The resistance R between terminals of this ammeter can be obtained from the equation $RI_F = V_G$:

Fig. 3. A DC ammeter. The symbols I_F, I_G, V_G refer to *full-scale* deflection.

$$R = \frac{V_G}{I_F} = \frac{0.001 \text{ v}}{10 \text{ amp}} = 0.0001\ \omega.$$

The resistance of a good ammeter should be low, so that when the ammeter is introduced as a series element in a circuit it does not appreciably change the current in the circuit by introduction of added resistance. An ammeter always measures correctly the current through itself *after* it is connected. Only if its resistance is negligible compared to the other resistances in the circuit is this current the same as the current before it was inserted in the circuit. The last equation above shows that the ammeter best from the standpoint of low resistance is the one made with the galvanometer of greatest voltage sensitivity (lowest V_G).

PROBLEMS

1. What shunt resistance is required in an ammeter whose galvanometer element has a resistance of 5 ohms and gives full-scale deflection on 50 mv, if the ammeter is to read 25 amp full scale?   Ans.: $0.00200\ \omega$.

2. What shunt resistance is required in a milliammeter whose galvanometer element has a resistance of 50 ohms and gives full-scale deflection on 1 ma, if the milliammeter is to read 60 ma full-scale?

NOTE: In measuring a resistance (Fig. 4) by the voltmeter-ammeter method, the ammeter is placed in series with the resistance, but the voltmeter can be connected in two ways:

(a) across the resistor alone,

(b) across the resistor and the ammeter in parallel.

Method (a) has the disadvantage that the ammeter measures the current through the voltmeter as well as that through the resistor; (b) has the disadvantage that the voltmeter measures the voltage drop across the ammeter as well as that across the resistor. We call the ratio V/I of voltmeter to ammeter reading the *apparent* resistance of the resistor being measured. In Probs. 3, 4, 5, and 6, we contemplate measuring a 20.00-ohm resistor by using a dry cell as a current source, together with a 1.5-v full-scale voltmeter and a 50-ma full-scale milliammeter. In each case, the current is adjusted by an external rheostat so that the milliammeter reads full scale.

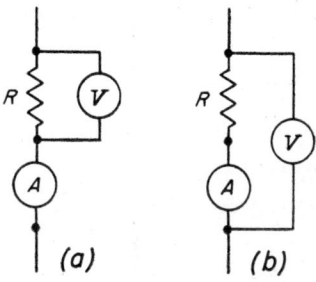

Fig. 4.

3. (See note above.) If the voltmeter has a resistance of 500 ohms and the milliammeter a resistance of 1 ohm, what is the apparent resistance in case (a)? in case (b)? *Ans:* (a) 19.23 ω; (b) 21.00 ω.

4. (See note above.) If the voltmeter has a resistance of 15,000 ohms and the milliammeter a resistance of 1 ohm, what is the apparent resistance in case (a)? in case (b)?

5. (See note above.) If the voltmeter has a resistance of 500 ohms and the milliammeter a resistance of 0.001 ohm, what is the apparent resistance in case (a)? in case (b)? *Ans:* (a) 19.23 ω; (b) 20.00 ω.

6. (See note above.) If the voltmeter has a resistance of 15,000 ohms and the milliammeter a resistance of 0.001 ohm, what is the apparent resistance in case (a)? in case (b)?

7. For connection (a) of Fig. 4, show that if I is the ammeter reading, V the voltmeter reading, R_A the ammeter resistance, and R_V the voltmeter resistance, then the true resistance of the resistor is given by $R = V/(I - V/R_V)$. Show also that if $R_{app} = V/I$, then $R = R_{app}(1 + R/R_V)$, so that connection (a) is most satisfactory when the resistance of the voltmeter is large compared to the resistance being measured.

8. For connection (b) of Fig. 4, show that if I is the ammeter reading, V the voltmeter reading, R_A the ammeter resistance, and R_V the voltmeter resistance, then the true resistance of the resistor is given by $R = (V/I) - R_A = R_{app} - R_A$, so that connection (b) is most satisfactory when the resistance of the ammeter is small compared to the resistance being measured.

9. Given a 50-ma, 50-mv, 1-ohm galvanometer, design a set of external shunts and multipliers that will convert this into a 1-amp, 5-amp, or 10-amp ammeter or a 15-volt, 75-volt, or 150-volt voltmeter.
Ans: Shunts of 0.0526, 0.0101, 0.00503 ω; multipliers of 299, 1499, 2999 ω.

10. Given a 1-ma, 50-mv, 50-ohm galvanometer, design a set of external shunts and multipliers that will convert this into a 10-ma, 50-ma, or 100-ma milliammeter, or a 50-mv, 100-mv, or 500-mv millivoltmeter.

4. THE ELECTRODYNAMOMETER

The electrodynamometer of Fig. 5 differs from the galvanometer of Fig. 1 in that the electrodynamometer contains no permanent magnet. Rather, the magnetic field in which the moving coil rotates is created by a pair of fixed coils carrying current supplied from outside through a pair of binding posts separate from those that supply current to the moving coil. The net effect of this coil arrangement is that a given pointer reading corresponds to a definite value of the product I_1I_2 of the currents in the fixed and moving coils, and the scale may be calibrated to read I_1I_2.

While the deflection is not strictly proportional to the product I_1I_2, so that the scale must be calibrated by sending known currents through the coils, the deflection is approximately proportional to I_1I_2, and the marks corresponding to $I_1I_2 = 0$, $I_1I_2 = 1$ ma^2, $I_1I_2 = 2$ ma^2, $I_1I_2 = 3$ ma^2, and so on, are approximately equally spaced on the scale.

The most important thing to understand is that a given pointer position rigorously corresponds to a definite value of the product I_1I_2 and that the pointer will stand at the position marked $I_1I_2 = 4$ ma^2, for example, whether $I_1 = 2$ ma and $I_2 = 2$ ma, $I_1 = 1$ ma and $I_2 = 4$ ma, $I_1 = 0.5$ ma and $I_2 = 8$ ma, or even $I_1 = -4$ ma and $I_2 = -1$ ma. To demonstrate this property, note that the pointer position of Fig. 5 is intended to represent the equilibrium position of the springs, and hence the position of the pointer when there are no currents in the coils. A current I_1 in the fixed coils in the direction shown will set up a magnetic field in the indicated direction. With a current I_2 in the moving coil in the direction shown, the moving coil will have a magnetic moment represented by a vector in the direction perpendicular to its plane and pointing in the same direction as the pointer. The coil in the magnetic field experiences a torque tending to turn its magnetic moment into the direction of the field, that is, a

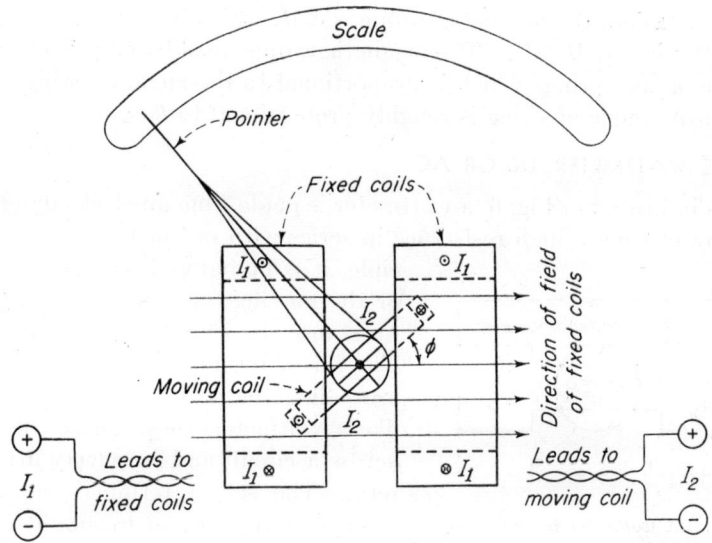

Fig. 5. The electrodynamometer. The pivoted moving coil rotates in the space interior to the fixed coils. A light framework extending through the gap between the fixed coils carries the pointer and the springs supplying the restoring torque. In this diagram the pointer is in the equilibrium position for no current.

clockwise torque tending to swing the pointer to the right. The pointer will move to the right until the countertorque of the springs just balances the magnetic torque. Suppose now that we increase the current I_1 by a factor k to kI_1, at the same time dropping I_2 by a factor k to I_2/k, so that the product I_1I_2 is unchanged. Then the force on each element of the coil, $\mathcal{B}I_2\,dl$, will be unchanged because the field $\mathcal{B}$ at each point is rigorously proportional to I_1, and this field increases by a factor k at the same times that I_2 drops by a factor k. Hence, the magnetic torque will be unchanged and will still balance the spring torque at the same pointer position. Similarly, if I_1 and I_2 are both reversed in direction but unchanged in magnitude, the magnetic torque and the pointer position will not change, for both the magnetic field and the current in the moving coil are exactly reversed, with the force on each current element unchanged.

Thus, we see that a given pointer position corresponds to a definite value of $I_1 I_2$. We can now show that the angle of pointer swing from the equilibrium position is *approximately proportional* to the value of $I_1 I_2$. The magnetic field ℬ is approximately uniform. For a uniform field, the magnetic torque would be $ℬM \cos\phi$, where M is the magnetic moment of the coil and ϕ is the angle between the plane of the coil and the magnetic field as in Fig. 5. Now to a very rough approximation we can set $\cos\phi = 1$, because ϕ is never greater than 30 or 40 degrees. To this rough approximation, the magnetic torque is $ℬM$, which is *proportional* to $I_1 I_2$, since $ℬ \propto I_1$ and $M \propto I_2$. The magnetic torque must balance the restoring torque of the springs which is proportional to the angle of swing. Consequently, angle of swing is roughly proportional to $I_1 I_2$.

5. THE WATTMETER, DC OR AC

As indicated in Fig. 6, a wattmeter is made from an electrodynamometer by putting a high resistance in series with one of the coils (in principle, it is immaterial whether the fixed or the moving coil is selected) and a low resistance in parallel with the other. The set of terminals marked V in Fig. 6 are called the *voltage terminals* because, like a voltmeter, they can be connected across a circuit and draw very little current. The set of terminals marked I are called the *current terminals* because the resistance between them is very low and, like an ammeter, they can be connected in series with a circuit without introducing much additional resistance.

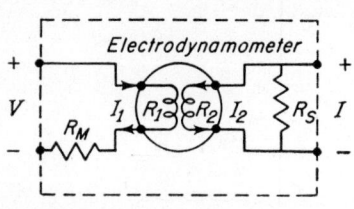

Fig. 6. A *wattmeter* is made from an electrodynamometer.

The wattmeter is connected to measure the power expended in a load as indicated in Fig. 7, with the voltage terminals in parallel with the load

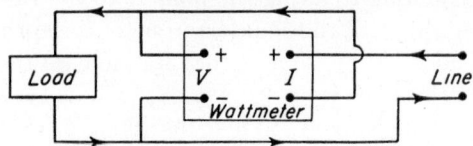

Fig. 7. Connections to a wattmeter to measure the power expended in a load. Arrows indicate current direction for a DC circuit, positive sense of current for an AC circuit.

and the whole load current flowing through the current terminals, which are in series with the load. The instrument will work equally well for

DC or AC. We shall discuss the DC case first. In this case the current I_1 through the voltage coil of the electrodynamometer is proportional to the voltage V across the load. The current I_2 through the current coil is proportional to the load current I (actually to the load current plus the current flowing through the voltage terminals of the wattmeter, but the latter current can usually be assumed negligible). Since the pointer position is a measure of the product $I_1 I_2$, and $I_1 \propto V$ and $I_2 \propto I$, the pointer position is a measure of VI, and the scale can be calibrated directly in watts.

If we write
$$I_1 = K_1 V, \tag{4}$$
we see, from Fig. 6, that $K_1 = 1/(R_1 + R_M)$. If we write
$$I_2 = K_2 I, \tag{5}$$
we see, also from Fig. 6, that $R_2 I_2 = R_S(I - I_2)$, or $R_2 I_2 + R_S I_2 = R_S I$, or $I_2 = I R_S/(R_2 + R_S)$, so that $K_2 = R_S/(R_2 + R_S)$. These considerations are just like those in the case of the voltmeter and the ammeter, respectively, and will be illustrated by problems at the end of this section. We then have
$$I_1 I_2 = K_1 K_2 \, VI = K_1 K_2 \, P, \tag{6}$$
where P is power in watts. If the value of $I_1 I_2$ for full-scale reading of the electrodynamometer is known, and $K_1 K_2$ is known, this equation will give the power P for full-scale reading of the wattmeter.

The ordinary commercial wattmeter will read power correctly on 60-$\sim$ AC as well as on DC, although it will not work on AC of frequency much above 60 cycles/sec. This versatility is possible because the electrodynamometer coils have such low inductive reactance (being air-cored, their self inductance is really quite low) compared to their resistance that even for 60-$\sim$ AC they are the practical equivalent of a pure resistance and carry a current in phase with the voltage across them. Consequently, equations (4) and (5) remain true for the AC case if the symbols are taken to refer to instantaneous values of currents and voltages.

The electrodynamometer movement has sufficient inertia and sufficient damping that it will not follow the rapid variations of magnetic torque that arise when 60-$\sim$ currents are introduced into its coils. Rather, it will set itself at such a position that the spring torque is equal and opposite to the *average* value of the magnetic torque. Since at a given position the instantaneous magnetic torque is proportional to the product $I_1 I_2$, the average magnetic torque will be proportional to the average of this product, which we denote by $\langle I_1 I_2 \rangle_\text{av}$. Hence, the scale reading will be a measure of $\langle I_1 I_2 \rangle_\text{av}$.

Now let Fig. 7 represent an AC circuit, with instantaneous voltage
$$V = \sqrt{2} \, V_0 \sin 2\pi f t,$$

where V_0 is the *effective* value of the AC voltage. Since the current I will generally differ in phase from the voltage, we write

$$I = \sqrt{2}\, I_0 \sin(2\pi ft + \theta),$$

where I_0 is the *effective* current and the phase angle θ is positive for a leading current, negative for a lagging current. Now, from (4) and (5),

$$I_1 I_2 = K_1 K_2\, VI,$$

or
$$\langle I_1 I_2 \rangle_{av} = K_1 K_2 \langle VI \rangle_{av}.$$

But we have shown in Chap. 40 that the power drawn by the load is

$$P = \langle VI \rangle_{av} = V_0 I_0 \cos\theta,$$

so that
$$\langle I_1 I_2 \rangle_{av} = K_1 K_2\, P.$$

Since the scale reading is a measure of $\langle I_1 I_2 \rangle_{av}$, comparison of this equation with (6) shows that the same pointer reading will correspond to the same power as in the DC case.

Note that *the wattmeter reads true power* $V_0 I_0 \cos\theta$, not the product $V_0 I_0$. Thus, if a load is drawing a large current at 90° phase angle with the voltage, so that it is drawing no power, the average magnetic torque in the electrodynamometer would be zero, and the meter would read zero watts.

PROBLEMS

NOTE: Although in principle it does not matter which of the coils of the electrodynamometer is used as the current and which as the voltage coil of the wattmeter, in practice it is most convenient to make the fixed coil of low resistance and to use it as the current coil. The fixed coil is made from a few turns of heavy wire and usually has sufficiently low resistance that it can be used without a shunt. The moving coil is made of many turns of fine wire and is used as the potential coil with a multiplier in series.

1. It is desired to make a wattmeter from an electrodynamometer that gives full-scale deflection with $I_1 I_2 = 0.01$ amp² by placing a high resistance in series with the moving coil and using this as the potential coil. If the moving coil has a resistance of 200 ohms and the wattmeter is to read 100 watts full scale, what series resistance is needed? *Ans*: 9800 ohms.

2. It is desired to make a wattmeter from an electrodynamometer that gives full-scale deflection with $I_1 I_2 = 0.05$ amp² by placing a high resistance in series with the moving coil and using this as the potential coil. If the moving coil has a resistance of 500 ohms and the wattmeter is to read 1000 watts full scale, what series resistance is needed?

3. Show that in the wattmeter connection of Fig. 7 the reading of the wattmeter *exceeds* the power consumed in the load by the power expended in the voltage circuit within the wattmeter itself. Show that the ratio of voltage-circuit power to load power equals (in the DC case) the ratio of load resistance to voltage-circuit resistance, so that this connection is most suitable when the voltage circuit of the wattmeter has a resistance high compared to the load resistance.

4. An alternative wattmeter connection, which in practice is frequently more desirable than that of Fig. 7, is shown in Fig. 8. Show that for this connection the reading of the wattmeter *exceeds* the power consumed in the load by the power expended in the current circuit within the wattmeter itself. Show that the ratio of current-circuit power to load power is equal (in the DC case) to the ratio of current-circuit resistance to load resistance, so that this connection is most suitable when the current circuit of the wattmeter has a resistance small compared to the load resistance.

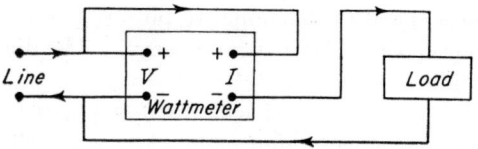

Fig. 8. Alternative connection of wattmeter to load.

5. A wattmeter designed for operation on 110 volts is connected to a load consisting of a condenser in series with a variable resistance, connected to 110 volts AC. As the value of the resistance is decreased, the power reading increases to about half scale on the wattmeter and then begins to decrease—and then the current coil of the wattmeter burns out! Explain this sequence of events.

6. THE WATT-HOUR METER

The DC watt-hour meter is shown schematically in Fig. 9. It is essentially a very small shunt motor in which the magnetic field is set up

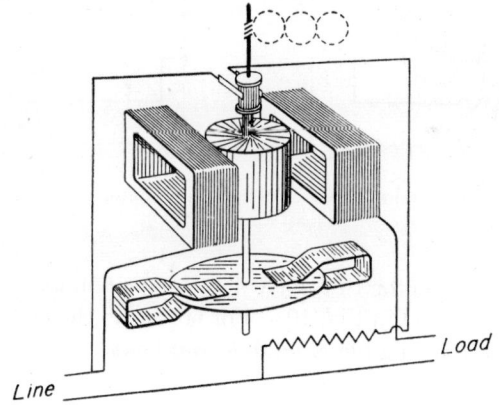

Fig. 9. The DC watt-hour meter.

by low-resistance coils connected in series with the line, so that the magnetic field is proportional to the line current. The armature, in series with a high resistance, is connected across the line, so that the armature receives a small current proportional to the line voltage. The torque of this motor is thus proportional to the product of voltage and current, that is, to the power taken by the load.

The principal resistance to turning of the motor is furnished by an eddy-current brake, which has the characteristic of offering a resisting torque proportional to speed of rotation. Since the motor will run at such speed that the magnetic torque equals the resisting torque, it is seen that the speed of the motor will be proportional to the magnetic torque, and hence to the power taken by the load. Dials driven through reduction gears thus turn at a speed proportional to power, so the dial readings are proportional to power × time, that is, to energy. The dials are calibrated in watt-hours or kilowatt-hours.

The instrument just described will run fairly satisfactorily on AC as well as on DC, but most AC watt-hour meters are essentially little induction motors so constructed that average torque is proportional to average power $V_0 I_0 \cos\theta$. The resistance is again furnished by an eddy-current brake. We shall not go further into the details of this AC instrument.

7. VOLTMETERS AND AMMETERS FOR USE ON AC

For low-frequency (60-∼) AC, an electrodynamometer may be made into a voltmeter or an ammeter by connecting the two coils in series and adding either a series or shunt resistance in the same way as in the con-

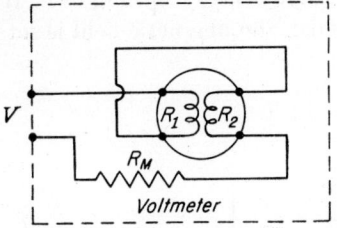 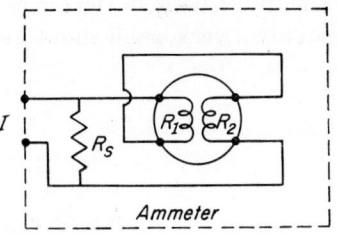

Fig. 10. Conversion of an electrodynamometer into a voltmeter or an ammeter.

version of a galvanometer to a DC voltmeter or ammeter. This type of instrument is illustrated in Fig. 10. For 60-∼ AC, the coils of the electrodynamometer have negligible reactance and behave like pure resistances. The instruments of Fig. 10 work equally well on DC or 60-∼ AC.

Let us consider the voltmeter first. Here the current in each coil is proportional to the applied voltage, so that the pointer swing is a measure of the square of the applied voltage and is approximately proportional to it. For the AC case, the pointer position depends on $\langle V^2 \rangle_{av} = V_0^2$, with the result that the same instrument reads either DC voltage or effective value of AC voltage.

Of course the scale is marked with values of voltage rather than of (voltage)^2. This calibration makes the scale extremely nonlinear. For example, if the meter swings full scale on voltage V, voltage $\frac{1}{2}V$ will make it swing only about $\frac{1}{4}$ scale, since the swing is approximately proportional to the square of the voltage. Such a nonlinear scale is illustrated in Fig. 11; it is usually used only for voltages above half the full-scale voltage, because below this point the finer divisions, not shown in Fig. 11, become too close for the scale to be read with accuracy.

The electrodynamometer-type ammeter similarly reads DC current or effective value of AC current on a nonlinear scale like that of Fig. 11.

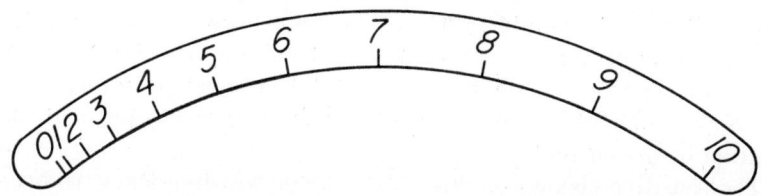

Fig. 11. Typical non-linear scale of an instrument whose swing is proportional to the square of the quantity being measured.

Electrodynamometer instruments are not ordinarily used for direct currents because they are definitely inferior to the permanent-magnet galvanometer type discussed earlier. Since the electrodynamometer element is much less sensitive than the galvanometer element, a galvanometer-type voltmeter can be made of much higher resistance, and an ammeter of much lower resistance, than the corresponding electrodynamometer type. Consequently, DC instruments are in general much more satisfactory than AC instruments.

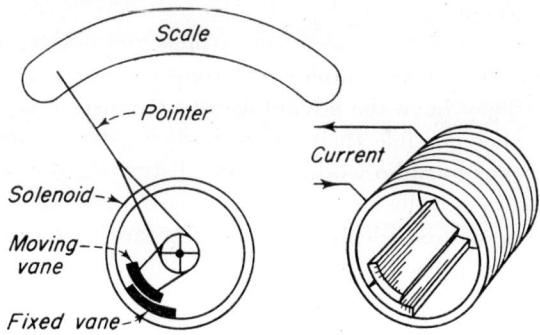

Fig. 12. Sensitive element of soft-iron type of meter. The perspective view on the right shows just the solenoid and the soft-iron vanes. The position illustrated is that of zero current.

A cheaper type of meter, which works on either DC or low-frequency AC, is the *soft-iron* type. In this type, which is in wide usage for small instruments, the sensitive element consists of a fixed iron vane and a moving iron vane, both contained within a solenoid as in Fig. 12. Soft iron with very low hysteresis is used for the vanes. When current flows in the solenoid, the magnetic field that is set up magnetizes both of the vanes in the direction of their length. The vanes then behave like two bar magnets placed side by side with N poles together and S poles together; they repel each other, causing the pointer attached to the moving vane to swing across the scale. The motion is resisted by spiral springs (not shown in Fig. 12) whose equilibrium position determines the zero position of the pointer. The scale is not linear but is less distorted than the scale of Fig. 11. Ammeters and voltmeters using this type of sensitive element are made by adding shunt or series resistance. When such an instrument is used with DC, the reading is independent of the direction of the current.

The sensitive element of Fig. 12 works on low-frequency AC because the magnetization follows the current. The polarity of the vanes reverses with the frequency of the current, but the vanes always repel each other because their like poles are always at the same end. Hysteresis causes less trouble with AC than with DC.

The above instruments cannot be used for high frequencies (audio or radio frequencies). The sensitive element of a *high-frequency meter* usually depends on the heating effect of a current. The temperature rise of a fine wire is measured by means of a thermocouple or by means of the linear expansion of a tightly stretched wire. The temperature rise is a measure of the square of the effective current in the wire. Ammeters and voltmeters employing such a sensitive element are made by adding shunt or series resistance as discussed above. A wattmeter cannot be made on this principle.

There are also various types of electronic voltmeters, some suitable for DC, some for AC. These employ electronic circuits which we shall not discuss here. They have the advantage of extremely high input impedance, which makes possible their use in high-resistance, low-current circuits such as occur in radio work, without disturbing the currents in the circuit. Currents in radio circuits are frequently measured by measuring the voltage drop, with an electronic voltmeter, across a known resistance already contained in the circuit.

PROBLEM

1. Why is the scale of a wattmeter approximately linear, whereas that of an AC voltmeter is highly nonlinear, although both are based on an electrodynamometer type of galvanometer?

8. MEASUREMENTS OF RESISTANCE, INDUCTANCE, AND CAPACITANCE

Accurate measurements (or rather comparisons) of resistance are made by means of the Wheatstone bridge which we have discussed on p. 888. For measurement of very low resistances, another bridge-type circuit, called the *Kelvin double bridge*, is more suitable. We shall not describe this bridge here.

The common *ohmmeter* measures the resistance of a resistor by measuring the current flowing through the resistor when the voltage across it is adjusted to a certain definite value by means of a knob and a built-in auxiliary meter. It is a convenient but not a highly precise instrument.

Measurements of unknown capacitances and inductances in terms of known ones are carried out by bridge circuits somewhat resembling the Wheatstone-bridge circuit, except that AC power is furnished to the bridge. The arms contain inductances or capacitances, and the galvanometer is replaced by a detector of alternating currents, for example a telephone headset if audio-frequency current is used. Such bridges are described in detail in books on electrical measurements.

9. ACCURATE COMPARISON OF VOLTAGES: THE POTENTIOMETER

The potentiometer is one of the most important instruments in any electrical laboratory making precision measurements. In principle it is a device for accurately measuring the ratio of two voltages. Since one of these is usually the accurately known voltage V_S of a standard cell, the potentiometer serves for precision measurement of the other, unknown, voltage V. It also serves for precision measurement of currents by measuring the voltage across a precision resistor through which the current passes. In this way the potentiometer is used for calibration of both ammeters and voltmeters in terms of the voltage of a standard cell.

The basic circuit of the potentiometer is shown in Fig. 13. A constant current, usually furnished by a lead storage battery, flows through the resistor shown in this figure. *The whole resistance R across the storage battery remains constant,* but in a commercial instrument this resistance is made up of a combination of fixed resistances and a precision slide wire, all in series, in such a way that *the resistances R_1 and R_2 can be varied and accurately read on knobs and dials.*

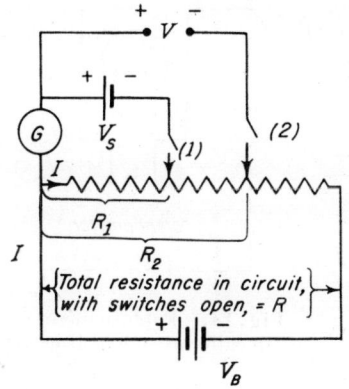

Fig. 13. The basic circuit of the *potentiometer*, arranged to compare the unknown voltage V with the voltage V_S of a standard cell.

In use, first the switch (*1*) is closed, switch (*2*) left open, and R_1 adjusted until the galvanometer G reads zero. When this adjustment has been made,

$$V_S = IR_1, \qquad I = V_B/R,$$

by Kirchhoff's second law.

Then switch (*1*) is opened, switch (*2*) is closed, and R_2 is adjusted until the galvanometer again reads zero. In this case,

$$V = IR_2, \qquad I = V_B/R.$$

Since V_B and R have not been changed between the two adjustments, I does not change, so by taking ratios we see that

$$\frac{V_S}{V} = \frac{R_1}{R_2}, \tag{7}$$

which determines V in terms of V_S and the known resistances R_1 and R_2.

It is not necessary to know either V_B or I. The fact that they have not changed between settings can be checked by alternated closing switches (1) and (2) and verifying that the galvanometer continues to

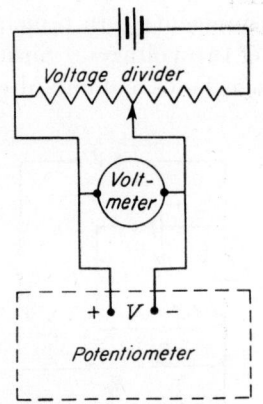

Fig. 14. Potentiometer used to calibrate a DC voltmeter.

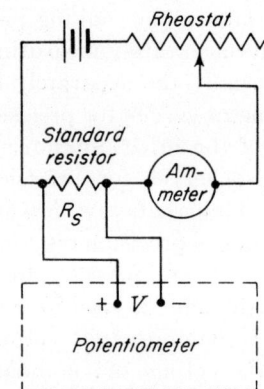

Fig. 15. Potentiometer used to calibrate a DC ammeter.

read zero. The two switches are never both closed at the same time, and the commercial instrument is constructed so that simultaneous closing is impossible.

Figures 14 and 15 show how the potentiometer can be used to calibrate a DC voltmeter or a DC ammeter. The potentiometer terminals marked $+ V -$ correspond to the terminals at the top of Fig. 13. The potentiometer is used to read the voltage across these terminals, and gives the correct voltmeter reading in Fig. 14. In connection with Fig. 15, notice that the potentiometer measures the voltage V without drawing current (galvanometer reading zero in Fig. 13). Since no current is drawn through the terminals V in Fig. 15, the potentiometer reading is R_S times the correct ammeter reading in Fig. 15.

Note that in common parlance a *voltage divider* such as that shown in

Fig. 14 is sometimes called a 'potentiometer.' This is a misusage. The word *potentiometer* means 'a device for *measuring* potential'; a voltage divider merely *divides* the battery potential and furnishes a fraction of it between the end of the rheostat and the sliding contact.

PROBLEMS

1. In Fig. 13, if $V_S = 1.0183$ volts is the known voltage of a Weston standard cell, $R_1 = 101.83$ ohms, and $R_2 = 126.35$ ohms, what is the voltage V of the unknown cell being measured?

2. In Fig. 15, if $R_S = 10.000$ ohms, and the potentiometer reads 1.0014 volts when the milliammeter is set at 100 ma exactly, what is the percentage error in the milliammeter reading? Does it read too high or too low?

10. THE FLUXMETER; THE BALLISTIC GALVANOMETER

The most convenient instrument for measurement of flux changes is the *fluxmeter*. This instrument resembles a d'Arsonval galvanometer, but its scale is calibrated in weber-turns.* If the fluxmeter is connected

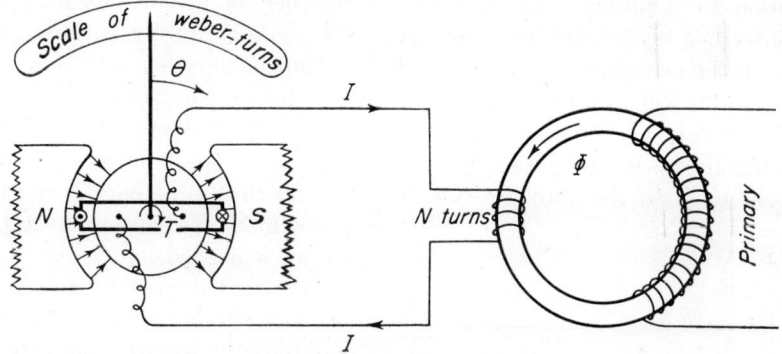

Fig. 16. The *fluxmeter* used to measure flux changes in a ring of ferromagnetic material. Arrows denote the positive sense of I, θ, and Φ as employed in the text discussion.

to an N-turn search coil, and the flux linking the search coil changes by $\Delta\Phi$ webers, the fluxmeter pointer will move from zero to the reading $N \Delta\Phi$ weber-turns. The fluxmeter reads the product of the flux change in the search coil to which it is connected by the number of turns in that search coil. Hence the expression *weber-turns*. The search coil may be a secondary coil wound around an iron ring as in Fig. 16 if it is desired to determine the change of flux in the ring for a given change in the primary current in an investigation of the magnetic properties of the material of the ring. Or the search coil may be a small flat coil placed between the

---

* Or in maxwell-turns. The maxwell is the cgs unit of flux; the weber the mks unit. One weber = 10^8 maxwells. See Sec. 1 of the Appendix.

poles of a magnet and then withdrawn from the field of the magnet to determine that field.

The great convenience of the fluxmeter arises from the fact that *its reading is independent of the resistance of the search-coil circuit and also independent of the time required for the flux to change.* Theoretically, these statements are true without limit; for practical instruments it is best to keep the search-coil resistance under about 100 ohms, and the time required for the flux change under about 15 seconds—these restrictions cause no practical inconvenience.

The fluxmeter differs from the d'Arsonval galvanometer only in that it has *no control springs* and *no damping frame.* Consequently, if the fluxmeter is not connected into an external circuit, the pointer is free to wander around at will. When it is connected into an external circuit, however, any incipient motion of the pointer will, by generator action, cause a current to flow in such a direction as to resist the motion. The movement is thus effectively damped if the circuit resistance is not too high. When not in use the fluxmeter is kept shorted to prevent excessive motion in handling. Because of the absence of control springs, the pointer has no definite zero position. The scale is usually marked with zero in the center so that it will read flux changes in either direction, but the pointer will remain wherever it is put. Therefore an auxiliary circuit, not shown in Fig. 16, is provided by means of which a small current can be introduced in either desired direction to move the pointer by motor action back to the zero position before a reading is taken. Provision is also made for continuous application, if needed, of a very small voltage to balance out any thermal EMF's that might exist in the search-coil circuit and which would cause the pointer to 'drift' slowly away from its initial or final position.

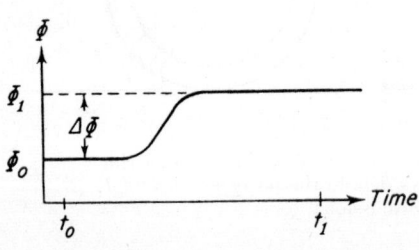

Fig. 17. Change of flux by $\Delta\Phi$. t_0 is a time at which the fluxmeter reads $\theta=0$, before the flux starts changing. t_1 is a time after the flux has stopped changing and after the fluxmeter has settled down to a new reading $\theta=\Theta$.

In use, the fluxmeter is adjusted to zero position ($\theta=0$) while the flux Φ is constant, say $\Phi=\Phi_0$. The flux Φ is then changed by an amount $\Delta\Phi$ to a new constant value Φ_1, as indicated in Fig. 17. The fluxmeter pointer will not follow the curve of Φ accurately; it will tend to overshoot its final position and oscillate back and forth a few times, but will rapidly settle down to a new steady position, say $\theta=\Theta$.

It is easy to demonstrate that the final steady pointer angle Θ is proportional to the flux-linkage change $N\,\Delta\Phi$. During the time between t_0 and t_1 in Fig. 17, current I will flow in the fluxmeter coil. The current will vary with time but will be zero at $t=t_0$ and also at $t=t_1$ when we have again reached a steady state. When current I flows in the fluxmeter coil of Fig. 16 in the direction indicated by the dot and cross, there will be a motor torque T tending to turn the coil in the direction indicated by the curved arrow. This motor torque will be proportional to I. Say that

$$T = KI,$$

where K is a positive constant which we know how to compute but do not need to bother to compute. This is the only torque that can act on the fluxmeter coil, and hence this torque equals the moment of inertia of the pivoted system times its angular acceleration:

$$T = J\, d\omega/dt = KI. \tag{8}$$

Here we use J for moment of inertia to avoid confusion with the symbol for current; ω represents the angular velocity $d\theta/dt$. We note that $\omega = 0$ at $t=t_0$ and at $t=t_1$ when the motion has stopped. Hence from (8):

$$I\, dt = (J/K)\, d\omega$$

and
$$\int_{t_0}^{t_1} I\, dt = \frac{J}{K} \int_{t_0}^{t_1} d\omega = \frac{J}{K}\left[\omega\right]_{t_0}^{t_1} = 0, \tag{9}$$

since $\omega = 0$ at t_0 and t_1. This result, that $\int I\, dt = 0$, we shall have occasion to use presently.

We must now analyze the EMF's that cause current I to flow. There are three sources of EMF in the circuit:

(1) If the fluxmeter coil is turning at positive angular velocity $\omega = d\theta/dt$, there will be a generated voltage proportional to ω in a direction opposite to the positive current direction defined by Fig. 16, as can be seen by a simple analysis of the motion of the conductors in the magnetic field. We can write this EMF as

$$-A\, d\theta/dt, \tag{10}$$

where A is a positive constant that we need not trouble to compute.

(2) If the flux Φ set up by the primary winding is increasing, there will be the induced EMF

$$N\, d\Phi/dt, \tag{11}$$

which will be in the positive direction of I, by Lenz's law.

(3) Finally, if the whole self-inductance of the fluxmeter, search-coil circuit be denoted by L, there will be the back EMF of self-induction,

$$-L\, dI/dt. \tag{12}$$

The current at any instant is determined by equating the sum of the three EMF's given by (10), (11), and (12), to IR, where R is the whole resistance of the fluxmeter, search-coil circuit:

$$-A\frac{d\theta}{dt}+N\frac{d\Phi}{dt}-L\frac{dI}{dt}=IR.$$

Multiplication of this equation by dt and integration from t_0 to t_1 gives

$$-A\int_{t_0}^{t_1}d\theta+N\int_{t_0}^{t_1}d\Phi-L\int_{t_0}^{t_1}dI=R\int_{t_0}^{t_1}I\,dt=0,$$

where the right side can be set equal to zero, by (9). We then have

$$-A\left[\theta\right]_{t_0}^{t_1}+N\left[\Phi\right]_{t_0}^{t_1}-L\left[I\right]_{t_0}^{t_1}=0.$$

Now at $t=t_0$, $\theta=0$, $\Phi=\Phi_0$, and $I=0$, whereas at $t=t_1$, $\theta=\Theta$, $\Phi=\Phi_1$, and $I=0$. Putting in these values, we have

$$-A\Theta+N(\Phi_1-\Phi_0)=0$$

or
$$N\,\Delta\Phi=A\Theta. \tag{13}$$

This equation proves that the change $N\,\Delta\Phi$ in flux-turns in the search coil is proportional to the deflection Θ of the fluxmeter, the proportionality constant being the constant A that governs the generator action of the fluxmeter. It is seen that the resistance of the circuit does not enter this relation.

The *ballistic galvanometer* can also be used for measurement of flux changes. This is a suspended-coil d'Arsonval galvanometer with comparatively *high* restoring torque and *high* resistance to keep down the damping. The maximum amplitude of the first swing is read after a rapid flux change takes place in the search coil. We do not give the theory here because it is rather complex. To a certain approximation, the amplitude of the first swing is proportional to the change in flux linkage, but it is not at all independent of the resistance of the circuit nor of the time occupied by the flux change. The flux change must take place so rapidly that the galvanometer coil does not move appreciably during the time occupied by the change.

The student will undoubtedly meet the ballistic galvanometer in his laboratory work, although in modern magnetic-laboratory practice it has been almost entirely superseded by the fluxmeter. For accurate and sensitive work, a suspended-coil type of fluxmeter is used. This is essentially a d'Arsonval galvanometer of extremely *low* restoring torque and *low* inertia used in a *low* resistance circuit so that it is highly damped. A null method may be employed in which a known and an unknown flux change are balanced against each other.

The *ballistic galvanometer* may also be used for capacitance measurements, although in this application it has largely been superseded by capacitance bridges. When a condenser is discharged through a properly designed ballistic galvanometer, the instrument gives an initial throw proportional to the charge on the condenser.

Part VI
MODERN PHYSICS

CHAPTER 43

ELECTRONICS

The term *modern physics* refers to the many new physical phenomena and laws that have been discovered since about 1890. At that time the physical phenomena that we have discussed so far (with the exception of the quantum character of radiation and the nuclear and electronic structure of matter) were quite well understood, and more than one famous physicist was rueing the fact that 'all the fundamental laws of physics have now been discovered and all that remains is to determine the next decimal place.' Such prognostications proved to be woefully in error. However, the development of a phase of physics, known as *classical physics*, had been substantially completed. Classical physics is concerned largely with physical phenomena that are anthropomorphic in magnitude—phenomena perceptible to the senses, of bodies having anthropomorphic or terrestrial sizes and speeds. Modern physics is concerned largely with phenomena outside this range—with bodies of atomic or nuclear size, bodies moving at enormous speeds, radiations imperceptible to the human senses, or energies enormous compared to those released in chemical processes such as combustion. In the following three chapters we shall discuss briefly most of the important developments of modern physics.

Many of the discoveries of modern physics are concerned with the properties of fundamental particles and of electromagnetic radiation, and these discoveries could not have been made without the developments of high-vacuum techniques that took place near the turn of the century. In this chapter we shall be concerned principally with the vacuum tubes used in electrical circuits.

Electrical circuits containing vacuum tubes have come to be used in almost every branch of science and engineering. In fact, the development of vacuum tubes and vacuum-tube circuits of various types has become so important and so specialized that it has almost become a separate branch of engineering in its own right. The name *electronics* is usually applied to this field. In the present chapter we shall describe only the simplest types of vacuum tubes and shall show some of their uses in electronic rectifiers, in amplifiers, in oscillator circuits, and in photoelectric applications. Our treatment of the subject of electronics must of necessity be brief, and we shall not be able to do more than survey the essential features of vacuum-tube circuits. It should be pointed out, however, that the complex circuits used in radio systems, in television systems, and in many other applications consist in large part of various combinations of simple circuits of the types we shall discuss.

We conclude the chapter with brief discussions of the generation of X rays and of the conduction of electricity through gases.

1. THERMIONIC EMISSION

The conduction of electricity through a metal—the familiar electric current—has been described as a relatively slow drift of 'free' electrons within the metal. An applied EMF produces this slow drift velocity, which is superimposed on the high random velocities of thermal agitation. The thermal motion of the electrons is not important to the process of conduction in a metal but is of great importance in the phenomenon of *thermionic emission* of electrons from a heated metal.

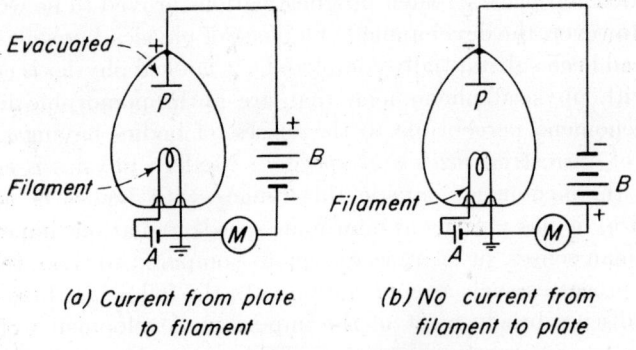

Fig. 1. Edison's discovery.

This phenomenon was first observed by Thomas Edison in the course of experiments (1879–1885) concerned with the development of the incandescent lamp. Edison found that if an electrode P were sealed into an evacuated lamp in the manner indicated in Fig. 1 a *current* could pass from this electrode to the heated filament but could not be made to flow in the reverse direction. In the arrangement shown in this figure, battery A of small EMF (commonly called the *A-battery*) is used to heat the filament to incandescence, and battery B of large EMF (commonly called the *B-battery*) is connected between the electrode P (called the *plate*) and the filament. When the plate is positive with respect to the filament as in part (a) of the figure, the meter M indicates a current from the plate to the filament; when the plate is negative with respect to the filament as in part (b), there is no current between filament and plate.

These observed effects can be explained if we assume that electrons are emitted from the hot filament. When the plate P is positive with respect to the filament, the emitted electrons are pulled to the plate, and therefore the meter indicates an electric current flowing from the plate to the filament; when the plate is negative with respect to the filament, there is no tendency for electrons emitted from the filament to pass toward the plate, and hence no current flows. The cold plate furnishes no electrons for the process of conduction through the tube. Likewise, if the A-battery is removed and the filament becomes cold, no current will flow in either direction through the evacuated tube (unless extremely high voltages are applied).

Since conduction in metals takes place by movement of 'free' electrons, it might be thought that a free electron coming toward a metal surface from within the metal could readily pass through the metal surface and escape. The results of the Edison experiment indicate that appreciable numbers of electrons can ordinarily escape from a metal only when the metal is hot. Electrons within a metal can be regarded as 'free' so far as electric current *within* the metal is concerned, but they are confronted by a 'barrier' at the surface of the metal. In order to escape from the metal, an electron must have sufficient energy to pass through the surface barrier. The minimum energy an electron must have in order to escape may be called the 'height of the potential barrier' at the metal surface. If an electron has just the minimum energy necessary to pass through the barrier, it will have no kinetic energy when it reaches the outside of the metal; electrons having more than the minimum energy will have appreciable kinetic energies after penetrating the barrier.

This minimum energy for escape is ordinarily measured in electron-volts and has different values for different metallic surfaces. At low temperatures very few electrons have sufficient energy to escape from a filament, but as the temperature of the filament is raised, the kinetic energies of the electrons inside the metal increase and the number of electrons capable of escaping increases. The whole phenomenon is closely analogous to the evaporation of molecules from the surface of a liquid. Just as the rate of evaporation increases rapidly with temperature, so does the rate of emission of electrons from a metal. The minimum energy for escape is analogous to the latent heat of vaporization, which could be expressed in electron-volts per molecule if desired.

The escape of electrons from the surface of an isolated metal electrode in a vacuum tube leaves the metal positively charged. The electrons that have escaped are therefore attracted by the metal and form a 'negative charge cloud' or *space charge* around the electrode. Ordinarily, an equilibrium is quickly established between the number of electrons escaping from a metal surface and the number returning to the surface from the space charge. If, however, as in Edison's experiment, a second near-by electrode is maintained at a higher potential than the first, electrons in the space charge are attracted to it; and as long as the potential difference is maintained, there will be a steady movement of electrons from the first electrode to the second. The first electrode is called the *cathode;* the second is called the *anode* or *plate*. A vacuum tube containing two electrodes of this type is called a *diode*. The cathode may be a hot *filament* or a cylindrical electrode heated by an internal hot-wire

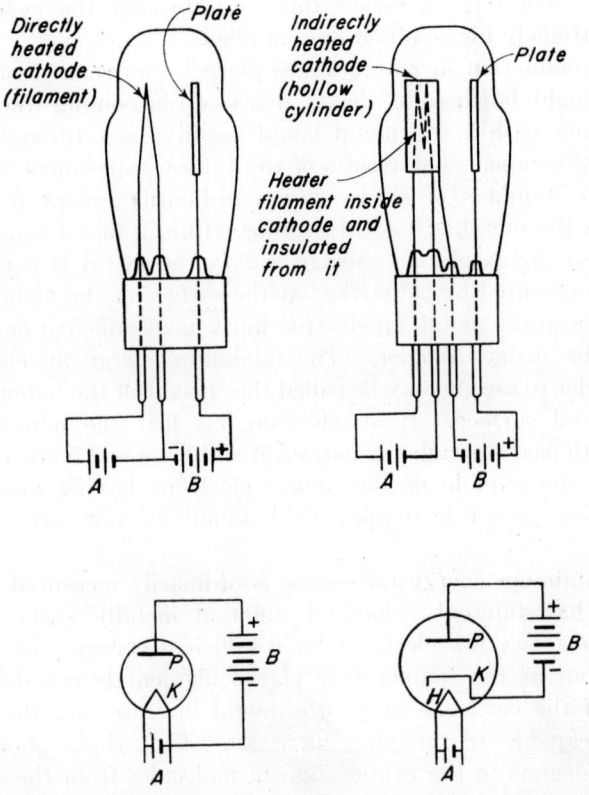

Fig. 2. Diodes: schematic diagrams and circuit symbols.

element called a *heater;* the second type of cathode is called an *indirectly heated cathode* and is electrically insulated from its heater. These two types of diodes are shown schematically in Fig. 2; beneath each sketch is shown the symbol used for the tube in drawing a circuit diagram. Instead of being flat as shown in the schematic diagram, the plate is usually a cylinder surrounding the cathode.

In order to study the characteristics of a diode, the arrangement shown in Fig. 3 may be used. In this circuit the milliameter MA gives the plate current I_p for various values of plate voltage V_p, which can be varied by means of the indicated voltage-divider arrangement popularly called a 'potentiometer' and can be read from the voltmeter V. If the potential difference V_p between plate and cathode is small, only a few of the emitted electrons reach the plate. Most of the emitted electrons penetrate only a short distance into the space charge and then return to the cathode. As the plate potential is increased, more and more of the emitted electrons reach the plate, and with sufficiently high potential difference *all* the emitted electrons arrive at the plate. Further increase of the plate voltage V_p does not increase the plate current, which is said to be *saturated*.

A typical graph of plate current I_p as a function of plate voltage V_p for a given heater current is shown in Fig. 4(a). As indicated, the plate current I_p is not quite zero even when the plate voltage V_p is zero; some

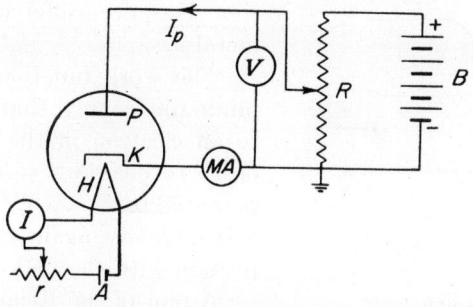

Fig. 3. Circuit for obtaining characteristic curves of plate current *vs* plate voltage for a diode.

of the emitted electrons still have appreciable kinetic energy after penetrating the potential barrier at the cathode surface, and the more rapidly moving ones are able to penetrate the space charge and reach the plate even when there is no accelerating potential. A small retarding potential Oa (exaggerated in the figure) is sufficient to prevent these fastest electrons from reaching the plate. The saturation current I_s is equal to the total emission current from the cathode, since at saturation *all* the electrons emitted by the cathode are being drawn to the plate.

For a given tube, the magnitude of the saturation current increases rapidly when the cathode temperature is increased by increasing the heater current. Figure 4(b) shows plate current as a function of plate voltage for three different cathode temperatures $T_1 > T_2 > T_3$. The relation between saturation or total emission current and cathode temperature is given by a relation derived first by O. W. Richardson and later in a different manner by Saul Dushman:

$$J_s = A\ T^2\ e^{-\phi/kT}, \tag{1}$$

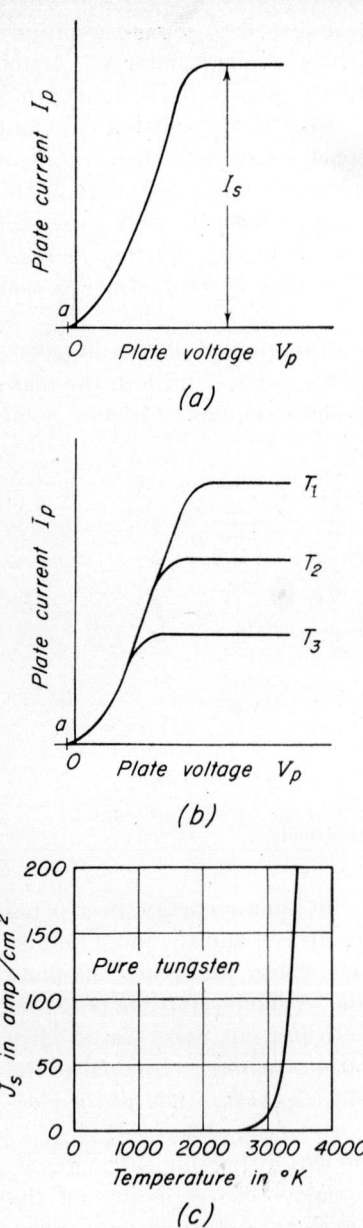

Fig. 4. (a) Typical characteristic curve for a diode: plate current *vs* plate voltage. I_S gives the saturation current. (b) Typical characteristic curve for a diode at various cathode temperatures $T_1 > T_2 > T_3$. (c) Saturation current density *vs* temperature for a tungsten filament.

where J_S is the total emission current per unit area at the cathode surface, A is a constant that is characteristic of the cathode surface, T is the absolute temperature of the cathode surface, k is the Boltzmann constant (see p. 392), and ϕ is called the *work function* of the surface, a quantity related to the 'height of the potential barrier.' The constant A appearing in Richardson's equation is approximately the same for all pure metal surfaces $(A = 60.2 \text{ amp/cm}^2 \cdot (\text{K deg})^2$ for pure metals) but the work function is quite different for different metals.

The work function represents the minimum energy that must be given to an electron in the 'cold' metal in order to enable it to escape over the potential barrier. We shall encounter this quantity again in Sec. 6 in connection with the photoelectric effect.

A plot of the Richardson equation (1) for a pure tungsten filament is shown in Fig. 4(c). For tungsten the work function ϕ is 4.52 electron-volts and ϕ/k is 52,500° K, since $k = 8.617 \times 10^{-5}$ ev/K deg. The controlling factor in (1) is the exponential, which prevents the expression from having appreciable values until T is about $\frac{1}{20}$ of ϕ/k, and then starts rising very rapidly with increasing T.

In selecting a material for use as a cathode surface, one is usually interested in choosing a material that has high emission at easily attainable temperatures. It can be seen from (1) that the work function should be *small*. The cathode materials in regular use are tungsten, thoriated tungsten, and metals coated with alkaline-earth or rare-earth oxides. As compared with pure tungsten, the work function may be reduced by about 50 per cent if a small amount of thorium is added to the tungsten. Because of the controlling nature of the exponential in (1), the addition of thorium reduces by approximately 50 per cent the temperature required to get copious thermionic emission. The work functions of oxide-coated surfaces are even lower than that of thoriated tungsten.

Tungsten filaments must usually be operated at high temperatures (a brilliant white) in order to emit sufficient numbers of electrons for vacuum-tube operation. Thoriated-tungsten filaments are operated at much lower temperatures, in the neighborhood of 1700° C (a bright yellow), and are therefore more economical of power required for heating than are pure tungsten filaments. Alkaline-earth oxides are usually deposited as thick coatings on nickel elements for use as cathodes. An oxide coating requires only a very low temperature of 700–750° C (a dull red) to produce a copious supply of electrons. Coated filaments operate very efficiently and require relatively little filament power.

It should be noted that in most vacuum-tube applications employing indirectly heated cathodes, the heater current is actually AC obtained from a step-down transformer instead of DC from the A-battery indicated in Figs. 2 and 3. The positive DC plate voltage is usually obtained from an electronic power supply instead of from the B-battery. It is still customary to speak of the high voltage as the B+-supply. Such an arrangement is shown in Fig. 5; the arrangement shown is similar *in essentials* to the circuit shown in Fig. 3.

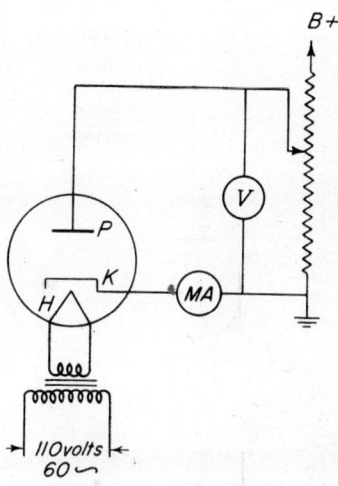

Fig. 5. A diode with AC heater supply and with plate voltage obtained from an electronic power supply B+.

PROBLEMS

1. The total emission current from a certain thoriated-tungsten filament in a diode is found to be 4.0 ma when the filament temperature is 1327° C. By means of the Richardson equation, calculate the total emission current when the filament temperature is 1727° C. (Assume a work function $\phi = 2.25$ ev.) Ans: 163 ma.

2. The total emission current from a certain thoriated-tungsten filament in a diode is 100 ma when the filament temperature is 1727° C. By means of the Richardson equation, calculate the total emission current when the temperature of the filament is 1227° C. (Assume a work function of $\phi = 2.50$ ev.)

3. Draw schematic plate-current *vs* plate-voltage curves for the diode containing the filament described in Prob. 1 for the two filament temperatures given.

4. Draw schematic plate-current *vs* plate-voltage curves for the diode containing the filament described in Prob. 2 for the two filament temperatures given.

5. From the Richardson equation and the constants given in the text, find the saturation-current density for pure tungsten at 2500, 3000, and 3500° K and compare with Fig. 4(c).

2. DIODE APPLICATIONS

Consideration of the curve shown in Fig. 4(a) immediately suggests one of the most important applications of a diode: its use as a *rectifier*. It will be seen that the application of positive voltages to the plate causes the tube to conduct, whereas the application of negative voltages greater

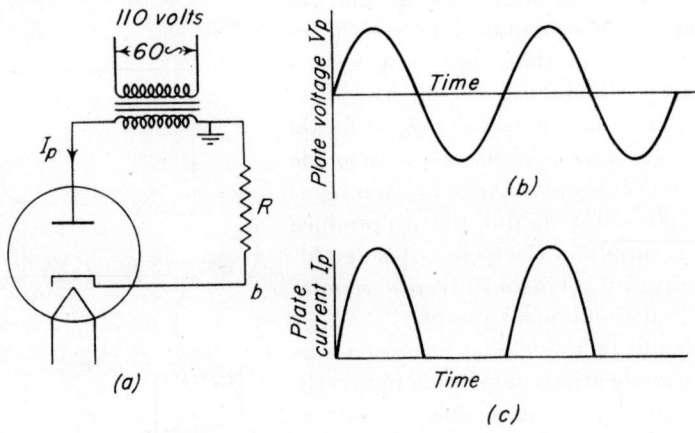

Fig. 6. (a) Diode used as a half-wave rectifier. (Voltage supply for heater is omitted from this and succeeding figures.) (b) Plate potential as a function of time, relative to the indicated ground. (c) Plate current as a function of time. Note that the instantaneous voltage across the load resistance R is simply $I_p R$.

than the small voltage Oa, which we can ignore, immediately stops the flow of current through the tube. The diode is thus a one-way conductor and behaves like a *valve*,* allowing current to flow from plate to cathode but not in the reverse direction.

The diode can be used to *rectify* an alternating current by means of the arrangement shown in Fig. 6(a). In this circuit the ungrounded end of the transformer secondary is connected directly to the plate and furnishes the plate voltage V_p. The cathode is connected through a high resistance R back to ground. If R is large and V_p is positive, only a small fraction of V_p represents voltage drop through the tube; the remainder represents $I_p R$-drop through R.† If R is large, to a first approximation

---

* Thermionic vacuum tubes are called 'thermionic valves' in Great Britain.

† In Fig. 4 the abscissa represents voltage drop through the tube. The figure refers to the case of a grounded cathode; if the cathode is not grounded, the abscissa should read $V_p - V_k$, the difference between plate and cathode potentials. The student should note that in discussing electronic circuits it is customary to refer all potentials

$V_p = I_p R$ when V_p is positive; the tube offers little obstruction to the flow of current, and most of the voltage V_p appears across R. On the other hand, when V_p is negative and the transformer attempts to send current in the other direction, the current is blocked by the tube as if it had infinite resistance.

The plate voltage V_p obtained from the secondary of the transformer is shown as a function of time in Fig. 6(b). When the plate is positive, the tube conducts; when the plate is negative, there is no current flow. The resulting plate current is plotted as a function of time in Fig. 6(c). It will be noted that the application of an *alternating* voltage to the plate has produced a pulsating *unidirectional current* through the load resistance R. The instantaneous voltage across the resistance is proportional to the current. It will also be noted that the *lower* end of the resistance in the figure is *positive* with respect to the grounded upper end: the potential at point b is positive whenever the tube is conducting. Since the diode conducts appreciably only during the half cycle in which the plate is positive, the diode is called a *half-wave rectifier*. In this diagram, we have assumed that the maximum plate current is insufficient to cause saturation; saturation would flatten the tops of the current loops.

Full-wave rectification can be obtained by using two diodes as shown in Fig. 7(a) or by using a single 'diode' with twin plates as shown in Fig. 7(b). Let us consider the situation depicted in Fig. 7(a). Voltage is applied to the diode plates from the secondary of a transformer; the center point of the transformer is 'tapped' for the purpose of grounding in the manner shown. Whenever the end of the secondary attached to the plate of tube 1 is positive, current flows through tube 1 and passes through load resistance R to the grounded center point of the secondary winding; during this time the plate of tube 2 is negative and no current is conducted through tube 2. During the next half cycle, the plate of tube 2 is positive and current is supplied through tube 2 to the load, but the plate of tube 1 is negative and no current is conducted by tube 1. In other words, whenever tube 1 is conducting, tube 2 is nonconducting, and vice versa, but a current through *either* tube will flow in the same direction through the load resistance R. Plots of plate voltage and plate current as a function of time are shown in parts (c), (d), (e), and (f) of Fig. 7 and serve to illustrate graphically the performance just described. The plot of current through the load resistance R is given in part (g) of Fig. 7. As may be seen from this plot, the current in the load is a pulsating *direct current*. The diodes shown in part (a) of this figure act as a *full-wave rectifier*. The single 'diode' with twin plates shown in part (b) of Fig. 7 is electrically identical with the two-tube arrangement; during one half cycle,

---

to a zero at the point of the circuit that is grounded (connected to the shielding chassis), so that he should be careful to indicate the location of the ground on each circuit diagram.

current from plate 1 is conducted through the tube to the load; during the other half cycle, current from plate 2 is conducted through the tube to the load.

The diode arrangements shown in Figs. 6 and 7 operate from an AC primary power supply and furnish DC power to a load such as the resistance R. The fact that DC power is delivered to the load in 'spurts' is frequently undesirable. It is possible to deliver DC power to the load at

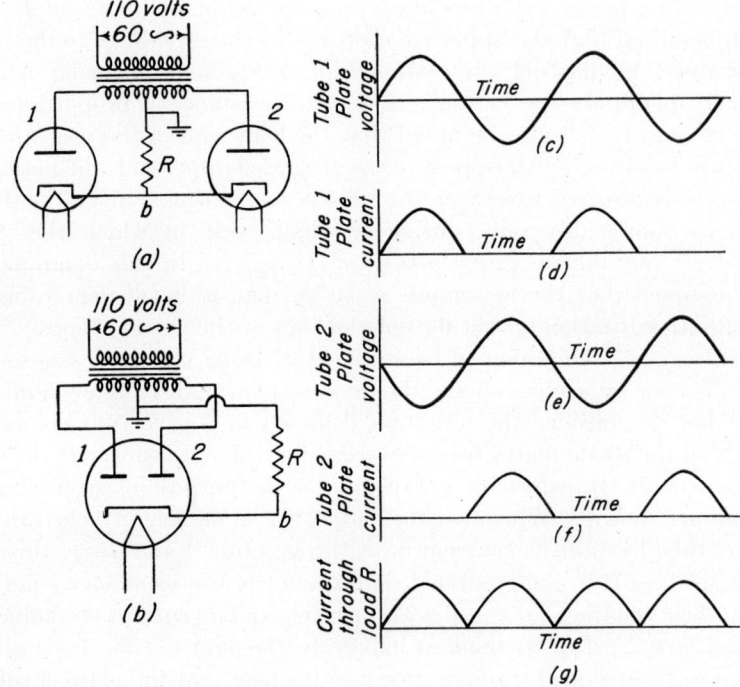

Fig. 7. The use of diodes in a full-wave rectifier.

more nearly constant voltage by adding a 'filter' as in Figs. 8, 9, or 10. In these diagrams, the upper ungrounded end of R is the same as point b in Figs. 6 and 7; R has been turned the other way up to conform to the conventional representation of filter elements.

One simple type of filter consists of a large condenser placed in parallel with a large load resistance R as shown in Fig. 8(a). Since the rate at which the condenser C is *charged* is limited only by the small effective resistance r of the diode circuit (time constant rC), the voltage across the condenser can *rise* almost as rapidly as the half-sine-wave voltage at the cathode. The condenser cannot discharge through the diode but only through R. The rate at which the condenser can *discharge* through load

R is determined by the time constant RC; hence, if the product RC is large, the condenser discharges slowly and the voltage across the condenser *falls* much more slowly than the sine-wave voltage that is being rectified. The net result of this rapid charging rate and slow discharge rate is that after a few cycles the condenser is charged nearly to the peak voltage from the transformer. Thereafter, the voltage between the

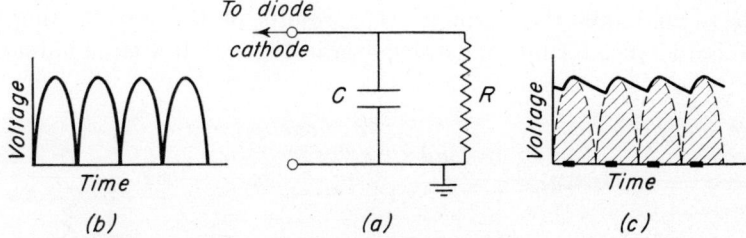

Fig. 8. (a) Condenser used as a filter. (b) Voltage across load when condenser is omitted. This is sometimes called the 'voltage input to the filter.' (c) Voltage across load when condenser is present. This is sometimes called the 'voltage output from the filter.'

condenser plates, which is also the voltage across the load R, remains *near* this peak value but shows the ripple indicated in Fig. 8(c). Comparison of Fig. 8(c) with Fig. 8(b) shows the pronounced 'smoothing action' of the condenser. When the condenser is present, the diodes conduct only when the plate voltage exceeds the voltage across the condenser. In a good condenser filter, this conduction occurs during

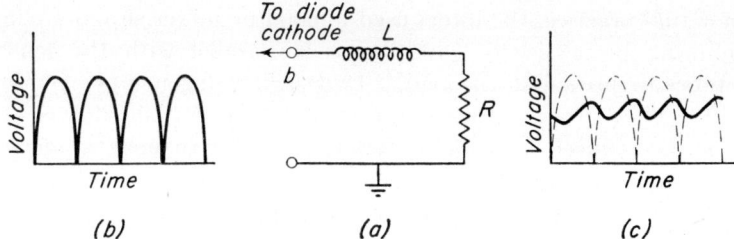

Fig. 9. (a) Series inductance used as a filter. (b) Voltage across load when inductance is omitted: 'voltage input to filter.' (c) Voltage across load when inductance is present: 'voltage output from filter.'

only a small fraction of a cycle, as shown by the small rectangles on the time axis of Fig. 8(c). In using the condenser as a filter, we make use of the fact that electrical energy can be stored in a charged condenser during part of the cycle and supplied to the load during the periods when energy is not being supplied through the rectifier tubes.

In a somewhat analogous way, we can make use of the fact that energy can be stored in the magnetic field of an inductance. Since an inductance tends to resist changes in the magnitude of the current flowing through it, an inductance can be placed in series with the load in order to minimize change in the current through the load. When the load current is increasing, the EMF induced in the inductance opposes the increase; when the load current is decreasing, the EMF induced in the inductance tends to maintain the current. The results of the introduction of a series inductance for filtering are shown in Fig. 9. If a large inductance

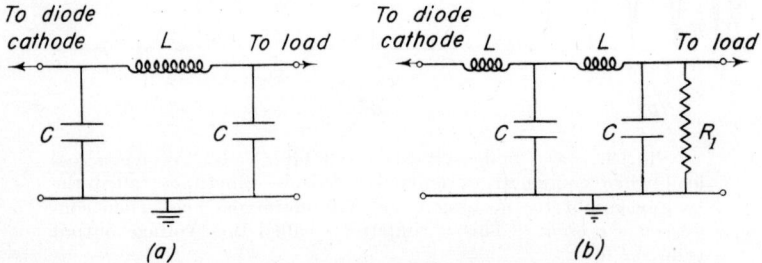

Fig. 10. Composite filters: (a) condenser input; (b) inductance input.

is available, the voltage ripple can be almost eliminated. However, since the inductance is in *series* with the load, the voltage across the load never attains the peak values it would attain if the inductance were omitted.

In actual practice, the filters used in good DC power supplies combine the filtering properties of capacitance in parallel with the load and inductance in series with the load. Two such arrangements are shown in Fig. 10. The 'ripple voltage' transmitted by composite filters of this type can be reduced to a value that is negligible in most applications. To meet more exacting requirements, it is possible to use glow-tube regulators or electronic regulation. Glow-tube regulation will be discussed on p. 1136.

PROBLEMS

1. The saturation current from the cathode of the diode shown in Fig. 6 is 10 ma and is attained when the plate voltage is only 20 v above that of the cathode. If the resistance $R = 10{,}000$ ohms and the voltage applied to the plate is given by the equation $V = 300 \sin 120\pi t$ v, plot an approximate curve showing the voltage drop across R as a function of time. Ans: max voltage = 100 v; voltage wave is almost a 'square wave.'

2. If the filament current of the diode described in the preceding problem is increased until the saturation current is 20 ma and is attained when the plate voltage is 30 v, plot a curve showing the voltage drop across R as a function of time when a voltage $V = 300 \sin 120\pi t$ v is applied to the plate of the diode.

3. Discuss the action of the filter shown in Fig. 8 when the output voltage from a half-wave rectifier, such as that shown in Fig. 6 is, applied. Would the filter be more effective in minimizing 'ripple' when used with a half-wave or with a full-wave rectifier?

4. Discuss the action of the filter shown in Fig. 9 when it is used with a half-wave rectifier of the type shown in Fig. 6. Would the filter be more effective in minimizing 'ripple' when used with a half-wave or with a full-wave rectifier?

3. THE CONTROL GRID: TRIODE APPLICATIONS

We have already seen in Fig. 4(a) and in the subsequent discussion that before saturation has been attained, the plate current I_p in a diode operating with the cathode at a constant temperature can be varied by

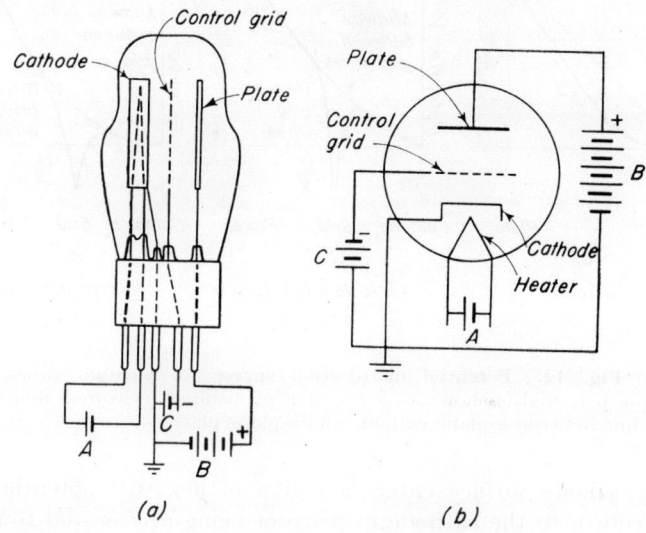

Fig. 11. The triode. (a) Schematic diagram. The grid is actually a helix between a cylindrical cathode and a cylindrical plate and is coaxial with them in the common triode. (b) Conventional symbolism for the triode. The 'A-battery' operates the heater; the 'B-battery' supplies the plate voltage, and the 'C-battery' gives the control grid a negative bias voltage.

changing the plate voltage V_p. Lee De Forest, in 1907, discovered that if a third electrode called a *control grid* be inserted between the cathode and plate of a thermionic vacuum tube, the potential of this third electrode exerts much greater 'control' over the plate current than does the plate voltage itself. The grid is usually an open mesh or a helix of fine wire, which allows the electrons to pass through the openings. A schematic diagram of a tube containing a control grid is shown in Fig. 11. Since small variations in grid voltage produce relatively large variations in plate current, the three-electrode tube or *triode* can be used as an *amplifier*.

Before discussing applications of the *triode*, we shall give a brief qualitative analysis of the action of the control grid on the flow of electrons from cathode to plate. It will be recalled that the negative space charge around the cathode of a diode tends to limit the plate current except for high values of the plate voltage. This limitation occurs because the region immediately around the cathode becomes a region of negative potential relative to the cathode as a result of the presence of electrons emitted from the cathode. Thus, an electron just emerging

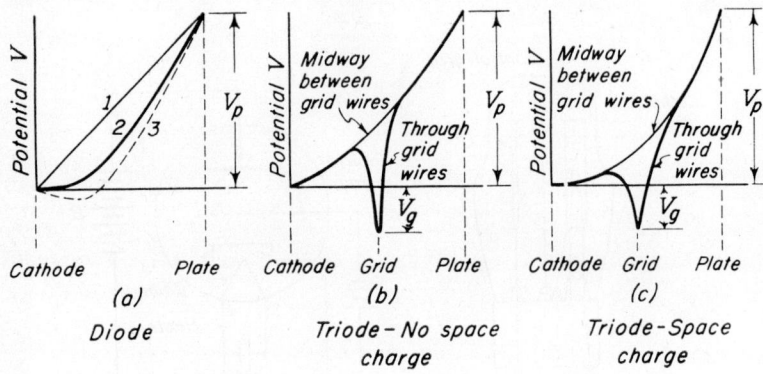

Fig. 12. Potential distribution curves for vacuum tubes. The potential is shown as a function of distance measured along a line between a plane cathode and a plane plate.

from the cathode surface enters a region of negative potential and is likely to return to the cathode in place of being accelerated toward the plate. The potentials existing in the inter-electrode space of a diode are shown in Fig. 12(a); in plotting the potential distribution curves for this figure, the plate and the cathode have, for the sake of simplicity, been treated as parallel infinite planes, with the cathode at zero potential. In the case of no space charge, the potential distribution curve 1 is a straight line. In the case of space charge, the potential-distribution curve is curved and is of the shape shown by curve 3 when the current is below saturation and of the shape shown by curve 2 when saturation current is flowing.

Recalling that the accelerating force on a charge q is given by

$$F = -q\, dV/dx,$$

we see that for an electron ($q = -e$) the accelerating force toward the plate is given by

$$F = e\, dV/dx.$$

Sec. 3] THE CONTROL GRID: TRIODE APPLICATIONS 1111

Thus, for our idealized diode, an electron will be subjected to a constant force toward the plate when there is no space charge. If the space charge is such that curve 2 applies, no accelerating force will act on the electron between the cathode and the point at which the potential begins to rise but the electron will be accelerated toward the plate when it is in the region where the potential curve is rising. If the space charge is such that curve 3 applies, the force acting on the electron will tend to return the electron to the cathode when the electron is in the region of decreasing potential and will tend to accelerate the electron toward the plate when the electron is in the region of increasing potential.

In a *triode*, a *negatively charged* grid, consisting of a plane network of widely spaced fine wires, is placed between the cathode and plate of the diode. In the case of no space charge, the curves in Fig. 12(b) apply. Because of the distortion of the electric field produced by the irregularity of the grid structure, it is not possible to represent the entire potential distribution by a single curve. In the figure we have drawn two limiting curves. The upper curve represents the potential distribution along a line from the cathode to the plate passing midway between the grid wires, and the lower curve gives the potential along a line from the cathode to the plate through the center of a wire in the grid; the potential distributions along lines passing from cathode to plate through any other part of the grid mesh fall between the two limiting curves in this figure. Figure 12(c) gives similar limiting potential curves for a triode in which there is space charge.

Along the lines passing through points midway between the widely spaced grid wires, the potential distribution is somewhat similar to the potential distribution along similar lines between the cathode and plate of a diode, and the grid has little effect on electrons on these lines. However, along lines from cathode to anode passing through points near the grid wires, the potential distribution curves have minima in the plane of the grid; and electrons on such lines in the region of decreasing potential experience forces that tend to return them to the cathode. Hence, many electrons which would reach the plate in a diode are repelled toward the cathode in a triode containing a negatively charged grid. Therefore, the plate current can be regulated by the grid potential. If the grid potential has a high negative value, the plate current is small and may even be zero; when the negative grid potential is decreased, the plate current rises; if the grid potential becomes positive, the plate current increases still further but current also begins to flow between the grid and cathode. Such *grid current* is usually undesirable, so the application of positive voltages to the control grid is avoided in circuit design.

To summarize our discussion of the action of the control grid: A negatively charged control grid is very effective in limiting the flow of electrons from cathode to plate by repelling electrons toward the cathode. As a result of this property, it is possible to apply relatively small signal voltages to the grid and thereby produce large changes in plate current. Since the grid current is negligible and the grid-filament capacitance very low, the *energy* and the *current* that must be supplied to the grid to furnish plate-current control are very low.

Commercial triodes are usually operated at potentials much lower than would be required to draw saturation current. The plate current of a triode is a function of cathode temperature, plate voltage, and grid voltage. It cannot be expressed conveniently as an algebraic function of

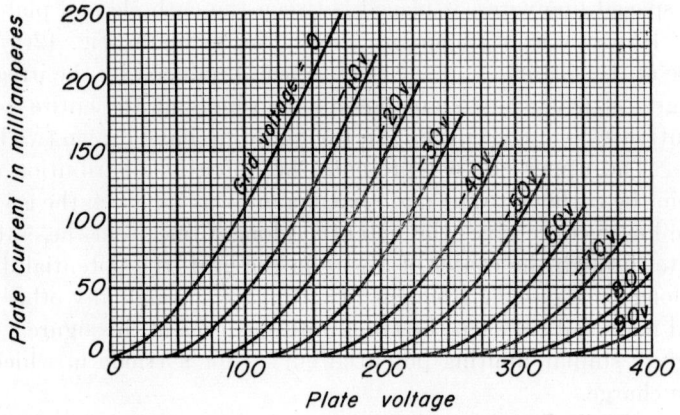

Fig. 13. Average plate characteristics for a 2A3 triode. Filament is heated by an A-battery of 2.5 volts.

these variables but is customarily expressed by graphs of characteristic curves like those shown in Fig. 13 for a 2A3 tube. The filament or heater of a commercial tube is usually operated by a fixed voltage prescribed by the manufacturer, and hence the curves in the graph give the plate current for various grid and plate voltages measured relative to the cathode at a fixed A-battery voltage of 2.5. In the figure the individual curves show plate current as functions of plate voltage when the control-grid voltage is kept constant at the values shown. For example, when the grid voltage is -20 v and the plate voltage is 200 v, the plate current is 140 ma. The data represented by the curves in Fig. 13 are obtained by means of the arrangement shown schematically in Fig. 14. The battery from which the grid voltages are obtained is traditionally called the 'C-battery.'

The interrelations between various electrode potentials and currents are commonly expressed in terms of *tube factors*, the values of which can be determined from the characteristic curves shown in Fig. 13. The

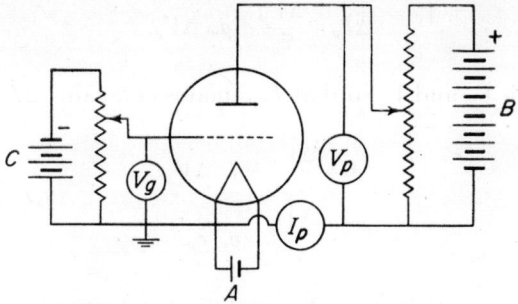

Fig. 14. Arrangement for obtaining data for characteristic curves of a triode.

most useful of the tube factors are (a) the *amplification factor* μ, (b) the *plate conductance* g_p (or its reciprocal, the *plate resistance* r_p), and (c) the *transconductance* g_m. These tube factors are defined in the following way:

(a) The *amplification factor* μ is defined as the negative of the ratio of a small change in plate voltage to a small change in grid voltage when the plate current is kept constant. It measures the ratio of the effectiveness of a change in control-grid voltage and of a change plate voltage in controlling the plate current. The amplification factor is given by the relation

$$\mu = -\Delta V_p/\Delta V_g \quad (I_p = \text{const}), \tag{2}$$

where the small changes ΔV_p and ΔV_g are read from a plot of the characteristic curves such as that shown in Fig. 13. The amplification factor of the 2A3 is approximately 4 for the straight portions of the curves.

(b) The *plate conductance* g_p is defined as the ratio of a small change in plate current to a small change in plate voltage when the grid voltage is kept constant. The plate resistance r_p is the reciprocal of the plate conductance and is evaluated from the relation

$$r_p = 1/g_p = \Delta V_p/\Delta I_p \quad (V_g = \text{const}), \tag{3}$$

where the small changes may be read directly from the appropriate characteristic curve. The plate conductance is a measure of the effect of changes in plate voltage on plate current. The plate resistance of the 2A3 is in the neighborhood of 500 ohms for the straight portions of the curves of Fig. 13.

(c) The *transconductance* g_m is defined as the ratio of a small change in plate current to a small change in grid voltage at constant plate voltage:

$$g_m = \Delta I_p/\Delta V_g \quad (V_p = \text{const}), \tag{4}$$

where ΔI_p and ΔV_g are read from a plot similar to that in Fig. 13. The transconductance is a measure of the effect of changes of grid voltage on plate current. The transconductance of the 2A3 is approximately 0.008 mho for the straight portions of the characteristic curves.

The plate current increases with increase of either the plate potential V_p or the grid potential V_g. For small changes in these potentials we can write, in accordance with (3) and (4),

$$\Delta I_p = \frac{\Delta V_p}{r_p} + g_m \Delta V_g. \tag{5}$$

If we alter both V_p and V_g so that I_p remains constant ($\Delta I_p = 0$), we have, from (5),

$$0 = \frac{\Delta V_p}{r_p} + g_m \Delta V_g$$

or

$$-\frac{\Delta V_p}{\Delta V_g} = g_m r_p.$$

But, from (2), this ratio equals the amplification factor μ, so the three tube factors are connected by the relation

$$\mu = g_m r_p. \tag{6}$$

Equation (5) can now be rewritten in the form

$$\Delta I_p = \frac{\Delta V_p + \mu \Delta V_g}{r_p}, \tag{7}$$

which shows again that grid-voltage changes have μ times as much effect on plate current as equal plate-voltage changes.

As an example of the use of a triode as an amplifier, let us consider the diagram shown in Fig. 15(a), in which a small signal voltage is applied to the control grid. If a small positive signal voltage ΔV_g is applied to the grid, the plate current through the tube will increase by a certain amount ΔI_p, and consequently the voltage at the plate will decrease because of the increased RI_p-drop in the load resistance R between the plate and the B-supply. Similarly, if a small negative signal voltage is applied to the grid, the plate current will decrease and the voltage at the plate will increase. If the tube is operating under conditions in which the characteristic curves like those of Fig. 13 approximate uniformly spaced straight lines, we shall show in the next paragraph that the change in plate voltage is approximately μ times the change in grid voltage (for R large compared to r_p), and of the opposite sign. Thus, the application of a small sinusoidal input voltage to the grid as in Fig. 15(b) will result in an amplified sinusoidal output voltage at the plate. Similarly, the application of any other wave shape of signal voltage on the grid will result in a faithfully amplified and inverted output wave shape at the plate so long as the signal amplitude remains small. A vacuum-tube amplifier is able to follow faithfully voltage variations at frequencies of many megacycles per second such as occur in radio.

The exact relation between ΔV_p and ΔV_g is easy to derive. In Fig. 15(a) we see that the instantaneous voltage V_p between the plate and ground must equal the voltage V_B of the B-battery minus the IR-drop in R. Hence, we can write

$$V_p = V_B - RI_p.$$

Since V_B and R are constant, we then have

$$\Delta V_p = -R\,\Delta I_p.$$

If we substitute here the expression for ΔI_p given by (7), we obtain the equation

$$\Delta V_p = -(R/r_p)(\Delta V_p + \mu\,\Delta V_g).$$

Solution of this equation for ΔV_p gives the desired relation:

$$\Delta V_p = -\left(\frac{R}{R+r_p}\right)\mu\,\Delta V_g. \tag{8}$$

The coefficient of ΔV_g on the right of this equation is known as the *voltage gain* of the one-stage amplifier. It is equal to μ, the amplification

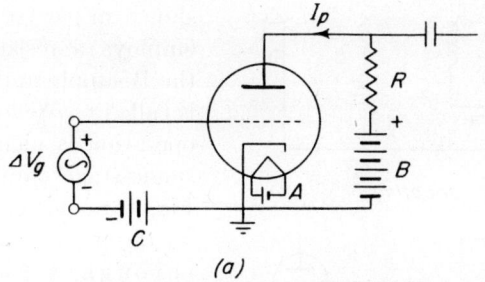

(a)

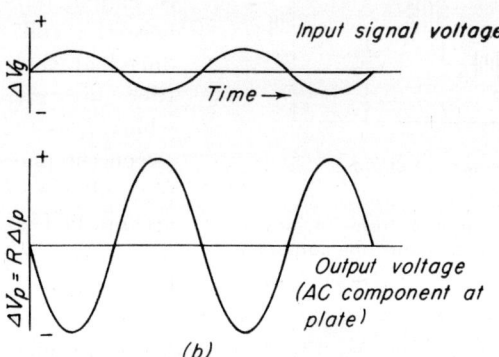

(b)

Fig. 15. Triode amplifier.

factor of the tube, if $R \gg r_p$. If $R = r_p$, the voltage gain is only $\tfrac{1}{2}\mu$. In a resistance-coupled stage such as that in Fig. 15, a tube such as the 2A3 would always be used with a load resistance R large compared to its plate resistance of about 500 ohms.

It should be noted that the sinusoidal output voltage ΔV_p of Fig.

15(b) is superposed on a quiescent positive plate voltage. If the output voltage is to be applied to another circuit element, connection is usually made through a condenser or some other circuit element that will pass only the AC component.

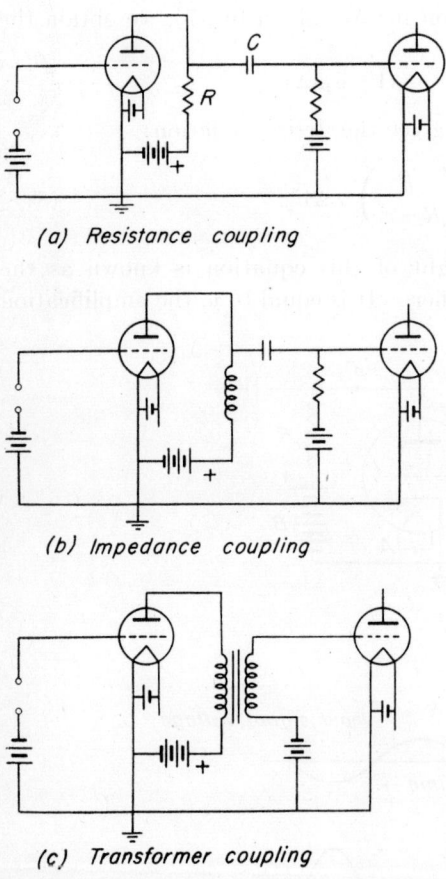

(a) Resistance coupling

(b) Impedance coupling

(c) Transformer coupling

Fig. 16. Three common forms of interstage coupling used in vacuum tube amplifiers.

If a single-stage amplifier does not provide sufficient voltage gain it is necessary to use additional stages of amplification. Several different methods of coupling between successive stages are shown in Fig. 16. The type of coupling shown in part (a) of this figure employs a resistance between the B-supply and the plate and is called *resistance coupling;* the operation is identical with the single-stage amplifier shown in Fig. 15; connection to the grid of the next tube is made through a condenser. The coupling shown in Fig. 16(b) is called *impedance coupling;* here the voltage changes produced at the plate of the first tube are given by $L\, dI_p/dt$, where L is the inductance between the plate and the B-supply. These voltage changes are applied to the grid of the next tube through a condenser.

Figure 16(c) shows an example of *transformer coupling;* changes in the plate current of the first tube induce voltages in the transformer secondary, and these produce voltage changes at the grid of the second tube. All of these types of interstage coupling find application.

One of the important applications of vacuum tubes is in circuits for the generation of high-frequency electrical oscillations. We have seen how the application of small AC voltages to the grid of a triode can result in the production of larger AC voltages at the plate of the triode. If a part of the AC voltage at the plate of a triode is returned to the grid in proper phase through a 'feed-back network,' larger grid voltages are produced and these larger grid voltages will in turn produce still larger plate voltages. If the plate and grid are both properly coupled to LC circuit elements, the circuits begin to oscillate. An LC circuit will oscillate at its natural frequency $1/2\pi\sqrt{LC}$, provided that energy is supplied to the circuit at proper times and at the same rate as energy is removed from the circuit by resistance heating or other dissipative losses. The triode is able to deliver the needed energy from its B-supply when properly connected.

As an example of an oscillator circuit, let us consider the Hartley oscillator shown in Fig. 17(a). In this circuit the grid and plate are both

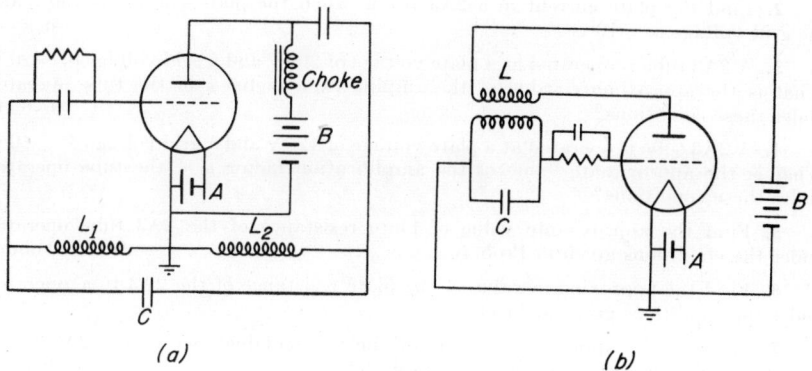

Fig. 17. (a) The Hartley oscillator. (b) A 'tuned-grid' oscillator.

connected by condensers to a single LC circuit in the manner indicated. The inductance is actually composed of two parts, L_1 and L_2, with the cathode connected as shown. The choke coil connected between the plate and the B-supply is a large inductance and presents a high impedance to high-frequency voltages but permits the passage of the DC plate current. Voltages from the LC 'tank circuit' are applied to the grid in proper phase to maintain oscillation. The oscillation frequency of the circuit is $1/2\pi\sqrt{(L_1+L_2)C}$. The action of the grid is to cause energy to be supplied from the B-supply to the oscillating LC circuit at the proper times so that oscillations are maintained. Oscillation of the LC circuit sets in as soon as the tube is turned on, since any slight change in plate current is sufficient to start oscillation, and the small oscillating voltages applied to the grid result in more energy being supplied to the oscillating circuit until the rate at which energy is supplied to the LC circuit becomes equal to the rate at which energy is dissipated in this circuit.

A second type of oscillator is shown in Fig. 17(b); in this circuit power from the plate circuit is fed back inductively to the grid circuit.

Vacuum-tube oscillators are used to produce the high-frequency oscillations needed in radio communications, which we shall discuss in the next chapter.

Shortly after De Forest introduced the control grid, it was found that additional grids could be used to advantage in thermionic vacuum tubes. A treatment of these multi-element tubes is beyond the scope of our present interest, but it might be remarked that vacuum tubes with as many as eight electrodes are now in common use.

PROBLEMS

NOTE: Problems 1–10 are based on the characteristic curves shown in Fig. 13 for a 2A3 triode operated with an A-battery of 2.5 v.

1. A 2A3 triode is operated with plate voltage of 250 v and with a grid bias of -30 v. Find the plate current. Ans: 145 ma.

2. Find the plate current in a 2A3 triode when the plate voltage is 150 v and the grid voltage is -10 v.

3. A 2A3 tube is operated at a plate voltage of 200 v and a grid voltage of -20 v. What is the approximate value of the amplification factor μ of the tube operated under these conditions? Ans: 4.0.

4. A 2A3 tube is operated at a plate voltage of 125 v and a grid voltage of -10 v. What is the approximate value of the amplification factor μ of the tube operated under these conditions?

5. Find the approximate value of plate resistance of the 2A3 tube operated under the conditions given in Prob. 3. Ans: 500 ohms.

6. Find the approximate value of the plate resistance of the 2A3 tube operated under the conditions given in Prob. 4.

7. What is the approximate value of the transconductance of the 2A3 triode operated under the conditions given in Prob. 3? Ans: 0.008 mho.

8. What is the approximate value of the transconductance of a 2A3 triode operated under the conditions stated in Prob. 4?

9. What is the approximate value of the plate conductance of a 2A3 triode operated under the conditions stated in Prob. 3? Ans: 0.002 mho.

10. What is the approximate value of the plate conductance of a 2A3 triode operated under the conditions stated in Prob. 4?

11. The load resistor R in the plate circuit of the amplifier stage shown in Fig. 15(a) is 10,000 ohms. When a sinusoidal signal voltage $V_g = 0.5 \sin 2\pi ft$ v is applied to the grid, it produces an approximately sinusoidal variation in plate current of 0.5 ma amplitude. Find the resulting variation in the plate voltage of the tube and the voltage gain. Ans: $-5 \sin 2\pi ft$ v; 10.

12. The load resistor R in the plate circuit of the amplifier stage shown in Fig. 15(a) is 100,000 ohms. When a sinusoidal signal voltage of maximum value 0.5 v is applied to the grid, an approximately sinusoidal variation in plate current of maximum value 0.1 ma results. Find the resulting variation in the plate voltage of the tube and the voltage gain.

13. Give a qualitative analysis of the operation of a Hartley oscillator.

14. Give a qualitative analysis of the operation of a tuned-grid oscillator.

4. THE ELECTRON-RAY OSCILLOGRAPH*

As we have seen in Chap. 42, most of the instruments used in the measurement of AC voltages and currents involve moving mechanical parts. The inertia of moving coils or wires with pointers or mirrors

* This section may be omitted without loss of continuity.

attached is too great to permit these moving parts to follow the rapid variations in applied torque and hence they measure average or effective values, not instantaneous values. However, with the development of thermionic vacuum tubes it has been possible to construct instruments that do record 'instantaneous' values of AC voltages and currents and hence permit observation of AC voltage or current 'waveforms.' These instruments are called *electron-ray* or *cathode-ray oscillographs*. The 'moving part' in this instrument is a narrow beam or pencil of electrons emitted from a hot cathode. Because of its almost negligible inertia, this beam is an ideal indicator for a rapidly changing function.

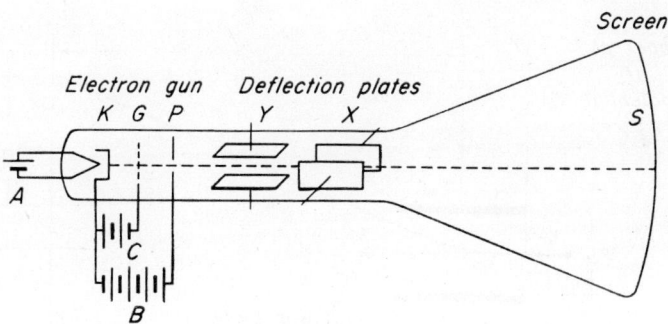

Fig. 18. Simplified drawing of an electron-ray tube. A stream of electrons from the 'electron gun' passes between deflecting plates Y and X and strike fluorescent screen S.

The essential features of an electron-ray tube are shown in Fig. 18. The tube itself is made of glass and is evacuated. Electrons (cathode rays) are emitted by the cathode K and are accelerated toward an anode P maintained at a potential of several hundred or several thousand volts positive with respect to the cathode. Most of the electrons strike the anode, but a narrow beam passes through a small hole in the anode and eventually strikes the screen S, which is a coating on the glass wall of the tube. The screen fluoresces and emits light when bombarded by electrons. The intensity of the light spot on the screen can be controlled by the grid G between cathode and anode in the 'electron gun.'

In going from the anode to the screen, the electrons pass between two sets X and Y of deflecting plates that control the horizontal and vertical deflections of the beam. The extremely small inertia of the electrons enables the electron stream to follow, with practically no time lag, the variations in electric fields produced when voltages are applied to the deflecting plates. If no voltages are applied to the deflecting plates, a bright spot is observed in the center of the fluorescent screen. If a voltage is applied across the Y plates that makes the upper plate positive,

the spot on the screen immediately moves upward; if it makes the upper
Y plate negative, the spot moves downward. If the X deflecting plates
are connected to a source of voltage that rises gradually at a constant
rate to a maximum value and then suddenly drops back to zero or to a
negative value (a 'saw-tooth' voltage variation), the beam may be made
to move periodically in such a way that the bright spot moves across the
screen at a uniform speed and then snaps back to its starting point. A
circuit that will provide such a 'saw-tooth' voltage is called a *sweep circuit;* such circuits can be constructed fairly easily by the employment of
vacuum tubes. With a saw-tooth voltage applied to the X plates and an
unknown periodic AC voltage applied to the Y plates, a plot of the

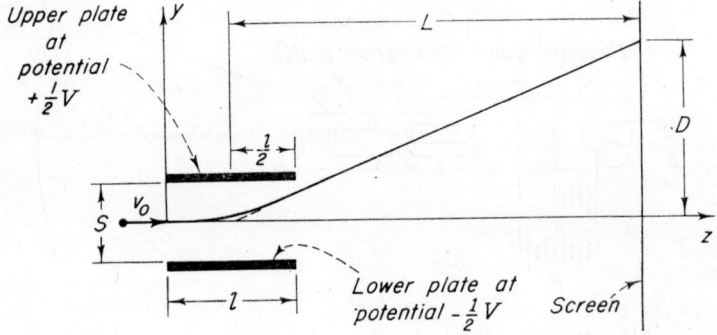

Fig. 19. Deflection of electrons by an electric field.

unknown voltage as a function of time is obtained on the screen, provided
the period of the saw-tooth voltage is equal to a multiple of the period of
the unknown AC voltage. The observed curve on the screen is really a
snapshot of one or more cycles of the unknown voltage and thus exhibits
the waveform of the unknown voltage. The electron-ray oscillograph is
at present an almost indispensable laboratory tool.

In order to see that the deflection of the spot on the screen is proportional to the DP applied to the deflecting plates, it will be necessary for us
to consider in detail the motion of an electron in the tube shown diagrammatically in Fig. 19. An electron from the gun enters the space between
the deflecting plates with a speed v_0 in the z-direction. When the
electron enters the space between the plates, it is subjected to a force in
the y-direction. The plates have a length l and are separated a distance
S. When a DP V is applied, an electric field is set up between the upper
plate and the lower plate. For simplicity, we shall consider that the
field is uniform and does not extend beyond the ends of the plates. The
value of the field is given by

$$\mathcal{E}_y = -V/S.$$

The force f_y on the negative electron is given by $-e\mathcal{E}_y$, and hence the acceleration experienced by the electron of mass m is

$$a_y = f_y/m = -e\mathcal{E}_y/m = eV/mS.$$

The final y-component of the velocity of the electron as it leaves the deflecting plates is equal to $a_y t_1$, where t_1 is the time spent by the electron in the region between the plates. Since the z-component of the electron's velocity remains unchanged, the time t_1 is simply $t_1 = l/v_0$, and the final y-component of the velocity is given by the relation

$$v_y = \frac{eV}{mS} \frac{l}{v_0}.$$

After the electron leaves the region between the deflecting plates, it travels in a straight line of slope

$$\frac{dy}{dz} = \frac{v_y\,dt}{v_0\,dt} = \frac{v_y}{v_0}.$$

This line intersects the z-axis at the center of the plates at $z = \tfrac{1}{2}l$; proof of this statement is left as a problem. Let L be the distance along the z-axis from this point to the screen. Then the deflection D will be given by

$$D = v_y T,$$

where T is the time required for the electron to pass from point $z = \tfrac{1}{2}l$, $y = 0$ to the screen. This time is given by $T = L/v_0$, and the final expression for the deflection becomes

$$D = \frac{eVl}{mSv_0}\frac{L}{v_0} = \frac{elL}{mSv_0^2} \times V = \text{const} \times V.$$

Thus, the screen deflection is shown to be proportional to the voltage V applied between the deflecting plates.

The electron-ray tube we have just described employs electrostatic deflection and is of the type most frequently used. Another type of tube utilizes magnetic deflecting coils in place of electrostatic deflecting plates. An electron moving at speed v in a direction perpendicular to a magnetic field $\mathcal{B}$ experiences a force of magnitude $\mathcal{B}ev$ at right angles to $\mathcal{B}$ and to the direction of motion (cf. p. 965). Thus, an oscillograph tube can be constructed with the deflecting coils arranged as shown schematically in Fig. 20(a). In Fig. 20(b) the electron beam is approaching the reader; with the current directions shown, the horizontal-control coils X would deflect the electron beam toward the left and the vertical-control coils Y would deflect the beam downward. For small deflections, the deflection of the spot on the screen is proportional to the magnetic flux density, as can be seen from a consideration of Fig. 21. In this figure the electrons from the electron gun enter the magnetic field from the left; for simplicity we shall consider a magnetic field of circular cross section. If the field is directed away from the reader, the electrons will be deflected as shown in the figure. The path is circular, and we may set mass times centripetal acceleration equal to $\mathcal{B}ev_0$:

$$mv_0^2/R = \mathcal{B}ev_0.$$

From this equation we obtain for the radius of curvature R the expression

$$R = mv_0/\mathcal{B}e.$$

The angle θ, which gives the change in direction of the beam, is given by

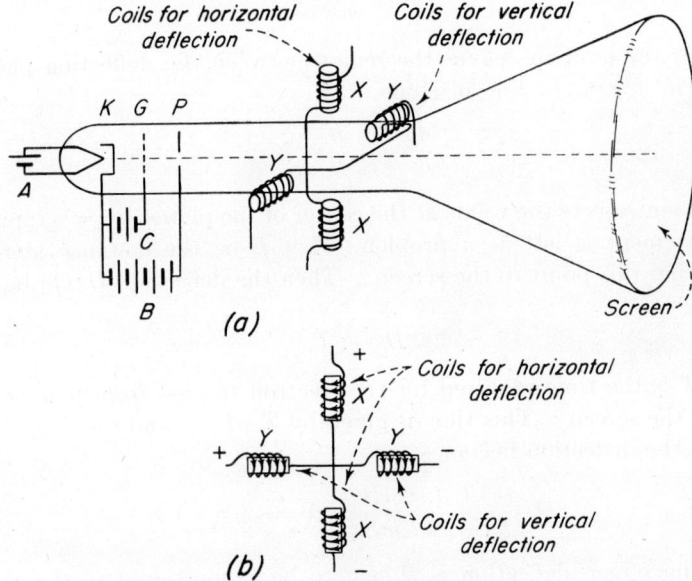

Fig. 20. (a) Schematic drawing of electron-ray tube using magnetic deflection. (b) An electron beam coming toward the reader is deflected downward and toward the left.

$\theta = P/R$, where P is the length of the curved path of the electrons in the magnetic field. The screen deflection D can be expressed as $D = L\tan\theta$, where L is measured from the center of the cross section of the magnetic field to the screen. For small angles, we may set $\tan\theta = \theta$ and write

$$D = L\theta = LP/R;$$

also, for small angles, P can be set equal to the diameter d of the cross section of the magnetic field, since from simple trigonometry we see that $d = 2R\tan\tfrac{1}{2}\theta \approx R\theta = P$. Making this substitution and putting in the value for R, we get

$$D = \frac{Ld}{R} = \frac{Ld\mathcal{B}e}{mv_0} = \left(\frac{Lde}{mv_0}\right)\mathcal{B} = \text{const} \times \mathcal{B}.$$

Since $\mathcal{B}$ is proportional to the current in the deflecting coils, the deflection is proportional to this current.

Magnetic-deflection tubes cannot be used to advantage at high frequencies since the inductance of the coils presents a high impedance to a high-frequency signal. A saw-tooth current for horizontal displacement also becomes increasingly difficult as the frequency increases.

Magnetic-deflection tubes are useful in certain applications where a polar plot is desired. Here a single set of deflection coils is used. Since the coils are external to the tube, they can be rotated in synchronism with other pieces of equipment; rotation of the deflection coils causes rotation

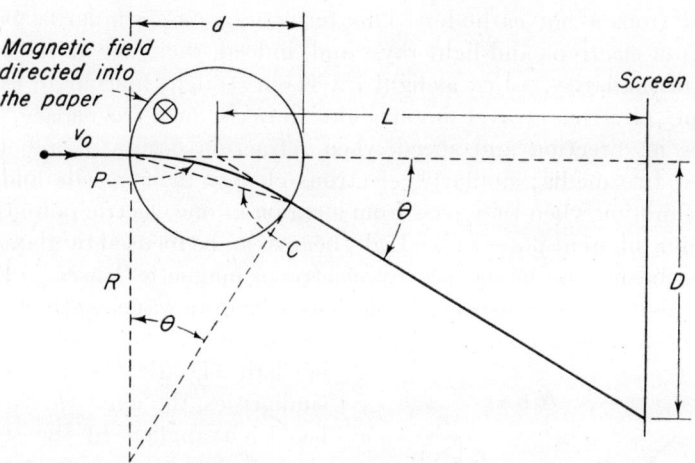

Fig. 21. Deflection of an electron beam by a magnetic field of circular cross section. Note the relation between the path P traversed by electrons in the magnetic field, the chord C, and the diameter d of the cross section of the field: $d > P > C$. As θ approaches zero, P approaches d.

of the radius to the spot on the screen and gives a polar plot. This type of rotation, coupled with a radial sweep, is widely used in radar ('radio direction and ranging') work. Signals applied to the grid of the tube vary the intensity of the spot in accordance with the strength of a reflected ultrashort-wave radio pulse in such a way that a dimensionally accurate radar map of the area being surveyed is plotted on the screen. This type of presentation is called a *polar intensity-modulated display*.

PROBLEMS

1. Consider the portion of the electron trajectory in the region between the deflecting plates in Fig. 19. Show that the straight line giving the electron's trajectory after the electron leaves the region between the deflecting plates will intersect the z-axis exactly at the center of the deflecting plates.

2. In the text, it is shown that the screen deflection D in an electron-ray tube is proportional to the deflecting voltage V in the electrostatic-deflection type and to the current I in the deflecting coils of the magnetic-deflection type of instrument. It is desirable to make the ratios D/V and D/I large if the oscillograph is to be a reasonably sensitive instrument. What effect does changing the accelerating voltage in the electron gun have on these ratios? What are the limitations on varying the accelerating voltage in obtaining higher sensitivity?

5. THE ELECTRON MICROSCOPE*

In connection with our discussion of the oscillograph, we have had occasion to use the term *electron rays* to describe the streams of electrons emitted from a hot cathode. This term suggests a similarity between streams of electrons and light rays, and, indeed, there are actually many points of similarity. Just as light travels in straight lines in an isotropic medium, electrons travel in straight lines in field-free space. Light changes in direction and speed when refraction occurs at a boundary between two media; similarly, electrons change their speeds and directions of motion when they pass from a region at one electric potential to a region at a different potential. Light beams can be focused by glass lenses; electron beams can be focused by electric or magnetic 'lenses.' Finally, just as light of a given spectral color has a definite wavelength, a definite wavelength is associated with an electron of a given speed, as we shall see in Chap. 44. Because of these many similarities, the name *electron optics* has been applied to the study of electron trajectories in electric and magnetic fields. We shall wish to consider this subject briefly in order to understand the general principles used in the electron microscope.

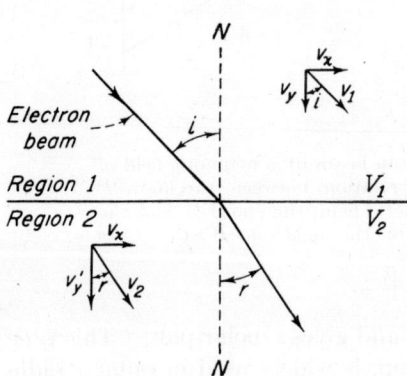

Fig. 22. Change in the direction of an electron beam in passing from a region of potential V_1 to a region of potential V_2 where $V_2 > V_1$.

First, let us consider the processes involved in electric focusing. As we have already indicated, the law of refraction has its counterpart in electron optics. Consider an electron beam to travel as shown in Fig. 22 from a region of constant potential V_1 to another of value V_2, which is higher than V_1. As a physical situation, this is highly idealized, but its consideration will help us understand the phenomenon of electrostatic focusing. When an electron crosses the boundary in Fig. 22, downward forces act on it

---

* This section may be omitted without loss of continuity.

momentarily. An electron will change its direction toward the normal NN in crossing the boundary, because the y-component of its velocity normal to the boundary will be increased, whereas the x-component of its velocity parallel to the boundary will be unchanged. Let the electron speed in region 1 be v_1 and that in region 2 be v_2. We see from Fig. 22 that $\sin i = v_x/v_1$ and $\sin r = v_x/v_2$. Hence, we may write

$$\frac{\sin i}{\sin r} = \frac{v_2}{v_1},$$

which in electron optics is analogous to Snell's law.

It should be noted that the speed ratio is the reciprocal of that appearing in ordinary optics. The ratio v_2/v_1 gives the index of refraction of region 2 relative to region 1. This index can be readily evaluated in terms of the potentials V_1 and V_2. The work done on an electron crossing the boundary is $e(V_2 - V_1)$; this is equal to the change in the kinetic energy of the electron:

$$e(V_2 - V_1) = \tfrac{1}{2}mv_2^2 - \tfrac{1}{2}mv_1^2,$$

where m is the mass of the electron. If we choose the zero of potential at the location where the electron has zero kinetic energy, then the initial kinetic energy $\tfrac{1}{2}mv_1^2$ is equal to the work eV_1 that was done on the electron when it passed from a region of zero potential to the region of potential V_1, and it follows also that $eV_2 = \tfrac{1}{2}mv_2^2$. Consequently, we may write

$$\frac{v_2^2}{v_1^2} = \frac{V_2}{V_1} \quad \text{or} \quad \frac{v_2}{v_1} = \sqrt{\frac{V_2}{V_1}}.$$

Hence

$$\frac{\sin i}{\sin r} = \sqrt{\frac{V_2}{V_1}},$$

which gives the refractive index of 2 with respect to 1 in terms of the potentials.

The abrupt bending of an electron beam as described shows the analogy with the abrupt bending of a light ray entering a dense medium at oblique incidence. In practice, however, electrostatic potentials change gradually, and consequently electron paths bend gradually as the electron passes through a region of changing potential. The forces tending to accelerate the electron act along the normals to the equipotential surfaces and bend the electron beam toward these normals when the potential increases. Thus, Fig. 23 shows in cross section a simple arrangement consisting of two cylindrical tubes T_1 and T_2 held at different potentials. The curved lines are sections of the axially symmetrical equipotential surfaces in the region in which the potential is changing from V_1 to V_2. The potential gradient is greatest midway between the tubes, where the equipotential surfaces are drawn closest together; it is in this region that the greatest forces are exerted on electrons that pass from T_1 into T_2. The arrangement shown is equivalent to a converging lens and can be used as a simple electron microscope. In order to explain this action, let us suppose that electrons are emitted from surface K at the upper end of T_1. The beam of electrons from each point on K diverges and reaches the electrostatic lens between the tubes; as a result of the forces acting on these electrons at the curved equipotential surfaces, the beam of electrons is focused at a point on the fluorescent screen S at the lower end of T_2. In this manner an inverted image of surface K is formed on the screen S. The magnification can be made large and the focusing precise by placing additional anode rings charged to appropriate potentials near the emitting surface K. The image on the screen can be brought into focus by varying the potentials V_1 and V_2 on the tubes, thereby changing the focal length of the electrostatic lens.

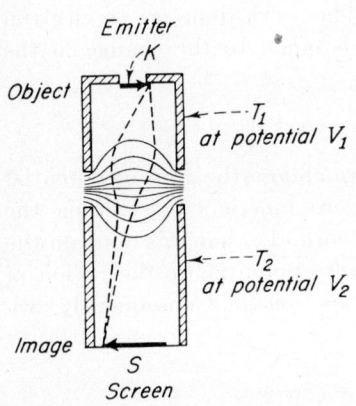

Fig. 23. Schematic drawing of a simple electron microscope using a single electrostatic lens.

In most electron microscopes, magnetic rather than electrostatic focusing is employed. The magnetic lens has been used for various purposes since 1899, when Wiechert discovered that a beam of electrons could be brought to a sharp focus by passing them down a solenoid carrying an electric current. As an aid in understanding the operation of an electron microscope using magnetic lenses, let us first consider the motion of electrons in a uniform magnetic field and then give a qualitative discussion of the action of a modern magnetic lens.

It will be recalled that no force is exerted on an electron that is moving in a direction parallel to magnetic lines; hence, the motion of such an electron is not influenced by the magnetic field. When an electron is moving with speed v in a direction perpendicular to magnetic lines, a force perpendicular to $\mathcal{B}$ and to the electron's direction of motion is exerted on the electron; and, as we have pointed out in Sec. 4, the electron moves in a circular path of radius R given by the relation

$$R = (m/\mathcal{B}e)\, v,$$

which indicates that the radius of the path traversed by an electron in a constant magnetic field is directly proportional to the electron's velocity component perpendicular to the field, and that the time taken to go once around the circular path is independent of the speed, as we have already pointed out on p. 966.

Now consider an electron moving with an initial velocity v_0 at an angle θ to $\mathcal{B}$ as indicated in Fig. 24. The component of the velocity parallel to $\mathcal{B}$ is given by $v_0 \cos\theta$. This component is unaffected by the magnetic field and does not change with time. The component of the initial velocity perpendicular to $\mathcal{B}$ is $v_0 \sin\theta$, and the force exerted on the electron by the field is $\mathcal{B}ev_0 \sin\theta$ in a direction perpendicular to $\mathcal{B}$ and to the velocity. Although the magnitude of the velocity component $v_0 \sin\theta$ perpendicular to $\mathcal{B}$ does not change, its direction changes continuously in such a way that the component motion perpendicular to $\mathcal{B}$ is circular, with radius

$$R = mv_0 \sin\theta / \mathcal{B}e.$$

The electron never moves more than a distance of $2R$ in a direction perpendicular to $\mathcal{B}$. Hence, the effect of the magnetic field is to limit the distance the electron can move perpendicular to $\mathcal{B}$ and

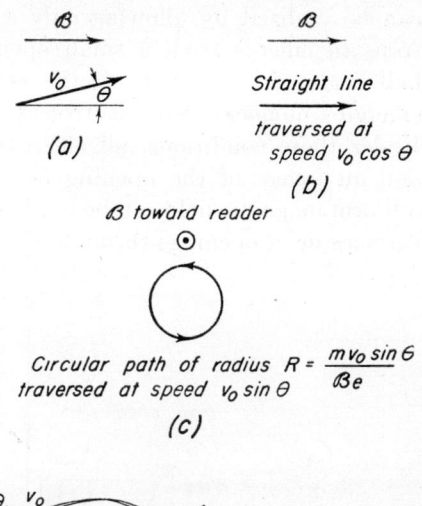

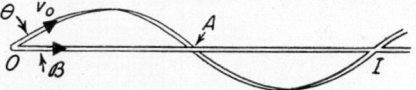

Fig. 24. Motion of an electron moving at speed v_0 in a uniform magnetic field. Parts (b) and (c) show the two components of the motion; part (d) shows the resultant motion.

to return the electron periodically to the $\mathcal{B}$-line on which the path started.

The path of the electron then consists of two parts: (1) uniform motion at speed $v_0 \cos\theta$ parallel to the $\mathcal{B}$ direction, combined with (2) motion in a circle normal to $\mathcal{B}$, of radius $mv_0 \sin\theta/\mathcal{B}e$, with period of revolution $2\pi m/\mathcal{B}e$. The combination of these paths is a helix of the type shown in Fig. 24(d). The 'pitch' of this helix is determined solely by the velocity component $v_0 \cos\theta$ parallel to $\mathcal{B}$. Consequently electrons leaving point O in Fig. 24(d), at any angle θ, will reach point I, provided their velocity components parallel to $\mathcal{B}$ are equal. Experimentally, this equality

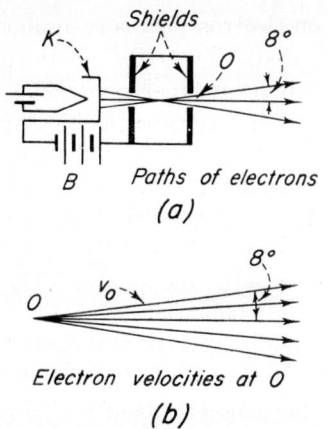

Fig. 25.

can be realized by allowing only a narrow cone of monoenergetic electrons to emerge from a small opening at position O in Fig. 25; if the half angle of the cone is 8°, the velocity components parallel to $\mathcal{B}$ of all emerging monoenergetic electrons will be the same to within one per cent. Under these conditions, all electron paths will pass very near point I and an image of the opening O will be formed at point I. Thus, a uniform magnetic field can be used as a lens to produce images of emitting surfaces or of openings through which electrons pass. No magnification

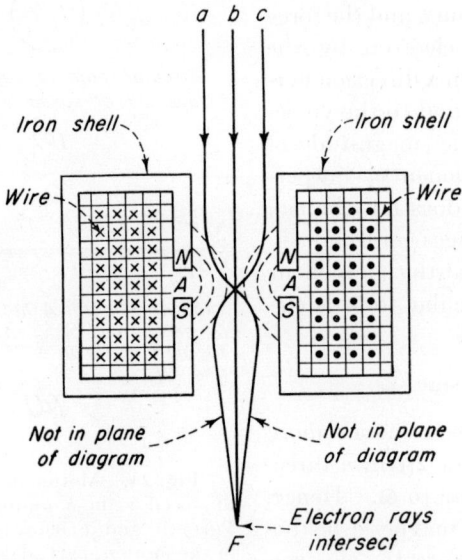

Fig. 26. A modern magnetic lens.

can be produced by such a lens, but its effect on electron beams is similar in some respects to magnetic lenses actually used. The chief point to be remembered is that electrons spiral around the magnetic flux lines and are prevented from moving very far in any direction perpendicular to the flux lines.

Figure 26 shows a cross section of a modern magnetic lens. This lens consists of a coil of wire surrounded by a thin iron shell that has an annular opening AA cut in such a way that the poles NN and SS produce a magnetic field represented by the dotted curves in the figure. The axial electrons on path b are not deviated by the magnetic field. Electrons entering the lens along paths a and c have a velocity component perpendicular to the flux lines and are therefore bent out of the plane of the diagram and follow a spiral path in the magnetic field. These electrons appear to have a counterclockwise motion in the magnetic field when viewed from below. They leave the magnetic field with a velocity component directed toward the axis of the lens and intersect the axial electrons at point F, which is the principal focus of the lens. The focal length of the lens can be varied by changing the current through the coils. This magnetic lens can be used to form electron images of electron 'sources' close to the lens axis. It should be noted that electron rays are twisted in passing through a magnetic lens in a manner that has no counterpart in optics.

A complete electron microscope is shown schematically in Fig. 27. A stream of high-speed electrons from an electron gun diverges through an opening S into the microscope tube, which is maintained at high vacuum. In passing the condensing lens C, the electrons become a parallel beam. At O_1 this beam strikes an object that is mounted on a thin film or mesh. The electrons pass readily through some parts of the object and are partially absorbed and partially scattered by other parts. Divergent electron rays from each point of the object are focused by objective lens L_1 to form the image I_1 as indicated in the figure. A second-stage magnification of a part O_2 of the first image I_1 is effected by a second lens L_2 in such a way that the final image I_2 is formed on a fluorescent screen or photographic plate. Direct linear magnifications of 30,000 are thus obtained; this is more than 10 times the magnification obtainable with optical microscopes. Because of the short wavelength (see Chap. 44) associated with electrons, the resolving power of an electron microscope can be made much greater than that attainable with ordinary microscopes.

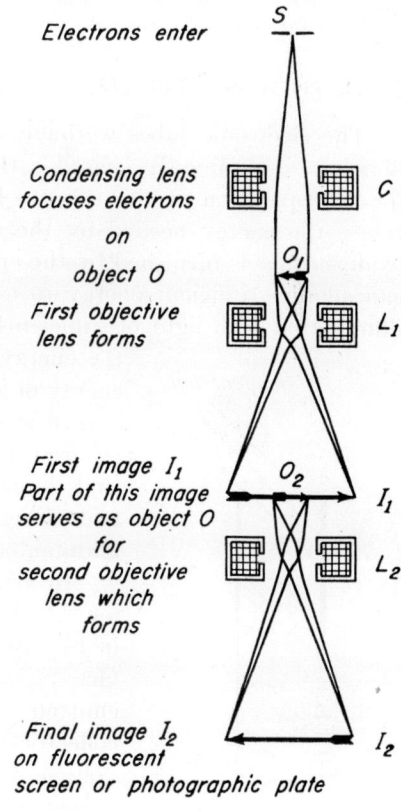

Fig. 27. Schematic drawing of an electron microscope.

PROBLEMS

1. An electron with a kinetic energy of 5000 ev enters a uniform magnetic field of 0.02 weber/m² that is perpendicular to the electron's direction of motion. What is the radius of the path of this electron in the magnetic field?   Ans: 1.19 cm.

2. An electron moving with a kinetic energy of 4000 ev enters a uniform magnetic field of 0.01 weber/m² that is perpendicular to the electron's direction of motion. What is the radius of the path of this electron in the magnetic field?

3. An electron enters a uniform magnetic field. Its initial path makes an angle of 45° with the magnetic-field direction. In the magnetic field, it traverses a helical path. If the 'radius' of the helix is 1 cm, what is the 'pitch' of the helix?

Ans: 2π cm.

4. An electron enters a uniform magnetic field. Its initial velocity makes an angle of 60° with the field direction. In the magnetic field, it traverses a helical path. If the 'radius' of the helix is 2 cm, what is the 'pitch' of the helix?

6. THE PHOTOELECTRIC EFFECT

The electronic tubes we have discussed thus far have employed hot filaments or indirectly heated cathodes to emit the electrons necessary for the operation of the tubes. In the emission of electrons in these tubes, the energy needed by the electron to escape from the metal or oxide surface is furnished by the energy of thermal agitation. Electrons can acquire sufficient energy to escape from cold metal if the metal is illuminated with light of sufficiently short wavelength. In this process, the energy needed for escape is furnished by the energy of a light quantum. This phenomenon is known as the *photoelectric effect* and was first discovered in 1887 by Heinrich Hertz, who noticed that a spark would jump more readily between two charged spheres when their surfaces were illuminated by light from another spark.

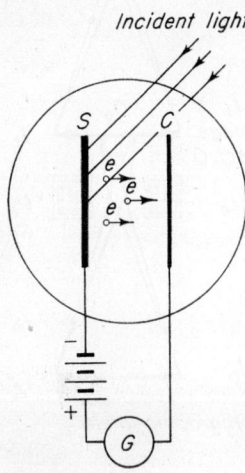

Fig. 28. A photoelectric cell circuit. Light striking the metal surface S ejects electrons which are drawn to collector C.

An arrangement that can be used for observing the photoelectric effect is shown schematically in Fig. 28. A beam of light strikes a metal surface S in an evacuated tube. Electrons are emitted by the surface and are drawn to the collector C, normally maintained at a positive voltage with respect to S. The current can be measured by the galvanometer G. It is found that for a given surface S, the frequency of the incident light must be greater than a certain frequency, called the *threshold frequency*, before any electrons are emitted by the surface at all. The threshold frequency for most metals is in the ultraviolet, but for some materials like potassium and cesium oxide it is in the visible region.

For light frequencies well above threshold, some of the electrons are emitted from S with considerable speed, as can be demonstrated by removing the battery from the circuit in Fig. 28 and noting that a small current still flows. The speed of the fastest electrons can be determined by finding the *negative* voltage that must be applied to the collector C in order to stop the current completely. Experiments show that *the maximum speed of emitted electrons depends only on the frequency of the incident light*. The number of electrons emitted per second (as determined from measurements of saturation currents) depends on the intensity of the incident light, but the maximum speed of the electrons is independent of the intensity of the incident light and depends only on the frequency.

The correct explanation of the photoelectric effect was given by Einstein in 1906. Einstein used the quantum theory that had been proposed earlier by Planck to account for the shape of the black-body-radiation curves (see Chap. 30). According to this theory, light is not emitted and absorbed continuously, but in small bundles or quanta. The energy W of each quantum is proportional to the frequency and is given by the relation

$$W = hf,$$

where h is *Planck's constant*. According to Einstein's theory, when a light quantum or photon is absorbed at a metal such as S in Fig. 28, its total energy hf is imparted to a single electron within the metal. The energy acquired by the electron may enable it to penetrate the potential barrier at the surface of the metal and escape if it is moving in the proper direction with sufficient speed. In penetrating the barrier, the electron loses a certain energy ϕ, called the *work function* of the surface; if the energy hf received from the incident light quantum is greater than ϕ, the electron retains kinetic energy after leaving the surface. The maximum kinetic energy $\frac{1}{2}mv_{max}^2$ of electrons emitted from a metal on which light of frequency f is incident is given by the Einstein photoelectric equation

$$\tfrac{1}{2}mv_{max}^2 = hf - \phi.$$

The experimental results are described accurately and completely by this expression, which is based on quantum theory and cannot be explained by classical electromagnetic theory. The work function here is the same as the work function introduced in Sec. 1 in connection with thermionic emission.

Modern photoelectric cells of the type shown in Fig. 28 have many uses. The currents obtainable with most vacuum phototubes is small and is of the order of a few microamperes per lumen of incident light. The currents available from a given beam of incident light is much greater in the *electron-multiplier tube*. In electron multipliers, the electrons ejected from one sensitive surface are accelerated toward a second surface, which ejects other electrons by so-called *secondary emission* when the original electrons strike it. The number of secondary electrons may be two or three times as great as the number of primary electrons. One commercial electron-multiplier tube contains nine stages of 'multiplication'; in this tube an average of 1.6 secondaries are emitted per primary at each surface, and the final current reaching the collector is $(1.6)^9$ or approximately 230,000 times the initial photoelectric current from the first surface.

The *photovoltaic cell* or *barrier-layer cell* is a different type of photocell that is widely used in 'light meters' and 'exposure meters.' In this type of cell, action of the light generates an EMF; hence this cell requires no external battery for its operation. In one common type of photovoltaic cell, a thin, almost transparent, layer of some metal deposited on cuprous oxide forms a coating for a copper disk. Incident light causes electrons to be ejected from the cuprous oxide into the copper, leaving the oxide and its thin metal coating positively charged and giving the copper a negative charge. When the two outer layers are connected externally as shown in Fig. 29, an external current flows from the metal coating to the copper.

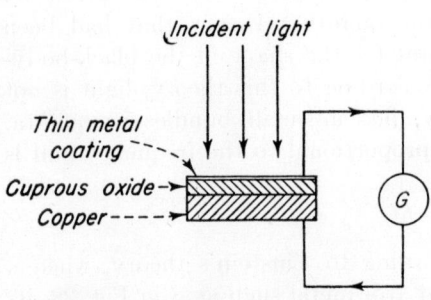

Fig. 29. Photovoltaic cell.

PROBLEMS

1. The photoelectric threshold of tungsten is 273 mμ. Determine the maximum kinetic energy of the electrons ejected from a tungsten surface by ultraviolet light of wavelength 180 mμ. Ans: 2.35 ev.

2. What is the maximum kinetic energy of electrons ejected from tungsten by ultraviolet light of wavelength 100 mμ if the photoelectric threshold is 273 mμ?

3. When a copper surface is illuminated by light of wavelength 253.7 mμ from a mercury arc, the value of the retarding potential required to stop the emission of electrons is 0.59 volt. What is the photoelectric threshold for copper? Ans: 288 mμ.

4. When a copper surface with photoelectric threshold at 288 mμ is illuminated by light of wavelength 200 mμ, what retarding potential is required to stop the emission of electrons?

5. If the photoelectric threshold of tungsten is 273 mμ, what is its work function in electron-volts? Compare with the value given in Sec. 1. Ans: 4.58 ev.

6. If the photoelectric threshold of copper is 288 mμ, what is its work function in electron-volts?

7. X RAYS

Incident light quanta cause the emission of electrons from a metal surface in the photoelectric effect. The inverse process—the ejection of light quanta from matter by incident electrons—results in the production of X rays.

In 1895, Wilhelm Konrad Roentgen discovered that when high-speed electrons impinge upon the walls of discharge tubes or upon metal electrodes, penetrating radiation is given off. The name *X rays* was applied because the nature of the radiation was not known. Today we know that X rays are similar in nature to light but have extremely short wavelengths and high frequencies.

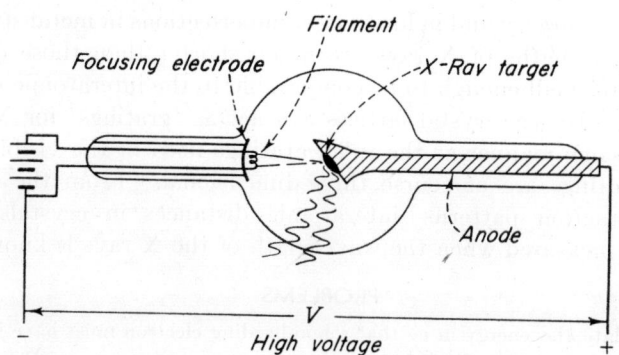

Fig. 30. X-ray tube. Electrons emitted by the filament strike the target button on the anode. X-rays are emitted from the target.

When an electron with an energy of several thousand electron-volts strikes a metal target, X rays are emitted from the surface. The maximum frequency f_{max} of the emitted radiation can be obtained from the Einstein photoelectric equation

$$hf_{max} = \tfrac{1}{2}mv^2,$$

where v is the speed of the incident electrons; in the case of X rays the effect of the work function ϕ is so small that it can be neglected. Any value of energy up to the electron's full kinetic energy can appear in a quantum of X radiation. Hence the target in an X-ray tube emits X rays of all frequencies below the *maximum* frequency, and the spectrum of the emitted X rays extends indefinitely from the wavelength corresponding to f_{max} toward longer wavelengths. With the usual *thick* targets, the spectral intensity is a maximum somewhat below the maximum frequency. The spectrum emitted from a heavy-metal X-ray target is continuous, but superimposed on this continuous spectrum are 'bright lines' corresponding to *characteristic X rays*. The frequencies of the bright lines are determined by the material of which the target is made. Spectral series of characteristic X rays arise from changes in energy of the inner electrons of the atoms of which the target is composed. Just as the atoms of every element have characteristic emission lines in the visible spectrum when properly excited, so the atoms of the heavy elements have characteristic lines in the X-ray spectrum. Visible spectra appear as the result of energy changes of a few electron-volts involving the *outer electrons;* X-ray spectra appear as the result of energy changes of thousands of electron-volts involving the *inner electrons.*

The penetrating properties of X rays are so well known that they will not be discussed in detail here. They are widely utilized in the fields of medicine and surgery and in location of imperfections in metal structures.

The wavelengths of X rays are much shorter than those of visible light and are small enough to be comparable to the interatomic distances in crystals. Hence, crystal lattices can act as 'gratings' for X rays in much the same manner as the ruled gratings used in the visible region. Crystal gratings are of course three-dimensional. From the observed X-ray diffraction patterns, interatomic distances in crystals can be accurately measured when the wavelength of the X rays is known.

PROBLEMS

1. Calculate the energy in ev that a bombarding electron must have in order to produce X rays of wavelength 0.1 mμ. Ans: 12,400 ev.

2. One of the characteristic X rays from molybdenum has a wavelength of 0.0708 mμ. What minimum energy must bombarding electrons have in order to excite this radiation?

3. What is the shortest wavelength produced in an X-ray tube to which 50,000 volts are applied? Ans: 0.0248 mμ.

4. What is the shortest wavelength produced in an X-ray tube operated at 1 million volts?

8. CONDUCTION OF ELECTRICITY THROUGH GASES

Air and other gases at normal pressure can for most purposes be considered as good insulators unless the electric field is so great as to produce spark discharges. There is, however, some conduction through air under normal laboratory conditions, as is evidenced by the gradual collapse of the leaves of a charged electroscope, even when there is no leakage along the solid insulators. The processes involved in conduction through gases are more complicated than those involved in conduction through metals. The conduction mechanism in gases involves positive and negative ions as well as free electrons; recombination of the ions is taking place continuously to some extent, and consequently the number of 'carriers' may not be constant as in the case of metallic conduction. Let us consider ways in which ions can be formed in the region between cathode and anode in a discharge tube.

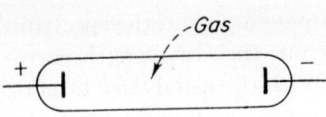

Fig. 31. A gas-discharge tube.

A neutral molecule is *ionized*, to produce a positive ion and a free negative electron, when energy is supplied to it in such a way as to remove an electron from the molecule. Frequently, the free electron becomes attached to another molecule to produce a negative ion. Ionization of gas molecules can be produced by photoelectric processes involving visible light, ultraviolet light, or X rays, by radiations from radioactive materials, and by the cosmic radiation that comes to the earth's atmosphere from outer space. Ions formed by these processes are called *primary ions*. Recombination of positive and negative ions gradually takes place; but when a potential difference exists between two electrodes in the gas, some of the positive ions will migrate to the cathode and some of the electrons and negative ions will migrate to the anode before recombination occurs, thereby producing a measurable current through the gas. As the potential difference between the electrodes is increased, the speeds of the ions and electrons increase, and consequently more of these 'primary' ions reach the electrodes before recombination, thereby increasing the current. As the potential is further increased, a 'saturation current' is attained when all the primary ions reach the electrodes before recombination.

With a sufficiently high voltage between the electrodes, the primary ions attain such high speeds that they produce *secondary ions* by collision with neutral molecules. This process greatly increases the number of ions available for the conduction process, eventually resulting in a luminous spark or glow discharge. Light from the discharge can increase the number of electrons available for conduction by causing photoelectric emission from the cathode, while bombardment of the cathode by positive ions can also produce electrons.

When the gas between the electrodes is at atmospheric pressure, raising the potential causes 'electrical breakdown' in the form of a typical spark discharge along an irregular, threadlike path. If the pressure is gradually decreased, the discharge spreads out and appears to fill the whole discharge tube in a glow discharge of the type used in a neon sign. Glow discharges take place at pressures of the order of a few millimeters of mercury when the mean free path of ions in the gas is much longer than it is at atmospheric pressure. The spark discharge is distinctly different in nature from a glow discharge; a spark discharge is an essentially discontinuous process, although a succession of spark discharges may take place so rapidly as to appear continuous. Once established, a glow discharge is continuous and is said to be 'self-sustaining'; the gas in the tube has a very low 'resistance' compared with the gas under normal conditions.

The relation between the applied voltage and the current in a glow discharge is shown in Fig. 32. Application of this unusual relationship is made in 'voltage-regulator tubes,' which are used to advantage in arrangements like those shown in Fig. 33. The voltage drop across these glow tubes is constant over fairly wide ranges of current from about 5 to 40 ma. In part (a) of Fig. 33, the glow tube is connected in series with a limiting resistance R_1 across the output of a filtered power supply. The voltage from this power supply must be higher than the *starting voltage*, which is usually about 30% higher than the *operating voltage* of the glow tube. The load resistance R_L is connected in parallel

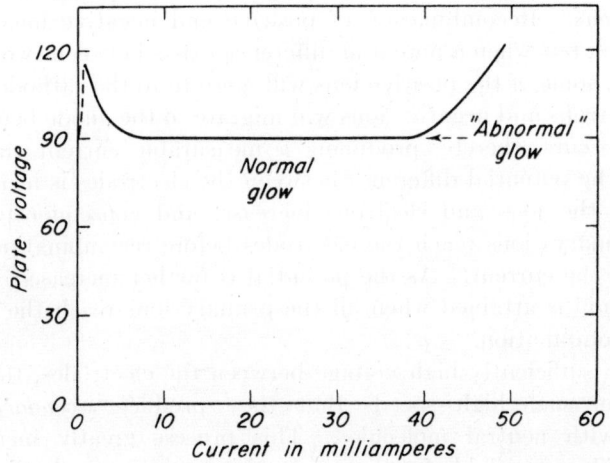

Fig. 32. Relation between voltage and current in the case of glow tube type VR-90.

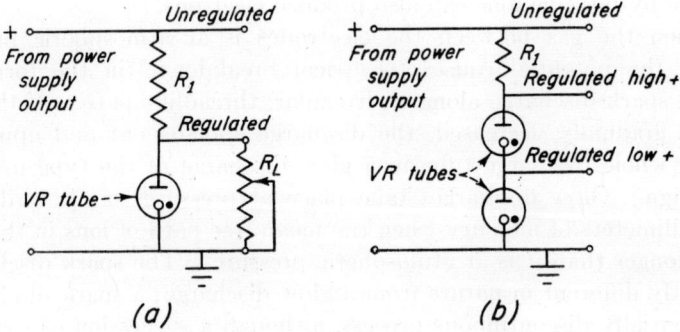

Fig. 33. The use of glow tubes for voltage regulation.

with the glow tube. For a range of currents through the load resistance R_L from 0 to about 35 ma, the voltage across R_L is accurately stabilized at 90 v in the case of the VR–90 tube. Glow tubes are commercially available for regulated voltages of 75, 90, 105, and 150 v. Two or more glow tubes can be used in series as indicated in part (b) of Fig. 33.

The character of the discharge in a tube such as that of Fig. 31 varies greatly with the gas pressure. This variation is best discussed in terms of the mean free path (mean distance between collisions) of the molecules. The effective period for acceleration of an ion by the electric field is the period determined by the mean free path, because at a collision the ion loses a good part of its kinetic energy and also starts off in a new direction. At high pressures (above a few cm) the mean free path is extremely short so an enormous field is required to give an ion sufficient kinetic energy during a mean free path so that it can produce secondary ions on collision. When such a field does exist, enormous numbers of secondary ions are produced and a spark discharge results. At pressures of the order of a few mm, mean free paths are much longer ($\sim 10^{-3}$ cm long, still small compared to the tube dimensions), the field required for secondary ionization is smaller, but when secondary ionization does occur the rate of production of secondaries per unit volume is smaller. Under these conditions a glow discharge fills the tube. At an extremely low pressure (called a *hard vacuum*), the mean free path becomes comparable to the tube dimensions. Practically no secondaries result from collisions because there are practically no collisions. The discharge is non-luminous and secondary ions are produced principally by X rays emitted at the anode and electrons knocked out of the cathode by positive ion bombardment. Under these conditions the current that can be carried by the tube is very small.

Two other types of gaseous discharge should be mentioned. The *arc discharge* is a discharge that involves high currents between relatively closely spaced electrodes. An arc discharge can be initiated by placing two electrodes in contact and then separating them. A *corona* involves the partial ionization of air in regions of high electric field, for example near the conductors of high-voltage transmission lines. In the region where the voltage gradient exceeds the breakdown strength of air (about 3 megavolts/meter), a corona results. The ionization of the air in a corona is accompanied by a faint glow, which can sometimes be seen at night near a high-voltage transmission line.

CHAPTER 44

ELECTROMAGNETIC WAVES

We have discussed the ways in which electrical oscillations can be set up in circuits containing capacitance and inductance. In circuits of this type, the energy is stored alternately in the electric field of the capacitive circuit elements and in the magnetic field of the inductive elements, just as the energy of an oscillating pendulum is alternately potential at the ends of the swing and kinetic when the bob passes the center point of the swing. Some of the energy of an oscillating circuit is dissipated in heating resistive elements in the circuit; if the oscillations are to be sustained, energy must be supplied to the circuit at a rate equal to the rate at which electrical energy is dissipated. Energy also escapes from an oscillating circuit in the form of electromagnetic radiation that passes outward through the space surrounding the circuit; this emission of radiant energy from an oscillating circuit becomes increasingly important as the frequency of oscillation is increased.

When the current through a coil increases, the magnetic field $\mathcal{B}$ in and around the coil increases. Work equal to $\frac{1}{2}LI^2$ must be done in the process of setting up this field, as we have seen. Mathematical analysis shows that this work is equal to the integral throughout space of $\mathcal{B}^2/(8\pi \times 10^{-7})$, in joules/m³, which is therefore called the *energy density* associated with the magnetic field. We have also seen that when the current decreases and the magnetic field disappears, energy equal to the work done in setting up the field is supplied to the electrical circuit. The energy of the field is said to be *returned* to the circuit. Exactly similar remarks may be made concerning the energy $\frac{1}{2}CV^2$ required to charge a condenser. This energy may be considered as residing in the electric field with energy density $\mathcal{E}^2/(8\pi \times 10^{-7}c^2)$, in joules/m³. This energy is returned to the circuit as the condenser discharges.

Up to now we have completely ignored one important question: *How fast* are these electric and magnetic fields set up? We have tacitly assumed that the electric and magnetic fields arising from a system of charges and currents are instantaneously determined, at all points of space, by the distribution of charges and currents at that particular instant. Maxwell, in 1864, showed by theoretical analysis that this assumption is not valid, but rather that the influences of charges and currents, as represented by the fields they set up, are propagated outward at a finite speed, which turns out to be the speed of light. Thus, if we charge a sphere at $t=0$, the (small) electric field of the sphere at a point a mile away does not appear for 1/186,000 second. During this time interval the (small) energy required to set up the electric field at a distance of a mile and more must be thought of as traveling outward in space at the speed of light. The times involved are small and the speed of energy propagation is high; consequently, if the sphere is *slowly* charged and discharged, the energy that is stored in the field, even a mile away, has plenty of time to get back to the sphere and reappear in the electrical circuit connected to the sphere. But if the sphere is alternately charged and discharged very rapidly (say a million times a second), the energy sent out from the sphere to a point a mile away cannot be recalled in time by the sphere as it discharges because the recall signal can go out only with the speed of light. The result is that the sphere can recall only the energy within a certain radius before it is again being charged and is sending out more energy. The net result of this situation is that some energy goes on traveling out through space indefinitely. Exactly the same arguments apply to the magnetic fields set up by currents. The energy sent out into space constitutes electromagnetic radiation.

It should appear reasonable from the above picture that the amount of electromagnetic radiation sent out into space by a given system of charges and currents depends strongly on the frequency. This conclusion is true, and Maxwell's theoretical analysis shows that the rate of radiation varies as the fourth power of the frequency. It is low so long as all regions where static electric and magnetic fields would be appreciable can be reached by signals transmitted with the speed of light in a time small compared to the period of oscillation, but it increases rapidly at higher frequencies. For example, ordinary radio transmission employs frequencies of 500,000 cycles/second or higher, for which the distance of signal propagation in ½ cycle is 1000 feet or less. The broadcasting station uses a very long antenna, for which the *static* fields would be appreciable beyond this distance of 1000 feet. Thus a high *radiated* power is achieved.

The fact that energy does propagate outward in the form of electromagnetic waves such as radio waves furnishes a justification of the assumption that the energy does reside in the electric and magnetic fields in the way mentioned above.

In the present chapter, we cannot go into the analytical details of the theory sketched above, but we shall discuss the radiation emitted from a simple antenna and indicate some of the ways in which this radiation is used in radio communication systems.

Electromagnetic waves are emitted whenever an electric charge is accelerated. We shall review the different regions of the 'electromagnetic spectrum,' which extends from the longest radio waves to the extremely short gamma rays emitted by radioactive materials.

1. ELECTROMAGNETIC RADIATION: THE WORK OF HERTZ

In Chapter 30 we mentioned Clerk Maxwell's electromagnetic theory of light, which was published in 1864 before electromagnetic waves were produced and detected by electrical methods in the laboratory. Maxwell's theory indicated that light waves *could* be electromagnetic in character and gave a description of the much longer and at that time unknown electromagnetic waves now used in radio communication. Long electromagnetic waves were first produced and detected in 1886

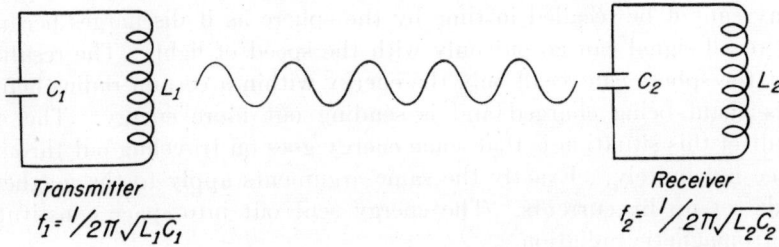

Fig. 1. Electromagnetic waves of frequency f_1 are sent out when the transmitter circuit is properly excited. Some of the electromagnetic radiation will excite the receiver circuit provided C_2 and L_2 are adjusted in such a way that $f_2 = f_1$.

by Heinrich Hertz, a German physicist. Hertz found that these waves, predicted by Maxwell, have properties similar to those of light even though the waves he used were a meter or more in length; they could be reflected, refracted, diffracted, and polarized with suitable equipment. Thus, Maxwell's theory received complete experimental verification and has since Hertz's time been accepted as the correct description of light waves as well as of long radio waves.

The apparatus used by Hertz in his experiments was crude, but the principles involved are precisely the same as those used today in the transmission and reception of radio waves. A diagram of the basic circuits used by Hertz is shown in Fig. 1. When the transmitter circuit is properly excited, electrical oscillations of frequency $f_1 = 1/2\pi\sqrt{L_1 C_1}$ are produced in this circuit, and electromagnetic waves of this frequency are sent out from the transmitter. If the receiver circuit is properly 'tuned,' that is, if L_2 and C_2 are adjusted so that $f_2 = 1/2\pi\sqrt{L_2 C_2} = f_1$, energy will be transferred to the receiver circuit by electromagnetic waves from the transmitter and can be detected in the receiver circuit by appropriate methods, which will be described.

In the transmitter used in the early experiments of Hertz, a condenser was allowed to discharge through a spark between electrodes in air. The discharge is oscillatory but is highly damped, as indicated in Fig. 3. A schematic diagram of one form of apparatus used by Hertz is shown in Fig. 2. The capacitance consisted of two square sheets of metal measuring 40 cm on a side. These were placed about 60 cm apart. Two highly polished metal balls 2 or 3 cm apart were connected to the plates

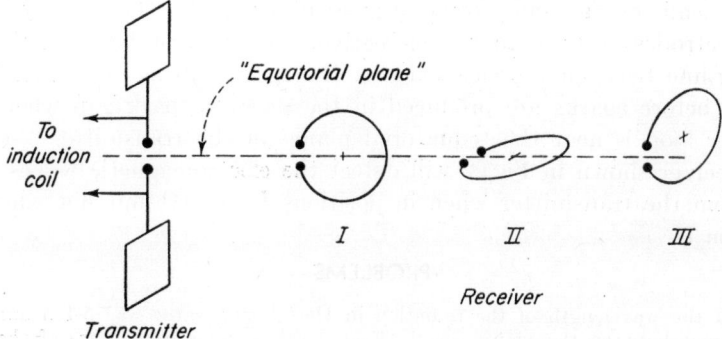

Fig. 2. Schematic diagram of Hertz' apparatus. With the receiver loop properly 'tuned,' sparks were produced at the gap in the receiver circuit when the loop was in positions I and III but not in position II, where the receiver gap is perpendicular to the transmitter gap.

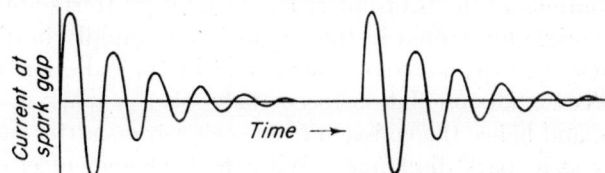

Fig. 3. Damped oscillations in the Hertz transmitter circuit.

by light metal rods. The plates were connected to the terminals of an induction coil. Whenever the potential difference between the balls reached a value sufficient to render the air in the gap conducting, an oscillatory discharge occurred and was accompanied by radiation of electromagnetic waves. The inductance in this circuit is merely the inductance of the straight current path connecting the condenser plates. Since both the inductance and the capacitance were very small, the frequency was very high. Interference measurements showed that the wavelength of the emitted radiation was about $\lambda = 4.5$ meters, corresponding to a frequency $f = c/\lambda = 3 \times 10^8 \text{(m/sec)}/5.4 \text{ m} = 56 \times 10^6$ cycles/sec = 56 megacycles/sec.

In order to receive and detect the radiation from this transmitter, Hertz employed a circular wire loop 35 cm in radius with a small gap at one point in the loop. 'Tuning' of the receiver loop was accomplished chiefly by proper selection of the loop diameter, but 'fine' tuning was provided by a micrometer screw arrangement for adjusting the spacing of the discharge points at the receiver gap. Sparks could be produced at the gap when radiation was falling upon this receiving circuit in the proper manner. The orientation of the receiver loop with respect to the transmitter was found to be of great importance. The line between the electrodes at the gap in the receiver circuit must be parallel to a similar line between the electrodes at the spark gap in the transmitter circuit before sparks are produced in the receiver spark gap when the receiver loop is near the 'equatorial plane' of the transmitter. Thus, the receiver shown in Fig. 2 will detect the electromagnetic waves sent out from the transmitter when in positions I and III but not when in position II.

PROBLEMS

1. If the wavelength of the radiation in Hertz's apparatus was 5.4 m and the capacitance between the plates was 1.33 $\mu\mu$f, what was the inductance of the discharge circuit between the plates?   Ans: 6.17 μhenry.

2. With a capacitance of 1.33 $\mu\mu$f, what is the inductance in Hertz's apparatus, if the wavelength of the radiation is 6.5 m?

2. RADIATION FROM A DIPOLE ANTENNA

The oscillations in the transmitter circuit used by Hertz are damped, since energy originally stored in the circuit is lost rapidly in dissipative effects at the spark gap and to a smaller extent by the radiation of electromagnetic waves. The oscillations occur only when a spark discharge is taking place, and hence the emission from such a transmitter takes place as erratically as a spark discharge. With the development of electronic vacuum tubes, it has been possible to construct circuits in which oscillations are sustained; the Hartley and the tuned-grid oscillator circuits described in Chap. 43 are examples. These circuits can be used to excite circuit elements that radiate *continuous* electromagnetic waves. Any oscillating circuit will radiate some electromagnetic waves, but the radiated power can be increased by the introduction of a special circuit element called an *antenna*. Of the numerous types of antennas that have been designed, the 'oscillating-dipole' type is one of the simplest; the oscillating circuit of the Hertz transmitter acts as an antenna of this type.

An oscillating-dipole antenna, as shown schematically in Fig. 4, consists of a straight conductor with a source of alternating EMF, usually part of a vacuum-tube oscillator circuit, at its center. The two halves of the straight conductor can be considered as the 'plates' of a condenser.

When the right half is positive, the left half is negative, and vice versa; hence the name *oscillating dipole*. The charge and current distributions at certain stages of the alternator cycle are shown in Fig. 4.

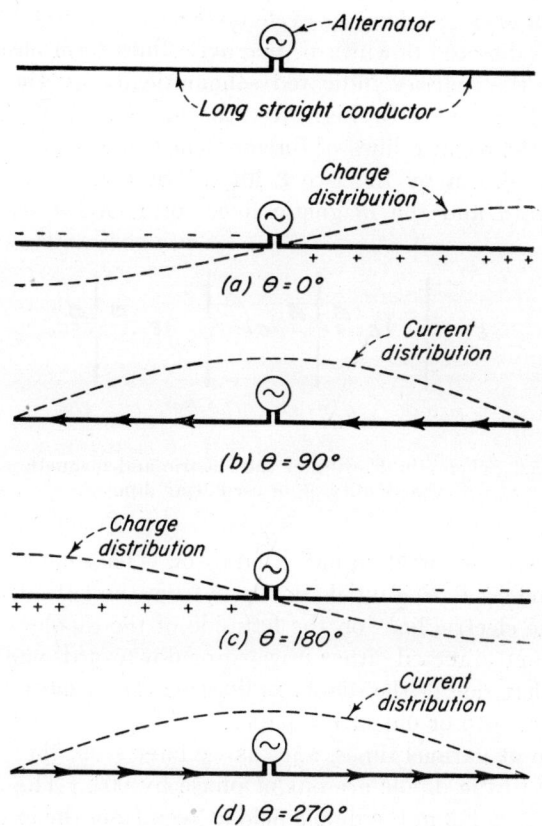

Fig. 4. An oscillating-dipole antenna: a long straight conductor with an alternator at its midpoint. (a) Initial condition: right end positive, left end negative, and current zero. (b) Condition at end of quarter period: no net charge, current directed toward the left. (c) Condition at end of half period: right end negative, left end positive, and current zero. (d) Condition at three-quarters of period: no net charge, current directed toward the right.

The electric and magnetic fields around this antenna are continually changing, but there are several points in the cycle at which we can get some idea of their configuration from our earlier discussion of electric and magnetic fields. These are shown as parts (a), (b), (c), and (d) of Fig. 5. Except for the fact that we have drawn the antenna vertical in Fig. 5, these parts correspond exactly to the charge and current distribution shown for the four stages of oscillation in parts (a), (b), (c), and (d) of Fig. 4. When the upper half of the dipole is positive as in Fig. 5(a), electric lines of force pass from the upper half to the lower half, as indicated schematically by the two $\mathcal{E}$ lines shown; since the current is zero, there are no $\mathcal{B}$ lines. A quarter-cycle later there are no $\mathcal{E}$ lines, but since the current is directed downward, magnetic lines form circles about the conductor in the manner indicated schematically by the directions of $\mathcal{B}$ shown in Fig. 5(b). In Fig. 5(c), the lower half of the antenna is positive and the electric lines of force extend from the lower half to the upper half as shown by the two $\mathcal{E}$ lines. In Fig. 5(d), the current is directed upward and the magnetic lines form circles around the con-

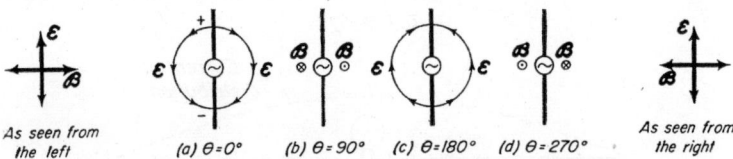

Fig. 5. Schematic drawing of the electric and magnetic lines in the vicinity of an oscillating dipole.

ductor and have the direction indicated by $\mathcal{B}$. Thus, an observer looking directly at the oscillating dipole in Fig. 5 from the left edge of the paper would see the electric lines on the left side of the dipole as lines *parallel to the dipole* and directed either upward or downward, and the magnetic lines on the left side of the dipole as lines *perpendicular to the dipole* and directed either into or out of the paper. These lines vary in magnitude and direction at various times, and, as we have seen, the $\mathcal{E}$ lines and the $\mathcal{B}$ lines close to the dipole are out of phase by 90°. The 'views' of the directions of $\mathcal{E}$ and $\mathcal{B}$ in the dipole field as seen from the left and from the right edges of the paper are also shown in Fig. 5.

The schematic pictures of the magnetic and electric fields we have shown in Fig. 5 are only partially correct, since we have shown two pictures, parts (a) and (c), that represent the *electric fields for static charge distributions* and two other pictures, parts (b) and (d), that represent the *magnetic fields for steady currents*. Actually, the *charge distribution and the currents at the dipole antenna are both changing*. If the dipole oscillated extremely slowly, the simple pictures we have shown would apply fairly well. The electric lines of force would slowly appear while the ends of the antenna were being charged, would slowly disappear while the charges were being neutralized, and then would slowly reappear with reversed direction while the ends of the antenna were being charged with reversed polarity. Similarly, the magnetic lines would gradually appear while the current was increasing, would slowly disappear while the current was dropping to zero, and then would slowly reappear with reversed direction while the reversed current built up. Actually, the electric and magnetic lines do not disappear completely, but some of the

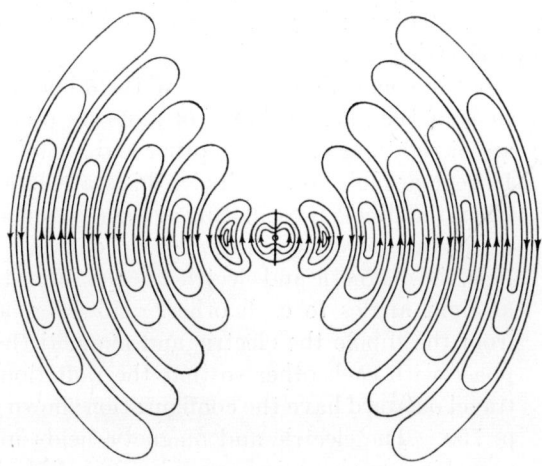

Fig. 6. Schematic representation of the electric lines of force around an oscillating dipole.

lines appear to become 'disengaged' from the dipole and move away from the dipole as *electromagnetic radiation*. This effect becomes more pronounced as the frequency is increased. We cannot give here a rigorous theoretical treatment of the processes taking place during the emission of electromagnetic radiation, but we shall give a brief qualitative description of the emission process in terms of the electric and magnetic lines.

The manner in which electric lines of force break away from a rapidly oscillating dipole antenna and travel outward in closed loops is illustrated in Fig. 6. In this picture the loops must be imagined to be generated at the antenna and to travel outward at the speed of light. The electric field decreases in strength as the loop moves outward.

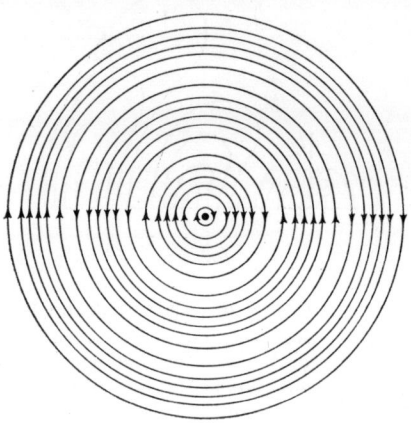

Fig. 7. Magnetic lines moving outward from an oscillating dipole. The antenna is shown in end view.

It will be recalled that electric lines of force cannot exist in the form of closed loops in a static field, in which an electric line always begins and ends on electric charges; but closed loops do occur in radiation fields.

Like the electric lines, some of the magnetic lines continue to move outward from the antenna. This movement is indicated in Fig. 7, which shows closed lines spreading outward in the 'equatorial plane' of an oscillating dipole. This process is somewhat easier to visualize than the corresponding electrical process.

As we pointed out in connection with Fig. 5, the $\mathcal{E}$ lines of the electric field and the $\mathcal{B}$ lines of the magnetic field of a slowly oscillating dipole are at right angles to each other and are 90° out of phase. In regions close to the dipole, this statement is true even when the dipole is oscillating at high frequencies. As the magnetic and electric lines spread outward from the dipole, the magnetic and electric lines continue to be oriented at right angles to each other. However, at a distance from the dipole the electric and magnetic fields get into phase with each other so that the radiation waves that travel outward have the configuration shown in Fig. 11 on p. 750. The electric and magnetic fields in a wave approaching an observer have the orientation shown in Fig. 8. The vectors $\mathcal{E}$ and $\mathcal{B}$ at points remote from a source of radiation are always in phase with each other and are perpendicular to the direction of propagation. It might be noted that if one looks in the direction of propagation, a clockwise or right-hand-screw motion will rotate $\mathcal{E}$ toward

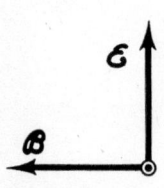

Fig. 8. An electromagnetic wave approaching the reader.

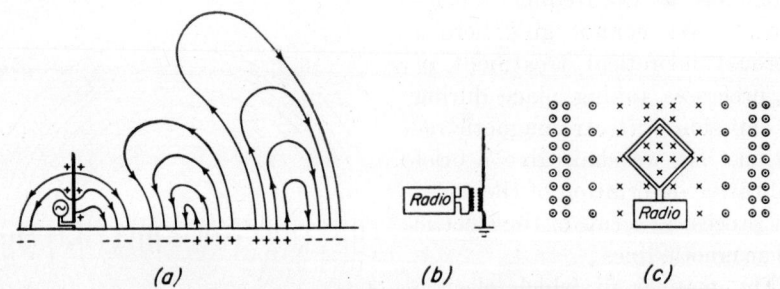

Fig. 9. (a) A 'half-dipole' transmitting antenna. (b) A vertical receiving antenna, which responds to the electric component. (c) A 'loop' antenna, which responds to the rate of change of magnetic flux as the magnetic lines indicated by crosses and dots move past it in their progress outward from the transmitter.

$\mathcal{B}$; this rule helps in remembering the relative orientation of the displacements. In an advancing electromagnetic wave, $\mathcal{E}$ and $\mathcal{B}$ are tangential to the wave-front and the direction of propagation is given by the 'ray,' which, as will be recalled, is always perpendicular to the wave-front.

Most radio transmitting antennas are not a whole dipole as in

Figs. 4–7, but a 'half dipole' standing vertically as in Fig. 9(a), where only the electric lines are indicated. Because the ground is an electrical conductor, it is capable of supplying the charges needed on the ends of the electric lines where they reach the ground.

Two types of receiving antennas are indicated in Fig. 9(b) and (c). One is a vertical antenna, which responds to the electric component of the radio wave. The other is a 'loop' antenna, which responds to the magnetic component. The loop antenna is directional in character and hence can be used as a radio direction finder. In the orientation shown in Fig. 9(c), the loop is threaded by magnetic flux, first in one direction and then the other as the wave moves across the loop, and the voltage $N\, d\Phi/dt$ is generated. If, however, the loop were turned through 90° about a vertical axis, it would not be threaded by any flux lines, and no signal would be received. A loop antenna is built into most home radio receivers.

3. RADIO COMMUNICATION SYSTEMS

The electromagnetic waves sent outward from the antenna of a transmitter can be received by appropriate methods at distant positions. The waves can be detected by means of a vacuum-tube amplifier tuned to the same frequency as the alternator or high-frequency oscillator in the transmitter. Just as an antenna is used for increasing the amount of radiation emitted from an oscillator, an antenna is used in connection with the amplifier employed to receive the radiation. The radiation produces current in the antenna that is amplified by the vacuum-tube amplifier.

The radiation from a transmitter travels outward in straight lines and therefore could be received only at receiving stations located within the line of sight from the transmitting antenna if it were not for atmospheric effects. Ionized layers in the upper atmosphere are effective in reflecting radiation of certain frequencies back toward the earth's surface. Radiation of these frequencies can be received at great distances from the transmitter. The frequencies used in the 'standard broadcast band' lie in the range between 540 and 1650 kilocycles/second (kc). Other frequency ranges or bands are used for various purposes.

In order to be useful in a communications system, the waves sent out from the antenna of a transmitter must be *modulated*. The high-frequency electromagnetic wave train is called the radio-frequency (RF) *carrier* and the process of *modulation* consists of producing periodic variations in either (a) the *amplitude* of the carrier (AM), (b) the *frequency* of the carrier (FM), or (c) the *phase* or wave-shape of the RF carrier (PM) in such a manner that these variations may be observed and interpreted at the receiving station. We shall first consider amplitude modulation at the audio frequencies produced by the human voice and shall consider a simple one-tube transmitter and a one-tube receiver.

The simple transmitter shown in Fig. 10 consists essentially of a Hartley oscillator tuned for radio-frequency oscillation. This circuit is

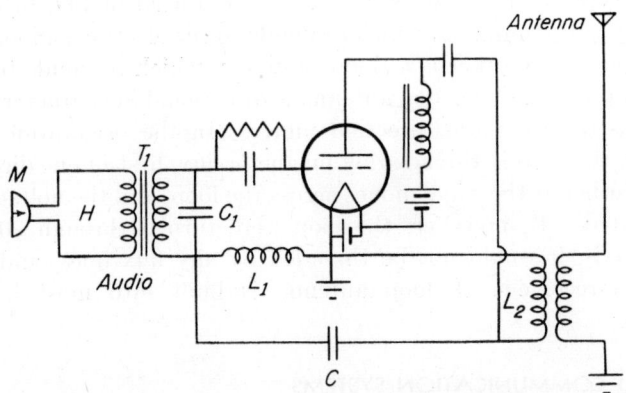

Fig. 10. A schematic diagram of a one-tube transmitter.

coupled through an RF transformer to a long straight wire that serves as antenna. In the grid circuit is the secondary winding of a transformer T_1, which is used to apply audio-frequency voltages to the grid. Since the transformer T_1 has high inductance, its impedance for radio frequencies is high, and condenser C_1 is placed in parallel with the transformer secondary in order to 'by-pass' RF currents. The primary winding of transformer T_1 is connected to a microphone M. The microphone M consists essentially of a diaphragm that supports a small coil of wire between the poles of a stationary magnet. A sound wave causes the diaphragm to vibrate at the frequency of the sound and an EMF of this audio frequency (AF) is induced in the coil.

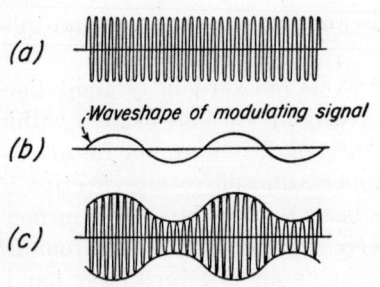

Fig. 11. Graphical presentation of amplitude modulation: (a) unmodulated RF carrier; (b) AF modulating voltage; (c) modulated carrier.

When no sound is reaching the microphone, a carrier wave of the type shown in Fig. 11(a) is radiated from the antenna. When sound waves strike the microphone M, variations in the current in circuit H are produced; these are sometimes called 'voice currents' and are shown in Fig. 11(b). These current variations in the transformer primary produce corresponding voltage changes in the secondary, and these voltage changes are applied to the grid of the oscillator tube. These AF voltages at the grid of the tube cause variations or modulations in the amplitude of the RF oscillation. Hence, the wave radiated from the antenna has the form shown in Fig. 11(c); this is the amplitude-modulated wave. In an actual case, the frequency of the RF signal would be much higher compared to the AF. For example, if the sound is 1 kc and the carrier 1000 kc, the carrier would oscillate 1000 times for each sound oscillation. This high frequency ratio is necessary in order for the envelope of the carrier to reproduce accurately the details of the audio wave-shape, which in general will be much more complicated than the simple sine curve of Fig. 11(b).

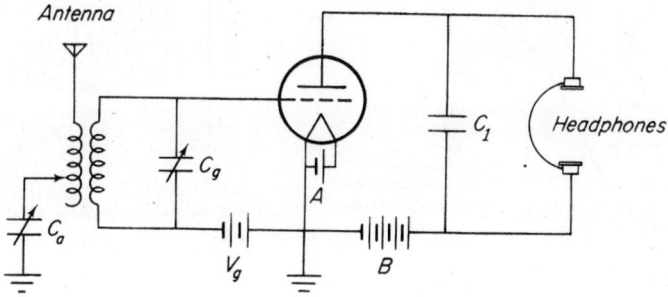

Fig. 12. Schematic diagram of a one-tube receiver.

The modulated waves sent out from the antenna of a transmitter may be received by the arrangement shown in Fig. 12. The amplitude-modulated electromagnetic waves produce detectable signals at the receiver, when the receiver is tuned to the carrier frequency, if the RF power level of the receiver antenna is sufficiently high. The receiver tuning is accomplished in the circuit shown in the figure by adjusting the variable condensers in the antenna and the grid circuits so that both circuits are tuned to the carrier frequency. The antenna circuit is coupled inductively to the grid circuit.

Variations in the grid potential produce changes in the plate current of the triode tube, which is arranged to act as a *detector*. The term *detector* is used for a 'nonlinear' circuit element* employed in the manner to be described. For the triode to be used successfully as a detector, the grid 'bias' V_g must be chosen in such a manner that the tube is operating at a curved portion of its characteristic curve of plate current *vs* grid voltage. Such a characteristic curve for constant plate voltage is shown in Fig. 13. If the grid bias is made negative by the amount V_g

---

* A nonlinear circuit element is one in which the current change is not proportional to the change in applied voltage. In the usual detector, applied positive voltages produce larger current changes than negative voltages of equal magnitude.

shown, it is seen that a superposed positive grid signal causes the plate current to increase substantially, whereas a superposed negative grid signal causes it to decrease only slightly, as shown in the small plots of signal against time.

Part (a) of Fig. 13 shows the variation in grid voltage produced when the modulated wave strikes the antenna. Part (b) shows the instantaneous high-frequency current produced in the condenser C_1; since the grid bias voltage V_g has been chosen in the manner described above, the magnitude of the current through C_1 is greater during the positive part of the RF cycle than during the negative part. The headphones cannot

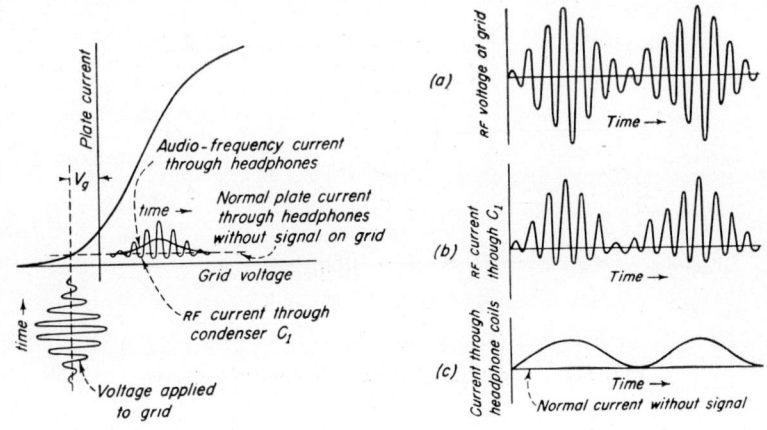

Fig. 13. Operating conditions for the simple receiver of Fig. 12.

follow the RF oscillations, but they can follow oscillations at audio frequency; therefore, they 'average' the RF current and give a response to the AF modulation.

The current through the headphone coils is shown in Fig. 13(c); it will be noted that this current has a waveform that is very similar to that of the original sound wave at the microphone of the transmitter, shown in Fig. 11(b). The magnetic-field variations in the headphone coils cause vibrations in diaphragms made of a ferromagnetic material, and the vibrations of the diaphragms in turn set up sound waves in the air.

The simple transmitter and receiver we have just described will operate satisfactorily for communication over short distances, but more power from the transmitter and greater sensitivity in the receiver are both needed in order to transmit messages over great distances. Both of these requirements can be met by using vacuum-tube amplifiers. The general schemes used are shown in the block diagrams of Fig. 14. In the transmitter a radio-frequency oscillator whose frequency is maintained as nearly constant as possible is followed by a 'buffer' stage of radio-frequency amplification before audio-frequency modulation is produced; the buffer stage is desirable, since the introduction of the audio signal to the oscillator directly would cause some frequency modulation in addition to the desired amplitude modulation. After further radio-frequency amplification, the modulated radio-frequency voltage is applied to the antenna. In the simple receiver shown, the signal from the

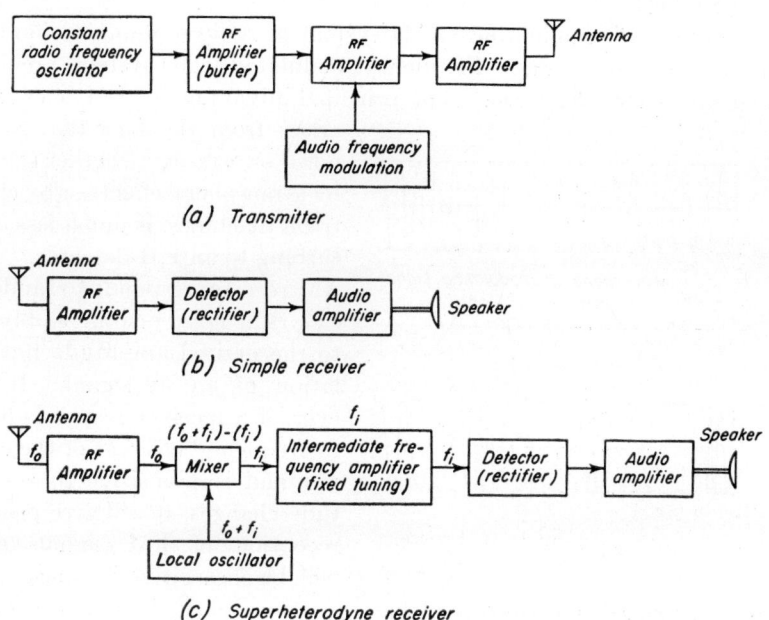

Fig. 14. Block diagrams of transmitter and superheterodyne receiver used in AM radio communication.

antenna undergoes several stages of radio-frequency amplification before detection, which is followed by one or more stages of audio-frequency amplification; a diode may be used as the detector. If extreme 'high gain' is desired, the construction of this simple receiver presents difficulties; the gain obtainable by audio amplification is limited because of local electrical noise, and the construction of an RF amplifier with many stages that can be simultaneously tuned also presents difficulties. In the *superheterodyne receiver* a part of the needed amplification can be accomplished at some *intermediate frequency* f_i with an amplifier that has fixed tuning. In the superheterodyne the RF signal of frequency f_0, after one or two stages of RF amplification, is applied to the control grid of a multielement tube called a *mixer*. To another grid of the mixer is applied a voltage of frequency f_0+f_i produced by a local oscillator in the receiver. The 'beat' frequency $f_0+f_i-f_0=f_i$ from the mixer is amplified by the permanently-tuned, intermediate-frequency amplifier. Since the amplitude of the local oscillator signal is kept constant, the amplitude of the intermediate-frequency signal has the same amplitude modulation as the modulated wave at the antenna of the receiver. The output of the intermediate-frequency amplifier is applied to the detector, which is followed by an audio-frequency amplifier that operates the headphones or loudspeaker.

The amplitude-modulated (AM) system of radio communication has been used for many years. Frequency-modulated (FM) systems are now coming into widespread use. The principal advantage of FM over AM arises from the fact that radio noise or 'static,' whether set up by atmospheric effects or by electrical machines, is much less disturbing to an FM detector. An AM receiver responds to random electrical noise just as readily as to the desired amplitude modulation of an RF signal. However, if a receiver responds *only* to frequency changes of the carrier and is insensitive to amplitude changes, it will give proper reception of FM signals and will be insensitive to noise. It should be pointed out, however, that the RF power at the receiver must exceed a certain *threshold* value before the advantages of FM are realized. Figure 15 gives a graphical presentation of a frequency-modulated wave.

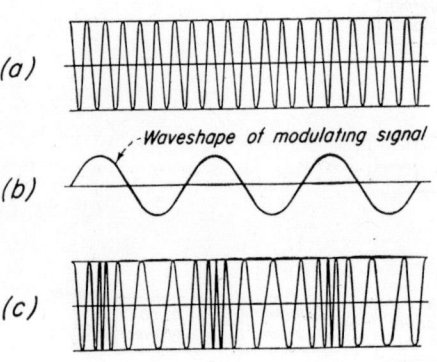

Fig. 15. A frequency-modulated wave.

The possibilities of phase modulation (PM) have not yet been fully explored in communication work.

PROBLEMS

1. The intermediate-frequency amplifier in a superheterodyne receiver is permanently tuned to a frequency of 275 kc. If the receiver is tuned to a broadcasting station whose carrier frequency is 550 kc, what should be the frequency of the local oscillator?
Ans: 825 kc.

2. If the receiver in Prob. 1 were tuned to a station whose carrier frequency is 1430 kc, what should be the frequency of the local oscillator?

4. THE ELECTROMAGNETIC SPECTRUM

We have seen in Chap. 43 how sustained oscillations can be produced in a circuit containing a condenser of capacitance C and a coil of inductance L. The frequency f of the electrical oscillations in such a circuit is given by $f = 1/2\pi \sqrt{LC}$. When L and C are both very large, oscillations of frequency well below the lower audio limit of 16 cycles/sec can be produced. If smaller condensers and coils are inserted in the circuit, the frequency increases to the radio-frequency range. It might appear at first glance that continued reduction in the size of condensers and coils would result in continued frequency increase without limit. Eventually, however, the electrical capacitance and inductance of the circuit wiring place a limit on the frequencies obtainable with a given circuit geometry. The capacitance and inductance of the circuit wiring can be reduced by the use of short straight wires, but finally a limit is imposed by the interelectrode capacitances of ordinary electronic vacuum tubes. This limit is of the order of 100 megacycles/sec.

In order to produce electrical oscillations of frequencies higher than this value a somewhat different approach is used. For an understanding of the principles involved, let us consider once again the dipole antenna shown in Fig. 4. In our previous discussion, we said nothing about the geometrical dimensions of the straight conductor. It is found that the effectiveness of the antenna can be increased considerably by the proper choice of antenna length. For a given frequency, there are certain lengths at which the antenna is 'resonant.' The antenna shown in Fig. 4 should be approximately one-half wavelength long; that of Fig. 9 approximately one-quarter wavelength long. Under these circumstances electrical standing waves are produced in the conductor by the alternator, with the ends of the antenna as antinodes and the center as a node of charge distribution. Considered from the standpoint of current distribution, the center of the antenna is an antinode and the ends are nodes. These statements follow from the same arguments as were used in the case of standing sound waves, and the fact that the speed of propagation of a voltage or current wave on an isolated straight conductor is approximately equal to the speed of light.

The important fact illustrated by the above discussion is that *a metal object shows electrical resonance to certain frequencies, and the wavelengths of the electromagnetic waves at these frequencies are of the same order of magnitude as the physical dimensions of the object.* This fact has been used in the production of ultra-high-frequency electromagnetic waves. Waves of frequency above about 1000 Mc or one billion cycles per second (wavelength below about 30 cm) are called *microwaves*.

The major problem involved in producing microwaves is to find effective methods of exciting electrical oscillations in small metal objects. To take an acoustical analogy, a stretched string will vibrate at certain definite acoustical frequencies; but in order for sound waves of these frequencies to be emitted, the string must be plucked by hand, stroked by a violin bow, struck by a small hammer, or excited mechanically in some other way. The problem of exciting electrical oscillations in a small object is more difficult. One of the first methods tried was that of producing an electrical spark between electrodes immersed in oil that held small metal filings in suspension. Extremely short electromagnetic waves were produced by this method early in the present century, but the method is extremely inefficient and the electrical oscillations produced in the filings were highly damped. Owing to the differences in the sizes and shapes of the metal particles and other factors, the frequencies of the radiation produced covered a broad band, and 'monochromatic' radiation was not obtained.

Somewhat different methods have been used in recent years. The modern methods of exciting ultra-high-frequency radiation involve the

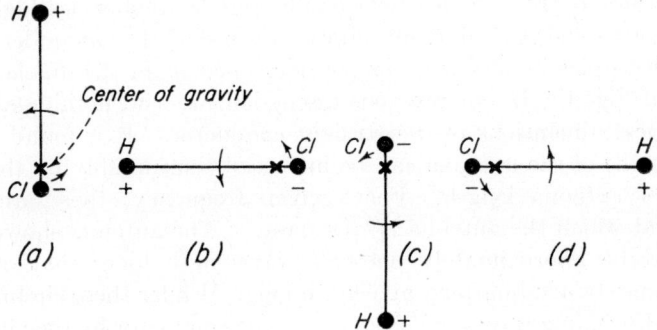

Fig. 16. The rotation of the polar molecule, HCl. The axis of rotation passes through the center of gravity of the molecule—actually much closer to the chlorine nucleus than shown in the figure.

excitation of *resonant cavities* in metal objects. Again, there is an acoustical analogy; just as standing sound waves can be set up in the air column inside an organ pipe, so also can standing electromagnetic waves be set up in a properly designed cavity inside a metal body. Just as sustained acoustical oscillations can be maintained in an organ pipe by energy derived from a suitably directed air jet, so may sustained electrical oscillations be maintained by energy derived from a suitably directed electron beam. The *klystron* and *magnetron* are oscillator tubes in which this excitation process is accomplished; we shall not discuss the details of their operation. Appreciable power has been obtained from tubes of these types at frequencies as high as 48,000 megacycles/sec, corresponding to a wavelength of 6 mm.

Electromagnetic waves in the microwave region can be focused by parabolic metal mirrors in a manner similar to the focusing procedures used for visible light beams. The antenna used for microwaves is a simple dipole like that of Fig. 4, about half a wavelength long. It is frequently placed at the focus of a parabolic mirror to give a concentrated unidirectional beam just as in a searchlight. The receiving antenna is similar. Radiations of 10-cm and of 3-cm wavelength are used in radar equipment (see Chap. 23, p. 587).

In the microwave region, the spectrum produced by electrical oscillators in the laboratory begins to overlap the solar spectrum. The presence of 3-cm radiation in the solar spectrum can be detected by directing the antenna of a good microwave receiver (a parabolic reflector with a dipole antenna at its focal point) toward the sun; it will be recalled that the observed solar spectrum is essentially a black-body spectrum with some modification because of absorption by the cooler outer gases of the sun and by the gases in the earth's atmosphere. Hence, we can say that the gap between radio wavelengths and the wavelengths emitted by black bodies has been bridged experimentally. This statement is true not only for sources that emit continuous spectra but also for sources of characteristic line or band spectra, since absorption lines arising from excitation of rotation and vibration of molecules have been observed in the microwave region.

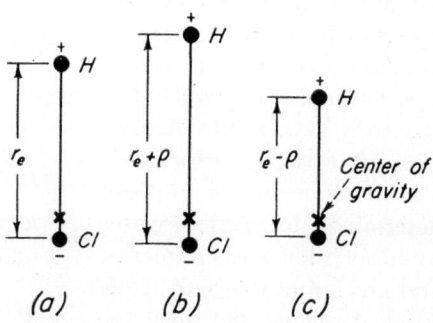

Fig. 17. Classical representation of a vibrating HCl molecule. The separation between H and Cl nuclei is given by $r = r_e + \rho \sin 2\pi ft$, where r_e is the equilibrium separation and ρ is the amplitude of the vibration.

In order to get a classical picture of the way in which molecular rotation can produce electromagnetic waves, let us consider the schematic diagram of an HCl molecule shown in Fig. 16. The center of the positive charges in this molecule lies nearer the hydrogen atom and the center of the negative charges lies nearer the chlorine atom; hence, the molecule is an electric dipole. If the molecule is rotating in the plane of the paper about an axis through its center of gravity, the electric dipole also rotates, but to an observer at the edge of the paper this rotation would resemble the motion of charges in an oscillating-dipole antenna. Hence, classically, we should expect the rotating molecule to emit electromagnetic waves in the observer's direction in a manner analogous to the way in which radiation is emitted from a dipole antenna; radiation of energy would continue until rotation ceased. However, we must recall (Chap. 30) that *quantum mechanics* must be applied to the emission and absorption processes in atoms and molecules. According to quantum mechanics, there are certain stationary energy states or energy levels in which an atom or molecule can exist, and energy is emitted or absorbed only when the atom or molecule passes from one of these stationary states to another. Thus, the HCl molecule will emit or absorb radiation only when it changes its energy of rotation, passing from one rotational energy level W_R to another level $W_{R'}$. The energy emitted or absorbed is given by the relation

$$hf_{RR'} = W_R - W_{R'},$$

where $f_{RR'}$ is the frequency of the emitted radiation. Only radiation of certain characteristic frequencies is emitted or absorbed as a result of rotational energy changes. These frequencies have been determined for various gases by absorption measurements, and are found to occur in the spectral region between the microwave region and the near infrared—a range of wavelengths extending from a few centimeters down to about 20 μ.

In the near-infrared region extending from 0.8 μ to 25 μ, the characteristic radiation produced by changes in the *vibrational* energy of molecules is observed. In connection with the emission of radiation from a vibrating molecule, let us consider Fig. 17, which shows another schematic diagram of the HCl molecule.

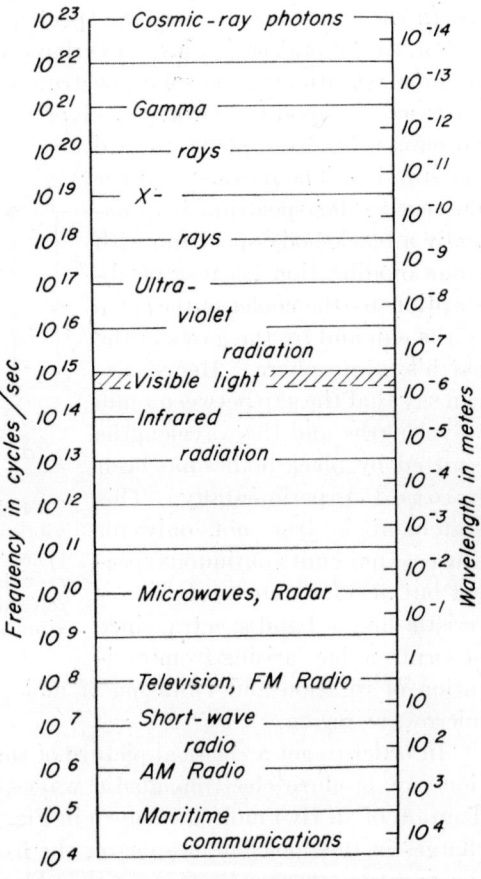

Fig. 18. The electromagnetic spectrum.

In the HCl molecule, the nuclei can vibrate in the manner indicated in the figure about their positions at equilibrium separation. As the vibration takes place, the dipole moment of the molecule changes, becoming smaller than its equilibrium value when the nuclei are closer together than in the equilibrium position, larger when they are farther apart. Thus, the vibrating molecule behaves somewhat like a dipole antenna that does not actually reverse in polarity but in which the magnitude of the charges on the ends of the conductor does change; we might therefore consider a vibrating molecule as a large permanent dipole plus a smaller oscillating dipole. Classically, we should expect the small oscillating dipole to emit radiation continuously until vibration ceased, but again we must recall that radiation of frequency $f_{vv'}$ is emitted in quanta of magnitude $hf_{vv'} = W_v - W_{v'}$ when the molecule makes a transition from one vibrational energy level W_v to another of energy $W_{v'}$.

In the visible and ultraviolet region of the spectrum, atoms and molecules have characteristic emission and absorption spectra that are produced by transitions between *electronic* energy levels involving the outermost or valence electrons (see Chap. 30). In the far ultraviolet, electronic energy changes involving the inner electrons of atoms produce characteristic line spectra, which overlap the characteristic X-ray lines produced in the manner described in Chap. 43. At still higher frequencies, γ-radiation from radioactive nuclei and extremely penetrating electromagnetic cosmic radiation are observed.

A complete chart of the known electromagnetic spectrum is shown in Fig. 18.

5. PHOTONS; WAVES ASSOCIATED WITH MATERIAL PARTICLES

In our discussion of the quantum theory of radiation, we have pointed out that energy is always emitted or absorbed in discrete units or quanta. If the frequency of the radiation is f, the energy E of a single quantum is given by

$$E = hf.$$

When the frequency is low, the energy of a single quantum is so small that it is impossible for any physical instrument to detect a single quantum. Table I gives the energy per quantum of various frequencies, and the number of quanta equivalent to one joule. It is apparent that at low frequencies the number of quanta equivalent to one joule of radiant energy is enormous, whereas at frequencies in the X-ray region the number is comparatively much smaller.

TABLE I
QUANTUM ENERGY AT VARIOUS FREQUENCIES

Type of radiation	Frequency (cycles/sec)	Energy per quantum (joules)	Number of quanta equivalent to 1 joule
Radio broadcast	10^6	6.624×10^{-28}	1.527×10^{27}
3.33-cm microwave	10^{10}	6.624×10^{-24}	1.527×10^{23}
3.33-μ infrared	10^{14}	6.624×10^{-20}	1.527×10^{19}
500-mμ visible	6×10^{14}	3.974×10^{-19}	2.547×10^{18}
1-mμ X-Ray	3×10^{19}	1.987×10^{-14}	5.090×10^{13}
0.01-mμ hard X-Ray	3×10^{21}	1.987×10^{-12}	5.090×10^{11}

In any type of radiation detector, such as a radio set, a photocell, or the eye, a natural limit to sensitivity is imposed by random fluctuations arising from thermal agitation of the molecules of which the detector is composed. For a 'perfect' detector at room temperature, this limit is such that energy of the order of 10^{-21} joule must arrive within a period comparable to the period of the radiation to which the detector is sensitive, if this energy is to be distinguished from the 'thermal noise.'

Thus, for radio frequencies a large number of quanta must be received in order for any detecting instrument to give a response. The reception of large numbers of quanta with the energy of each quantum extremely small gives the impression of a *continuous* process of reception, analogous to our feeling that light energy enters our eyes and produces stimuli continuously and not by discontinuous processes.

If the quantum energy of Table I is compared with the thermal energy limit of 10^{-21} joule mentioned above, it is seen that for wavelengths in the infrared we first have the possibility of detecting a single quantum. Photocells can be made to work in the near-infrared region and detect a single quantum.

The human eye comes close to being able to detect a single quantum. The completely dark-adapted eye is amazingly sensitive. Careful experiments show that if two adjacent rod cells on the retina each receive a quantum within $1/_{70}$ second, the eye will just perceive a flash of light. To achieve this sensitivity, the light must be at the wavelength of maximum sensitivity (510 mμ, in the blue-green, for a dark-adapted eye) and must be received by rods in a region subtending less than 10' of arc, located 20° off the center of the retina, where dark vision is most acute.

At X-ray frequencies, *a single quantum can easily be detected*, even by a relatively insensitive detector. This fact gives us further evidence that emission and absorption are actually quantum processes. The individual quanta have such distinctive properties that they have many of the characteristics of particles and have been given the name of *photons*. This name is actually applied to a quantum of radiation of any frequency, but the particle properties show up conspicuously only in the X-ray and γ-ray regions.

At X-ray frequencies, the properties of the individual quanta or photons in their interaction with matter can easily be studied. Many of the properties of X-ray photons are actually similar to those of particles. One interesting property is illustrated by the *Compton effect*. Arthur H. Compton, in 1924, discovered that when a monochromatic beam of X rays of frequency f is scattered at an angle θ as in Fig. 19, *two frequencies are present in the scattered beam*. One frequency f is equal to the frequency of the original unscattered X rays in the incident beam; this frequency was to be expected on the basis of the classical electromagnetic theory of scattering. The other frequency f', not expected from classical theory, is always less than the frequency of the incident X rays and is dependent on the scattering angle θ. By experiment, Compton found the following relationship for the wavelength λ' of the radiation scattered at angle θ:

$$\lambda' = \lambda + (h/mc)(1-\cos\theta),$$

where h is Planck's constant, m is the mass of the electron, c is the speed of light, and λ is the wavelength of the incident radiation.

Compton was able to account for the change in frequency of the scattered radiation by considering the incident photon as a 'particle' with energy hf and with momentum of magnitude hf/c. Scattering is assumed to take place as a result of a collision between the incident photon and an electron in the scattering material. As a result of the collision, a part of the energy and momentum of the incident photon is transferred to the electron, so that the final energy hf' and momentum hf'/c of the scattered photon are less than those of the incident photon. By writing the conservation-of-energy and the conservation-of-momentum relations for a collision of this type, Compton was able to obtain an expression identical with the empirical relationship between λ, λ', and θ that we have given above. We shall not go through the calculation, but shall merely point out that *we can explain the results of Compton's scattering experiment by treating the X-ray photon as a particle of energy hf having momentum of magnitude $hf/c = h/\lambda$.* Observations of the recoil electrons knocked out of the scattering material have shown that they do indeed have the momentum and energy to be expected from the momentum and energy equations for a collision with a particle with the initial momentum and energy assumed for the photon.

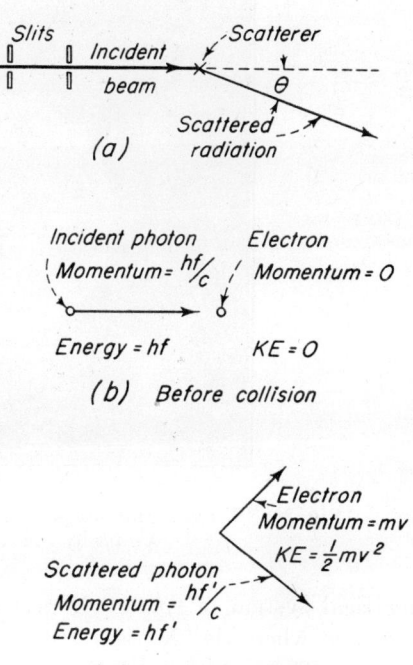

Fig. 19. The Compton effect. In this sketch, it is assumed that the initial kinetic energy and momentum of the scattering electron are negligible.

On the basis of the Compton effect, we might be led to the conclusion that X rays consist of particles and are not waves at all. However, there are other X-ray phenomena that can be explained only on the basis of wave properties. The wavelength of X rays is of the same order of magnitude as the distance between the atoms or ions in crystals, and crystals can be used as three-dimensional diffraction gratings for X rays. The diffraction pattern produced when a pencil of X rays passes through powdered steel is shown in Fig. 20. Owing to the random orientation of the small crystals in the powder, a symmetrical pattern of concentric rings is formed around the spot at the central maximum of the pattern. The diffraction pattern produced by a single crystal consists of a sym-

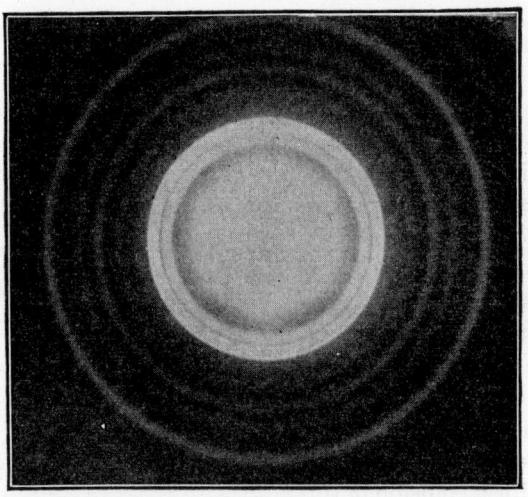

Fig. 20. X-ray diffraction pattern of powdered steel. [From *Applied X-rays* by Clark (McGraw-Hill).]

metrical system of spots. X rays can be diffracted by ruled reflection gratings when the X rays strike the grating surface at oblique incidence. Thus, there is abundant evidence that X rays also have wave characteristics.

This dual nature of X rays—particle nature in the Compton effect and wave nature in diffraction—was for a time quite disturbing, but this dualism is now regarded as characteristic not only of electromagnetic radiation but of matter as well. Just as we were accustomed to think of *light* as consisting of *waves*, so also we were accustomed to think of *matter* as consisting of *particles*. Visible light and radio waves do not have a readily observable particle nature, and particles large enough to be seen do not have a readily observable wave nature. However, as we have seen (Chap. 30), the behavior of submicroscopic 'particles' such as atoms and molecules cannot be described in terms of the classical mechanics based on Newton's laws of motion but must be treated from a quantum standpoint; thus, these submicroscopic 'particles' cannot be regarded as having properties identical with small visible bodies like dust particles.

In 1924, Louis Victor de Broglie suggested that *the motion of an electron or of any other particle is associated with a wave motion of wavelength*

$$\lambda = h/mv,$$

where h is Planck's constant, m is the mass of the particle, and v is the speed of the particle. For an electron having an energy of V ev, the wavelength in mμ given by the above expression is

$$\lambda = \frac{1.2263}{\sqrt{V}} \, \text{m}\mu.$$

Thus, an electron with an energy of 100 ev should be expected, according to de Broglie, to have a characteristic wavelength of 0.12263 mμ. This wavelength is comparable to the wavelengths of X rays. Therefore, if de Broglie's hypothesis is correct, an electron beam passing through a thin film of powdered crystal or through a metal film should experience diffraction similar to that experienced by an X-ray beam. Diffraction of an electron beam was observed experimentally in 1927 by C. J. Davisson and L. H. Germer. A photograph of an electron diffraction pattern is shown in Fig. 21. The essential similarity between this diffraction pattern and the X-ray diffraction pattern shown in Fig. 20 is at once apparent. We are led to the conclusion that the de Broglie hypothesis is correct. Consideration of the above expression for the de Broglie wavelength reveals

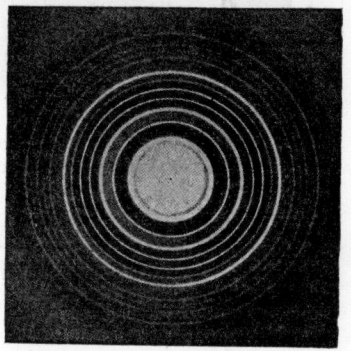

Fig. 21. Electron diffraction pattern of cesium iodide. [From *Particles of Modern Physics* by Stranathan (Blakiston).]

that for particles of large mass, the associated wavelength is so small, even for the low speeds of thermal agitation, that no diffraction phenomena can be observed, and hence the wave nature of large particles cannot be readily detected.

The de Broglie hypothesis was taken over by Erwin Schrödinger and Werner Heisenberg, who used it in the development of modern *quantum mechanics*, or, as it is sometimes called, *wave mechanics*. As we have already pointed out (Chap. 30), quantum mechanics must be used to describe the behavior of atoms and molecules in terms of characteristic energy levels. The quantum mechanics of Schrödinger and Heisenberg enables us to predict correctly the characteristic energy levels of an atom or molecule from certain perfectly general equations. When quantum mechanics is applied to a system involving macroscopic bodies, the number of characteristic energy levels is so great and the levels are so close together that the results become equivalent to those obtained by classical or Newtonian mechanics.

Thus, we see that both matter and photons have properties of the character that we ordinarily ascribe to 'particles,' and properties of the character that we ordinarily ascribe to 'waves.' The 'particle' properties of radio-frequency photons are not apparent because only a very large number of photons can be detected. The 'wave' properties of macroscopic matter are not apparent because the wavelength is undetect-

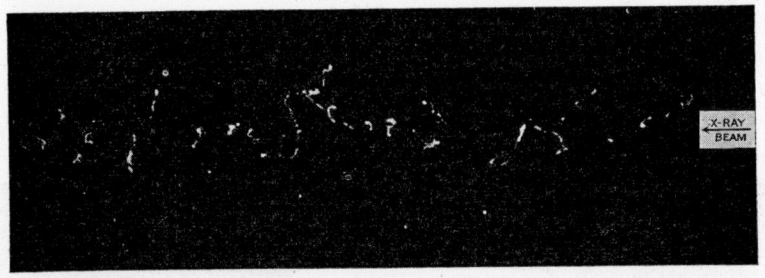

Fig. 22. Electron tracks produced by the passage of a narrow beam of X-rays through a cloud chamber. [From C. T. R. Wilson, *Proc. Roy. Soc.*, **104A.** 1, (1923).]

ably small. In the X-ray region, photons show both 'particle' and 'wave' properties very strikingly; in the γ-ray region, only the 'particle' properties are apparent because again the wavelength is undetectably small. Figure 22 shows tracks of Compton-effect electrons ejected by X rays. As discussed on p. 1159, these electrons arise from a manifestation of particle properties of the X rays. Slow-speed electrons and neutrons have detectably large wavelengths, so their 'wave' properties are apparent.

Both photons and matter particles have energy, momentum, and wavelength. 'Wave' properties are apparent only if the wavelength is detectable, which means in practice that it is at least sufficiently large to be comparable to the 'grating' spacing of crystals. Properties ordinarily associated with 'particles' are apparent only if the energy and momentum are sufficiently large so that individuals can be detected.

The above discussion is not intended to imply that there is not a fundamental difference between photons and material particles. In spite of the fact that they share similar physical properties such as energy, momentum, and wavelength, there is one fundamental difference: a photon always moves with speed c (relative to any observer, in fact, according to the experimental evidence that led to the formulation of Einstein's theory of relativity), whereas a material particle always moves with a speed that is less than c (relative to any observer). There are other fundamental differences in behavior that we are unable to discuss here.

PROBLEMS

1. How many quanta of visible light of wavelength 500 mμ would have a total energy equivalent to the energy of a single quantum of X radiation of wavelength 0.1 mμ? Ans: 5000.

2. How many quanta of radiation of 30 m wavelength would have a total energy equal to the energy of a single X-ray quantum of wavelength 2 mμ?

3. The distance between adjacent planes in a certain crystal is 0.15 mμ. Taking this distance as the equivalent grating interval, find the angle at which the first-order diffraction maximum would occur if X rays of wavelength 0.075 mμ strike the hypothetical grating at normal incidence? Ans: 30°.

4. At what angle would the first-order diffraction pattern from the crystal grating of Prob. 3 be observed if X radiation of 0.1-mμ wavelength struck the grating at normal incidence?

5. Calculate the energy and momentum of a photon of X radiation of wavelength 0.1 mμ. Ans: 1.99×10^{-15} joule; 6.62×10^{-24} kg·m/sec.

6. Find the energy and momentum of a photon of X radiation of wavelength 0.03 mμ.

7. From the expression for the de Broglie wavelength, $\lambda = h/mv$, verify the correctness of the relation $\lambda = 1.2263/\sqrt{V}$ mμ for the wavelength associated with an electron of energy V electron-volts.

8. Calculate the wavelengths associated with electrons that have been accelerated through potential differences of 1 volt, 10 volts, 100 volts, and 1000 volts.

9. From the de Broglie relation, calculate the wavelength associated with a 'thermal' neutron of kinetic energy $\frac{1}{30}$ ev. Ans: 0.157 mμ.

10. Calculate the wavelength of a 1-Mev proton, a 1-Mev neutron, and a 1-Mev alpha particle. How do these wavelengths compare in order of magnitude with the radius ($\sim 10^{-15}$ m) of atomic nuclei?

CHAPTER 45

ELEMENTARY PARTICLES

Throughout this book we have made frequent reference to atomic theory and have indicated that electrons and nuclei are the constituent parts of atoms. Electrons make up the outer structure of the atoms of the elements. The arrangement of the outermost of these electrons determines the chemical properties of the element; these electrons act as links between the atoms in diatomic and polyatomic molecules, being shared between atoms in homopolar molecules and being transferred from one atom to another in ionic molecules. The electron is called an *elementary particle*.

> An elementary particle is a particle that up to the present has not been shown to be composed of two or more simpler particles held together by some type of forces.

There are other elementary particles that are associated with the nuclei of atoms and still other elementary particles that have a transitory existence. We shall in this concluding chapter give a brief discussion of these elementary particles and of the structure of atomic nuclei. We shall also consider the ways in which energy can be obtained from nuclear reactions, but in order to do so we shall have to learn the principles of the theory of relativity.

1. CHEMICAL ELEMENTS; ATOMS

The modern concept of chemical elements originated with Robert Boyle. In his book, *The Sceptical Chymist*, published in 1661, Boyle stated that the chemist should regard as elements all those substances which could not be split up by chemical reactions into simpler constituents. This idea is so much like our modern point of view that it is difficult to realize how revolutionary it must have seemed to the scientists of Boyle's time, many of whom still held the medieval view that mercury, salt, and sulfur were the only elements. During the eighteenth century, the work of Joseph Black, Joseph Priestley, Henry Cavendish, Carl Wilhelm Scheele, and A. L. Lavoisier added so much to the basic knowledge of the chemical elements and of chemical reactions that in 1808 it was possible for John Dalton to advance the atomic theory of matter. According to Dalton, each chemical element is made up of indivisible units or *atoms*, which can combine with each other or with the atoms of other elements but which maintain their identity during chemical reactions.

On the basis of measurements of the combining weights of the elements, it was possible to determine the chemical atomic weights or the relative weights of the atoms of the chemical elements. In measuring chemical atomic weights, oxygen was arbitrarily assigned an atomic weight of 16 and the atomic weights of the other elements were measured in terms of oxygen; the assignment of 16 as the atomic weight of oxygen was made merely as a matter of convenience in laboratory measurements since 16 is the minimum integral atomic weight that could be assigned to oxygen and still give an atomic weight of over unity for hydrogen, the lightest element. The most recent values for the atomic weights of the elements are given in a table in Sec. 4 of the Appendix. These atomic weights are on the newer *physical scale*, which has been discussed on p. 894, rather than on the chemical scale.

As more elements were discovered and their chemical properties determined, it was observed that the elements could be grouped into families, the members of which have similar chemical properties; the halogen family, consisting of fluorine, chlorine, bromine, and iodine, is an example. In 1869 the Russian chemist Dmitri I. Mendeleev discovered that if the elements were placed in order of increasing atomic weight, there were certain periodic repetitions of chemical properties. For example, oxygen commonly has a negative valence of 2, and sulfur, the eighth element beyond oxygen in order of increasing atomic weight, also has a negative valence of 2 and has chemical properties similar to those of oxygen; lithium has a positive valence of 1, and sodium, the eighth element beyond lithium, has a positive valence of 1 and has properties similar to those of lithium. Mendeleev arranged the elements in a *periodic table*, one form of which is shown in Sec. 3 of the Appendix. The order in which the elements appear in the periodic table is the order of increasing *atomic number* Z, rather than the order of increasing atomic weight. It will be recalled from p. 788 that the atomic number is the number of electrons in the neutral atom or the number of elementary charges on the atomic nucleus. When the elements are arranged according to atomic number, only two pairs (A, K, $Z=18$, 19; and Co, Ni, $Z=27$, 28) fail to fall strictly in the order of increasing atomic weight.

Although nineteenth-century chemists regarded atoms of a given element as indestructible and immutable units, developments that took place during the closing days of the nineteenth century did much to alter this view. The clear recognition of the electron as an elementary particle which could be removed from material bodies by thermal and photoelectric emission processes indicated that the electron is a constituent part of atoms. The discovery of natural radioactivity indicated that the atoms of some of the heaviest elements—uranium, thorium, and actinium

—are spontaneously disintegrating to produce elements of lower atomic weight and in the process are emitting charged particles at high speed. The charged particles emitted were identified as electrons (called *beta particles*) and positively charged helium nuclei (called *alpha particles*). These discoveries indicated that *atoms* are not really indivisible, as the name *atom* implies, but are composed of simpler elementary particles, of which the electron was the first to be discovered.

PROBLEMS

1. The atomic weight of oxygen is 16.0044 on the physical scale. Using Avogadro's number, find the average mass of one oxygen atom. Ans: 2.66×10^{-26} kg.

2. Taking 6.942 as the atomic weight of lithium on the physical scale, and using Avogadro's number, calculate the average mass of one lithium atom.

3. Using the atomic weights given in the table in Sec. 4 of the Appendix, find the molecular weight of carbon dioxide (CO_2). How much carbon is present in 100 g of CO_2? What is the mass of a single CO_2 molecule?
Ans: 44.0234; 27.3 g; 7.31×10^{-26} kg.

4. What is the molecular weight of dry lithium oxide, (Li_2O)? How much lithium is present in 100 g of Li_2O? What is the mass of a single Li_2O molecule?

2. THE NUCLEAR MODEL OF THE ATOM

The approximate sizes of atoms and lighter molecules (diameters of the order of 0.1 mμ or 10^{-10} m) were known at the beginning of the present century from interpretation of the observed properties of gases on the basis of kinetic theory. After the discovery that electrons formed a part of the structure of atoms, Sir J. J. Thomson (1856–1940) proposed a model of the atom in which the electrons were embedded in a matrix of positive electrical charge like plums in a pudding. The positive charge was supposed to have approximately the same dimensions as those obtained from kinetic theory for monatomic molecules. According to Thomson's theory, the electrons had certain equilibrium positions in the positive matrix. Vibration of the electrons about these positions of equilibrium was supposed to result in the emission of light. The Thomson model was not particularly satisfactory, since, although it gave proper qualitative explanations of the Zeeman and Stark effects (Chap. 30),

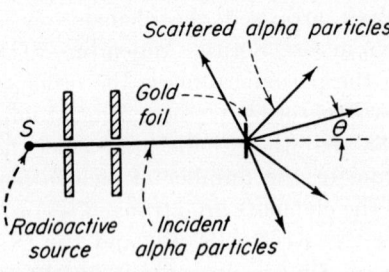

Fig. 1. Schematic diagram of arrangement used by Rutherford in his experiments on the scattering of alpha particles.

observed atomic spectra could not be interpreted in terms of this model. The Thomson model was discarded in 1911 in favor of a nuclear model proposed by Sir Ernest Rutherford (1871–1937).

Rutherford proposed the nuclear model to account for results obtained in his experiments on the scattering of high-speed, doubly charged helium atoms (alpha particles) by matter. A schematic diagram of the experimental arrangement he used is shown in Fig. 1. Alpha particles emitted by a radioactive source were allowed to pass through a hole in a metal shield and strike a thin gold foil which acted as a scatterer. The alpha particles scattered at various angles θ with the incident beam were counted by observing the scintillations produced when the particles impinged upon a fluorescent screen. On the basis of the Thomson model, there should be no electric fields near or within the gold atoms large enough to produce scattering at large angles. In the experiment, however, it was observed that some of the alpha particles were scattered through angles even greater than 90°; that is, some alpha particles emerged from the gold foil on the same side they entered. In order to explain such large-angle scattering of high-speed alpha particles, Rutherford was forced to assume the existence of an intense electric field within the atom. To provide the intense intra-atomic field, Rutherford assumed that the entire positive charge of the atom was concentrated in a very small nucleus and that electrons occupied the space outside the nucleus. Subsequent careful scattering experiments substantiated Rutherford's theory and showed that the positive charge Ze on the nucleus of an atom must be concentrated within a region of the order of 10^{-15} m in diameter (only 1/100,000 of the diameter of the atom) in order to give a sufficiently intense repulsive field to account for the observed scattering. Further evidence of the essential correctness of the Rutherford model was obtained when Bohr successfully used it in his theory of the hydrogen spectrum (Chap. 30). The analysis of the spectra of the atoms of other elements has enabled us to obtain detailed information on the arrangement of the extranuclear electrons in various atoms and has given additional evidence for the correctness of the nuclear model.

Careful measurement of the electronic charge e and independent measurements of the ratio of charge to mass, e/m, for the electron indicate that the mass of an electron is extremely small compared with the total mass of an atom. Hence, almost all of the mass of an atom is concentrated in the atomic nucleus. It might be desirable to sketch briefly the methods by which e and e/m are determined.

Between 1909 and 1917, R. A. Millikan carefully determined the electronic charge itself by observations of charged oil droplets in an electric field. A schematic diagram of Millikan's apparatus is shown in Fig. 2. Oil droplets from an atomizer are introduced into the space between the parallel plates. X rays passing through the air produce ionization and electrons become attached to the oil droplets; actually, some of the oil droplets become charged as the result of frictional effects in the atomizer. The motion of one of the oil droplets of mass M is observed by means of a microscope. Let us suppose that the oil droplet has a single electron attached. If the condenser plates are not charged, the oil droplet is subjected to a gravitational force $f = M\mathbf{g}$ and will move downward; owing to the viscosity of the air, the downward motion will be slow. From the rate of fall, the weight of the oil droplet can be determined by known laws of hydrodynamics—a tiny sphere falls at the constant velocity for which the viscous resistance of the air just balances the force of gravity. After the rate of fall of a particular droplet has been determined, the plates are charged so as to exert an upward electrostatic force just sufficient to make the downward motion of the droplet cease. When there is no resultant vertical motion, the upward force $e\mathcal{E}$ is exactly equal and opposite to the gravitational force. Hence,

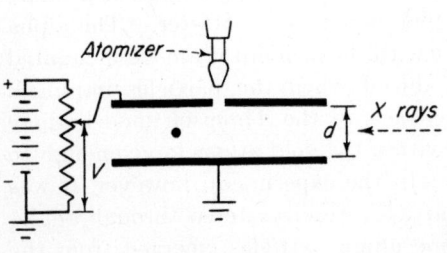

Fig. 2. Schematic diagram of the arrangement used in Millikan's oil-droplet experiment.

$$e\mathcal{E} = Mg, \quad \text{and} \quad e = Mg/\mathcal{E} = Mgd/V,$$

where V is the voltage between the plates and d is their separation.

The values of charge obtained by Millikan were not the same on all droplets, but the value was always a small integer (from 1 to 9) times the least charge observed. This least charge could then be assumed to be the charge on a single electron, with some of the droplets carrying more than one electron. By careful measurements, Millikan was able to obtain data on which the accurate value for e given in the table in Sec. 2 of the Appendix is based.

The value of e/m for the electron is obtained by superposing electric and magnetic deflecting fields on an electron beam. The electric and magnetic fields are arranged so that the forces they exert on the electrons in the beam are in opposite directions, and the fields are adjusted so as to produce no deflection. When there is no resultant deflection, the force $f = e\mathcal{E}$ exerted by the electric field is equal and opposite to the force $f = \mathcal{B}ev$ exerted by the magnetic field:

$$e\mathcal{E} = \mathcal{B}ev, \quad \text{or} \quad \mathcal{E} = \mathcal{B}v, \tag{1}$$

where v is the speed of the electrons. The speed can be written in terms of the accelerating voltage V used in the electron gun. For ordinary accelerating voltages of a few kv, relativistic effects (cf. Sec. 5) do not need to be considered, and we can use the classical relation

$$\tfrac{1}{2}mv^2 = eV, \quad \text{or} \quad v^2 = 2eV/m.$$

Substitution of this value for v^2 in $\mathcal{E}^2 = \mathcal{B}^2 v^2$ leads to the formula

$$e/m = \mathcal{E}^2/2V\mathcal{B}^2,$$

where the electric field $\mathcal{E}$, the magnetic field $\mathcal{B}$, and the accelerating voltage V are all easily determinable quantities. The best available value for e/m is given in the table of constants in Sec. 2. of the Appendix.

From the measured values of e and e/m listed in the table, the value of the electronic mass m can be determined. This mass is approximately $1/1838$ that of the hydrogen atom. Thus, even in the lightest element, the mass of the nucleus is far greater than the mass of the associated electron. The effective radius of the extranuclear electronic charge cloud of an atom is of the order of 10^{-10} m, and the effective radius of the nucleus is of the order of 10^{-15} m. Thus, most of the mass of an atom is localized in an extremely small fraction of the volume that is effectively occupied by the atom.

The nucleus of the ordinary hydrogen atom is an elementary particle called the *proton*. As indicated above, the mass of the proton is approximately 1837 times that of the electron. Since the proton with one associated electron forms a *neutral* hydrogen atom, *the charge of a proton is equal in absolute magnitude to that of the electron but is positive.*

In much the same way that the mass of the electron could be determined by e/m measurements once e had been determined, the masses of atoms can be determined or compared from analagous q/m measurements on ions of known charge q. A device for making such measurements is called a *mass spectrograph*. A schematic diagram of a modern form of mass spectrograph is shown in Fig. 3. Positive ions (charge $q = +e$) of the element being studied are formed in a discharge tube; after acceleration, a narrow beam of high-speed ions passes through slits S_1 and S_2 into a region containing a uniform magnetic field of flux density $\mathcal{B}'$ directed away from the reader, and containing a uniform electric field $\mathcal{E}$ set up by the plates of a parallel-plate condenser. By varying the voltage on the condenser plates, the force $\mathcal{E}q$ exerted on the ions by the electric field can be made equal and opposite to the force $\mathcal{B}'qv$ exerted by the magnetic field on ions having speed v; when this is done, equation (1) shows that all ions with speed $v = \mathcal{E}/\mathcal{B}'$ will pass through the third slit S_3 regardless of differences in mass. These ions pass through slit S_3 into a second uniform magnetic field $\mathcal{B}$ directed away from the reader. The force acting on each ion is given by

$$\mathcal{B}qv = Mv^2/R.$$

Solving this equation for M, we may write

$$M = (\mathcal{B}q/v) \times R = \text{const} \times R,$$

which indicates that all ions of a given charge q traverse circular paths of radius R proportional to the mass. With the arrangement shown in Fig. 3, the ions strike a photographic plate after traversing one semicircle and produce darkened traces on the photographic plate. From the position of the trace on the plate, R can be accurately determined. If $\mathcal{B}$, q, and v are also accurately known, the absolute value of the ion mass M can be calculated. In actual practice, the mass spectrograph is

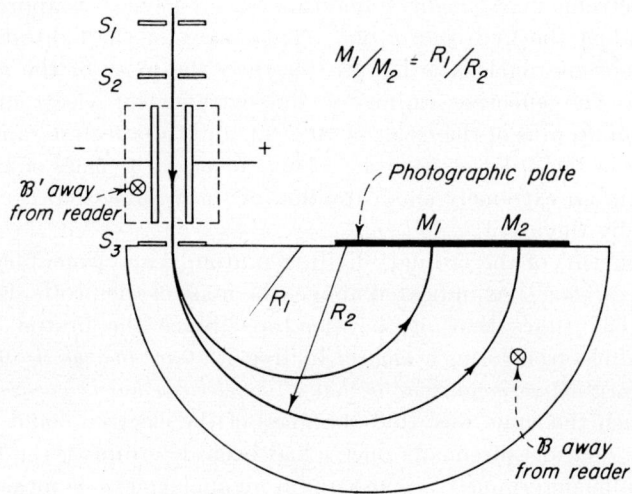

Fig. 3. Schematic diagram of a mass spectrograph (*after Bainbridge*).

usually used for comparing masses; for example, if two types of ions of mass M_1 and M_2 are present in the beam entering slit S_3, M_1 can be determined in terms of M_2 by the relation

$$M_1/M_2 = R_1/R_2.$$

One discovery made by J. J. Thomson in 1913 with a prototype of the mass spectrograph was that not all the atoms of a given element have the same mass. Most of the elements have two or more *isotopes*.*

Isotopes are atoms of different mass but equal nuclear charge.

Since the different isotopes of an element have the same number and arrangement of electrons, they are chemically indistinguishable. Isotopes cannot in general be separated by chemical means. They can only be separated by physical methods (mass spectrographs, diffusion columns, etc.) which distinguish between atoms of different *mass*.

* The literal meaning of the word *isotope* is 'same place.' The term indicates that the *isotopes* occupy the *same place in the periodic table*.

Sec. 2] THE NUCLEAR MODEL OF THE ATOM 1171

Some elements have numerous isotopes; for example, tin has ten isotopes. Figure 4 is a photograph of the mass spectrum of tin.

Hydrogen has an isotope called *deuterium* of approximately twice the mass of the ordinary hydrogen atom; the hydrogen isotopes are of particu-

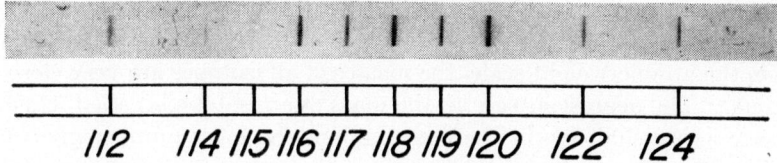

Fig. 4. The mass spectrum of tin (*courtesy of K. T. Bainbridge*). The numbers are mass numbers (see p. 1172).

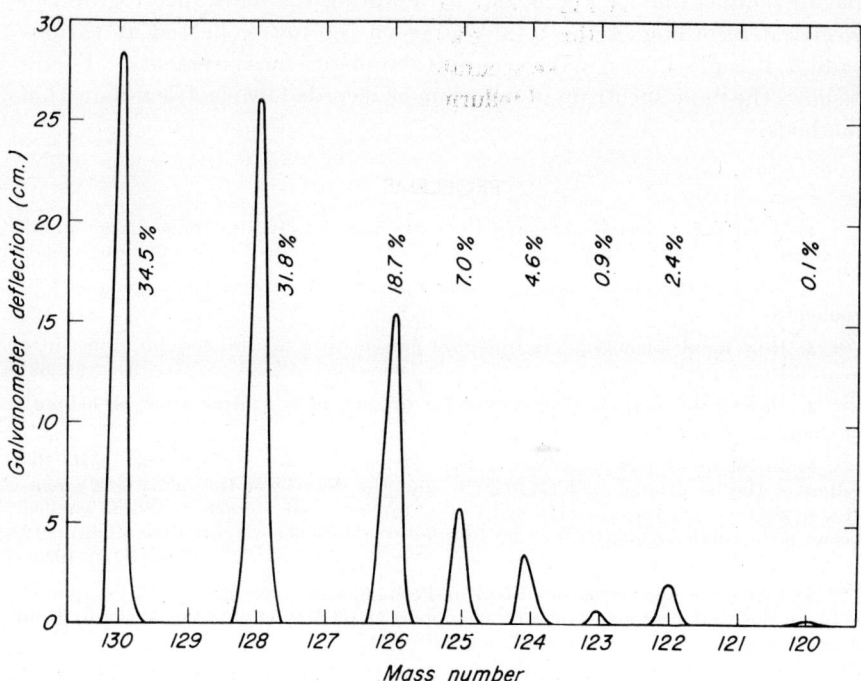

Fig. 5. The mass spectrum of tellurium as observed by an electrical method of detection (*D. Williams and P. Yuster*).

lar interest because of their large mass ratio. The deuterium nucleus, called the *deuteron*, has the simplest known nuclear structure except for the proton itself. There is also an unstable hydrogen isotope of approximately three times the mass of ordinary hydrogen, called *tritium*.

Oxygen has three stable isotopes, of masses approximately 16, 17, and 18 times the mass of hydrogen. As we have already remarked in Chap. 34, the assignment of 16 exactly for the chemical atomic weight of oxygen refers to the average mass in the normal mixture of these isotopes. In the specification of isotopic masses, a *physical-atomic-weight* scale is used in which the number 16 exactly is assigned to the mass of the lightest of the three oxygen isotopes. Chapter 34 contains further discussion of these scales.

On the atomic-weight scale, the masses of all isotopes are very close to integers. The nearest integer to the mass of an isotope is called its *mass number;* as we shall see in the next section, the mass number gives the number of nucleons in the nucleus.

It is impossible to make a very accurate determination of the relative abundance of the different isotopes of an element from a photographic record such as that of Fig. 4, but by adapting the mass spectrograph to electrical recording of the total charge on the ions collected at various radii R, it is possible to make accurate abundance measurements. Figure 5 shows the mass spectrum of tellurium as recorded by electrical-detection methods.

PROBLEMS

1. What is the electric charge of the oxygen nucleus in electronic-charge units? in coulombs? Ans: $+8e$; 1.28×10^{-18} coul.

2. What is the charge of the uranium nucleus in electronic-charge units? in coulombs?

3. How many planetary electrons are present in a neutral sodium atom? in a neutral lead atom? Ans: 11; 82.

4. How many planetary electrons are present in a neutral atom of helium? of chlorine? of bromine?

5. In an oil-droplet experiment, the condenser plates are 1.60 cm apart, the radius of the oil droplet is 2.8×10^{-4} cm, and the density of the oil is 0.92 g/cm^3. If a single excess electron is attached to the droplet, what voltage should be applied between the condenser plates in order to counterbalance the weight of the oil droplet? Ans: 5.18×10^4 v.

6. Using the apparatus described in Prob. 5, what voltage should be applied between the condenser plates in order to support an oil droplet of radius 5.52×10^{-4} cm if two excess electrons are attached to the droplet?

7. In an arrangement for measuring e/m for the electron, the accelerating voltage is 10 kv. The distance between the deflecting plates is 0.8 cm and the voltage between the deflecting plates is 500 volts. Find the strength of the magnetic field that must be applied in the region between the deflecting plates in order to give zero deflection. Ans: 1.05×10^{-3} weber/m^2.

8. If the accelerating voltage used in the arrangement described in the preceding problem were reduced to 5 kv, what should be the value of the magnetic field if the voltage between the deflecting plates is maintained at 500 volts?

9. Chlorine has two isotopes of masses 34.980 and 36.978 amu. If the radius of the path described by the lighter isotope in the Bainbridge spectrograph is 5.0 cm, find the separation between the traces produced by the two isotopes on the photographic plate. Ans: 0.571 cm.

10. Find the plate separation for the lithium isotopes of mass numbers 6 and 7 if the radius of the path of the lighter isotope in a Bainbridge mass spectrograph is 5.0 cm. (See Sec. 5 of the Appendix for isotopic masses).

3. NUCLEAR STRUCTURE

As already noted, analysis of both scattering experiments and atomic spectra indicates that the nucleus of the atom of an element of atomic number Z has a positive charge of magnitude Ze. The mass of the nucleus of an atom can be determined by means of the mass spectrograph. The masses of all nuclei are *approximately* equal to integral multiples of the proton mass; the exact values will be discussed in Sec. 4. The approximate mass of any nucleus is given by an integer called the mass number A, which for naturally occurring elements varies from 1 for the proton itself to 238 for the heaviest uranium isotope. The *nuclear charge* and *nuclear mass number* for most types of nuclei are well known. They are listed in the table in Sec. 5 of the Appendix.

We shall use a symbol of the type $_{92}U^{238}$ to denote the uranium *nucleus*, with $Z=92$, $A=238$. For the uranium *atom* that contains this nucleus and 92 electrons, we shall use the symbol U^{238} without the subscript.

Additional information concerning other properties of atomic nuclei has also been obtained. The earliest source of information concerning the structure of the nucleus was the phenomenon of natural radioactivity, discovered by Henri Becquerel in 1896. Practically all of the naturally occurring radioactive elements have atomic numbers between $Z=81$ and $Z=92$. As mentioned in Sec. 1 of this chapter, two types of natural radioactive disintegration processes have been observed for the elements in this range.

One of these involves the emission of *alpha particles* (helium nuclei). An example of this type of process is the disintegration of uranium 238; this nucleus spontaneously emits, after an average lifetime of 10^9 years, an alpha particle and becomes a thorium nucleus of mass number 234. We may write an equation for this process which is analogous to the equations used to describe chemical reactions. The equation for the disintegration of uranium 238 can be written

$$_{92}U^{238} \rightarrow {_{90}Th^{234}} + {_2He^4},$$

where *the left-hand subscripts give the atomic numbers and the superscripts give the mass numbers.* The effect of alpha-particle emission is to decrease the mass number of the parent nucleus by 4 units and the atomic number by 2 units. In equations of this kind the sum of the mass numbers of the product nuclei on the right is equal to the mass number of the original nucleus on the left; the same is true of the atomic numbers, since the atomic numbers measure charge, and electric charge is conserved. It might be noted, however, that the product nuclei have kinetic energy and also that a heavy product nucleus like $_{90}\text{Th}^{234}$ may be left in an excited energy state and reach its lowest or ground state only by the emission of one or more high-energy quanta called *gamma rays*. Gamma radiation is similar in character to high-frequency X radiation.

The second type of naturally occurring disintegration involves the emission of *beta particles*, which are high-energy electrons. A typical beta-emission process occurs when the *radium* isotope of mass number 228 disintegrates to form an actinium isotope of mass number 228 and an electron. The descriptive equation may be written as

$$_{88}\text{Ra}^{228} \rightarrow {}_{89}\text{Ac}^{228} + {}_{-1}\varepsilon^0,$$

where the electron ε is assigned an atomic number of -1 because of its negative charge and a mass number 0 because its mass is only a very small fraction of one atomic mass unit. When a beta particle is emitted, the atomic number of the product nucleus is always 1 greater than that of the parent nucleus, and the mass number is unchanged. The product nucleus may be left in an excited state and reach its ground state by gamma-ray emission.

Observations of the energies of the emitted beta particles show that, if energy and momentum are conserved in beta-emission processes, it is necessary to assume that another particle called a *neutrino* is emitted along with the beta particle. The neutrino has no charge and has a mass that is much smaller than the electron mass. Although this particle has never been observed directly, the above equation should probably be written as

$$_{88}\text{Ra}^{228} \rightarrow {}_{89}\text{Ac}^{228} + {}_{-1}\varepsilon^0 + {}_0\nu^0$$

where the symbol $_0\nu^0$ represents the neutrino.

The *neutrino* is regarded as a fundamental particle. That it has never been observed is not surprising, because an extremely light particle of no charge would be extraordinarily difficult to detect. The physicists of today are inclined to accept its existence because of several different lines of evidence that require either the existence of such a particle or radical revision of some of the most fundamental principles of physics, such as the laws of conservation of energy, momentum, and angular momentum.

Early studies of radioactivity showed that the 'activity' of a given sample of a radioactive element decreases with time. Taking the number of disintegrations per unit time as a measure of the activity, observers found that the activity of samples of some radioactive isotopes decreases very rapidly in a matter of seconds whereas the activity of samples of other radioactive isotopes decreases slowly over a period of years. Experiments reveal that *for a given radioactive material the number of disintegrations occurring per unit time, dN/dt, depends only on the total number N of* *radioactive atoms present in the sample and is proportional to this number.* This experimental result can be described by the equation

$$dN/dt = -\lambda N,$$

where the proportionality constant λ is called the *decay constant* of the radioactive material being studied. The negative sign is used because dN/dt, the number of disintegrations per unit time, is also the rate at which N, the number of unstable atoms, is *decreasing*. Separation of variables and integration of the above equation leads to

$$N = N_0 \, e^{-\lambda t}, \tag{2}$$

where N is the number of atoms remaining at time t and N_0 gives the number of atoms initially present in a given sample. The decay constant λ gives a measure of the fraction of the atoms dN/N disintegrating per unit time: $\lambda = -(dN/N)/dt$. The larger the decay constant of a material, the more rapidly the activity of a sample of this material will decrease.

Another quantity, perhaps more readily interpretable, is sometimes used to measure the activity of a radioactive material; this quantity is called the *half-life* of the material.

> The half-life T of a radioactive material is defined as the time required for the activity of a sample of the material to decrease to one-half of its initial value, or, what amounts to the same thing, the time for half the atoms of the sample to disintegrate.

Recalling that the activity of a sample is proportional to the number of atoms present, we see that $t = T$ when

$$N = \tfrac{1}{2}N_0 \quad \text{or} \quad \tfrac{1}{2}N_0 = N_0 \, e^{-\lambda T}.$$

Dividing this equation by N_0 and taking the natural logarithm of both sides, we obtain

$$\lambda T = \log 2 = 0.693, \quad \text{or} \quad T = 0.693/\lambda. \tag{3}$$

The half-lives of several radioactive materials are listed in Table I. It might be noted that the half-life of a radioactive isotope is a characteristic nuclear property and cannot be altered by any method now known.

Further knowledge of the properties of atomic nuclei has been obtained by using the alpha particles from radioactive materials as projectiles for the bombardment of other nuclei. As we have seen, Rutherford used alpha particles in his studies of scattering, and was thus led to the nuclear theory of atomic structure. Rutherford also used alpha particles to produce *nuclear reactions*.

> A nuclear reaction is a reaction involving a change from one nuclear species to another.

Because of their high energy, alpha particles can approach very close to the atomic nuclei of the lighter elements. In certain cases alpha particles can 'penetrate' the nucleus of an atom and cause a change to another type of nucleus. On the basis of a theory advanced by Bohr, a nuclear reaction of this type may be thought of as consisting of two steps. The first involves the capture of the bombarding alpha particles by a nucleus and the formation of a compound nucleus. The second is the almost

TABLE I

The Natural Radioactive Series*

Uranium series				Thorium series			
Radio-active nucleus	Half-life	Emitted particle	Resulting nucleus	Radio-active nucleus	Half-life	Emitted particle	Resulting nucleus
$_{92}U^{238}$	4.5×10^9 yr	α	$_{90}Th^{234}$	$_{90}Th^{232}$	1.65×10^{10} yr	α	$_{88}Ra^{228}$
$_{90}Th^{234}$	24.5 days	β	$_{91}Pa^{234}$	$_{88}Ra^{228}$	6.7 yr	β	$_{89}Ac^{228}$
$_{91}Pa^{234}$	1.14 min	β	$_{92}U^{234}$	$_{89}Ac^{228}$	6.13 hr	β	$_{90}Th^{228}$
$_{92}U^{234}$	10^6 yr	α	$_{90}Th^{230}$	$_{90}Th^{228}$	1.90 yr	α	$_{88}Ra^{224}$
$_{90}Th^{230}$	7.6×10^4 yr	α	$_{88}Ra^{226}$	$_{88}Ra^{224}$	3.64 days	α	$_{86}Rn^{220}$
$_{88}Ra^{226}$	1.6×10^2 yr	α	$_{86}Rn^{222}$	$_{86}Rn^{220}$	54.5 sec	α	$_{84}Po^{216}$
$_{86}Rn^{222}$	3.825 days	α	$_{84}Po^{218}$	$_{84}Po^{216}$	0.145 sec	α	$_{82}Pb^{212}$
$_{84}Po^{218}$	3.05 min	α	$_{82}Pb^{214}$	$_{82}Pb^{212}$	10.6 hr	β	$_{83}Bi^{212}$
$_{82}Pb^{214}$	26.8 min	β	$_{83}Bi^{214}$	$_{83}Bi^{212}$	60.5 min	β	$_{84}Po^{212}$
$_{83}Bi^{214}$	19.7 min	β	$_{84}Po^{214}$	$_{84}Po^{212}$	10^{-11} sec	α	$_{82}Pb^{208}$ (stable)
$_{84}Po^{214}$	10^{-6} sec	α	$_{82}Pb^{210}$				
$_{82}Pb^{210}$	25 yr	β	$_{83}Bi^{210}$				
$_{83}Bi^{210}$	5.0 days	β	$_{84}Po^{210}$				
$_{84}Po^{210}$	136.3 days	α	$_{82}Pb^{206}$ (stable)				

* From Rutherford, Chadwick, and Ellis, *Radiations from Radioactive Substances*, Cambridge University Press, 1930. This table shows only the principal chains of disintegrations; there is some 'branching' into alternative routes that we do not show.
There is also a third series starting from $_{92}U^{235}$ and ending in $_{82}Pb^{207}$.

immediate breaking up of the compound nucleus into the final products. As an example, let us consider one of the earliest observed nuclear reactions. When alpha particles pass through nitrogen gas in a cloud chamber, a few forked tracks like the one shown in Fig. 6 are observed; one of the branches is very heavy and is typical of a particle much heavier than an alpha particle, whereas the other is a very thin track typical of a light particle like a proton. The observed tracks can be explained on the basis of the nuclear reaction represented by the equation

$$_7N^{14} + _2He^4 \rightarrow (_9F^{18}) \rightarrow _8O^{17} + _1H^1.$$

The penetration of the alpha particle into the nitrogen nucleus produces the compound nucleus $_9F^{18}$, an unstable isotope of fluorine, which immediately breaks up into an isotope of oxygen and a proton. Many reactions of this type have been observed and are sometimes denoted by the symbol (α,p) where the first letter, α, indicates that the *bombarding* particle is an *alpha particle* and the second letter, p, indicates that the *emitted* particle is a *proton*.

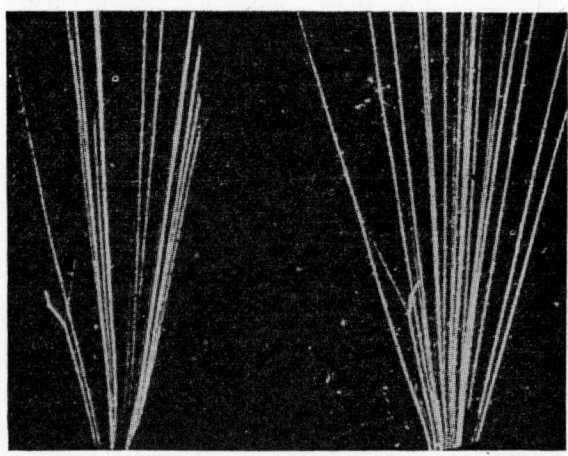

Fig. 6. Cloud-chamber photograph in which the forked track shows the (α, p) reaction of nitrogen and an alpha particle [from *Elements of Nuclear Physics* by Rasetti (Prentice-Hall, 1937).]

The capture of an alpha particle by a nucleus does not always result in the emission of a proton by the compound nucleus formed as a result of this capture. In one reaction, the bombardment of beryllium by alpha particles, a very penetrating type of 'radiation' is found to be emitted by the newly formed compound nucleus. It was at first assumed that this 'radiation' was gamma radiation resulting from the radiative capture process $_4Be^9 + _2He^4 \rightarrow (_6C^{13}) \rightarrow _6C^{13} + hf$, where hf represents an emitted photon. It was found that the emitted 'radiation' had the very interesting property of being able to knock protons out of paraffin and other hydrogenous materials. James Chadwick in 1932 performed a series of experiments on the recoil of various nuclei struck by the 'radiation' emitted from beryllium bombarded by alpha particles. By observing the energies of various recoil nuclei and attributing the observed recoil energies to collisions between incident photons and nuclei, Chadwick was unable to arrive at a unique value for the energy of the incident photons; experiments with recoil protons gave a value of 55 Mev for the photon energy, while experiments with nitrogen recoil nuclei led to a value of 90 Mev for the photon energy. However, Chadwick showed that this inconsistency disappeared if he adopted the hypothesis that the 'radiation' emitted when beryllium is bombarded with alpha particles does not consist of photons but consists of *neutral particles of mass very nearly equal to that of the proton*. These particles are called *neutrons* and are formed as a result of the reaction

$$_4Be^9 + {}_2He^4 \rightarrow ({}_6C^{13}) \rightarrow {}_6C^{12} + {}_0n^1, \tag{4}$$

where $_0n^1$ is the symbol for the neutron, showing that it has zero charge and mass number unity. Thus was discovered a new fundamental particle, the *neutron*. Many nuclear reactions of this type (α,n) have since been observed for light elements.

The discovery of the neutron gave further insight into the structure of the nucleus. Prior to the neutron's discovery, it had been thought that the nucleus consisted of protons and electrons, but this assumption was very unsatisfactory for a number of reasons which we cannot enumerate here. According to presently accepted theory,

The nucleus is composed of protons and neutrons.

The number of protons in a given nucleus is equal to its atomic number Z and the number of neutrons $(A-Z)$ is just sufficient to make up the remainder of the mass number A; for example, the $_2He^4$ nucleus contains 2 protons and 2 neutrons, while the $_{92}U^{238}$ nucleus contains 92 protons and 146 neutrons. The neutrons and protons that compose the nucleus are together called *nucleons*.

A nucleon is a constituent particle of atomic nuclei.

The neutrons emitted by a nucleus in a process such as the (α,n) reaction described above behave quite differently from charged particles such as electrons, protons, and alpha particles. As a result of their charges, charged particles with large kinetic energy interact strongly with the planetary electrons of atoms and usually fritter away their energy by ionizing the atoms or molecules of the materials through which they pass. Protons and alpha particles lose energy very rapidly and are brought to rest and neutralized after passage through only a few centimeters of air or through thin metal foils. Electrons of comparable energies are more penetrating but gradually lose energy by producing ionization, and after being slowed down become attached to positive ions, which thereby become neutral atoms or molecules, or to neutral atoms or molecules to form negative ions. Neutrons, possessing no electric charge, have no tendency to interact with the extranuclear portion of atoms and are consequently more penetrating than charged particles of comparable energy. Neutrons interact strongly only with nuclei; a neutron may have elastic collisions with nuclei, but eventually it is captured by a nucleus. One type of capture process is that in which a neutron is captured by nitrogen as described in the equation

$$_7N^{14} + {}_0n^1 \rightarrow ({}_7N^{15}) \rightarrow {}_6C^{14} + {}_1H^1.$$

In this (n,p) process, the product nucleus $_6C^{14}$ is unstable and eventually achieves stability by the beta-emission process

$$_6C^{14} \rightarrow {}_7N^{14} + {}_{-1}\varepsilon^0 + {}_0\nu^0.$$

Other neutron capture processes will be described in Sec. 7.

The exact nature of the interaction between a neutron and a nucleus is not yet clearly understood, but it has been established that slow neutrons are more readily captured than fast neutrons. Fast neutrons, on passing through hydrogenous materials, are slowed down as a result of elastic collisions with protons and are thereafter captured by nuclei in processes similar to the one given above. Certain nuclei such as those of cadmium absorb neutrons more readily than other nuclei. The use of neutrons as projectiles for bombarding atomic nuclei has added much to our knowledge of the properties of nuclei; we shall say more of this in a later section.

On the presently accepted picture in which nuclei are believed to contain only neutrons and protons, the electrons that are emitted when a nucleus undergoes a beta process must be thought of as *created* when a neutron changes to a proton in the nucleus. When a neutron changes to a proton, an electron must be emitted in order that the total charge may be conserved. The reverse process, in which a proton changes into a neutron and a *positron* (a particle of electronic mass but charge $+e$) will be considered in Sec. 6. There is recent experimental proof that a free neutron (one not in a nucleus) spontaneously changes to a proton and an electron (plus a neutrino, probably). This process, which is analogous to natural beta radioactivity, has a half-life of the order of 15 minutes.

We shall now define a very useful measure of the probability of a nuclear reaction, called the *cross section* for the reaction. Consider any nuclear reaction—for example the (α,n) reaction in Be^9 whose equation is given in (4). Now consider a very thin sheet of pure Be^9 that contains N atoms of Be^9 per square meter, with a beam of alpha particles of a certain energy directed against the sheet. Of the alpha particles, suppose that a fraction p ($p \ll 1$) cause reaction (4) in Be^9 nuclei, the rest of the alpha particles either passing right through or being scattered or perhaps causing some different reaction. Then, for a sufficiently thin sheet, it will be found that p is proportional to N, which in turn is proportional to the thickness of the sheet. Now imagine that we draw on the surface of the sheet N tiny nonoverlapping circles, each of tiny area A, one for each nucleus in the square meter of our sheet. We choose A so that the total area NA of the circles is p meter^2, which is very much less than 1 m^2. Then we can consider that the probability that an alpha particle cause a nuclear reaction is given by playing the following game: If an alpha particle is projected at the sheet, it will cause a reaction if it happens to pass through one of the circles; if it does not, it will not cause a reaction. Since the circles occupy a fraction p of the whole area, this game will give the correct probability. Since there is one circle for each nucleus, the area of the circle is called the cross section of the nucleus for the particular reaction. The cross sections are in general of the same order of magnitude as the projected area of a nucleus. A typical nuclear size is 10^{-14} m in diameter, or roughly 10^{-28} m^2 in projected area. The area 10^{-28} m^2 is called *one barn* ('big as a barn door'), and cross sections for nuclear reactions are measured in *barns*. They vary from less than 0.001 barn to over 1000 barns. This cross section gives an easily visualizable measure of the probability of a nuclear reaction, because we need merely assign an area A to each nucleus, and the probability of the reaction taking place is the probability that our bombarding particle pass through one of these areas; or, the number of reactions taking place is the number of particles passing through such areas.

PROBLEMS

1. The uranium isotope U^{234} spontaneously disintegrates by alpha-particle emission. Write the equation describing this process.

2. The thorium isotope Th^{232} spontaneously disintegrates by alpha-particle emission. Write the equation describing this process.

3. The thorium isotope Th^{234} spontaneously disintegrates by beta-particle emission. Write the equation describing this process.

4. The isotope produced by the process mentioned in Prob. 3 is a beta emitter. Write the equation describing this second beta process.

5. The radioactive decay constant for Th^{232} is 1.33×10^{-18} sec^{-1}. What is the half-life of this isotope? In a given sample of Th^{232}, what fraction of the Th^{232} nuclei decays each second? Ans: 1.65×10^{10} years; 1.33×10^{-18}.

6. The half-life of U^{238} is 4.5×10^9 years. What is the radioactive decay constant for U^{238}? What fraction of the U^{238} nuclei in a given sample of uranium decays each second?

7. When boron is bombarded with alpha particles, a reaction involving B^{10} results. In the reaction protons are ejected. Write an equation describing this (α,p) reaction.

8. When sulfur is bombarded with alpha particles, an (α,p) reaction involving S^{32} results. Write an equation describing this reaction.

9. When boron is bombarded with alpha particles, a reaction of type (α,n) results. The isotope B^{11} is involved. Write the equation describing this reaction.

10. Write the equation for the (α,n) process produced when Li^7 is bombarded by alpha particles.

11. The cross section for the (α,n) reaction in Be^9 is 0.43 barns for 3-Mev α-particles. If a sheet of Be having a mass of 1 mg/cm^2 is bombarded with a cyclotron beam of 1 microampere of alpha particles, how many reactions take place per second? Ans: 8.97×10^7.

12. The average cross section for the (n,γ) reaction in natural Cd is 2500 barns for thermal neutrons. What fraction of the thermal neutrons incident on a sheet of Cd having a mass of 1 mg/cm^2 is captured?

4. PARTICLE ACCELERATORS

The use of alpha particles from naturally radioactive sources as projectiles for nuclear bombardment produced valuable results in the Rutherford scattering experiments and in the discovery of the (α,p) and (α,n) reactions. However, the numbers of alpha particles obtainable per second from natural radioactive sources is relatively small compared with the numbers of charged particles present in electron or ion beams, and the alpha-particle energies are in general limited to values less than 10 Mev. These limitations of natural radioactive sources were soon recognized, and much effort has gone into the development of devices—the so-called 'atom smashers'—that accelerate charged particles, such as protons, deuterons, and electrons, to be used as projectiles in the study of nuclei. We shall describe briefly several of these devices.

At first thought it might appear that the simplest method of producing high-energy projectiles would be to allow charged particles such as protons in an evacuated tube to pass from a region of very high potential to a region of low potential. This process is simple in principle, but serious experimental problems are encountered in producing potentials of the order of several million volts and applying them to the electrodes of an evacuated tube in which the ions are to be accelerated. Insulation problems make it impossible to use the conventional arrangement involving a step-up transformer, a rectifier, and a filter of the type used in electronic power supplies. One device for producing high voltages for the accelerating ions is the *Van de Graaff generator*, described on pp. 839 and 892.

In the Van de Graaff machine at the Westinghouse Research Laboratories (Fig. 7), the spherical electrode has a diameter of 15 ft and is located at the center of a pear-shaped tank having a diameter of 30 ft, as in Fig. 15, p. 853. When the tank is at atmospheric pressure, electrical breakdown occurs across the $7\frac{1}{2}$-ft gap between sphere and tank when the sphere reaches a potential of 1.2 million volts. However, when the tank is filled with dry air at a high pressure, the breakdown voltage is 4 million volts. In some pressurized Van de Graaff machines, pressures of 150 lbf/in² are used and Freon or sulfur hexafluoride is added to increase the dielectric strength of the dry air in the tank. Potentials as high as 5 million volts have been attained, and machines are being built that should give 10 million volts. The voltage of the sphere can be maintained constant to 0.1 per cent.

In accelerating positive ions, the voltage from the high-voltage electrode is applied to a long vacuum tube, one end of which is in the sphere itself and contains an ion source that supplies protons, deuterons, or doubly charged helium ions. The other end of the vacuum tube is at ground potential and contains the 'target' to be bombarded. A number of electrodes at intermediate potentials are inserted in the vacuum tube between the high voltage end and ground. These electrodes serve to focus the ion beam on the target. With the sphere at 5 million volts, 5 Mev protons and deuterons or 10 Mev helium ions (α particles) can be produced and focused to a small spot on the target. Beam currents

Fig. 7. The Westinghouse electrostatic accelerator (*courtesy of Westinghouse Electric Company*).

are at present limited to values of less than 5 microamperes, but the fact that the ions are more strictly monoenergetic than those obtainable with other accelerators makes the Van de Graaff machine an exceedingly valuable tool in research work.

Larger beam currents of high-energy ions are obtainable with the *cyclotron* developed by E. O. Lawrence and his coworkers at the University of California. In this device, positive ions are made to pass repeatedly through the same accelerating potential, and finally to acquire energies corresponding to a fall through a potential many times greater than that actually applied at any one time between electrodes in the cyclotron. For example, if a proton is made to pass 1000 times through a potential difference of 10,000 volts, its final kinetic energy is 10 Mev. The arrangement of the electrodes in the cyclotron is illustrated schematically in Fig. 8. Two semicircular hollow copper boxes are arranged in the manner indicated; these boxes are called 'dees' because their shape resembles the letter D. The dees are placed in an evacuated enclosure between the pole faces of a huge magnet like that in Fig. 7, p. 993, so that there is a strong magnetic field perpendicular to the flat faces of the dees. An alternating potential of the order of 10 kv is applied between the dees at a frequency of the order of 10 megacycles/sec.

In order to understand the scheme of operation of the cyclotron, let us suppose that there is a supply of low-energy positive ions at point P midway between the dees. Ions are produced in this region of a cyclotron by electron bombardment of gas introduced at low pressure; the gas introduced is usually hydrogen, deuterium, or helium. During a half-cycle these ions will be accelerated toward one of the dees B. Once these ions enter the hollow electric-field-free space within the dee, they will no longer be accelerated by the alternating electric field and will move at constant *speed*. However, since they are traveling perpendicular to a constant magnetic field $\mathcal{B}$, they will traverse a circular path and will finally return to the gap between the dees. If the frequency of the alternating potential is such that the time required to describe this semicircle corresponds to one half-cycle, then the ions will arrive at the gap at just the proper time to be further accelerated by the now reversed electric field. The ions are now moving faster after entering the second dee A and will therefore traverse a circular path of greater radius. However, as we have seen on p. 966 and again on p. 1162, the *time* required for an ion to traverse a circular path, or half a circular path, in a magnetic field is independent of the speed of the ion. The time for a half-revolution is given by $\pi m/\mathcal{B}q$, where m and q are the mass and charge of the ion.

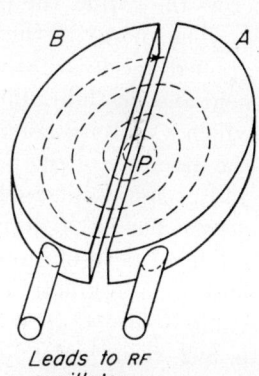

Fig. 8. Schematic diagram of the electrodes (dees) and the ion path in a cyclotron.

Thus, for an ion to arrive at the gap between the dees at just the proper instant to experience further acceleration after each half-revolution, the oscillator must have a period equal to the time of two half-revolutions of the ion, or $2\pi m/\mathcal{B}q$, in seconds, corresponding to a frequency of $\mathcal{B}q/2\pi m$, in cycles/sec. For a proton of mass 1.67×10^{-27} kg and charge 1.60×10^{-19} coul, with a field of 1.5 weber/m^2, this is a frequency of 23 megacycles/sec. For deuterons of twice the mass and the same charge, the frequency would be half this value, or 11.5 megacycles/sec. Since alpha particles have twice the mass and twice the charge of a deuteron, they would require the same frequency.

The ions describe a series of semicircles of increasing radius, gradually spiraling outward and finally emerging at the outer edge of the dees, where they may be concentrated on a target by means of an electrostatic deflecting plate. The ions emerge with an energy equivalent to a fall through a potential many times higher than that used in the accelerating process. We have considered an ion that is in the gap between the dees at the optimum times for acceleration. Ions crossing the gap before or after the peak of the alternating potential acquire less energy on each traversal of the gap but, by making more revolutions, eventually arrive at the periphery with the same total kinetic energy as ions that cross the gap at the peak of the voltage wave.

The energy of the emerging ions does not depend on the value of the applied accelerating voltage but only on the strength of the magnetic field and on the radius of the dees, which is made equal to the radius for which a uniform magnetic field is available from the magnet—essentially the diameter of the pole pieces. The ion will continue to acquire energy and to spiral outward until the radius of its path is R, the radius of the dees. We have derived on p. 966 the expression $R = mv/\mathcal{B}q$ for the radius of path of an ion of speed v. If we solve this expression for v, we find, for the kinetic energy of an ion moving in a path of radius R, the value $\frac{1}{2}mv^2 = \frac{1}{2}R^2\mathcal{B}^2q^2/m$, in joules. Using the conversion factor on p. 892, from joules to electron-volts, we see that this kinetic energy can be written as $3.15 \times 10^{12} R^2\mathcal{B}^2q^2/m$, in Mev. For a deuteron in a field of 1.5 weber/m², of radius ½ m, this formula gives an energy of 13.5 Mev. This was about the size of the earlier cyclotrons.

It is customary to design a cyclotron with a fixed-frequency oscillator and to adjust the magnetic field to satisfy accurately the required relation between field and frequency. If the maximum available field is used for deuterons and alpha particles, the field must be reduced to half this value in the case of protons, if the frequency is to be kept the same. For the example discussed above, the cyclotron would be operated with a field of 0.75 weber/m² when protons are being accelerated, and the protons would acquire only half the energy of the deuterons, or 6.8 Mev. For the same cyclotron with alpha particles, the field would be 1.5 weber/m², and the alpha particles would acquire twice the deuteron energy, or 27 Mev. Since, because of the saturation properties of ferromagnetic materials, it is impossible to set up extensive fields much more intense than 1.5 or 2 weber/m², the only way to increase the energy of the accelerated particles much above these figures is to increase the radius R of the magnetic field, which means building larger and much more expensive electromagnets. Thus magnets have been built with pole pieces of diameter 42, 60, and 184 inches. The 'size' of a cyclotron is usually specified by giving the diameter in inches of its pole faces.

The ions arriving at the cyclotron target are fairly homogeneous in energy but are not so nearly monoenergetic as those obtainable with a Van de Graaff machine. On the other hand, larger ion-beam currents and higher ion energies are obtainable with a cyclotron than with a Van de Graaff machine. For example, at the University of California the 200-ton cyclotron with pole faces 60 inches in diameter has produced

Fig. 9. The 184-inch frequency-modulated cyclotron at the University of California (*courtesy of the Radiation Laboratory of the University of California*).

8-Mev protons at a beam current of 25 microamperes when the beam is removed from the dees and a current of 100 microamperes within the dees; this cyclotron will also produce 16-Mev deuterons and 32-Mev alpha particles.

As we shall see in the next section, the mass of a moving particle is not actually constant but increases as the speed of the particle approaches the speed of light. When the ions in a conventional cyclotron of the type we have described reach very high speeds, the cyclotron ceases to function properly, since the time $\pi m/\mathscr{B}q$ required between accelerations is no longer constant but increases as the mass of the ion increases. This difficulty becomes of importance for protons of about 50 Mev energy and for electrons of about 25 kev energy, and prevents the operation of an ordinary cyclotron above those energies. Thus, the simple cyclotron is not at all useful in connection with the acceleration of electrons. In the case of protons and heavier particles, this difficulty has been overcome by using a *frequency-modulated cyclotron* with a pulsed ion source. Using a frequency-modulated cyclotron with pole pieces 184 inches in diameter, Lawrence and his associates have produced ions with energies of 300 Mev. Figure 9 is a photograph of this cyclotron. A still larger cyclotron, designed for the production of 1000-Mev particles, is being constructed (1950) at the University of California.

Although the cyclotron and the Van de Graaff electrostatic generator have thus far been the most successful and most widely used devices for the production of high-energy projectiles for use in nuclear experiments, other accelerators are in use or in process of development.

Fig. 10. The linear accelerator at the University of California (*courtesy of Luis Alvarez*).

One of these devices is the *linear accelerator*, in which charged particles traversing a straight-line path in a tube are subjected to repeated small accelerations by applying potentials at proper times to a number of electrodes placed at appropriate distances along the tube; the voltages are supplied by radio-frequency oscillators. Linear accelerators to produce ions of 200 Mev energy are being constructed. Figure 10 is a photograph of the linear accelerator at the University of California.

Another type of accelerator is the *synchrotron*, which is used to accelerate *electrons* introduced into a magnetic field at fairly high speed and subjected to repeated accelerations as in the cyclotron. However, in the synchrotron the time t between accelerations, $t = \pi m / \mathcal{B} e$, is maintained constant by increasing the magnetic field $\mathfrak{B}$ as the mass m increases; furthermore, $\mathfrak{B}$ can also be varied in such a manner as to keep the path radius r a constant, and hence the large central portion of the cyclotron magnet is unnecessary. The synchrotron gives brief repeated pulses of high-energy electrons; synchrotrons for the production of 1000-Mev electrons have been proposed.

Fig. 11. Photograph of a 'race-track' synchrotron model (*courtesy of H. R. Crane*).

Finally, we should mention the *betatron* or *induction accelerator*, which uses the induced EMF produced by a changing magnetic field to accelerate *electrons* to high energy. Consider a stream of electrons describing a circular path inside an evacuated doughnut-shaped vacuum tube located in a magnetic field. If the flux Φ linking the circular electron path changes at the rate $d\Phi/dt$, the electrons are subjected to an accelerating force proportional to $d\Phi/dt$. Just as a circular wire at this location would have an induced EMF of $V = d\Phi/dt$ volts, this accelerating force does work $d\Phi/dt$ electron-volts on the electron *per revolution*. While this force is increasing the momentum mv of the electrons, the magnetic flux density through the 'orbit' traversed by the electrons is increased in such a way that the radius of the orbit remains constant. The electrons make several hundred thousand revolutions while the central flux Φ is increasing, and with each revolution acquire additional energy. When the flux Φ produced by coils supplied from a 60-$\sim$ AC line reaches a maximum, a sudden change is made in the flux density $\mathcal{B}$ at the orbit to change the electron path and allow it to strike a target located near

Fig. 12. Photograph of a betatron (*courtesy of Donald Kerst*).

the point at which the electrons were originally injected. Betatrons have been constructed to give electron energies up to 100 Mev. Figure 12 is a photograph of the betatron at the University of Illinois, where it was invented by Donald Kerst in 1940.

When high-energy electrons are used in nuclear work, they are allowed to strike a target and the emitted high-energy photons (X rays) are used to produce nuclear reactions. One such 'photodisintegration' is

$$_1H^2 + hf \rightarrow {}_1H^1 + {}_0n^1,$$

in which a deuteron absorbs a photon, whose energy must be greater than 2.17 Mev, and divides into a proton and a neutron.

The accelerators we have described provide abundant sources of different types of atomic projectiles for use in the study of the nucleus.

PROBLEMS

1. The high-voltage electrode in a pressurized Van de Graaff generator is maintained at a potential of 4 million volts. Calculate the maximum energies that can be imparted to protons, deuterons, and alpha particles by this machine.

Ans: 4 Mev; 4 Mev; 8 Mev.

2. If an ion source could be devised that could completely strip the electrons from atoms, what kinetic energies could be imparted to the 'projectiles' obtained when (a) lithium, (b) carbon, and (c) sulfur nuclei were accelerated by the generator of Prob. 1?

3. In a certain cyclotron the radio-frequency oscillator operates at a frequency of 10 megacycles/sec and applies a peak voltage of 10 kv between the dees. Find the time required for protons to describe a semicircular path inside one of the dees. What should be the flux density of the magnetic field in this cyclotron? If the effective diameter of the pole faces measured to the periphery of the dees in this cyclotron is 1.5 m, what is the maximum kinetic energy that can be imparted to protons?

Ans: 5×10^{-8} sec; 0.656 webers/m²; 11.6 Mev.

4. If the frequency and the peak value of the RF voltage in the cyclotron of Prob. 3 were maintained constant, what should be the magnetic-field strength if deuterons are to be accelerated? What would be the maximum kinetic energy imparted to the deuterons? Make a similar calculation for doubly charged helium ions.

5. THE THEORY OF RELATIVITY

Experiments on the ratio e/m, by Kaufmann, Bücherer, and others, beginning in 1906, showed that this ratio, for the high-speed electrons (beta particles) emitted from radioactive substances, is less than the ratio for electrons of moderate speed. The ratio was found to decrease as the speed increased. If this decrease is interpreted as an increase of mass with speed, charge being constant, the experimental data on the mass of the electron as a function of speed are given by the points of Fig. 13.

This departure from the Newtonian idea of an invariant mass is one of the predictions of the *theory of relativity*, formulated by Albert Einstein in 1905. Einstein made a critical re-examination of the fundamental principles of mechanics and electrodynamics in the light of available experimental data and concluded that our basic philosophical ideas of space and time were in need of complete revision. Einstein concluded that distances and time intervals between 'events' would be given different values by different 'observers' moving relative to each other, even though these observers were using identically constructed meter sticks and clocks. The difference must be such that *each observer will always find the same value, $c = 3 \times 10^8$ m/sec, for the speed of light relative to* *himself, regardless of the direction of travel of the light beam.* The statement in italics was an experimental conclusion from the observations of Michelson and Morley who, in 1881, showed by a careful interferometric technique that the observed speed of light is a constant, unaffected by the earth's high orbital speed around the sun at any time of the day or year or for any direction of propagation relative to the earth.

We cannot go further here into the foundations of the theory of relativity, but it is necessary that we learn some of the results of this theory that are fundamental to an understanding of modern particle

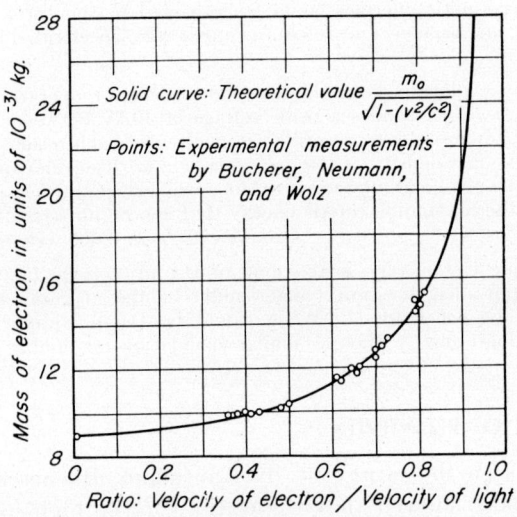

Fig. 13. Electron mass as a function of speed.

physics. The theory gives a revised mechanical law to replace Newton's second law; the two laws do not give results that are detectably different for bodies whose speed is small compared to the speed of light (say less than 3×10^6 m/sec or 6,000,000 mi/hr), but they give quite different results for particles moving at speeds close to that of light. We need to learn the relativistic law if we are to understand the motion of the particles in modern high-energy accelerators such as those discussed in the preceding section.

By logical arguments, Einstein not only predicted the observed increase of mass with speed, but made other startling predictions, such as that of the equivalence of mass and energy. This equivalence, which was not verified until much later, is fundamental to an understanding of the release of atomic energy in nuclear reactions. We shall discuss first the new second law, then the equivalence of mass and energy.

I. *The new second law of relativistic mechanics.* If we write the momentum of a particle as $m\mathbf{v}$, then the mass of the particle is not a constant but increases with increasing speed in such a way as to approach infinity as the speed of the particle approaches that of light. The relation is

$$m = \frac{m_0}{\sqrt{1-(v^2/c^2)}}, \tag{5}$$

where m_0, called the *rest mass*, is the Newtonian mass—the apparent mass of the particle when at rest or when moving with a speed very small

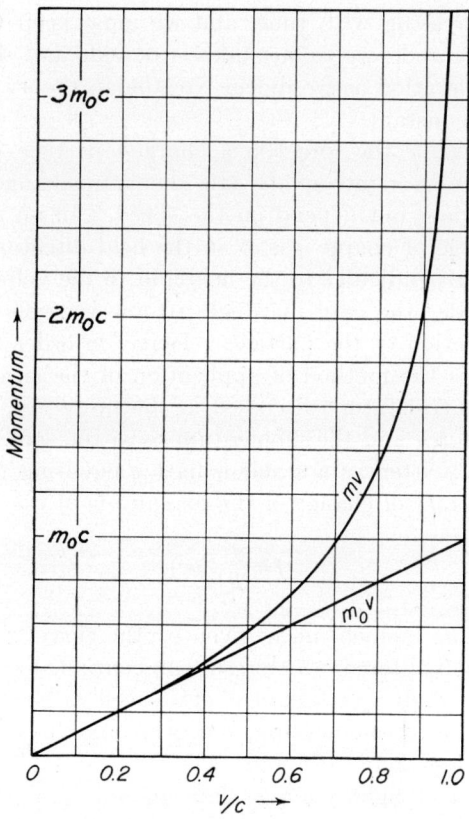

Fig. 14. The momentum of a particle as a function of speed: comparison of Newtonian and relativistic formulas.

compared to the speed of light. A plot of (5) for the case of the electron, with $m_0 = 9.1 \times 10^{-31}$ kg, is given in the solid curve of Fig. 13.

The momentum of the particle is now given by the vector $m\mathbf{v}$ (whereas on Newtonian theory it would be $m_0\mathbf{v}$). A comparison of the momentum magnitude mv with the Newtonian value m_0v, as a function of v/c, is given in Fig. 14.

The first and third of Newton's laws remain the same in relativistic mechanics as in Newtonian. The second law must be written as the vector equation

$$\boldsymbol{f} = \frac{d}{dt}(m\boldsymbol{v}) \tag{6}$$

—force equals time rate of change of momentum. This equation has the same outward form as the one applicable in Newtonian mechanics, but now we must remember that if the speed is increasing with time, the mass is also increasing with time, and we must keep the m inside the differentiation symbol; we *cannot* take m outside and set force equal to mass times acceleration as we did in Newtonian theory where mass was considered as a constant.

The formulas for the force on a charged particle in an electric or magnetic field go over into relativistic theory unchanged. The magnitude of charge does not depend on the speed. In an electric field, the force on a particle of charge q is $q\mathcal{E}$ in the field direction; in a magnetic field it is $\mathcal{B}qv$, perpendicular to the field and to the velocity.

Let us consider the case in which a force is applied by an electric field in the direction of the particle velocity, in order to accelerate the particle. This is the method of application of the accelerating force in all the particle accelerators discussed in the preceding section. In this case, since the force and the momentum have the same direction, equation (6) can be written as a scalar equation equating the magnitude of the force to the rate of change of the magnitude of the momentum:

$$f = \frac{d}{dt}(mv). \qquad (\boldsymbol{f}\|\boldsymbol{v}) \tag{7}$$

But now since the momentum is given by the curve mv of Fig. 14, continued application of force, which results in continued increase of momentum, will never result in attainment of a speed as great as that of light, because any value of momentum, however large, still corresponds to a value of speed less than, although perhaps close to, the speed of light. Thus, the speed of light plays a limiting role, and *it is impossible to accelerate a particle to a speed greater than that of light.*

Now let us consider the case in which a force is applied in a direction normal to the velocity $\boldsymbol{v}$, and hence normal to the momentum $m\boldsymbol{v}$. In this case the force has no tendency to change the *magnitude* of the momentum but only to change its *direction*. Since the magnitude of the momentum remains constant, the magnitude of the velocity also remains constant (compare Fig. 14), and hence the mass remains constant [compare (5)]. In this case the mass *can* be taken outside the parenthesis in (6), and we can write $f = ma$. The acceleration is transverse, with magnitude $a = v^2/R$, where R is the radius of curvature of the path. Hence,

$$f = mv^2/R, \qquad (f \perp v) \quad (8)$$

just as in Newtonian theory, except that now m is the mass given by equation (5) and depends on the speed.

The experiments of Kaufmann and Bücherer on the ratio e/m of high-speed beta particles were arranged in principle exactly like the mass spectrograph of Fig. 3. In this apparatus, all forces are applied transversely. Hence, the classical analysis of the mass spectrograph which we gave on p. 1169 is valid without change, so long as it is recognized that m should stand for the relativistic mass (5). This type of apparatus first balances transverse forces from crossed electric and magnetic fields to get a velocity selection according to the equations

$$q\mathcal{E} = \mathcal{B}'qv, \qquad v = \mathcal{E}/\mathcal{B}';$$

then it deflects particles of this known speed into a circular path in a magnetic field to determine q/m according to the equations

$$\mathcal{B}qv = mv^2/R, \qquad q/m = v/R\mathcal{B}.$$

All these equations are relativistically satisfactory. Hence, experiments on the ratio e/m of electrons of different speed will give decreasing values of e/m and increasing values of m, as the speed increases. Experimental values of m determined in this way are compared with the theoretical curve for electron mass in Fig. 13.

II. *Energy considerations in relativistic mechanics. The equivalence of mass and energy.* The work done by the force acting on a particle is defined as $\int f \, ds$, where f is the force component in the direction of the velocity and ds is an element of distance along the path of the particle. If f is the net force component in the direction of motion, it is related to the rate of change of the magnitude of the momentum by (7). The work necessary to increase the speed of the particle from 0 up to some value v is *defined* as the *kinetic energy* of the particle at speed v. Let us compute the relativistic expression for the kinetic energy; this is expected to agree with the Newtonian formula only for speeds small compared with that of light.

We can write

$$\int f \, ds = \int \frac{d}{dt}(mv) \, ds = \int \frac{d}{dt}(mv) \frac{ds}{dt} \, dt.$$

But ds/dt is the speed v, by definition, so that

$$\int f \, ds = \int v \frac{d}{dt}(mv) \, dt = \int \left[mv \frac{dv}{dt} + v^2 \frac{dm}{dt} \right] dt.$$

Now it can readily be shown* that

$$mv\frac{dv}{dt}+v^2\frac{dm}{dt}=c^2\frac{dm}{dt}.$$

Hence we can write

$$\int f\,ds = \int c^2\frac{dm}{dt}\,dt = c^2\int dm.$$

This is a very simple expression; the element of work, $f\,ds$, is just equal to c^2 times the increase of mass dm. When the speed increases from 0 to some value v, the mass increases from the rest mass m_0 to some higher value m given by (5); and the work done, which by definition is the kinetic energy, is

$$\text{K.E.} = c^2\int_{m_0}^{m} dm = c^2\,m\Big]_{m_0}^{m} = c^2(m-m_0). \tag{9}$$

The kinetic energy of a particle equals c^2 times the difference between its mass and its rest mass. That this strange formula does reduce to the Newtonian expression $\frac{1}{2}m_0 v^2$ for kinetic energy at low speeds is easily verified. By expanding (5) in a series of powers of v^2/c^2, we find

$$m = m_0\left[1-\frac{v^2}{c^2}\right]^{-\frac{1}{2}} = m_0\left[1+\frac{1}{2}\frac{v^2}{c^2}+\frac{3}{8}\frac{v^4}{c^4}+\cdots\right];$$

whence

$$\text{K.E.} = c^2(m-m_0) = \frac{1}{2}m_0 v^2 + \frac{3}{8}m_0\frac{v^4}{c^2}+\cdots = \frac{1}{2}m_0 v^2\left[1+\frac{3}{4}\frac{v^2}{c^2}+\cdots\right].$$

The Newtonian formula $\frac{1}{2}m_0 v^2$ is valid for small values of v/c such that the second term in the last bracket is negligible in comparison with unity.

The fact that the kinetic energy of a particle is directly proportional to the difference between the mass of the particle and its rest mass leads one to suspect that perhaps mass and energy are just two different measures of the same physical quantity. Further consideration along the lines we have begun above led Einstein to the conclusion that this is indeed so—that mass is associated with all forms of energy: kinetic, potential, elastic, thermal, and electromagnetic—and that whenever a

---

* By multiplying the numerator and denominator of (5) by c, we can write

$$m = \frac{m_0 c}{\sqrt{c^2-v^2}}.$$

By differentiation,

$$\frac{dm}{dt} = \frac{m_0 c v}{(c^2-v^2)^{3/2}}\frac{dv}{dt}.$$

Multiplication of both sides of this equation by (c^2-v^2) gives

$$(c^2-v^2)\frac{dm}{dt} = \frac{m_0 c}{\sqrt{c^2-v^2}}v\frac{dv}{dt} = mv\frac{dv}{dt},$$

from which

$$mv\frac{dv}{dt}+v^2\frac{dm}{dt}=c^2\frac{dm}{dt},$$

the relation required in the text.

body changes in energy it changes in mass correspondingly. The conversion factor in all cases is c^2, the change in energy ΔE in joules being related to the change in mass Δm in kg by

$$\Delta E = c^2 \, \Delta m, \tag{10}$$

with c in m/sec. Thus, *mass and energy are measures of the same physical quantity*, the conversion factor being given by

$$\left. \begin{array}{l} 1 \text{ kg} = c^2 \text{ joules} = 8.987 \times 10^{16} \text{ joules}; \\ 1 \text{ joule} = 1.113 \times 10^{-17} \text{ kg}. \end{array} \right\} \tag{10a}$$

The extremely small size of the factor 1.1×10^{-17} accounts for the fact that it is impossible to detect the mass changes associated with ordinary energy changes such as occur in thermal heating and chemical reactions. Thus, to heat 1 kg of water from 0° C to 100° C, we must add 418,500 joules of energy. This addition increases the mass of the water by 5×10^{-12} kg, which is undetectably small. Again, the energy release in the complete combustion of *3 tons* of carbon makes the combustion products only *1 milligram* lighter than the *11 tons* of carbon and oxygen entering the reaction.

Only since 1932 has there been direct experimental confirmation of the relation (10). This relation has now been extensively and accurately confirmed in nuclear reactions in which the release of energy is so large that the accompanying mass changes are readily measured in a mass spectrograph.

Following Einstein, we assert that there is energy E associated with any mass m, and mass m associated with any energy E, the relation between energy and mass being

$$E = mc^2, \tag{11}$$

the conversion factor having the value (10a). By this identification of mass and energy, the *law of conservation of energy* and the *law of conservation of mass* become *one and the same physical law*, not two distinct laws as in classical theory.

Relation (11) would assign mass hf/c^2 to a *photon* of energy hf. Since the photon moves at speed c, it would have momentum $(hf/c^2)c = hf/c$. This is the value of momentum that had to be assigned to the photon to explain the Compton effect, which we discussed on p. 1159.

PROBLEMS

1. Calculate the mass of an electron moving at 0.9 of the speed of light. Give the result in terms of the rest mass m_0 and in kg.   Ans: 2.29 m_0; 2.09×10^{-30} kg.

2. What is the mass of an electron moving at a speed of 0.95 c?   0.99 c?   Give the results in terms of the rest mass and in kg.

3. What is the total energy E associated with an electron moving with a speed of $0.9\,c$? What is the classical value for the kinetic energy of this electron? What is the relativistic value for the kinetic energy of this electron?

Ans: 1.88×10^{-13} joules; 0.331×10^{-13} joules; 1.06×10^{-13} joules.

4. Find the total energy, the classical value for the kinetic energy, and the relativistic value for the kinetic energy for each electron mentioned in Prob. 2.

6. MASS-ENERGY TRANSFORMATIONS; NUCLEAR MASSES

For a free fundamental particle, we have, from (9),

$$mc^2 = m_0 c^2 + \text{K.E.}$$

Einstein called mc^2 the *total energy* of the particle and $m_0 c^2$ its *rest energy* (energy associated with the rest mass of the particle because of its mere existence). At the time the theory of relativity was first formulated, there was no evidence that the rest energy of a fundamental particle could ever change to another form of energy, but since the discovery of the *positron* in 1932 (see below) the process of the disappearance of material particles (electrons and positrons) with the complete conversion of their rest energy into the energy of light quanta has become familiar, as has the inverse process, that of the 'materialization' of the energy of light quanta as the rest energy of electrons and positrons. There is now no reason to suppose that it will not be possible, when experiment reaches into the realm of still higher energies (the billion-volt range) to observe the disappearance and materialization of heavier particles such as protons and neutrons.

For a compound particle such as a nucleus which is composed of protons and neutrons (collectively called *nucleons*), we can write for the total energy

$$Mc^2 = M_0 c^2 + \text{K.E.},$$

where K.E. refers to the kinetic energy of translation of the nucleus as a whole, corresponding to the speed of its center of gravity. In this case the rest energy $M_0 c^2$ of the nucleus is not equal to the sum of the rest energies the constituent nucleons would have if free, because there are also the internal kinetic and potential energies to be considered. If we denote the internal energy by I.E., we have

$$M_0 c^2 = \sum_{\text{nucleons}} m_0 c^2 + \text{I.E.} \qquad (12)$$

The internal energy I.E. *is a negative quantity* because of the negative potential energy of the strong attractive forces between nucleons that hold the nucleus together. *The rest mass of a nucleus is less than the sum of the rest masses of the constituent nucleons.* The mass (energy) difference would be released in the process of formation of the nucleus from the nucleons; the difference would have to be supplied in order to break the nucleus up into its constituent nucleons. This energy difference, which

Sec. 6] MASS-ENERGY TRANSFORMATIONS; NUCLEAR MASSES

in this case is so large as to be capable of manifesting itself as a mass difference, is quite analogous to a chemical heat of reaction.

The masses of atoms, nuclei, and elementary particles are conveniently given in atomic mass units (amu) on a scale in which the O^{16} *atom* ($_8O^{16}$ nucleus plus 8 electrons) is assigned the rest mass 16 amu. On this scale we have the following rest masses:

electron:	0.0005486 amu	deuteron:	2.01418 amu
neutron:	1.0089 amu	H^2 atom:	2.01473 amu
proton:	1.00758 amu	α-particle:	4.00279 amu
H^1 atom:	1.00813 amu	He^4 atom:	4.00389 amu.

The energies of nuclear reactions are ordinarily specified in Mev, so that we need to know the relation between the amu and the Mev. We have enough data available to compute this relation. We have shown [(9), p. 373] that 1 amu = 1.6597×10^{-27} kg; equation (10a) gives the relation between the kilogram and the joule; equation (1), p. 892, gives the relation 1 ev = 1.6020×10^{-19} joule. From these data we find the conversion factor

$$1 \text{ amu} = 931.0 \text{ Mev.} \tag{13}$$

Thus the energy equivalent of the rest masses of the electron and proton are

electron: 0.511 Mev   proton: 939 Mev.

This equivalent, for the electron, is directly observed in connection with annihilation and creation of electrons and positrons, as we shall now discuss.

In 1932, C. D. Anderson discovered a new elementary particle called a *positron* in the cosmic radiation. This particle has a mass equal to that of the electron and has a *positive* charge equal in absolute magnitude to the electron's charge. The positron has a transitory existence on the earth, and therefore had not been previously observed in investigations of atomic structure. Anderson found that positrons are created in a process called *pair production*, in which *a gamma-ray photon disappears and an electron-positron pair is created*. In other words, *the radiant energy of the photon is converted into matter*. The energy relationship for this process is

$$(hf)_{\text{photon}} = (m_0c^2 + \text{K.E.})_{\text{electron}} + (m_0c^2 + \text{K.E.})_{\text{positron}}.$$

Since the rest energies of the positron and the electron are each equal to 0.511 Mev, the energy of the photon must be greater than 1.02 Mev before pair production can occur. A cloud-chamber picture showing the formation of an electron-positron pair is shown in Fig. 15. The energy of the incident photon is known to be 5.7 Mev. Measurements of the radii of curvature of the paths of the created particles in a magnetic field lead to a value of 4.7 Mev for the total kinetic energy. Thus, about 1 Mev of the photon's energy has gone into the creation of the two particles, a result in agreement with theory.

Fig. 15. Cloud-chamber photograph showing pair production. A gamma-ray photon incident on the lead plate at the top of the photograph creates an electron and a position whose tracks have opposite curvatures in the magnetic field that is normal to the paper (*courtesy of H. R. Crane*).

It has been found that positrons are sometimes emitted from the nuclei of unstable isotopes. For example, the bombardment of carbon with deuterons leads to the nuclear reaction

$$_6C^{12} + {_1H^2} \rightarrow {_7N^{13}} + {_0n^1},$$

where the product nucleus $_7N^{13}$ is unstable and eventually achieves stability by the emission of a positron

$$_7N^{13} \rightarrow {_6C^{13}} + {_{+1}\varepsilon^0}.$$

When traversing matter, a positron is ultimately annihilated, along with an electron, by a process with the following energy balance:

$$(m_0c^2)_{\text{positron}} + (m_0c^2)_{\text{electron}} = 2\,(hf)_{\text{photon}}.$$

It is observed that *two* photons appear as the result of the annihilation of the positron-electron pair; each photon has an energy of approximately 0.5 Mev, which indicates that the electron and positron have little kinetic energy when they are annihilated. Hence K.E. terms have been omitted on the left of the above equation.

Energy (including rest energy), momentum, and electric charge are all conserved in the processes of pair production and annihilation. *Pair production takes place only in the vicinity of some heavy nucleus* such as that of lead; recoil of the heavy nucleus in connection with the pair-production process is necessary in order to satisfy the condition for conservation of momentum. In annihilation, the two photons travel in opposite directions, as would be expected from momentum considerations since the electron and positron velocities are small at the time when annihilation occurs. Charge conservation requires that electrons and positrons be created or annihilated in pairs, not individually.

We have seen above that the energies involved in ordinary chemical reactions like the combustion of carbon are so small that there is no experimentally detectable difference between the rest mass of the reactants (carbon and oxygen) and the rest mass of the reaction product (CO_2). Now let us consider the analogous problem of the formation of a stable atomic nucleus from protons and neutrons. Although we cannot, in general, produce stable nuclei from neutrons and protons in the laboratory in a manner comparable with the way in which we can produce carbon dioxide from carbon and oxygen, we can make very accurate measurements of atomic masses by means of the mass spectrograph; and from these masses we can determine the energy that would be released in the formation of a nucleus from neutrons and protons. Accurate masses have been measured by F. W. Aston, A. J. Dempster, K. T. Bainbridge, and others; values in amu for the naturally occurring isotopes are given in the table in Sec. 5 of the Appendix.

A neutral atom of atomic number Z and mass number A is built of Z protons and $A-Z$ neutrons in the nucleus and Z extranuclear electrons. Since the binding energy of the extranuclear electrons is quite negligible when expressed in amu, we can consider that this atom would have the same mass as Z neutral H^1 atoms and $A-Z$ neutrons were it not for the internal energy of the nucleus. If we call the rest energy of the neutral atom M, that of the H^1 atom m_H, and that of the neutron m_n, the internal energy of the nucleus is given, in amu, by

$$\text{I.E.} = M - Zm_H - (A-Z)m_n,$$

which comes from (12). The values of m_H (determined mass-spectroscopically) and m_n (determined indirectly from the energetics of various nuclear reactions) are given on p. 1197.

Thus, for $_8O^{16}$,

$$\begin{aligned}\text{I.E.} &= 16.0000 - 8(1.0081) - 8(1.0089) \\ &= 16.0000 - 8.0648 - 8.0712 = -0.1360 \text{ amu}.\end{aligned}$$

The O^{16} nucleus has 0.1360 amu or 126 Mev *less energy* than its constituent particles—this amount of energy would be released on formation of O^{16} from its constituent particles.

The size of the internal energy is a measure of the stability of a nucleus—the lower the internal energy, the more stable the nucleus. The negative of the internal energy is frequently called the *binding energy*—this is the energy that would have to be supplied to the nucleus to break

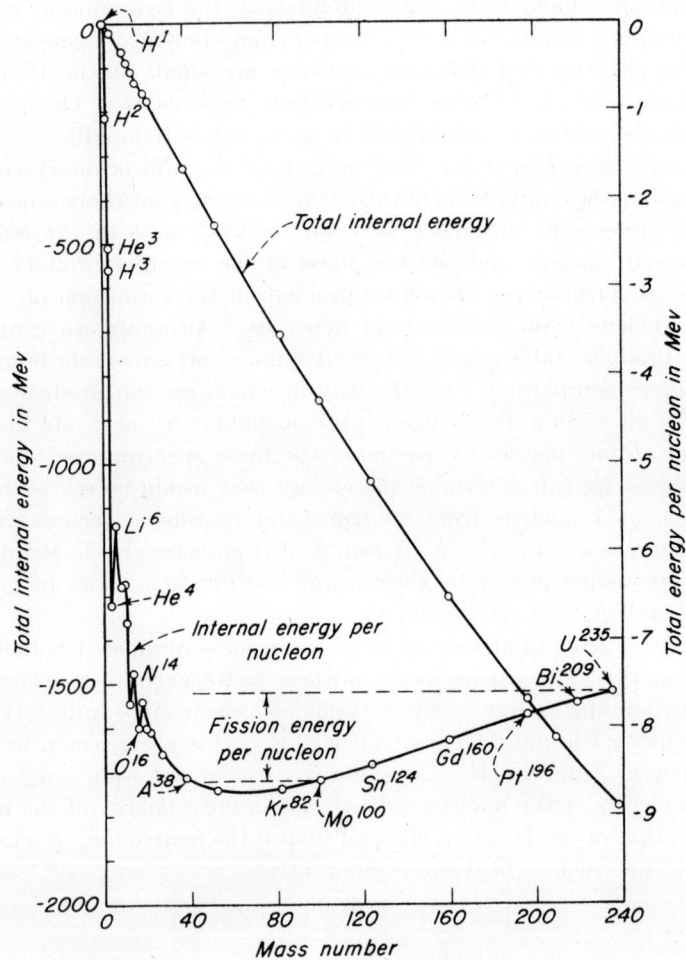

Fig. 16. Total internal energy and internal energy per nucleon as functions of mass number. While the points show representative nuclei, all nuclei lie close to these curves.

it up into its constituent parts; the binding energy is 0.1360 amu or 126 Mev for O^{16}.

Figure 16 shows the internal energies of various nuclei plotted against mass number. One curve shows the total internal energy (in Mev) computed as in the example above. For the other curve, the internal energy is divided by the mass number A to give the internal energy per nucleon. This second curve is of the greatest interest because it shows that those nuclei with mass numbers between 50 and 80 give the lowest internal energy per nucleon and hence represent the most stable arrangements of nucleons. Both lighter and heavier nuclei are relatively less stable.

If we could develop some method of causing two or more light nuclei to combine to form a nucleus with intermediate mass number, a great deal of energy would be released; similarly, by splitting a heavy nucleus into two or more nuclei with intermediate mass numbers, we could also release large amounts of energy. Self-sustaining reactions of the first type, which form the basis of the proposed 'hydrogen bomb' discussed briefly in Sec. 7, have not yet been produced on the earth but undoubtedly occur in the interiors of stars where temperatures are sufficiently high for the thermal energies of nuclei to be sufficient to initiate such nuclear reactions. Such reactions are believed to furnish the source of stellar energy. One such sequence of reactions begins with a reaction between two protons to form a deuteron:

$$_1H^1 + {}_1H^1 \rightarrow ({}_2He^2) \rightarrow {}_1H^2 + {}_{+1}\varepsilon^0.$$

The deuteron captures two protons in succession to form an α-particle:

$$_1H^2 + {}_1H^1 \rightarrow {}_2He^3,$$

$$_2He^3 + {}_1H^1 \rightarrow ({}_3Li^4) \rightarrow {}_2He^4 + {}_{+1}\varepsilon^0.$$

If we add four electrons to the protons on the left in the above equations, we see that the net result of this sequence is the conversion of four hydrogen atoms into one helium atom. Two of the electrons of the hydrogen atoms are needed to form the helium atom; the other two are needed to annihilate the two positrons that are produced. Since the mass of four hydrogen atoms is $4 \times 1.0081 = 4.0324$ amu, whereas the mass of a helium atom is only 4.0039 amu, the energy released in this process would be 0.0285 amu $= 26.5$ Mev, or 6.6 Mev per nucleon, as plotted in Fig. 16.

Self-sustaining reactions of the second type, in which heavy nuclei are split into nuclei of intermediate mass number with consequent release of energy of about 1 Mev per nucleon as indicated in Fig. 16, have been produced and are used in the chain-reacting pile and in the atomic bomb. These reactions will be considered further in the next section.

As an example of the verification of the relation between mass and energy in a simple nuclear reaction, let us consider the first nuclear reaction observed with particles accelerated by a laboratory accelerator. In 1932, J. D. Cockcroft and E. T. S. Walton, using a transformer-rectifier outfit, accelerated protons to 700 kev and observed the following reaction to result from lithium bombardment:

$$_3Li^7 + {}_1H^1 + K.E. \rightarrow {}_2He^4 + {}_2He^4 + K.E.$$

The kinetic energy of the proton on the left is 0.7 Mev. Cockcroft and Walton observed that each alpha particle on the right had kinetic energy of about 8.5 Mev, making a total kinetic energy on the right of about 17.0 Mev. Let us determine what the kinetic energy on the right should be from the mass-spectroscopically determined masses. If we add 4 electrons to each side of this equation to obtain neutral atoms, we find from Sec. 5 of the Appendix that the total energy on the left is

$$Li^7 = 7.0182 \text{ amu}$$
$$H^1 = 1.0081$$
$$0.7 \text{ Mev} = \underline{0.0008}$$
$$\text{total} = 8.0271 \text{ amu}$$

From this total, we subtract the mass of two helium atoms, $2 \times 4.0039 = 8.0078$ amu, to get the kinetic energy on the right as $8.0271 - 8.0078 = 0.0193$ amu $= 18.0$ Mev. The agreement with Cockcroft and Walton's rather crudely determined value of 17.0 Mev is as good as could be expected. Later work, in which kinetic energies have been determined with high accuracy, has given very accurate confirmation of Einstein's relation between mass and energy in a large number of nuclear reactions.

PROBLEMS

1. By measurement of tracks in a Wilson cloud chamber, it is found that the total kinetic energy of an electron-positron pair is 6.25 Mev. What was the energy of the original photon responsible for the production of the electron-positron pair?
Ans: 7.27 Mev.

2. A photon of energy 8.00 Mev produces an electron-positron pair. What is the kinetic energy associated with the electron-positron pair?

3. Using the values given in the table in Sec. 5 of the Appendix, compute the total binding energy for the sulfur isotope $_{16}S^{32}$. What is the binding energy per nucleon? Ans: 2.71 Mev; 8.46 Mev.

4. Compute the total binding energy and the binding energy per nucleon for the isotopes $_7N^{14}$ and $_{11}Na^{23}$.

5. Calculate the total energy released in the series of reactions described on p. 1201 if four moles of protons combine to form a single mole of helium.
Ans: 2.56×10^{12} joules.

6. Calculate the total energy in joules released if a mole of hydrogen atoms combines with a mole of lithium atoms to form two moles of helium atoms.

7. If $_4Be^9$ is bombarded with 3.00-Mev alpha particles to form $_6C^{12}$ and a neutron in accordance with the reaction on p. 1178, find the resulting kinetic energy. This kinetic energy will be shared between the neutron and the recoil carbon but will mostly reside in the lighter neutron. Ans: 8.57 Mev.

8. When $_7N^{14}$ is bombarded with 3.00-Mev alpha particles to form $_8O^{17}$ and a proton, as in the reaction on p. 1176, find the resulting kinetic energy in Mev. This kinetic energy will be shared between the proton and the recoil oxygen, but will mostly reside in the lighter proton.

7. ATOMIC ENERGY

Beginning in the year 1934, Enrico Fermi and his collaborators began a systematic study of nuclear reactions involving the capture of neutrons by various atomic nuclei. When slow neutrons were used as projectiles, many reactions of the (n,γ) type were observed; such a reaction is

$$_{48}Cd^{113} + {}_0n^1 \rightarrow {}_{48}Cd^{114} + hf,$$

in which a neutron is captured by $_{48}Cd^{113}$ and the product nucleus $_{48}Cd^{114}$ achieves stability by emission of a gamma-ray photon of energy hf. This process is called *radiative capture*. With slow neutrons, (n,p) and (n,α) processes are also sometimes observed. When fast neutrons are used as projectiles, several types of reactions are possible; these include (n,p), (n,α), and (n,2n) processes.

Many readily interpretable experiments involving neutron bombardment of elements of low, intermediate, and high mass numbers were performed; however, neutron bombardment of uranium led to results that were not immediately interpretable. These results were correctly interpreted in 1939 by O. R. Frisch and Lise Meitner, then refugees in Copenhagen, when their former collaborators, Otto Hahn and F. Strassmann in Berlin, identified *barium* as one of the reaction products appearing when uranium is bombarded by neutrons. The appearance of barium as a reaction product was interpreted as evidence that the uranium nucleus on capturing a neutron split into nuclei of intermediate mass number; this process is called *nuclear fission*. Since the energy per nucleon of nuclei of intermediate mass number is, as indicated in Fig. 16, appreciably smaller than the energy per nucleon of uranium, large amounts of energy are released in the fission process. Energy of approximately 200 Mev is released by each nucleus that undergoes fission. This enormous quantity of energy is released when a slow neutron with only thermal energy (approximately $\frac{1}{30}$ ev) is captured by a uranium nucleus; hence, it was immediately obvious that if large numbers of thermal neutrons were available, the fission process could be used in power production.

Further studies of uranium fission showed that it was the relatively rare isotope $_{92}U^{235}$ that was split by slow neutrons and that *in addition to two elements of intermediate mass number, several neutrons are usually present among the reaction products*. For example, the following fission reaction might occur:

$$_{92}U^{235} + {}_0n^1 \rightarrow {}_{56}Ba^{144} + {}_{36}Kr^{89} + 3\ {}_0n^1.$$

The fission products $_{56}Ba^{144}$ and $_{36}Kr^{89}$ are both unstable since their mass numbers are larger than those associated with atomic numbers 56 and 36 in stable elements; in other words, these two isotopes contain too many neutrons and too few protons. However, by a series of beta-particle emissions, they eventually achieve stability, since the emission of a beta particle results in a reduction of the number of neutrons by 1 and an increase in the number of protons by 1 in a nucleus. It should be noted that the reaction given above is only one of many possible fission reactions. The known fission products are elements near the middle of the periodic table having atomic numbers in the range from $Z = 34$ to $Z = 58$ and mass numbers in the range from $A = 70$ to $A = 166$; the number of neutrons released apparently varies. Careful measurements indicate that the average initial kinetic energy of fission products is in the neighborhood of 160 Mev. Since the total energy released by the fission products is about 200 Mev, the remainder of the energy appears as kinetic energy of the neutrons and as energy associated with beta and gamma radiation from the fission products.

The uranium isotope $_{92}U^{235}$ seems to be the only known naturally occurring nucleus that undergoes a fission reaction produced by neutrons of thermal energy. However, two other nuclei, which have been produced as a result of radiative capture of neutrons, can also be split by slow neutrons. One of these is the uranium isotope $_{92}U^{233}$ formed when neutrons are captured by $_{90}Th^{232}$:

$$_{90}Th^{232} + _0n^1 \rightarrow {}_{90}Th^{233}.$$

The isotope $_{90}Th^{233}$ undergoes two beta-emission processes to form U^{233}:

$$_{90}Th^{233} \rightarrow {}_{91}Pa^{233} + _{-1}\varepsilon^0, \qquad _{91}Pa^{233} \rightarrow {}_{92}U^{233} + _{-1}\varepsilon^0.$$

The other artificially produced fissionable nucleus is an isotope of element *plutonium*, which can be produced as a result of radiative capture of slow neutrons by $_{92}U^{238}$ in the following reactions:

$$_{92}U^{238} + _0n^1 \rightarrow {}_{92}U^{239}, \qquad _{92}U^{239} \rightarrow {}_{93}Np^{239} + _{-1}\varepsilon^0, \qquad _{93}Np^{239} \rightarrow {}_{94}Pu^{239} + _{-1}\varepsilon^0.$$

The elements neptunium Np ($Z = 93$) and Pu ($Z = 94$) are called *transuranic elements*. Four more transuranic elements have now been artificially produced by similar nuclear reactions. These are $Z = 95$ and 96 (americium and curium) and $Z = 97$ and 98 (tentatively called berkelium and californium).

The fission processes produced when samples containing $_{92}U^{233}$ and $_{94}Pu^{239}$ are irradiated with slow neutrons are similar in essentials to the fission processes we have described for $_{92}U^{235}$.*

We pointed out above that it was early realized that nuclear fission could be used for power production, provided an abundant supply of neutrons were available to initiate fission processes. When it was found that two or three neutrons are released in every fission process, it became apparent that nuclear *chain reactions*† might be produced by using these released neutrons to produce additional fissions. In order to understand

* Fission of various heavy nuclei other than $_{92}U^{233}$, $_{92}U^{235}$, and $_{94}Pu^{239}$ can be induced by *high-energy* neutrons, protons, deuterons, alpha particles, and photons.

† The term *chain reaction* has long been used by chemists to describe a series of individual reactions in which a reaction product of the first reaction produces a second reaction, a reaction product of the second reaction products a third reaction, etc.

how this process is possible, consider the schematic diagram in Fig. 17. In part (a) of this figure, a single neutron produces fission of a $_{92}U^{235}$ nucleus in a block of uranium metal, and, in addition to the fission product nuclei, three neutrons are assumed to be released. These neutrons are 'lost' either by escaping from the space occupied by the uranium or in

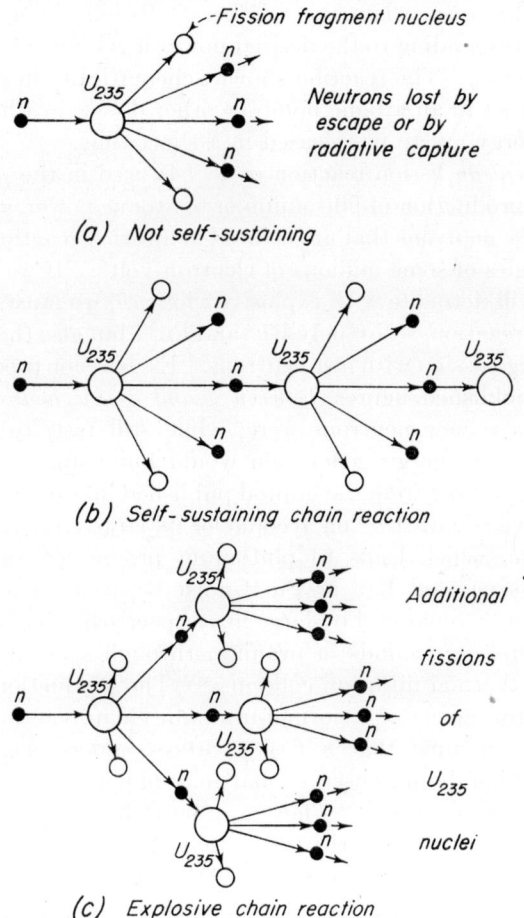

Fig. 17. Schematic diagram illustrating fission phenomena.

radiative capture by $_{92}U^{238}$ or some other nucleus that may be present. Hence, this reaction is not self-sustaining. In part (b) of this figure is shown a chain reaction that is just self-sustaining. In each fission one of the released neutrons produces the fission of another $_{92}U^{235}$ nucleus and two are lost by escape or by radiative capture. In part (c) is shown a chain reaction which involves high 'multiplication'; in this case, every neutron released by a fission process produces additional fission of a $_{92}U^{235}$ nucleus. Hence, assuming 3 neutrons per fission, we would expect 3^n fissions in the nth 'generation'; remembering that 200 Mev energy is released during each process, we see that a great deal of energy would be produced in a very short time. The reaction shown schematically in part (b) of Fig. 15 would be the type desirable for sustained power production. In this case, when the number of fission chains had reached some value corresponding to the desired power level, each chain should be just self-sustaining. The reaction shown schematically in part (c) is the type to be desired in an atomic bomb or other device in which enormous amounts of energy are to be released in a short time.

The *slow-neutron* fission reaction of U^{235} is used in the *pile* or *nuclear reactor* for the production of plutonium or of atomic power, as we shall discuss later. The neutrons that are created in a fission reaction are initially *fast*, with energies of some millions of electron-volts. If we wish to make a bomb that will detonate with explosive violence, we must utilize a *fast-neutron* fission reaction. Not only U^{235} and Pu^{239} but also the common isotope U^{238} undergo fission with fast neutrons. Each fission process generates, according to published figures, *between 2 and 3 new neutrons*. If *more than one* of these new neutrons were, while still fast, to cause a new fission, the rate of energy generation would build up. Apparently, as well as can be gathered from the limited published literature, this build-up will not take place with U^{238} on account of its large cross section for resonance capture, which leads to plutonium production rather than to fission; either separated U^{235} or Pu^{239} must be used for a bomb. The U^{235} isotope can be separated by large mass spectrographs, by diffusion of gaseous or liquid compounds of uranium through specially constructed barriers, or in thermal diffusion columns.* The production of $_{94}Pu^{239}$ is accomplished by means of a normal-uranium chain-reacting pile.

Let us now assume that a fission process takes place within the material of our bomb and observe what may happen to the two or three neutrons that are generated. They may be radiatively captured in the bomb material or in an impurity; they may be elastically scattered and start to slow down; they may pass out of the material and escape—none of these processes is useful from the standpoint of generating an explosion. Finally, K of the two or three neutrons may cause a fast-neutron fission. K is known as the *reproduction factor;* and if K is appreciably greater than 1, the bomb will explode. The value of K depends on the *purity*, the *geometry*, and the *quantity* of fissionable material. The probability of the fission process in the bomb can be kept to a maximum as compared with the probability of elastic scattering or radiative-capture processes by

---

* A detailed account of the various schemes used will be found in *Atomic Energy for Military Purposes*, by H. D. Smyth (United States Government Printing Office, 1945).

using pure U^{235} or Pu^{239}. The *geometry factor* determines the probability of neutron loss by *escape;* since a sphere has a minimum surface area for a given volume, a solid spherical body of fissionable material has the optimum *geometry*. Therefore, let us consider a spherical mass of pure $_{92}U^{235}$ or $_{94}Pu^{239}$ and see what happens if we gradually increase the radius of this sphere; this will tell us something of the effect of quantity of fissionable material. When the sphere is very small, the total production of neutrons is limited and many of those produced escape, since their mean free path is large compared to the diameter of the sphere; under this condition the reproduction factor is less than unity. As we progressively increase the diameter of the sphere, the probability of neutron loss by escape decreases until, for a certain radius, the loss of neutrons by escape is just balanced by the production of neutrons by fission. The system is then said to be *critical*, and the mass of fissionable material is called the *critical mass*. For a critical system, the reproduction factor K is equal to unity and the number of neutrons in the assembly is constant. If our $_{92}U^{238}$ sphere were made *slightly* larger than the critical size, K would become larger than unity, multiplication would take place and a great deal of energy would be released by fission; however, the temperature of the sphere would rise sufficiently for the sphere to expand or melt and this would cause the reaction rate to drop. In order to be useful as an explosive device, fissionable material must be assembled into a highly supercritical mass with K substantially greater than 1, so that a great deal of energy can be released by nuclear-fission processes before the assembly is blown apart as a result of elevation of its temperature.

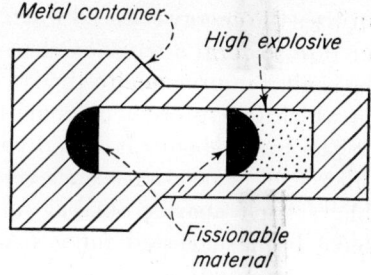

Fig. 18. A suggested atomic-bomb mechanism.

One method of achieving this result might be to use the arrangement shown in Fig. 18. In this arrangement, the fissionable material is molded into two hemispherical bodies, each of which is subcritical. One hemisphere, the target, is embedded in a large mass of dense material at one end of a gun barrel; the other hemisphere, the projectile, is near the other end of the gun barrel just in front of a large charge of high explosive. Each hemisphere is subcritical when separated from the other by the length of the gun barrel, but ignition of the propellant charge brings the projectile hemisphere and the target hemisphere together at high speed. Meeting at the end of the gun, the two masses are welded together and form one highly supercritical mass in which a nuclear chain reaction immediately starts. The restraint imposed upon the supercritical mass by the heavy casing around the target and the large momentum of the projectile might be expected to keep the supercritical assembly together long enough for a large number of fissions to occur. If this is the case, the suggested mechanism would be an effective bomb.

In an actual bomb, the fissioning of $_{92}U^{235}$ nuclei releases sufficient energy to convert the uranium metal into highly compressed uranium gas at a temperature of about 10 million degrees Centigrade. In expanding, this hot gas forms a blast wave of enormous intensity in the surrounding atmosphere; the destructive properties of the blast wave at Hiroshima are said to be equivalent to that produced by the detonation of 20,000 tons of TNT. The highly compressed high-temperature gas expands as a 'ball of fire' which gives off intense ultraviolet, visible, and infrared radiation capable of igniting combustible material and causing severe burns. Neutrons, gamma rays, and highly radioactive fission products in lethal quantities are also produced when an atomic bomb is detonated.

In view of the momentary high temperatures produced during the explosion of a uranium or plutonium fission bomb, it is possible that a *fission* bomb could be used as a detonator for a *nuclear fusion bomb* that utilizes the energy released when the nuclei of very light elements combine or fuse to form a single nucleus of greater mass. Such a reaction would be similar in principle to the set of reactions (mentioned earlier in Sec. 6) in which four protons combine to produce a helium nucleus. However, in the fusion bomb it would be necessary to use a single reaction rather than a set of reactions, since very little time is available before the bomb blows itself apart. Several such reactions involving hydrogen isotopes have been suggested for a fusion bomb, which therefore is popularly termed a 'hydrogen bomb.' Some of the suggested reactions with the resulting energy releases are given below:

$$_1H^2 + {}_1H^2 \rightarrow {}_1H^3 + {}_1H^1 + 4 \text{ Mev}$$
$$_1H^2 + {}_1H^2 \rightarrow {}_2He^3 + {}_0n^1 + 4 \text{ Mev}$$
$$_1H^3 + {}_1H^3 \rightarrow {}_2He^4 + 2{}_0n^1 + 11 \text{ Mev}$$
$$_1H^3 + {}_1H^2 \rightarrow {}_2He^4 + {}_0n^1 + 18 \text{ Mev}.$$

Any of these reactions could, in principle, be used, provided sufficiently high temperatures—tens of millions of degrees—were available to *start* the reaction; once started, the reaction (like a TNT chemical reaction) could be self-sustaining until the bomb blew itself apart. Since these reactions would not be 'self-starting' for any quantity of reactants, there is in principle no upper limit on the amount of energy that could be released by such a bomb; the energy released would be determined by the number of fusion reactions that occur and this number would depend on the amount of reactants present and the manner in which the reactants were held together.

Now let us describe the principles involved in the construction and operation of a *nuclear reactor* or *pile*. In setting up a pile, we are interested in producing a nuclear chain reaction different in many respects from the type of chain reaction desired in a bomb. In a bomb, a rapid and uncontrolled reaction with a high reproduction factor is desired; in a pile, a continuous and well-controlled reaction must be maintained. In a bomb, *fast neutrons* are the 'links' in the chain reaction; a pile depends for its operation chiefly on slow neutrons. Whereas the bomb utilizes $_{94}Pu^{239}$ or the rare uranium isotope $_{92}U^{235}$, a pile can use *normal uranium* as 'fuel.' Pile operation and design are complicated by the radioactive hazards associated with the fission process; piles must be well shielded and must be operated by remote control without direct access of personnel to the pile itself.

Figure 19 gives a schematic diagram of a simple pile using normal uranium. Graphite blocks, each with a circular hole through the center, are stacked in the form of a large cake. The holes in the graphite blocks are arranged so that long normal-uranium rods may be inserted inside the holes. These uranium rods, known as *fuel rods*, are placed horizontally in the pile. In addition to the uranium rods, several control rods containing cadmium or other neutron-absorbing material can be inserted in the pile; these are shown as vertical rods in the sketch in Fig. 19. The positioning of these rods determines the rate at which the chain reaction is built up and the level at which the reaction is maintained. Fast-neutron induced fission cannot be used to support a chain reaction in natural uranium, since the most abundant uranium isotope, $_{92}U^{238}$, has a high probability for radiative capture, a nonfission process that traps many neutrons of high and moderate energies. If, however, a 'moderator' material such as graphite is used to slow neutrons down to thermal speeds by elastic collisions, these thermal neutrons can be used to produce enough fissions of the rarer isotope $_{92}U^{235}$ to make a self-sustained chain reaction possible.

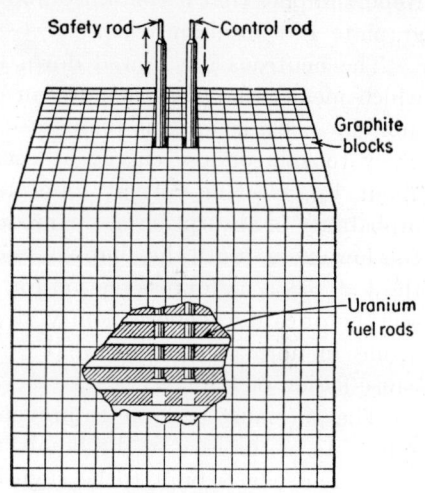

Fig. 19. Schematic drawing of a uranium-graphite pile. [From *Nuclear Radiation Physics* by Lapp and Andrews (Prentice-Hall, 1947).]

It is important to try to understand the function of the moderator. Apparently, an infinite block of pure natural uranium will not support a chain reaction. Those of the high-energy neutrons released in a fission process that escape immediate fission or nonfission capture and start to slow down are almost certain to undergo radiative capture by U^{238} in the resonance region below 1000 ev, where the capture cross section is very high. No neutrons will get down to thermal energies, where the fission cross section of U^{235} is extremely high and the radiative-capture cross section of U^{238} is very low. But if we could slow the neutrons down to thermal energies *outside the uranium* and then let them re-enter the uranium, we could take advantage of these properties at thermal energies. This is the function of the moderator; it 'moderates' the energy. A large fraction of the high-speed neutrons created in fission escape immediately from the uranium rods and enter the moderator. The moderator is of low atomic weight, so that it is efficient in absorbing energy from neutrons in elastic collisions; it must have a negligible cross section for neutron capture and be free from impurities liable to capture neutrons. Hydrogen, deuterium, helium, beryllium, heavy water, and carbon would all be suitable. The first self-sustaining pile operated in Chicago on December 2, 1942, with graphite as a moderator. The Smyth Report implies that it contained about 6 tons of uranium metal as well as graphite and uranium oxide.

The neutrons are slowed down in the moderator to thermal speed, which means that they acquire an energy distribution like that of the molecules of a gas at the temperature of the moderator and are equally likely to gain or lose energy at each collision. The average energy is about $\frac{1}{40}$ electron-volt at room temperature. Except for the small probability of absorption in the moderator, the neutrons wander about at this low energy until they happen to enter a uranium rod. At this energy the U^{235} has a high cross section for fission and the U^{238} a very low cross section for capture; consequently, in spite of the fact that only $\frac{1}{140}$ of the atoms in normal uranium are U^{235}, most of the thermal neutrons will cause fission of U^{235}.

The pile must be large to prevent escape of the neutrons to the outside. As in the case of the bomb, this limitation sets a certain critical size. The pile is built to be slightly supercritical and then its rate of operation is controlled at the desired level by inserting or removing cadmium rods which have an extremely large cross section for radiative capture of thermal neutrons.

A uranium pile simultaneously produces heat (from the fission energy) and plutonium (from the radiative capture in U^{238}). At least one of the neutrons from each fission must produce a new fission if the reaction is to be self-sustaining; as a result, less than two of the neutrons (probably considerably less) are available to produce plutonium. In other words, to produce plutonium we must also produce considerable heat. Smyth estimates that to produce a kilogram a day of plutonium, piles must produce heat at a rate of about a million kilowatts. During World War II the plutonium plant at Hanford, Wash., used the heat only to warm the Columbia River, but evidently this heat will be the source of our peacetime atomic power when the problems of using it to generate mechanical energy are solved. The simultaneous production of plutonium is not a disadvantage from this point of view, because the plutonium is capable of replacing the U^{235}, which is being consumed, as the fuel. Thus, the pile simultaneously burns U^{235} to give energy and produces new fuel from the U^{238} in the form of Pu. In principle, then, the whole of the uranium can be burned to give energy.

In the Hanford pile, the plutonium was chemically extracted from the uranium to give bomb material. The separation can be effected by chemical methods, since these are two different chemical elements. This separation is a very much simpler problem than the separation of U^{235} by physical methods of isotope separation.

Within a pile there is a very high neutron flux which can be used to irradiate material samples placed in the pile for the production of radioactive isotopes. Such radio-isotopes are being widely used as tracers in biological science and in industrial processes, and they are also finding medical use. By placing gold in the pile at Oak Ridge, the pure stable Hg^{198} isotope has been produced in gram quantities for the use of the National Bureau of Standards in the fabrication of wavelength standards. As we have pointed out on p. 690, this pure isotope has the advantage of giving a single sharp monochromatic green line, entirely free from the fine structure of the line in ordinary mercury that arises from the presence of several isotopes.

PROBLEMS

1. Taking 200 Mev as the energy released during the fission of a single U^{235} nucleus, compute the number of fission processes taking place each second in a reactor operating at a power level of 1 watt. Ans: 3.12×10^{10}.

2. When the experimental pile at Harwell, England, is operated at a power level of 6000 kw, how many fission processes occur each second?

3. How much U^{235} (mass 235 amu) is consumed each day in a nuclear reactor operating at a power level of 1 watt? How much bituminous coal (heat of combustion 7500 kcal/kg) would be required to release this amount of energy? Ans: 1.05×10^{-6} g; 2.75 g.

4. How much U^{235} (mass 235 amu) is consumed each day in the Harwell pile when the pile operates at the rated power level of 6000 kw? How much anthracite (heat of combustion 8000 kcal/kg) would be required to release an equivalent amount of energy?

5. What is the total decrease each day in the total *mass* of the material in a uranium pile operating at a power level of 1 watt? Ans: 9.61×10^{-10} g.

6. How much mass is converted into energy each day in the Harwell pile?

7. The fuel value of coal is measured by the heat of combustion. Using 200 Mev as the energy release per fission, calculate the 'heat of fission' for pure U^{235} in joules/kg and in kcal/kg. Ans: 8.21×10^{13} joules/kg; 1.96×10^{10} kcal/kg.

8. Recalling that the ratio of U^{235} to U^{238} in normal uranium is $1/140$, calculate the 'heat of fission' for slow-neutron fission of normal uranium. How does the fuel value of normal uranium compare with that of anthracite?

9. According to official estimates, the atomic bomb at Hiroshima was equivalent to 20,000 tons of TNT. Assuming 3.8×10^9 joules as the energy released by detonation of 1 ton of TNT, find the number of fissions occurring, the total amount of U^{235} consumed, and the total mass decrease involved in the explosion of the bomb.

Ans: 2.37×10^{24}; 0.925 kg; 8.45×10^{-4} kg.

8. NUCLEAR FORCES; THE MESON

Thus far, we have described the nucleus only by saying that it is composed of protons and neutrons; we have said very little about the forces that hold these particles together. Actually, very little is known about the nature of these forces. The known facts are these: (a) a proton at a relatively large distance $r > 10^{-15}$ m from a nucleus of charge Ze is acted on only by the force of ordinary electrostatic repulsion, but at a shorter distance the proton is strongly attracted by so-called *short-range forces*; (b) a neutron at a large distance $r > 10^{-15}$ m from a nucleus experiences no appreciable force, but at a shorter distance the neutron is strongly attracted by forces similar to those experienced by a proton. These short-range forces are much stronger than can be accounted for in terms of any gravitational, electrostatic, or magnetic effects now known.

The short-range nuclear forces show *saturation effects* analogous to the saturation of chemical forces in homopolar compounds. For example, in the case of valence forces, we say that a carbon atom has four valence bonds and is *saturated* when all four of these bonds are utilized in forming links with atoms of other elements. Thus, in methane (CH_4) there is saturation; and if more H atoms are brought close to the methane molecule, the C atom has no tendency to combine with them. Evidence for the saturation of nuclear forces is found in the energy curve shown in Fig. 16. If short-range forces existed between a given proton or neutron and *all* the other particles in a nucleus of mass number A, we should expect the total binding energies of various nuclei to be proportional to A^2, and the curve of total internal energy in Fig. 16 should be a parabola. However, the curve is almost a straight line, which would be expected if each nuclear particle exerted short-range forces only on its immediate neighbors. The forces between nearest neighbors in a nucleus are therefore somewhat analogous to the forces between neighboring water molecules in a water droplet.

In 1935, Hideki Yukawa, a Japanese physicist, developed a theory that pictured short-range forces between particles in nuclei as 'exchange' forces similar to the chemical exchange forces between adjacent atoms in homopolar compounds. In a homopolar chemical bond between two atoms, electrons are *shared* between the two atoms. In order to account for the short-range nuclear forces on a similar basis, Yukawa had to postulate the existence of a particle of mass intermediate between the electron and proton masses. In Yukawa's theory this particle, called the *meson* or *mesotron*, played a role analogous to that played by the electrons in homopolar chemical bonds. Yukawa's hypothetical particle was supposed to have the property of disintegrating into an electron and a neutrino.

In the years following 1936 Carl D. Anderson and others found conclusive evidence for the existence of such a particle in cosmic radiation. In fact, there is now evidence for the existence of several varieties of meson. One of these is apparently formed high in the atmosphere by primary cosmic-ray particles; the mass of this cosmic-ray meson is approximately 200 electron masses. This meson has been observed to decay and the resulting electron has been observed. The penetrating power of the cosmic-ray mesons is enormous; although they are produced high in the atmosphere, they penetrate many hundreds of feet below the surface of the earth. Positive and negative cosmic-ray mesons have been observed. Another type of meson, of about 300 times the mass of the electron, has been produced in the laboratory at the University of California when 380-Mev alpha particles from the new 184-in cyclotron strike a target. As yet, very little is understood of the properties of mesons or of the role they may play in the nucleus.

9. ELEMENTARY-PARTICLE PHYSICS

Let us now summarize the 'elementary particles' thus far detected. These include

(a) the light particles: the electron, the positron, and the neutrino*;
(b) the particles of intermediate mass: positive and negative mesons of different masses, and possibly neutral mesons†;
(c) the heavy particles: the proton and the neutron.

The number of known elementary particles has increased enormously since 1930, when just the electron and proton were known. One wonders whether it will not appear later that these particles, which we now regard tentatively as 'elementary,' are actually themselves composed of simpler particles. Much attention is being given to this question.

At present we are only beginning studies of the behavior of particles having energies approaching a billion electron-volts (Bev). The directions being taken in these studies are twofold. First, exhaustive studies of cosmic rays are in progress. The cosmic rays reaching the earth's surface consist chiefly of high-energy electrons, positrons, mesons, neutrons, and photons. These and other particles are apparently produced by charged primary particles of unknown origin that enter the earth's atmosphere with energies of 6 Bev or more. Studies of the behavior of matter when bombarded with particles of this range of energies would throw addi-

---

* Only indirect evidence of the existence of this particle has been obtained.

† The existence of a neutral meson or 'neutretto' has been postulated to describe proton-proton and neutron-neutron exchange forces.

tional light on many elementary-particle problems yet unsolved. Second, studies of nuclear reactions produced by the less energetic but much more abundant projectiles available with recently developed new types of accelerators are in progress. These studies will add much to our knowledge of the elementary particles and some day may lead to atomic-energy developments that will greatly overshadow the present developments depending upon binary nuclear fission.

Fig. 20. Photograph showing the 'explosion' of a silver nucleus produced by a cosmic-ray particle *(courtesy of L-Leprince-Ringuet)*

In closing this volume, we include in Fig. 20 a recent photograph of a nuclear disruption produced by a high-energy cosmic-ray particle. This photograph shows the 'explosion' of the nucleus of a silver atom in a photographic emulsion when the silver nucleus was struck by a particle with energy somewhat greater than 1 Bev. The silver nucleus was split into *thirty-four* charged heavy fragments that produced tracks in the photographic emulsion; in addition to these charged heavy fragments there were probably also some neutrons and mesons which left no record. Processes of this type are not yet understood, but furnish intriguing hints of the many strange phenomena likely to be encountered in new and unexplored fields of the physics of particles of ultra-high energy.

APPENDIX

1. SYSTEMS OF ELECTRICAL AND MAGNETIC UNITS

In the course of the historical development of electricity and magnetism, three different systems of units were introduced: a CGS *electrostatic system* for handling problems in *electrostatics;* a CGS *electromagnetic system* for handling problems in *magnetism;* and the *practical system* employed by engineers for problems in *current electricity.* Since these three subjects are not at all independent, it was formerly necessary to learn not only all three systems of units, but a complex set of relations between them. The practical units—the coulomb, ampere, ohm, and volt—had been chosen as certain multiples of the *electromagnetic* units that would be of convenient practical size. It was Giorgi, in 1901, who first pointed out that if an MKS, rather than a CGS system of fundamental mechanical units was employed, a single complete and consistent system of electrical and magnetic units could be devised that would embody the practical units of current, DP, and resistance. This Giorgi system was adopted in 1935 by the International Electrotechnical Commission, and is rapidly replacing the older CGS systems in scientific and technical work. It is this system, in the so-called 'rationalized' form, that we have employed in this book. Since, however, all the older treatments of the subject employ the CGS systems, it is desirable to see how the latter are set up and to give the relations between the units in these systems and those we have learned.

The *electrostatic unit* (ESU) of charge is defined by the equation

$$f = Q_1 Q_2 / d^2 \qquad (1)$$

for the force between charges. With f in dynes* and d in cm, Q is in *statcoulombs.* By comparison with (2), p. 791, we see that

$$1 \text{ coulomb} = 3 \times 10^9 \text{ statcoulombs.} \qquad (2)\dagger$$

Current in *statamperes* is defined as statcoulombs per second, so

$$1 \text{ ampere} = 3 \times 10^9 \text{ statamperes.} \qquad (3)$$

* One dyne is the force that gives a mass of 1 gram an acceleration of 1 cm/sec²; 1 erg = 1 cm·dyne; compare with Sec. 1 of the Appendix to vol. I, which discusses these CGS mechanical units.

† Throughout this section the number '3' stands for 2.99776, the numerical constant occurring in the metric value of the speed of light. Conversion factors accurate to four figures are given in the tables of Sec. 6.

Difference of potential in *statvolts* is defined by the equation $W = QV$, with W in ergs. Comparison with the definition of the DP in volts as number of joules/coulomb shows that

$$1 \text{ statvolt} = 300 \text{ volts}. \tag{4}$$

Finally, the *statohm* and the *statfarad* are defined by $R = V/I$ and $C = QV$, and we see that

$$1 \text{ statohm} = 9 \times 10^{11} \text{ ohms}, \tag{5}$$

and
$$1 \text{ farad} = 9 \times 10^{11} \text{ statfarads}. \tag{6}$$

Instead of the above names with the prefix 'stat-,' units in this system are frequently designated as ESU of charge, current, potential, and so forth.

The *electromagnetic unit* (EMU) of current, the *abampere*, may be defined by using the formula

$$f = 2I^2/a \tag{7}$$

for the force in dynes per cm length between two parallel wires a distance a (in cm) apart, each carrying current I. When this is compared with (10), p. 945, we see that

$$1 \text{ abampere} = 10 \text{ amperes}. \tag{8}$$

Defining the abcoulomb from $Q = It$, with t in sec, the abvolt from $W = QV$, with W in ergs, and the abohm from $R = V/I$, we see that

$$1 \text{ abcoulomb} = 10 \text{ coulombs}, \tag{9}$$

$$1 \text{ abvolt} = 10^{-8} \text{ volt}, \tag{10}$$

$$1 \text{ abohm} = 10^{-9} \text{ ohm}. \tag{11}$$

In this electromagnetic system, we may define the magnetic field strength $\mathcal{B}$ in *gausses* by means of the formula $f = \mathcal{B}lI$, in dynes, for the force on a length l (in cm) of wire carrying current I (in abamperes) perpendicular to the field. Comparison of this formula with (4), p. 931, shows that

$$1 \text{ weber/m}^2 = 10^4 \text{ gausses}. \tag{12}$$

Flux in *maxwells* is given by $\Phi = \mathcal{B}A$, with A in cm^2; hence

$$1 \text{ weber} = 10^8 \text{ maxwells}. \tag{13}$$

The magnetizing force $\mathcal{H}$ in *oersteds* is defined in this system by the equation

$$\mathcal{H} = \mathcal{B} - 4\pi \mathcal{M},$$

with magnetic moment per unit volume $\mathcal{M}$ in abampere·cm^2/cm^3. Comparison with (1), p. 983, shows that

$$1 \text{ ampere-turn/meter} = 4\pi \times 10^{-3} \text{ oersted}. \tag{14}$$

It is noted that in this system $\mathcal{B} = \mathcal{H}$ except in ferromagnetic materials. For a toroid, MMF $= \mathcal{H}l$, with l in cm. The unit of MMF is called the *gilbert*. Hence

$$1 \text{ ampere-turn} = 0.4\pi \text{ gilberts.} \tag{15}$$

If the reluctance of a toroid is defined by $\Phi = \text{MMF}/\mathcal{R}$, the formula for reluctance is $l/\mu A$, with l in cm, A in cm^2, and $\mu = \mathcal{B}/\mathcal{H}$. As we have already noted in the footnote on p. 994, the permeability μ has the same value in the two systems. The relation between the reluctance units is seen to be

$$1 \frac{\text{ampere-turn}}{\text{weber}} = \frac{4\pi}{10^9} \frac{\text{gilbert}}{\text{maxwell}}. \tag{16}$$

In the electromagnetic system, electromotive force is given by rate of change of flux, just as in the practical system, the same factor 10^8 occurring in the flux units (13) and the EMF units (10).

Now let us look at the physical dimensions of the units in the various systems. We have summarized the dimensions assigned to the practical MKS units in Sec. 7 of Chap. 41. In this system, we can write

$$1 \text{ amp} = 1 \sqrt{\text{nt}}, \quad 1 \text{ coul} = 1 \sqrt{\text{nt}} \cdot \text{sec}, \quad 1 \text{ v} = 1 \sqrt{\text{nt}} \cdot \text{m/sec}, \tag{17}$$

and so forth.

The electromagnetic units are defined by equations similar to those used in defining the practical units, but with *different numerical constants* [compare (7) above with (1), p. 1066]. In this system we could write

$$1 \text{ abamp} = 1 \sqrt{\text{dyne}}, \quad 1 \text{ abcoul} = 1 \sqrt{\text{dyne}} \cdot \text{sec}, \quad 1 \text{ abv} = 1 \sqrt{\text{dyne}} \cdot \text{cm/sec}. \tag{18}$$

From (1) we see that in electrostatic units we could write 1 statcoulomb $= 1 \sqrt{\text{dyne}} \cdot \text{centimeter}$, and hence

$$1 \text{ statamp} = 1 \sqrt{\text{dyne} \cdot \text{cm/sec}}, \quad 1 \text{ statcoul} = 1 \sqrt{\text{dyne} \cdot \text{cm}}, \quad 1 \text{ statv} = 1 \sqrt{\text{dyne}}. \tag{19}$$

One realizes very quickly that (17), (18), and (19) are *logically inconsistent*. Comparing (17) and (18) we should conclude, since $1 \text{ nt} = 10^5$ dynes, that

$$1 \text{ amp} = 1 \sqrt{\text{nt}} = 10^{5/2} \sqrt{\text{dyne}} = 10^{5/2} \text{ abamp,}$$

which is *incorrect* [see (8)]. This inconsistency arises because different numerical constants were used in defining the amp and the abamp.

A more egregious inconsistency is observed when (19) is compared with (17) or (18). According to these equations, the electrostatic units do not even have the same physical dimensions as the electromagnetic or the practical units—in other words, they do not seem to represent the same kinds of physical quantities. But of course they *really do* represent the same physical quantities.

These inconsistencies point up the fact that *the dimensions* (17) *that we have assigned to electrical and magnetic units in terms of mechanical units have no fundamental significance.* However, so long as we adhere to a single consistent system of units, as we have done in this text, such an assignment is very convenient.

To achieve logical consistency between different systems of electrical and magnetic units, we must introduce a fifth *fundamental* unit (in addition to those of length, mass, time, and temperature). It is convenient to assume that the unit of *current* is a fundamental unit, *not expressible in terms of mechanical units.* The equation

$$1 \text{ amp} = \tfrac{1}{10} \text{ abamp} = 3 \times 10^9 \text{ statamp} \tag{20}$$

defines the relative size of the units of current in the different systems.

With the assumption that the units in (20) are not expressible in terms of mechanical units, we must rewrite the definition of the current in amperes in the form

$$I = C_1 \sqrt{10^7 af/2},$$

where C_1 is a *dimensional constant* to which is assigned the value

$$C_1 = 1 \text{ amp}/\sqrt{\text{nt}}.$$

Similarly, the current in abamperes is defined by

$$I = C_2 \sqrt{af/2},$$

with $\qquad C_2 = 1 \text{ abamp}/\sqrt{\text{dyne}};$

and the statcoulomb must be defined in terms of the force f in dynes between two equal charges Q a distance d in cm apart by the equation

$$Q = C_3 \sqrt{f}\, d,$$

with $\qquad C_3 = 1 \text{ statcoul}/\sqrt{\text{dyne}\cdot\text{cm}} = 1 \text{ statamp}\cdot\text{sec}/\sqrt{\text{dyne}\cdot\text{cm}}.$

In this system of fundamental units, the following relations replace (17), (18), and (19):

$$1 \text{ amp} = 1 \text{ amp}, \quad 1 \text{ coul} = 1 \text{ amp}\cdot\text{sec}, \quad 1 \text{ v} = 1 \text{ watt}/\text{amp}; \tag{17'}$$

$$1 \text{ abamp} = 1 \text{ abamp}, \quad 1 \text{ abcoul} = 1 \text{ abamp}\cdot\text{sec}, \quad 1 \text{ abv} = 1 \text{ erg}/\text{abamp}\cdot\text{sec}; \tag{18'}$$

$$1 \text{ statamp} = 1 \text{ statamp}, \quad 1 \text{ statcoul} = 1 \text{ statamp}\cdot\text{sec}, \quad 1 \text{ statv} = 1 \text{ erg}/\text{statamp}\cdot\text{sec}. \tag{19'}$$

It is clear that these relations are logically consistent.

The same type of argument applies to other electrical and magnetic quantities. These quantities are not fundamentally expressible in terms of mechanical units; one more fundamental electrical unit must be introduced. Table I gives the units of all electrical and magnetic quantities in terms of mechanical units and the unit of current. This table is

TABLE I
Electrical and Magnetic Units in the Three Systems

	Practical MKS unit	Electromagnetic EMU	Electrostatic ESU
Length l	1 meter	1 centimeter	1 centimeter
Mass m	1 kilogram	1 gram	1 gram
Time t	1 second	1 second	1 second
Force f	1 newton = 1 kg·m/sec^2	1 dyne = 1 g·cm/sec^2	1 dyne = 1 g·cm/sec^2
Energy W	1 joule = 1 m·nt	1 erg = 1 cm·dyne	1 erg = 1 cm·dyne
Power P	1 watt = 1 joule/sec	1 erg/sec	1 erg/sec
Current I	1 ampere	1 abampere	1 statampere
Charge $Q = It$	1 coul = 1 amp·sec	1 abcoul = 1 abamp·sec	1 statcoul = 1 statamp·sec
Electric potential $V = P/I$	1 volt = 1 watt/amp	1 abvolt = 1 erg/abamp·sec	1 statvolt = 1 erg/statamp·sec
Resistance $R = V/I$	1 ohm = 1 watt/amp^2	1 abohm = 1 erg/abamp^2·sec	1 statohm = 1 erg/statamp^2·sec
Electric intensity $\mathcal{E} = V/l = f/Q$	1 volt/meter = 1 nt/coul = 1 nt/amp·sec	1 abvolt/cm = 1 dyne/abcoul = 1 dyne/abamp·sec	1 statvolt/cm = 1 dyne/statcoul = 1 dyne/statamp·sec
Capacitance $C = Q/V$	1 farad = 1 coul/v = 1 amp^2·sec/watt	1 abf = 1 abcoul/abv = 1 abamp^2·sec^2/erg	1 statf = 1 statcoul/statv = 1 statamp^2·sec^2/erg
Dielectric displacement $\mathfrak{D}$*	1 coul/m^2 = 1 amp·sec/m^2	1 EMU = $(1/4\pi)$ abamp·sec/cm^2	1 ESU = $(1/4\pi)$ statamp·sec/cm^2
Electric inductive capacity $\epsilon_e = \mathfrak{D}/\mathcal{E}$*	1 farad/meter = 1 amp^2·sec/watt·m	1 EMU = $(1/4\pi)$ abamp^2·sec^2/erg·cm	1 ESU = $(1/4\pi)$ statamp^2·sec^2/erg·cm
Magnetic flux density $\mathfrak{B} = f/lI$	1 weber/m^2 = 1 nt/amp·m	1 gauss = 1 dyne/abamp·cm	1 ESU = 1 dyne/statamp·cm
Magnetic flux $\Phi = \mathfrak{B}A$	1 weber = 1 joule/amp	1 maxwell = 1 erg/abamp	1 ESU = 1 erg/statamp
Magnetic moment $M = IA$	1 amp·m^2	1 abamp·cm^2	1 statamp·cm^2
Magnetization $\mathfrak{M} = M/v$	1 amp/m	1 abamp/cm	1 statamp/cm
Magnetizing force $\mathcal{H}$	1 amp-turn/meter	1 oersted = $(1/4\pi)$ abamp-turn/cm	1 ESU = $(1/4\pi)$ statamp-turn/cm
Magnetomotive force MMF = $\mathcal{H}l$	1 ampere-turn	1 gilbert = $(1/4\pi)$ abamp-turn	1 ESU = $(1/4\pi)$ statamp-turn
Reluctance $\mathcal{R} = \text{MMF}/\Phi$	1 amp-turn/weber = 1 amp^2/joule	1 gilbert/maxwell = $(1/4\pi)$abamp^2/erg	1 ESU = $(1/4\pi)$ statamp^2/erg
Inductance L or M $= V/(dI/dt)$	1 henry = 1 ohm·sec = 1 joule/amp^2	1 abhenry = 1 abohm·sec = 1 erg/abamp^2	1 stathenry = 1 statohm·sec = 1 erg/statamp^2
Magnetic inductive capacity $\epsilon_m = \mathfrak{B}/\mathcal{H}$*	1 henry/meter = 1 nt/amp^2	1 gauss/oersted = 4π abhenry/cm = 4π dyne/abamp^2	1 ESU = 4π stathenry/cm = 4π dyne/statamp^2
Dielectric constant K	dimensionless and equal in the three systems		
Permeability μ	dimensionless and equal in the three systems		

* These quantities are not defined in this text. The factors containing 4π that occur in these and other lines arise because the MKS units are 'rationalized,' the CGS units 'unrationalized'; the meaning of the term 'rationalization' is explained in more advanced texts.

logically consistent, and the relations between the units in the three systems can be obtained from this table by using (20) and the known relations between mechanical quantities. Some of the conversion factors are given in the tables of Sec. 6.

We note again that if one is willing to adhere to a *single* system of units, as we have done in this text and as is recommended by the International Electrotechnical Commission, it is logically consistent and most convenient to express all electrical units in terms of mechanical units. This we have done in Sec. 7 of Chap. 41, but we must realize that this usage is one of convenience and not one of fundamental significance.

2. FUNDAMENTAL PHYSICAL CONSTANTS

The following values are based on R. T. Birge, REVIEWS OF MODERN PHYSICS **13**, 233 (1941) and J. W. M. DuMond and E. R. Cohen, *ibid* **20**, 28 (1948). All data in this table are on the physical scale of atomic weights (see p. 894).

Gravitation constant (G) .... $(6.670 \pm 0.005) \times 10^{-11}$ nt·m^2/kg^2
Volume of mole of ideal gas at NTP .... $(22,420.7 \pm 0.6)$ cm^3
Standard atmosphere .... $(101,324.6 \pm 0.4)$ nt/m^2
Ice-point .... $273.16° \pm 0.01°$ K
Mechanical equivalent of heat (number of joules equal to one kilocalorie) .... 4185.5 ± 0.4
Avogadro's number (number of molecules in one mole) .... $(6.0251 \pm 0.0004) \times 10^{23}$
Atomic weight of natural oxygen on physical scale .... 16.00436 ± 0.00009
Ratio of atomic weights on physical scale to those on chemical scale $(16.00436/16)$ ...... 1.000272 ± 0.000005
Atomic mass unit (amu) .... $(1.6597 \pm 0.0001) \times 10^{-27}$ kg
Density of mercury at NTP .... $(13,595.04 \pm 0.06)$ kg/m^3
Universal gas constant (R) .... (8316.6 ± 0.4) joules/kg·K deg
 $= (1.9870 \pm 0.0002)$ kcal/kg·K deg
Boltzmann's constant (k) .... $(1.3803 \pm 0.0001) \times 10^{-23}$ joule/K deg
Speed of light (c) .... $(2.99776 \pm 0.00004) \times 10^8$ m/sec
Faraday (charge carried by 1 mole of monovalent ions) .... $96,522 \pm 7$ coul
Electronic charge (e) .... $(1.6020 \pm 0.0002) \times 10^{-19}$ coul
Electron-volt (ev) .... 1.6020×10^{-19} joule
Planck's constant (h) .... $(6.623 \pm 0.001) \times 10^{-34}$ joule·sec
 $= 4.134 \times 10^{-15}$ ev·sec
Constant in Stefan-Boltzmann law (σ) .... $(5.672 \pm 0.002) \times 10^{-8}$
 joule/(K deg)^4·m^2·sec
Constant in Wien's displacement law (A) ..... $(2.8972 \pm 0.0004) \times 10^{-3}$ m·K deg

Particles:

	atomic weight	mass	charge
electron	$(5.4862 \pm 0.0006) \times 10^{-4}$	$(9.105 \pm 0.001) \times 10^{-31}$ kg	$-e$
proton	1.007582 ± 0.000003	$(1.6723 \pm 0.0001) \times 10^{-27}$ kg	$+e$
neutron	1.00895 ± 0.00003	$(1.6746 \pm 0.0001) \times 10^{-27}$ kg	0
deuteron	2.014176 ± 0.000006	$(3.3429 \pm 0.0002) \times 10^{-27}$ kg	$+e$
α-particle	4.00276 ± 0.00003	$(6.6434 \pm 0.0004) \times 10^{-27}$ kg	$+2e$

3. PERIODIC TABLE OF THE ELEMENTS

H 1																	He 2
Li 3	Be 4											B 5	C 6	N 7	O 8	F 9	Ne 10
Na 11	Mg 12											Al 13	Si 14	P 15	S 16	Cl 17	A 18
K 19	Ca 20	Sc 21	Ti 22	V 23	Cr 24	Mn 25	Fe 26	Co 27	Ni 28	Cu 29	Zn 30	Ga 31	Ge 32	As 33	Se 34	Br 35	Kr 36
Rb 37	Sr 38	Y 39	Zr 40	Nb 41	Mo 42	Tc 43	Ru 44	Rh 45	Pd 46	Ag 47	Cd 48	In 49	Sn 50	Sb 51	Te 52	I 53	Xe 54
Cs 55	Ba 56	Lu 71	Hf 72	Ta 73	W 74	Re 75	Os 76	Ir 77	Pt 78	Au 79	Hg 80	Tl 81	Pb 82	Bi 83	Po 84	At 85	Rn 86
Fr 87	Ra 88																

Transition elements

Rare earths

La 57	Ce 58	Pr 59	Nd 60	Pm 61	Sm 62	Eu 63	Gd 64	Tb 65	Dy 66	Ho 67	Er 68	Tm 69	Yb 70
Ac 89	Th 90	Pa 91	U 92	Np 93	Pu 94	Am 95	Cm 96	— 97	— 98				

4. PHYSICAL PROPERTIES OF THE ELEMENTS

ATOMIC WEIGHTS FROM *Journal of the American Chemical Society* **70,** 3532 (1948), CHANGED TO THE PHYSICAL SCALE BY MULTIPLICATION BY 1.000272.
OTHER DATA MOSTLY FROM *U.S. National Bureau of Standards Circular* C447 (1943).

Element	Symbol	Atomic number	Atomic weight	Density at 20° C (g/cm³)	Melting point (° C)	Boiling point (° C)	Electrical resistivity (10^{-8} ohm·m)
Actinium	Ac	89	227	—	—	—	—
Aluminum	Al	13	26.98	2.70	660.0	2056	2.65 (20° C)
Americium	Am	95	—	—	—	—	—
Antimony	Sb	51	121.79	6.62	630.5	1440	39.0 (0° C)
Argon	A	18	39.955	1.663×10^{-3}	−189.4	−185.8	gaseous
Arsenic	As	33	74.93	5.73	subl.	610	35 (20° C)
Astatine	At	85	211	—	—	—	—
Barium	Ba	56	137.40	3.5	700	1638	60 (20° C)
Beryllium	Be	4	9.015	1.82	1280	1500	5.88 (0° C)
Bismuth	Bi	83	209.06	9.80	271.3	1420	107 (0° C)
Boron	B	5	10.82	2.3	2300	2550	10^{12} (0° C)
Bromine	Br	35	79.938	3.12	−7.2	58	liquid
Cadmium	Cd	48	112.44	8.65	320.9	765	6.83 (0° C)
Calcium	Ca	20	40.09	1.54	850	1487	3.43 (0° C)
Carbon (graphite)	C	6	12.013	2.22	3700	4827	1370 (0° C)
Cerium	Ce	58	140.17	6.90	600	1400	78 (20° C)
Cesium	Cs	55	132.95	1.87	28	690	18.8 (0° C)
Chlorine	Cl	17	35.467	2.995×10^{-3}	−101	−34.7	gaseous
Chromium	Cr	24	52.02	7.14	1800	2482	14.1 (20° C)
Cobalt	Co	27	58.96	8.9	1495	3000	5.60 (0° C)
Copper	Cu	29	63.56	8.96	1083.2	2595	1.72 (20° C)
Curium	Cm	96	—	—	—	—	—
Dysprosium	Dy	66	162.50	—	—	—	—
Erbium	Er	68	167.2	(4.77)	—	—	—
Europium	Eu	63	152.0	—	—	—	—
Fluorine	F	9	19.01	0.790×10^{-3}	−220	−188.2	gaseous
Francium	Fr	87	223	—	—	—	—
Gadolinium	Gd	64	156.9	—	—	—	—
Gallium	Ga	31	69.74	5.91	29.8	2071	53.4 (0° C)
Germanium	Ge	32	72.62	5.36	960	2700	10^5 (0° C)
Gold	Au	79	197.3	19.3	1063.0	2966	2.19 (0° C)
Hafnium	Hf	72	178.6	11.4	(1700)	>3700	32 (20° C)
Helium	He	2	4.004	0.166×10^{-3}	−271.4	−268.9	gaseous
Holmium	Ho	67	164.98	—	—	—	—
Hydrogen	H	1	1.0083	0.0838×10^{-3}	−259.4	−252.7	gaseous
Indium	In	49	114.79	7.31	156.4	1450	8.37 (0° C)
Iodine	I	53	126.95	4.93	114	183	10^{15} (20° C)
Iridium	Ir	77	193.2	22.4	2454	~5300	5.3 (20° C)
Iron	Fe	26	55.87	7.87	1539	3000	9.71 (20° C)
Krypton	Kr	36	83.7	3.49×10^{-3}	−157	−152	gaseous
Lanthanum	La	57	138.96	6.15	826	1800	59 (18° C)
Lead	Pb	82	207.27	11.3	327.3	1744	20.6 (20° C)
Lithium	Li	3	6.942	0.534	186	1372	8.55 (0° C)
Lutetium	Lu	71	175.04	—	—	—	—
Magnesium	Mg	12	24.33	1.74	650	1107	4.33 (18° C)
Manganese	Mn	25	54.94	7.44	1260	2151	23 (20° C)
Mercury	Hg	80	200.66	13.6	−38.9	357	94.1 (0° C)
Molybdenum	Mo	42	95.98	10.2	2620	4800	5.17 (0° C)
Neodymium	Nd	60	144.31	7.05	840	—	79 (18° C)
Neon	Ne	10	20.188	0.839×10^{-3}	−248.6	−246.0	gaseous

Element	Symbol	Atomic number	Atomic weight	Density at 20° C (g/cm³)	Melting point (° C)	Boiling point (° C)	Electrical resistivity (10^{-8} ohm·m)
Neptunium	Np	93	(237)	—	—	—	—
Nickel	Ni	28	58.71	8.90	1455	2732	6.84 (20° C)
Niobium	Nb	41	92.94	8.57	2500	3300	21 (20° C)
Nitrogen	N	7	14.012	1.165×10^{-3}	−210.0	−195.8	gaseous
Osmium	Os	76	190.3	22.5	2700	~5500	9.5 (20° C)
Oxygen	O	8	16.0044	1.332×10^{-3}	−218.8	−183.0	gaseous
Palladium	Pd	46	106.7	12.0	1555	2200	10.8 (20° C)
Phosphorus (yellow)	P	15	30.99	1.82	44.1	280	10^{17} (11° C)
Platinum	Pt	78	195.28	21.4	1773	4407	9.81 (0° C)
Plutonium	Pu	94	(239)	—	—	—	—
Polonium	Po	84	210	—	(600)	—	—
Potassium	K	19	39.107	0.86	63	774	6.15 (0° C)
Praseodymium	Pr	59	140.96	6.63	940	—	88 (18° C)
Promethium	Pm	61	—	—	—	—	—
Protactinium	Pa	91	231	—	(3000)	—	—
Radium	Ra	88	226.11	5.0	700	1140	metallic
Radon	Rn	86	222	9.07×10^{-3}	−71	−61.8	gaseous
Rhenium	Re	75	186.36	20.5	3170	~5900	18.9 (20° C)
Rhodium	Rh	45	102.94	12.4	1966	~4500	4.3 (0° C)
Rubidium	Rb	37	85.50	1.53	39	679	12.5 (20° C)
Ruthenium	Ru	44	101.7	12.2	2500	~4900	10 (18° C)
Samarium	Sm	62	150.47	7.7	>1300	—	—
Scandium	Sc	21	45.11	(2.5)	1200	(2400)	—
Selenium	Se	34	78.98	4.81	220	680	10^{13} (20° C)
Silicon	Si	14	28.07	2.42	1420	2287	10^5 (20° C)
Silver	Ag	47	107.909	10.5	960.5	2212	1.62 (20° C)
Sodium	Na	11	23.003	0.97	97.7	892	4.2 (0° C)
Strontium	Sr	38	87.65	2.6	770	1384	22.8 (20° C)
Sulfur (rhombic)	S	16	32.075	2.07	112.8	444.6	10^{23} (20° C)
Tantalum	Ta	73	180.93	16.6	3000	~6100	14.6 (18° C)
Technetium	Tc	43	—	—	—	—	—
Tellurium	Te	52	127.64	6.24	450	1087	—
Terbium	Tb	65	159.2	—	327	—	—
Thallium	Tl	81	204.45	11.8	300	1457	17.6 (0° C)
Thorium	Th	90	232.18	11.5	1800	~5200	18.6 (20° C)
Thulium	Tm	69	169.4	—	—	—	—
Tin	Sn	50	118.73	7.30	231.8	2270	11.5 (20° C)
Titanium	Ti	22	47.91	4.54	1800	~5100	80 (0° C)
Tungsten (see wolfram)							
Uranium	U	92	238.13	18.7	1133	~4300	60 (18° C)
Vanadium	V	23	50.96	5.68	1740	3000	58.8 (20° C)
Wolfram	W	74	183.97	19.3	3400	5927	5.5 (20° C)
Xenon	Xe	54	131.3	5.45×10^{-3}	−112	−108.0	gaseous
Ytterbium	Yb	70	173.09	—	1800	—	—
Yttrium	Y	39	88.94	5.51	1500	~4600	—
Zinc	Zn	30	65.40	7.14	419.4	907	5.92 (20° C)
Zirconium	Zr	40	91.24	6.4	1800	~5000	41.0 (0° C)

5. MASSES AND ABUNDANCES OF NATURALLY OCCURRING ISOTOPES

The following isotopic masses are those of the neutral atom—nucleus plus Z electrons—in atomic mass units on the physical scale of atomic weights. *Naturally occurring radioactive isotopes are indicated by italic type.*

SOURCES OF DATA: J. Mattauch, *Nuclear Physics Tables*, Interscience Publishers, New York, 1946; G. T. Seaborg and I. Perlman, REVIEWS OF MODERN PHYSICS **20**, 585 (1948).

Atomic number Z	Chemical Symbol	Mass number A	Abundance (%)	Isotopic mass (amu)	Atomic number Z	Chemical Symbol	Mass number A	Abundance (%)	Isotopic mass (amu)
1	H	1	99.984	1.008131	19	K	39	93.3	38.976
		2	0.016	2.014725			*40*	*0.011*	—
2	He	3	10⁻⁴	3.01699			41	6.7	—
		4	100	4.00386	20	Ca	40	96.96	—
3	Li	6	7.39	6.01692			42	0.64	—
		7	92.61	7.01816			43	0.15	—
							44	2.06	—
4	Be	9	100	9.01496			46	0.003	—
							48	0.19	—
5	B	10	18.83	10.01617					
		11	81.17	11.01290	21	Sc	45	100	44.9698
6	C	12	98.9	12.00388	22	Ti	46	7.95	—
		13	1.1	13.00756			47	7.75	—
							48	73.45	47.9657
7	N	14	99.62	14.00753			49	5.51	48.964
		15	0.38	15.00487			50	5.34	49.963
8	O	16	99.757	16					
		17	0.039	17.00450	23	V	51	100	50.9604
		18	0.204	18.0049	24	Cr	50	4.49	—
9	F	19	100	19.0045			52	83.78	51.959
							53	9.43	—
10	Ne	20	90.51	19.99890			54	2.30	—
		21	0.28	21.0000	25	Mn	55	100	—
		22	9.21	21.9986					
11	Na	23	100	22.9964	26	Fe	54	5.81	53.961
							56	91.64	55.957
12	Mg	24	78.60	23.9930			57	2.21	—
		25	10.11	24.9946			58	0.34	—
		26	11.29	25.9901					
					27	Co	59	100	—
13	Al	27	100	26.9907	28	Ni	58	67.76	57.9597
14	Si	28	92.28	27.9872			60	26.16	59.9498
		29	4.67	28.9865			61	1.25	60.954
		30	3.05	29.9840			62	3.66	61.9496
15	P	31	100	30.9844			64	1.16	63.9474
16	S	32	95.06	31.9825	29	Cu	63	69.09	62.957
		33	0.74	32.9819			65	30.91	64.955
		34	4.18	33.9798	30	Zn	64	48.89	63.957
		36	0.016	—			66	27.81	65.953
17	Cl	35	75.4	34.9788			67	4.07	—
		37	24.6	36.97770			68	18.61	67.955
							70	0.620	69.954
18	A	36	0.307	35.9773					
		38	0.060	37.9746	31	Ga	69	60.2	68.956
		40	99.633	39.9755			71	39.8	70.954

NATURALLY OCCURRING ISOTOPES

Atomic number Z	Chemical Symbol	Mass number A	Abundance (%)	Isotopic mass (amu)	Atomic number Z	Chemical Symbol	Mass number A	Abundance (%)	Isotopic mass (amu)
32	Ge	70	20.55	—	45	Rh	103	100	102.949
		72	27.37	—	46	Pd	102	0.8	—
		73	7.61	—			104	9.3	—
		74	36.74	—			105	22.6	—
		76	7.67	—			106	27.2	105.946
33	As	75	100	—			108	26.8	—
34	Se	74	0.87	—			110	13.5	109.944
		76	9.02	—	47	Ag	107	51.35	106.950
		77	7.58	—			109	48.65	108.949
		78	23.52	—	48	Cd	106	1.215	—
		80	49.82	—			108	0.875	—
		82	9.19	—			110	12.39	—
35	Br	79	50.5	—			111	12.75	—
		81	49.5	—			112	24.07	—
36	Kr	78	0.342	77.945			113	12.26	—
		80	2.223	—			114	28.86	—
		82	11.50	81.938			116	7.58	—
		83	11.48	—	49	In	113	4.23	—
		84	57.02	83.939			115	95.77	—
		86	17.43	85.939	50	Sn	112	0.90	—
37	Rb	85	72.8	—			114	0.61	—
		87	27.2	—			115	0.35	—
38	Sr	84	0.56	—			116	14.07	115.943
		86	9.86	—			117	7.54	—
		87	7.02	—			118	23.98	117.940
		88	82.56	—			119	8.62	118.938
39	Y	89	100	—			120	33.03	—
40	Zr	90	51.46	—			122	4.78	121.946
		91	11.23	—			124	6.11	123.945
		92	17.11	—	51	Sb	121	57.25	—
		94	17.40	—			123	42.75	—
		96	2.80	—	52	Te	120	0.091	—
41	Nb	93	100	—			122	2.49	—
42	Mo	92	15.86	—			123	0.89	—
		94	9.12	93.945			124	4.63	—
		95	15.7	94.945			125	7.01	—
		96	16.5	95.946			126	18.72	—
		97	9.45	96.945			128	31.72	—
		98	23.75	97.944			130	34.46	—
		100	9.62	99.939	53	I	127	100	—
43	Tc	none	—	—	54	Xe	124	0.094	—
44	Ru	96	5.68	95.945			126	0.088	—
		98	2.22	—			128	1.90	—
		99	12.81	98.944			129	26.23	128.946
		100	12.70	—			130	4.07	—
		101	16.98	—			131	21.17	—
		102	31.34	—			132	26.96	131.946
		104	18.27	—			134	10.54	—
							136	8.95	—

Atomic number Z	Chemical Symbol	Mass number A	Abundance (%)	Isotopic mass (amu)	Atomic number Z	Chemical Symbol	Mass number A	Abundance (%)	Isotopic mass (amu)
55	Cs	133	100	—	67	Ho	165	100	—
56	Ba	130	0.101	—	68	Er	162	0.1	—
		132	0.097	—			164	1.5	—
		134	2.42	—			166	32.9	—
		135	6.59	—			167	24.4	—
		136	7.81	—			168	26.9	—
		137	11.32	—			170	14.2	—
		138	71.66	—					
57	La	138	0.089	—	69	Tm	169	100	—
		139	99.911	—	70	Yb	168	0.06	—
58	Ce	136	0.193	—			170	4.21	—
		138	0.250	—			171	14.26	—
		140	88.48	—			172	21.49	—
		142	11.07	—			173	17.02	—
							174	29.58	—
59	Pr	141	100	—			176	13.38	—
60	Nd	142	27.13	—	71	Lu	175	97.5	—
		143	12.20	—			176	2.5	—
		144	23.87	—					
		145	8.30	—	72	Hf	174	0.18	—
		146	17.18	145.964			176	5.30	—
		148	5.72	147.964			177	18.47	—
		150	5.60	149.970			178	27.10	—
							179	13.84	—
61	Pm	none	—	—			180	35.11	—
62	Sm	144	3.16	—	73	Ta	181	100	—
		147	15.07	—					
		148	11.27	—	74	W	180	0.122	—
		149	13.84	—			182	25.77	—
		150	7.47	—			183	14.24	—
		152	26.63	—			184	30.68	—
		154	22.53	—			186	29.17	—
63	Eu	151	47.77	—	75	Re	185	37.07	—
		153	52.23	—			187	62.93	—
64	Gd	152	0.20	—	76	Os	184	0.018	—
		154	2.15	—			186	1.59	—
		155	14.78	154.977			187	1.64	—
		156	20.59	155.977			188	13.3	—
		157	15.71	156.976			189	16.1	—
		158	24.78	157.976			190	26.4	190.04
		160	21.79	159.976			192	41.0	192.038
65	Tb	159	100	—	77	Ir	191	38.5	191.04
							193	61.5	193.04
66	Dy	156	0.052	—	78	Pt	192	0.78	—
		158	0.090	—			194	32.8	194.039
		160	2.294	—			195	33.7	195.039
		161	18.88	—			196	25.4	196.039
		162	25.53	—			198	7.23	198.044
		163	24.97	—					
		164	28.18	—	79	Au	197	100	197.039

NATURALLY OCCURRING ISOTOPES

Atomic number Z	Chemical Symbol	Mass number A	Abundance (%)	Isotopic mass (amu)	Atomic number Z	Chemical Symbol	Mass number A	Abundance (%)	Isotopic mass (amu)
80	Hg	196	0.15	—	85	At	215	—	—
		198	10.1	—			216	—	—
		199	17.0	—			218	—	—
		200	23.3	—	86	Rn	219	—	—
		201	13.2	—			220	—	—
		202	29.6	—			222	—	—
		204	6.7	—	87	Fr	223	—	—
81	Tl	203	29.1	203.059	88	Ra	223	—	—
		205	70.9	205.059			224	—	—
		207	—	—			226	—	—
		208	—	—			228	—	—
		210	—	—					
82	Pb	204	1.5	—	89	Ac	227	—	—
		206	23.6	206.061			228	—	—
		207	22.6	—	90	Th	227	—	—
		208	52.3	208.060			228	—	—
		210	—	—			230	—	—
		211	—	—			231	—	—
		212	—	—			232	100	—
		214	—	—			234	—	—
83	Bi	209	100	209.056	91	Pa	231	—	—
		210	—	—			234	—	—
		211	—	—	92	U	234	0.005	—
		212	—	—			235	0.71	—
		214	—	—			238	99.28	—
84	Po	210	—	—	93	Np	none	—	—
		211	—	—					
		212	—	—	94	Pu	239	—	—
		214	—	—	95	Am	none	—	—
		215	—	—	96	Cm	none	—	—
		216	—	—	97	—	none	—	—
		218	—	—	98	—	none	—	—

6. TABLES OF CONVERSION FACTORS

Plane Angle

	°	′	″	rad	rev
1 degree =	1	60	3600	1.745×10^{-2}	2.778×10^{-3}
1 minute =	1.667×10^{-2}	1	60	2.909×10^{-4}	4.630×10^{-5}
1 second =	2.778×10^{-4}	1.667×10^{-2}	1	4.848×10^{-6}	7.716×10^{-7}
1 radian =	57.30	3438	2.063×10^{5}	1	0.1592
1 revolution =	360	2.16×10^{4}	1.296×10^{6}	6.283	1

$1 \text{ rev} = 2\pi \text{ rad} = 360°$ $1° = 60' = 3600''$
1 artillery mil = $\frac{1}{6400}$ rev = 0.0009817 rad = 0°05625

Solid Angle
1 sphere = 4π steradians = 12.57 steradians

Length

	cm	m	km	in	ft	mi
1 centimeter =	1	10^{-2}	10^{-5}	0.3937	3.281×10^{-2}	6.214×10^{-6}
1 meter =	100	1	10^{-3}	39.37	3.281	6.214×10^{-4}
1 kilometer =	10^{5}	1000	1	3.937×10^{4}	3281	0.6214
1 inch =	2.540	2.540×10^{-2}	2.540×10^{-5}	1	8.333×10^{-2}	1.578×10^{-5}
1 foot =	30.48	0.3048	3.048×10^{-4}	12	1	1.894×10^{-4}
1 statute mile =	1.609×10^{5}	1609	1.609	6.336×10^{4}	5280	1

1 foot = $\frac{1200}{3937}$ meter 1 micron (μ) = 10^{-6} m 1 fathom = 6 ft
1 meter = $\frac{3937}{1200}$ feet 1 millimicron (mμ) = 10^{-9} m 1 yard = 3 ft
1 angstrom (A) = 10^{-10} m 1 light-year = 9.4600×10^{12} km 1 rod = 16.5 ft
1 X-unit = 10^{-13} m 1 parsec = 3.084×10^{13} km 1 mil = 10^{-3} in
1 nautical mile = 1.15157 statute miles = 6080.27 ft

Area

	m²	cm²	ft²	in²	circ mil
1 square meter =	1	10^{4}	10.76	1550	1.974×10^{9}
1 square centimeter =	10^{-4}	1	1.076×10^{-3}	0.1550	1.974×10^{5}
1 square foot =	9.290×10^{-2}	929.0	1	144	1.833×10^{8}
1 square inch =	6.452×10^{-4}	6.452	6.944×10^{-3}	1	1.273×10^{6}
1 circular mil =	5.067×10^{-10}	5.067×10^{-6}	5.454×10^{-9}	7.854×10^{-7}	1

1 square mile = 27,878,400 ft² = 640 acres   1 acre = 43,560 ft²
1 barn = 10^{-28} m²

Volume

	m^3	cm^3	l	ft^3	in^3
1 cubic meter =	1	10^6	1000	35.31	6.102×10^4
1 cubic centimeter =	10^{-6}	1	1.000×10^{-3}	3.531×10^{-5}	6.102×10^{-2}
1 liter =	1.000×10^{-3}	1000	1	3.531×10^{-2}	61.02
1 cubic foot =	2.832×10^{-2}	2.832×10^4	28.32	1	1728
1 cubic inch =	1.639×10^{-5}	16.39	1.639×10^{-2}	5.787×10^{-4}	1

1 U.S. fluid gallon = 4 U.S. fluid quarts = 8 U.S. fluid pints = 128 U.S. fluid ounces = 231 in^3.

1 British Imperial gallon = the volume of 10 lb of water at 62° F = 277.42 in^3.

1 liter = the volume of 1 kg of water at its maximum density = 1000.028 cm^3.

Mass

	g	kg	oz	lb	slug	ton
1 gram =	1	0.001	3.527×10^{-2}	2.205×10^{-3}	6.852×10^{-5}	1.102×10^{-6}
1 kilogram =	1000	1	35.27	2.205	6.852×10^{-2}	1.102×10^{-3}
1 ounce (Avoirdupois) =	28.35	2.835×10^{-2}	1	6.250 $\times 10^{-2}$	1.943×10^{-3}	3.125×10^{-5}
1 pound (Avoirdupois) =	453.6	0.4536	16	1	3.108×10^{-2}	0.0005
1 slug =	1.459×10^4	14.59	514.8	32.17	1	1.609×10^{-2}
1 ton =	9.072×10^5	907.2	3.2×10^4	2000	62.16	1

1 Avoirdupois pound = 7000 grains

1 Troy or Apothecaries' pound = 12 Troy or Apothecaries' ounces = 5760 grains = 0.8229 Avoirdupois pound

1 long ton = 2240 lb
1 metric ton = 1000 kg = 2205 lb
1 lb = 453.5924277 g
1 stone = 14 lb
1 carat = 0.2 g
1 kg = 2.2046223 lb
1 hundredweight (cwt) = 112 lb
1 pennyweight (dwt) = 24 grains
1 slug = 32.17398 lb

1 atomic mass unit (amu) = 1.6597×10^{-27} kg

Time

	yr	day	hr	min	sec
1 year =	1	365.2	8.766×10^3	5.259×10^5	3.156×10^7
1 day =	2.738×10^{-3}	1	24	1440	8.640×10^4
1 hour =	1.141×10^{-4}	4.167×10^{-2}	1	60	3600
1 minute =	1.901×10^{-6}	6.944×10^{-4}	1.667×10^{-2}	1	60
1 second =	3.169×10^{-8}	1.157×10^{-5}	2.778×10^{-4}	1.667×10^{-2}	1

1 year = 365.24219879 days

Density

	slug/ft³	lb/ft³	lb/in³	kg/m³	g/cm³
1 slug per ft³ =	1	32.17	1.862×10^{-2}	515.4	0.5154
1 pound per ft³ =	3.108×10^{-2}	1	5.787×10^{-4}	16.02	1.602×10^{-2}
1 pound per in³ =	53.71	1728	1	2.768×10^4	27.68
1 kilogram per m³ =	1.940×10^{-3}	6.243×10^{-2}	3.613×10^{-5}	1	0.001
1 gram per cm³ =	1.940	62.43	3.613×10^{-2}	1000	1

Speed

	ft/sec	km/hr	m/sec	mi/hr	knot
1 foot per second =	1	1.097	0.3048	0.6818	0.5921
1 kilometer per hour =	0.9113	1	0.2778	0.6214	0.5396
1 meter per second =	3.281	3.6	1	2.237	1.943
1 mile per hour =	1.467	1.609	0.4470	1	0.8684
1 knot =	1.689	1.853	0.5148	1.152	1

1 knot = 1 nautical mile/hr   1 mi/min = 88 ft/sec = 60 mi/hr

Force

	dyne	gf	kgf	nt	lbf	pdl
1 dyne =	1	1.020×10^{-3}	1.020×10^{-6}	10^{-5}	2.248×10^{-6}	7.233×10^{-5}
1 gram-force =	980.7	1	0.001	9.807×10^{-3}	2.205×10^{-3}	7.093×10^{-2}
1 kilogram-force =	9.807×10^5	1000	1	9.807	2.205	70.93
1 newton =	10^5	102.0	0.1020	1	0.2248	7.233
1 pound-force =	4.448×10^5	453.6	0.4536	4.448	1	32.17
1 poundal =	1.383×10^4	14.10	1.410×10^{-2}	0.1383	3.108×10^{-2}	1

1 kgf = 9.80665 nt   1 lbf = 32.17398 pdl

Pressure

	atm	dyne/cm²	inch of water	cm Hg	kgf/m²	nt/m²	lbf/in²	lbf/ft²
1 atmosphere =	1	1.013×10^6	406.8	76	1.033×10^4	1.013×10^5	14.70	2116
1 dyne per cm² =	9.869×10^{-7}	1	4.015×10^{-4}	7.501×10^{-5}	1.020×10^{-2}	0.1	1.450×10^{-5}	2.089×10^{-3}
1 inch of water at 4° C* =	2.458×10^{-3}	2491	1	0.1868	25.40	249.1	3.613×10^{-2}	5.202
1 centimeter of mercury at 0° C* =	1.316×10^{-2}	1.333×10^4	5.353	1	136.0	1333	0.1934	27.85
1 kilogram-force per m² =	9.678×10^{-5}	98.07	3.937×10^{-2}	7.356×10^{-3}	1	9.807	1.422×10^{-3}	0.2048
1 newton per m² =	9.869×10^{-6}	10	4.015×10^{-3}	7.501×10^{-4}	0.1020	1	1.450×10^{-4}	2.089×10^{-2}
1 pound-force per in² =	6.805×10^{-2}	6.895×10^4	27.68	5.171	703.1	6.895×10^3	1	144
1 pound-force per ft² =	4.725×10^{-4}	478.8	0.1922	3.591×10^{-2}	4.882	47.88	6.944×10^{-3}	1

* Where the acceleration of gravity has the standard value 9.80665 m/sec².

1 bar = 1 dyne/cm²   1 millibar = 10^{-3} dyne/cm²

Energy, Work, Heat

	BTU	erg	ft·lbf	hp·hr	joule	kcal	kwh
1 British thermal unit =	1	1.055×10^{10}	777.9	3.929×10^{-4}	1055	0.2520	2.930×10^{-4}
1 erg =	9.481×10^{-11}	1	7.376×10^{-8}	3.725×10^{-14}	10^{-7}	2.389×10^{-11}	2.778×10^{-14}
1 foot·pound-force =	1.285×10^{-3}	1.356×10^{7}	1	5.051×10^{-7}	1.356	3.239×10^{-4}	3.766×10^{-7}
1 horsepower·hour =	2545	2.685×10^{13}	1.980×10^{6}	1	2.685×10^{6}	641.4	0.7457
1 joule =	9.481×10^{-4}	10^{7}	0.7376	3.725×10^{-7}	1	2.389×10^{-4}	2.778×10^{-7}
1 kilocalorie =	3.968	4.186×10^{10}	3087	1.559×10^{-3}	4186	1	1.163×10^{-3}
1 kilowatt·hour =	3413	3.6×10^{13}	2.655×10^{6}	1.341	3.6×10^{6}	860.1	1

1 electron-volt (ev) = 1.6020×10^{-19} joules
1 m·kgf = 9.807 joules
1 watt·sec = 1 joule = 1 m·nt
1 cm·dyne = 1 erg

Relativistic energy equivalents:
1 kg = 8.9866×10^{16} joules
1 amu = 1.4915×10^{-10} joules
(see table on p. 1236)

Power

	BTU/hr	ft·lbf/min	ft·lbf/sec	hp	kcal/sec	kw	w
1 British thermal unit per hour =	1	12.97	0.2161	3.929×10^{-4}	7.000×10^{-5}	2.930×10^{-4}	0.2930
1 foot·pound-force per minute =	7.713×10^{-2}	1	1.667×10^{-2}	3.030×10^{-5}	5.399×10^{-6}	2.260×10^{-5}	2.260×10^{-2}
1 foot·pound-force per second =	4.628	60	1	1.818×10^{-3}	3.239×10^{-4}	1.356×10^{-3}	1.356
1 horsepower =	2545	3.3×10^{4}	550	1	0.1782	0.7457	745.7
1 kilocalorie per second =	1.429×10^{4}	1.852×10^{5}	3087	5.613	1	4.186	4186
1 kilowatt =	3413	4.425×10^{4}	737.6	1.341	0.2389	1	1000
1 watt =	3.413	44.25	0.7376	1.341×10^{-3}	2.389×10^{-4}	0.001	1

1 watt = 1 joule/sec

Quantity of Electricity, Electric Charge

	abcoul	amp·hr	coul	faraday	statcoul
1 abcoulomb (1 EMU) =	1	2.778×10^{-3}	10	1.036×10^{-4}	2.998×10^{10}
1 ampere·hour =	360	1	3600	3.730×10^{-2}	1.079×10^{13}
1 coulomb =	0.1	2.778×10^{-4}	1	1.036×10^{-5}	2.998×10^{9}
1 faraday =	9652	26.81	9.652×10^{4}	1	2.893×10^{14}
1 statcoulomb (1 ESU) =	3.336×10^{-11}	9.266×10^{-14}	3.336×10^{-10}	3.456×10^{-15}	1

1 electronic charge $= 1.6020 \times 10^{-19}$ coul   1 faraday $= 96{,}522$ coul

Electric Current

	abamp	amp	statamp
1 abampere (1 EMU) =	1	10	2.998×10^{10}
1 ampere =	0.1	1	2.998×10^{9}
1 statampere (1 ESU) =	3.336×10^{-11}	3.336×10^{-10}	1

Electric Potential, Electromotive Force

	abv	v	statv
1 abvolt (1 EMU) =	1	10^{-8}	3.336×10^{-11}
1 volt =	10^{8}	1	3.336×10^{-8}
1 statvolt (1 ESU) =	2.998×10^{10}	299.8	1

Electric Resistance

	abohm	ohm	statohm
1 abohm (1 EMU) =	1	10^{-9}	1.113×10^{-21}
1 ohm =	10^{9}	1	1.113×10^{-12}
1 statohm (1 ESU) =	8.987×10^{20}	8.987×10^{11}	1

Electric Resistivity

	abohm·cm	µohm·cm	ohm·cm	statohm·cm	ohm·m	ohm·circ mil/ft
1 abohm-centimeter (1 EMU) =	1	0.001	10^{-9}	1.113×10^{-21}	10^{-11}	6.015×10^{-3}
1 microhm-centimeter =	1000	1	10^{-6}	1.113×10^{-18}	10^{-8}	6.015
1 ohm-centimeter =	10^9	10^6	1	1.113×10^{-12}	0.01	6.015×10^6
1 statohm-centimeter (1 ESU) =	8.987×10^{20}	8.987×10^{17}	8.987×10^{11}	1	8.987×10^9	5.406×10^{18}
1 ohm-meter =	10^{11}	10^8	100	1.113×10^{-10}	1	6.015×10^8
1 ohm-circular mil per foot =	166.2	0.1662	1.662×10^{-7}	1.850×10^{-19}	1.662×10^{-9}	1

Capacitance

	abf	f	µf*	statf
1 abfarad (1 EMU) =	1	10^9	10^{15}	8.987×10^{20}
1 farad =	10^{-9}	1	10^6	8.987×10^{11}
1 microfarad =	10^{-15}	10^{-6}	1	8.987×10^5
1 statfarad (1 ESU) =	1.113×10^{-21}	1.113×10^{-12}	1.113×10^{-6}	1

* This unit is frequently abbreviated mf.

Inductance

	abhenry	henry	microhenry	millihenry	stathenry
1 abhenry (1 EMU) =	1	10^{-9}	0.001	10^{-6}	1.113×10^{-21}
1 henry =	10^9	1	10^6	1000	1.113×10^{-12}
1 microhenry =	1000	10^{-6}	1	0.001	1.113×10^{-18}
1 millihenry =	10^6	0.001	1000	1	1.113×10^{-15}
1 stathenry (1 ESU) =	8.987×10^{20}	8.987×10^{11}	8.987×10^{17}	8.987×10^{14}	1

Magnetic Flux

	maxwell	kiloline	weber
1 maxwell (1 line or 1 EMU) =	1	0.001	10^{-8}
1 kiloline =	1000	1	10^{-5}
1 weber =	10^8	10^5	1

$1 \text{ ESU} = 299.776 \text{ weber}$

Magnetic Flux Density ℬ

	gauss	kiloline/in²	weber/m²	milligauss	γ
1 gauss (line per square centimeter) =	1	6.452×10^{-3}	10^{-4}	1000	10^5
1 kiloline per square inch =	155.0	1	1.550×10^{-2}	1.550×10^5	1.550×10^7
1 weber per square meter =	10^4	64.52	1	10^7	10^9
1 milligauss =	0.001	6.452×10^{-6}	10^{-7}	1	100
1 gamma =	10^{-5}	6.452×10^{-8}	10^{-9}	0.01	1

$1 \text{ ESU} = 2.99776 \times 10^6 \text{ weber/m}^2$

Magnetomotive Force

	abamp-turn	amp-turn	gilbert
1 abampere-turn =	1	10	12.57
1 ampere-turn =	0.1	1	1.257
1 gilbert =	7.958×10^{-2}	0.7958	1

$1 \text{ pragilbert} = 4\pi \text{ amp-turn}$ $1 \text{ ESU} = 2.65456 \times 10^{-11} \text{ amp-turn}$

Magnetizing Force ℋ

	abamp-turn/cm	amp-turn/cm	amp-turn/in	amp-turn/m	oersted
1 abampere-turn per centimeter =	1	10	25.40	1000	12.57
1 ampere-turn per centimeter =	0.1	1	2.540	100	1.257
1 ampere-turn per inch =	3.937×10^{-2}	0.3937	1	39.37	0.4947
1 ampere-turn per meter =	0.001	0.01	2.540×10^{-2}	1	1.257×10^{-2}
1 oersted =	7.958×10^{-2}	0.7958	2.021	79.58	1

1 oersted = 1 gilbert/cm
1 pra-oersted = 4π amp-turn/m
1 ESU = 2.65456×10^{-9} amp-turn/m

Relativistic Mass-Energy Equivalents

	kg	amu	joule	Mev
1 kilogram =	1	6.025×10^{26}	8.987×10^{16}	5.610×10^{29}
1 atomic mass unit =	1.660×10^{-27}	1	1.492×10^{-10}	931.0
1 joule =	1.113×10^{-17}	6.705×10^{9}	1	6.242×10^{12}
1 million electron-volts =	1.783×10^{-30}	1.074×10^{-3}	1.602×10^{-13}	1

1 kg = 8.9866×10^{16} joules
1 amu = 1.4915×10^{-10} joules
1 kcal = 4.6575×10^{-14} kg
1 ev = 1.6020×10^{-19} joules
1 amu = 931.04 Mev

MATHEMATICAL
TABLES

7. NATURAL TRIGONOMETRIC FUNCTIONS

sin

	.0	.1	.2	.3	.4	.5	.6	.7	.8	.9	
0°	.0000	.0017	.0035	.0052	.0070	.0087	.0105	.0122	.0140	.0157	.0175	89°
1°	.0175	.0192	.0209	.0227	.0244	.0262	.0279	.0297	.0314	.0332	.0349	88°
2°	.0349	.0366	.0384	.0401	.0419	.0436	.0454	.0471	.0488	.0506	.0523	87°
3°	.0523	.0541	.0558	.0576	.0593	.0610	.0628	.0645	.0663	.0680	.0698	86°
4°	.0698	.0715	.0732	.0750	.0767	.0785	.0802	.0819	.0837	.0854	.0872	85°
5°	.0872	.0889	.0906	.0924	.0941	.0958	.0976	.0993	.1011	.1028	.1045	84°
6°	.1045	.1063	.1080	.1097	.1115	.1132	.1149	.1167	.1184	.1201	.1219	83°
7°	.1219	.1236	.1253	.1271	.1288	.1305	.1323	.1340	.1357	.1374	.1392	82°
8°	.1392	.1409	.1426	.1444	.1461	.1478	.1495	.1513	.1530	.1547	.1564	81°
9°	.1564	.1582	.1599	.1616	.1633	.1650	.1668	.1685	.1702	.1719	.1736	80°
10°	.1736	.1754	.1771	.1788	.1805	.1822	.1840	.1857	.1874	.1891	.1908	79°
11°	.1908	.1925	.1942	.1959	.1977	.1994	.2011	.2028	.2045	.2062	.2079	78°
12°	.2079	.2096	.2113	.2130	.2147	.2164	.2181	.2198	.2215	.2233	.2250	77°
13°	.2250	.2267	.2284	.2300	.2317	.2334	.2351	.2368	.2385	.2402	.2419	76°
14°	.2419	.2436	.2453	.2470	.2487	.2504	.2521	.2538	.2554	.2571	.2588	75°
15°	.2588	.2605	.2622	.2639	.2656	.2672	.2689	.2706	.2723	.2740	.2756	74°
16°	.2756	.2773	.2790	.2807	.2823	.2840	.2857	.2874	.2890	.2907	.2924	73°
17°	.2924	.2940	.2957	.2974	.2990	.3007	.3024	.3040	.3057	.3074	.3090	72°
18°	.3090	.3107	.3123	.3140	.3156	.3173	.3190	.3206	.3223	.3239	.3256	71°
19°	.3256	.3272	.3289	.3305	.3322	.3338	.3355	.3371	.3387	.3404	.3420	70°
20°	.3420	.3437	.3453	.3469	.3486	.3502	.3518	.3535	.3551	.3567	.3584	69°
21°	.3584	.3600	.3616	.3633	.3649	.3665	.3681	.3697	.3714	.3730	.3746	68°
22°	.3746	.3762	.3778	.3795	.3811	.3827	.3843	.3859	.3875	.3891	.3907	67°
23°	.3907	.3923	.3939	.3955	.3971	.3987	.4003	.4019	.4035	.4051	.4067	66°
24°	.4067	.4083	.4099	.4115	.4131	.4147	.4163	.4179	.4195	.4210	.4226	65°
25°	.4226	.4242	.4258	.4274	.4289	.4305	.4321	.4337	.4352	.4368	.4384	64°
26°	.4384	.4399	.4415	.4431	.4446	.4462	.4478	.4493	.4509	.4524	.4540	63°
27°	.4540	.4555	.4571	.4586	.4602	.4617	.4633	.4648	.4664	.4679	.4695	62°
28°	.4695	.4710	.4726	.4741	.4756	.4772	.4787	.4802	.4818	.4833	.4848	61°
29°	.4848	.4863	.4879	.4894	.4909	.4924	.4939	.4955	.4970	.4985	.5000	60°
30°	.5000	.5015	.5030	.5045	.5060	.5075	.5090	.5105	.5120	.5135	.5150	59°
31°	.5150	.5165	.5180	.5195	.5210	.5225	.5240	.5255	.5270	.5284	.5299	58°
32°	.5299	.5314	.5329	.5344	.5358	.5373	.5388	.5402	.5417	.5432	.5446	57°
33°	.5446	.5461	.5476	.5490	.5505	.5519	.5534	.5548	.5563	.5577	.5592	56°
34°	.5592	.5606	.5621	.5635	.5650	.5664	.5678	.5693	.5707	.5721	.5736	55°
35°	.5736	.5750	.5764	.5779	.5793	.5807	.5821	.5835	.5850	.5864	.5878	54°
36°	.5878	.5892	.5906	.5920	.5934	.5948	.5962	.5976	.5990	.6004	.6018	53°
37°	.6018	.6032	.6046	.6060	.6074	.6088	.6101	.6115	.6129	.6143	.6157	52°
38°	.6157	.6170	.6184	.6198	.6211	.6225	.6239	.6252	.6266	.6280	.6293	51°
39°	.6293	.6307	.6320	.6334	.6347	.6361	.6374	.6388	.6401	.6414	.6428	50°
40°	.6428	.6441	.6455	.6468	.6481	.6494	.6508	.6521	.6534	.6547	.6561	49°
41°	.6561	.6574	.6587	.6600	.6613	.6626	.6639	.6652	.6665	.6678	.6691	48°
42°	.6691	.6704	.6717	.6730	.6743	.6756	.6769	.6782	.6794	.6807	.6820	47°
43°	.6820	.6833	.6845	.6858	.6871	.6884	.6896	.6909	.6921	.6934	.6947	46°
44°	.6947	.6959	.6972	.6984	.6997	.7009	.7022	.7034	.7046	.7059	.7071	45°
		.9	.8	.7	.6	.5	.4	.3	.2	.1	.0	

cos

sin

	.0	.1	.2	.3	.4	.5	.6	.7	.8	.9		
45°	.7071	.7083	.7096	.7108	.7120	.7133	.7145	.7157	.7169	.7181	.7193	44°
46°	.7193	.7206	.7218	.7230	.7242	.7254	.7266	.7278	.7290	.7302	.7314	43°
47°	.7314	.7325	.7337	.7349	.7361	.7373	.7385	.7396	.7408	.7420	.7431	42°
48°	.7431	.7443	.7455	.7466	.7478	.7490	.7501	.7513	.7524	.7536	.7547	41°
49°	.7547	.7559	.7570	.7581	.7593	.7604	.7615	.7627	.7638	.7649	.7660	40°
50°	.7660	.7672	.7683	.7694	.7705	.7716	.7727	.7738	.7749	.7760	.7771	39°
51°	.7771	.7782	.7793	.7804	.7815	.7826	.7837	.7848	.7859	.7869	.7880	38°
52°	.7880	.7891	.7902	.7912	.7923	.7934	.7944	.7955	.7965	.7976	.7986	37°
53°	.7986	.7997	.8007	.8018	.8028	.8039	.8049	.8059	.8070	.8080	.8090	36°
54°	.8090	.8100	.8111	.8121	.8131	.8141	.8151	.8161	.8171	.8181	.8192	35°
55°	.8192	.8202	.8211	.8221	.8231	.8241	.8251	.8261	.8271	.8281	.8290	34°
56°	.8290	.8300	.8310	.8320	.8329	.8339	.8348	.8358	.8368	.8377	.8387	33°
57°	.8387	.8396	.8406	.8415	.8425	.8434	.8443	.8453	.8462	.8471	.8480	32°
58°	.8480	.8490	.8499	.8508	.8517	.8526	.8536	.8545	.8554	.8563	.8572	31°
59°	.8572	.8581	.8590	.8599	.8607	.8616	.8625	.8634	.8643	.8652	.8660	30°
60°	.8660	.8669	.8678	.8686	.8695	.8704	.8712	.8721	.8729	.8738	.8746	29°
61°	.8746	.8755	.8763	.8771	.8780	.8788	.8796	.8805	.8813	.8821	.8829	28°
62°	.8829	.8838	.8846	.8854	.8862	.8870	.8878	.8886	.8894	.8902	.8910	27°
63°	.8910	.8918	.8926	.8934	.8942	.8949	.8957	.8965	.8973	.8980	.8988	26°
64°	.8988	.8996	.9003	.9011	.9018	.9026	.9033	.9041	.9048	.9056	.9063	25°
65°	.9063	.9070	.9078	.9085	.9092	.9100	.9107	.9114	.9121	.9128	.9135	24°
66°	.9135	.9143	.9150	.9157	.9164	.9171	.9178	.9184	.9191	.9198	.9205	23°
67°	.9205	.9212	.9219	.9225	.9232	.9239	.9245	.9252	.9259	.9265	.9272	22°
68°	.9272	.9278	.9285	.9291	.9298	.9304	.9311	.9317	.9323	.9330	.9336	21°
69°	.9336	.9342	.9348	.9354	.9361	.9367	.9373	.9379	.9385	.9391	.9397	20°
70°	.9397	.9403	.9409	.9415	.9421	.9426	.9432	.9438	.9444	.9449	.9455	19°
71°	.9455	.9461	.9466	.9472	.9478	.9483	.9489	.9494	.9500	.9505	.9511	18°
72°	.9511	.9516	.9521	.9527	.9532	.9537	.9542	.9548	.9553	.9558	.9563	17°
73°	.9563	.9568	.9573	.9578	.9583	.9588	.9593	.9598	.9603	.9608	.9613	16°
74°	.9613	.9617	.9622	.9627	.9632	.9636	.9641	.9646	.9650	.9655	.9659	15°
75°	.9659	.9664	.9668	.9673	.9677	.9681	.9686	.9690	.9694	.9699	.9703	14°
76°	.9703	.9707	.9711	.9715	.9720	.9724	.9728	.9732	.9736	.9740	.9744	13°
77°	.9744	.9748	.9751	.9755	.9759	.9763	.9767	.9770	.9774	.9778	.9781	12°
78°	.9781	.9785	.9789	.9792	.9796	.9799	.9803	.9806	.9810	.9813	.9816	11°
79°	.9816	.9820	.9823	.9826	.9829	.9833	.9836	.9839	.9842	.9845	.9848	10°
80°	.9848	.9851	.9854	.9857	.9860	.9863	.9866	.9869	.9871	.9874	.9877	9°
81°	.9877	.9880	.9882	.9885	.9888	.9890	.9893	.9895	.9898	.9900	.9903	8°
82°	.9903	.9905	.9907	.9910	.9912	.9914	.9917	.9919	.9921	.9923	.9925	7°
83°	.9925	.9928	.9930	.9932	.9934	.9936	.9938	.9940	.9942	.9943	.9945	6°
84°	.9945	.9947	.9949	.9951	.9952	.9954	.9956	.9957	.9959	.9960	.9962	5°
85°	.9962	.9963	.9965	.9966	.9968	.9969	.9971	.9972	.9973	.9974	.9976	4°
86°	.9976	.9977	.9978	.9979	.9980	.9981	.9982	.9983	.9984	.9985	.9986	3°
87°	.9986	.9987	.9988	.9989	.9990	.9990	.9991	.9992	.9993	.9993	.9994	2°
88°	.9994	.9995	.9995	.9996	.9996	.9997	.9997	.9997	.9998	.9998	.9998	1°
89°	.9998	.9999	.9999	.9999	.9999	1.000	1.000	1.000	1.000	1.000	1.000	0°
	.9	.8	.7	.6	.5	.4	.3	.2	.1	.0		

cos

tan

	.0	.1	.2	.3	.4	.5	.6	.7	.8	.9	
0°	.0000	.0017	.0035	.0052	.0070	.0087	.0105	.0122	.0140	.0157	.0175	89°
1°	.0175	.0192	.0209	.0227	.0244	.0262	.0279	.0297	.0314	.0332	.0349	88°
2°	.0349	.0367	.0384	.0402	.0419	.0437	.0454	.0472	.0489	.0507	.0524	87°
3°	.0524	.0542	.0559	.0577	.0594	.0612	.0629	.0647	.0664	.0682	.0699	86°
4°	.0699	.0717	.0734	.0752	.0769	.0787	.0805	.0822	.0840	.0857	.0875	85°
5°	.0875	.0892	.0910	.0928	.0945	.0963	.0981	.0998	.1016	.1033	.1051	84°
6°	.1051	.1069	.1086	.1104	.1122	.1139	.1157	.1175	.1192	.1210	.1228	83°
7°	.1228	.1246	.1263	.1281	.1299	.1317	.1334	.1352	.1370	.1388	.1405	82°
8°	.1405	.1423	.1441	.1459	.1477	.1495	.1512	.1530	.1548	.1566	.1584	81°
9°	.1584	.1602	.1620	.1638	.1655	.1673	.1691	.1709	.1727	.1745	.1763	80°
10°	.1763	.1781	.1799	.1817	.1835	.1853	.1871	.1890	.1908	.1926	.1944	79°
11°	.1944	.1962	.1980	.1998	.2016	.2035	.2053	.2071	.2089	.2107	.2126	78°
12°	.2126	.2144	.2162	.2180	.2199	.2217	.2235	.2254	.2272	.2290	.2309	77°
13°	.2309	.2327	.2345	.2364	.2382	.2401	.2419	.2438	.2456	.2475	.2493	76°
14°	.2493	.2512	.2530	.2549	.2568	.2586	.2605	.2623	.2642	.2661	.2679	75°
15°	.2679	.2698	.2717	.2736	.2754	.2773	.2792	.2811	.2830	.2849	.2867	74°
16°	.2867	.2886	.2905	.2924	.2943	.2962	.2981	.3000	.3019	.3038	.3057	73°
17°	.3057	.3076	.3096	.3115	.3134	.3153	.3172	.3191	.3211	.3230	.3249	72°
18°	.3249	.3269	.3288	.3307	.3327	.3346	.3365	.3385	.3404	.3424	.3443	71°
19°	.3443	.3463	.3482	.3502	.3522	.3541	.3561	.3581	.3600	.3620	.3640	70°
20°	.3640	.3659	.3679	.3699	.3719	.3739	.3759	.3779	.3799	.3819	.3839	69°
21°	.3839	.3859	.3879	.3899	.3919	.3939	.3959	.3979	.4000	.4020	.4040	68°
22°	.4040	.4061	.4081	.4101	.4122	.4142	.4163	.4183	.4204	.4224	.4245	67°
23°	.4245	.4265	.4286	.4307	.4327	.4348	.4369	.4390	.4411	.4431	.4452	66°
24°	.4452	.4473	.4494	.4515	.4536	.4557	.4578	.4599	.4621	.4642	.4663	65°
25°	.4663	.4684	.4706	.4727	.4748	.4770	.4791	.4813	.4834	.4856	.4877	64°
26°	.4877	.4899	.4921	.4942	.4964	.4986	.5008	.5029	.5051	.5073	.5095	63°
27°	.5095	.5117	.5139	.5161	.5184	.5206	.5228	.5250	.5272	.5295	.5317	62°
28°	.5317	.5340	.5362	.5384	.5407	.5430	.5452	.5475	.5498	.5520	.5543	61°
29°	.5543	.5566	.5589	.5612	.5635	.5658	.5681	.5704	.5727	.5750	.5774	60°
30°	.5774	.5797	.5820	.5844	.5867	.5890	.5914	.5938	.5961	.5985	.6009	59°
31°	.6009	.6032	.6056	.6080	.6104	.6128	.6152	.6176	.6200	.6224	.6249	58°
32°	.6249	.6273	.6297	.6322	.6346	.6371	.6395	.6420	.6445	.6469	.6494	57°
33°	.6494	.6519	.6544	.6569	.6594	.6619	.6644	.6669	.6694	.6720	.6745	56°
34°	.6745	.6771	.6796	.6822	.6847	.6873	.6899	.6924	.6950	.6976	.7002	55°
35°	.7002	.7028	.7054	.7080	.7107	.7133	.7159	.7186	.7212	.7239	.7265	54°
36°	.7265	.7292	.7319	.7346	.7373	.7400	.7427	.7454	.7481	.7508	.7536	53°
37°	.7536	.7563	.7590	.7618	.7646	.7673	.7701	.7729	.7757	.7785	.7813	52°
38°	.7813	.7841	.7869	.7898	.7926	.7954	.7983	.8012	.8040	.8069	.8098	51°
39°	.8098	.8127	.8156	.8185	.8214	.8243	.8273	.8302	.8332	.8361	.8391	50°
40°	.8391	.8421	.8451	.8481	.8511	.8541	.8571	.8601	.8632	.8662	.8693	49°
41°	.8693	.8724	.8754	.8785	.8816	.8847	.8878	.8910	.8941	.8972	.9004	48°
42°	.9004	.9036	.9067	.9099	.9131	.9163	.9195	.9228	.9260	.9293	.9325	47°
43°	.9325	.9358	.9391	.9424	.9457	.9490	.9523	.9556	.9590	.9623	.9657	46°
44°	.9657	.9691	.9725	.9759	.9793	.9827	.9861	.9896	.9930	.9965	1.000	45°
		.9	.8	.7	.6	.5	.4	.3	.2	.1	.0	

cot

tan

	.0	.1	.2	.3	.4	.5	.6	.7	.8	.9	
45°	1.000	1.003	1.007	1.011	1.014	1.018	1.021	1.025	1.028	1.032	1.036	44°
46°	1.036	1.039	1.043	1.046	1.050	1.054	1.057	1.061	1.065	1.069	1.072	43°
47°	1.072	1.076	1.080	1.084	1.087	1.091	1.095	1.099	1.103	1.107	1.111	42°
48°	1.111	1.115	1.118	1.122	1.126	1.130	1.134	1.138	1.142	1.146	1.150	41°
49°	1.150	1.154	1.159	1.163	1.167	1.171	1.175	1.179	1.183	1.188	1.192	40°
50°	1.192	1.196	1.200	1.205	1.209	1.213	1.217	1.222	1.226	1.230	1.235	39°
51°	1.235	1.239	1.244	1.248	1.253	1.257	1.262	1.266	1.271	1.275	1.280	38°
52°	1.280	1.285	1.289	1.294	1.299	1.303	1.308	1.313	1.317	1.322	1.327	37°
53°	1.327	1.332	1.337	1.342	1.347	1.351	1.356	1.361	1.366	1.371	1.376	36°
54°	1.376	1.381	1.387	1.392	1.397	1.402	1.407	1.412	1.418	1.423	1.428	35°
55°	1.428	1.433	1.439	1.444	1.450	1.455	1.460	1.466	1.471	1.477	1.483	34°
56°	1.483	1.488	1.494	1.499	1.505	1.511	1.517	1.522	1.528	1.534	1.540	33°
57°	1.540	1.546	1.552	1.558	1.564	1.570	1.576	1.582	1.588	1.594	1.600	32°
58°	1.600	1.607	1.613	1.619	1.625	1.632	1.638	1.645	1.651	1.658	1.664	31°
59°	1.664	1.671	1.678	1.684	1.691	1.698	1.704	1.711	1.718	1.725	1.732	30°
60°	1.732	1.739	1.746	1.753	1.760	1.767	1.775	1.782	1.789	1.797	1.804	29°
61°	1.804	1.811	1.819	1.827	1.834	1.842	1.849	1.857	1.865	1.873	1.881	28°
62°	1.881	1.889	1.897	1.905	1.913	1.921	1.929	1.937	1.946	1.954	1.963	27°
63°	1.963	1.971	1.980	1.988	1.997	2.006	2.014	2.023	2.032	2.041	2.050	26°
64°	2.050	2.059	2.069	2.078	2.087	2.097	2.106	2.116	2.125	2.135	2.145	25°
65°	2.145	2.154	2.164	2.174	2.184	2.194	2.204	2.215	2.225	2.236	2.246	24°
66°	2.246	2.257	2.267	2.278	2.289	2.300	2.311	2.322	2.333	2.344	2.356	23°
67°	2.356	2.367	2.379	2.391	2.402	2.414	2.426	2.438	2.450	2.463	2.475	22°
68°	2.475	2.488	2.500	2.513	2.526	2.539	2.552	2.565	2.578	2.592	2.605	21°
69°	2.605	2.619	2.633	2.646	2.660	2.675	2.689	2.703	2.718	2.733	2.747	20°
70°	2.747	2.762	2.778	2.793	2.808	2.824	2.840	2.856	2.872	2.888	2.904	19°
71°	2.904	2.921	2.937	2.954	2.971	2.989	3.006	3.024	3.042	3.060	3.078	18°
72°	3.078	3.096	3.115	3.133	3.152	3.172	3.191	3.211	3.230	3.251	3.271	17°
73°	3.271	3.291	3.312	3.333	3.354	3.376	3.398	3.420	3.442	3.465	3.487	16°
74°	3.487	3.511	3.534	3.558	3.582	3.606	3.630	3.655	3.681	3.706	3.732	15°
75°	3.732	3.758	3.785	3.812	3.839	3.867	3.895	3.923	3.952	3.981	4.011	14°
76°	4.011	4.041	4.071	4.102	4.134	4.165	4.198	4.230	4.264	4.297	4.331	13°
77°	4.331	4.366	4.402	4.437	4.474	4.511	4.548	4.586	4.625	4.665	4.705	12°
78°	4.705	4.745	4.787	4.829	4.872	4.915	4.959	5.005	5.050	5.097	5.145	11°
79°	5.145	5.193	5.242	5.292	5.343	5.396	5.449	5.503	5.558	5.614	5.671	10°
80°	5.671	5.730	5.789	5.850	5.912	5.976	6.041	6.107	6.174	6.243	6.314	9°
81°	6.314	6.386	6.460	6.535	6.612	6.691	6.772	6.855	6.940	7.026	7.115	8°
82°	7.115	7.207	7.300	7.396	7.495	7.596	7.700	7.806	7.916	8.028	8.144	7°
83°	8.144	8.264	8.386	8.513	8.643	8.777	8.915	9.058	9.205	9.357	9.514	6°
84°	9.514	9.677	9.845	10.02	10.20	10.39	10.58	10.78	10.99	11.20	11.43	5°
85°	11.43	11.66	11.91	12.16	12.43	12.71	13.00	13.30	13.62	13.95	14.30	4°
86°	14.30	14.67	15.06	15.46	15.89	16.35	16.83	17.34	17.89	18.46	19.08	3°
87°	19.08	19.74	20.45	21.20	22.02	22.90	23.86	24.90	26.03	27.27	28.64	2°
88°	28.64	30.14	31.82	33.69	35.80	38.19	40.92	44.07	47.74	52.08	57.29	1°
89°	57.29	63.66	71.62	81.85	95.49	114.6	143.2	191.0	286.5	573.0	∞	0°
	.9	.8	.7	.6	.5	.4	.3	.2	.1	.0	

cot

8. TABLE OF LOGARITHMS TO BASE 10

N	0	1	2	3	4	5	6	7	8	9	\multicolumn{5}{c}{P. P.}
											1	2	3	4	5
10	0000	0043	0086	0128	0170	0212	0253	0294	0334	0374	4	8	12	17	21
11	0414	0453	0492	0531	0569	0607	0645	0682	0719	0755	4	8	11	15	19
12	0792	0828	0864	0899	0934	0969	1004	1038	1072	1106	3	7	10	14	17
13	1139	1173	1206	1239	1271	1303	1335	1367	1399	1430	3	6	10	13	16
14	1461	1492	1523	1553	1584	1614	1644	1673	1703	1732	3	6	9	12	15
15	1761	1790	1818	1847	1875	1903	1931	1959	1987	2014	3	6	8	11	14
16	2041	2068	2095	2122	2148	2175	2201	2227	2253	2279	3	5	8	11	13
17	2304	2330	2355	2380	2405	2430	2455	2480	2504	2529	2	5	7	10	12
18	2553	2577	2601	2625	2648	2672	2695	2718	2742	2765	2	5	7	9	12
19	2788	2810	2833	2856	2878	2900	2923	2945	2967	2989	2	4	7	9	11
20	3010	3032	3054	3075	3096	3118	3139	3160	3181	3201	2	4	6	8	11
21	3222	3243	3263	3284	3304	3324	3345	3365	3385	3404	2	4	6	8	10
22	3424	3444	3464	3483	3502	3522	3541	3560	3579	3598	2	4	6	8	10
23	3617	3636	3655	3674	3692	3711	3729	3747	3766	3784	2	4	5	7	9
24	3802	3820	3838	3856	3874	3892	3909	3927	3945	3962	2	4	5	7	9
25	3979	3997	4014	4031	4048	4065	4082	4099	4116	4133	2	3	5	7	9
26	4150	4166	4183	4200	4216	4232	4249	4265	4281	4298	2	3	5	7	8
27	4314	4330	4346	4362	4378	4393	4409	4425	4440	4456	2	3	5	6	8
28	4472	4487	4502	4518	4533	4548	4564	4579	4594	4609	2	3	5	6	8
29	4624	4639	4654	4669	4683	4698	4713	4728	4742	4757	1	3	4	6	7
30	4771	4786	4800	4814	4829	4843	4857	4871	4886	4900	1	3	4	6	7
31	4914	4928	4942	4955	4969	4983	4997	5011	5024	5038	1	3	4	6	7
32	5051	5065	5079	5092	5105	5119	5132	5145	5159	5172	1	3	4	5	7
33	5185	5198	5211	5224	5237	5250	5263	5276	5289	5302	1	3	4	5	6
34	5315	5328	5340	5353	5366	5378	5391	5403	5416	5428	1	3	4	5	6
35	5441	5453	5465	5478	5490	5502	5514	5527	5539	5551	1	2	4	5	6
36	5563	5575	5587	5599	5611	5623	5635	5647	5658	5670	1	2	4	5	6
37	5682	5694	5705	5717	5729	5740	5752	5763	5775	5786	1	2	3	5	6
38	5798	5809	5821	5832	5843	5855	5866	5877	5888	5899	1	2	3	5	6
39	5911	5922	5933	5944	5955	5966	5977	5988	5999	6010	1	2	3	4	6
40	6021	6031	6042	6053	6064	6075	6085	6096	6107	6117	1	2	3	4	5
41	6128	6138	6149	6160	6170	6180	6191	6201	6212	6222	1	2	3	4	5
42	6232	6243	6253	6263	6274	6284	6294	6304	6314	6325	1	2	3	4	5
43	6335	6345	6355	6365	6375	6385	6395	6405	6415	6425	1	2	3	4	5
44	6435	6444	6454	6464	6474	6484	6493	6503	6513	6522	1	2	3	4	5
45	6532	6542	6551	6561	6571	6580	6590	6599	6609	6618	1	2	3	4	5
46	6628	6637	6646	6656	6665	6675	6684	6693	6702	6712	1	2	3	4	5
47	6721	6730	6739	6749	6758	6767	6776	6785	6794	6803	1	2	3	4	5
48	6812	6821	6830	6839	6848	6857	6866	6875	6884	6893	1	2	3	4	4
49	6902	6911	6920	6928	6937	6946	6955	6964	6972	6981	1	2	3	4	4
50	6990	6998	7007	7016	7024	7033	7042	7050	7059	7067	1	2	3	3	4
51	7076	7084	7093	7101	7110	7118	7126	7135	7143	7152	1	2	3	3	4
52	7160	7168	7177	7185	7193	7202	7210	7218	7226	7235	1	2	2	3	4
53	7243	7251	7259	7267	7275	7284	7292	7300	7308	7316	1	2	2	3	4
54	7324	7332	7340	7348	7356	7364	7372	7380	7388	7396	1	2	2	3	4

TABLE OF LOGARITHMS TO BASE 10

NOTE: $\log_e N = \log_e 10 \, \log_{10} N = 2.3026 \log_{10} N$
$\log_{10} e^x = x \log_{10} e = 0.43429 \, x$

N	0	1	2	3	4	5	6	7	8	9	P.P. 1	2	3	4	5
55	7404	7412	7419	7427	7435	7443	7451	7459	7466	7474	1	2	2	3	4
56	7482	7490	7497	7505	7513	7520	7528	7536	7543	7551	1	2	2	3	4
57	7559	7566	7574	7582	7589	7597	7604	7612	7619	7627	1	2	2	3	4
58	7634	7642	7649	7657	7664	7672	7679	7686	7694	7701	1	1	2	3	4
59	7709	7716	7723	7731	7738	7745	7752	7760	7767	7774	1	1	2	3	4
60	7782	7789	7796	7803	7810	7818	7825	7832	7839	7846	1	1	2	3	4
61	7853	7860	7868	7875	7882	7889	7896	7903	7910	7917	1	1	2	3	4
62	7924	7931	7938	7945	7952	7959	7966	7973	7980	7987	1	1	2	3	3
63	7993	8000	8007	8014	8021	8028	8035	8041	8048	8055	1	1	2	3	3
64	8062	8069	8075	8082	8089	8096	8102	8109	8116	8122	1	1	2	3	3
65	8129	8136	8142	8149	8156	8162	8169	8176	8182	8189	1	1	2	3	3
66	8195	8202	8209	8215	8222	8228	8235	8241	8248	8254	1	1	2	3	3
67	8261	8267	8274	8280	8287	8293	8299	8306	8312	8319	1	1	2	3	3
68	8325	8331	8338	8344	8351	8357	8363	8370	8376	8382	1	1	2	3	3
69	8388	8395	8401	8407	8414	8420	8426	8432	8439	8445	1	1	2	3	3
70	8451	8457	8463	8470	8476	8482	8488	8494	8500	8506	1	1	2	2	3
71	8513	8519	8525	8531	8537	8543	8549	8555	8561	8567	1	1	2	2	3
72	8573	8579	8585	8591	8597	8603	8609	8615	8621	8627	1	1	2	2	3
73	8633	8639	8645	8651	8657	8663	8669	8675	8681	8686	1	1	2	2	3
74	8692	8698	8704	8710	8716	8722	8727	8733	8739	8745	1	1	2	2	3
75	8751	8756	8762	8768	8774	8779	8785	8791	8797	8802	1	1	2	2	3
76	8808	8814	8820	8825	8831	8837	8842	8848	8854	8859	1	1	2	2	3
77	8865	8871	8876	8882	8887	8893	8899	8904	8910	8915	1	1	2	2	3
78	8921	8927	8932	8938	8943	8949	8954	8960	8965	8971	1	1	2	2	3
79	8976	8982	8987	8993	8998	9004	9009	9015	9020	9025	1	1	2	2	3
80	9031	9036	9042	9047	9053	9058	9063	9069	9074	9079	1	1	2	2	3
81	9085	9090	9096	9101	9106	9112	9117	9122	9128	9133	1	1	2	2	3
82	9138	9143	9149	9154	9159	9165	9170	9175	9180	9186	1	1	2	2	3
83	9191	9196	9201	9206	9212	9217	9222	9227	9232	9238	1	1	2	2	3
84	9243	9248	9253	9258	9263	9269	9274	9279	9284	9289	1	1	2	2	3
85	9294	9299	9304	9309	9315	9320	9325	9330	9335	9340	1	1	2	2	3
86	9345	9350	9355	9360	9365	9370	9375	9380	9385	9390	1	1	2	2	3
87	9395	9400	9405	9410	9415	9420	9425	9430	9435	9440	0	1	1	2	2
88	9445	9450	9455	9460	9465	9469	9474	9479	9484	9489	0	1	1	2	2
89	9494	9499	9504	9509	9513	9518	9523	9528	9533	9538	0	1	1	2	2
90	9542	9547	9552	9557	9562	9566	9571	9576	9581	9586	0	1	1	2	2
91	9590	9595	9600	9605	9609	9614	9619	9624	9628	9633	0	1	1	2	2
92	9638	9643	9647	9652	9657	9661	9666	9671	9675	9680	0	1	1	2	2
93	9685	9689	9694	9699	9703	9708	9713	9717	9722	9727	0	1	1	2	2
94	9731	9736	9741	9745	9750	9754	9759	9763	9768	9773	0	1	1	2	2
95	9777	9782	9786	9791	9795	9800	9805	9809	9814	9818	0	1	1	2	2
96	9823	9827	9832	9836	9841	9845	9850	9854	9859	9863	0	1	1	2	2
97	9868	9872	9877	9881	9886	9890	9894	9899	9903	9908	0	1	1	2	2
98	9912	9917	9921	9926	9930	9934	9939	9943	9948	9952	0	1	1	2	2
99	9956	9961	9965	9969	9974	9978	9983	9987	9991	9996	0	1	1	2	2

9. TABLE OF EXPONENTIALS

$$e^x$$

x	0	1	2	3	4	5	6	7	8	9
0.0	1.000	1.010	1.020	1.031	1.041	1.051	1.062	1.073	1.083	1.094
0.1	1.105	1.116	1.127	1.139	1.150	1.162	1.174	1.185	1.197	1.209
0.2	1.221	1.234	1.246	1.259	1.271	1.284	1.297	1.310	1.323	1.336
0.3	1.350	1.363	1.377	1.391	1.405	1.419	1.433	1.448	1.462	1.477
0.4	1.492	1.507	1.522	1.537	1.553	1.568	1.584	1.600	1.616	1.632
0.5	1.649	1.665	1.682	1.699	1.716	1.733	1.751	1.768	1.786	1.804
0.6	1.822	1.840	1.859	1.878	1.896	1.916	1.935	1.954	1.974	1.994
0.7	2.014	2.034	2.054	2.075	2.096	2.117	2.138	2.160	2.181	2.203
0.8	2.226	2.248	2.270	2.293	2.316	2.340	2.363	2.387	2.411	2.435
0.9	2.460	2.484	2.509	2.535	2.560	2.586	2.612	2.638	2.664	2.691
1.0	2.718	2.746	2.773	2.801	2.829	2.858	2.886	2.915	2.945	2.974
1.1	3.004	3.034	3.065	3.096	3.127	3.158	3.190	3.222	3.254	3.287
1.2	3.320	3.353	3.387	3.421	3.456	3.490	3.525	3.561	3.597	3.633
1.3	3.669	3.706	3.743	3.781	3.819	3.857	3.896	3.935	3.975	4.015
1.4	4.055	4.096	4.137	4.179	4.221	4.263	4.306	4.349	4.393	4.437
1.5	4.482	4.527	4.572	4.618	4.665	4.712	4.759	4.807	4.855	4.904
1.6	4.953	5.003	5.053	5.104	5.155	5.207	5.259	5.312	5.366	5.419
1.7	5.474	5.529	5.585	5.641	5.697	5.755	5.812	5.871	5.930	5.989
1.8	6.050	6.110	6.172	6.234	6.297	6.360	6.424	6.488	6.554	6.619
1.9	6.686	6.753	6.821	6.890	6.959	7.029	7.099	7.171	7.243	7.316
2.0	7.389	7.463	7.538	7.614	7.691	7.768	7.846	7.925	8.004	8.085
2.1	8.166	8.248	8.331	8.415	8.499	8.585	8.671	8.758	8.846	8.935
2.2	9.025	9.116	9.207	9.300	9.393	9.488	9.583	9.679	9.777	9.875
2.3	9.974	10.07	10.18	10.28	10.38	10.49	10.59	10.70	10.80	10.91
2.4	11.02	11.13	11.25	11.36	11.47	11.59	11.70	11.82	11.94	12.06
2.5	12.18	12.30	12.43	12.55	12.68	12.81	12.94	13.07	13.20	13.33
2.6	13.46	13.60	13.74	13.87	14.01	14.15	14.30	14.44	14.59	14.73
2.7	14.88	15.03	15.18	15.33	15.49	15.64	15.80	15.96	16.12	16.28
2.8	16.44	16.61	16.78	16.95	17.12	17.29	17.46	17.64	17.81	17.99
2.9	18.17	18.36	18.54	18.73	18.92	19.11	19.30	19.49	19.69	19.89
3.0	20.09	20.29	20.49	20.70	20.91	21.12	21.33	21.54	21.76	21.98
3.1	22.20	22.42	22.65	22.87	23.10	23.34	23.57	23.81	24.05	24.29
3.2	24.53	24.78	25.03	25.28	25.53	25.79	26.05	26.31	26.58	26.84
3.3	27.11	27.39	27.66	27.94	28.22	28.50	28.79	29.08	29.37	29.67
3.4	29.96	30.27	30.57	30.88	31.19	31.50	31.82	32.14	32.46	32.79

x	.0	.1	.2	.3	.4	.5	.6	.7	.8	.9
3	20.09	22.20	24.53	27.11	29.96	33.12	36.60	40.45	44.70	49.40
4	54.60	60.34	66.69	73.70	81.45	90.02	99.48	109.9	121.5	134.3
5	148.4	164.0	181.3	200.3	221.4	244.7	270.4	298.9	330.3	365.0
6	403.4	445.9	492.7	544.6	601.8	665.1	735.1	812.4	897.8	992.3
7	1097	1212	1339	1480	1636	1808	1998	2208	2441	2697
8	2981	3295	3641	4024	4447	4915	5432	6003	6634	7332
9	8103	8955	9897	10938	12088	13360	14765	16318	18034	19930

$$\log_{10} e^x = x \log_{10} e = 0.43429\, x$$

TABLE OF EXPONENTIALS

$$e^{-x}$$

x	0	1	2	3	4	5	6	7	8	9
0.0	1.000	.9900	.9802	.9704	.9608	.9512	.9418	.9324	.9231	.9139
0.1	.9048	.8958	.8869	.8781	.8694	.8607	.8521	.8437	.8353	.8270
0.2	.8187	.8106	.8025	.7945	.7866	.7788	.7711	.7634	.7558	.7483
0.3	.7408	.7334	.7261	.7189	.7118	.7047	.6977	.6907	.6839	.6771
0.4	.6703	.6637	.6570	.6505	.6440	.6376	.6313	.6250	.6188	.6126
0.5	.6065	.6005	.5945	.5886	.5827	.5769	.5712	.5655	.5599	.5543
0.6	.5488	.5434	.5379	.5326	.5273	.5220	.5169	.5117	.5066	.5016
0.7	.4966	.4916	.4868	.4819	.4771	.4724	.4677	.4630	.4584	.4538
0.8	.4493	.4449	.4404	.4360	.4317	.4274	.4232	.4190	.4148	.4107
0.9	.4066	.4025	.3985	.3946	.3906	.3867	.3829	.3791	.3753	.3716
1.0	.3679	.3642	.3606	.3570	.3535	.3499	.3465	.3430	.3396	.3362
1.1	.3329	.3296	.3263	.3230	.3198	.3166	.3135	.3104	.3073	.3042
1.2	.3012	.2982	.2952	.2923	.2894	.2865	.2837	.2808	.2780	.2753
1.3	.2725	.2698	.2671	.2645	.2618	.2592	.2567	.2541	.2516	.2491
1.4	.2466	.2441	.2417	.2393	.2369	.2346	.2322	.2299	.2276	.2254
1.5	.2231	.2209	.2187	.2165	.2144	.2122	.2101	.2080	.2060	.2039
1.6	.2019	.1999	.1979	.1959	.1940	.1920	.1901	.1882	.1864	.1845
1.7	.1827	.1809	.1791	.1773	.1755	.1738	.1720	.1703	.1686	.1670
1.8	.1653	.1637	.1620	.1604	.1588	.1572	.1557	.1541	.1526	.1511
1.9	.1496	.1481	.1466	.1451	.1437	.1423	.1409	.1395	.1381	.1367
2.0	.1353	.1340	.1327	.1313	.1300	.1287	.1275	.1262	.1249	.1237
2.1	.1225	.1212	.1200	.1188	.1177	.1165	.1153	.1142	.1130	.1119
2.2	.1108	.1097	.1086	.1075	.1065	.1054	.1043	.1033	.1023	.1013
2.3	.1003	*9926	*9827	*9730	*9633	*9537	*9442	*9348	*9255	*9163
2.4	0.0 9072	8982	8892	8804	8716	8629	8544	8458	8374	8291
2.5	0.0 8208	8127	8046	7966	7887	7808	7730	7654	7577	7502
2.6	0.0 7427	7353	7280	7208	7136	7065	6995	6925	6856	6788
2.7	0.0 6721	6654	6587	6522	6457	6393	6329	6266	6204	6142
2.8	0.0 6081	6020	5961	5901	5843	5784	5727	5670	5613	5558
2.9	0.0 5502	5448	5393	5340	5287	5234	5182	5130	5079	5029
3.0	0.0 4979	4929	4880	4832	4783	4736	4689	4642	4596	4550
3.1	0.0 4505	4460	4416	4372	4328	4285	4243	4200	4159	4117
3.2	0.0 4076	4036	3996	3956	3916	3877	3839	3801	3763	3725
3.3	0.0 3688	3652	3615	3579	3544	3508	3474	3439	3405	3371
3.4	0.0 3337	3304	3271	3239	3206	3175	3143	3112	3081	3050

x		.0	.1	.2	.3	.4	.5	.6	.7	.8	.9
3	0.0	4979	4505	4076	3688	3337	3020	2732	2472	2237	2024
4	0.0	1832	1657	1500	1357	1228	1111	1005	*9095	*8230	*7447
5	0.00	6738	6097	5517	4992	4517	4087	3698	3346	3028	2739
6	0.00	2479	2243	2029	1836	1662	1503	1360	1231	1114	1008
7	0.000	9119	8251	7466	6755	6112	5531	5004	4528	4097	3707
8	0.000	3355	3035	2747	2485	2249	2035	1841	1666	1507	1364
9	0.000	1234	1117	1010	*9142	*8272	*7485	*6773	*6128	*5545	*5017
10	0.0000	4540	4108	3717	3363	3043	2754	2492	2254	2040	1846

$$\log_{10} e^{-x} = -x \log_{10} e = -0.43429\, x$$

VOLUMES I AND II

INDEX

A

A-battery 1098
Abampere 1216
Abcoulomb 1216
Aberration
 chromatic 648, 721
 lens 647
 of light 583
 spherical 618, 647
Abohm 1216
Absolute
 ampere 1065
 electrical units 930, 1065, 1215
 humidity 420
 pressure 82
 systems of units 134, 455
  electrical 930, 1065, 1215
 volt 1066
 zero of temperature 323, 441
Absorber, perfect 771
Absorption
 of light 573, 734, 769
 of radiation 767
  Kirchoff's law 770
 of sound 557
  coefficients, TABLE 560
  measurement 560
 of waves 508
 spectra 769
Absorptivity 769
Abvolt 1216
AC 1011ff, 1033ff
 circuits 1033–1063
  parallel 1055
  power relations for 1050
  rotating vector for 1037
  vector diagram for 1033
 generators 1011
 motors 1018, 1022
Accelerated motion 99
 with constant acceleration 104–106
Acceleration 91, 99–104
 angular, *definition* 184
 average, *definition* 99
 centripetal 118
 instantaneous, *definition* 100

Acceleration (*cont.*)
 of center of gravity 205
 of charged particles 1181
 of gravity 107; TABLE 110
 tangential 188
Accelerators for particles 1181–1189
Accommodation 671
Achromatic lenses 647, 721
Acoustic amplifiers 517
Acoustics, architectural 558
Addition of vectors 12, 20–24
Adiabatic processes 426–432; *definition* 427
Adiabatics, GRAPH 430
Aerodynamics 292–309
Aeronautics 303–309
Air columns, vibrations of 523, 526–529
Airfoil 306
Air speed, indicated 306
Albedo 769
Alnico 973
Alpha particles 1166, 1173
Alternating current (*see* AC)
ALVAREZ, LUIS 1186
Ambient temperature 360
American Standard Definitions of Electrical Terms 785
American Wire Gauge 866
Ammeter 856, 1078, 1086
Ampère, André Marie 855, 856, 922, 939
Ampere, *definition* 856, 1064, 1065
Ampere-hour 913, 916
Ampère's law 939, 940
Ampère's line-integral law 956
Amperian currents 922
Amplification factor (μ) 1113
Amplifier, electronic 1115, 1116
 audio 535
Amplitude
 of a wave, *definition* 482
  sound 548
 of simple harmonic motion, *definition* 275
 angular, *definition* 280
Amplitude modulation (AM) 1147
Analogues, rotational, TABLE 202
 of Newton's laws 192, 265

1247

Analyzer 743
  harmonic 502
ANDERSON, C. D. 1197, 1213
Aneroid barometer 83
Angle 9–10; CONVERSION FACTORS 458, 1228
  critical 555, 629
  of dip 928, 980
  of incidence 552, 606, 625
  of reflection 552, 606
  of refraction 625
  of repose 66
  of shear 230
  of slip 66
  phase 274
  polarizing 745
  solid 459, 581, 1228
Angular
  acceleration, *definition* 184
  displacement, *definition* 182
  impulse 266
  momentum 265
  simple harmonic motion 279–281
  velocity, *definition* 183
Animate prime movers 178, 180
Anions 897
Anisotropic medium 752
Annihilation of matter 1199
Anode 897, 1100
Antenna
  electric-dipole 1142
  half-dipole 1146
  loop 1146
Antinode 500
Aperture 612
Aqueous humor 670
Arc discharge 1137
  lamp 590
ARCHIMEDES 82
Archimedes' theorem 80–82
Architectural acoustics 558
Area, CONVERSION FACTORS 458, 1228
Armature 1011, 1014, 1016, 1021
Astigmatism 648, 672
ASTON, FRANCIS W. 1199
Astronomical telescope 663
Atmosphere 82–85, 364–368, 377–380, 555–557, 632–634
  circulation patterns 367–368
  pressure and density at various heights 377
  (pressure unit), *definition* 83; VALUES 83, 371, 457; CONVERSION FACTORS 461, 1231
  refraction of light by 633
  refraction of sound by 555
  stratosphere 366
  temperature at various levels 379
  tropopause 366

Atmosphere (*cont.*)
  troposphere 366
  wind systems 367
Atom 1164
  Bohr model 781, 1167
  nuclear model 1166
  Rutherford's model 1166
  Thomson's model 1166
Atomic
  bomb 1201, 1207
  energy 1202
  mass unit (AMU), *definition* 373, 1197; VALUE 457, 1220
  nucleus 1167
  number (Z) 1165
  weights 370, 893; TABLE 458, 1222–1223
    chemical and physical scales 370, 457, 894, 1165, 1172
Atom smashers 1181
Attenuation 508
Atwood's machine 138–140
Audibility
  range of 534
  threshold 530
Audio-frequency modulation 1148
Auroral zones 980
Avogadro's law 370
Avogadro's number 373, 893–894; VALUE 373, 457, 1220
Axis 17, 181–182 (*see also* Coordinate systems *and* Rotation)
  fixed 191–193
  instantaneous 212
  of nutation 310–311
  of precession 310–311
  of rotation 30
  of spin 310–311
  principal, of inertia 205
  torque 30–34

B

B-battery 1098
Back-EMF 1009
BAINBRIDGE, K. T. 1170, 119
Bainbridge mass spectrograph 1172
Ballistic galvanometer 1091, 1094
Ballistics, external 143
BALMER, JOHANN JACOB 779
Balmer series 779
Band spectra 727, 782
Barn (unit of area) 1180
Barometer 82–87
Barrier-layer cell 1132
Battery (*see also* Cell) 909–917
  charge and discharge 874, 875
  storage 874, 912–916
  voltaic 858, 909–917

INDEX 1249

Beams, light 576
Beats 520, 562
BECQUEREL, HENRI 1173
Bel 530
BELL, ALEXANDER GRAHAM 530
Bell Telephone Laboratories 533
BERNOULLI, DANIEL 295
Bernoulli's theorem 292–299
  aeronautical applications 303–309
Beta particle 1166, 1174
Betatron 1187
Bimetallic strip 333
Binding energy of nuclei 1200
Binocular vision 580
BIRGE, R. T. 457, 1220
BLACK, JOSEPH 1164
Black body 594, 767; *definition* 770
  radiation 772, 774, 775, 1131
Black surface 771
Blind spot 671
BOHR, NIELS 781, 973, 1167
Bohr atom 781, 1167
Bohr magneton 970
Boiling 418–419
  points of various materials 328; TABLE 348, 1222
BOLTZMANN, LUDWIG 318, 394, 772
Boltzmann's constant (k), *definition* 392; VALUE 457, 1220
Bomb calorimeter 350–351
Boundary conditions 510
Boundary layer 301
Bound charges 844
Bourdon pressure gauge 85
BOYLE, ROBERT 369, 1164
Boyle's law 369
BOZORTH, R. M. 994
Brackett series 779
BRADLEY, JAMES 583
BRAHE, TYCHO 145
Brake, Prony 203
Breaking strength 216, 238
BREWSTER, DAVID 745
Brewster's angle 745
Brewster's law 746
British engineering system of units 134, 455
British thermal unit (BTU), *definition* 342
Broadcast bands for radio 1147
BROWN, ROBERT 397
Brownian motion 396–397
BÜCHERER 1189
Bulk modulus 227–230; TABLE 224
Bunsen grease-spot photometer 600
Buoyant forces 87–89
Bureau of Standards, U.S. 8, 137, 328, 594, 596, 1064, 1211

C

C-battery 1112
Cable, coaxial 833–958
California, University of 1182, 1185, 1186, 1213
Caloric 318
Calorie, *definition* 342
Calorimeter 341, 350
Calorimetry 341–352
Camera
  photographic 656
  pinhole 577
Candle 594
  new standard 594
Candlepower 593, 598
  mean 598
Capacitance 833–854; *definition* 836; UNITS 836, 1215; CONVERSION FACTORS 1234
  measurement of 1088
  role in AC circuits 1037, 1044, 1055
Capacitive reactance 1039
Capacitor (*see* Condenser)
Capacity (*see* Capacitance)
Capture, radiative 1203
Carbon, electrical conductivity of 871
Carnegie Institution of Washington 981
CARNOT, SADI 432
Carnot cycle 432–437
  efficiency 444
  performance coefficient 446
Carrier, RF 1147
Cathode
  of electrolytic cell 897
  of vacuum tube 1100
  reactions 904, 896–901
  surfaces 1102
Cathode-ray oscillograph (*see also* Electron-ray oscillograph) 797, 1119
Cations 897
Caustic curve 618
CAVENDISH, HENRY 136, 1164
Cavitation 298
Cell
  Daniell 902
  dry 874, 911
    polarization of 911
  primary 909
  standard 909
  storage 909, 912
    Edison 912
    lead-acid 912, 915
  Weston standard 910
Center of curvature 612
Center of gravity 51–58; *definition* 53
  acceleration of 205
  moment of inertia about axis through 197

Center of gravity (*cont.*)
  momentum associated with 247
  motion of, for a system 248–249
  potential energy determined by position of 207
  rotation about axis through 205
Center of mass (*see* Center of gravity), *definition* 247
Center of oscillation (percussion) 285
Centimeter, *definition* 9
Centripetal acceleration 118
Centripetal force 144
CGS system of units 455–456
  electromagnetic 1215
  electrostatic 1215
CHADWICK, JAMES 1177
Chain reaction 1204
  pile 1204, 1206, 1208
Characteristic curves for vacuum tubes
  diode 1102
  triode 1112
Charge (*see also* Electric charge) 785
Charging by induction 790, 820
Charles' law 370
Chemical elements 1164, 1221; TABLES 1221, 1222, 1224
Chemical energy 161, 350–352, 858, 891, 901, 905
  of fuels 178–179; TABLE 351
  source of EMF 858
Choke coil 1043
Chromatic aberration 648, 721
Chromosphere 728
Circle of confusion 658
Circuits (*see also* Electric circuits and Magnetic circuits)
  containing R and C 1037
  containing R and L 1041
  containing R, C, and L 1044
  DC 876–881
  magnetic 982–998
Circular mil, *definition* 863
Circular motion 116–118, 267–270
Classical physics 1097
Claude apparatus 451
CLAUSIUS 318
Cloud chamber 431
  photographs 967, 968, 1162, 1177, 1198
Coaxial cable 833, 958
COCKCROFT, J. D. 1201
Coefficient of (*see quantity involved*)
Coercive force 997
COHEN, E. R. 457, 1220
Collimator 716
Collisions 249–261
  elastic 249–254; *definition* 250
  imperfectly elastic 254–258; *definition* 255
  inelastic 259–261; *definition* 250

Color 731, 732, 734
  of light 731, 732
  of pigments 734
  sensation 731
Combination tones 564
Combustion, heat of 350–352; TABLE 351
Commutator 1015
  ripple 1015
Components
  force 28
  rectangular 15
  vector 24
Composition of vectors 12
Compound lens 722
Compound microscope 660
Compression 227
  of a gas 426, 432
COMPTON, A. H. 1158, 1195
Compton effect 1158, 1195
Concave mirror 611
Concentric conductors 833, 837
Concurrent forces 41
Condensation 402–409
Condensations (in longitudinal wave) 479
Condensers (electrical) 833–854
  cylindrical 833
  current from 855, 1038
  energy of 847
  in electrical filters 1106
  in parallel and series 849
  parallel-plate 841
  spherical 837
Conductance, *definition* 859
Conduction of electricity
  electrolytic 896
  in gases 1134
  in metals 862
Conduction of heat 353–359
  coefficient of 355; TABLE 357
Conductivity
  electrical 866
  thermal 355; TABLE 357
Conductor of electricity 789
Cones (receptors) 671
Conservation
  of angular momentum 265–266
  of energy 148, 158–164
  of linear momentum 240, 244–249
  of mechanical energy 148, 156, 159
Constants, fundamental physical, TABLE 458, 1220
Continuous spectra 726
Continuous wave 482
Control grid 1109
Convection 353, 359–363
Convergent light beams 576
Converging lens 636
Conversion factors, TABLES 458–462, 1228–1236

Convex mirror 612
Cooling 360–364
  Newton's law of 360
  of water 363
  time constant of 361
Coordinate systems 10–12
  inertial 304
Coplanar forces 45–51
Coplanar vectors 22
Copper plating 899
Copper wire, electrical properties of, TABLE 865
Cornea 670
Corner reflector 611
Corona discharge 1137
Cosines, TABLE 464–465, 1238–1239
Cosmic rays 1214
Cotangents, TABLE 466–467, 1240–1241
COTTON, A. A. 764
Cotton-Mouton effect 764
COULOMB, CHARLES AUGUSTIN 787
Coulomb, *definition* 791, 1064
Coulometer 900
Counter-EMF 1009
CRANE, H. R. 1187
Crest 478
Critical
  angle 555, 629
  constants, TABLE 413
  damping 289, 1075, 1076
  mass 1207
  point 412–414
  pressure 413
  temperature 413
Crystalline lens 670
Crystals 398–399
Current (*see also* Electric current, AC, *and* DC) 855
  a fundamental quantity 1218
  units, CONVERSION FACTORS 1233
Current balance 1064
Current element 925
  forces on 931, 932, 937
CURTIS, H. L. 1065
Curvature, center of 612
Cycle 367
  Carnot 432–437
  Rankine 443–444
Cyclotron 965, 1182, 1185, 1213
  magnet 992, 993

D

DALTON, JOHN 373, 1164
Dalton's law of partial pressures 372–374
Damped harmonic motion 387–388
Damping
  critical 289
  force 387

Damping (*cont.*)
  galvanometer 1075
  over- 289
Daniell cell 902
  electrode reactions in 903
D'Arsonval galvanometer 1074
DAVISSON, C. J. 1161
Day, *definition* 93
DC (direct current) 855–890
  dynamo, homopolar 1006
  generator 874, 932, 934, 1017
    series wound 1017
    shunt wound 1017
    voltage, current, power relations for 1010
  power supply 1106
DE BROGLIE, LOUIS VICTOR 1161
Deceleration 101
Decibel, *definition* 530
Declination 980
DEFOREST 1109
Deformation 216–220, 222
Deforming force 217
Degree (*see* Angle, Electrical, Temperature)
  of freedom 395
DEMPSTER, A. J. 1199
Density, *definition* 126; CONVERSION FACTORS 460, 1230; TABLES 125, 1222
  flux (*see* Flux)
  of air 414
  of CO_2 415
  of gases 369–379
  of H_2O 417
  of solids and liquids, TABLE 125
  of water, VALUES 338
  specific volume of water, TABLE 404–405
Department of Weights and Measures, USSR 1064
Depth of focus 658
DESCARTES, RENÉ 626
Detectors 1149
  of radiation 1158
Deuterium 1171
Deuteron 1171
Deviation of light by prism 631
  angle of, minimum 632
Dew point, definition 421
Dextrorotatory liquids 760
Diamagnetism 969
Dielectric 789
  constant 843; *definition* 845; TABLE 846
  polarization 794, 844
  strength 843; *definition* 852; TABLE 846
Diesel engine 427
Difference of potential (DP), *definition* 806

Diffraction 574, 690–711
  grating 708
  of electrons 1161
  of light 574, 690
    Fraunhofer 693, 701
    Fresnel 693
  of sound 564
  of X rays 1160
  patterns 693, 708
Diode 1102, 1104
Diopter, *definition* 644
Dip, angle of 928, 980
Dipole
  electric 804, 1142
  magnetic 953–954
  moment (magnetic) 949
  oscillating 1143
Direct current (*see* DC)
Disintegration, radioactive 1173
Dispersion 574, 713, 719
  angular 719
  linear 719
Dispersive medium 497
Dispersive power, *definition* 719
  mean 722
Displacement 17–20
  angular, *definition* 182
  flux (electric) 815
Dissipation of mechanical energy 160–161, 318–319
Dissipative forces 148
Distorting force 217
Distortion of sounds 518
Divergent light beams 576
Diverging lens 636
Doldrums 366
Domain, magnetic 974
Doppler effect 564
Double refraction 751–759
Doubly refracting medium 753
Drag (fluid dynamics) 366
Driving force 288
Dry cell 874, 911
  polarization of 911
DuMond, J. W. M. 457, 1220
Dushman, Saul 1101
Dynamic pressure 306
Dynamics 17, 120–134
  of fluids 292–309
  of gyroscopic motion 311–313
  of pure rotation 181, 191–193
  of rotation and translation in a plane 204–208
  of translation 120–124
Dynamo 874, 1006–1008
  power relationships 1008
Dynamometer (Electro-) 1080
Dyne, *definition* 455

E

Ear 532
Earth, atmosphere of 364–368, 377–380
  magnetic field of 976–981
  mass of 146
Echoes 551
Eddy current 1018
  brake 1019
  production 1019
Edison, Thomas Alva 591, 913, 1098
Effective values of current and voltage 1050
Efficiency, *definition* 164–165
  of a heat engine 432–435, 444
  of light sources 604
    fluorescent lamps, TABLE 604
    luminous, *definition* 605
    tungsten lamps, TABLE 604
  of machine 164–165, 176
Einstein, Albert 304, 1131, 1133, 1189, 1194, 1195
Einstein's photoelectric equation 1131, 1133
Einstein's relativity theory 1162
Elastic (*see also* Elasticity)
  body, *definition* 215
  collision 249–258; *definition* 250
  constants (moduli of elasticity), TABLE 224
    relations between 235–237
  force 216, 218
  limit 216, 237–239; TABLE 239
  potential energy 152, 218
  properties of rubber 220
Elasticity 26, 27, 215–239
  bulk modulus 227–230; *definition* 228
  moduli of, TABLE 224
  modulus of, in tension, *definition* 223
  of length 221–227
  of shape 230–235
  Poisson's ratio, *definition* 236
  shear modulus (modulus of rigidity) 230–235; *definition* 232
  volume 227–230
  Young's modulus, *definition* 223
Electric (*see also* Electrical)
  charge 785
    net 789
    on conductor 812
    point 787
    surface density 816
    units, CONVERSION FACTORS 1233
  circuits (*see also* Circuits) 876–890, 1037, 1041–1045
  current (*see also* Current) 855
    alternating (*see also* AC) 1033–1063
    direct (*see also* DC) 857
    direction of 855

INDEX 1253

Electric (*cont.*)
  current (*cont.*)
    effective 1050
    in a magnetic field 932
    magnetic effects of 922
    thermal effects of 860
    transient 857
    units, CONVERSION FACTORS 1233
  current element 925, 931
    forces on 931, 937
  dipole 1142
  field 750, 796
    average 816
    propagation of 1139
    resultant 801
    strength 797
  flux, *definition* 815
    through a tube of force 831
  intensity 796, 800; *definition* 797
    units 808
  lens 1124
  line of force 799
  potential 806
  vector of light waves 740
  vibrations 751
Electrical (*see also* Electric)
  breakdown in gases 1135
  conductivity, *definition* 866
    of carbon 871
  degrees 1034
  energy 861, 874
  filters 1106
  networks 881
  resistance (*see also* Resistance) 1233
  resistivity (*see also* Resistivity) 862
  resonance 1046
  systems of units 792, 930, 1064, 1215, 1219
Electricity (*see also* Electric charge) 26, 785ff
  conduction of 789, 896, 1134
  negative, *definition* 786
  positive, *definition* 786
Electrochemical equivalent 901
Electrochemical series 905; TABLE 906
Electrochemistry 891
Electrode 896, 1098, 1109
  reactions 899, 904
Electrolux refrigerator 445
Electrolysis 896–897, 901
Electrolytic cell 896
  local fields in 899
Electrolytic conduction 896
Electromagnetic
  induction 999
  radiation 1140
    from an oscillating dipole 1145
  spectrum 575, 1152; CHART 1156

Electromagnetic (*cont.*):
  system of units 791, 1068, 1215
    CGS 791, 1215
    MKS 1064–1073, 1215
  theory 767
  waves 750, 1138
Electromagnetism 922
Electromotive force (*see* EMF)
Electromotive series 905
Electron 788, 793, 1213
  charge 793; VALUE 1220
  deflection of 1119
  diffraction 1161
  free 789, 1099
  microscope 1124, 1129
  multiplier tube 1131
  optics 1124
  ray oscillograph 797, 1118, 1123
  rays 1124
  spin 970
  wave properties 1161
Electron-volt, *definition* 891
Electronic
  amplifiers 535, 1097, 1114
  charge (*e*) 793, 1167; VALUE 1220
    specific (*e/m*) 1168
  energy levels 1157
Electronics 923, 1097
Electro-optical effects 763
Electrophorus 821
Electroscope 822
  measurement of potential by 824
Electrostatic
  deflection of electrons 1121
  lens 1126
  shielding 818
  system of units 791, 1215
  voltmeter 825
Electrostatics 785–854, 922
Electrotechnical Laboratory, Japan 1064
Elementary particles 1164; LIST 1213
Elements, chemical 1164; TABLES 1221, 1222, 1224
Elliptical polarization of light 757
ELVIOS 324
EMF (electromotive force) 858
  chemical energy as source of 858
  counter- 1009
  induced 999, 1003
  of Edison cell 916
  of lead-acid cell 916
  sources of 858, 873
  thermal 920
  units, CONVERSION FACTORS 1233
Emission
  of electrons 1098, 1101, 1130
    secondary 1131
  of light 575

Emission (*cont.*)
  of radiation 767
    Kirchhoff's law 770
  spectra 726
Emissive power 769
  spectral 774
Emissivity, *definition* 773
Endothermic reaction 350
Energy 148, 151–155; CONVERSION FACTORS 462, 1232
  chemical 161, 178–179, 350–352, 858
  conservation 148, 158–164, 1195
  dissipation of mechanical 160–161, 318–319
  electrical 161
    of a condenser 847
  environmental 179
  equipartition of 394–396
  internal 380–382
    of nuclei 1200
  kinetic 151–153; *definition* 152
    molecular 391
    rotational 153, 199–200
    translational 153
  level diagrams 780
  macroscopic mechanical 319
    associated with a wave 494
  magnetic 161
    associated with a coil 1027
  mass equivalent 1193–1196; CONVERSION FACTORS 1236
  materialization of 1196
  mechanical 155–156
  microscopic mechanical 319
  nuclear 161, 1193–1196, 1206–1208
  potential 151–152; *definition* 152
    elastic 152, 218
    gravitational 151, 153–155
  radiant (*see also* Radiation) 161, 180, 353, 767
  relations in relativity theory 1193
  rest 1196
  solar 364–365, 1201
  thermal 161; *definition* 320
  transformations 155–158, 161, 1196
Engines (*see also* Heat engines) 432–445
Enlargement, *definition* 651
Entropy 430
Equation of state 370–371
Equilibrium 40–51
  concurrent forces 41–43
  coplanar forces 45–51, 58–61
  fluid 73–90
  noncoplanar forces 71–72
  of a particle 41–43
  of a rigid body 45–51
  position in harmonic motion 271
  rotational 40
  translational 40

Equipartition of energy 294–296
Equipotential surfaces 808
Equivalence of mass and energy 1193, 1195; CONVERSION FACTORS 1236
Erect image 617
Erecting telescope 667
EWING, ALFRED 972
Excited states 781
Exothermic reactions 350
Expansion (*see also* Thermal expansion)
  of a gas 426, 432
Exponential functions, TABLES 470–471, 1244–1245
Exposure meter 1132
External
  ballistics 143
  force 38, 122
  work 380–382
Extraordinary ray 759
Eye 669–675, 1158
  sensitivity 675, 1158
Eyepiece 600, 664

F

f-number 657
FAHRENHEIT, GABRIEL DANIEL 324
Fahrenheit scale of temperature 324
Falling bodies 106–111
Farad, *definition* 836
FARADAY, MICHAEL 763, 836, 858, 900, 999
Faraday, *definition* 893, 895
Faraday effect 763
Faraday's laws of electrolysis 900ff
Fathometer 569
Feed-back networks 1116
FERMI, ENRICO 1116, 1202
Ferromagnetism 969, 971, 972
Filament (cathode) 1098–1103
  oxide-coated 1102, 1103
  thoriated-tungsten 1103
  tungsten 1102
Filters
  electrical 1106–1108
  optical 733, 737
Field (*see* Electric *and* Magnetic)
First law (*see* Newton's laws *and* Thermodynamics)
Fission, nuclear 1203, 1208
FIZEAU, A. H. L. 584
FLETCHER, HARVEY 532
Flicker photometer 602
Flow
  steady 292, 293
  supersonic 292, 309, 431
  through orifice 296
Flowmeter 298

Fluid 73-82, 292-309; *definition* 75
  dynamics 292-309
  equilibrium 80
  normal forces exerted by 74
  pressure 73-77
  statics 73-82
  viscosity 293, 300-303
Fluorescent lamps 592
  efficiency, TABLE 604
Flux
  displacement 815
  electric 815
    through a tube of force 831
  light 593
  luminous 593
  magnetic 947
    density 948
  radiant 605
Fluxmeter 984, 1091-1094
Focal length 614, 639
Focal point, principal 614, 639
Focus
  depth of 658
  principal 614, 639
Food, chemical energy of 179, 342; TABLE 351
Foot, *definition* 9
Foot-candle, *definition* 593
Foot·pound-force (ft·lbf), *definition* 150
Force 13, 25-30, 122, 126-128
  buoyant 87-89
  centripetal 144
  damping 287
  deforming 217
  dissipative 148
  distorting 217, 220
  driving 288
  elastic 216-218
  electrical 785
  external 38, 122
  frictional 63
  gravitational 26, 131-136
  impulsive 242
  magnetic 929, 933, 949
  normal 63, 65
  nuclear 1212
  reaction 36, 130, 217, 220, 263
  restoring 271
  resultant 29, 38
  units 27-28, 128, 131-135, 455-457; CONVERSION FACTORS 461, 1231
Force constant of a spring, *definition* 271, 273
Forced vibrations 288-291
FOUCAULT, J. B. L. 314, 585
Foucault pendulum 304
FOURIER 501
Fourier series 502
  theorem 501

Fovea centralis 672
FPS system of units 128, 455
FRANCK, JAMES 782
FRAUNHOFER, JOSEPH VON 728
Fraunhofer diffraction 693, 701
Fraunhofer lines 728
Free charges 844
  electrons 789, 1099
Freedom, degrees of 395
Free-expansion experiment 381
Freezing 398-402
  of water 363, 400
  points, TABLE 348, 1222
French Academy 521
Frequency, *definition* 267
  fundamental 511
  measurements 518
  modulation 1147, 1152
  natural 290
  of angular simple harmonic motion 280
  of generated voltage 1014
  of physical pendulum 284
  of simple harmonic motion 274
  of simple pendulum 282
  of sinusoidal waves 482
  resonant 291
  threshold 1130
FRESNEL, AUGUST JEAN 677
Fresnel
  bi-prism 678
  diffraction 693
  double mirror 678
  experiments 677
  zones 693
Friction 26, 61-69, 71
  coefficient of, TABLE 65
  kinetic 62, 64
  laws of 64, 70-71
  skin 302
  static 62, 64
  torque produced by 209
  work done against 160-161, 211, 318
FRISCH, OTTO R. 1203
Fundamental frequency, *definition* 511
Fundamental physical constants, TABLE 457, 1220
Fusion 346-349, 398-402
  latent heat of, *definition* 347, 401; TABLE 348

G

Galilean telescope 668
GALILEO 106, 121, 131, 241, 581, 668
Galton whistle 568
Galvanic pile 858
Galvanometer 1074
  ballistic 1091, 1094
  D'Arsonval 1074

Gamma (magnetic field unit), *definition* 977
Gamma ray 1158, 1174
  photons 1197
Gas 73, 369–397, 414–417
  constant (R) 371–372; VALUE 372, 374, 385, 457, 1220
  external work done by 380–382
  ideal 369
  internal energy 380–382
  laws 369–377
  mole of 371
  specific heats 382–388, 394–396; VALUES 385–386
    at constant pressure 383–388
    at constant volume 382–383
    ratio of 387
  thermometer 375
  work done by 383
Gases
  kinetic theory of 388–396
  liquefaction of 450–452
  mixtures of 419–423
  properties of 369–397
  real 414–417
  specific heats of 382–388, 394–396
Gas-discharge tube 1134
Gauge pressure 82
Gauges, pressure 82, 85
GAUSS, KARL FRIEDRICH 930
Gauss, *definition* 994, 1216
Gauss's theorem 826
GAY-LUSSAC 370
General gas law 370
Generator, electric 874, 1001, 1007, 1011, 1016
Geomagnetic axis and equator 977
Geometrical optics 606, 676
Geophysical methods of prospecting 137
GERMER, L. H. 1161
GIBBS, WILLARD 318
Gibbs-Helmholtz relation 909
Gilbert, *definition* 1217
GIORGI 1215
Glow-discharge lamp 591
Glow-discharge tube 1135
GOUDSMIT, SAMUEL 970
Gradient, potential 808
Grating 708–710, 724–725
  diffraction 708
  reflection 710
  replica 710
  spectrograph 724
  spectrometer 725
  transmission 709
Gravitation, universal 26, 135–138
  constant (G) 136; VALUE 457
Gravitational systems of units 131–135, 455

Gravity
  acceleration of 107; TABLE 110
  center of (*see also* Center of gravity) 51–58
  force of 26, 131–136
  standard 131, 455
Gravity meter 138
Gray body 773
Greenhouse effect 365
Grid, control 1109–1111
  current 1111
Ground state 781
Group velocity 497
GURNEY, R. W. 891
Gyration, radius of 195
Gyrocompass 314
Gyroscope 311–314
  directional 314
  free 313
Gyroscopic motion 310–314

H

$\mathcal{H}$, line integral law for 990
HAHN, OTTO 1203
Half-life 1175
Hanford pile 1210
Harmonic analysis 502
Harmonic motion 270–279
  damped 287–288
Harmonics 511
Hartley oscillator 1117
Harwell pile 1211
Heat 148, 161, 317ff; *definition* 321; CONVERSION FACTORS 462, 1232
  conduction 353–359
    coefficient of, *definition* 355; TABLE 357
  conductivity, *definition* 355; TABLE 357
  engines 179, 432–435
  insulators 356
  latent 346–350; TABLE 348
    of sublimation and vaporization for H_2O, TABLE 404–405
  of combustion 350–352; TABLE 351
  of reaction 350, 895
  produced by electric current 860
  pump 448–449
  quantity 341–346
  reversible 907
  specific 343–346
    of gases 383–388, 394–396; VALUES 385–386
    of solids and liquids, TABLE 344
    of water, VALUES 344
  transfer methods 353–354
    in atmosphere 364–368
HEISENBERG, WERNER 782, 973, 1161

INDEX

Helmholtz 148, 318, 674
Helmholtz coils 947
Henry, Joseph 858, 999, 1023
Henry, *definition* 1023
Hertz, Gustav 782
Hertz, Heinrich 1130, 1140
Hertzian waves 1141
Heyl, P. R. 137
Hiroshima 1208, 1212
Hooke 216
Hooke's law 215–221
   generalization 221–227
Horizontal, *definition* 26
Horse latitudes 367
Horsepower, *definition* 173
Horsepower·hour, *definition* 174
Human voice 528
Humidity 419–422
   absolute, *definition* 420
   relative, *definition* 420
Huygens, Christian 690
Huygens' principle 691
Hydraulic machines (elevator, jack, press) 90, 172
Hydraulics 292
Hydrodynamics 292
Hydrogen atom 781
   bomb 1201, 1208
   electrode 906
Hydrometer 89
Hydrometry 419–423
Hydrophone 522
Hypermetropia 672
Hysteresis loop 997

I

Ideal
   gas 369
   heat engine 432–435
   mechanical advantage 165
   radiator 768
   refrigerator 435
Illinois, University of 1188
Illumination 590, 593, 599; *definition* 596
Image 608ff
   distance 614
   erect 617
   inverted 617
   real 614
   virtual 609
Impacts 249–261
Impedance 1040ff, 1042, 1045
Imperfectly elastic collisions 354–358
Impulse 240, 242–244
   angular 266
   turbine 260
Impulsive forces 242
Inanimate prime movers 178

Incandescent lamp 591
Incidence, angle of 552, 606, 625
Inclination, angle of 580
Inclined plane (as a machine) 166
Incompressibility 292
Index of refraction 626, 628; tables 628, 720
Indicator diagram 442
Induced charges 789
Induced emf 999ff, 1003
Inductance 1022ff, 1088
   in circuits 1028, 1041–1044
   mutual 1022–1023
   self 1024ff
      energy of 1027
   units, conversion factors 1234
Induction
   accelerator 1187
   charging by 790ff, 820ff
   coil 1024
   electromagnetic 999ff
   motor 1020
Inductive reactance 1042
Industrial Revolution 180, 442
Inelastic collisions 259–261
Inelastic materials 216
Inertia 38, 122
   factor in harmonic motion 280
   moment of 192, 193–198, 205; *definition* 193
   rotational 192
Inertial coordinate systems 304
Infrared radiation 575, 1156
   spectrograph 730
Infrasonic waves 509
Insulator
   electric 789
   heat 356
Intensity
   electric 797
   magnetic 924
   of light sources 592ff
   of sound waves 529ff, 545
      relation to frequency 548
      relation to pressure variations 549
      relation to wave amplitude 548
Interactions 122
Interference 496ff, 501, 676ff, 682
   constructive 498
   destructive 498
   of light waves 574
      fringes 678
      in thin films 679
      patterns 678, 684
      Young's experiments 692
   of sound waves 561
Interferometer 687
   measurement of wavelength by 689
Intermediate frequency (if) 1151

1258 INDEX

Internal
  energy 380–382
  forces 416, 222–232
    gas 416
    solid 222–232
  resistance 874
Internal-combustion engine 427
International
  Bureau of Weights and Measures 7, 27, 125
  candle 594
  Committee on Weights and Measures 594, 1064
  electrical units 1065
  Electrotechnical Commission 1215
    recommendations 1220
  meter, optical reproduction 690
Inverted images 617
Ionization processes 1135
Ions 896ff, 1135ff
  electrolytic 896
  in gases 1134–1135
IR-drop 874ff
Iris 670
Iron, magnetic properties of 969, 994
Isentropic process 430
Isothermal process 414, 415, 417, 429, 430
Isotopes 370, 1170
  masses and abundances 1172; TABLE, 1224
  oxygen 893
Isotropic optical medium 751

J

Jackscrew 168
Jet propulsion 264
JOULE, JAMES PRESCOTT 148, 318, 381
Joule, *definition* 150
Joule's free-expansion experiment 381

K

KAUFMANN 1189
Kaufmann-Bücherer experiment 1193
KELVIN, LORD 318, 325, 440
Kelvin double bridge 1088
Kelvin temperature scale 327, 440
KEPLER 145
KERR, JOHN 764
Kerr effect 764
KERST, DONALD 1188
Kilocalorie, *definition* 342
  per mole, *definition* 893
Kilogram force (kgf), *definition* 27, 132
Kilogram mass (kg), *definition* 125
Kilowatt, *definition* 173
Kilowatt-hour, *definition* 174

Kinematics 91–119, 181–187, 310–311
  of gyroscopic motion 310–311
  of rotation 181–187
  of translation 91–119
Kinetic energy 151; *definition* 152
  in relativity 1193
  of rotation 199–200
  of translation 151–153
Kinetic friction 62–71
  coefficient of, *definition* 64; TABLE 65
Kinetic theory of gases 388–394
KIRCHHOFF 770, 871, 881
Kirchhoff's laws
  of electrical networks 878, 881–883
  of emission and absorption 770
Klystron 1154
Krakatao explosion 556
Kundt's tube 539, 560

L

Laboratoire Central d'Électricité 1064
Lag angle in AC 1034
Laminated armature 1019
Lamps 591ff
LAND, EDWIN H. 742
LAPLACE 542
Latent heat (*see* Fusion, Vaporization, *or* Sublimation)
Laval nozzle 431
LAVOISIER 1164
LAWRENCE, E. O. 1182, 1186
Lead-acid cell 916
Lead angle in AC 1034
Least confusion, circle of 658
Le Châtelier-Braun principle 452–453, 908, 918, 1002
Length 7–10, 13; CONVERSION FACTORS 458, 1228
Lens 636ff
  aberrations of 647
  achromatic 647, 721
  axis 636
  combinations of 645
  converging 636
  diverging 636
  electrostatic 1124, 1126
  equation 639
  focal length 639
  focal point, principal 639
  magnetic 1124
  negative 644
  optical center 640
  positive 644
  power of 644
  principal rays for 640
  thick 647
  wave treatment of 711
Lensmaker's equation 644

INDEX 1259

Lenz, H. F. E. 1004
Lenz's law 1004
Lever 167
Lever arm, *definition* 31
Lift (aerodynamic) 306
Light 573–782
  aberration of 583
  beams 576
  diffraction of 574, 690ff
  dispersion of 574, 713ff
  emission of 575, 767, 726
  flux 593
  interference 574, 678ff
  meter 602, 1132
  nature of 573
  particle theory 683
  polarization of 574, 740ff
  ray 576
  rectilinear propagation 575
  reflection 574, 606ff
  refraction 574, 606, 624ff
  scattering 738
  sources 590, 598
    efficiency of 604
    intensity of 592
    isotropic point 592
    standard 594
  speed of 581, 585, 1139, 1189
    a limiting speed 1192
  waves 574, 740ff
Limit, elastic 216, 237–239
Linde apparatus 451
Line of force, electric 799, 804, 817
Line-integral law
  Ampère's 956
  for $\mathcal{H}$ 990
Linear
  accelerator 1186
  displacement (*see also* Translation) 17
  expansion 330–331
  momentum (*see also* Momentum) 241–242
  motion 104–106
Linnaeus 324
Liquefaction of gases 450–452
Liquids (*see also* Fluids) 73, 336–338, 398–414
Local oscillator 1151
Lodestone 922
Logarithms, TABLE 468–469, 1242–1243
Longitudinal wave 479ff, 485ff
Looming 634
Loop antenna 1146
Loops 500
Loudness 529
Loudspeaker 536–537
Lumen 593; 595–596
Luminous efficiency 605
Luminous flux 593, 595

Lummer-Brodhun photometer 601
Lyman series 779

M

Machines 164–172
  efficiency of 164–165
  ideal mechanical advantage of 165
  mechanical advantage of 164
Magdeburg hemispheres 87
Magnet, permanent 953, 967ff, 973
  field of 953–954
  forces 952
  torque on 929
Magnetic
  alloys 996
  circuit 982ff, 985, 988
    air gaps in 992
    parallel 993
    series 990
  compass 922, 925, 928
  deflection of elections 1120, 1122
  dipole 953
  dipping needle 928
  domains 974
  effects of electric current 922ff
  field 922ff
    energy stored in 1027, 161
    force on a moving charge in 964
    force on conductor in 932
    force on current element in 931, 937
    force on electron in 965, 1127
    of a coaxial cable 958
    of a circular coil 942
    of a long straight wire 941, 947, 957
    of a solenoid 942, 950ff, 953, 961, 963
    of a square coil 941
    of a toroid 954, 959
    of the earth 976ff
      effect of sunspots on 980
    produced by electric current 938ff
    propagation of 1139
    strength $\mathcal{B}$ 123ff; *definition* 925, 930;
      UNITS AND CONVERSION FACTORS 931, 1255
  flux 947; CONVERSION FACTORS 1235
    density 923ff, 930
    fringing in air gaps 993
    residual 997
    through a thin solenoid 955
    through a tube 947
  forces between moving changes 923
  induction $\mathcal{B}$ 924
  intensity $\mathcal{H}$ 924
  lens 1124, 1128
  lines 927ff, 939
  materials 973ff, 982, 994
    hard 973
    ideal 982–983

Magnetic (cont.)
  materials (cont.)
    real 982, 994
    soft 973
  mine 946, 1006
  moment 925ff, 930; definition 930
    of a bar magnet 949
    of a coil 926ff, 930, 936
    per unit volume 974
  needle 925
  pole (concept) 949ff, 950
    force on 949, 954
  storms 980
  tube, 947
  vector $\mathcal{B}$ 924, 926
Magnetism 26, 922ff, 949ff, 973ff
Magnetization
  curve 995, 996
  intensity of 995
  of a toroid 984
Magnetizing force $\mathcal{H}$ 983–985; CONVERSION FACTORS 1236
  inside a permanent magnet 998
Magnetomotive force (MMF) 986; CONVERSION FACTORS 1235
Magneton 970
Magneto-optical effects 763
Magnetostatics 922
Magnetostriction oscillators 568
Magnification 651
Magnifier, simple 652
Magnifying glass 652
Magnifying power 651
Magnitude of a vector 7, 12, 13
MALUS, ETIENNE LOUIS 745
Manometer 85
Mass 122–126, 1189–1191; CONVERSION FACTORS 459, 1229
  conservation of 1195
  energy equivalence 1193–1196; CONVERSION FACTORS 1236
  Newtonian invariant 1189
  number 1172
  of the earth 146
  of the sun 145
  relativistic relations 1191
  rest 1191
  spectrograph 965, 1169–1173
  spectrum 1171
  standard 8, 125
Mathematical tables 464–471, 1238–1245
MATTAUCH, J. 1224
Matter
  annihilation of 1199
  electrical structure of 788
MAXWELL, JAMES CLERK 318, 394, 767, 1138, 1140
Maxwell, definition 1091, 1216
Maxwellian distribution 393

MAYER 148
Mean free path 388–389
Mean solar day, definition 93
Mechanical advantage 164–165
Mechanical energy 155–156
  conservation of 156, 159
  dissipation of 160
  environmental 179
  macroscopic 319
  microscopic 313
  transmission by waves 494
Mechanical equivalent of heat 343, 425, 457, 1220
Mechanical units, systems of 455–457
Mechanical waves 476ff
Mechanics 7ff
  quantum 121, 782, 1161
  relativistic 1191
Medium, optical 751, 752
MEITNER, LISE 1203
Melting points 328, 348, 400; TABLES 348, 1222
MENDELEEF, DMITRI I. 1165
Mercury-vapor lamp 591
Meson (mesotron) 1212–1213
Meter, definition 7, 8
MICHELSON, A. A. 585, 687, 1190
Michelson's interferometer 687–689
Michelson's measurement of the speed of light 585
Michelson-Morley experiment 1190
Michigan, University of 1187
Micron, definition 9
Microphone 536
Microscope 653, 660ff
  compound 660
  electron 1124–1129
  simple 653
Microwaves 587, 1153
MILLIKAN, ROBERT A. 1167
Millimicron, definition 574
Minimum deviation 632
Mirage 634
Mirror
  concave 611, 612
  convex 612
  equation 616
  focal length 614
  parabolic 618
  plane 608
  spherical 612, 621
Mixer 1151
Mho, definition 859
MKS system of units 8, 128, 134, 150, 173, 455
  electrical 1064, 1215, 1219
Modern physics 1097
Modulation 1147, 1148, 1152
Modulus (see Elastic and Elasticity)

Mole, *definition* 371, 895
Molecular spectra 1155
Molecular translational kinetic energy 391
Molecular weight, *definition* 370
Molecule, polar 1155
Moment of inertia 192–198; *definition* 265
  of particle 192
  of rigid bodies 193–198
  parallel-axis theorem 195
Momentum
  angular, *definition* 265
    conservation of 265–266
    time rate of change of 265
  linear, *definition* 241
    change of (impulsive force) 243
    conservation of 244–246
    of system of particles 247
    time rate of change of 241
MORLEY 1190
Motion (*see also* Dynamics *and* Kinematics)
  accelerated 99
  Brownian 396–397
  circular 116–119, 267–270
  gyroscopic 310–314
  of center of gravity 248–249
  of charges in electric and magnetic fields 1118–1130
  of pendulum 281–287
  periodic 267
  projectile 112–116
  rectilinear 18
  rotational 181–203
  simple harmonic (*see* Simple harmonic *and* Frequency)
  translational 91–119, 120–134
  uniform 38
  vibratory 267–291
  wave 475ff
Motors
  AC 1008, 1018–1022
  DC 874, 932, 934, 1010, 1017
Mount Palomar telescope 666
MOUTON, H. 746
Musical scales 529–530
Myopia 672

N

National Advisory Committee on Aeronautics 379
National Bureau of Standards 8, 137, 328, 594, 596, 1064, 1211
National Physical Laboratory, Great Britain 1064
Natural frequency 290
  of *LC* circuit 1057
Naval observatory 519
Negative charge (*see* Electric charge)
Negative lens 644

Networks, electrical 881
Neutretto 1213
Neutrino 1174, 1213
NEWTON, SIR ISAAC 145, 241, 304, 360, 542, 574, 683, 714
Newton (unit of force), *definition* 128;
  CONVERSION FACTORS 461, 1231
Newtonian
  mechanics (*see* Newton's laws of mechanics)
  principle of relativity 304
Newton's
  law of cooling 360
  law of universal gravitation 135
  laws of mechanics (or motion) 121ff, 1162, 1192
    first law 37–41, 121–122, 246
      rotational analogue 265
    second law 126–129, 241
      in relativistic mechanics 1192
      rotational analogue 192, 265
    third law 36–37, 129–131
  particle theory of light 574
  rings 683
NIELSEN, C. E. 968
Nodes 500
Noise 529, 532
  thermal 1158
Noncoplanar forces 71–72
Noncoplanar vectors 23
Nonlinear circuit elements 1149
Nonreflecting films 684
Normal temperature and pressure (NTP), *definition* 371
NTP 371
Nuclear
  abundances, TABLE 1224
  chain reaction 1204
  charge 1173
  cross section 1179
  energy 161, 1196
  fission 1203, 1208
  forces 1212
  masses 1196; TABLE 1224
  model of the atom 1166
  reactions 1175, 1178–1180
  structure 1173
Nucleon, *definition* 1178, 1196
Nucleus 788, 1166–1180
  compound 1178
  internal energy of 1196
  structure 1178
Number, atomic 1165

O

Oak Ridge pile 1211
Object 608
  virtual 643, 645

1262 INDEX

Object distance 614
Objective 660, 664
Obliquity factor 692
Octave 530
OERSTED, HANS CHRISTIAN 922
Oersted, *definition* 994, 1216
OHM, GEORG SIMON 859
Ohm, *definition* 859
Ohm-meter 1089
Ohm's law 859
Oil-drop experiment 1167
Opera glass 668
Operational approach 2
Optical
  activity 760
  center of a lens 640
  density 625
  filters 733
    subtractive effects 737
  instruments 651
  lever 610
  path length, *definition* 681
  pyrometer
Optic nerve 671
Optics 573ff
  electron 1124
  geometrical 606, 676
  physical 606, 676
Ordinary ray 759
Organ pipes 526ff
Oscillation (*see also* Harmonic motion *and* Vibratory motion) 274
  center of 285
  electrical 1057, 1117
  fundamental mode of 510
  higher modes of 510
  normal modes of 510
    air column, 526
    circular membrane 514
    drum head 514
    metal plate 515
    rod 575
    string 513
    tuning fork 516
  torsional 279-281
Oscillator, electronic 1117ff
  Hartley 1117
  tuned-grid 1117
Oscillograph (cathode-ray or electron-ray) 1118-1123
Overtones 510ff
  in harmonic 512

P

Paints 736
Pair production 1197
Parabolic mirror 618
Parallel-axis theorem 195

Parallel
  beam of light 576
  condensers in 849
  -plate condenser 841
  resistors in 876
  wires, magnetic field of 947
Paramagnetism 969
Partial pressure 373
Particle, *definition* 41
  theory of light 574, 683
Particles, elementary 1164ff; LIST 1213
Pascal's principle 89-90
Pascal's vases 88
Paschen series 779
PELTIER, J. C. A. 918
Peltier effect 918
Pelton wheel 260
Pendulum 281-287
  equivalent simple 285
  Foucault 304
  physical 283
  simple 281
  torsion 281
Penumbra 577
Percussion, center of 285
Perfect
  gas 369
  radiator 768
Performance coefficient of a refrigerator 446
Period, *definition* 267
  of pendulum 283
  of simple harmonic motion 274
Periodic motion, *definition* 267
Periodic table 1165, 1221
PERLMAN, I. 1224
Permalloy 996
Permanent magnet 969, 973, 998
Permanent set 274
Permeability (μ) 983
  definition 983
  initial 996
  maximum 996
  of iron 995
Pfund series 779
Phase
  angle 274
    in AC circuits 1034
  modulation (PM) 1147
  velocity 497
Phases of matter 398-419
Phonograph 538
Photoelasticity 759
Photoelectric effect 1130-1132
  Einstein's equation 1131, 1133
Photographic camera 656ff
  speed of 657
Photometers 600ff
  Bunsen's grease spot 600

INDEX 1263

Photometers (*cont.*)
  flicker 602
  Lummer-Brodhun 601
Photometric quantities 592
Photometry 590, 599–603
Photon 1157
  mass of 1195
Photosphere 728
Photosynthesis 180
Photovoltaic cell 1132
Physical constants, fundamental, TABLE 458, 1220
Physical optics 606, 676
Physical pendulum, 283
Physical properties of elements, TABLE 1222
Physics, *definition* 1, 2
Physikalisch-Technische Reichsanstalt 1064
PICTET, RAOUL 450
Pigments 736
Pile, nuclear chain-reaching 1204ff, 1206
Pinhole camera 577
Pitch 529–530
Pitot-static tube 305
PLANCK, MAX 767, 776, 1131
Planck's
  constant 776; VALUE 1220
  quantum theory 776
  radiation law 776
Plane angle (*see* Angle)
Plane mirrors 608ff
Plane of polarization 744
Planetary motion 144–145
Plate
  conductance 1113
  resistance 1113
  vacuum tube electrode 1100
Plutonium production 1204
Point
  charge 787
  focal 614, 639
  source of light 592
Poise (viscosity unit), *definition* 301
POISEUILLE 301
Poisson's ratio, *definition* 236
Polarimeter 760
Polariscope 756
Polarization
  dry cells 911
  electrical (dielectric) 844
  light 574, 740–766
    by reflection 745
    by scattering 748
    by selective absorption 741
    circular 755
    elliptical 757
    partial 746
    plane 743, 744

Polarizer 743
Polarizing angle 745
Polar molecule 1155
Polaroid 742
Poles, magnetic 949, 950
  force between 954
Positions, methods of specifying 10–12
Positive charge (*see* Electric charge)
Positive lens 644
Positron 1179, 1196, 1197, 1213
Potential 806–811
  barrier 1079, 1131
  difference (DP), *definition* 806–811
  gradient, *definition* 808
  zero 810
Potential energy (*see also* Energy) 151–155; *definition* 152
  elastic 218
  gravitational 151, 153–155
  in simple harmonic motion 277–278, 280
Potentiometer 1089
Pound (lb), *definition* 126
Pound-force (lbf), *definition* 27, 133
Poundal, *definition* 128, 455
Power 148, 172–178; *definition* 173; CONVERSION FACTORS 462, 1232
  associated with torque 199
  dispersive 719, 722
  factor 1053, 1055
    meter 1053
  of a lens 644
  production 178
  relations in electric circuits
    AC 1050
    DC 860
    motors and generators 1008
  supplies, electronic 1106
  thermoelectric 921
  units 173
Practical electrical units 791
Precession 310–313
Pressure 74, 77; CONVERSION FACTORS 461, 1231
  absolute 82
  atmospheric 83, 377
  critical 413
  dynamic 306
  fluid 73–77
  gauge 82–87
  normal 371
  partial 373
  stagnation 306
  static 305
  vapor 82, 402–409
PRIESTLEY, JOSEPH 1164
Primary cells 909
Primary wave-front 691

Prime movers 148, 178–180
Principal
  axis of inertia 205
  focus 614
  planes 647
  points 647
  rays 617, 640
Principle of Le Châtelier-Braun 452–453, 908, 918, 1002
Prism
  binoculars 668
  deviation of light by 631ff
  dispersion by 715
  reflecting 630
  spectrograph 715ff
Projectiles 112–116, 261–265
  acceleration of 261–265
  motion of 112–116
  range of 113
  trajectory 112
Projection lantern 658
Prony brake 203
Propagation of electric and magnetic fields 1139
Proportional limit, *definition* 238
Proton 793, 1169
Psychrometer 422
Pulleys 169, 172
Pupil 670
Pyrometer 778, 920
  optical 778
  radiation 920

Q

Q of a circuit 1048
Quality of sounds 529, 531
Quanta, energy for various frequencies, TABLE 1157
Quantity of electricity (*see* Electric charge)
Quantum 774ff
  definition 776
  hypothesis 777
  mechanics 121, 782, 1161
  Planck's theory 774
Quarter-wave plate 759

R

R (*see* Gas constant)
Radar 587
  frequencies 1153–1155
Radial acceleration 118, 188
Radian, *definition* 9
Radiant energy (*see also* Radiation) 161, 180, 353
Radiation 353, 359–363
  absorption of 767
  black-body 772, 1131

Radiation (*cont.*)
  detectors 1158
  electromagnetic 1140, 1145
  emission of 767
  infrared 575, 1156
  pyrometer 920
  solar 180, 364–365; TABLE 365
  total 772
  ultraviolet 575, 1157
  visible 574
Radiative capture 1203
Radiator, ideal 768
Radioactive decay 1173–1176
Radio communication 1147ff
  AM systems 1151
  receiver 1149
  transmitter 1148
Radius of gyration 195
Range of a projectile 113
Rankine diagram 443–444
Rankine temperature scale 327
Rarefaction 479
Rationalized units 1215, 1219
Ray 576
  principal 617, 640
Rayleigh disk 549, 550
Rayleigh's criterion for resolution 707
Reactance
  capacitive 1039
  inductive 1042
Reaction
  heat of (chemical) 350, 895
  nuclear 1175–1180, 1203
    probability of 1180
Reaction forces 36, 130, 217, 220, 263
  acceleration of projectiles by 263
  in turbine 263
  normal 65
Reactor, nuclear 1206
Reading glass 654
Real image 614
Reaumur temperature scale 325
Recoil 262
Recording of sound 537
Rectangular components of a vector 15
Rectangular component vectors 24
Rectification 1015
Rectifier 871, 1104–1105
Rectilinear motion 18
Reflecting telescope 665
Reflection 606ff
  factor 769
  of light 544, 606
    at plane surfaces 606
    by spherical mirrors 611, 621
  laws of 606
  polarization by 745
  specular 607
  total 555, 629

Reflection (cont.)
  of sound 551, 552
  of waves 503
Reflectivity 769
Reflector, retrodirective 611
Refracting angle of prism 631
Refracting telescope 663
Refraction 624–650
  of light 574, 606ff, 624
    atmospheric 633
    by a prism 631, 715
    double 751
    index of 626, 628
    laws of 625
  of sound 553
  of waves 506
Refractive index, TABLES 628, 720
Refrigeration 445–450
Refrigerator, ideal 435
REGNAULT 522
Relative humidity 420
Relativity 121, 304, 1162, 1189ff
  Einstein's theory of 1162, 1189ff
    energy relations in 1193
    mass in 1191
    second law of mechanics in 1191
  Newtonian principle of 304
Reluctance ($\mathcal{R}$), definition 986
Replica grating 710
Repose, (limiting) angle of 66
Reproduction of sound 537ff
Resistance (electrical) 855, 859; CONVERSION FACTORS 1233
  internal 874
  measurement of 1088
  of insulators, semi-conductors and liquids 870
  plate 1113
  temperature coefficient of 867, 871
  thermometer 869
Resistivity 862ff; CONVERSION FACTORS 1234
  of copper, GRAPH 868
  of liquids 872
  of metals, TABLE 863, 864
  of solutions 872
  temperature coefficients of 867, 871
  units 863
Resistors 874, 876
  parallel and series combinations 879
Resolution
  of a force 28
  of a vector 24–25
  optical, limit of 706
Resolving power 706ff
  Rayleigh's criterion 707
Resonance 288–291
  acoustical 517, 523
  electrical 1044–1046, 1153–1155

Resonance (cont.)
  mechanical 288–291
Resonant
  cavities 1154
  circuits 1046
  frequency 291
Restitution, coefficient of, definition 256; TABLE 256
Rest mass 1191
Resultant
  displacement 19
  force 29, 126–129
  torque 38, 192
  vector 19
Retardation, total, definition 682
Retina 670
Retrodirective reflector 611
Reverberation 559
Reversible heat 907
Reversing layer 728
Revolution 10
RF carrier 1147
RICHARDSON, O. W. 1101
Richardson's equation 1102
Right-hand rule
  for magnetic field of wire 927
  for magnetic moment of coil 926
  for torque vector 34
Rigidity, modulus of 232
Ripples 480
Ritz combination principle 781
Rockets 264
Rod receptors 671
ROEMER, OLAUS 582
ROENTGEN, WILHELM KONRAD 1132
Rolling 208–214
Rotating vector for AC 1037ff
Rotation 181–213
  dynamics of 181, 204–208
  instantaneous axis 212
  kinematics of 181–187
  with translation 204–208, 211
Rotation, pure, definition 181
  dynamics of 191–198
  effect of torques on 31, 191–198
  energy relations in 198–203
  kinetic energy of 199
  power relations in 198–203
  work in 198–203
Rotational analogues of Newton's laws 192, 265
Rotational analogues of quantities describing rectilinear motion, TABLE 202
Rotational equilibrium 40
Rotational inertia 192
Rotational motion 181–213
  motion of a point in 187–191
  simple harmonic 280

Rotational motion (*cont.*)
  with translation in a plane 204–214
Rotor, dynamo (*see also* Armature) 934, 1007
ROWLAND 729
Rubber, elastic properties of 220
RUMFORD, COUNT 148, 318
RUTHERFORD, LORD ERNEST 1166, 1175
Rutherford
  model of atom 1166
  scattering experiments 1167
Rydberg constant 779

S

SABINE 558
Saccharimeter 760
Sagitta formula 712
Saturated vapor 402
Saturation
  current (vacuum tube) 1101
  magnetic 995
Scalar quantity 7, 13
Scattering of alpha particles 1167
Scattering of light 738ff
  polarization by 748
SCHEELE, CARL WILHELM 1164
SCHRÖDINGER, ERWIN 1161
SEABORG, G. T. 1224
Second (time unit), *definition* 93
Second law (*see* Newton's laws *and* Thermodynamics)
  Newton's, in relativistic mechanics 1191
Secondary emission 1131
Secondary waves 691
SEEBECK, THOMAS JOHANN 918
Seebeck effect 918
Self inductance 1024ff
  energy of 1027
Semiconductors 871
Series connections
  condensers 849
  resistors 879
Series, spectral 779ff
Shadows 577ff
Shape, elasticity of 230–235
Shear 230
  angle of 230
  modulus of, *definition* 232; TABLE 224
Shearing strain 231
Shearing stress 231
Shielding, electrostatic 812, 818
Shock wave 309
Sidereal day 93
Simple harmonic motion 270–276; *definition* 271
  angular 279–281
Simple machines 164–172

Simple pendulum 281
Sines, TABLE 464–465, 1238–1239
Siphon 297
Siren, disk 519
Skin-friction drag 302
Sling psychrometer 422
Slip, angle of 66
Slip rings 1014
Slug, *definition* 133, 456
SMYTH, H. D. 1206, 1210
Smyth Report 1206, 1210
SNELL, WILLEBRORD 626
Snell's law 626
  analogue in electron optics 1125
Solar day, *definition* 93
Solar energy (incident on earth), TABLE 365
  source of 1201
Solar radiation 180, 364–365
Solenoid, magnetic field of 942, 950–953, 961–963
Solid angle, unit of 459, 1228; *definition* 581
Solids, thermal properties of 329–336, 398–402
Sonar systems 569
Sound 509–569
  absorption of 557, 560
  box 517
  characteristics 509, 529
  diffraction of 564
  frequency of 509, 518
  intensity of 529, 545, 548
  interference of 561
  loudness of 529
  pitch of 531
  production of 509
  quality 529, 531
  reflection 551, 552
  refraction 553
  reproduction 537
  sources 510
  speed 521, 524, 539, 542–544
    in gases, TABLE 543
    in liquids, TABLE 541
    in solids, TABLE 541
  track 538
  transmission in atmosphere 556
  waves 539, 546
Space charge 797, 1099
Specific
  heat (*see also* Heat) 343–346; *definition* 343
  inductive capacity (*see also* Dielectric constant) 845
  internal energy 381–383, 395
  volume, TABLE for H_2O 404–405
  weight 79; TABLE 84

INDEX

Spectra
  absorption 728
  band 727, 782
  continuous 726
  electronic 1157
  emission 726
  infrared 730, 731, 1155
  line 727, 779
  mass 1171
  molecular 1155
  ultraviolet 726
  visible 726
Spectral emissive power 774
Spectral lines 716
Spectrochemical analysis 730
Spectrogram 717
Spectrograph 724, 730
  mass 965, 1169
Spectrometer 717, 725
Spectroscope 715
Spectroscopy 730
Spectrum (*see also* Spectra)
  black body 774
  electromagnetic 575, 1152; CHART 1156
Specular reflection 607
Speed 91–94; CONVERSION FACTORS 460, 1230
  average 91–92
  instantaneous 91–92
  of light 581, 585ff, 1139, 1189, 1192
  of longitudinal waves 493
  of sound 521, 524, 539–544
  of transverse waves 490, 493
Spherical aberration 618, 647
Spherical condenser 837ff
Spherical mirrors 612ff
Spin 310–311
  electronic 970
Squirrel-cage rotor 1021
Stagnation point 308
Stagnation pressure 306
Standard
  atmosphere 83
  candle 592, 594
  cells 509
  gravity 131
  light source 594
  pressure 371
  temperature 371
Standards
  electrical 1064–1073
  of mass, length, and time
    length (meter) 7, 8
    mass (kilogram) 8, 125
    time (mean solor day) 93
Standards Office, Westminster 27
Standing waves 499ff
  in air columns 523
  in a string 505

STARK, JOHANNES 766
Stark effect 766, 1166
Statampere, *definition* 1215
Statcoulomb, *definition* 1215
Statfarad, *definition* 1215
Static electricity (*see* Electrostatics)
Static pressure 305
Statics 27, 36–72
  of fluids 73–90
Statohm, *definition* 1216
Statvolt, *definition* 1216
Steam engine 442–445
STEFAN, JOSEF 772
Stefan-Boltzmann law 773
Steradian 581
Stiffness 217
  factor 280
Storage battery 874, 909–912
  reactions in 915
Strain 221–227
  longitudinal, *definition* 222
  shearing, *definition* 231
  volume, *definition* 228
STRASSMANN, F. 1203
Stratosphere 366
Streamlines 293
Streamlining 307
Stream tube 293
Strength, dielectric 843
Strength of materials 237–239
  breaking 216, 238
  ultimate 238; TABLE 239
Stress 221–227
  longitudinal, *definition* 222
  shearing, *definition* 231
  volume, *definition* 228
Stroboscope 520
Sublimation 404–405, 409–412
  latent heat for H_2O, TABLE 404
  of ice 404–405
Subtropical high 367
Summation tone 564
Sun, mass of 145
Sunspot activity 980
Superconductivity 867
Superheterodyne receiver 1151
Supermalloy 997
Superposition principle 496
Supersonic flow 292, 309
Supersonic wind tunnel 431
Surface tension 403
Surface waves 480
Susceptibility, magnetic 983
Synchronous motor 1022
Synchrotron 1186, 1187

T

Tangential acceleration 188
Tangents, TABLE 466–467, 1240–1241

Telescope
  astronomical 663
  erecting 667
  Galilean 668
  reflecting 665
  refracting 663
  terrestrial 667
Telluric absorption lines 729
Temperature 317, 321–329; *definitions* 321, 323
  absolute zero 323, 441
  ambient 354
  atmospheric 379
  coefficient of resistance 867, 871
  critical 413
  gradient 354
  normal 371
  scales 324–329, 440–442
Tension 63, 223, 237–239
  surface 403
Term frequencies 780
Term values 780, 781
Terminal velocity 111
Terminal voltage 873
Terminals, positive and negative 873
Terrestrial telescope 667
Thermal
  conductivity, *definition* 355; TABLE 357
  current (thermoelectric) 920
  efficiency of heat engines 444
  EMF 920
  energy 161; *definition* 320
  expansion 329–340, 370–372
    anomalous, of water 337–338
    coefficients of, TABLES 331, 336
    of liquids 336–340
    of solids 329–336
  noise 1158
  properties of gases 369–388, 414–419
  properties of solids and liquids 398–414
  radiation 767
Thermionic emission 1098
  Richardson's equation 1101
Thermionic valve 1104
Thermocouple 918
Thermodynamic temperature scale 440–442
Thermodynamics 318, 424–453
  first law of 380, 424–426
  second law of 322, 436–440
Thermoelectric effects 918
Thermoelectric power 921
Thermometers 324–326
  gas 375
  resistance 869
  wet- and dry-bulb 421–422
Thermopile 920
Thermostat 333

Thick lens 647
Thin lens 636ff
Third law (*see* Newton's laws of mechanics)
THOMPSON, BENJAMIN 318
THOMSON, J. J. 1166
THOMSON, WILLIAM 440
Thomson model of the atom 1166
Thorium series 1176
Threshold frequency 1130
Timbre 531
Time 13, 92–93; CONVERSION FACTORS 460, 1230
Time-constant of a circuit containing inductance 1029
Time-constant of cooling or warming 361
Top 310
Toroid, magnetic field of 954, 959
Torque 29–32, 192; *definition* 31
  about an axis 30–33
  about a point 33–35
  axis 34
  effect on rotational motion 29, 192–193
  frictional 209
  on a coil or bar magnet in a magnetic field, 933, 951
  power associated with 199
  resultant 32, 38
  work done by 198
Torque vector 33–35
  right-hand rule 34
TORRICELLI, EVANGELISTA 82, 296
Torricelli's theorem 296
Torsion constant 220
Torsion pendulum 281
Torsional wave 479
Total reflection 555, 629
Total retardation, *definition* 682
Tourmaline crystals 741
Trajectories of projectiles 112–116, 248
Transconductance 1113
Transfer of heat 253–263
Transformations of energy 155–158, 161, 1193, 1196
Transformer 1023ff, 1058ff
  power relations for 1062
  vector diagrams for 1062
Transient electric current 857
Transition elements 972
Translation 17, 181
  dynamics of 120–135
  kinematics of 91–119
  with rotation 204–208, 211
Translational equilibrium 40
Translational kinetic energy 153
  molecular 391
Transmission grating 709
Transmission of light 767
Transuranic elements 1204

Transverse waves, *definition* 478
  equation 482
  speed of 481
Trigonometric functions, TABLES 464–467, 1204–1207
Triode 1109ff
  amplifier 1109–1110, 1115
  characteristic curves 1112
Triple point 410–412
  diagram for CO_2 411
  diagram for H_2O 410
Tritium 1171
Tropopause 366
Troposphere 366
Trough 477
Tube of force 814, 836
Tubes, vacuum 1102ff
  electron-ray 797, 1131
  factors 1112, 1114
  gas discharge 1134, 1135
  voltage regulator 1135, 1136
Tungsten lamps 591
  efficiencies of, TABLE 604
Tuning forks 516
Turbine 260
Turbulence 292

U

UHLENBECK, G. 970
Ultimate strength (tension), *definition* 238; TABLE 239
Ultrasonic waves 509, 568
Ultraviolet radiation 575
Umbra 577
Underwater sound 569
Uniform motion 38
United States Public Health Service 553
Units, TABLES OF CONVERSION FACTORS 458–463, 1228–1236
  prefixes for decimal multiples 8
  systems of
    electrical 1064–1073, 1215–1220
    mechanical 455–457
Universal gas constant (R) (*see* Gas constant)
Universal gravitation 135–138
Uranium
  disintegration 1173
  fission 1203, 1208
  series 1176

V

Vacuum gauge 82
Vacuum tubes 1097ff, 1098, 1110, 1117
VAN DE GRAAFF, R. J. 839

Van de Graaff generator 839, 853, 892, 1181, 1185, 1186
Vapor pressure 82, 402–409
Vaporization 402–409
  latent heat of 346–356; TABLE 348; TABLE for H_2O 404–405
  of CO_2 411–412
  of various liquids 408
  of water 404–406
Vapors and gases 419–423
Varley loop 889
Vector
  components 24
  definition 13
  diagram for transformer 1062
  diagrams for AC circuits 1033
  electric ($\mathcal{E}$) 797
  magnetic ($\mathcal{B}$) 924
  notation 17
  rectangular components of 15
  representation 16
  resolution of 24–25
Vectors 12–17
  addition of 12, 20–24
  composition of 12
  coplanar 22
  noncoplanar 23
  sum of 19
Velocities, Maxwellian distribution of 393
Velocity 91, 94–99; CONVERSION FACTORS 460, 1230
  angular, *definition* 183
  average 95, 102; *definition* 95
  group 497
  instantaneous 96, 100; *definition* 97
  of light (*see* Speed)
  of sound (*see* Speed)
  phase 497
  recoil 262
  relation to speed 97
  terminal 111
Vena contracta 297
Venturi flowmeter 298
Verdet's constant 764
Vertical, *definition* 26
Vibrating solids 510
Vibration spectra 1155
Vibrations, forced 288–291
Vibratory motion 267–290
Virtual image 609
Virtual object 643, 645
Viscosity, fluid 293, 300–303
  coefficient of, magnitude 301; *definition* 300
Visible radiation, wavelengths of 574
Vision 579
  distance of most distinct 652
  Young-Helmholtz theory 674

Visual purple 674
Vitreous humor 670
VOLTA, ALESSANDRO 806, 858
Volt, absolute, *definition* 806, 1066
Voltage 806
 accurate determinations 1089
 divider 1090
 effective 1050
 generated 1007
  frequency of 1014
 regulation 1135–1136
Voltaic battery 858
Voltmeter 1076, 1086
 electrostatic 825
Volume, CONVERSION FACTORS 459, 1229
Volume elasticity 227–230
 strain 228
 stress 228
Volumetric thermal expansion 333, 336
VON GUERICKE, OTTO 87
VR-tubes 1136

W

Wake 303
WALTON, E. T. S. 1201
Water
 anomalous expansion of 337
 cooling of 363
 density, VALUES 338
 freezing of 363
 latent heat, TABLE 404–405
 specific heat, VALUES 344
 specific volume, TABLE 404–405
 thermodynamic data for 404–405
 triple-point diagram for 410
 vapor pressure, TABLE 404–405
WATT, JAMES 442
Watt (power unit), *definition* 173
Wattmeter 1082
Watt-hour meter 1085
Wave mechanics 1161
Wave nature of electron 1161
Wave theory of light 544
Wavelength 483, 484
Waves 475ff
 absorption of 508
 amplitude of 482
 continuous 482
 electromagnetic 750, 1138
 equations of 482, 487
 Hertzian 1141
 infrasonic 509
 light 544
  electric vector in 740, 1138
 longitudinal 479, 485
  speed of 493
  wavelength of 484

Waves (*cont.*)
 mechanical 476
 reflection of 503
 refraction of 506
 shape of 532
 shock 309
 sinusoidal 482
 sound 509ff, 539ff
 standing 499, 505, 523
 transverse 478ff
  speed of 481
  transmission of energy by 494
  wavelength 483
 ultrasonic 509, 568
WEBER, WILHELM 930, 972
Weber 930; *definition* 948
Weber per square meter, *definition* 930
Wedge 171
Weight 26, 51, 128, 131–135
 molecular 370
 specific 76; TABLE 84
Westinghouse Research Laboratory 1181
Weston standard cell 910
Wheatstone bridge 888, 1088
WIECHERT 1126
Wiedermann-Franz law 356
WIENER, FRANCIS M. 532
WIEN, WILHELM 776
Wien's displacement law 776
WILLIAMS, D. 1171
Wilson cloud chamber 431, 1162
WOLLASTON, WILLIAM HYDE 728
WOOD, R. W. 710
Work 148–151; *definition* 149; CONVERSION FACTORS 462, 1232
 done against friction 160–161, 318
 done by a gas 383
 done by friction 211
 done on a gas 380–382
 in rotational motion 198–203
Work function 1102, 1131
WWV 519

X

X rays 840, 1132, 1157
 characteristic 1133
 diffraction of 1160
 particle nature 1159
 spectra 1133
 wave nature 1160

Y

Yard, *definition* 9
Yerkes Observatory 665

Yield point, *definition* 238
YOUNG, THOMAS 674, 677, 692
Young's interference experiments 692
Young's modulus, *definition* 223; TABLE 224
YUKAWA, HIDEKI 1212
YUSTER, P. 1171

Z

ZEEMAN, PETER 765
Zeeman effect 765, 1166
Zero of temperature, absolute 323
Zone of silence 556
Zone plates 695, 698
Zones, Fresnel 693